GREAT SEA STORIES
OF ALL NATIONS

GREAT SEA STORIES OF ALL NATIONS

BY

GIOVANNI BOCCACCIO · DAVID BONE · JOSEPH CONRAD
CAPTAIN DINGLE · ANATOLE FRANCE · VICTOR HUGO
JONAS LIE · BASIL LUBBOCK · JOHN MASEFIELD
HERMAN MELVILLE · EDGAR ALLAN POE · FELIX
RIESENBERG · MORLEY ROBERTS
ERNEST SHACKLETON
H. G. WELLS

*And Many Others from Ancient
Greece to Modern Japan*

EDITED AND WITH AN INTRODUCTION BY

H. M. TOMLINSON

G·C·P

GARDEN CITY PUBLISHING CO., INC.

GARDEN CITY, NEW YORK

1937
GARDEN CITY PUBLISHING CO., INC.

ACKNOWLEDGMENT

MISS ELIZABETH D'OYLEY is mainly responsible for the task of making the selection, from the vast amount of material available, which it is hoped is fairly representative of the prose literature of the sea; and the editor here makes complete acknowledgment of her good taste, wide reading, and industry, without which, for his part, there would have been no anthology.

A word is necessary relative to the arrangement of the Contents. When the episode is taken from real life it is placed under the country to which the event belongs and not classified according to the nationality of the author. So with the chronological order: the description of an actual occurrence is put in its right place, that of a fictitious event takes the date of its author.

A FOREWORD

It is not easy to gather an anthology from the sea. The sea has few convincing flowers, as we learn with disappointment when we seek their corresponding beauty in English poetry. Byron assures us that

> There is society, where none intrudes,
> By the deep sea, and music in its roar;

but one will feel little of the confidence shown by that brave man when there is only the society of an iron stanchion on the weather side of the deck, with wind and sea getting up, as the day goes down in the western ocean, the month being February. And that music in its roar! I think I dimly understand what the noble poet means, yet, when holding fast and bracing oneself for it as she rolls and pitches, one would have to be an immortal to enjoy fully from a small steamer in the twilight of a winter's day the antiphon of gale and breaking seas. In the Greek Anthology there is an epitaph to one Theris, which some of us might think to be much nearer to the bitter mind of a man looking out on a bad Atlantic night when his only support is a wet iron rail:

> Not even in death shall I, Theris, tossed shipwrecked upon land by the waves, forget the sleepless shores; for beneath the spray-beaten reefs, nigh the disastrous main, I found a grave at the hands of strangers, and for ever do I wretchedly hear roaring even among the dead the hated thunder of the sea.

The hated thunder of the sea! There is something hearty and genuine about that. It is true it is only the shade of a Levantine seaman of long ago, one whom to-day with gross impropriety we would call a Dago, who thus exclaims; nevertheless, he is nearer to our hearts, in the last count, than all the poets who have become lyrical when they remembered a wet sheet and a flowing sea. Anthologies of verse inspired by the sea have been for the most part of artificial flowers. Most seamen, I fear, would wonder what the fuss was all about. And seamen, too, would be just as surprised by the traveller in "The Old Margate Hoy." Elia saw from such a craft the sea for the first time, and then surmised that, even out of sight of land, there would be "but a flat watery horizon about him, nothing comparable to the vast o'er-curtaining of the sky, his familiar object, seen daily without dread or amazement"; and consequently he felt tempted to exclaim with Charoba, in the poem of Gebir:

> Is this the mighty ocean?—is this *all?*

No, dear Elia, not by a good deal.

How much more then?

It may be possible to judge from this abundant garnering of stories of the sea. Miss D'Oyley, who most diligently collected and arranged these stories, selecting representative passages from the literatures of all those peoples who should know what the sea is, necessarily turned to the pedestrian work of prose writers; and they, we find, had chanced to be pioneers and adventurers, seamen, fishermen, whalers, and marine engineers; or seasoned travellers and sympathetic men and women who knew well the seaboard and the sound of wind and combers when friends had not returned to port; and their more sober evidence is somewhat different. They are occasionally lyrical, but it is not, as a rule, the sight of the deep and dark blue ocean which moves them, but sorrow for absent seafarers, and anxiety for their welfare, and, in the back of their minds, fear of the sea, the ancient enemy of man, because they know that man's restless curiosity, and his need to be up and doing, will send him into the open, whatever the way of the wind. You will certainly miss in this book some of your favourite passages. I can assure you that they were well known to Miss D'Oyley, who occasionally failed to secure the privilege of including a little masterpiece.

On the whole, in this prose collection, you will find more of the strangeness, dread, and compulsion of Ultima Thule, where the seafarer must chance his luck, and of fallow waters, than you will of Trade-Wind weather. Except from some of the Latins, there is here little flattery of the sea. You will find in the Exeter Book an Anglo-Saxon poem called "The Sea-Farer," and that anonymous poet tells us (in the translation of his poem by Mr L. Iddings):

> Benumbed by the cold, oft the comfortless night watch hath held me
> At the prow of my craft as it tossed about under the cliffs.
> My feet were imprisoned with frost, were fettered with ice-chains,
> Yet hotly were wailing the querulous sighs round my heart;
> And hunger within me, sea-wearied, made havoc of courage.
> This he, whose lot happily chances on land, doth not know;
> Nor how I on the ice-cold sea passed the winter in exile,
> In wretchedness, robbed of my kinsmen, with icicles hung.
> The hail flew in showers about me; and there I heard only
> The roar of the sea, ice-cold waves, and the song of the swan;
> For pastime the gannet's cry served me; the kittiwake's chatter
> For laughter of men; and for mead-drink the call of the sea mews.

But the reading of that heartfelt plaint will never deter youth from packing his bolster, and setting out for the quays and a likely ship; he listens to the relations of his elders, home from sea, yarns which usually are not without what Americans call "rough-stuff," or he reads such stories as are gathered here, but not for warnings; all he wants is the cause of excitement and the quickening of his desire. There was the sailor who, during the War, was asked what he would do when released at last from the prow of his ship, where he watched for mines and periscopes and the loom of dirt of all kinds. "Well," he answered, "I shall put an oar over my shoulder, and walk up-country with it, and walk and walk till I come to a place where they'll point to the oar and say, 'What's that?' That'll be the place for me. I'll settle down there." Is it likely we shall think that story has more in it than fun, who never watched for periscopes and dirt by the Dogger Bank when the wind was hard at northeast? Not in the least. What most of us will remember, and will take as the truth of it, are such words as we read in *The Lusiad:* "And now they sailed in Indian Seas, and came in sight of the region where the sun rose." Or look again at the opening chapter of *Moby Dick*, and you will learn from it all there is to be said for those irrational men who know the worst that can be said of the sea, and have even sworn they will have no more of it, yet embark once more:

> Whenever I find myself growing grim about the mouth; whenever it is a damp, drizzly November in my soul; whenever I find myself involuntarily pausing before coffin warehouses, and bringing up the rear of every funeral I meet; and especially whenever my hypos get such an upper hand of me that it requires a strong moral principle to prevent me from deliberately stepping into the street, and methodically knocking people's hats off— then, I account it high time to get to sea as soon as I can. This is my substitute for pistol and ball.

It would be useless to look for common sense in that. It has no more of it than we should find in much else which moves men to do this, that, and the other thing. It has been hinted there is fair presumptive evidence for the existence of an immortal soul in man in the fact that he is so easily bored. "I am a stranger here; Heaven is my home." Therefore he would go to sea again, because it is better than suicide, or he would sail the Indian Ocean, and go on till he comes to the region where day is born. In the meantime, since it is not easy to escape from the compulsion of the morning train to the city and the task, and since we must endure the coffin warehouses as best we may, our escape, usually, is vicarious; so first we read the *Swiss Family Robinson*, and after that go on to Hakluyt's *Principall Navigations*, or any other book which reflects the light which never was on any sea, though the horizons of all seas suggest that it is just beyond.

Sailors in half mockery may tell their tales of hardships and hard tack, as some of them do in this volume, as well as they please. If, for example, you read Shackleton's account of the voyage in the ship's boat, from his book *South*, which is included here, a simple and nervous yarn, excellently told, you will find that it is enough to daunt even an experienced mariner. Yet it will have the opposite effect on many landsmen, for there will always be boys in the world, and light-hearted oldsters who will adventure as though they had access to the fountain of life. Young men and fools have never listened to the warning of Safety First, and never will. After all, not even good dogs do that. Says a Greek to his son in a story which is included here, warning him against the life of a sailor: "Keep away from the lying monster. She has no faith or mercy. Worship her as you will—honour her—she never moves from her own aim. Don't look at her deceiving smile, promising her countless wealth. Sooner or later she will dig a grave for you, or she will cast you on the world a useless ruin, with nothing to own but your skin and bones. Sea or woman—it's all the same." With a sigh, other oldsters told that youth: "There's no more bread to be gained from the sea. Let me have just a root of vine on the solid earth and I would throw a black stone behind me."

What is the good of talking to young men like that? Luckily, it is no good. While life lasts our interest in it will be maintained by youth and dreaming lunatics; they will continue to do things by the stars and the phases of the moon, and will keep us awake to the dangerous mutability of the eternal hills. And there is no telling the chance consequences of their apparently irrational doings. Columbus went west to reach Asia that way, and thought he had found it; and as one result we have the United States of America and the Monroe Doctrine. The greater part of the American continent was disclosed by men while looking for something else. For centuries they were obsessed by the notion, for one thing, of a north-west passage to Cathay, and it was the search for that sea-route which brought Hudson's Bay to light, and caused the penetration of Canada westward. Then again there was that Golden City of Manoa, about which Raleigh and others were quite sure, though they had never seen it. The search for it, though it could not succeed—for doubtless that city was but a variation of the vision of Zion—opened to traffic the Orinoco and the Amazon, and gave us rubber tyres, as well as some good reading here.

We are sometimes reminded that the higher and better sort of man, unless he is a seaman, never travels far, because he is more properly occupied in reading the signs of the times in his native village. The sufficient answer to this is that St Paul was no sailor, though he behaved stoutly on that voyage to Rome; and though Thomas Hardy never strayed from Dorset, Charles Montagu Doughty was a wanderer, and those two writers, widely different in temper, gave us books which are the major summits in late English literature. It was in his stars that Doughty should go to Arabia and suffer, in the way that another man is fated to go to sea. Yet let us note that it is no good talking romantically of the "great open spaces of the world" to such men. They would wonder what we meant. Though they may be romantic—for it is evident that the motives which stir them will lead to no material profit—yet they are also realists, for they know well enough what measure of knowledge, skill, and fortitude will be demanded of them, if they would succeed in surviving to indigence in old age. Those other phrases, equally popular, with a meaning too deep for coherent translation, the Open Road, the

Back of Beyond, Far Horizons, Unknown Coasts and Uncharted Seas, and Wanderlust, affect a sailor or seasoned traveller mournfully, just as a young poet's public avowal affects his elders when he declares the love-light in her eyes. It is better not to speak earnestly and aloud of such stirrings within, because it may make one who overhears us, and knows, not sympathetically solemn, but restive. It is better to remember the sailor walking inland with the experimental oar on his shoulder.

What has this to do, it may be asked, with the appeal of travel and exploration and of the sea in literature? Maybe everything, for honesty must be at the back of all literature, whether it concerns ships and the sea or anything else. Once, for example, I left London with the determination to visit the Mergui Archipelago before that voyage was over. I was romantic. The Mergui Islands are the islands of the Sea Gypsies. Late in the journey I had but five minutes to make up my mind: should I embark on a coasting steamer for Mergui, or take a liner for London which then was at the quay, soon to sail? There was no hesitation about it. I will be honest, and show that when one is stranded on a tropical beach one's thoughts are not invariably romantic. My baggage was in the liner for London that morning. I had but just arrived from a long journey in the interior of that country, and a still longer journey among other tropical islands, and at the moment this traveller felt that he had had quite enough of it. Yet had he? Only now he picks up a volume he had with him then, the *Sailing Directions for the East Indies*—a very proper book to have at hand while writing this foreword—and he notices again some names: Kuala Pahang, Tanjong Labuan, Sula Besi Channel, Molucca Passage, Menado Roads, Ceram Laut, Tanjong Kaju Merah, and Gillolo Passage. His need to go on writing this foreword was forgotten for a few minutes; except in the body he was no longer present. He would have given much to have sniffed again the smell of durian shards; and if you have ever been shocked by the smell of a durian then you must be convinced that his emotion was as sincere as that of the young fellow who could rest assured of that love-light. Though he has no illusion about the sea, it would be unwise to try him again with the choice between Mergui and London. And as to that sailor with the oar (which we will suppose has long stood as a symbol in an inland garden) if another sailor drifted into that village, then the two of them would gossip of nothing but the ships they used to know and the ports of other days. If we chanced to approach them they would stop talking, and the visiting sailor might shyly pretend to be admiring his friend's hollyhocks, yet we could safely assume they both knew of fuller days than these, and of places far away that never again will be seen at their best, for the best was when they were there.

Sir James Barrie once told us that memory was given to us that we might have roses in December. The beauty of such roses is that they may bloom from thistles or cabbage stalks, for man's chief distinction is

that he is not a rational animal; that he is sometimes even an Arctic explorer. In any case, no man ever embarked on a voyage in order to provide roses for a distant December. He went to catch fish, or to try to
round Africa, as did Diaz, or to bring tea from China or guano from
Chincha, or to look for El Dorado, or to watch from an island in the
South Seas the transit of a planet, as did James Cook. A man but em-
barks—which in itself is a great trial—resolute to face the pleasures as
they come, and never to ask for trouble. All sorts of things will happen
to him, if they are not designed.

That means, we must suppose, that it is possible for men to be happy
without being conscious of it at the time. Let us suppose a traveller
does at last find himself unexpectedly on that "uncharted coast of an
unknown sea"—a description which has its full measure of bunkum. He
does not meet fun there. There is no time for day-dreaming. He becomes
too tired at essential tasks to bother much over the moonlight on tropic
shores and the palms and the fireflies; he will merely groan at night because of the heat and the mosquitoes. He becomes preoccupied with an
uncertain and arduous track, knowing that it will melt into the swamp
with one downfall of rain; he doubts whether his supplies will last till
he can reach a replenishing point; his men may be good, but it would
be absurd to expect that their patience is other than perishable; and
he knows that only a trifling accident may put his little party into a pass
from which he could not extricate it. There seems hardly enough in this
far horizon to make the voyage worth the time and money. He continues
to travel in a land where the very native names are delectable, and—
when afterward we see them in print—able to form the right sounds for a
song about the lotus. But he himself never notices the lotus buds, except
as a botanist. He has no time to remember that he ought to enjoy himself.
His simple concern from day to day is to protect his company from
unlucky surprises. Yet afterward, as you will discover when reading
these stories by many travellers, his senses were free to refresh themselves with the new things about him, the face of the waters, the colours
of the ice, the shapes in the forest, the loom of the headlands, the new
smells, the perplexing sounds, or the subduing silence of the wastes.
His senses, as we now see, must have recovered a juvenile receptivity
after their apathy in a city of civilization. Though the mind was busy
with the affairs of the day, the body was looking after itself, and did
not plague its owner because it was fatigued. This left the mind little to
do except its appointed task. It was not annoyed with grievances from
the body over the hard going, and hunger and thirst. Only afterward did
the traveller remember, with surprise at the clearness of the recollection, the evening which came at the end of the longest and most tiring
day of the journey. The fragrance of the smoke of the camp or the galley
fire becomes as memorable as though his nose had never smelt anything
better. Why was the hearing so acute, too, when he was not even listening

at the time? There were sounds below the silence. Nothing to eat all day, either; not even a draw at a pipe. That did not appear to matter, though hunger was as sharp as a threat. As for his fatigue, he felt, with a pipe, that it was a luxury; for the job was done. And, now it is all long ago, the clear reports come in, without the assistance of note-book and diary. The traveller remembers the trivialities of the hardest days, though he was too busy to give them more than a glance at the time. Every patch of light and shade in a camp, or the sails that were set, are seen, and the shapes and colours of the clouds. He can hear the plunge of the bows and the murmur of the wash alongside; or the dry rustling of the palm fronds along the beach in the off-shore wind at sunset. There is no doubt about it, he was fully alive then, though he felt he was worn out. That is why some of these stories of the sea and narratives of travel are so brisk and sharp. The unknown Anglo-Saxon Seafarer, for instance, who assures us dolefully that hail is "coldest of grain," and who "for mead-drink had the call of the sea-mews," was the more alert when things were at their dreariest, and so he compels our sympathy in his voyaging, though he stood his last night watch perhaps a thousand years ago.

In Shackleton's *Last Voyage* you will find a chapter called "The Ice." For a time Commander Wild forgets his anxieties over his ship, and he had many. The *Quest* was in considerable danger. She was a light-headed little thing to be engaged in a desperate Antarctic adventure. But her captain forgets his worries over her to record that at daybreak, one morning, "the old floes passed from pale pink to crimson . . . to the palest and most delicate heliotrope. The darker newly-frozen ice changed from bronze to light apple-green."

That is not prose-poetry, as some unwary enthusiasts name a kind of pleasing wool-work in words. It is merely what a master mariner notes in his log, for his own satisfaction—navigators were given to that, at one time, and even to embellishing the pages with pictures of terns, whales, dolphins, and boobies. We do not pause to admire the sailor's words; we merely see at once what took his attention one morning. The captain of the *Quest* had been logging many things before that entry, and most of them leave us in doubt as to whether or not we should have enjoyed a life on the ocean wave in the *Quest*. One of her officers called her a "she-devil." She had a trick of assaulting her protectors, when she was not making the most case-hardened of them sick. We understand the loneliness of that ship's company in the Southern Ocean, where even the sight of a seal or a penguin was an event, and we guess with what assiduity they must have nursed the thin hope that their vessel could sneak sufficiently northward before winter shut and bolted the door against them. But one morning, when that hope was heartbreaking to look at, Commander Wild simply forgets it, and notes in his log that the old ice changed from bronze to apple-green; and he regrets that he cannot describe the beauty of the scene.

But in his book he does try, nevertheless, to do something much more difficult than the description of a beautiful morning. He endeavours to put into words the effect upon a witness of tranquil and impersonal beauty; and that, if it is not impossible, is rarely done after seriously considering the wonder. Says Beowulf, telling of his fortunate morning after his strife with the sea: "Light came from the east, the bright beacon of God. The waves were stilled until I might see the sea-nesses, the windy walls." You sometimes come upon such directness and lucidity, revealing the deeps as though by lucky chance, in the narratives of the Elizabethan voyagers. The effect is not translated by arranging in order a number of sentences. It is not a trick, so it cannot be learned. The words which do it are exactly the same as those which do not. They might be uttered by a child, or a seaman. What is this virtue then? Nobody really knows. A man will be telling his tale, when suddenly luck touches him, and then, like the ice which was not changed in nature yet somehow was different, his words take on a meaning that is startling, if hard to define; they have another import and a light which does not belong to them.

Now, Commander Wild succeeds no more than other philosophers in making reasonable the spell put upon us by light in some of its chance incidences. For his part he was watching ice change colour in the Antarctic; yet we understand him well enough when he turns from the memory of that uncharitable glow and tells us with irrelevance that "few people who have travelled away from the beaten track and spent long unbroken periods face to face with Nature can hope to escape the sudden feeling of restlessness and disquietude which come upon one without warning and drive one to pace up and down, to face the rain on a gusty night, or do anything so long as one can be alone for a while." What has that to do with ice changing its colour? Not a little, we may suspect, though we cannot justify it; it would be as reasonable to explain to the nightingale that his song reminded us of the sad heart of Ruth when she stood in tears amid the alien corn. The navigator of the *Quest* tells us, too, that he has seen even the dogs standing on deck with ears cocked, and gazing into the silence and splendour of the Polar twilight, listening. He asks us, listening for what?

Well, no doubt the dogs saw the men doing it, and dogs are sociable creatures. There, however, in any case, the men were, gazing entranced into the empty distance of that region, and listening, though knowing they would hear nothing, and gain nothing, except frost-bite and a feeling of disquietude. It does not surprise us to learn that a sailor who once upon a time saw a big moon poised just above the bergs and floes, turning them to gold in a waste where man ventured at his peril, may suddenly pick up his hat, at home, to the surprise of his comfortable family, and go out on a wet and gusty night, without a word of explanation, to be alone on Tooting Common. Men sometimes do that sort of thing when they remember the moon. They go out without a word of explanation because there isn't one. And what odd corners of the earth and unsought prospects affect us in this way! Why should a man remember just one corner of a trench, and one instant there, as if it were charged with all the mystery of the War? The corner has gone. It is wheat to-day. His mates who knew it have gone. The place has no name now. Yet it survives, the very smell of it, with that tangle of rusty wire jutting from its clay wall, a surviving tuft of grass shivering on the parapet, a pal beyond on the fire-step, motionless, as if already dead, and not a sound, as though all were over, the days of earth counted, and he the last man, forgotten on an abandoned earth; there the trench still is, though it never was worth remembering, with a meaning that is disquieting, whenever the wind sits in a certain quarter, and he is alone. He never mentions it to anyone because he doesn't know what there is to say about it, yet he feels that something of the truth may be there, if only he could get at it. He goes out alone now on a wet and windy night to think it over.

And that, when one has read all these stories, appears to be about as much as is ever got out of an adventure. That is its chief reward. It sends you out on a wet night to think it over in disquietude. The reward is not marketable. Indeed, it is hardly communicable. Of what use is disquietude, and a privy matter which is so compelling that even the wind and rain after dark in a London street are overlooked? Drake went round the world to find the islands from which the spices came; without spices to disguise its flavour, meat was soon uneatable in his day. There was no cold storage then. Spices were an urgent matter in Tudor days. First the Chinese brought those spices to the Isthmus of Suez, or took them to India for transhipment; though that was long before Elizabeth's day. Then the Arabs were the carriers to the isthmus, from whence the Italians distributed Oriental commodities over Europe. But at last Diaz and Da Gama found Africa could be rounded; and India and the Strait of Malacca were reached. In a few years more the Portuguese were busy among the islands of the Moluccas, which were attained later still by the survivors of Magellan's men; and Drake followed Magellan. They wanted pepper, cloves, and nutmegs, and intrigued cunningly and fought each other bitterly, mixed with obstinate and tough Dutchmen, for the trade; but we have forgotten what all the fuss was about. So much enterprise and courage for nutmegs seem ridiculous. It is not often that the motives of a hero or an ardent pioneer will bear close examination in the light of later days; we read his log, in after years, for his quality when surmounting trouble, his encouraging spirit when his companions threw up their hands, his faith in his star when it had vanished behind enduring clouds. It is little to us now that stout old Diaz found there was an end to the obstructing west coast of Africa, and so a direct way to commerce with India; but we think of him, with not a little awe, sticking to it in his tiny craft, heading south, away from everything known, because of a lee shore to larboard, till he entered the terrific seas which wheel freely round this planet to the south of all the continents. Then he stood eastward again to look for Africa, and failed to find it, so made his course northerly, which presently showed him that Africa itself trended east and west. It seems simple now, but I think any sailor must respect the nerve of that Portugee. And perhaps as good a passage as there is in *The World Encompassed* is where Parson Fletcher tells us how the *Golden Hind* grounded on coral, probably between Tubalai of the Sula Islands and the east coast of Celebes. We know very little of the Sula Islands to-day; and Drake had just come out of the long narrow Gulf of Gorontalo (Celebes); and literally, he did not know where he was. He had assumed, wrongly, that that gulf was the way home. He came out of it, turned south, and ran on a reef. English sailors then were ignorant of the nature of coral reefs. *The Golden Hind* was hard and fast, and on the other side of the world. Her men were thoroughly frightened, and fell on their knees "and so preparing as it were our neckes unto the blocke, we every minute expected the finall stroake to be given unto us"; but as soon as their prayers were ended, "our Generall (exhorting us to have the especiallest care of the better part, to wit, the soule, and adding many comfortable speeches, of the joyes of that other life, which wee now alone looked for) incouraged us all to bestire ourselves, showing us the way thereto by his own example; and first of all the pump being well plyed . . ." and so on till they floated again. Drake was not one to lay his neck on the block in meekness and prayer without looking round him for a way out. When we read to-day *The World Encompassed*, it is not because we see extended therein the fortunes of Gloriana and the English Realm; we read it for signs which Master Fletcher did not knowingly leave for us to decipher.

In truth, we should be hard put to it if we were asked to name the best things in life, and it is no easier to explain why a book or a place is particularly comfortable to us. Once I myself happened to be in the Moluccas. As did Drake, I stayed at Ternate. It is as Master Fletcher assures us, a delectable island; but now I do not dwell fondly on its possibilities for British commerce, or its clove gardens, and palm walks, or the friendliness of its people. The Moluccas, as I remember the sight of them, were remote and unsubstantial, and no more than was Canaan to Moses; for I saw them once, for five minutes, from the high summit of Ternate, as it were from a raft of stones which was anchored on the shining clouds of the south-west monsoon. There are no bearings for that. I could see all the northern Moluccas and over Gillolo to the Pacific. It was clear then that this planet is a celestial body, a fact which I had not noticed in the market place of Ternate, then far below, and lost in a gulf of sapphire. Yet it was a fact in travel, though I did not know how to log it; nor can I see now that it would be of any use as a safe direction for other travellers. It would not lead them anywhere, and is useless for statistical purposes. It might indeed lead them astray.

And, for that matter, many of the best stories in this book resemble it in that particular. Their sea-light is evasive and strange. It should be sufficient for us that Miss D'Oyley has done as much as was possible, I think, in her selection from the great sea-stories of the world, to show how the sea has moved the wonder of men, and has troubled their minds with surmises which went beyond the edge of the earth. These men ventured mostly for fish or cargoes, or to fight over the right to collect them—there is a deplorable amount of fighting in this volume—but they brought to light also, and usually without knowing it, a treasure which is greater than the victory of Lepanto or the doubling of Cape Horn. In this book you will find here and there indications to further and fuller reading which might profitably occupy the curious for a long spell. It ought not to be news to us, though perhaps it is, that one of the most direct and nervous narratives of sea travel in English is to be found in the *Acts of the Apostles*. And if a reader does not want more of Beowulf, Malory, and Hakluyt, than he finds herein, then the purpose of this book is frustrate. To most of us, probably, the *Dangerous Voyage of Captain Thomas James, told by Himself*, will be a surprise. Even now we do not know the name of his ship. James does not give it; we know only that she was Bristol built. James was a seventeenth-century mastermariner who deserves a place in Valhalla. His story should be read in full, and I imagine the long extracts from it, to be found here, will send readers to it. His ship was the first to winter in Hudson's Bay, by Charlton Island, which he named. Her men scuttled her, to save her from the ice, and she rested on the bottom all the winter. When spring broke they raised her. It was not done as easily as that, as you may suppose. We are surprised that James and his men managed to survive their privations; but James was a great seaman and a first-rate leader. And now note this: they raised their ship, and got her going again in a forbidding and unknown sea, yet instead of heading for Bristol they endeavoured to make west, for their object had been the North-West Passage. A reader, it is almost certain, will want more of Captain James. Nor should that reader imagine that he has sighted *Moby Dick* because something of that portentous whale's bulk is suggested in a page or two, in this collection. The virtue of that great book of the sea—I think, the greatest in our language—altogether escapes an extract. One cannot see Mount Everest, because an enthusiastic climber, who has essayed its glacial steeps, has presented us with a nice fragment of its substance for an interesting paper-weight. An extract or a quotation has no value unless, as did Ali Baba, we know what Open Sesame will do for us.

H. M. TOMLINSON

CONTENTS

GREAT BRITAIN

GREAT SEA STORIES
OF ALL NATIONS

ANCIENT GREECE

HOW ODYSSEUS MADE HIMSELF A RAFT, AND HOW POSEIDON, SHAKER OF THE EARTH, OVERWHELMED HIM WITH A STORM[1]

Homer

(c. 1000 B. C.)

SO SOON as early Dawn shone forth, the rosy-fingered, anon Odysseus put on him a mantle and doublet, and the nymph clad her in a great shining robe, light of woof and gracious, and about her waist she cast a fair golden girdle, and a veil withal upon her head. Then she considered of the sending of Odysseus, the great-hearted. She gave him a great axe, fitted to his grasp, an axe of bronze double-edged, and with a goodly handle of olive wood fastened well. Next she gave him a polished adze, and she led the way to the border of the isle where tall trees grew, alder and poplar, and pine that reacheth unto heaven, seasoned long since and sere, that might lightly float for him. Now after she had shown him where the tall trees grew, Calypso, the fair goddess, departed homeward.

And he set to cutting timber, and his work went busily. Twenty trees in all he felled, and then trimmed them with the axe of bronze, and deftly smoothed them, and over them made straight the line. Meanwhile Calypso, the fair goddess, brought him augers, so he bored each piece and jointed them together, and then made all fast with trenails and dowels. Wide as is the floor of a broad ship of burden, which some man well skilled in carpentry may trace him out, of such beam did Odysseus fashion his broad raft. And thereat he wrought, and set up the deckings, fitting them to the close-set uprights, and finished them off with long gunwales, and therein he set a mast, and a yard-arm fitted thereto, and moreover he made him a rudder to guide the craft. And he fenced it with wattled osier withies from stem to stern, to be a bulwark against the wave, and piled up wood to back them. Meanwhile Calypso, the fair goddess, brought him web of cloth to make him sails; and these too he fashioned very skilfully. And he made fast therein braces and halyards and sheets, and at last he pushed the raft with levers down to the fair salt sea.

It was the fourth day when he had accomplished all. And, lo, on the fifth, the fair Calypso sent him on his way from the island, when she had

---

[1]From *The Odyssey*, translated by S. H. Butcher and Andrew Lang. Reprinted by permission of the Executors of the translators and of Macmillan & Co., Ltd.

bathed him and clad him in fragrant attire. Moreover, the goddess placed on board the ship two skins, one of dark wine, and another, a great one, of water, and corn too in a wallet, and she set therein a store of dainties to his heart's desire, and sent forth a warm and gentle wind to blow. And goodly Odysseus rejoiced as he set his sails to the breeze. So he sate and cunningly guided the craft with the helm, nor did sleep fall upon his eyelids, as he viewed the Pleiads and Boötes, that setteth late, and the Bear, which they likewise call the Wain, which turneth ever in one place, and keepeth watch upon Orion, and alone hath no part in the baths of Ocean. This star, Calypso, the fair goddess, bade him to keep ever on the left as he traversed the deep. Ten days and seven he sailed traversing the deep, and on the eighteenth day appeared the shadowy hills of the land of the Phæacians, at the point where it lay nearest to him; and it showed like a shield in the misty deep.

Now the lord, the shaker of the earth, on his way from the Ethiopians, espied him afar off from the mountains of the Solymi: even thence he saw Odysseus as he sailed over the deep; and he was mightily angered in spirit, and shaking his head he communed with his own heart. "Lo now, it must be that the gods at the last have changed their purpose concerning Odysseus, while I was away among the Ethiopians. And now he is nigh to the Phæacian land, where it is ordained that he escape the great issues of the woe which hath come upon him. But, methinks, that even yet I will drive him far enough in the path of suffering."

With that he gathered the clouds and troubled the waters of the deep, grasping his trident in his hands; and he roused all storms of all manner of winds, and shrouded in clouds the land and sea; and down sped night from heaven. The East Wind and the South Wind clashed, and the stormy West, and the North, that is born in the bright air, rolling onward a great wave. Then were the knees of Odysseus loosened and his heart melted, and heavily he spake to his own great spirit:

"Oh, wretched man that I am! what is to befal me at the last? I fear that indeed the goddess spake all things truly, who said that I should fill up the measure of sorrow on the deep, or ever I came to mine own country; and lo, all these things have an end. In such wise doth Zeus crown the wide heaven with clouds, and hath troubled the deep, and the blasts rush on of all the winds; yea, now is utter doom assured me. Thrice blessed those Danaans, yea, four times blessed, who perished on a time in wide Troy-land, doing a pleasure to the sons of Atreus! Would to God that I too had died, and met my fate on that day when the press of Trojans cast their bronze-shod spears upon me, fighting for the body of the son of Peleus! So should I have gotten my dues of burial, and the Achæans would have spread my fame; but now it is my fate to be overtaken by a pitiful death."

Even as he spake, the great wave smote down upon him, driving on in terrible wise, that the raft reeled again. And far therefrom he fell,

and lost the helm from his hand; and the fierce blast of the jostling winds
came and brake his mast in the midst, and sail and yard-arm fell afar
into the deep. Long time the water kept him under, nor could he speedily
rise from beneath the rush of the mighty wave: for the garments hung
heavy which fair Calypso gave him. But late and at length he came up,
and spat forth from his mouth the bitter salt water, which ran down in
streams from his head. Yet even so forgat he not his raft, for all his
wretched plight, but made a spring after it in the waves, and clutched
it to him, and sat in the midst thereof, avoiding the issues of death;
and the great wave swept it hither and thither along the stream. And as
the North Wind in the harvest tide sweeps the thistle down along the
plain, and close the tufts cling each to other, even so the winds bare the
raft hither and thither along the main. Now the South would toss it to
the North to carry, and now again the East would yield it to the West
to chase.

But the daughter of Cadmus marked him, Ino of the fair ankles,
Leucothea, who in time past was a maiden of mortal speech, but now in
the depths of the salt sea she had gotten her share of worship from the
gods. She took pity on Odysseus in his wandering and travail, and she
rose, like a sea-gull on the wing, from the depth of the mere, and sat
upon the well-bound raft and spake saying:

"Hapless one, wherefore was Poseidon, shaker of the earth, so wondrous wroth with thee, seeing that he soweth for thee the seeds of many
evils? Yet shall he not make a full end of thee, for all his desire. But do
even as I tell thee, and methinks thou art not witless. Cast off these
garments, and leave the raft to drift before the winds, but do thou swim
with thine hands and strive to win a footing on the coast of the Phæacians,
where it is decreed that thou escape. Here, take this veil imperishable
and wind it about thy breast; so is there no fear that thou suffer aught
or perish. But when thou hast laid hold of the mainland with thy hands,
loose it from off thee and cast it into the wine-dark deep far from the
land, and thyself turn away."

With that the goddess gave the veil, and for her part dived back into
the heaving deep, like a sea-gull: and the dark wave closed over her.
But the steadfast goodly Odysseus pondered, and heavily he spake to
his own brave spirit:

"Ah, woe is me! Can it be that some one of the immortals is weaving
a new snare for me, that she bids me quit my raft? Nay, verily, I will
not yet obey, for I had sight of the shore yet a long way off, where she
told me that I might escape. I am resolved what I will do—and methinks
on this wise it is best. So long as the timbers abide in the dowels, so long
will I endure steadfast in affliction, but so soon as the wave hath shattered my raft asunder, I will swim, for meanwhile no better counsel
may be."

While yet he pondered these things in his heart and soul, Poseidon,

shaker of the earth, stirred against him a great wave, terrible and grievous, and vaulted from the crest, and therewith smote him. And as
when a great tempestuous wind tosseth a heap of parched husks and
scatters them this way and that, even so did the wave scatter the long
beams of the raft. But Odysseus bestrode a single beam, as one rideth on
a courser, and stript him of the garments which fair Calypso gave him.
And presently he wound the veil beneath his breast, and fell prone into
the sea, outstretching his hands as one eager to swim. And the lord,
the shaker of the earth, saw him and shook his head, and communed
with his own soul. "Even so, after all thy sufferings, go wandering over
the deep, till thou shalt come among a people, the fosterlings of Zeus.
Yet for all that I deem not that thou shalt think thyself too lightly
afflicted." Therewith he lashed his steeds of the flowing manes, and
came to Ægea, where is his lordly home.

And Athene, daughter of Zeus, turned to new thoughts. Behold,
she bound up the courses of the other winds, and charged them all to
cease and be still; but she roused the swift North and brake the waves
before him, that so Odysseus, of the seed of Zeus, might mingle with the
Phæacians, lovers of the oar, avoiding death and the fates.

So for two nights and two days he was wandering in the swell of the
sea, and much his heart boded of death. But when at last the fair-tressed
Dawn brought the full light of the third day, thereafter the breeze
fell, and lo, there was a breathless calm, and with a quick glance ahead,
(he being upborne on a great wave,) he saw the land very near. And
even as when most welcome to his children is the sight of a father's life,
who lies in sickness and strong pains long wasting away, some angry
god assailing him; and to their delight the gods have loosed him from his
trouble; so welcome to Odysseus showed land and wood; and he swam
onward being eager to set foot on the strand. But when he was within
earshot of the shore, and heard now the thunder of the sea against the
reefs—for the great wave crashed against the dry land belching in terrible
wise, and all was covered with foam of the sea—for there were no harbours for ships nor shelters, but jutting headlands and reefs and cliffs;
then at last the knees of Odysseus were loosened and his heart melted,
and in heaviness he spake to his own brave spirit:

"Ah me! now that beyond all hope Zeus hath given me sight of land,
and withal I have cloven my way through this gulf of the sea, here there
is no place to land on from out of the grey water. For without are sharp
crags, and round them the wave roars surging, and sheer the smooth
rock rises, and the sea is deep thereby, so that in no wise may I find
firm foothold and escape my bane, for as I fain would go ashore, the
great wave may haply snatch and dash me on the jagged rock—and a
wretched endeavour that would be. But if I swim yet further along the
coast to find, if I may, spits that take the waves aslant and havens of the
sea, I fear lest the storm-winds catch me again and bear me over the

teeming deep, making heavy moan; or else some god may even send forth against me a monster from out of the shore water; and many such pastureth the renowned Amphitrite. For I know how wroth against me hath been the great Shaker of the Earth."

Whilst yet he pondered these things in his heart and mind, a great wave bore him to the rugged shore. There would he have been stript of his skin and all his bones been broken, but that the goddess, grey-eyed Athene, put a thought into his heart. He rushed in, and with both his hands clutched the rock, whereto he clung till the great wave went by. So he escaped that peril, but again with backward wash it leapt on him and smote him and cast him forth into the deep. And as when the cuttle-fish is dragged forth from his chamber, the many pebbles clinging to his suckers, even so was the skin stript from his strong hand against the rocks, and the great wave closed over him. There of a truth would luckless Odysseus have perished beyond that which was ordained, had not grey-eyed Athene given him sure counsel. He rose from the line of the breakers that belch upon the shore, and swam outside, ever looking landwards, to find, if he might, spits that take the waves aslant and havens of the sea. But when he came in his swimming over against the mouth of a fair-flowing river, whereby the place seemed best in his eyes, smooth of rocks, and withal there was a covert from the wind, Odysseus felt the river running, and prayed to him in his heart:

"Hear me, O king, whosoever thou art; unto thee am I come, as to one to whom prayer is made, while I flee the rebukes of Poseidon from the deep. Yea, reverend even to the deathless gods is that man who comes as a wanderer, even as I now have come to thy stream and to thy knees after much travail. Nay pity me, O king; for I avow myself thy suppliant."

So spake he, and the god straightway stayed his stream and withheld his waves, and made the water smooth before him, and brought him safely to the mouths of the river. And his knees bowed and his stout hands fell, for his heart was broken by the brine. And his flesh was all swollen and a great stream of sea water gushed up through his mouth and nostrils. So he lay without breath or speech, swooning, such terrible weariness came upon him. But when now his breath returned and his spirit came to him again, he loosed from off him the veil of the goddess, and let it fall into the salt flowing river. And the great wave bare it back down the stream, and lightly Ino caught it in her hands. Then Odysseus turned from the river, and fell back in the reeds, and kissed earth, the grain-giver.

HOW THE GREEKS DEFEATED THE PERSIANS OFF THE ISLE OF SALAMIS[1]

Æschylus

(525 B. C.–456 B. C.)

O YE cities of the whole land of Asia! O realm of Persia, and mighty haven of opulence, how hath the ample weal been demolished by a single stroke, and the flower of the Persians is fallen and gone! The shores of Salamis, and all the adjoining region, are full of the corpses of those who miserably perished. For our bows availed us nought, and our whole host perished, beaten down by the collision of the beaks of the vessels. O name of Salamis, most hateful to our ears! Alas! how I sigh when I remember Athens. Xerxes himself lives, and beholds the light. But Artembares, leader of a myriad of horse, is dashed against the rugged shores of Sileniæ. And Dadaces the chiliarch, beneath the stroke of the spear, bounded a light leap out of his vessel. Tenagon too, the true-born chieftain of the Bactrians, haunts the sea-beat isle of Ajax. Lilæus, and Arsames, and Argestes third, overcome, keep butting against the hard shore around the dove-breeding isle. Arcteus, too, that dwelt near the sources of Egyptian Nile, Adeues, and Pheresseues the third, Pharnuchus, these fell from one vessel. Matallus of Chrysa, commander of a myriad, leader of a body of thirty thousand black cavalry, in his death, tinged his bright auburn beard, changing its colour with a stain of purple. And Arabus the Mage, and Artames the Bactrian, a settler on the rugged land, perished there. Amestris, and Amphistreus who wielded a spear that did great execution, and brave Ariomardus, occasioning grief to Sardis, and Sesames the Mysian; Tharybis, too, commander of five times fifty ships, of Lyrnæan race, a hero of fair form, lies wretched, having died by no means happily. And Syennesis, foremost in gallantry, governor of the Cilicians, that with his single arm occasioned much trouble to the foe, fell gloriously.

So far as numbers are concerned, the barbarians had the advantage with their ships: for the whole number of those of the Greeks amounted to ten squadrons of thirty, and beside these there were ten of surpassing excellence. But Xerxes, for I know this also, had a thousand, the number of those which he led; and those which exceeded in swiftness were two hundred and seven; thus runs report. 'Twas some divinity that thus depressed the balance with a counterpoise of fortune.

A Greek that had come from the host of the Athenians, told thy son Xerxes this, that, when the gloom of murky night should come, the Greeks would not remain, but, springing on the benches of their vessels,

[1] From T. A. Buckley's translation of *The Persians*. (G. Bell & Sons, Ltd.)

would severally, in different directions, save their lives by stealthy flight. And he, as soon as he heard it, not aware of the stratagem of the Greek, nor of the jealousy of the gods, publishes this order to all his captains, that when the sun should have ceased to illumine the earth with his rays, and darkness tenant the temple of the firmament, they should draw up the squadron of the ships in three lines, to guard the outlets, and the murmuring passes of the sea, and others in a circle around the isle of Ajax; so that if the Greeks should elude fatal destruction by discovering any escape for their ships by stealth, it was decreed that they all should be deprived of their heads. To this effect he spake from a frantic spirit; for he knew not that which was pre-ordained by the gods. And they, without disorder, and with obedient mind, both provided supper for themselves, and the mariner lashed his oar to the well-fitted rowlock. And when the light of the sun had waned, and night had come on, every man, master of an oar, went on board his ship, and every one that had sway over arms; and one line of ships of war cheered on another line, and they made sail as each had been appointed, and all the live-long night the commanders of the ships were keeping the whole naval host occupied in sailing about.

And night withdrew, and the force of the Greeks by no means made a stealthy escape in any direction. But when Day, drawn by white steeds, had occupied the whole earth, of radiance beautiful to behold, first of all a shout from the Greeks greeted Echo like a song, and Echo from the island-rock at the same instant shouted forth an inspiring cry: and terror fell on all the barbarians, baulked of their purpose; for not as in flight were the Greeks then chaunting the solemn paean, but speeding on to the fight with gallant daring of soul. And the trumpet, with its clang, inflamed their whole line; and forthwith, with the collision of the dashing oar, at the word of command they smote the roaring brine. And quickly were they conspicuous to view. The right wing, well marshalled, led on foremost in good order, and secondly, their whole force was coming forth against us, and we could at the same time hear a mighty shout: SONS OF THE GREEKS! ON! FREE YOUR COUNTRY, AND FREE YOUR CHILDREN, YOUR WIVES, THE ABODES TOO OF THE GODS OF YOUR FATHERS, AND THE TOMBS OF YOUR ANCESTORS; NOW IS THE CONFLICT FOR THEM ALL!

And sooth to say, a murmur of the Persian tongue met them from our line, and no longer was it the moment to delay, but forthwith ship dashed her brazen prow at ship. And a Grecian vessel commenced the engagement, and breaks off the whole of the figure-head of a Phœnician ship: and each commander severally directed his bark against another of the enemy's. At first, indeed, the torrent of the Persian armament bore up against them: but when the multitude of our ships were crowded in the strait, and no assistance could be given to one another, they were struck by their own brazen beaks, and were smashing their entire equipment of oars, and the Grecian vessels, not without science, were smiting them in a circle on all sides, and the hulls of our vessels were upturned, and the sea was no longer to behold, filled as it was with wrecks and the slaughter of men. The shores, too, and the rugged rocks were filled with the dead; and every ship, as many as ever there were in the barbaric armament, was rowed in flight without order. But the Greeks kept striking, hacking us as it were tunnies, or any draught of fishes, with fragments of oars, and splinters of wrecks; and wailing filled the ocean brine with shrieks, until the eye of murky night removed it. But for the multitude of our woes—no, not if I should recite them in order for ten days, could I complete the tale for thee.

HOW THE SHIP *ARGO* PASSED BETWEEN THE CLASHING ROCKS[1]

Apollonius Rhodius

(c. 235 B. C.–   )

NOW when the sun, rising from the east, shone upon the dewy hills, and awoke shepherds, in that hour they loosed their cables from the stem of the bay tree, and putting their booty on board, even all that they had need to carry, they steered with the wind along the swirling Bosphorus. Then did a wave like to a steep mountain rush upon them in front as though it were charging them, rearing itself ever above the clouds, and never wouldst thou have said they would escape a horrid fate, for it hung arching right over the middle of the ship in all its fury; but yet even this grows smooth, if but you possess a clever pilot. So then they too came forth, unscathed, though much afeared, through the skill of Tiphys. And on the next day they anchored over against the Bithynian land.

Here Phineus, son of Agenor, had his home beside the sea; he who by reason of the divination that the son of Leto granted him aforetime, suffered most awful woes, far beyond all men; for not one jot did he regard even Zeus himself in foretelling the sacred purpose to men unerringly. Wherefore Zeus granted him a weary length of days, but reft his eyes of the sweet light, nor suffered him to have any joy of all the countless gifts, which those who dwelt around and sought him for oracles, were ever bringing to his house. But suddenly through the clouds the Harpies darted nigh, and kept snatching them from his mouth or hands in their talons. Sometimes never a morsel of food was left him, sometimes a scrap that he might live and suffer.

At once when he heard the sound and noise of a company, he per-

[1]From Edward P. Coleridge's translation of *The Argonautica*. Reprinted by permission of G. Bell & Sons, Ltd.

ceived that they were the very men now passing by, at whose coming an oracle from Zeus had said that he should enjoy his food. Up from his couch he rose, as it were a lifeless phantom, and leaning on his staff, came to the door on his wrinkled feet, feeling his way along the walls; and as he went, his limbs trembled from weakness and age; and his skin was dry and caked with filth, and nought but the skin held his bones together. So he came forth from his hall, and sat down with heavy knees on the threshold of the court, and a dark mantle wrapped him, and seemed to sweep the ground below all round; and there he sank with never a word, in strengthless lethargy.

But they, when they saw him, gathered round and were astonished. And he, drawing a laboured breath from the bottom of his chest, took up his parable for them, and said:

"Hearken, choice sons of all the Hellenes, if 'tis you in very truth, whom now Jason, at the king's chill bidding, is leading on the ship *Argo* to fetch the fleece. 'Tis surely you. Still doth my mind know each thing by its divining. Wherefore to thee, my prince, thou son of Leto, do I give thanks even in my cruel sufferings. By Zeus, the god of suppliants, most awful god to sinful men, for Phoebus' sake and for the sake of Hera herself, who before all other gods hath had you in her keeping as ye came, help me, I implore; rescue a hapless wretch from misery, and do not heedlessly go hence and leave me thus. For not only hath the avenging fiend set his heel upon my eyes, not only do I drag out to the end a tedious old age, but yet another most bitter pain is added to the tale. Harpies, swooping from some unseen den of destruction, that I see not, do snatch the food from my mouth. Them 'tis heaven's decree that the sons of Boreas shall check; and they shall ward them off, for they are my kinsmen, if indeed I am that Phineus who, in days gone by, had a name amongst men for my wealth and divination, whom Agenor my sire, begat."

So spake the son of Agenor, and deep sorrow took hold on each of the heroes, but especially on the two sons of Boreas. But they wiped away a tear and drew nigh, and thus spake Zetes, taking in his the hand of the suffering old man.

"Ah! poor sufferer, methinks there is no other man more wretched than thee. Why is it that such woes have fastened on thee? Is it that thou hast sinned against the gods in deadly folly through thy skill in divination? Wherefore are they so greatly wroth against thee? Lo! our heart within us is sorely bewildered, though we yearn to help thee, if in very truth the god hath reserved for us twain this honour. For plain to see are the rebukes that the immortals send on us men of earth. Nor will we check the coming of the Harpies, for all our eagerness, till that thou swear that we shall not fall from heaven's favour in return for this."

So spake he, and straight that aged man opened his sightless eyes and lifted them up, and thus made answer:

"Hush! Remind me not of those things, my son. The son of Leto be
my witness, who of his kindness taught me divination be witness that
ill-omened fate that is my lot, and this dark cloud upon my eyes, and the
gods below, whose favour may I never find if I die perjured thus, that
there shall come no wrath from heaven on you by reason of your aid."

Then were those twain eager to help him by reason of the oath, and
quickly did the young men make ready a feast for the old man, a last
booty for the Harpies; and the two stood near to strike them with their
swords as they swooped down. Soon as ever that aged man did touch the
food, down rushed those Harpies with whirr of wings at once, eager for
the food, like grievous blasts or like lightning darting suddenly from the
clouds. But those heroes, when they saw them in mid air, shouted; and
they at the noise sped off afar across the sea. And the two sons of Boreas
started in pursuit of them with their swords drawn, for Zeus inspired
them with tireless courage and 'twas not without the will of Zeus that
they followed them, for they would dart past the breadth of the west
wind, what time they went to and from Phineus. As when upon the hill-
tops dogs skilled in the chase run on the track of horned goats or deer,
and straining at full speed just behind, in vain do gnash their teeth
upon their lips, even so Zetes and Calais, darting very nigh to them, in
vain grazed them with their finger-tips. And now, I trow, they would
have torn them in pieces against the will of the gods on the floating islands, after they had come afar, had not swift Iris seen them, and darting
down from the clear heaven above stayed them with this word of rebuke:

"Ye sons of Boreas, 'tis not ordained that ye should slay the Harpies,
the hounds of mighty Zeus, with your swords, but I, even I, will give you
an oath that they will come no more nigh Phineus."

Therewith she sware by the stream of Styx, most dire and awful oath
for all the gods, that these should never again draw near unto the house
of Phineus, son of Agenor, for even so was it fated. So they yielded to
her oath, and turned to hasten back to the ship. And so it is that men
call those isles "the isles of turning," though aforetime they called them
"the floating isles." And the Harpies and Iris parted; they entered their
lair in Crete, the land of Minos, but she sped up to Olympus, soaring on
her swift pinions.

Meantime the chieftains sat them down and feasted, and with them
Phineus fell a-feasting ravenously, cheering his heart as in a dream.
Then when they had taken their fill of food and drink, they sat up all
night awaiting the sons of Boreas. And in their midst beside the hearth
sat that ancient one himself, telling them of the ends of their voyage
and the fulfilment of their journey.

"Hearken then. All ye may not learn of a surety, but as much as is
heaven's will I will not hide. First of all, when ye have gone hence from
me, ye shall see the two Cyanean rocks at the place where two seas
meet. Through these, I trow, none can win a passage. For they are not

fixed on foundations below, but oft they clash together upon each other, and much salt water boils up from beneath, rearing its crest, and loud is the roar round the bluff headland.

"Wherefore now give heed to my exhorting, if in sooth ye make this voyage with cautious mind and due regard for the blessed gods: perish not then senselessly by a death of your own choosing, nor rush on at the heels of youthful rashness. First I bid you let loose from the ship a dove, and send her forth before you to try the way. And if she fly safely on her wings through those rocks to the sea, no longer do ye delay your voyage for any time, but stoutly ply the oars in your hands and cleave through the strait of sea, for now your life will depend not so much on your prayers as on your stalwart arms. Wherefore leave all other things alone and exert yourselves bravely to the utmost, yet ere you start I do not forbid you to entreat the gods. But if the dove be slain right in mid passage, fare ye back again, for far better it is to yield to the deathless gods. For then could ye not escape an evil doom at the rocks, no, not if Argo were made of iron.

"And these things shall be even as they may. But if ye escape the clashing of the rocks and come scathless inside Pontus, forthwith keep the Bithynian land upon your right, and sail cautiously amid the breakers, till that ye round the swift current of the river Rhebas and the Black headland, and be come to a haven in the Thynian isle. Thence return a short stretch across the sea, and beach your ship on the opposite shore of the Mariandyni. There is a path down to Hades, and the headland of Acherusia juts out and stretches itself on high, and swirling Acheron, cutting through the foot of the cliff, pours itself forth from a mighty ravine. Very nigh to it shall ye pass by many hills of the Paphlagonians, over whom Pelops first held sway in Enete, of whose blood they avow them to be. Now there is a certain cliff that fronts the circling Bear, on all sides steep: men call it Carambis; above it the gusty north is parted in twain; in such wise is it turned toward the sea, towering to heaven. At once when a man hath rounded it a wide beach stretches before him, and at the end of that wide beach nigh to a jutting cliff the stream of the river Halys, terribly discharges, and after him, but flowing near, the Iris rolls into the sea, a lesser stream with clear ripples. Here in front a great and towering bend stands out; next, Thermodon's mouth flows into a sleeping bay near the Themiscyrean headland, from its meandering through a wide continent. There is the plain of Doias, and hard by are the triple cities of the Amazons; and after them the Chalybes inhabit a rough and stubborn land, of all men most wretched, labourers they, busied with working of iron. Near them dwell the Tibareni, rich in sheep, beyond the Gentæan headland, where is a temple of Zeus, lord of hospitality. Next beyond this, but nigh thereto, the Mossynæci hold the woody mainland and the foot of the mountain, men that have builded houses of timber with wooden battlements and chambers deftly finished, which they call Mossynæ, and hence they have their name.

"Coast on past them, and anchor at a smooth isle, after ye have driven off with all the skill ye may those ravening birds, which, men say, do roost upon this desert isle in countless numbers. Therein the queens of the Amazons builded a temple of stone to Ares, even Otrere and Antiope, what time they went forth to battle. Now here shall there come to you from out the bitter sea a help ye looked not for, wherefore of good will I bid you there to stay. But hold! why should I once more offend by telling everything from beginning to end in my divining? In front of the island, on the mainland opposite, dwell the Philyres: higher up, beyond them, are the Macrones: and yet beyond these, the countless tribes of the Becheiri. Next to them dwell the Sapeires, and their neighbours are the Byzeres, and right beyond them come next the warlike Colchians themselves.

"But cleave on your way, until ye come nigh to the inmost sea. There across the Cytæan mainland, from the Amarantian hills afar, and the plain of Circe, the swirling Phasis rolls his broad stream into the sea. Drive your ship into the mouth of that river, and ye shall see the towers of Cytæan Æetes and the shady grove of Ares, where a dragon, dire monster to behold, watches from his ambush round the fleece as it hangs on the top of an oak; nor night nor day doth sweet sleep o'ercome his restless eyes."

So spake he, and as they hearkened, fear fell on them forthwith. Long were they struck with speechlessness: at last spake the hero, the son of Æson, sorely at a loss:

"Old man, lo! now hast thou rehearsed the end of our toilsome voyage, and the sure sign which, if we obey, we shall pass through those loathèd rocks to Pontus; but whether there shall be a return again to Hellas for us, if we do escape them, this too would I fain learn of thee. How am I to act, how shall I come again over so wide a path of sea, in ignorance myself and with a crew alike ignorant? For Colchian Æa lieth at the uttermost end of Pontus and the earth."

So spake he, and to him did that old man make answer:

"My child, as soon as thou hast escaped through those rocks of death, be of good cheer, for a god will guide thee on a different route from Æa; and toward Æa there shall be plenty to guide thee. Yea, friends, bethink you of the crafty aid of the Cyprian goddess. For by her is prepared a glorious end to your toils. But question me no further of these matters."

So spake the son of Agenor, and the two sons of Thracian Boreas came glancing down from heaven, and set their rushing feet upon the threshold beside them. Up sprang the heroes from their seats, when they saw them coming near. And among the eager throng Zetes made harangue, drawing great gasps for breath after his toil, and told them how far they had journeyed, and how Iris prevented them from slaying the Harpies, and how the goddess in her favour gave them an oath, and those others slunk away in terror 'neath the vast cavern of the cliff of Dicte. Glad then were all their comrades in the house, and Phineus himself, at the news.

And anon, in no long space, as they talked the dawn appeared, and the neighbouring folk came round Phineus, they who even aforetime gathered thither day by day, ever bringing a portion of food for him. And unto all of them that aged man with good will gave oracles; wherefore they would visit and care for him. With these came Peræbius, the man most dear to him, and glad was he to hear them in his house. For long before had he himself declared that an expedition of chieftains, on its way from Hellas to the city of Æetes, should fasten its cables to the Thynian land, and they should restrain by Zeus's will the Harpies from coming to him.

And the chiefs abode there by constraint, and every day the Thynians sent forth good store of gifts for the strangers, out of favour for Phineus.

After this, when they had builded an altar to the twelve blessed gods on the edge of the sea opposite, and had offered sacrifice upon it, they went aboard their swift ship to row away, nor did they forget to take with them a timorous dove, but Euphemus clutched her in his hand, cowering with terror, and carried her along, and they loosed their double cables from the shore.

Nor, I ween, had they started ere Athene was ware of them, and forthwith and hastily she stepped upon a light cloud, which should bear her at once for all her weight; and she hasted on her way seaward, with kindly intent to the rowers. As when a man goes wandering from his country, as oft we men do wander in our hardihood, and there is no land too far away, for every path lies open before his eyes, when lo! he seeth in his mind his own home, and withal there appeareth a way to it over land or over sea, and keenly he pondereth this way and that, and searcheth it out with his eyes, even so the daughter of Zeus, swiftly darting on, set foot upon the cheerless strand of Thynia.

Now they, when they came to the strait of the winding passage, walled in with beetling crags on either side, while an eddying current from below washed up against the ship as it went on its way; and on they went in grievous fear, and already on their ears the thud of clashing rocks smote unceasingly, and the dripping cliffs roared; in that very hour the hero Euphemus clutched the dove in his hand, and went to take his stand upon the prow, while they, at the bidding of Tiphys, son of Hagnias, rowed with a will, that they might drive right through the rocks, trusting in their might. And as they rounded a bend, they saw those rocks opening for the last time of all. And their spirit melted at the sight; but the hero Euphemus sent forth the dove to dart through on her wings, and they, one and all, lifted up their heads to see, and she sped through them, but at once the two rocks met again with a clash; and the foam leapt up in a seething mass like a cloud, and grimly roared the sea, and all around the great firmament bellowed. And the hollow caves echoed beneath the rugged rocks as the sea went surging in, and high on the cliffs was the white spray vomited as the billow dashed upon them. Then did the current spin the ship round. And the rocks cut off just the tail-feathers of the dove, but she darted away unhurt. And loudly the rowers cheered, but Tiphys himself shouted to them to row lustily, for once more the rocks were opening.

Then came trembling on them as they rowed, until the wave with its returning wash came and bore the ship within the rocks. Thereon most awful fear seized on all, for above their head was death with no escape; and now on this side and on that lay broad Pontus to their view, when suddenly in front rose up a mighty arching wave, like to a steep hill, and they bowed down their heads at the sight. For it seemed as if it must indeed leap down and whelm the ship entirely. But Tiphys was quick to ease her as she laboured to the rowing, and the wave rolled with all his force beneath the keel, and lifted up the ship herself from underneath, far from the rocks, and high on the crest of the billow she was borne. Then did Euphemus go amongst all the crew, and call to them to lay on to their oars with all their might, and they smote the water at his cry. So she sprang forward twice as far as any other ship would have yielded to rowers, and the oars bent like curved bows as the heroes strained. In that instant the vaulted wave was past them, and she at once was riding over the furious billow like a roller, plunging headlong forward o'er the trough of the sea.

But the eddying current stayed the ship in the midst of the Clashers, and they quaked on either side, and thundered, and the ship-timbers throbbed. Then did Athene with her left hand hold the stubborn rock apart, while with her right she thrust them through upon their course; and the ship shot through the air like a wingèd arrow. Yet the rocks, ceaselessly dashing together, crushed off in passing the tip of the carved stern. And Athene sped back to Olympus, when they were escaped unhurt. But the rocks closed up together, rooted firm for ever; even so was it decreed by the blessed gods, whenso a man should have passed through alive in his ship. And they, I trow, drew breath again after their chilling fear, as they gazed out upon the sky, and the expanse of sea spreading far and wide. For verily they deemed that they were saved from Hades, and Tiphys first made harangue:

"Methinks we have escaped this danger sure enough, we and the ship, and there is no other we have to thank so much as Athene, who inspired the ship with divine courage, when Argus fastened her together with bolts; and it is not right that she should be caught. Wherefore, son of Æson, no more fear at all the bidding of thy king, since God hath granted us to escape through the rocks, for Phineus, son of Agenor, declared that, after this, toils easy to master should be ours."

Therewith he made the ship speed past the Bithynian coast across the sea. But the other answered him with gentle words:

"Ah! Tiphys, why comfort my heavy heart thus? I have sinned, and upon me has come a grievous blindness I may not cope with; for I should have refused this journey outright at once when Pelias ordained it, even though I was to have died, torn ruthlessly limb from limb; but now do I endure exceeding terror, and troubles past bearing, in deadly dread to sail across the chill paths of the deep, in deadly dread whene'er we land. For on all sides are enemies. And ever as the days go by, I watch through the dreary night, and think of all since first ye mustered for my sake; and lightly dost thou speak, caring only for thine own life, while I fear never so little for myself, but for this man and for that, for thee and the rest of my comrades do I fear, if I bring you not safe and sound to Hellas."

So spake he, making trial of the chieftains; but they cried out with words of cheer. And his heart was glad within him at their exhorting, and once more he spake to them outright.

"My friends, your bravery makes me more bold. Wherefore now no more will I let fear fasten on me, even though I must voyage across the gulf of Hades, since ye stand firm amid cruel terrors. Nay, since we have sailed from out the clashing rocks, I trow there will be no other horror in store such as this, if we surely go our way, following the counsel of Phineus."

HOW LUCIAN OF SAMOTHRACE VOYAGED TO THE MOON AND HOW HE WAS AFTERWARD SWALLOWED BY A WHALE[1]

Lucian of Samothrace
(125 A. D.–180 A. D.)

DISANKERING on a time from the pillars of *Hercules*, the winde fitting mee well for my purpose, I thrust into the West Ocean: the occasion that moved mee to take such a voyage in hand, was onely a curiositie of minde, a desire of novelties, and a longing to learne out the bounds of the Ocean, and what people inhabit the farther shoare: for which purpose, I made plentifull provision of victualls and fresh-water, got fiftie companions of the same humour to associate mee in my travells, furnished my self with store of munition, gave a round summe of money to an expert pilot that could direct us in our course, and new rigd, and repair'd a tall ship strongly, to hold a tedious and difficult journey: Thus sailed wee forward a day and a night with a prosperous winde, and as long as wee had any sight of land, made no great hast on our way: but the next morrow about sunne rising, the winde blew high, and the waves began to swell, and a darknesse fell upon us, so that wee could not see to

[1]From *The True History*, translated by Mr. Francis Hickes (1634).

strike our sailes, but gave our ship over to the winde and weather: thus were we tost in this tempest, the space of three-score and nineteene daies together, on the fourescorth day, the sunne upon a sudden brake out, and we descried not farre off us, an Island full of mountaines and woods, about the which the seas did not rage so boisterously, for the storme was now reasonably well calm'd: there we thrust in, and went on shoare, and cast our selves upon the ground, and so lay a long time, as utterly tired with our miserie at sea. . . .

On the morrow wee put to sea againe, the winde serving us weakely, but about noone, when wee had lost sight of the Island, upon a suddaine a whirlewinde caught us, which turned our shippe round about, and lifted us up some three thousand furlongs into the aire, and suffered us not to settle againe into the sea, but wee hung above ground, and were carried aloft with a mightie wind which filled our sailes strongly. Thus for seven daies space and so many nights, were wee driven along in that manner, and on the eighth day, wee came in view of a great countrie in the aire, like to a shining Island, of a round proportion, curiously glittering with light, and approaching to it, we there arrived, and tooke land, and surveying the countrie, wee found it to be both inhabited and husbanded: and as long as the day lasted we could see nothing there, but when night was come many other Islands appeared unto us, some greater and some lesse, all of the colour of fire, and another kind of earth underneath, in which were cities, and seas, and rivers, and woods, and mountaines, which we conjectured to be the earth by us inhabited: and going further into the land, we were met withall and taken by those kind of people, which they call *Hippogypians:* these *Hippogypians* are men riding upon monstrous vultures: which they use instead of horses: for the vultures there are exceeding great, every one with three heads apiece: you may imagine their greatnesse by this: for every feather in their wings was bigger and longer than the mast of a tall ship: their charge was to flie about the countrie, and all the strangers they found to bring them to the King: and their fortune was then to seize upon us, and by them wee were presented to him: As soone as he saw us, he conjectured by our habit what country-men we were, and said:

"Are not you strangers *Grecians?*"

Which when wee affirmed,

"And how could you make way," said hee, "thorow so much aire as o get hither?"

Then wee delivered the whole discourse of our fortunes to him, whereupon hee began to tell us likewise of his owne adventures, how that hee also was a man, by name *Endymion*, and rapt up long since from the earth, as hee was asleep, and brought hither, where hee was made King of the Countrie, and said it was that region: which to us below seemed to bee the Moone, but hee bad us be of good cheare, and feare no danger, for wee should want nothing wee stood in need of. . . .

Then we tooke our leaves of the King, and tooke shipping, and departed: at which' time *Endymion* bestowed upon mee two mantles made of their glasse, and five of brasse, with a compleat armour of those shells of.lupines all which I left behinde in the whale; and sent with us a thousand of his *Hippogypians* to conduct us five hundred furlongs on our way: In our course wee coasted many other countries, and lastly arrived at the Morning Starre now newly inhabited, where wee landed, and tooke in fresh water: from thence wee entred the *Zodiake*, passing by the Sunne, and leaving it on our right hand tooke our course neare unto the shoare, but landed not in the countrie, though our companie did much desire it, for the winde would not give us leave. . . .

Wee made forwards, all the next night and day, and about eveningtide following wee came to a citie called *Lychnopolis*, still holding on our course downwards: this citie is seated in the aire betweene the *Pleiades* and the *Hyades*, somewhat lower than the *Zodiake*, and arriving there, not a man was to be seene, but lights in great numbers running to and fro, which were imployed, some in the market-place, and some about the haven, of which many were little, and as a man may say, but poore things, some againe were great and mightie, exceeding glorious and resplendent, and there were places of receipt for them all: every one had his name as well as men, and we did heare them speake: these did us no harme, but invited us to feaste with them, yet wee were so fearfull, that we durst neither eate nor sleepe as long as we were there. . . .

And on the next morrow we returned to our ship: and sailing neare unto the clouds had a sight of the citie *Nephelococcygia*, which wee beheld with great wonder, but entred not into it, for the winde was against us. . . . The third day after, the Ocean appeared plainly unto us, though wee could see no land, but what was in the aire: and these countries also seemed to be fierie and of a glittering colour: the fourth day about noone, the wind gently forbearing, settled us faire and leasurely into the sea: and as soon as wee found our selves upon water, we were surprised with incredible gladnesse, and our joy was unexpressible: we feasted and made merrie with such provision as wee had, wee cast our selves into the sea, and swamme up and downe for our disport, for it was a calme. But oftentimes it falleth out that the change to the better, is the beginning of greater evils: for when wee had made onely two daies saile in the water, as soone as the third appeared, about Sun-rising, upon a suddaine wee saw many monstrous fishes and whales: but one above the rest containing in greatnesse fifteene hundred furlongs: which came gaping upon us and troubled the sea round about him, so that hee was compassed on every side with froth and fome, shewing his teeth a farre off, which were longer than any beech trees are with us, all as sharpe as needles, and as white as Ivorie; then wee tooke, as wee thought, our last leaves one of another, and embracing together, expected our ending day: the monster was presently with us, and swallowed us up shippe and all: but by chance,

he caught us not betweene his chops, for the ship slipt thorow the void
passages downe into his entralls: when wee were thus got within him we
continued a good while in darknesse and could see nothing, till hee began
to gape, and then wee perceived it to be a monstrous whale of a huge
breadth and high, bigge enough to containe a citie that would hold tenne
thousand men: and within wee found small fishes, and many other
creatures chopt in pieces, and the masts of ships, and ankers, and bones
of men, and luggage. In the midst of him was earth and hills, which
were raised, as I conjectured, by the settling of the mudde which came
down his throat: for woods grew upon them and trees of all sorts, and all
manner of hearbes, and it looked as if it had beene husbanded: the
compasse of the land was two hundred and fortie furlongs: there were
also to be seene all kinds of sea-fowle, as gulls, halcyons, and others that
had made their nests upon the trees: then we fell to weeping abundantly:
but at the last I rows'd up my companie and propt up our ship: and
stroke fier: then wee made ready supper of such as wee had, for abundance of all sort of fish lay ready by us, and wee had yet water enough
left which wee brought out of the Morning Starre: the next morning
we rose to watch when the whale should gape: and then looking out, we
could sometimes see mountaines, sometimes onely the skies, and many
times Islands: for we found that the fish carried himselfe with great
swiftnesse to every part of the sea: when wee grew wearie of this, I tooke
seaven of my company and went into the wood to see what I could finde
there, and wee had not gone above five furlongs, but we light upon a
temple erected to *Neptune*, as by the title appeared: and not farre off wee
espied many sepulchers and pillars placed upon them, with a fountaine
of cleare water close unto it; we also heard the barking of a dogge, and
saw smoake rise a farre off, so that wee judged there was some dwelling
thereabout: wherefore making the more hast, wee lighted upon an old
man and a youth, who were very busie in making a garden and in conveying water by a channall from the fountaine into it: whereupon wee
were surprised both with joy and feare: and they also were brought into
the same taking, and for a long time remained mute: but after some
pause, the old man said:

"What are yee, you strangers? any of the sea spirits? or miserable men
like unto us? for wee that are men by nature, borne and bred in the earth,
are now sea-dwellers, and swimme up and downe within the Continent
of this whale, and know not certainly what to think of our selves: wee
are like to men that be dead; and yet believe our selves to be alive."

Whereunto I answered:

"For our parts, father, we are men also, newly come hither, and swallowed up ship and all but yesterday: and now come purposely within this
wood, which is so large and thicke: some good angell, I thinke, did guide
us hither to have the sight of you, and to make us know, that wee are
not the onely men confin'd within this monster: tell us therefore your

fortunes wee beseech you, what you are, and how you came into this place."

But hee answered:

"You shall not heare a word from mee, nor aske any more questions, untill you have taken part of such viands as wee are able to afford you."

So hee tooke us, and brought us into his house, which was sufficient to serve his turne, his pallets were prepared, and all things else made readie: then hee set before us herbes, and nuts, and fish, and fild out of his owne wine unto us: and when wee were sufficiently satisfied, hee then demanded of us what fortunes wee had endured, and I related all things to him in order that had betide unto us, even till our diving into the whale: whereat hee wondered exceedingly, and began to deliver also what had befalne to him, and said:

"By linage, O yee strangers, I am of the Island of *Cyprus*, and travelling from mine owne countrie as a marchant, with this my sonne you see here, and many other friends with mee, made a voyage for *Italie* in a great ship full fraught with marchandise, which perhaps you have seene broken in pieces in the mouth of the whale: wee sailed with faire weather, till wee were as farre as *Sicilie:* but there wee were overtaken with such a boistrous storme, that the third day wee were driven into the Ocean, where it was our fortune to meete with this whale which swallowed us all up, and onely wee two escaped with our lives, all the rest perished, whom wee have here buried and built a temple to *Neptune:* ever since wee have continued this course of life, planting hearbs and feeding upon fish and nuts: here is wood enough you see, and plentie of vines which yield most delicate wine: wee have also a well of excellent coole water, which it may be you have seene: wee make our beddes of the leaves of trees, and burne as much wood as we will: wee chace after the birds that flie about us, and goe out upon the gills of the monster to catch after live fishes: here wee bath our selves when wee are disposed, for wee have a lake of salt water not farre off, about some twentie furlongs in compasse, full of sundrie sorts of fish, in which wee swimme and saile upon it in a little boat of mine owne making; This is the seven and twentieth yeare of our drowning, and with all this wee might be well enough contented, if our neighbours, and borderers about us were not perverse and troublesome, altogether insociable and of sterne condition."

"Is it so indeed?" said I, "that there should be any within the whale but your selves?"

"Many," said hee, "and such as are unreconcileable towards strangers, and of monstrous and deformed proportions: the westerne countries and the taile-part of the wood, are inhabited by the *Tarychanians*, that looke like eeles, with faces like a lobster: these are warlike, fierce, and feed upon raw fish: they that dwell towards the right side, are called *Tritonomenditans*, which have their upper parts like unto men, their lower parts like cattes, and are lesse offensive than the rest: On the left side inhabit the *Cancinochirians* and the *Thinocephalians*, which are in league one with another: the middle region is possest by the *Pagurodians*, and the *Psittopodians*, a warlike nation and swift of foot: eastwards towards the mouth is for the most part desart, as overwasht with the sea: yet am I faine to take that for my dwelling, paying yearly to the *Psittopodians*, in way of tribute, five hundred oysters: of so many nations doth this countrie consist: wee must therefore devise among our selves, either how to be able to fight with them, or how to live among them."

"What number may they all amount unto?" said I.

"More than a thousand," said hee.

"And what armour have they?"

"None at all," said hee, "but the bones of fishes."

"Then were it our best course," said I, "to incounter them, being provided as wee are, and they without weapons; for if wee prove too hard for them we shall afterward live out of feare."

This wee concluded upon, and went to our ship to furnish our selves with armes: the occasion of war we gave by Nonpayment of tribute, which then was due: for they sent their messengers to demand it, to whom hee gave a harsh and scornfull answer, and sent them packing with their arrant: but the *Psittopodians* and *Pagurodians*, taking it ill at the hands of *Scintharus*, for so was the man named, came against us with great tumult; and wee suspecting what they would do, stood upon our guard to wait for them, and laid five and twentie of our men in ambush, commanding them as soone as the enemie was past bye, to set upon them: who did so, and arose out of their ambush, and fell upon the reare: we also being five and twentie in number (for Scintharus and his sonne were marshalled among us) advanced to meet with them, and encountred them with great courage and strength: but in the end wee put them to flight and pursued them to their very dennes: of the enemies were slain an hundred three-score and tenne: and but one of us beside *Trigles* our pilot, who was thrust thorow the backe with a fishes ribbe: all that day following, and the night after, we lodged in our trenches, and set on end a drie backe bone of a Dolphin, instead of a Trophie: The next morrow, the rest of the countrie people perceiving what had happened, came to assault us: the *Tarichanians*, were ranged in the right wing, with *Pelamus* their Captaine: the *Thynocephalians* were placed in the left wing, the *Carcinochirians* made up the maine battell: for the *Tritonomenditans* stirred not, neither would they joyne with either part: about the temple of *Neptune* we met with them, and joyned fight with a great crie; which was answered with an eccho out of the whale as if it had beene out of a cave: but wee soone put them to flight being naked people, and chased them into the wood, making our selves masters of the countrie: soone after they sent Embassadores to us, to crave the bodies of the dead, and to treat upon conditions of peace: but we had no purpose to hold friendship with them, but set upon them the next day and put them all to the sword, except the *Tritonomenditans,* who seeing how it fared with the rest of their fellows, fled away thorow the gills of the fish, and cast themselves into the sea. Then wee travelled all the countrie over, which now was desart, and dwelt there afterwards without feare of enemies, spending the time in exercise of the body, and in hunting, in planting vineyards, and gathering fruit of the trees, like such men as live delicately, and have the world at will, in a spatious and unavoidable prison: this kind of life led wee for a yeare and eight moneths: but when the fifth day of the ninth moneth was come, about the time of the second opening of his mouth (for so the whale did once every howre, whereby we conjectured how the houres went away) I say about the second opening, upon a sudden, we heard a great cry, and a mighty noise, like the calls of mariners, and the stirring of oares, which troubled us not a little: wherefore we crept up to the very mouth of the fish, and standing within his teeth, saw the strangest sight that ever eye beheld: men of monstrous greatnesse, halfe a furlong in stature, sailing upon mightie great Islands as if they were upon ship board: I know you will think this smells like a lie, but yet you shall have it: the Islands were of a good length indeed, but not very high, containing about an hundred furlongs in compasse, everie of these carried of those kinde of men, eight and twentie, of which some sate on either side of the Island, and rowed in their course with great *Cypres* trees, branches, leaves, and all, instead of oares: on the sterne or hinder part, as I take it, stood the governour, upon a high hill, with a brasen rudder of a furlong in length in his hand: on the forepart stood fortie such fellows as those: armed for the fight, resembling men in all points, but in their haire, which was all fire and burnt clearly, so that they needed no helmets: instead of sailes, the wood growing in the Island did serve their turnes, for the winde blowing against it, drave forward the Island like a ship, and carried it which way the governour would have it, for they had Pilots to direct them, and were as nimble to be stird with oares as any long boate: at the first wee had the fight but of two or three of them: afterwards appeared no lesse than sixe hundred, which dividing themselves in two parts, prepared for incounter, in which many of them by meeting with their barkes together were broken in pieces: many were turned over and drowned: they that closed, fought lustily, and would not easily be parted, for the souldiers in the front shewed a great deale of valour, entring one upon another, and kill'd all they could, for none were taken prisoners: instead of iron grapples, they had mightie great *Polypodes* fast tied, which they cast at the other, and if they once laid hold on the wood, they made the Isle sure enough for stirring: they darted and wounded one another with oisters that would fill a waine, and spunges as bigge as an acre: the leader of the one side was *Æolocentaurus,* and of the other *Thalassopotes:* the quarrell, as it seemes, grew about taking a bootie: for they said that *Thalassopotes* drave away many flockes of dolphins that belonged to *Æolocentaurus,* as we heard by their clamours one to another, and calling upon the names of their kings: but *Ælocentaurus* had the better of the day and sunke one hundred and fiftie of the enemies Islands, and three they tooke with the men and all: the rest withdrew themselves and fled, whom the other pursued, but not farre, because it grew towards evening, but returned to those that were wrackt and broken, which they also recovered for the most part, and tooke their own awaie with them: for on their part there were no lesse than fourscore Islands drowned: then they erected a Trophie for a monument of this Island fight, and fastned one of the enemies Islands with a stake upon the head of the whale: that night they lodged close by the beast, casting their cables about him, and ankered neare unto him: their ankers are huge and great made all of glasse, but of a wonderfull strength: the morrow after when they had sacrificed upon the top of the whale, and there buried their dead, they sailed away, with great triumph and songs of victorie, and this was the manner of the Islands fight.

Upon this we began to be wearie of our abode in the whale, and our tarriance there did much trouble us, we therefore set all our wits aworke to finde out some means or other to cleare us from our captivitie: first, we thought it would do well to digge a hole thorow his right side, and make our escape that way forth, which we began to labour at lustily: but after we had pierced him five furlongs deep, and found it was to no purpose, we gave it over: Then wee devised to set the wood on fire, for that would certainly kill him without all question, and being once dead, our issue would be easie enough: this wee also put in practice, and began our project at the taile end, which burnt seven daies, and as many nights, before hee had any feeling of our fire workes: upon the eighth and nineth daies we perceived he began to grow sickly: for he gaped more dully than hee was wont to do, and sooner closed his mouth againe: the tenth and eleventh he was thoroughly mortified, and began to sinke: upon the twelfth day we bethought our selves, though almost too late, that unless we underpropt his chops, when he gaped next, to keepe them from closing, we should be in danger of perpetuall imprisonment within his dead carcasse, and there miserably perish, we therefore pitcht long beames of timber upright within his mouth to keepe it from shutting, and then made our ship in a readinesse, and provided our selves with store of fresh water, and all other things necessary for our use, *Scintharus* taking upon him to be our pilot, and the next morrow the whale died: then we haled our ship thorow the void passages, and fastning cables about his teeth, by little and little setled it into the Sea.

THE MIGHT OF THE WHALE[1]

Oppian

(fl. c. A. D. 177–A. D. 180)

THE Sea-monsters that are nurtured in the midst of the seas are very many in number and of exceeding size. And not often do they come up out of the brine, but by reason of their heaviness they keep the bottom of the sea below. And they rave for food with unceasing frenzy, being always anhungered and never abating the gluttony of their terrible maw: for what food shall be sufficient to fill the void of their belly or enough to satisfy and give a respite to their insatiable jaws? Moreover, they themselves also destroy one another, the mightier in valour slaying the weaker, and one for the other is food and feast. Often too they bring terror to ships when they meet them in the Iberian sea in the West, where chiefly, leaving the infinite water of the neighbouring Ocean, they roll upon their way, like unto ships of twenty oars. Often also they stray and come nigh the beach where the water is deep inshore: and there one may attack them.

For all the great beasts of the sea, save the Dog-fishes, travelling is heavy-limbed and not easy. For they neither see far nor do they travel over all the sea, burdened as they are with their vast limbs, but very tardily they roll upon their way. Wherefore also with all of them there travels a companion fish, dusky to the eye and long of body and with a thin tail: which conspicuously goes before to guide them and show them their path in the sea; for which cause men call it the Guide. But to the Whale it is a companion that hath found wondrous favour, as guide at once and guard; and it easily bringeth him whither he will. For that is the only fish that he follows, the ever-loyal comrade of a loyal friend. And it wheels about near him and close by the eyes of the Whale it extends its tail, which tells the monster everything—whether there is some prey to seize or whether some evil threatens nigh, or if there is a shallow depth of sea which it were better to avoid. Even as if it had a voice, the tail declares all things to him truly, and the burden of the water obeys. For that fish is to the beast champion at once and ears and eyes: by it the Whale hears, by it he sees, to it he entrusts the reins of his life for keeping. Even as a son lovingly entreats his aged father, by anxious care of his years repaying the price of his nurture, and zealously attends and cherishes him, weak now of limb and dim of eye, reaching him his arm in the street and himself in all works succouring him—sons are a new strength to an aged sire: so that fish for love cherishes the monster of the

---

[1] From A. W. Mair's translation of *Halieutica*, in the Loeb Classical Library. Reprinted by permission of the editors.

brine, steering as it were a ship by the guiding helm. Surely it had blood
akin to his from earliest birth or he took it of his own will and made it
his companion. Thus neither valour nor beauty hath such profit as
wisdom, and strength with unwisdom is vain. A little man of good counsel sinks or saves the man of might; for even the invincible Whale
with its unapproachable limbs takes for its friend a tiny fish. Therefore
one should first capture that scouting Guide, entrapping it with might
of hook and bait; for while it lives thou shalt never overpower and conquer the monster, but when it is gone, his destruction will be swifter. For
he no longer knows surely the paths of the violet brine nor knows to
shun the evil that is at hand, but, even as a merchant vessel whose
steersman has perished, he wanders idly, defenceless and helpless, wherever the grey water carries him, and is borne in darkling and unguessed
ways, widowed of his helpful charioteer. Many a time in his wandering
he runs aground on rock or beach: such darkness is spread upon his eyes.
Thereupon with eager thoughts the fishers hasten to the labour of the
hunt, praying to the blessed gods of whale-killing that they may capture
the dread monster of Amphitrite. As when a strong company of foemen,
having waited for midnight, stealthily approach their enemy and find
by favour of Ares the sentinels asleep before the gates and fall upon
them and overcome them: thereupon they haste confidently to the high
city and the very citadel, carrying the weapon of fire, the doom of the
city, even the brand that wrecks the well-builded walls: even so confidently do the fisher host haste after the beast, unguarded now that his
pilot is slain. First they conjecture in their minds his weight and size;
and these are the signs that tell the measure of his limbs. If, as he rolls
amid the waves of the sea, he rise a little above it, showing the top of his
spine and the ridge of his neck, then verily he is a mighty beast and
excellent: for not even the sea itself can easily support and carry him.
But if some portion of his back also appears, that does not announce so
great a weight: for feebler beasts travel a more buoyant path. For these
monsters the line is fashioned of many strands of well-woven cord, as
thick as the forestay of a ship, neither very large nor very small, and in
length suitable to the prey. The well-wrought hook is rough and sharp
with barbs projecting alternately on either side, strong enough to take a
rock and pierce a cliff and with deadly curve as great as the gape of the
beast can cover. A coiled chain is cast about the butt of the dark hook—a
stout chain of beaten bronze to withstand the deadly violence of his
teeth and the spears of his mouth. In the midst of the chain are set round
wheels close together, to stay his wild struggles and prevent him from
straightway breaking the iron in his bloody agony, as he tosses in deadly
pain, but let him roll and wheel in his fitful course. For fatal banquet
they put upon the hook a portion of the black liver of a bull or a bull's
shoulder suited to the jaws of the banqueter. To accompany the hunters,
as it were for war, are sharpened many strong harpoons and stout

tridents and bills and axes of heavy blade and other such weapons as are forged upon the noisy anvil. Swiftly they go on board their well-benched ships, silently nodding to one another as need may be, and set forth. With quiet oars they gently make white the sea, carefully avoiding any noise, lest the great Whale remark aught and dive into the depths for refuge, and the task of the fishers be undertaken in vain. But when they draw nigh to him and close with their task, then boldly from the prow they launch for the giant beast the fatal snare. And when he espies the grievous banquet, he springs and disregards it not, obedient to his shameless belly, and rushing upon the hookèd death he seizes it; and immediately the whetted hook enters within his wide throat and he is impaled upon the barbs. Then, roused by the wound, first, indignant, he shakes his deadly jaw against them and strives to break the brazen cord; but his labour is vain. Then, next, in the anguish of fiery pain he dives swiftly into the nether gulfs of the sea. And speedily the fishers allow him all the length of the line; for there is not in men strength enough to pull him up and to overcome the heavy monster against his will. For easily could he drag them to the bottom, benched ship and all together, when he set himself to rush. Straightway as he dives they let go with him into the water large skins filled with human breath and fastened to the line. And he, in the agony of his pain, heeds not the hides but lightly drags them down, all unwilling and fain for the surface of the foamy sea. But when he comes to the bottom with labouring heart, he halts, greatly foaming in his distress. As some horse when it has accomplished its sweaty labour to the utmost goal, in a bloody foam grinds his teeth in the crooked bit, while the hot panting breath comes through his mouth: so, breathing hard, the Whale rests. But the skins allow him not, even if he would, to remain below, but swiftly speed upward and leap forth from the sea, buoyed by the breath within them; and a new contest arises for the Whale. Then first he makes a vain rush with his jaws, eager to defend himself against the hides which pull him up. But these fly upward and await him not, but flee like living things seeking escape. And he indignant rushes again to the innermost deep of the brine, and many a twist and turn he makes, now perforce, now of his own will, pulling and being pulled in turn. As when woodcutters labour busily at the joint labour of the saw, when they haste to make a keel or other needful matter for mariners: both men in turn draw to them the rough edge of iron pressing on the wood and the row of its teeth is never turned in one path, but urged from either side it sings loudly as it saws and evermore is drawn the other way: even such is the contest between the hides and the deadly beast—he being dragged up, while they are urged the other way. Much bloody spume he discharges over the sea as he struggles in his pain, and his panting breath as he rages resounds under the sea, and the water bubbles and roars around; thou wouldst say that all the blasts of Boreas were housed and hidden beneath the waves: so violently he pants in his fury. And round about many a swirling eddy the swelling waves make a hollow in the waters and the sea is divided in twain. As by the mouth of the Ionian and Tyrrhenian seas the dividing waters of the Strait roll raging under the violent panting of Typhaon and dread straining swirls curve the swift wave and dark Charybdis circles round, drawn by her eddying tides: even so by the panting blasts of the Whale the space of the sea around is lashed and whirled about. Then should one of the whalers row his hollow skiff and come to land and make fast the line to a rock upon the shore and straightway return—even as a man makes fast a ship by cables from the stern. Now when the deadly beast is tired with his struggles and drunk with pain and his fierce heart is bent with weariness and the balance of hateful doom inclines, then first of all a skin comes to the surface, announcing the issue of victory and greatly uplifts the hearts of the fishers. Even as, when a herald returns from dolorous war in white raiment and with cheerful face, his friends exulting follow him, expecting straightway to hear favourable tidings, so do the fishers exult when they behold the hide, the messenger of good news, rising from below. And immediately other skins rise up and emerge from the sea, dragging in their train the huge monster, and the deadly beast is hauled up all unwillingly, distraught in spirit with labour and wounds. Then the courage of the fishers is roused and with hasting blades they row their well-oared boats near. And much noise and much shouting resound upon the sea as they haste and exhort one another to the struggle. Thou wouldst say thou wert beholding the toil of men in war; such valour rises in their hearts and there is such din and such desire for battle. Far away some goatherd hears their horrid noise, or some shepherd tending his woolly flock in the glens, or woodcutter felling the pine, or hunter slaying wild beasts, and astonished he draws near to sea and shore and standing on a cliff beholds the tremendous toil of the men in this warfare of the sea and the issue of the wondrous hunt, while quenchless lust of war in the water stirs the men. Then one brandishes in his hands the long-barbed trident, another the sharp-pointed lance, others carry the well-bent bill, another wields the two-edged axe. All toil, the hands of all are armed with mighty blade of iron, and close at hand they smite and wound the beast with sweeping blows. And he forgets his mighty valour and is no more able, for all his endeavour, to stay the hasting ships with his jaws, but with heavy sweep of flippers and with the end of his tail he ploughs up the waves of the deep and drives back the ships sternward and turns to naught the work of the oars and the valour of the men, even as a contrary wind that rolls the waves against the prow. The cries of the men resound as they set themselves to work, and all the sea is stained with the gory filth poured forth by his deadly wounds. The infinite water boils with the blood of the beast and the grey sea is reddened. As when in winter a river comes down from the hills of red earth into a billowy gulf and the blood-coloured mud is rolled down by the rush of the water, mingling with the eddying waves; and afar the water is reddened by the ruddy dust and the sea is as if covered with blood: even so in that hour the gory waters are stained with the blood of the beast, rent amid the waves by the shafts of the fishermen. Then they draw and drop into his wounds a bitter stream of bilge-water; and the salt mingling in his sores like fire kindles for him deadliest destruction. As when the fire of heaven smites with the lash of Zeus a bark that is traversing the sea, and the flaming onset that devours the ship is stirred and made yet fiercer by the sea mingling with the torches of heaven: even so his cruel wounds and pains are made more fierce by the cruel water of the putrid evil-smelling bilge. But when, overcome by the pains of many gashes, fate brings him at last to the gates of dismal death, then they take him in tow and joyfully haul him to the land; and he is dragged all unwilling, pierced with many barbs as with nails and nodding as if heavy with wine in the issue of deathly doom. And the fishers, raising the loud paean of victory, while they speed the boat with their oars, make the sea resound, singing their shrill song to hasting blades. As when after the decision of a battle at sea the victors take in tow the ships of the vanquished and haste joyfully to bring to land the foemen who man the ships, shouting loud to the oarsmen the paean of victory in a fight at sea, while the others against their will sorrowfully follow their foe perforce: even so the fishers take in tow the dread monster of the brine and joyfully bring him ashore. But when he comes nigh the land, then destruction real and final rouses him, and he struggles and lashes the sea with his terrible fins, like a bird upon the well-built altar tossing in the dark struggle of death. Unhappy beast! verily an effort he makes to reach the waves but the strength of his valour is undone and his limbs obey him not and panting terribly he is dragged to land: even as a merchant ship, broad and many-benched, which men draw forth from the sea and haul up on the dry land when winter comes, to rest from its seafaring toil, and heavy is the labour of the sailors: so they bring the mighty-limbed whale to land. And he fills all the beach with his unapproachable limbs as they lie, and he is stretched out dead, terrible to behold.

THE DOLPHIN—LORD OF FISHES[1]

Oppian

(fl. c. A. D. 177–A. D. 180)

NOW all the viviparous denizens of the sea love and cherish their young but diviner than the Dolphin is nothing yet created; for indeed they were aforetime men and lived in cities along with mortals,

---

[1]From A. W. Mair's translation of *Halieutica*, in the Loeb Classical Library. Reprinted by permission of the editors.

but by the devising of Dyonysus they exchanged the land for the sea
and put on the form of fishes; but even now the righteous spirit of men
in them preserves human thought and human deeds. For when the twin
offspring of their travail come into the light, straightway, soon as they
are born they swim and gambol round their mother and enter within her
teeth and linger in the maternal mouth; and she for her love suffers them
and circles about her children gaily and exulting with exceeding joy.
And she gives them her breasts, one to each, that they may suck the
sweet milk; for god has given her milk and breasts of like nature to those
of women. Thus for a season she nurses them; but, when they attain the
strength of youth, straightway their mother leads them in their eagerness to the way of hunting and teaches them the art of catching fish; nor
does she part from her children nor forsake them; until they have attained the fulness of their age in limb and strength, but always the
parents attend them to keep watch and ward. What a marvel shalt thou
contemplate in thy heart and what sweet delight, when on a voyage,
watching when the wind is fair and the sea is calm, thou shalt see the
beautiful herds of Dolphins, the desire of the sea; the young go before in
a troop like youths unwed, even as if they were going through the changing circle of a mazy dance; behind and not aloof their children come the
parents great and splendid, a guardian host, even as in spring the shepherds attend the tender lambs at pasture. As when from the works of the
Muses children come trooping while behind there follow, to watch them
and to be censors of modesty and heart and mind, men of older years: for
age makes a man discreet; even so also the parent Dolphins attend their
children, lest aught untoward encounter them. . . .

But, notwithstanding, even the Dolphins have foes who meet their
encounter, the fish called Amia, which care not for the Dolphin but alone
fight them face to face. These have a weaker body than the Tunny and
are clothed in feeble flesh, but in their ravenous mouth bristles sharp a
dense array of teeth; wherefore also they have great courage and do not
cower before the mighty lord of fishes. For when they see one that has
wandered away alone from the rest of the herd of Dolphins, then from
this quarter and from that, as a great army at command, they gather
in a body together and set forth to battle dauntlessly, like shielded
warriors against the tower of the foe. And the bearded Dolphin, when the
crowd meets him, at first recks not of them but rushes among them,
seizing and rending now one and now another, finding a banquet after
his heart. But when the ranks of war surround him on every side, and
encircle him with their great and dense array, then trouble at length enters his heart and he knows that sheer destruction is upon him, hemmed
about as he is, alone among countless foes; and the toil of battle appears.
For furiously they fall in a body about the limbs of the Dolphin and fix
in him the might of their teeth; everywhere they bite him and cling to
him relentlessly, many clutching his head, others his grey jaws, while yet

others cleave to his very fins; many in his flanks fix their deadly teeth, others seize the end of his tail, others his belly beneath, others feed upon his back above, others hang from his mane, others from his neck. And, full of manifold distress, he rushes over the sea and his frenzied heart within him is racked with agony and his spirit is afire with pain. Every way he leaps and turns, rushing blindly in the spasms of agony. Like a diver, now he runs over the deep waves like a whirlwind, now he plunges to the nether deeps; and often he springs up and leaps above the foam of the sea, if haply the bold swarm of overweening fishes may let him go. But they, relentless, no wise abate their violence but cling to him all the same; when he dives, they dive along with him; when he leaps up again, they likewise spring forth from the sea in his train. You would say that the Shaker of the Earth had gotten a new and monstrous birth, half Dolphin and half Amia; so grievous the bond of teeth wherewith he is bound. As when a cunning physician drains a swollen wound, within which is gathered much unwholesome blood, and he applies to the flesh of the sufferer the watery brood, the dark-hued reptiles of the marsh to feast on his black blood; and straightway they become arched and rounded and draw the filth and abate not until having drained the strong drink of blood they roll of themselves from the flesh and fall like drunken men; even so the fury of the Amia abates not until they have devoured with the mouth the flesh which they once seize. But when they leave him and the Dolphin gets a breathing-space from toil, then shalt thou behold the rage of the angry lord of fishes and deadly doom appears for the Amia. They flee; and he behind working havoc, like hurricane of evil noise, lays all waste, devouring them incontinently, and with ravening jaws reddens the sea with blood; and he avenges the despite that he suffered. . . .

This other excellent deed of the Dolphins have I heard and admire. When fell disease and fatal draws nigh to them, they fail not to know it but are aware of the end of life. Then they flee the sea and the wide waters of the deep and come aground on the shallow shores. And there they give up their breath and receive their doom upon the land; that so perchance some mortal man may take pity on the holy messenger of the Shaker of the Earth when he lies low, and cover him with mound of shingle, remembering his gentle friendship; or haply the seething sea herself may hide his body in the sands; nor any of the brood of the sea behold the corse of their lord, nor any foe do despite to his body even in death. Excellence and majesty attend them even when they perish, nor do they shame their glory even when they die.

ANCIENT ROME

HOW ROME BUILT HER FIRST SHIPS AND HOW C. DUILIUS NEPOS DEFEATED THE CARTHAGINIANS THEREWITH[1]

Polybius

(205 B. C.–123 B. C.)

AMONG the motives, which induced me to enter into a more minute description of the War in Sicily, this was not the least: that I might take occasion to explain the time, and manner, in which the Romans first equipped a Naval armament, together with the causes that gave birth to that attempt.

Their design then was, to bring the war to a speedy and effectual conclusion. With this view, they resolved to build a hundred Quinqueremes, and twenty Triremes. But one great difficulty occurred. Their builders were entirely unacquainted with the manner of constructing Quinqueremes; the use of which was then unknown in Italy. But in this design we may observe a most conspicuous proof of that bold and daring spirit, which is peculiar to the Romans: who, though destitute of all the means that such an enterprise required, and before they had even gained the least degree of knowledge or experience in maritime affairs, could at once conceive and carry into execution, so vast a project, and make the first trial of their forces against the Carthaginians, who had received from their ancestors the undisputed sovereignty of the sea. The following fact may serve to confirm the truth of this reflection. When this people first resolved to send their forces over to Messana, they had neither any decked vessels, or ship of transport, nor even a single shallop. But having borrowed among the Tarentines, Eleates, Locrians, and Neapolitans, some Boats of fifty oars, and a few Triremes, they boldly embarked the legions in those vessels.

The Carthaginians bore down upon them in their passage: when one of their Quinqueremes, advancing to fight with too great eagerness struck upon the sands, and was taken by the Romans. This vessel was now made use of, as the model of their fleet: and indeed without some such accident, their want of skill must soon have forced them to abandon the design.

While the workmen were busy in building and fitting the ships, others were employed to draw together a body of sailors, and instruct them in the exercise of the oar. This was done in the following manner. They

---

[1]From the translation of *The Histories*, by Mr Hampton (1772).

placed benches along the shore, upon which the rowers were ranged in the same order as at sea, with a proper officer among them to give the command. In this situation they accustomed themselves to perform all the necessary motions of the body: to fall back together, and again to bend forwards, to contract and extend their arms; to begin, or leave off, according to the signals. After this preparation, the vessels being now completely finished, they sailed out to sea, and, when they had spent some little time in perfecting their exercise, advanced along the coast of Italy, agreeable to the orders which they had before received.

For Cn. Cornelius, who commanded the naval forces, had sailed a few days before with seventeen ships towards Messana, to provide whatever might be wanted for the fleet: and had left directions with the other Captains, that they should follow him as soon as they were ready. But while he lay at Messana, having received some intelligence which gave him hopes of taking the town of Lipara by surprize, he too easily engaged in the design, and steered his course towards the place, with the ships just mentioned. But on the news of this attempt, Annibal, who then was stationed at Panormus, immediately sent away the Senator Boodes, with twenty ships. Boodes, sailing to the place by night, blocked up the Romans in the port. As soon as day appeared, the sailors all fled from their ships, and escaped to land: and Cornelius, being struck with terror, and perceiving no means of safety, surrendered himself to the enemy, who immediately returned back again to Annibal, carrying with them the Roman Consul, and all his squadron. Not many days after this exploit, while the misfortune of the Romans was still fresh and recent, an accident of the same kind proved almost fatal to Annibal himself. For having received information, that the whole Roman fleet had steered their course along the coast of Italy, and were now at no great distance, he presently advanced with fifty vessels, designing to take a view of their numbers, and of the order in which they sailed. But he had scarcely doubled the promontory of Italy, when he found himself at once in the very midst of the enemy, who were all disposed in perfect order, and ready to engage. A great part of his ships were taken: but himself escaped with the rest, though not without the greatest difficulty. The Romans then held on their course to Sicily: and being there informed of what had happened to Cornelius, they sent messengers to Duilius who commanded the land forces in the island, and waited his arrival. At the same time, having received intelligence that the Carthaginians were at no great distance, they began to make the necessary preparations for an engagement. But because their ships were built with little skill, and were both slow and heavy in their motions, it was resolved to balance these defects by the use of certain Machines, which some person in the fleet had invented for the occasion, and which were afterwards called by the Romans, CORVI. The description of them is as follows. They erected on the prow of every vessel a round Pillar of wood, of about twelve feet in height, and of three palms breadth in diameter, with a Pully at the top. To this Pillar was fitted a kind of Stage, eighteen feet in length and four feet broad, which was made ladder-wise, of strong timbers laid across, and cramped together with iron: the Pillar being received into an oblong square, which was opened for that purpose, at the distance of six feet within the end of the Stage. On either side of the Stage lengthways was a Parapet, which reached just above the knee. At the farthest end of this Stage, or Ladder, was a bar of iron, whose shape was somewhat like a Pestle: but it was sharpened at the bottom, or lower point; and on the top of it was a Ring. The whole appearance of this Machine very much resembled those that are used in grinding corn. To the Ring just mentioned was fixed a Rope; by which, with the help of the Pully that was at the top of the Pillar, they hoisted up the Machines, and, as the vessels of the enemy came near, let them fall upon them, sometimes on their prow, and sometimes on their sides, as occasion best served. As the Machine fell, it struck into the decks of the enemy, and held them fast. In this situation, if the two vessels happened to lay side by side, the Romans leaped on board from all parts of their ships at once. But in case that they were joined only by the prow, they then entered two and two along the Machine: the two foremost extending their bucklers right before them, to ward off the strokes that were aimed against them in front; while those that followed rested the boss of their bucklers upon the top of the Parapet on either side, and thus covered both their flanks. Having in this manner prepared their vessels for the combat, they now only waited for the time to engage.

As soon as Duilius heard of the misfortune that had happened to the other Consul, he left the care of the army to the Tribunes, and hastened to the fleet: and having received information that the enemy were employed in ravaging the plain of Mylae, he presently steered his course that way. The Carthaginians beheld their approach with joy; and immediately drew out their fleet, which consisted of a hundred and thirty ships: despising the inexperience of the Romans, and flattering themselves with such assurance of success, that they even disdained to form their squadron into any kind of order, and, turning their prows towards the enemy, bore down instantly upon them, as to a certain spoil. The Commander of the fleet was the same Annibal, who made his retreat by night from Agrigentum. He sailed in a vessel of seven Banks of oars, which had formerly belonged to Pyrrhus. As they approached more nearly to the Roman fleet, the sight of those strange Machines, erected on the prow of every ship, occasioned some little hesitation and surprize. After some time however, as their contempt of the enemy again took place, they advanced with the same ardour as before. But when their vessels, as soon as they were joined in action, were grappled fast by these new instruments of war, and when the Romans, instantly advancing along the Machines towards them, maintained the fight upon their very decks, one part of the Carthaginians were immediately destroyed, and the rest threw down their arms, being struck with terror by this new kind of combat, which seemed so nearly to resemble an engagement upon land. The ships that had advanced the foremost of the fight, being thirty in number, were taken with their men. Among these was the General's ship. But Annibal himself found means to get on board a boat, and escaped, though not without the greatest hazard.

The rest of the squadron were now advancing to the fight: but having observed the fate of their companions, they at first turned aside, in order to elude the stroke of the Machines. But as their ships were light, and easy in their motions, they soon resumed their confidence, and began to fall upon the Roman vessels, some in stern, and some upon their sides; being persuaded, that, with this precaution, they should be secure from danger. But when they saw, with great astonishment, that, on which side soever they advanced, the CORVI still hung over them, they were at last content to seek their safety in flight, with the loss of fifty ships.

HOW ÆOLUS, KING OF THE WINDS, SENT FORTH A STORM AGAINST ÆNEAS[1]

Virgil

(70 B. C.–19 B. C.)

SCARCELY had the Trojans, losing sight of Sicily, with joy launched out into the deep, and were ploughing the foaming billows with their brazen prows, when Juno, harbouring everlasting rancour in her breast, thus with herself:

"Shall I then, baffled, desist from my purpose, nor have it in my power to turn away the Trojan king from Italy, because I am restrained by fate? Was Pallas able to burn the Grecian ships, and bury them in the ocean, for the offence of one, and the frenzy of Ajax, Oileus' son? She herself, hurling from the clouds Jove's rapid fire, both scattered their ships, and upturned the sea with the winds; him too she snatched away in a whirlwind, breathing flames from his transfixed breast, and dashed him against the pointed rock. But I, who move majestic, the queen of heaven, both sister and wife of Jove, must maintain a series of wars with one single race for so many years. And who will henceforth adore Juno's divinity, or humbly offer sacrifice on her altars?"

The goddess by herself revolving such thoughts in her inflamed breast, repairs to Æolia, the native land of storms, regions pregnant with boisterous winds. Here, in a vast cave, King Æolus controls with imperial sway the reluctant winds and sounding tempests, and confines

---

[1]From C. Davidson's translation of *The Æneid* (1866).

them with chains in prison. They roar indignant round their barriers, filling the mountain with loud murmurs. Æolus is seated on a lofty throne, wielding a sceptre, and assuages their fury, and moderates their rage. For, unless he did so, they, in their rapid career, would bear away sea and earth, and the deep heaven, and sweep them through the air. But the almighty Sire, guarding against this, hath pent them in gloomy caves, and thrown over them the ponderous weight of mountains and appointed them a king, who, by fixed laws, and at command, knows both to curb them, and when to relax their reins; whom Juno then in suppliant words thus addressed:

"Æolus, (for the sire of gods and the king of men hath given thee power both to smooth the waves and raise them with the wind,) a race by me detested sails the Tuscan Sea, transporting Ilium, and its conquered gods, into Italy. Strike force into thy winds, overset and sink the ships; or drive them different ways, and strew the ocean with carcasses. I have twice seven lovely nymphs, the fairest of whom, Deïopeia, I will join to thee in firm wedlock, and assign to be thine own for ever, that with thee she may spend all her years for this service, and make thee father of a beautiful offspring."

To whom Æolus replies:

"'Tis thy task, O Queen, to consider what you would have done: on me it is incumbent to execute your commands. You conciliate to me whatever of power I have, my sceptre, and Jove. You grant me to sit at the tables of the Gods; and you make me lord of storms and tempests."

Thus having said, whirling the point of his spear, he struck the hollow mountain's side: and the winds, as in a formed battalion, rush forth at every vent, and scour over the lands in a hurricane. They press upon the ocean, and at once, east, and south, and stormy south-west, plough up the whole deep from its lowest bottom, and roll vast billows to the shores. The cries of the seamen succeed, and the cracking of the cordage. In an instant clouds snatch the heavens and day from the eyes of the Trojans; sable night sits brooding on the sea, thunder roars from pole to pole, the sky glares with repeated flashes, and all nature threatens them with immediate death. Forthwith Æneas' limbs are relaxed with cold shuddering fear. He groans, and, spreading out both his hands to heaven, thus expostulates:

"O thrice and four times happy they, who had the good fortune to die before their parents' eyes, under the high ramparts of Troy! O thou, the bravest of the Grecian race, great Tydeus' son, why was I not destined to fall on the Trojan plains, and pour out this soul by thy right hand? where stern Hector lies prostrate by the sword of Achilles; where mighty Sarpedon lies; where Simois rolls along so many shields, and helmets, and bodies of heroes snatched away beneath its waters."

While uttering such words a tempest, roaring from the north, strikes across the sail, and heaves the billows to the stars. The oars are shattered: then the prow turns away, and exposes the side to the waves. A steep mountain of waters follows in a heap. These hang on the towering surge; to whose eyes the wide-yawning deep discloses the earth between two waves; the whirling tide rages with mingled sand. Three other ships the south wind, hurrying away, throws on hidden rocks; rocks in the midst of the ocean, which the Italians call Altars, a vast ridge rising to the surface of the sea. Three from the deep the east wind drives on shoals and flats, a piteous spectacle! and dashing on the shelves, it encloses them with mounds of sand. Before the eyes of Æneas himself, a mighty billow, falling from the height, dashes against the stern of one which bore the Lycian crew, and faithful Orontes: the pilot is tossed out and rolled headlong, prone into the waves: but her the driving surge thrice whirls around in the same place, and the rapid eddy swallows up in the deep. Then floating here and there on the vast abyss, are seen men, their arms, and planks, and the Trojan wealth, among the waves. Now the storm overpowered the stout vessel of Ilioneus, now that of brave Achates, and that in which Abas sailed, and that in which old Alethes; all, at their loosened and disjointed sides, receive the hostile stream, and gape with chinks.

Meanwhile Neptune perceived that the sea was in great uproar and confusion, a storm sent forth, and the depths overturned from their lowest channels. He, in violent commotion, and looking forth from the deep, reared his serene countenance above the waves; sees Æneas' fleet scattered over the ocean, the Trojans oppressed with the waves and the ruin from above. Nor were Juno's wiles and hate unknown to her brother. He calls to him the east and west winds; then thus addresses them:

"And do you thus presume upon your birth? Dare you, winds! without my sovereign leave, to embroil heaven and earth, and raise such mountains? Whom I—— But first it is right to assuage the tumultuous waves. A chastisement of another nature from me awaits your next offence. Fly apace, and bear this message to your king: That not to him the empire of the sea, and the awful trident, but to me by lot are given: his dominions are the mighty rocks, your proper mansions, Eurus: in that palace let King Æolus proudly boast and reign in the close prison of the winds."

So he speaks, and, more swiftly than his speech, smooths the swelling seas, disperses the collected clouds, and brings back the day. With him Cymothoë, and Triton with exerted might, heave the ships from the pointed rock. He himself raised them with his trident; lays open the vast sandbanks, and calms the sea; and in his light chariot glides along the surface of the waves. And as when a sedition has perchance arisen among a mighty multitude, and the minds of the ignoble vulgar rage; now firebrands, now stones fly; fury supplies them with arms: if then, by chance, they espy a man revered in piety and worth, they are hushed, and stand with ears erect; he, by eloquence, rules their passions and calms their breasts. Thus all the raging tumult of the ocean subsides, as soon as the sire, surveying the seas, and wafted through the open sky, guides his steeds, and flying, gives the reins to his easy chariot.

The weary Trojans direct their course towards the nearest shores, and make the coast of Libya. In a long recess, a station lies; an island forms it into a harbour by its jutting sides, against which every wave from the ocean is broken, and divides itself into receding curves. On either side vast cliffs, and two twin-like rocks, threaten the sky; under whose summit the waters all around are calm and still. Above is a sylvan scene with waving woods, and a dark grove with awful shade hangs over. Under the opposite front a cave is of pendant rocks, within which are fresh springs, and seats of living stone, the recess of nymphs. Here neither cables hold, nor anchors with crooked fluke moor the weather-beaten ships. To this retreat Æneas brings seven ships, collected from all his fleet; and the Trojans, longing much for land, disembarking, enjoy the wished-for shore, and stretch their brine-drenched limbs upon the beach.

HOW JULIUS CÆSAR, TAKING FORTUNE FOR HIS COMRADE, PUT OUT INTO THE TUMULT OF THE SEA[1]

Lucan

(39 A. D.–65 A. D.)

ANTONY was the leader, daring in all warfare, even then, in civil war, training for Leucas.[2] Him delaying full oft by threats and by entreaties does Cæsar summon forth:

"O cause of woes so mighty to the world, why dost thou retard the Gods of heaven and the Fates? The rest has been effected by my speed; Fortune demands thee as the finishing hand to the successes of the hastened warfare. Does Libya, sundered with her shoaly quicksands, divide us with uncertain tides? Have I in any way entrusted thy arms to an untried deep, and art thou dragged into dangerous unknown? Sluggard, Cæsar commands thee to come, not to go! I myself, the first, amid the foe touched upon sands in the midst of them, and under the sway of others. Dost thou fear my camp? I lament that the hours of fate are waiting; upon the winds and the waves do I expend my prayers. Keep not those back who desire to go on the shifting deep; if I judge aright, the youths would be willing by shipwreck even to repair to the arms of Cæsar. Now must I employ the language of grief; not on equal terms have we divided the world. Cæsar and the whole Senate occupy Epirus; thou alone dost possess Ausonia."

[1] From H. T. Riley's translation of *The Pharsalia*.

[2] It was off the Leucadian Promontory that Antony fought against Augustus in the Battle of Actium.

After he sees that he, summoned three or four times in this language, is still delaying, as he believes that it is he himself who is wanting to the Gods, and not the Deities to him, of his accord amid the unsafe shades of night he dares to try the sea, which they, commanded, stand in fear of, having experienced that venturous deeds have prospered under a favouring Divinity; and waves, worthy to be feared by fleets, he hopes to pass over in a little bark.

Night with its languor had now relaxed the wearied care of arms; rest was obtained for the wretched, into whose breasts by sleep a more humble lot inspires strength. Now was the camp silent; now had its third hour brought on the second watch; Cæsar with anxious step amid the vasty silence attempted things hardly by his servants to be dared; and, all left behind, Fortune alone pleased him as his companion. After he had gone through the tents, he passed over the bodies of the sentinels which had yielded to sleep, silently complaining that he was able to elude them. He passed along the winding shore, and at the brink of the waves found a bark attached by a cable to the rocks eaten away.

Not far from thence a house, free from all cares, propped up with no stout timbers, but woven with barren rushes and the reeds of the marsh, and covered on its exposed side with a boat turned bottom upwards, sheltered the pilot and the owner of the bark. Cæsar twice or thrice knocked with his hand at this threshold, that shook the roof. Amyclas arose from the soft couch, which the sea-weed afforded.

"What shipwrecked person, I wonder," said he, "repairs to my abode? Or whom has Fortune compelled to hope for the aid of our cottage?"

Thus having said, the tow now raised from the dense heap of warm ashes, he nourished the small spark into kindled flames; free from care of the warfare, he knew that in civil strife cottages are no prey. O safe the lot of a poor man's life, and his humble home! O gifts of the Deities not yet understood! What temples or what cities could this befall, to be alarmed with no tumult, the hand of Cæsar knocking?

Then, the door being opened, the chieftain says:

"Look for what is greater than thy moderate wishes, and give scope to thy hopes, O youth. If, obeying my commands, thou dost carry me to Hesperia, no more wilt thou be owing everything to thy bark, and by the hands dragging on a needy old age. Hesitate not to entrust thy fate to the God who wishes to fill thy humble abode with sudden wealth."

Thus he says, unable to be taught to speak as a private man, though clad in a plebeian garb. Then says the poor Amyclas:

"Many things indeed forbid me to trust the deep to-night. For the sun did not take down into the seas ruddy clouds, and rays of one hue; one portion of Phœbus invited the southern gales, another, with divided light, the northern. Dimmed, too, and languid in the middle of his orb, he set, not dazzling the eyes that looked on him, with his weakly light. The moon, also, did not rise, shining with slender horn, or hollowed with clear cavities in her mid orb; nor did she describe tapering points on her straitened horn, and with the signs of wind she was red; besides, pallid, she bears a livid aspect, sad with her face about to sink beneath the clouds.

"But neither does the waving of the woods, nor the lashings of the sea-shore, nor the fitful dolphin, that challenges the waves, please me; nor yet that the sea-gull loves the dry land; the fact, too, that the heron ventures to fly aloft, trusting to its hovering wing; and that, sprinkling its head with the waves, as though it would forestall the rain, the crow paces the seashore with infirm step. But if the weight of great events demands, I would not hesitate to lend my aid. Either I will touch the commanded shore, or, on the other hand, the seas and the winds shall deny it."

Thus having said and unmooring his craft, he spreads the canvas to the winds; at the motion of which, not only meteors gliding along the lofty air, as they fall, describe tracks in all quarters of the heavens; but even the stars which are held fixed in the loftiest skies, appear to shake. A dusky swell pervades the surface of the sea; with many a heaving along their lengthened track the threatening waves boil up, uncertain as to the impending blasts; the swelling seas betoken the winds conceived. Then says the master of the quivering bark:

"Behold, how vast dangers the raging sea is preparing. Whether it presages the Zephyrs, or whether the east winds, it is uncertain. On every side the fitful waves are beating against the bark. In the clouds and in the heavens are the southern blasts; if we go by the mumurs of the sea, Corus is skimming along the deep. In a storm thus mighty, neither will bark nor shipwrecked person reach the Hesperian shores. To despair of making our way, and to turn from the forbidden course, is our only safety. Let it be allowed me to make for shore with the tossed bark, lest the nearest land should be too distant."

Cæsar, confident that all dangers will give way for him, says:

"Despise the threats of the deep, and spread sail to the raging winds. If, heaven prompting thee, thou dost decline Italy, myself thy prompter, seek it. This alone is thy reasonable cause for fear, not to have known thy freight; one whom the Deities never forsake; of whom Fortune deserves badly then, when after his wishes expressed she comes. Secure in my protection, burst through the midst of the storms. This is the labour of the heavens and of the sea, not of our bark; that, trod by Cæsar, the freight will protect from the waves. Nor will long duration be granted to the raging fury of the winds; this same bark will advantage the waves. Turn not thy hands; avoid, with thy sails, the neighbouring shores; believe that then thou hast gained the Calabrian port, when no other land can be granted to the ship and to our safety. Art thou ignorant what, amid a tempest so great, is preparing? Amid the tumult of the sea and sky, Fortune is enquiring how she shall favour me."

No more having said, a furious whirlwind, the stern being struck, tears away the shrouds rent asunder, and brings the flapping sails upon the frail mast; the joints overstrained, the vessel groans. Then rush on perils gathered together from the whole universe. First, moving the tides, Corus, thou dost raise thy head from the Atlantic Ocean; now, as thou dost lift it, the sea rages, and uplifts all its billows upon the rocks. The cold Boreas meets it, and beats back the ocean, and doubtful stands the deep, undecided which wind to obey. But the rage of the Scythian north wind conquers and hurls aloft the waves, and makes shallows of the sands entirely concealed. And Boreas does not carry the waves on to the rocks, and he dashes his own seas against the billows of Corus; and the aroused waves, even with the winds lulled, are able to meet in conflict.

I would surmise that the threats of Eurus were not withheld, and that the winds of the South, black with showers, did not lie beneath the dungeons of the Æolian rocks; that all, rushing from their wonted quarters, with violent whirlwinds defended their own regions, and that thus the ocean remained in its place. No small seas do they speak of as having been carried along by the gales; the Tyrrhenian runs into the Ægean waves; the wandering Adriatic echoes in the Ionian sea. O how often did that day overwhelm mountains before beaten in vain by the waves! What lofty summits did the subdued earth permit to be overcome! Not on that shore do waves so tremendous rise, and, rolling from another region of the earth, from the vast ocean have they come, and the waves that encircle the world speed on their monstrous billows.

Thus did the ruler of Olympus aid his wearied lightnings against the world with his brother's trident, and the earth was added to the secondary realms of Neptune, when Tethys was unwilling to submit to any shores, content to be bounded by the skies alone. Now as well would the mass of sea so vast have increased to the stars, if the ruler of the Gods of heaven had not kept down the waves with clouds. That was not a night of the heavens; the air lay concealed infected with the paleness of the infernal abodes, and, oppressed with storms, was kept down, and the waves received the showers in the clouds. Even the light so dreadful is lost, and the lightnings flash not with their brilliance, but the cloudy atmosphere obscurely divides for their flashes.

Then do the convex abodes of the Gods of heaven resound, and the lofty skies re-echo, and, the structure strained, the poles re-echo. Nature dreads Chaos, the elements seem to have burst from their concordant repose, and night once more to return about to mingle the shades below with the Gods of heaven. The sole hope of safety is, that not as yet have they perished amid ruin of the universe so great. As far as from the Leucadian heights the calm deep is beheld below, so far do the trembling mariners look down upon the headlong sea from the summits of the waves; and when the swelling billows gape open once again, hardly does the mast stand above the surface. The clouds are touched by the sails, and the earth by the keel. For the sea, in the part where it is at rest, does not conceal the sands; it arises in mountains, and all the waters are in waves. Fears conquer the resources of art, and the pilot knows not which to break, to which wave to give way.

The discord of the sea comes to their aid in their distress, and billow is not able to throw over the vessel against billows; the resisting wave supports the yielding side, and the bark rises upright amid all the winds. They dread not the lowly Sason with its shallows, nor yet the rocky shores of curving Thessaly, and the dangerous harbours of the Ambracian coast; of the summits of rocky Ceraunia the sailors are in dread. Now does Cæsar believe there to be a danger worthy of his destiny.

"Is it a labour so great," says he, "with the Gods above to overwhelm me, who, sitting in a little bark, they have assaulted with seas so vast? If the glory of my end has been granted to the deep, and I am denied to the warfare, fearlessly will I receive whatever death, ye Deities, you send me. Although the day hurried on by the Fates should cut short my mighty exploits, things great enough have I done. The nations of the north have I conquered; hostile arms have I subdued with fear; Rome has beheld Magnus second to me. The commonalty ordered by me, I have obtained by warfare the fasces which were denied unto me. No Roman dignity will be wanting to my titles.

"No one will know this, except thee, Fortune, who alone art conscious of my wishes, that I, although I go loaded with honours and Dictator and Consul, to the Stygian shades, die as a private person. There is need, O Gods of heaven, of no funereal rites for me; retain my mangled carcase in the midst of the waves; let tomb and funeral pile be wanting to me, so long as I shall be always dreaded and looked for by every land."

Him, having thus said, a tenth wave, wondrous to be said, lifts with the frail bark on high; nor again does it hurl it down from the lofty heights of the sea, but the wave bears it along, and casts it on dry land, where the narrow shore is free from rugged cliffs.

HOW MARK ANTONY, FOLLOWING AFTER CLEOPATRA, FLED FROM THE BATTLE OF ACTIUM[1]

Plutarch

(50 A. D.–120 A. D.)

NOW Antonius was made so subject to a woman's will, that though he was a great deale the stronger by land, yet for Cleopatra's sake, he would needes have this battell tryed by sea; though he sawe before

---

[1] From Sir Thomas North's translation of *The Lives of the Most Noble Grecians and Romans* (1579).

his eyes, that for lacke of water men, his Captaines did presse by force all sorts of men out of Greece that they could take up in the field, as travellers, muletters, reapers, harvest men, and young boyes, and yet could they not sufficiently furnishe his gallies: so that the most part of them were empty, and could scant rowe, bicause they lacked water men enowe. But on the contrary side, Cæsar's shippes were not built for pompe, highe and great, onely for a sight and bravery, but they were light of yarage, armed and furnished with water men as many as they needed, and had them all in readiness, in the havens of Tarentum and Brundusium. So Octavius Cæsar sent unto Antonius, to will him to delay no more time, but to come on with his army into Italy: and that for his owne part he would give him safe harbour, to lande without any trouble, and that he would withdraw his armie from the sea, as farre as one horse could runne, until he had put his army on shore, and had lodged his men. Antonius on the other side bravely sent him word againe, and chalenged the combate of him man to man, though he were the elder: and that if he refused him so, he would then fight a battell with him in the fields of Pharsalia, as Julius Cæsar, and Pompey had done before.

Now whilest Antonius rode at anker, lying idely in harber at the head of Actium, in the place where the citie of Nicopolis standeth at this present: Cæsar had quickly passed the sea Ionium, and taken a place called Toryne, before Antonius understoode that he had taken shippe. Then began his men to be affraid, bicause his army by land was left behind. But Cleopatra making light of it: And what daunger, I pray you, said she, if Cæsar keepe Toryne? The next morning by breake of day, his enemies comming with full force of owers in battell against him, Antonius was affraid that if they came to joyne, they would take and cary away his shippes that had no men of warre in them. So he armed all his water men, and set them in order of battell upon the forecastell of their shippes, and then lift up all his rancks of owers towards the element, as well of the one side, as the other, with the prooes against the enemies, at the entry and mouth of the gulfe, which beginneth at the point of Actium, and so kept them in order of battell, as if they had bene armed and furnished with water men and souldiers. Thus Octavius Cæsar beeing finely deceyved by this stratageame, retyred presently, and therewithall Antonius very wisely and sodainely did cut him of from fresh water. For, understanding that the places where Octavius Cæsar landed, had very little store of water, and yet very bad; he shut them in with stronge ditches and trenches he cast, to keepe them from salying out at their pleasure, and so to goe seeke water further of.

Furthermore, he delt very friendely and curteously with Domitius, and against Cleopatra's mynde. For, he being sicke of an agewe when he went and tooke a little boate to goe to Cæsar's campe, Antonius was very sorry for it, but yet he sent after him all his caryage, trayne, and men: and the same Domitius, as though he gave him to understand that he repented his open treason, he died immediately after. There were certen kings also that forsooke him, and turned on Cæsar's side: as Amyntas, and Deiotarus. Furthermore, his fleete and navy that was unfortunate in all thinges, and unready for service, compelled him to chaunge his minde, and to hazard battell by land. And Canidius also, who had charge of his army by land, when time came to follow Antonius determination: he turned him cleane contrary, and counselled him to send Cleopatra backe againe, and himselfe to retyre into Macedon, to fight there on the maine land. And furthermore told him that Dicomes king of the Getes, promised him to ayde him with a great power: and that it should be no shame nor dishonour to him to let Cæsar have the sea, (bicause him selfe and his men both had beene well practised and exercised in battels by sea, in the warre of Sicilia against Sextus Pompeius) but rather that he should doe against all reason, he having so great skill and experience of battells by land as he had, if he should not employ the force and valliantnes of so many lusty armed footemen as he had ready, but would weaken his army by dividing them into shippes.

But now, notwithstanding all these good perswasions, Cleopatra forced him to put all to the hazard of battel by sea: considering with her selfe how she might flie, and provide for her safetie, not to helpe him to winne the victory, but to flie more easily after the battel lost.

Betwixt Antonius campe and his fleete of shippes, there was a great hie point of firme lande that ranne a good waye into the sea, the which Antonius often used for a walke, without mistrust of feare or daunger. One of Cæsar's men perceived it, and told his Maister that he would laugh and they could take up Antonius in the middest of his walke. Thereupon Cæsar sent some of his men to lye in ambush for him, and they missed not much of taking of him: for they tooke him that came before him, bicause they discovered to soone, and so Antonius scaped verie hardly.

So when Antonius had determined to fight by sea, he set all the other shippes a fire, but three score shippes of Egypt, and reserved onely but the best and greatest gallies, from three bancks, unto tenne bancks of owers. Into them he put two and twenty thowsand fighting men, with two thowsand darters and slingers. Now, as he was setting his men in order of battel, there was a Captaine, and a valliant man, that had served Antonius in many battels and conflicts, and had all his body hacked and cut: who as Antonius passed by him, cryed out unto him, and sayd: O noble Emperor, how commeth it to pass that you trust to these vile brittle shippes? what, doe you mistrust these woundes of myne, and this sword? let the Egyptians and Phœnicians fight by sea, and set us on the maine land, where we use to conquer, or to be slayne on our feet. Antonius passed by him, and sayd never a word, but only beckoned to him with his hand and head, as though he willed him to be of good corage, although in deede he had no great corage him selfe. For when the Masters of the gallies and Pilots would have let their sailes alone, he made them clap them on, saying to culler the matter withall, that not one of his enemies should scape.

All that day, and the three dayes following, the sea rose so high, and was so boysterous, that the battel was put of. The fift day the storme ceased, and the sea calmed againe, and then they rowed with force of owers in battaile one against the other: Antonius leading the right wing with Publicola, and Cælius the left, and Marcus Octavius, and Marcus Justeius middest. Octavius Cæsar on thother side had placed Agrippa in the left winge of his armye, and had kept the right winge for himselfe. For the armies by lande, Canidius was generall of Antonius side, and Taurus of Cæsar's side: who kept their men in battell raye the one before the other, uppon the sea side, without stirring one agaynst the other. Further, touching both the Chieftaynes: Antonius being in a swift pinnase, was carried up and downe by force of owers through his army, and spake to his people to encourage them to fight valliantly, as if they were on maine land, bicause of the steadines and heavines of their ships: and commaunded the Pilots and masters of the gallies, that they should not sturre, none otherwise then if they were at anker, and so to receive the first charge of their enemies, and that they should not goe out of the straight of the gulfe.

Cæsar betymes in the morning going out of his tent to see his ships thorough out: met a man by chaunce that drave an asse before him. Cæsar asked the man what his name was. The poore man told him Eutychus, to say, fortunate: and his asses name Nicon, to say, Conqueror. Therefore Cæsar after he had wonne the battell, setting out the market place with the spurres of the gallies he had taken, for a signe of his victorie: he caused also the man and his asse to be set up in brasse.

When he had visited the order of his armie thorough out, he tooke a little pinnase, and went to the right wing, and wondered when he sawe his enemies lye stil in the straight, and sturred not. For, decerning them a farre of, men would have thought they had bene shippes riding at anker, and a good while he was so perswaded: so he kept his gallies eight furlong from his enemies. About noone there rose a little gale of wind from the sea, and then Antonius men waxing angry with tarying so long, and trusting to the greatness and height of their shipps, as if they had bene invincible: they began to march forward with their left wing. Cæsar seeing that, was a glad man, and began a little to give backe from the right wing, to allure them to come further out of the straight and gulfe: to thend that he might with his light shippes well manned with water men, turne and environe the gallies of the enemies, the which were heavy of yarage, both for their biggenes, as also for lacke of water men to row them.

When the skirmish began, and that they came to joyne, there was no great hurt at the first meeting, neither did the shippes vehemently hit one against the other, as they doe commonly in fight by sea. For on the one side, Antonius shippes for their heavines, could not have the strength and swiftnes to make their blowes of any force: and Cæsar's shippes on thother side tooke great heede, not to rushe and shocke with the forecastells of Antonius shippes, whose proues were armed with great brasen spurres. Furthermore they durst not flanck them, bicause their points were easily broken, which way soever they came to set upon his shippes, that were made of great mayne square peeces of tymber, bounde together with great iron pinnes: so that the battel was much like to a battel by land, or to speake more properly, to the assault of a citie. For there were alwaies three or foure of Cæsar's shippes about one of Antonius shippes, and the souldiers fought with their pykes, halberds, and darts, and threw pots and darts with fire. Antonius shippes on the other side bestowed among them, with their crosbows and engines of battery, great store of shot from their highe towers of woodde, that were apon their shippes.

Now Publicola seeing Agrippa put forth his left wing of Cæsar's army, to compasse in Antonius shippes that fought: he was driven also to loose of to have more roome, and going a little at one side, to put those further of that were affraid, and in the middest of the battel. For they were sore distressed by Aruntius. Howbeit the battell was yet of even hand, and the victorie doubtfull, being indifferent to both: when sodainely they saw the three score shippes of Cleopatra busie about their yard masts, and hoysing saile to flie. So they fled through the middest of them that were in fight, for they had bene placed behind the great shippes, and did marvelously disorder the other shippes. For the enemies them selves wondred much to see them saile in that sort, with ful saile towards Peloponnesus. There Antonius shewed plainely, that he had not onely lost the corage and hart of an Emperor, but also of a valliant man, and that he was not his owne man: (proving that true which an old man spake in myrth, that the soule of a lover lived in another body, and not in his owne) he was so caried away with the vaine love of this woman, as if he had bene glued unto her, and that she could not have removed without moving of him also. For when he saw Cleopatra's shippe under saile, he forgot, forsooke, and betrayed them that fought for him, and imbarked upon a galley with five bankes of owers, to follow her that had already begon to overthrow him, and would in the end be his utter destruction. When she knew this galley a farre of, she lift up a signe in the poope of her shippe, and so Antonius coming to it, was pluckt up where Cleopatra was, howbeit he saw her not at his first comming, nor she him, but went and sate down alone in the prowe of his shippe, and said never a word, clapping his head betwene both his hands.

In the meane time came certaine light brigantynes of Cæsar's that followed him hard. So Antonius straight turned the prowe of his shippe, and presently put the rest to flight, saving one Eurycles Lacedæmonian, that followed him neare, and prest upon him with great corage, shaking a dart in his hand over the prow, as though he would have throwen it unto Antonius. Antonius seing him, came to the forecastell of his ship, and asked him what he was that durst follow Antonius so neare? I am, aunswered he, Eurycles, the sonne of Lachares, who through Cæsar's good fortune seketh to revenge the death of my father. This Lechares was condemned of fellonie, and beheaded by Antonius. But yet Eurycles durst not venter on Antonius shippe, but set upon the other Admirall galley (for there were two) and fell with him with such a blowe of his brasen spurre, that was so heavy and bigge that he turned her round and tooke her, with another that was loden with very rich stuffe and cariage.

After Eurycles had left Antonius, he returned againe to his place, and sate downe, speaking never a word as he did before; and so lived three dayes alone, without speaking to any man. But when he arrived at the head of Tænarus, there Cleopatra's women first brought Antonius and Cleopatra to speake together, and afterwards, to suppe and lye together.

BIBLICAL LITERATURE

THE GATHERING TOGETHER OF THE WATERS[1]

IN THE beginning God created the heaven and the earth.
And the earth was without form, and void; and darkness was upon the face of the deep. And the Spirit of God moved upon the face of the waters.

And God said, Let there be light: and there was light.

And God saw the light, that it was good: and God divided the light from the darkness.

And God called the light Day, and the darkness he called Night. And the evening and the morning were the first day.

And God said, Let there be a firmament in the midst of the waters, and let it divide the waters from the waters.

And God made the firmament, and divided the waters which were under the firmament from the waters which were above the firmament: and it was so.

And God called the firmament Heaven. And the evening and the morning were the second day.

And God said, Let the waters under the heaven be gathered together unto one place, and let the dry land appear: and it was so.

And God called the dry land Earth; and the gathering together of the waters called he Seas: and God saw that it was good.

THE WATERS OF THE FLOOD[1]

BUT Noah found grace in the eyes of the Lord.
And God looked upon the earth, and, behold, it was corrupt; for all flesh had corrupted his way upon the earth.

And God said unto Noah, The end of all flesh is come before me; for the earth is filled with violence through them; and, behold, I will destroy them with the earth.

Make thee an ark of gopher wood; rooms shalt thou make in the ark, and shalt pitch it within and without with pitch.

And this is the fashion which thou shalt make it of: The length of the ark shall be three hundred cubits, the breadth of it fifty cubits, and the height of it thirty cubits.

A window shalt thou make to the ark, and in a cubit shalt thou finish it above; and the door of the ark shalt thou set in the side thereof; with lower, second, and third stories shalt thou make it.

---

[1]From the Book of Genesis.

And, behold, I, even I, do bring a flood of waters upon the earth, to destroy all flesh, wherein is the breath of life, from under heaven; and every thing that is in the earth shall die.

But with thee will I establish my covenant; and thou shalt come into the ark, thou, and thy sons, and thy wife, and thy sons' wives with thee.

And of every living thing of all flesh, two of every sort shalt thou bring into the ark, to keep them alive with thee; they shall be male and female.

Of fowls after their kind, and of cattle after their kind, of every creeping thing of the earth after his kind, two of every sort shall come unto thee, to keep them alive.

And take thou unto thee of all food that is eaten, and thou shalt gather it to thee; and it shall be for food for thee, and for them.

Thus did Noah; according to all that God commanded him, so did he.

And the Lord said unto Noah, Come thou and all thy house into the ark; for thee have I seen righteous before me in this generation.

Of every clean beast thou shalt take to thee by sevens, the male and his female: and of beasts that are not clean by two, the male and his female.

Of fowls also of the air by sevens, the male and the female; to keep seed alive upon the face of all the earth.

For yet seven days, and I will cause it to rain upon the earth forty days and forty nights; and every living substance that I have made will I destroy from off the face of the earth.

And Noah did according unto all that the Lord commanded him.

And Noah was six hundred years old when the flood of waters was upon the earth.

And Noah went in, and his sons, and his wife, and his sons' wives with him, into the ark, because of the waters of the flood.

Of clean beasts, and of beasts that are not clean, and of fowls, and of every thing that creepeth upon the earth.

There went in two and two unto Noah into the ark, the male and the female, as God had commanded Noah.

And it came to pass after seven days, that the waters of the flood were upon the earth.

In the six hundredth year of Noah's life, in the second month, the seventeenth day of the month, the same day were all the fountains of the great deep broken up, and the windows of heaven were opened.

And the rain was upon the earth forty days and forty nights: and the waters increased, and bare up the ark, and it was lift up above the earth.

And the waters prevailed, and were increased greatly upon the earth; and the ark went upon the face of the waters.

And the waters prevailed exceedingly upon the earth; and all the high hills, that were under the whole heaven, were covered.

Fifteen cubits upward did the waters prevail; and the mountains were covered.

And all flesh died that moved upon the earth, both of fowl, and of cattle, and of beast, and of every creeping thing that creepeth upon the earth, and every man:

All in whose nostrils was the breath of life, of all that was in the dry land, died.

And every living substance was destroyed which was upon the face of the ground, both man, and cattle, and the creeping things, and the fowl of the heaven; and they were destroyed from the earth: and Noah only remained alive, and they that were with him in the ark.

And the waters prevailed upon the earth an hundred and fifty days.

And God remembered Noah, and every living thing, and all the cattle that was with him in the ark: and God made a wind to pass over the earth, and the waters asswaged.

The fountains also of the deep and the windows of heaven were stopped, and the rain from heaven was restrained.

And the waters returned from off the earth continually: and after the end of the hundred and fifty days the waters were abated.

And the ark rested in the seventh month, on the seventeenth day of the month, upon the mountains of Ararat.

And the waters decreased continually until the tenth month: in the tenth month, on the first day of the month, were the tops of the mountains seen.

And it came to pass at the end of forty days, that Noah opened the window of the ark which he had made:

And he sent forth a raven, which went forth to and fro, until the waters were dried up from off the earth.

Also he sent forth a dove from him, to see if the waters were abated from off the face of the ground;

But the dove found no rest for the sole of her foot, and she returned unto him into the ark, for the waters were on the face of the whole earth: then he put forth his hand, and took her, and pulled her in unto him into the ark.

And he stayed yet other seven days: and again he sent forth the dove out of the ark;

And the dove came in to him in the evening; and, lo, in her mouth was an olive leaf pluckt off: so Noah knew that the waters were abated from off the earth.

And he stayed yet other seven days; and sent forth the dove; which returned not again unto him any more.

And it came to pass in the six hundredth and first year, in the first month, the first day of the month, the waters were dried up from off the earth: and Noah removed the covering of the ark, and looked, and, behold, the face of the ground was dry.

And in the second month, on the seven and twentieth day of the month, was the earth dried.

And God spake unto Noah, saying:

Go forth of the ark, thou, and thy wife, and thy sons, and thy sons' wives with thee.

Bring forth with thee every living thing that is with thee, of all flesh, both of fowl, and of cattle, and of every creeping thing that creepeth upon the earth: that they may breed abundantly in the earth, and be fruitful, and multiply upon the earth.

And Noah went forth, and his sons, and his wife, and his sons' wives with him:

Every beast, every creeping thing, and every fowl, and whatsoever creepeth upon the earth, after their kinds, went forth out of the ark.

JONAH AND THE WHALE[1]

NOW the word of the Lord came unto Jonah the son of Amittai, saying, Arise, go to Nineveh, that great city, and cry against it, for their wickedness is come up before me."

But Jonah rose up to flee unto Tarshish from the presence of the Lord, and went down to Joppa; and he found a ship going to Tarshish; so he paid the fare thereof, and went down into it, to go with them unto Tarshish from the presence of the Lord.

But the Lord sent out a great wind into the sea, and there was a mighty tempest in the sea, so that the ship was like to be broken. Then the mariners were afraid, and cried every man unto his god, and cast forth the wares that were in the ship into the sea to lighten it of them. But Jonah was gone down into the sides of the ship; and he lay, and was fast asleep.

So the shipmaster came to him, and said unto him,

What meanest thou, O sleeper? Arise, call upon thy God, if so be that God will think upon us, that we perish not.

And they said every one to his fellow,

Come, and let us cast lots, that we may know for whose cause this evil is upon us.

So they cast lots, and the lot fell upon Jonah.

Then said they unto him,

Tell us, we pray thee, for whose cause this evil is upon us. What is thine occupation? and whence comest thou? What is thy country? and of what people art thou?

And he said unto them,

I am an Hebrew, and I fear the Lord, the God of Heaven, which hath made the sea and the dry land.

---

[1] From the Book of Jonah.

Then were the men exceedingly afraid, and said unto him,
Why hast thou done this?
For the men knew that he fled from the presence of the Lord, because
he had told them. Then said they unto him,
What shall we do unto thee, that the sea may be calm unto us?
For the sea wrought and was tempestuous. And he said unto them,
Take me up, and cast me forth into the sea; so shall the sea be calm
unto you; for I know that for my sake this great tempest is upon you.
Nevertheless the men rowed hard to bring it to the land; but they could
not for the sea wrought and was tempestuous against them. Wherefore
they cried unto the Lord, and said,
We beseech thee, O Lord, we beseech thee, let us not perish for this
man's life, and lay not upon us innocent blood: for thou, O Lord, hast
done as it pleased thee.
So they took up Jonah and cast him forth into the sea, and the sea
ceased from her raging. Then the men feared the Lord exceedingly, and
offered a sacrifice unto the Lord, and made vows.
Now the Lord had prepared a great fish to swallow up Jonah. And
Jonah was in the belly of the fish three days and three nights.
Then Jonah prayed unto the Lord his God out of the fish's belly, and
said,
I cried by reason of mine affliction unto the Lord, and he heard me:
out of the belly of hell cried I, and thou heardest my voice. For thou
hadst cast me into the deep, in the midst of the seas, and the floods compassed me about: all thy billows and thy waves passed over me. Then I
said, I am cast out of thy sight, yet I will look again toward thy holy
temple. The waters compassed me about, even to the soul: the depth
closed me round about: the weeds were wrapped about my head. I went
down to the bottoms of the mountains: the earth with her bars was about
me for ever; yet hast thou brought up my life from corruption, O Lord
my God. When my soul fainted within me I remembered the Lord, and
my prayer came in unto thee, into thine holy temple. They that observe
lying vanities forsake their own mercy. But I will sacrifice unto thee with
the voice of thanksgiving. I will pay that that I have vowed. Salvation
is of the Lord.
And the Lord spake unto the fish, and it vomited out Jonah upon the
dry land.

THE SHIPWRECK OF ST PAUL[1]

AND when it was determined that we should sail into Italy, they
delivered Paul and certain other prisoners unto one named Julius,
a centurion of Augustus' band. And entering into a ship of Adramyttium,

[1]From the Acts of the Apostles.

we launched, meaning to sail by the coasts of Asia, one Aristarchus, a Macedonian of Thessalonica, being with us.

And the next day we touched at Sidon, and Julius courteously entreated Paul, and gave him liberty to go unto his friends to refresh himself. And when we had launched from thence, we sailed under Cyprus, because the winds were contrary. And when we had sailed over the sea of Cilicia and Pamphylia, we came to Myra, a city of Lycia. And there the centurion found a ship of Alexandria sailing into Italy, and he put us therein.

And when we had sailed slowly many days, and scarce were come over against Cnidus, the wind not suffering us, we sailed under Crete, over against Salmone. And, hardly passing it, came unto a place which is called The Fair Havens, nigh whereunto was the city of Lasea.

Now when much time was spent, and when sailing was now dangerous, because the fast was now already past, Paul admonished them, and said unto them:

Sirs, I perceive that this voyage will be with hurt and much damage, not only of the lading and ship, but also of our lives.

Nevertheless the centurion believed the master and the owner of the ship more than those things which were spoken by Paul, and because the haven was not commodious to winter in, the more part advised to depart thence also, if by any means they might attain to Phenice, and there to winter, which is an haven of Crete and lieth toward the south west and north west. And when the south wind blew softly, supposing that they had obtained their purpose, loosing thence, they sailed close by Crete.

But not long after there arose against it a tempestuous wind called Euroclydon; and when the ship was caught, and could not bear up into the wind, we let her drive. And running under a certain island which is called Clauda, we had much work to come by the boat, which when they had taken up, they used helps, undergirding the ship; and fearing lest they should fall into the quicksands, strake sail, and so were driven.

And we being exceedingly tossed with a tempest, the next day they lightened the ship. And the third day we cast out with our own hands the tackling of the ship; and when neither sun nor stars in many days appeared, and no small tempest lay on us, all hope that we should be saved was then taken away.

But after long abstinence Paul stood forth in the midst of them, and said,

Sirs, ye should have hearkened unto me, and not have loosed from Crete, and to have gained this harm and loss; and now I exhort you to be of good cheer, for there shall be no loss of any man's life among you, but of the ship. For there stood by me this night the angel of God, whose I am, and whom I serve, saying Fear not, Paul; thou must be brought before Cæsar: and lo, God hath given thee all them that sail with thee.

Wherefore, sirs, be of good cheer, for I believe God, that it shall be even as it was told me. Howbeit we must be cast upon a certain island.

But when the fourteenth night was come, as we were driven up and down in Adria, about midnight the shipmen deemed that they drew near to some country; and sounded and found it twenty fathoms. And when they had gone a little further, they sounded again, and found it fifteen fathoms. Then, fearing lest we should have fallen upon rocks, they cast four anchors out of the stern, and wished for the day.

And as the shipmen were about to flee out of the ship, when they had let down the boat into the sea, under colour as though they would have cast anchors out of the foreship, Paul said to the centurion and to the soldiers,

Except these abide in the ship, ye cannot be saved.

Then the soldiers cut off the ropes of the boat and let her fall off.

And while the day was coming on, Paul besought them all to take meat, saying,

This day is the fourteenth day that ye have tarried and continued fasting, having taken nothing. Wherefore I pray you to take some meat, for this is for your health; for there shall not an hair fall from the head of any of you.

And when he had thus spoken, he took bread and gave thanks to God in presence of them all, and when he had broken it he began to eat. Then were they all of good cheer, and they also took some meat. And we were in all in the ship two hundred threescore and sixteen souls. And when they had eaten enough, they lightened the ship, and cast out the wheat into the sea.

And when it was day, they knew not the land, but they discovered a certain creek with a shore, into the which they were minded, if it were possible, to thrust in the ship. And when they had taken up the anchors, they committed themselves unto the sea, and loosed the rudder bands, and hoisted up the mainsail to the wind, and made toward shore. And falling into a place where two seas met, they ran the ship aground, and the forepart stuck fast and remained unmoveable, but the hinder part was broken with the violence of the waves.

And the soldiers' counsel was to kill the prisoners lest any of them should swim out and escape. But the centurion, willing to save Paul, kept them from their purpose, and commanded that they which could swim should cast themselves first into the sea, and get to land, and the rest, some on boards, and some on broken pieces of the ship. And so it came to pass, that they escaped all safe to land.

ARABIA

THE FIRST VOYAGE OF ES-SINDIBÁD OF THE SEA[1]

KNOW, O masters, O noble persons, that I had a father, a merchant, who was one of the first in rank among the people and the merchants, and who possessed abundant wealth and ample fortune. He died when I was a young child, leaving to me wealth and buildings and fields; and when I grew up, I put my hand upon the whole of the property, ate well and drank well, associated with the young men, wore handsome apparel, and passed my life with my friends and companions, feeling confident that this course would continue and profit me; and I ceased not to live in this manner for a length of time. I then returned to my reason, and recovered from my heedlessness, and found that my wealth had passed away, and my condition had changed, and all (the money) that I had possessed had gone. I recovered not to see my situation but in a state of fear and confusion of mind, and remembered a tale that I had heard before, the tale of our lord Suleymán the son of Dáood (on both of whom be peace!), respecting his saying, Three things are better than three: the day of death is better than the day of birth; and a living dog is better than a dead lion; and the grave is better than the palace. Then I arose, and collected what I had, of effects and apparel, and sold them; after which I sold my buildings and all that my hand possessed, and amassed three thousand pieces of silver; and it occurred to my mind to travel to the countries of other people; and I remembered one of the sayings of the poets, which was this:

In proportion to one's labour, eminences are gained; and he who seeketh eminence passeth sleepless nights.
He diveth in the sea who seeketh for pearls, and succeedeth in acquiring lordship and good fortune.
Whoso seeketh eminence without labouring for it, loseth his life in the search of vanity.

Upon this I resolved, and arose, and bought for myself goods and commodities and merchandise, with such other things as were required for travel; and my mind had consented to my performing a sea-voyage. So I embarked in a ship, and it descended to the city of El-Basrah, with a company of merchants; and we traversed the sea for many days and nights. We had passed by island after island, and from sea to sea, and from land to land; and in every place by which we passed we sold and bought and exchanged merchandise. We continued our voyage until we

---

[1]From E. W. Lane's translation of *The Thousand and One Nights*.

arrived at an island like one of the gardens of Paradise, and at that island
the master of the ship brought her to anchor with us. He cast the anchor,
and put forth the landing-plank, and all who were in the ship landed upon
that island. They had prepared for themselves fire-pots, and they lighted
the fires in them; and their occupations were various: some cooked;
others washed: and others amused themselves. I was among those who
were amusing themselves upon the shores of the island, and the passengers were assembled to eat and drink and play and sport. But while
we were thus engaged, lo, the master of the ship, standing upon its side,
called out with his loudest voice, O ye passengers, whom may God
preserve! come up quickly into the ship, hasten to embark, and leave
your merchandise, and flee with your lives, and save yourselves from
destruction; for this apparent island, upon which ye are, is not really an
island, but it is a great fish that hath become stationary in the midst of
the sea, and the sand hath accumulated upon it, so that it hath become
like an island, and trees have grown upon it since times of old; and when
ye lighted upon it the fire, it felt the heat, and put itself in motion, and
now it will descend with you into the sea, and ye will all be drowned:
then seek for yourselves escape before destruction, and leave the merchandise!—The passengers, therefore, hearing the words of the master
of the ship, hastened to go up into the vessel, leaving the merchandise,
and their other goods, and their copper cooking-pots, and their fire-pots;
and some reached the ship, and others reached it not. The island had
moved, and descended to the bottom of the sea, with all that were upon
it, and the roaring sea, agitated with waves, closed over it.

I was among the number of those who remained behind upon the
island; so I sank in the sea with the rest who sank. But God (whose name
be exalted!) delivered me and saved me from drowning, and supplied me
with a great wooden bowl, of the bowls in which the passengers had been
washing, and I laid hold upon it and got into it, induced by the sweetness
of life, and beat the water with my feet as with oars, while the waves
sported with me, tossing me to the right and left. The master of the vessel
had caused her sails to be spread, and pursued his voyage with those who
had embarked, not regarding such as had been submerged; and I ceased
not to look at that vessel until it was concealed from my eye. I made sure
of destruction, and night came upon me while I was in this state; but
I remained so a day and night, and the wind and the waves aided me until
the bowl came to a stoppage with me under a high island, whereon were
trees overhanging the sea. So I laid hold upon a branch of a lofty tree,
and clung to it, after I had been at the point of destruction; and I kept
hold upon it until I landed on the island, when I found my legs be-
numbed, and saw marks of the nibbling of fish upon their hams, of which
I had been insensible by reason of the violence of the anguish and fatigue
that I was suffering.

I threw myself upon the island like one dead, and was unconscious of my existence, and drowned in my stupefaction; and I ceased not to remain in this condition until the next day. The sun having then risen upon me, I awoke upon the island, and found that my feet were swollen, and that I had become reduced to the state in which I then was. Awhile I dragged myself along in a sitting posture, and then I crawled upon my knees. And there were in the island fruits in abundance, and springs of sweet water: therefore I ate of those fruits; and I ceased not to continue in this state for many days and nights. My spirit had then revived, my soul had returned to me, and my power of motion was renewed; and I began to meditate, and to walk along the shore of the island, amusing myself among the trees with the sight of the things that God (whose name be exalted!) had created; and I had made for myself a staff from those trees, to lean upon it. Thus I remained until I walked, one day, upon the shore of the island, and there appeared unto me an indistinct object in the distance. I imagined that it was a wild beast, or one of the beasts of the sea; and I walked towards it, ceasing not to gaze at it; and, lo, it was a mare, of superb appearance, tethered in a part of the island by the sea-shore. I approached her; but she cried out against me with a great cry, and I trembled with fear of her, and was about to return, when, behold, a man came forth from beneath the earth, and he called to me and pursued me, saying to me, Who art thou, and whence hast thou come, and what is the cause of thine arrival in this place? So I answered him, O my master, know that I am a stranger, and I was in a ship, and was submerged in the sea with certain others of the passengers; but God supplied me with a wooden bowl, and I got into it, and it bore me along until the waves cast me upon this island. And when he heard my words, he laid hold of my hand and said to me, Come with me. I therefore went with him, and he descended with me into a grotto beneath the earth, and conducted me into a large subterranean chamber, and having seated me at the upper end of that chamber, brought me some food. I was hungry; so I ate until I was satiated and contented, and my soul became at ease. Then he asked me respecting my case, and what had happened to me; wherefore I acquainted him with my whole affair from beginning to end; and he wondered at my story.

And when I had finished my tale, I said, I conjure thee by Allah, O my master, that thou be not displeased with me; I have acquainted thee with the truth of my case and of what hath happened to me, and I desire of thee that thou inform me who thou art, and what is the cause of thy dwelling in this chamber that is beneath the earth, and what is the reason of thy tethering this mare by the sea-side. So he replied, Know that we are a party dispersed in this island, upon its shores, and we are the grooms of the King El-Mihráj, having under our care all his horses; and every month, when moon-light commenceth, we bring the swift mares, and tether them in this island, every mare that has not foaled, and conceal ourselves in this chamber beneath the earth, that they may attract the sea-horses. This is the time of the coming forth of the sea-horse; and afterwards, if it be the will of God (whose name be exalted!), I will take thee with me to the King El-Mihráj, and divert thee with the sight of our country. Know, moreover, that if thou hadst not met with us, thou hadst not seen any one in this place, and wouldst have died in misery, none knowing of thee. But I will be the means of the preservation of thy life, and of thy return to thy country.—I therefore prayed for him, and thanked him for his kindness and beneficence; and while we were thus talking, the horse came forth from the sea, as he had said. And shortly after, his companions came, each leading a mare; and, seeing me with him, they inquired of me my story, and I told them what I had related to him. They then drew near to me, and spread the table, and ate, and invited me: so I ate with them; after which, they arose, and mounted the horses, taking me with them, having mounted me on a mare.

We commenced our journey, and proceeded without ceasing until we arrived at the city of King El-Mihráj, and they went in to him and acquainted him with my story. He therefore desired my presence, and they took me in to him, and stationed me before him; whereupon I saluted him, and he returned my salutation, and welcomed me, greeting me in an honourable manner, and inquired of me respecting my case. So I informed him of all that had happened to me, and of all that I had seen from beginning to end; and he wondered at that which had befallen me and happened to me, and said to me, O my son, by Allah thou hast experienced an extraordinary preservation, and had it not been for the predestined length of thy life, thou hadst not escaped from these difficulties; but praise be to God for thy safety! Then he treated me with beneficence and honour, caused me to draw near to him, and began to cheer me with conversation and courtesy; and he made me his superintendent of the sea-port, and registrar of every vessel that came to the coast. I stood in his presence to transact his affairs, and he favoured me and benefited me in every respect; he invested me with a handsome and costly dress, and I became a person high in credit with him in intercessions, and in accomplishing the affairs of the people. I ceased not to remain in his service for a long time; and whenever I went to the shore of the sea, I used to inquire of the merchants and travellers and sailors respecting the direction of the city of Baghdád, that perchance some one might inform me of it, and I might go with him thither and return to my country; but none knew it, nor knew any one who went to it. At this I was perplexed, and I was weary of the length of my absence from home; and in this state I continued for a length of time, until I went in one day to the King El-Mihráj, and found with him a party of Indians. I saluted them, and they returned my salutations, and welcomed me, and asked me respecting my country; after which, I questioned them as to their country, and they told me that they consisted of various races. Among them are the Shákireeyeh, who are the most noble of their races, who oppress no one, nor offer violence to any. And among them are a class called the Bráhmans, a people who never drink wine; but they are persons of pleasure and joy and sport and merriment, and possessed of camels and horses and cattle. They informed me also that the Indians are divided into seventy-two classes; and I wondered at this extremely. And I saw, in the dominions of the King El-Mihráj, an island, among others, which is called Kásil, in which is heard the beating of tambourines and drums throughout the night, and the islanders and travellers informed us that Ed-Dejjál is in it. I saw too, in the sea in which is that island a fish two hundred cubits long, and the fishermen fear it; wherefore they knock some pieces of wood, and it fleeth from them: and I saw a fish whose face was like that of the owl. I likewise saw during that voyage many wonderful and strange things, such that, if I related them to you, the description would be too long.

I continued to amuse myself with the sight of those islands and the things that they contained, until I stood one day upon the shore of the sea, with a staff in my hand, as was my custom, and, lo, a great vessel approached, wherein were many merchants; and when it arrived at the harbour of the city, and its place of anchoring, the master furled its sails, brought it to an anchor by the shore, and put forth the landing-plank; and the sailors brought out everything that was in that vessel to the shore. They were slow in taking forth the goods, while I stood writing their account, and I said to the master of the ship, Doth ought remain in thy vessel? He answered, Yes, O my master; I have some goods in the hold of the ship; but their owner was drowned in the sea at one of the islands during our voyage hither, and his goods are in our charge; so we desire to sell them, and to take a note of their price, in order to convey it to his family in the city of Baghdád, the Abode of Peace. I therefore said to the master, What was the name of that man, the owner of the goods? He answered, His name was Es-Sindibád of the Sea, and he was drowned on his voyage with us in the sea. And when I heard his words, I looked at him with a scrutinizing eye, and recognized him; and I cried out at him with a great cry, and said, O master, know that I am the owner of the goods which thou hast mentioned, and I am Es-Sindibád of the Sea, who descended upon the island from the ship, with the other merchants who descended; and when the fish that we were upon moved, and thou calledst out to us, some got up into the vessel, and the rest sunk, and I was among those who sank. But God (whose name be exalted!) preserved me and saved me from drowning by means of a large wooden bowl, of those in which the passengers were washing, and I got into it, and began to beat the water with my feet, and the wind and the waves aided me until I arrived at this island, when I landed on it, and God (whose name be exalted!) assisted me, and I met the grooms of the King El-Mihráj, who took me with them and brought me to this city. They then led me in to the King El-Mihráj, and I acquainted him with my story; whereupon he bestowed benefits upon me, and appointed me clerk of the harbour of this city, and I obtained profit in his service, and favour with him. Therefore these goods that thou hast are my goods and my portion.

But the master said, There is no strength nor power but in God the High, the Great! There is no longer faith nor conscience in any one!—Wherefore, O master, said I, when thou hast heard me tell thee my story? He answered, Because thou heardest me say that I had goods whose owner was drowned: therefore thou desirest to take them without price; and this is unlawful to thee; for we saw him when he sank, and there were with him many of the passengers, not one of whom escaped. How then dost thou pretend that thou art the owner of the goods?—So I said to him, O master, hear my story, and understand my words, and my veracity will become manifest to thee; for falsehood is a characteristic of the hypocrites. Then I related to him all that I had done from the time that I went forth with him from the city of Baghdád until we arrived at that island upon which we were submerged in the sea, and I mentioned to him some circumstances that had occurred between me and him. Upon this, therefore, the master and the merchants were convinced of my veracity, and recognized me; and they congratulated me on my safety, all of them saying, By Allah, we believed not that thou hadst escaped drowning; but God hath granted thee a new life. They then gave me the goods, and I found my name written upon them, and nought of them was missing. So I opened them, and took forth from them something precious and costly; the sailors of the ship carried it with me, and I went up with it to the King to offer it as a present, and informed him that this ship was the one in which I was a passenger. I told him also that my goods had arrived all entire, and that this present was a part of them. And the King wondered at this affair extremely; my veracity in all that I had said became manifest to him, and he loved me greatly, and treated me with exceeding honour, giving me a large present in return for mine.

Then I sold my bales, as well as the other goods that I had, and gained upon them abundantly; and I purchased other goods and merchandise and commodities of that city. And when the merchants of the ship desired to set forth on their voyage, I stowed all that I had in the vessel and, going in to the King, thanked him for his beneficence and kindness; after which I begged him to grant me permission to depart on my voyage to my country and my family. So he bade me farewell, and gave me an abundance of things at my departure, of the commodities of that city; and when I had taken leave of him, I embarked in the ship, and we set sail by the permission of God, whose name be exalted! Fortune served us, and destiny aided us, and we ceased not to prosecute our voyage night and day until we arrived in safety at the city of El-Basrah. There we landed, and remained a short time; and I rejoiced at my safety, and my return to my country; and after that, I repaired to the city of Baghdád, the Abode of Peace, with abundance of bales and goods and merchandise of great value. Then I went to my quarter, and entered my house, and all my family and companions came to me. I procured for myself servants and other dependants, and memlooks and concubines and male black slaves, so that I had a large establishment; and I purchased houses and other immoveable possessions, more than I had at first. I enjoyed the society of my companions and friends, exceeding my former habits, and forgot all that I had suffered from fatigue, and absence from my native country, and difficulty, and the terrors of travel.

THE STORY OF 'ABD–ALLAH OF THE LAND AND 'ABD–ALLAH OF THE SEA[1]

THERE was a fisherman named 'Abd-Allah, who had a numerous family: he had nine children and their mother, and was very poor, possessing nothing but his net. He used to go every day to the sea to fish; and when he caught little, he sold it, and expended its price upon his children, according as God supplied him; but if he caught much, he would cook a good dish, and buy fruit, and cease not to expend until there remained not aught in his possession; whereupon he would say within himself, The supply necessary for to-morrow will come to-morrow. Now when his wife gave birth to another, his children became ten persons; and the man that day possessed not any thing whatever: so his wife said to him, O my master, seek for me something wherewith I may sustain myself. He answered her, Lo, I am going, relying upon the blessing of God (whose name be exalted!) to the sea this day, for the luck of this new-born child, that we may see its fortune. And she replied, Place thy dependence upon God. Accordingly he took the net, and repaired to the sea. He then cast the net for the luck of that little infant, and said, O Allah, make his subsistence easy, not difficult; and abundant, not little! He waited over it a while, and then drew it, and it came forth full of rubbish and sand and pebbles and grass; and he saw not in it any fish; neither many did he see, nor few. So he cast it a second time, and waited over it, and then drew it; but he saw not in it fish. And he cast a third time, and a fourth, and a fifth; but there came not up in it any fish. He therefore removed to another place, and begged his subsistence of God (whose name be exalted!), and ceased not to do thus till the close of the day; but caught not a single minnow. And he wondered in his mind, and said, Hath God created this new-born child without allotting it subsistence? This can never be: for He who hath opened the jaws hath undertaken to provide for them the necessary subsistence: and God (whose name be exalted!) is bountiful, a liberal supplier of the necessaries of life.

He then took up the net, and returned with broken spirit, his heart

---

[1]From E. W. Lane's translation of *The Thousand and One Nights*.

being occupied with care for his family, because he had left them without food, especially as his wife had just given birth to a child. He ceased not to walk on, saying within himself, What is to be done; and what shall I say to the children this night? Then he came before the oven of a baker, and saw a crowd before it. The time was a time of dearness; and in those days there existed not in the possession of the people more than a scanty supply of provisions, and the people were offering money to the baker, but he paid no attention to any one of them, on account of the greatness of the crowd. The fisherman however stood looking, and smelling the smell of the hot bread, and his soul desired it by reason of his hunger; and thereupon the baker saw him, and called out to him, saying, Come hither, O fisherman! So he advanced to him; and the baker said to him, Dost thou desire bread? And he was silent. The baker said to him, Speak, and be not abashed: for God is bountiful. If thou have not with thee money, I will give thee, and will have patience with thee until good shall betide thee.—The fisherman therefore replied, By Allah, O master, I have not money: but give me bread sufficient for my family, and I will leave this net in pawn with thee till to-morrow. But the baker said to him, O poor man, verily this net is as it were thy shop, and the door of thy subsistence; and if thou give it in pawn, with what wilt thou fish? Acquaint me then with the quantity that will suffice thee.—He replied, For ten nuṣf faddahs. And he gave him bread for ten nuṣfs; after which he gave him also ten nuṣf faddahs, and said to him, Take these ten nuṣfs, and cook for thee by their means a dish of food; so thou wilt owe twenty nuṣf faddahs, and to-morrow bring me their value in fish, or, if nought betide thee, come, receive thy bread and ten nuṣfs, and I will have patience with thee until good shall betide thee, and after that, bring me fish to the value of that which I shall be entitled to receive from thee.—So the fisherman replied, May God (whose name be exalted!) reward thee, and recompense thee for me with every thing good! He then took the bread and the ten nuṣf faddahs, and went away happy, and, having purchased for him what he easily could, went in to his wife; and he saw her sitting, soothing the children, who were weeping by reason of their hunger, and she was saying to them, This instant your father will bring something for you to eat. So when he went in to them, he put down for them the bread, and they ate; and he acquainted his wife with that which had happened to him; whereupon she said to him, God is bountiful.

And on the following day, he took up his net, and went forth from his house, saying, I beg thee, O Lord, to supply me, this day, with that which shall whiten my face in the eyes of the baker! And when he came to the sea, he proceeded to cast the net and draw it; but there came not forth in it any fish. He ceased not to do so until the close of the day, and got nothing. So he returned in great grief; and the way to his house led by the oven of the baker. He therefore said within himself, By what way can I go to my house? But I will quicken my pace, that the baker may not see me.—And when he came to the oven of the baker, he saw a crowd; and he hastened in his pace, by reason of his abashment at the baker, in order that he might not see him: but, lo, the baker raised his eyes towards him, and cried out, saying, O fisherman, come hither; receive thy bread and the money for thy expenditure; for thou hast forgotten! He replied, No, by Allah; I forgot not; but I was abashed at thee; for I have not caught any fish this day. The baker said to him, Be not abashed. Did I not say to thee, Take thy leisure, until good shall betide thee?— Then he gave him the bread and the ten nusfs, and he went to his wife, and informed her of the news; upon which she said to him, God is bountiful. If it be the will of God, good will betide thee, and thou shalt pay him all that is due to him.—And he ceased not to continue thus for the space of forty days, every day going to the sea, and remaining from the rising of the sun to its setting, and returning without fish, and receiving bread and money for his expenditure from the baker, who mentioned not to him the fish any day of those days, nor neglected him as men generally would have done, but gave him the ten nusfs and the bread; and every time that the fisherman said to him, O my brother, reckon with me,— he would reply, Go; this is not the time for reckoning: wait until good shall betide thee, and then I will reckon with thee. So he would pray for him, and depart from him, thanking him. And on the one and fortieth day, he said to his wife, I desire to cut up this net, and be relieved of this mode of life.—Wherefore? said she. He answered her, It seemeth that my supply of subsistence from the sea is ended. And how long, he added, shall this state continue? By Allah, I am dissolved by abashment at the baker, and I will no more go to the sea, that I may not pass by his oven; for there is no way for me save by his oven; and every time that I pass by it, he calleth me, and giveth me the bread, and the ten nusfs. How long then shall I run in debt to him?—But she replied, Praise be to God (whose name be exalted!) who hath moved his heart to favour thee so that he giveth thee the food! And what dost thou dislike in this?— He said, I now owe him a great sum of money, and inevitably he will demand his due. His wife said to him, Hath he vexed thee with words? He answered, No; nor would he reckon with me; but would say to me, Wait until good shall betide thee.—Then, replied his wife, when he demandeth of thee, say to him, Wait until the good that I and thou hope for shall betide. And he said to her, When will the good that we hope for come? She answered him, God is bountiful. And he replied, Thou hast spoken truth.

He then took up his net, and repaired to the sea, saying, O Lord, supply me, if only with one fish, that I may give it to the baker! Then he cast the net in the sea, and drew it, and found it heavy; and he ceased not to labour at it until he was violently fatigued; but when he drew it forth, he saw in it a dead ass, swollen, and of abominable odour: so his

soul was wearied. He extricated it from the net, and said, There is no
strength nor power but in God, the High, the Great! I have been tired
of saying to this woman, There remaineth for me no means of subsistence
in the sea: let me abandon this occupation:—and of her replying, God is
bountiful: good will betide thee. Is then this dead ass that good?—
Exceeding grief affected him, and he went to another place, that he
might be remote from the smell of the ass, and took the net, and cast it,
and waited over it some time. Then he drew it, and again found it heavy;
and he ceased not to labour at it until blood issued from the palms of his
hands; and when he had drawn forth the net, he saw in it a human being.
So he imagined that he was an 'Efreet, of those whom the lord Suleymán
used to imprison in bottles of brass, and cast into the sea, and that, the
bottle having broken by reason of the length of years, that 'Efreet had
issued from it, and come up in the net. He therefore fled from him, and
began to say, Mercy! Mercy! O' Efreet of Suleymán!—But the human
being cried out to him from within the net, saying, Come hither, O
fisherman! Flee not from me; for I am a human being like thee. Liberate
me then, that thou mayest obtain my recompense.—So when the fisherman heard his words, his heart became tranquillized, and he came to him
and said to him, Art thou not an 'Efreet of the Jinn? He answered,
No; but I am a man, a believer in God and his Apostle. The fisherman
said to him, And who cast thee into the sea? He replied, I am of the
children of the sea. I was going about, and thou threwest upon me the
net. We are nations obedient to the ordinances of God, and we are compassionate to the creatures of God (whose name be exalted!); and were
it not that I fear and dread being of the disobedient, I should have rent
thy net; but I willingly submit to that which God hath decreed to befall
me; and thou, if thou deliver me, wilt become my owner, and I shall become thy captive. Wilt thou then emancipate me with the desire of
seeing the face of God (whose name be exalted!), and make a covenant
with me, and become my companion? I will come to thee every day in
this place, and thou shalt come to me, and bring for me a present of the
fruits of the land. For with you are grapes and figs and water-melons and
peaches and pomegranates and other fruits, and everything that thou
wilt bring me will be acceptable from thee. And with us are coral and
pearls and chrysolites and emeralds and jacinths and other jewels. So I
will fill for thee the basket in which thou wilt bring me the fruits with
minerals consisting of the jewels of the sea. What then sayest thou, O
my brother, of this proposal?—The fisherman answered him, Let the
Fátehah be recited in confirmation of the agreement between me and
thee as to this proposal.

Accordingly each of them recited the Fátehah, and the fisherman
liberated him from the net, and said to him, What is thy name? He
answered, My name is 'Abd-Allah of the Sea; and if thou come to this
place, and see me not, call out and say, Where art thou, O 'Abd-Allah,

O thou of the Sea?—and I will be with thee instantly. And thou (he added), what is thy name?—The fisherman answered, My name is 'Abd-Allah. So the other replied, Thou art 'Abd-Allah of the Land, and I am 'Abd-Allah of the Sea. Now stay here while I go and bring thee a present. —And he said, I hear and obey. Then 'Abd-Allah of the Sea went into the sea; and thereupon 'Abd-Allah of the Land repented of his having liberated him from the net; and he said within himself, How do I know that he will return to me? He only laughed at me, so that I liberated him; and had I kept him, I might have diverted the people in the city with the sight of him, and received money from all the people for shewing him, and entered with him the houses of the great men.—Therefore he repented of his having liberated him, and said to himself, Thy prey hath gone from thy hand. But while he was lamenting his escape from his hand, lo, 'Abd-Allah of the Sea returned to him, with his hands filled with pearls and coral and emeralds and jacinths and other jewels, and said to him, Receive, O my brother, and blame me not; for I have not a basket; if I had I would have filled it for thee. So thereupon 'Abd-Allah of the Land rejoiced, and received from him the jewels; and 'Abd-Allah of the Sea said to him, Every day thou shalt come to this place before sunrise. He then bade him farewell, and departed, and entered the sea.

But as to the fisherman, he entered the city, joyful, and ceased not to walk on until he came to the oven of the baker, when he said to him, O my brother, good hath betided us: therefore reckon with me. The baker replied, No reckoning is necessary. If thou have with thee any thing, give me; and if thou have not with thee any thing, receive thy bread, and the money for thy expenditure, and go, and wait until good shall betide thee. So he said to him, O my companion, good hath betided me from the bounty of God, and I owe thee a large sum; but receive this. And he took for him a handful of pearls and corals and jacinths and other jewels, that handful being half of what he had with him; and he gave it to the baker, and said to him, Give me some money that I may expend it this day, until I shall sell these minerals. He therefore gave him all the money that he had at his command, and all the bread that was in the basket which he had with him; and the baker was rejoiced with those minerals, and said to the fisherman, I am thy slave and thy servant. He carried all the bread that he had with him on his head, and walked behind him to the house, and the fisherman gave the bread to his wife and his children. The baker then went to the market, and brought meat and vegetables and all kinds of fruit. He abandoned the oven, and remained all that day occupying himself with the service of 'Abd-Allah of the Land, and performing for him his affairs. So the fisherman said to him, O my brother, thou hast wearied thy-self. The baker replied, This is incumbent on me; for I have become thy servant, and thy beneficence hath inundated me. But the fisherman said to him, Thou wast my benefactor in the time of distress and dearness. And the baker passed the ensuing night with him, enjoying good eating; and he became a faithful friend to the fisherman. The fisherman informed his wife of his adventure with 'Abd-Allah of the Sea, whereat she rejoiced, and she said to him, Conceal thy secret, lest the magistrates tyrannize over thee. But he replied, If I conceal my secret from all other people, I will not conceal it from the baker.

He arose in the morning of the following day, having filled a basket with fruits of all kinds in the preceding evening, and he took it up before sunrise, and repaired to the sea, put it down on the shore, and said, Where art thou, O 'Abd-Allah, O thou of the Sea? And he answered him, At thy service:—and came forth to him. He therefore presented to him the fruit, and he took it up, and descended with it, diving into the sea, and was absent a while; after which he came forth, having with him the basket full of all kinds of minerals and jewels. So 'Abd-Allah of the Land put it upon his head, and departed with it; and when he came to the oven of the baker, the baker said to him, O my master, I have baked for thee forty shureyks, and sent them to thy house; and now I will bake bread of the finest flour, and when it is done, I will convey it to the house, and go to bring thee the vegetables and the meat. Upon this, 'Abd-Allah took for him, for the basket, three handfuls, and gave them to him, and went to the house, where he put down the basket, and took, of each kind of jewels, one jewel of great value. Then he repaired to the jewel-market, and, stopping at the shop of the Sheykh of the market, said, Purchase of me these jewels. He replied, Shew them to me. So he shewed them to him; and the Sheykh said to him, Hast thou any beside these? He answered, I have a basket full. The Sheykh said to him, Where is thy house? He answered him, In such a quarter. And the Sheykh took from him the jewels, and said to his servants, Lay hold of him; for he is the thief who stole the things of the Queen, the wife of the Sultán. He then ordered them to beat him, and they did so, and bound his hands behind his back; and the Sheykh arose, with all the people of the jewel-market, and they began to say, We have taken the thief. Some of them said, None stole the goods of such a one but this villain:—and others said, None stole all that was in the house of such a one but he:—and some of them said thus, and others said thus. All this while, he was silent; he returned not to any one of them a reply, nor did he utter to him a sentence, until they stationed him before the King; whereupon the Sheykh said, O King of the age, when the necklace of the Queen was stolen, thou sentest and acquaintedst us, and requiredst of us the capture of the offender; and I strove above the rest of the people, and have captured for thee the offender. Lo, here he is before thee, and these jewels we have rescued from his hand.—The King therefore said to the eunuch, Take these minerals, and shew them to the Queen, and say to her, Are these thy goods that thou hast lost? Accordingly the eunuch took them, and went in with them before the Queen: and when she saw them she wondered at them, and she sent to say to the King, I have found my necklace in my place, and these are not my property; but these jewels are better than the jewels of my necklace; therefore act not unjustly to the man; and if he will sell them, purchase them of him for thy daughter, Umm-es-So'ood, that we may put them for her upon a necklace.

So when the eunuch returned, and acquainted the King with that which the Queen had said, he cursed the Sheykh of the jewellers, him and his company, with the curse of 'Ád and Thamood; whereupon they said, O King of the age, we knew that this man was a poor fisherman; so we deemed those things too much for him to possess, and imagined that he had stolen them. But he replied, O base wretches, do ye deem good things too much for a believer? Wherefore did ye not ask him? Perhaps God (whose name be exalted!) hath blessed him with them in a way he did not reckon upon; and wherefore do ye assert him to be a thief, and disgrace him among the people? Go forth! May God not bless you!— They therefore went forth in a state of fear. The King then said, O man, may God bless thee in that which He hath bestowed on thee! And thou hast promise of indemnity. But acquaint me with the truth. Whence came to thee these jewels? For I am a King, and the like of them exist not in my possession.—So he answered, O King of the age, I have a basket full of them; and the case is thus and thus. And he informed him of his companionship with 'Abd-Allah of the Sea, and said to him, An agreement hath been made between me and him, that I shall every day fill for him the basket with fruits, and he shall fill it for me with these jewels. The King therefore said to him, O man, this is thy lot; but wealth requireth an exalted station, and I will prevent men's domineering over thee in these days. Perhaps, however, I may be deposed, or may die, and another may be appointed in my stead, and may slay thee on account of his love of worldly goods, and covetousness. I therefore desire to marry thee to my daughter, and to make thee my Wezeer, and bequeath to thee the kingdom after me, that no one may covet thy possessions after my death.—Then the King said, Take ye this man, and conduct him into the bath. So they took him, and washed him, and they clad him in apparel of the apparel of Kings, and led him forth into the presence of the King, who thereupon appointed him Wezeer unto him. He sent also the couriers, and the soldiers of the guard, and all the wives of the great men, to his house; and they clad his wife in the apparel of the wives of Kings, clad her children likewise, and mounted her in a litter; and all the wives of the great men, and the troops and the couriers, and the soldiers of the guard, walked before her, and conducted her to the King's palace, with the little infant in her bosom. They brought in her elder children to the King, who treated them with honour, took them upon his lap and seated them by his side. And they were nine male children; and the King was destitute of male offspring, not having been blessed with any child except that daughter, whose name was Umm-es-So'ood. And as to the Queen, she treated the wife of 'Abd-Allah of the Land with honour, and bestowed favours upon her, and made her Wezeereh to her. The King gave orders to perform the ceremony of the contract of the marriage of 'Abd-Allah of the Land to his daughter, and he assigned as her dowry all the jewels and minerals that he had, and they commenced the festivity; the King commanding that a proclamation should be made to decorate the city on account of the marriage-festivity of his daughter.

Then, on the following day, after 'Abd-Allah of the Land had introduced himself to the King's daughter, the King looked from the window, and saw 'Abd-Allah carrying upon his head a basket full of fruits. So he said to him, What is this that is with thee, O my son-in-law, and whither goest thou? He answered, To my companion, 'Abd-Allah of the Sea. The King said to him, O my son-in-law, this is not the time to go to thy companion. But he replied, I fear to be unfaithful to him with respect to the time of promise; for he would reckon me a liar, and say to me, Worldly matters have diverted thee from coming to me. And the King said, Thou hast spoken truth. Go to thy companion. May God aid thee!—So he walked through the city, on his way to his companion, and, the people having become acquainted with him, he heard them say, This is the son-in-law of the King, going to exchange the fruits for the jewels. And he who was ignorant of him, and knew him not, would say, O man, for how much is the pound? Come hither: Sell to me.—Whereupon he would answer him, Wait for me until I return to thee. And he would not vex any one. Then he went, and met 'Abd-Allah of the Sea, and gave him the fruits; and 'Abd-Allah of the Sea gave him for them jewels in exchange.—He ceased not to do thus, and every day he passed by the oven of the baker, and saw it closed. He continued thus for the space of ten days; and when he had not seen the baker, and saw his oven closed, he said within himself, Verily this is a wonderful thing! Whither can the baker have gone?—He then asked his neighbour, saying to him, O my brother, where is thy neighbour the baker, and what hath God done with him? He answered, O my master, he is sick: he doth not come forth from his house. So he said to him, Where is his house? The man answered him, In such a quarter. He therefore repaired thither, and inquired for him; and when he knocked at the door, the baker looked from the window, and saw his companion the fisherman with a full basket upon his head. So he descended to him, and opened to him the door; and 'Abd-Allah of the Land threw himself upon him, and embraced him, and said to him, How art thou, O my companion? For every day I pass by the oven and see it closed. Then I asked thy neighbour, and he informed me that thou wast sick. I therefore inquired for thy house, that I might see thee. —The baker replied, May God recompense thee for me with every thing good! I have no disease; but it was told me that the King had taken thee, because some of the people lied to him, and asserted that thou wast a thief: so I feared, and closed the oven, and hid myself.—'Abd-Allah of the Land said, Thou hast spoken truth. And he informed him of his case, and of the events that had happened to him with the King and the Sheykh of the jewel-market, and said to him, The King hath married me to his daughter, and made me his Wezeer. He then said to him, Take what is in this basket as thy lot, and fear not.

After that, he went forth from him, having dispelled from him his fear, and repaired to the King with the basket empty. So the King said to him, O my son-in-law, it seemeth that thou hast not met with thy companion 'Abd-Allah of the Sea this day. He replied, I went to him, and what he gave me I have given to my companion the baker; for I owe him kindness. The King said, Who is this baker? He answered, He is a man of kind disposition, and such and such events happened to me with him in the days of poverty, and he neglected me not any day, nor broke my heart. The King said, What is his name? He answered, His name is 'Abd-Allah the baker, and my name is 'Abd-Allah of the Land, and my other companion's name is 'Abd-Allah of the Sea. Upon this, the King said, And my name is 'Abd-Allah, and the servants of God are all brethren. Send therefore to thy companion the baker: bring him that we may make him Wezeer of the Left. Accordingly he sent to him; and when he came before the King, the King invested him with the apparel of Wezeer, and appointed him Wezeer of the Left, appointing 'Abd-Allah of the Land Wezeer of the Right. 'Abd-Allah of the Land continued in this state a whole year, every day taking the basket full of fruits, and returning with it full of jewels and minerals; and when the fruits were exhausted from the gardens, he used to take raisins and almonds and hazel-nuts and walnuts and figs and other things; and all that he took to him he accepted from him, and he returned to him the basket full of jewels as was his custom.

Now it happened, one day, that he took the basket full of dried fruits, according to his custom, and his companion received them from him; after which, 'Abd-Allah of the Land sat upon the shore, and 'Abd-Allah of the Sea sat in the water, near the shore, and they proceeded to converse together, talking alternately until they were led to mention the tombs. Thereupon 'Abd-Allah of the Sea said, O my brother, they say that the Prophet (may God bless and save him!) is buried among you in the land. Dost thou then know his tomb?—He answered, Yes. He asked, In what place? He answered, In a city called Teybeh. He said, And do men, the people of the land, visit his tomb? He answered, Yes. And 'Abd-Allah of the Sea said, May you derive enjoyment, O people of the land, from visiting this generous, benign, merciful Prophet, whose visitor meriteth his intercession! And hast thou visited him, O my brother?—He answered, No; for I was a poor man, and found not what I should expend on the way, and I have not been independent save from the time when I first knew thee and thou conferredst upon me this prosperity. But the visiting him, after I shall have performed the pilgrimage to the Sacred House of God, hath become incumbent on me; and nothing hath prevented my doing that but my affection for thee; for I cannot separate myself from thee for one day.—Upon this, he of the Sea said to him of the Land, And dost thou prefer thy affection for me above visiting the tomb of Moḥammad (may God bless and save him!), who will intercede for thee on the day of appearance before God, and will save thee from the fire, and by means of whose intercession thou wilt enter Paradise; and for the sake of the love of the world dost thou neglect to visit the tomb of thy Prophet Moḥammad, may God bless and save him? He answered, No, by Allah: verily the visitation of him is preferred by me above every thing else; but I desire of thee permission that I may visit him this year. He replied, I give thee permission to visit him; and when thou standest by his tomb, give him my salutation. I have also a deposite: so enter the sea with me, that I may take thee to my city, and conduct thee into my house, and entertain thee, and give thee the deposite, in order that thou mayest put it upon the grave of the Prophet (may God bless and save him!); and say thou to him, O Apostle of God, 'Abd-Allah of the Sea saluteth thee, and hath given to thee this present, and he beggeth thine intercession to save him from the fire.—So 'Abd-Allah of the Land said to him, O my brother, thou wast created in the water, and the water is thine abode, and it injureth thee not: then if thou come forth from it to the land, will injury betide thee? He answered, Yes; my body will dry up and the breezes of the land will blow upon me, and I shall die.— And he in like manner, replied, 'Abd-Allah of the Land was created on the Land, and the land is my abode; and if I enter the sea, the water will enter into my body, and suffocate me, and I shall die. But the other said to him, Fear not that; for I will bring thee an ointment, with which thou shalt anoint thy body, and the water will not injure thee, even if thou pass the remainder of thy life going about in the sea; and thou shalt sleep and arise in the sea, and nought will injure thee. So he replied, If the case be so, no harm. Bring me the ointment, that I may try it.

'Abd-Allah of the Sea said, Be it so. And he took the basket, and descended into the sea, and was absent a little while. He then returned, having with him some fat like the fat of beef, the colour of which was yellow, like gold, and its scent was sweet; and 'Abd-Allah of the Land said to him, What is this, O my brother? He answered him, this is the fat of the liver of a kind of fish called the dendán. It is the greatest of all kinds of fish, and the most violent of our enemies, and its form is larger than that of any beast of the land existing among you: if it saw the camel or the elephant, it would swallow it.—'Abd-Allah of the Land said to him, O my brother, and what doth this unlucky creature eat? He answered him, It eateth of the beasts of the sea. Hast thou not heard that it is said in the proverb, like the fish of the sea: the strong eateth the weak?—He replied, Thou hast spoken truth. But have you (he added) many of these dendáns among you in the sea? 'Abd-Allah of the Sea answered, Among us are such as none can number except God, whose name he exalted! Then said 'Abd-Allah of the Land, Verily I fear that, if I descend with thee, this kind of creature may meet me and devour me. But 'Abd-Allah of the Sea replied, Fear not; for when it seeth thee, it will know that thou art a son of Adam, and it will fear thee, and flee. It feareth not aught in the sea as it feareth a son of Adam; for when it hath eaten a son of Adam, it dieth instantly, because the fat of a son of Adam is a deadly poison to this kind of creature. And we collect not the fat of its liver save in consequence of a son of Adam's falling into the sea and being drowned: for his form becometh altered, and often his flesh is torn, and the dendán eateth it, imagining it to be of some of the animals of the sea, and dieth: then we happen to light on it dead, and take the fat of its liver, with which we anoint our bodies, and we go about in the sea. In whatever place is a son of Adam, if there be in that place a hundred or two hundred or a thousand or more of that kind of creature, and they hear the cry of the son of Adam, all of them die immediately at his crying once, and not one of them can move from its place.

Upon this, 'Abd-Allah of the Land said, I place my reliance upon God. He then pulled off the clothes that were upon him, and, having dug a hole on the shore, he buried his clothes; after which, he anointed his person from the parting of his hair to his feet with this ointment. Then he descended into the water, and dived; and he opened his eyes, and the water injured him not. He walked to the right and left; and if he would, he ascended; and if he would, he descended to the bottom. He saw the water of the sea forming as it were a tent over him, and it injured him not. And 'Abd-Allah of the Sea said to him, What seest thou, O my brother? He answered him, I see what is good, O my brother, and thou hast spoken truth in that which thou hast said; for the water doth not injure me. Then 'Abd-Allah of the Sea said to him, Follow me. So he followed him; and they ceased not to walk from place to place, while he saw before him, and on his right and on his left, mountains of water, and he diverted himself with the view of them and with the view of the different kinds of fish that were sporting in the sea, some great and some small. Among them were some resembling buffaloes, and some resembling oxen, and some resembling dogs, and some resembling human beings; and every kind to which they drew near fled at seeing 'Abd-Allah of the Land. He therefore said to him of the Sea, O my brother, wherefore do I see every kind to which we draw near flee from us? And he answered him, Through fear of thee; for every thing that God hath created feareth the son of Adam. He ceased not to divert himself with the sight of the wonders of the sea until they came to a high mountain, and 'Abd-Allah of the Land walked by the side of that mountain, and suddenly he heard a great cry: so he looked aside, and he saw something black descending upon him from that mountain, and it was as large as a camel, or larger, and cried out. He therefore said to his companion, What is this, O my brother? He answered him, This is the dendán: it is descending in pursuit of me, desiring to devour me: so cry out at it, O my brother, before it reacheth us; for otherwise it will seize me, and devour me. Accordingly, 'Abd-Allah of the Land cried out at it, and, lo, it fell down dead; and when he saw it dead, he said, Extolled be the perfection of God, and his praise! I struck it not with a sword, nor with a knife! How is it that, with the enormity of this creature, it could not bear my cry, but died?— But 'Abd-Allah of the Sea, said to him, Wonder not: for by Allah, O my brother, were there a thousand or two thousand of this kind, they would not be able to endure the cry of a son of Adam.

They then walked to a city, and they saw its inhabitants to be all damsels, no males being among them. So 'Abd-Allah of the Land said, O my brother, what is this city, and what are these damsels? And his companion answered him, This is the city of the damsels; for its inhabitants are of the damsels of the sea. The King of the Sea banisheth them to this city. Every one against whom he is incensed, of the damsels of the Sea, he sendeth hither, and she cannot come forth from it, for if she came forth from it any of the beasts of the sea that saw her would devour her. But in other cities than this, there are men and women.—Then 'Abd-Allah of the Land proceeded to divert himself with the view of these damsels, and saw that they had faces like moons, and hair like the hair of women; but they had arms and legs in the fore part of the body, and tails like the tails of fishes. His companion, having diverted him with the view of the inhabitants of this city, went forth with him, and walked before him to another city, which he saw to be filled with people, females and males, whose forms were like the forms of the damsels before mentioned; and they had tails; but they had no selling nor buying like the people of the land. And he said, O my brother, how do they manage their marriages? His companion answered him, They do not all marry; for we are not all of one religion: among us are Muslims, unitarians; and among us are Christians and Jews and other sects; and those of us who marry are chiefly the Muslims. Whoso desireth to marry, they impose upon him, as a dowry, the gift of a certain number of different kinds of fish, which he catcheth; as many as a thousand or two thousand, or more or less, according to the agreement made between him and the father of the wife. And when he bringeth what is demanded, the family of the bridegroom and the family of the bride assemble and eat the banquet. Then they introduce him to his wife. And after that, he catcheth fish and feedeth her; or, if he be unable, she catcheth fish and feedeth him.— 'Abd-Allah of the Sea then took him to another city, and after that to another, and so on, until he had diverted him with the sight of eighty cities; and he saw the inhabitants of each city to be unlike the inhabitants of another city; and he said, O my brother, are there any more cities in the sea? His companion said, And what hast thou seen of the cities of the sea, and its wonders? By the generous, benign, merciful Prophet, were I to divert thee for a thousand years, every day with the sight of a thousand cities, and shew thee in every city a thousand wonders, I should not shew thee a twenty-fourth part of the cities of the sea, and its wonders. I have only diverted thee with the view of our own region, and our land, and nothing more.—So 'Abd-Allah of the Land said to him, O my brother, since the case is so, enough for me is that with the sight of which I have diverted myself; for I have become weary of eating fish, and have spent eighty days in thy company, during which thou hast not fed me, morning and evening, with aught but raw fish, neither broiled nor cooked in any way. But thou hast not diverted me with a sight of thy city.— He replied, As to my city, we have gone a considerable distance beyond it, and it is near the shore from which we came.

Then he returned with him to his city, and when he came to it, he said to him, This is my city. And he saw it to be a small city in comparison with those with the sight of which he had diverted himself. He entered the city, accompanied by 'Abd-Allah of the Sea, who proceeded until he came to a cavern, when he said to him, This is my house; and all the houses of this city are likewise caverns, great and small, in the mountains, as are also all those of all the cities of the sea. For every one who desireth to make for himself a house, goeth to the King, and saith to him, I desire to make me a house in such a place. Thereupon the King sendeth with him a tribe of fish called the peckers, assigning as their wages a certain quantity of fish; and they have beaks which crumble rock. They come to the mountain that the intended owner of the house hath chosen, and excavate in it the house with their beaks; and the owner of the house catcheth fish for them, and putteth them into their mouths, until the cavern is completed, when they depart, and the owner of the house taketh up his abode in it. All the people of the sea are in this state: they transact not affairs of commerce, one with another, nor do they serve one another, save by means of fish; and their food is fish. Then he said to him, Enter. So he entered. And 'Abd-Allah of the Sea said, O my daughter! And, lo, his daughter advanced to him. She had a face round like the moon, and long hair and heavy hips, and black-edged eyes and a slender waist; but she had a tail. And when she saw 'Abd-Allah of the Land with her father, she said to him, O my father, what is this tail-less creature whom thou hast brought with thee? He answered her, O my daughter, this is my companion of the land, from whom I used to bring thee the fruits of the land. Come hither: salute him.—She therefore advanced and saluted him, with an eloquent tongue and fluent speech; and her father said to her, Bring some food for our guest, by whose arrival a blessing hath betided us. And she brought him two large fishes, each of them like a lamb; and he said to him, Eat. So he ate in spite of himself, by reason of his hunger; for he was weary of eating fish, and they had nothing else. And but a short time had elapsed when the wife of 'Abd-Allah of the Sea approached. She was of beautiful form, and with her were two children, each child having in his hand a young fish, of which he was craunching bits as a man craunceth bits of a cucumber. And when she saw 'Abd-Allah of the Land with her husband, she said, What is this tail-less creature? The two children also advanced with their sister and their mother, and they looked at 'Abd-Allah of the Land, and said, Yea, by Allah: verily he is tail-less! And they laughed at him. So 'Abd-Allah of the Land said to his companion, O my brother, hast thou brought me to make me a laughing-stock to thy children and thy wife? 'Abd-Allah of the Sea answered him, Pardon, O my brother: for he who hath no tail existeth not among us; and when one without a tail is found, the Sultan taketh him to laugh at him. But, O my brother, be not displeased with these young children and the woman, since their intellects are defective.—Then he cried out at his family, and said to them, Be ye silent! So they feared, and were silent; and he proceeded to appease his mind.

And while he was conversing with him, lo, ten persons, great, strong, and stout, advanced to him, and said, O 'Abd-Allah, it hath been told to the King that thou hast with thee a tail-less creature, of the tail-less creatures of the land. So he replied, Yes; and he is this man: for he is my companion: he hath come to me as a guest, and I desire to take him back to the land. But they said to him, We cannot go save with him; and if thou desire to say aught, arise and take him, and come with him before the King, and what thou sayest to us, say to the King. Therefore 'Abd-Allah of the Sea said to him, O my brother, the excuse is manifest, and it is impossible for us to disobey the King, but go with me to the King, and I will endeavour to liberate thee from him, if it be the will of God. Fear not; for when he seeth thee, he will know that thou art of the children of the land; and when he knoweth that thou art of the land, he will without doubt treat thee with honour, and restore thee to the land.— So 'Abd-Allah of the Land replied, It is thine to determine; and I will place my dependence upon God, and go with thee. He then took him and proceeded with him until he came to the King; and when the King saw him, he laughed, and said, Welcome to the tail-less! And every one who was around the King began to laugh at him, and to say, Yea, by Allah: verily he is tail-less! Then 'Abd-Allah of the Sea advanced to the King, and acquainted him with his circumstances, and said to him, This is of the children of the land, and he is my companion, and he cannot live among us; for he loveth not the eating of fish unless it be fried or otherwise cooked; and I desire that thou give me permission to restore him to the land. The King therefore replied, Since the case is so, and he cannot live among us, I give thee permission to restore him to his place after entertainment. Then the King said, Bring to him the banquet. And they brought him fish of various shapes and colours, and he ate in obedience to the command of the King; after which the King said to him, Demand of me what thou wilt. And 'Abd-Allah of the Land replied, I demand of thee that thou give me jewels. So he said, Take ye him to the jewel-house, and let him select what he requireth. Accordingly his companion took him to the jewel-house, and he selected as many as he desired. He then returned with him to his city, and, producing to him a purse, he said to him, Take this as a deposite, and convey it to the tomb of the Prophet, may God bless and save him! And he took it, not knowing what was in it.

Then 'Abd-Allah of the Sea went forth with him, to conduct him to the land; and he saw, in his way, people engaged in singing and festivity, and a table of fish spread; and the people were eating and singing, and in a state of great rejoicing. So he said to 'Abd-Allah of the Sea, Wherefore are these people in a state of great rejoicing? Is a wedding being celebrated among them?—And he of the Sea answered, There is no wedding being celebrated among them; but a person among them is dead. 'Abd-Allah of the Land therefore said to him, Do ye, when a person dieth among you, rejoice for him, and sing and eat? His companion answered, Yes. And ye, O people of the land, he added, what do ye? 'Abd-Allah of the Land answered, When a person among us dieth, we mourn for him, and weep, and the women slap their faces, and rend the bosoms of their garments, in grief for him who is dead. And upon this, 'Abd-Allah of the Sea stared at 'Abd-Allah of the Land, and said, Give me the deposite. So he gave it to him. Then 'Abd-Allah of the Sea took him forth to the land, and said to him, I have broken off my companionship with thee, and my friendship for thee, and after this day thou shalt not see me, nor will I see thee.—Wherefore, said 'Abd-Allah of the Land are these words? 'Abd-Allah of the Sea said, Are ye not, O people of the Land, a deposite of God?—Yes, answered he of the Land. And the other rejoined, Then how is it that it is not agreeable to you that God should take his deposite, but on the contrary ye weep for it? And how should I give thee the deposite for the Prophet (may God bless and save him!), seeing that ye, when the new-born child cometh to you, rejoice in it, though God (whose name be exalted!) putteth into it the soul as a deposite? Then, when He taketh that soul, how is it that it grieveth you, and ye weep and mourn? Such being the case, we have no need of your companionship.—He then left him, and went back to the sea.

So upon this, 'Abd-Allah of the Land put on his clothes, and took his jewels, and repaired to the King, who met him with a longing desire to see him, and rejoiced at his return, and said to him, How art thou, O my son-in-law, and what hath been the cause of thine absence from me during this period? He therefore told him his story, and what he had seen of the wonders in the sea; whereat the King wondered. He acquainted him also with that which 'Abd-Allah of the Sea had said; and he replied, Thou art the person who erred, in thy giving this information. 'Abd-Allah of the Land persevered for a length of time in going to the shore of the sea, and calling out to 'Abd-Allah of the Sea; but he answered him not, nor came to him. So 'Abd-Allah of the Land relinquished the

hope of seeing him again, and he and the King his father-in-law and
their family resided in the most happy state and in the practice of good
deeds until they were visited by the terminator of delights and the sepa
rator of companions, and they all died.—Extolled be the perfection of the
Living who dieth not, and to whom belongeth the dominion that is apparent and the dominion that is hidden, and who is able to accomplish
every thing, and is gracious and knowing with respect to his servants!

PERSIA

THE SAILOR AND THE PEARL MERCHANT[1]

IT IS related that in the city of Basrah there was a man, Abu'l
Fawaris, who was the chief of the sailors of the town, for in the
great ocean there was no port at which he had not landed. One day, as
he sat on the seashore, with his sailors round him, an old man arrived
in a ship, landed where Abu'l Fawaris was sitting, and said: "Friend,
I desire you to give me your ship for six months, and I will pay you whatever you desire." "I demand a thousand gold dinars," said the sailor,
and at once received the gold from the old man, who, before departing,
said that he would come again on the next day, and warned Abu'l Fawaris that there was to be no holding back.

The sailor took home his gold, made his ship ready, and then, taking
leave of his wife and sons, he went down to the shore, where he found the
old man waiting for him with a slave and twenty ass-loads of empty
sacks. Abu'l Fawaris greeted him, and together they loaded the ship and
set sail. Taking a particular star for their mark, they sailed for three
months, when an island appeared to one side of them. For this the old
man steered, and they soon landed upon it. Having loaded his slave with
some sacks, the old man with his companions set out towards a mountain
which they could see in the distance. This they reached after some hours
of travel, and climbed to the summit, upon which they found a broad
plain where more than two hundred pits had been dug. The old man then
explained to the sailor that he was a merchant, and that he had, on that
spot, found a mine of jewels. "Now that I have given you my confidence,"
he continued, "I expect faithfulness from you too. I desire you to go
down into this pit and send up sufficient pearls to fill these sacks. Half
I will give to you, and we shall be able to spend the rest of our lives in
luxury." The sailor thereupon asked how the pearls had found their way
into these pits, to which the old man replied that there was a passage
connecting the pits with the sea. Along this passage oysters swam, and
settled in the pits, where by chance he had come upon them. He explained
further that he had only brought the sailor because he needed help; but
he desired not to disclose the matter to any one else.

With great eagerness then the sailor descended into the pit, and there
found oysters in great numbers. The old man let down a basket to him,
which he filled again and again, until at last the merchant cried out that
the oysters were useless, for they contained no pearls. Abu'l Fawaris

[1]From Mr. Reuben Levy's translation of *The Three Dervishes*, in the World's Classics
Series. Reprinted by permission of the translator and of the Oxford University Press.

therefore left that pit, and descended into another, where he found pearls in great number. By the time night fell he was utterly wearied, and called out to the old man to help him out of the pit. In reply the merchant shouted down that he intended to leave him in the pit, for he feared that Abu'l Fawaris might kill him for the sake of the jewels. With great vehemence the sailor protested that he was innocent of any such intention, but the old man was deaf to his entreaties, and, making his way back to the ship, sailed away.

For three days Abu'l Fawaris remained, hungry and thirsty. As he struggled to find a way out he came upon many human bones, and understood that the accursed old man had betrayed many others in the same fashion. In desperation he dug about, and at last he saw a small opening, which he enlarged with his hands. Soon it was big enough for him to crawl through, and he found himself in the darkness, standing upon mud. Along this he walked carefully, and then felt himself suddenly plunged to his neck in water, which was salt to the taste; and he knew that he was in the passage that led to the sea. He swam along in this for some way, till, in front of him, there appeared a faint light. Greatly heartened by the sight of it, he swam vigorously until he reached the mouth of the passage. On emerging, he found himself facing the sea, and threw himself on his face to give thanks for his delivery. Then he arose, and a little distance from him he found the cloak which he had left behind when he set out for the mountain; but of the old merchant there was no sign, and the ship had disappeared.

Full of trouble and despondency, he sat down at the water's brink, wondering what he was to do. As he gazed at the sea there came into view a ship, and he saw that it was filled with men. At sight of it the sailor leaped from his place; snatching his turban from his head, he waved it with all his might in the air, and shouted at the top of his voice. But as they approached he decided not to tell his rescuers the truth of his presence there; therefore when they landed and asked how he came to be on the island he told them that his ship had been wrecked at sea, that he had clung to a plank and been washed to the shore.

They praised his good fortune at his escape, and in reply to his questions with regard to the place of their origin, told him that they had sailed from Abyssinia, and were then on their way to Hindustan. At this, Abu'l Fawaris hesitated, saying that he had no business in Hindustan. They assured him, however, that they would meet ships going to Basrah, and would hand him over to one of them. He agreed then to go with them, and for forty days they sailed without seeing any inhabited spot. At last he asked them whether they had not mistaken their way, and they admitted that for five days they had been sailing without knowing whither they were going or what direction to follow. All together therefore set themselves to praying, and remained in prayer for some time.

Soon afterwards, as they sailed, something in appearance like a minaret emerged from the sea, and they seemed to behold the flash of a Chinese mirror. Also they perceived that their ship without their rowing, and without any greater force of wind, began to move at great speed over the water. In great amazement the sailors ran to Abu'l Fawaris and asked him what had come to the ship that it moved so fast. He raised his eyes, and groaned deeply as in the distance he saw a mountain that rose out of the sea. In terror he clapped his hand to his eyes and shouted out: "We shall all perish! My father continually warned me that if ever I lost my way upon the sea I must steer to the East; for if I went to the West I would certainly fall into the Lion's Mouth. When I asked him what the Lion's Mouth was, he told me that the Almighty had created a great hole in the midst of the ocean, at the foot of a mountain. That is the Lion's Mouth. Over a hundred leagues of water it will attract a ship, and no vessel which encounters the mountain ever rises again. I believe that this is the place and that we are caught."

In great terror the sailors saw their ship being carried like the wind against the mountain. Soon it was caught in the whirlpool, where the wrecks of ten thousand ancient ships were being carried around in the swirling current. The sailors and merchants in the ship crowded to Abu'l Fawaris, begging him to tell them what they could do. He cried out to them to prepare all the ropes which they had in the ship; he would then swim out of the whirlpool and on to the shore at the foot of the mountain, where he would make fast to some stout tree. Then they were to cast their ropes to him and so he would rescue them from their peril. By great good fortune the current cast him out upon the shore, and he made the rope of his ship fast to a stout tree.

Then, as soon as was possible, the sailor climbed to the top of the mountain in search of food, for neither he nor his shipmates had eaten for some days. When he reached the summit he found a pleasant plain stretching away in front of him, and in the midst of it he saw a lofty arch, made of green stone. As he approached it and entered, he observed a tall pillar made of steel, from which there hung by a chain a great drum of Damascus bronze covered with a lion's skin. From the arch also hung a great tablet of bronze, upon which was engraved the following inscription: "O thou that dost reach this place, know that when Alexander voyaged round the world and reached the Lion's Mouth, he had been made aware of this place of calamity. He was therefore accompanied by four thousand wise men, whom he summoned and whom he commanded to provide a means of escape from this calamitous spot. For long the philosophers pondered on the matter, until at last Plato caused this drum to be made, whose quality is that if any one, being caught in the whirlpool, can come forth and strike the drum three times, he will bring out his ship to the surface."

When the sailor had read the inscription, he quickly made his way to the shore and told his fellows of it. After much debate he agreed to risk his life by staying on the island and striking the drum, on condition that they would return to Basrah on their escape, and give to his wife and sons one-half of what treasure they had in the ship. He bound them with an oath to do this, and then returned to the arch. Taking up a club he struck the drum three times, and as the mighty roar of it echoed from the hills, the ship like an arrow shot from a bow, was flung out of the whirlpool. Then, with a cry of farewell to Abu'l Fawaris from the crew, they sailed to Basrah, where they gave one-half the treasure which they had to the sailor's family.

With great mourning the wife and family of Abu'l Fawaris celebrated his loss; but he, after sleeping soundly in the archway and giving thanks to his Maker for preserving him alive, made his way again to the summit of the mountain. As he advanced across the plain he saw black smoke arising from it, and also in the plain were rivers, of which he passed nine. He was like to die of hunger and weariness, when suddenly he perceived on one side a meadow, in which flocks of sheep were grazing. In great joy he thought that he was at last reaching human habitation, and as he came towards the sheep, he saw with them a youth, tall in stature as a mountain, and covered with a tattered cloak of red felt, though his head and body were clad in mail. The sailor greeted him, and received greeting in reply, and also the question "Whence come you?" Abu'l Fawaris answered that he was a man upon whom catastrophe had fallen, and so related his adventures to the shepherd. He heard it with a laugh, and said: "Count yourself fortunate to have escaped from that abyss. Do not fear now, I will bring you to a village." Saying this he set bread and milk before him and bade him eat. When he had eaten he said: "You cannot remain here all day, I will take you to my house, where you may rest for a time."

Together they descended to the foot of the mountain, where stood a gateway. Against it leaned a mighty stone, which a hundred men could not have lifted, but the shepherd, putting his hand into a hole in the stone, lifted it away from the gateway and admitted Abu'l Fawaris. Then he restored the stone to its place, and continued on his way.

When the sailor had passed through the gateway he saw before him a beautiful garden in which were trees laden with fruit. In the midst of them was a kiosk, and this, the sailor thought, must be the shepherd's house. He entered and looked about from the roof, but though he saw many houses there was no person in sight. He descended therefore, and walked to the nearest house, which he entered. Upon crossing the threshold he beheld ten men, all naked and all so fat that their eyes were almost closed. With their heads down upon their knees, all were weeping bitterly. But at the sound of his footsteps they raised their heads and called out "Who are you?" He told them that the shepherd had brought him and offered him hospitality. A great cry arose from them as they heard this. "Here," they said, "is another unfortunate who has fallen, like ourselves, into the clutch of this monster. He is a vile creature, who in the guise of a shepherd goes about and seizes men and devours them. We are all merchants whom adverse winds have brought here. That div has seized us and keeps us in this fashion."

With a groan the sailor thought that now at last he was undone. At that moment he saw the shepherd coming, saw him let the sheep into the garden, and then close the gateway with the stone before entering the kiosk. He was carrying a bag full of almonds, dates, and pistachio nuts, with which he approached, and, giving it to the sailor, he told him to share it with the others. Abu'l Fawaris could say nothing, but sat down and ate the food with his companions. When they had finished their meal, the shepherd returned to them, took one of them by the hand, and then in sight of them all, slew, roasted, and devoured him. When he was sated, he brought out a skin of wine and drank until he fell into a drunken sleep.

Then the sailor turned to his companions and said: "Since I am to die, let me first destroy him; if you will give me your help, I will do so." They replied that they had no strength left; but he, seeing the two long spits on which the ogre had roasted his meat, put them into the fire until they were red hot, and then plunged them into the monster's eyes.

With a great cry the shepherd leaped up and tried to seize his tormentor, who sprang away and eluded him. Running to the stone, the shepherd moved it aside and began to let out the sheep one by one, in the hope that when the garden was emptier he could the more easily capture the sailor. Abu'l Fawaris understood his intention: without delay, he slew a sheep, put on the skin and tried to pass through. But the shepherd knew as soon as he felt him that this was not a sheep, and leaped after him in pursuit. Abu'l Fawaris flung off the pelt, and ran like the wind. Soon he came to the sea, and into this he plunged, while the shepherd after a few steps returned to the shore, for he could not swim.

Full of terror the sailor swam till he reached the other side of the mountain. There he met an old man who greeted him, and, after hearing his adventure, fed him and took him to his house. But soon, to his horror, Abu'l Fawaris found that his old man also was an ogre. With great cunning he told the ogre's wife that he could make many useful implements for her house, and she persuaded her husband to save him. After many days in the house, he was sent away to the care of a shepherd, and put to guard sheep. Day by day he planned to escape, but there was only one way across the mountain and that was guarded.

One day, as he wandered in a wood, he found in the hollow trunk of a tree a store of honey, of which he told the shepherd's wife when he went home. The next day, therefore, the woman sent her husband with Abu'l Fawaris, telling him to bring home some of the honey; but, on the way, the sailor leaped upon him and bound him to a tree. Then, taking the shepherd's ring, he returned and told the woman that her husband had given him leave to go, and that he sent his ring in token of this. But the woman was cunning and asked: "Why did not my husband come himself to tell me this?" Seizing him by the cloak, she told him that she would go with him and find out the truth. The sailor, however, tore himself free, and again fled to the sea, where he thought that he might escape death. In haste and terror he swam for many hours, until at last he espied a ship full of men, who steered towards him and took him on board. Full of wonder they asked how he came there, and he related to them all his adventures.

It happened by great good fortune that the ship's captain had business at one place only on the coast, and that from there he was sailing to Basrah. In the space of a month, therefore, Abu'l Fawaris was restored to his family, to the joy of them all.

The many dangers and sufferings of the sailor had turned his hair white. For many days he rested, and then, one day, as he walked by the seashore, that same old man who had before hired his ship again appeared. Without recognizing him, he asked if he would lend his ship on hire for six months. Abu'l Fawaris agreed to do so for a thousand dinars of gold, which the old man at once paid to him, saying that he would come in a boat on the morrow, ready to depart.

When the ancient departed, the sailor took home the money to his wife, who bade him beware not to cast himself again into danger. He replied that he must be avenged not only for himself, but also for the thousand Muslims whom the villainous old man had slain.

The next day, therefore, the sailor took on board the old man and a black slave, and for three months they sailed, until they once more reached the island of pearls. There they made fast the ship on the shore, and taking sacks, they ascended to the top of the mountain. Once arrived there, the old man made the same request to Abu'l Fawaris as before, namely, that he should go down into the pits and send up pearls. The sailor replied that he was unacquainted with the place, and preferred that the old man should go down first, in order to prove that there was no danger. He answered that there was surely no danger; he had never in his life harmed even an ant, and he would of a certainty never send Abu'l Fawaris down into the pits if he knew any peril lay there. But the sailor was obstinate, saying that until he knew how to carry it out, he could not undertake the task.

Very reluctantly, therefore, the old man allowed himself to be lowered into the first pit by a basket and a rope. He filled the basket with oysters and sent it up, crying out: "You see, there is nothing to do harm in this pit. Draw me up now, for I am an old man and have no more strength left." The sailor replied, "Now that you are there, it were better if you remained there to complete your task. To-morrow I myself will go into another pit and will send up so many pearls as to fill the ship." For a long time the old man worked, sending up pearls, and at last he cried out again, "O my brother, I am utterly wearied, draw me out now."

Then the sailor turned upon him with fury, and cried out: "How is it that thou dost see ever thine own trouble and never that of others? Thou misbegotten dog, art thou blind that thou dost not know me? I am Abu'l Fawaris, the sailor, whom long ago you left in one of these pits. By the favor of Allah I was delivered, and now it is your turn. Open your eyes to the truth and remember what you have done to so many men." The old man cried aloud for mercy, but it availed him nothing, for Abu'l Fawaris brought a great stone and covered up the mouth of the pit. The slave too he overwhelmed with threats, and then together they carried down the pearls to the ship, in which they set sail. In three months they arrived at Basrah. There Abu'l Fawaris related his adventures, to the amazement of all. Thenceforward he abandoned the sea and adopted a life of ease. Finally he died, and this story remains in memory of him. And Allah knoweth best.

HOW XERXES BRIDGED THE HELLESPONT[1]

Herodotus

(484 B. C.–424 B. C.)

PASSING by Anaua a City of Phrygia, and a Lake famous for the making of Salt, he (Xerxes) arriv'd at Colossa, a considerable City of the same Province; where the River Lycus falling into an Aperture of the Earth, disappears for the space of about five Stades in Length; and then rising again runs afterwards into the Meander. From this Place the Army advanc'd to the City of Cydra, built on the Borders of Phrygia and Lydia; where an Inscription engrav'd on a Pillar, which was erected by Crœsus, declares the Limits of each Country. After they had enter'd the Territories of Lydia, they found the Way divided into two Routes; one on the Left-hand leading to Caria, the other on the Right, to Sardis. Those who take the last of these Ways, are necessitated to pass the Meander, and to approach the City of Callatebus, in which Honey is made by Men, with Wheat and the Shrub Myrice. Xerxes taking his March by this Way, saw a Plane-tree so beautiful, that he adorn'd it with Gold; and having committed the Care of it to one of those Persians who go under the Name of Immortal, arriv'd the next day at Sardis, the Capital of Lydia. Upon his Arrival in that City he sent Heralds to Greece with Orders to demand Earth and Water, and to require all the Cities, except Athens and Lacedæmon, to provide everything necessary for the King's Table; not doubting that the Terror of his Arms would now induce all those to a ready Submission, who had formerly refus'd to comply with the like Demand, made on the part of his Father Darius.

[1] From the translation of *The History*, by Isaac Littlebury (1720).

When Xerxes had dispatch'd these Heralds, he prepar'd to march towards Abydus; and in the mean time commanded a Bridge to be laid over the Hellespont, in order to pass into Europe. The Coast of the Hellespontin Chersonesus, which faces the City of Abydus, and stretches along the Sea between Sestus and Madytus, is uneven, and of difficult Access. The Bridge was begun at Abydus, by Men appointed to that end, and carried on to the opposite Coast; which is seven Stades distant from that City; the Phœnicians making use of Cordage of white Hemp, and the Ægyptians of another sort called Byblus. But no sooner had they finish'd the Bridge, than a violent Storm arising, broke in pieces and dispers'd the whole Work: Which when Xerxes heard, he fell into such a Transport of Anger, that he commanded three hundred Stripes to be inflicted on the Back of the Waters, and a Pair of Fetters to be let down into the Hellespont. I have heard, he likewise order'd that Sea to be branded with Marks of Infamy. But nothing is more certain, than that he strictly enjoin'd those who were entrusted with the Execution of his Orders, to pronounce these barbarous and impertinent Words:

"O thou salt and bitter Water! thy Master has condem'd thee to this Punishment, for offending him without Cause, and is resolv'd to pass over thee in despite of thy Insolence. With reason all Men neglect to sacrifice to thee, because thou art both disagreeable and treacherous."

Thus having commanded the Hellespont to be chastised, he order'd the Heads of those who had the Direction of the Workmen to be taken off; which was all the Recompence they had for contriving the Bridge. In their place other Architects were employ'd, who prepar'd two Bridges in the following manner:

They brought three hundred and sixty Gallies into a Line, board by board, and facing the Euxin Sea. On the other hand they plac'd three hundred and fourteen more, with their Sides turned towards the Euxin, and their Heads to the Current of the Hellespont, in order to preserve the Cordage entire. This done, they drop'd their main Anchors, to secure the Vessels on one side against the Force of those Winds that blow from the Euxin, and on the other, from the South and Easterly Winds of the Ægean Sea; leaving three several Passages open to the Eastward, for the Convenience of those who should desire to pass from the Euxin, or to return thither. After that, they fasten'd Cables to the Shoar, and straining them with Engines of Wood prepar'd for that purpose, bound the Vessels together; allowing only two Ropes of white Hemp for every four made of Byblus. For tho the Thickness and Shape was the same, yet the former were of much greater Strength; every Cubit weighing a full Talent. Having carried on these Lines of Ships from one Shoar to the other, they cover'd the Cordage with Pieces of Timber, cut exactly to the Breadth of the Bridges, and strongly compacted together. Upon these again they laid Planks of Wood rang'd in order; and having thrown a Covering of Earth on the Top, they rais'd a Barrier on each side, that the Horses and other Cattle might not be terrified at the sight of the Sea.

When the Bridges were finish'd, and the Canal at Mount Athos secur'd by a Bank of Earth thrown up at each End, to prevent the Floods from choaking the Passage with Sand; the Army being inform'd that all things were ready, departed from Sardis, where they had winter'd, and directed their March towards Abydus. But as they were on the way thither, the Sun quitting his Seat in the Heavens, disappear'd; and tho the Air was perfectly serene, and free from Clouds, a sudden Night ensu'd in the place of day: Which Xerxes observing with Surprize, and no little Anxiety, enquir'd of the Mages what might be the meaning of the Prodigy. They answer'd, that the God by this Presage plainly foretold the Destruction of the Grecian Cities; because the Sun was the Protector of Greece, and the Moon of the Persians. Xerxes pleas'd with their Interpretation, resolv'd to continue his March. . . .

The rest of the Day was spent in disposing all things, in order to their Passage: And waiting the rising of the next Sun, they in the mean time burnt all sorts of Perfumes upon the Bridges, and strow'd the Way with Myrtles. When the Sun was risen, Xerxes pouring a Libation into the Sea out of a golden Cup, address'd a Prayer to the Sun, "That he might not meet with any Impediment so great, as to hinder him from carrying his conquering Arms to the utmost Limits of Europe." After which he threw the Cup into the Hellespont, with a Bowl of Gold, and a Persian Scymeter. But I cannot determine whether his Intention was to consecrate these things to the Sun, or whether he made this Donation to the Hellespont, by way of Satisfaction for the Stripes he had inflicted on that Sea. After this Ceremony, all the Foot and Horse of the Army pass'd over that Bridge, which was next to the Euxin; while the Servants and Draught-horses, with the Baggage, pass'd over the other, which was plac'd nearer to the Ægean Sea. The ten thousand Persians I mention'd before, led the Van, with Crowns on their Heads, and were followed by Troops promiscuously compos'd of all Nations. These pass'd the first Day. On the second, those Horse, who carried their Javelins pointed to the Ground, pass'd over first, wearing Crowns likewise. Then came the sacred Horses, the sacred Chariot; and Xerxes himself, followed by the Spearmen and one thousand Horse. All the rest of the Army clos'd the March; and at the same time the Ships made to the Coast of Europe. I have heard that Xerxes march'd in the Rear of all. But however that be, he saw his Forces compell'd by Blows to pass over the Bridge; which yet was not effected in less than seven Days and seven Nights, tho they continued to pass without Intermission during all that time.

After his Landing, a certain Man of that Country, as is said, cried out; "O Jupiter, why art thou come to destroy Greece in the Shape of a Persian, and under the Name of Xerxes, with all Mankind following thee; whereas thy own Power is sufficient to do this without their

Assistance?" When the Army began to march, a prodigious thing happen'd, yet not difficult to be understood, tho altogether neglected by Xerxes. A Mare cast a Hare instead of a Colt: From which one might easily conjecture, that after Xerxes had transported a mighty Army into Greece with great Vanity and Ostentation, he should be afraid for his own Life, and run away to the Place from whence he came. Another Prodigy had been seen before, during the time he staid at Sardis, where a Mule brought forth a Colt, with the Parts both of a Male and a Female, tho the former appear'd more perfect.

But Xerxes slighting both these Events, continued to advance with his Land-Forces; while the Fleet at the same time sailing out of the Hellespont, coasted along by the Shoar, and kept on a quite different Course. For they stood to the Westward for the Promontory of Sarpedon; where they were commanded to attend farther Orders: But the Land-Forces march'd by the way of Chersonesus, facing the East and the rising Sun.

CELTIC LITERATURE

THE VOYAGE OF MAILDUN[1]

THERE was once an illustrious man of the tribe of Owenaght of Ninus, Allil Ocar Aga by name, a goodly hero, and lord of his own tribe and territory. One time, when he was in his house unguarded, a fleet of plunderers landed on the coast, and spoiled his territory. The chief fled for refuge to the church of Dooclone; but the spoilers followed him thither, slew him, and burned the church over his head.

Not long after Allil's death, a son was born to him. The child's mother gave him the name of Maildun; and, wishing to conceal his birth, she brought him to the queen of that country, who was her dear friend. The queen took him to her, and gave out that he was her own child, and he was brought up with the king's sons, slept in the same cradle with them, and was fed from the same breast and from the same cup. He was a very lovely child; and the people who saw him thought it doubtful if there was any other child living at the time equally beautiful.

As he grew up to be a young man, the noble qualities of his mind gradually unfolded themselves. He was high-spirited and generous, and he loved all sorts of manly exercises. In ball-playing, in running and leaping, in throwing the stone, in chess-playing, in rowing, and in horse-racing, he surpassed all the youths that came to the king's palace, and won the palm in every contest.

One day, when the young men were at their games, a certain youth among them grew envious of Maildun; and he said, in an angry and haughty tone of voice:

"It is a cause of much shame to us that we have to yield in every game, whether of skill or of strength, whether on land or on water, to an obscure youth, of whom no one can tell who is his father or his mother, or what race or tribe he belongs to."

On hearing this, Maildun ceased at once from play; for until that moment he believed that he was the son of the king of the Owenaght, and of the queen who had nursed him. And going anon to the queen, he told her what had happened; and he said to her:

"If I am not thy son, I will neither eat nor drink till thou tell me who my father and mother are."

She tried to soothe him, and said:

"Why do you worry yourself searching after this matter? Give no heed to the words of this envious youth. Am I not a mother to you?

---

[1]From *Old Celtic Romances*, translated by P. W. Joyce. Reprinted by permission of Mr Philip Nutt.

And in all this country, is there any mother who loves her son better than I love you?"

He answered:

"All this is quite true; yet I pray thee let me know who my parents are."

The queen then, seeing that he would not be put off, brought him to his mother, and his mother told him the truth, saying,

"Your father was Allil Ocar Aga, of the tribe of Owenaght of Ninus."

Maildun then set out for his father's territory; and his three foster brothers, namely, the king's three sons, who were noble and handsome youths like himself, went with him.

Some time after this, it happened that a number of young people were in the churchyard of Dooclone—the same church in which Maildun's father had been slain—exercising themselves in casting a handstone. The game was to throw the stone clear over the charred roof of the church that had been burned; and Maildun was there contending among the others. A foul-tongued fellow named Brickna, a servant of the people who owned the church, was standing by; and he said to Maildun:

"It would better become you to avenge the man who was burned to death here, than to be amusing yourself casting a stone over his bare, burnt bones."

"Who was he?" inquired Maildun.

"Allil Ocar Aga, your father," replied the other.

"Who slew him?" asked Maildun.

"Plunderers from a fleet slew him and burned him in this church," replied Brickna, "and the same plunderers are still sailing in the same fleet."

Maildun was disturbed and sad after hearing this. He dropped the stone that he held in his hand, folded his cloak round him, and buckled on his shield. And he left the company, and began to inquire of all he met, the road to the plunderers' ships. For a long time he could get no tidings of them; but at last some persons, who knew where the fleet lay, told him that it was a long way off, and that there was no reaching it except by sea.

Now Maildun was resolved to find out these plunderers, and to avenge on them the death of his father. So he went without delay into Corcomroe to the druid Nuca, to seek his advice about building a curragh, and to ask also for a charm to protect him, both while building it, and while sailing on the sea afterwards.

The druid gave him full instructions. He told him the day he should begin to build his curragh, and the exact day on which he was to set out on his voyage; and he was very particular about the number of the crew, which, he said, was to be sixty chosen men, neither more nor less.

So Maildun built a large triple-hide curragh, following the druid's directions in every particular, chose his crew of sixty, among whom were his two friends, Germane and Diuran Lekerd; and on the day appointed put out to sea.

When he had got only a very little way from the land, he saw his three foster brothers running down to the shore, signalling and calling out to him to return and take them on board; for they said they wished to go with him.

"We shall not turn back," said Maildun; "and you cannot come with us; for we have already got our exact number."

"We will swim after you in the sea till we are drowned, if you do not return for us," replied they; and so saying, the three plunged in and swam after the curragh.

When Maildun saw this, he turned his vessel towards them, and took them on board rather than let them be drowned.

They sailed that day and night, as well as the whole of the next day, till darkness came on again; and at midnight they saw two small bare islands, with two great houses on them near the shore. When they drew near, they heard the sounds of merriment and laughter, and the shouts of revellers intermingled with the loud voices of warriors boasting of their deeds. And listening to catch the conversation, they heard one warrior say to another:

"Stand off from me, for I am a better warrior than thou; it was I who slew Allil Ocar Aga, and burned Dooclone over his head; and no one has ever dared to avenge it on me. Thou hast never done a great deed like that."

"Now surely," said Germane and Diuran to Maildun, "Heaven has guided our ship to this place! Here is an easy victory. Let us now sack this house, since God has revealed our enemies to us, and delivered them into our hands."

While they were yet speaking, the wind arose, and a great tempest suddenly broke on them. And they were driven violently before the storm all that night, and a part of next day, into the great and boundless ocean; so that they saw neither the islands they had left nor any other land; and they knew not whither they were going.

Then Maildun said:

"Take down your sail and put by your oars, and let the curragh drift before the wind in whatsoever direction it pleases God to lead us"; which was done.

He then turned to his foster-brothers, and said to them:

"This evil has befallen us because we took you into the curragh, thereby violating the druid's direction; for he forbade me to go to sea with more than sixty men for my crew, and we had that number before you joined us. Of a surety more evil will come of it."

His foster-brothers answered nothing to this, but remained silent.

For three days and three nights they saw no land but on the fourth day discovered a large, sandy island, on which when they came near, they saw a huge, fearful animal standing on the beach, and looking at them very attentively. He was somewhat like a horse in shape; but his legs were like the legs of a dog; and he had great, sharp claws of a blue colour.

Maildun, having viewed this monster for some time, liked not his look; and, telling his companions to watch him closely for that he seemed bent on mischief, he bade the oarsmen row very slowly towards land.

The monster seemed much delighted when the ship drew nigh the shore, and gambolled and pranced about with joy on the beach, before the eyes of the voyagers; for he intended to eat the whole of them the moment they landed.

"He seems not at all sorry to see us coming," said Maildun, "but we must avoid him and put back from the shore."

This was done. And when the animal observed them drawing off, he ran down in a great rage to the very water's edge, and digging up large, round pebbles with his sharp claws, he began to fling them at the vessel; but the crew soon got beyond his reach, and sailed into the open sea.

They suffered much from hunger and thirst this time, for they sailed a whole week without making land; but at the end of that time they came in sight of a high island, with a large and very splendid house on the beach near the water's edge. There were two doors—one turned inland, and the other facing the sea; and the door that looked towards the sea was closed with a great flat stone. In this stone was an opening, through which the waves, as they beat against the door every day, threw numbers of salmon into the house.

The voyagers landed, and went through the whole house without meeting any one. But they saw in one large room an ornamental couch, intended for the head of the house, and in each of the other rooms was a larger one for three members of the family; and there was a cup of crystal on a little table before each couch. They found abundance of food and ale, and they ate and drank till they were satisfied, thanking God for having relieved them from hunger and thirst.

After leaving this, they suffered again from hunger, till they came to an island with a high hill round it on every side. A single apple tree grew in the middle, very tall and slender, and all its branches were in like manner exceedingly slender, and of wonderful length, so that they grew over the hill and down to the sea.

When the ship came near the island, Maildun caught one of the branches in his hand. For three days and three nights the ship coasted the island, and during all this time he held the branch, letting it slide through his hand, till on the third day he found a cluster of seven apples on the very end. Each of these apples supplied the travellers with food and drink for forty days and forty nights.

The next island had a wall all round it. When they came near the shore, an animal of vast size, with a thick, rough skin, started up inside the wall, and ran round the island with the swiftness of the wind. When he had ended his race, he went to a high point, and standing on a large flat stone, began to exercise himself according to his daily custom, in the following manner. He kept turning himself completely round and round in his skin, the bones and flesh moving, while the skin remained at rest.

When he was tired of this exercise, he rested a little; and he then began turning his skin continually round his body, down at one side and up at the other like a mill-wheel; but the bones and flesh did not move.

After spending some time at this sort of work, he started and ran round the island as at first, as if to refresh himself. He then went back to the same spot, and this time, while the skin that covered the lower part of his body remained without motion, he whirled the skin of the upper part round and round like the movement of a flat-lying millstone. And it was in this manner that he spent most of his time on the island.

Maildun and his people, after they had seen these strange doings, thought it better not to venture nearer. So they put out to sea in great haste. The monster, observing them about to fly, ran down to the beach to seize the ship; but finding that they had got out of his reach, he began to fling round stones at them with great force and an excellent aim. One of them struck Maildun's shield and went quite through it, lodging in the keel of the curragh; after which the voyagers got beyond his range and sailed away.

After rowing for a long time, they had nothing to eat or drink; so that they suffered sorely under a hot sun, and their mouths and nostrils were filled with the briny smell of the sea. At last they came in sight of land— a little island with a large palace on it. Around the palace was a wall, white all over, without stain or flaw, as if it had been built of burnt lime, or carved out of one unbroken rock of chalk; and where it looked towards the sea it was so lofty that it seemed almost to reach the clouds.

The gate of this outer wall was open, and a number of fine houses, all snowy white, were ranged round on the inside, enclosing a level court in the middle, on which all the houses opened. Maildun and his people entered the largest of them, and walked through several rooms without meeting with any one. But on reaching the principal apartment, they saw in it a small cat, playing among a number of low, square, marble pillars, which stood ranged in a row; and his play was, leaping continually from the top of one pillar to the top of another. When the men entered the room, the cat looked at them for a moment, but returned to his play anon, and took no further notice of them.

Looking now to the room itself, they saw three rows of precious jewels ranged round the wall from one door-jamb to the other. The first was a row of brooches of gold and silver with their pins fixed in the wall, and their heads outwards; the second, a row of torques of gold and silver; and the third, a row of great swords, with hilts of gold and silver.

Round the room were arranged a number of couches, all pure white and richly ornamented. Abundant food of various kinds was spread on tables, among which they observed a boiled ox and a roast hog, and there were many large drinking horns, full of good, intoxicating ale.

"Is it for us that this food has been prepared?" said Maildun to the cat.

The cat, on hearing the question, ceased from playing, and looked at him; but he recommenced his play immediately. Whereupon Maildun told his people that the dinner was meant for them; and they all sat down, and ate and drank till they were satisfied, after which they rested and slept on the couches.

When they awoke, they poured what was left of the ale into one vessel; and they gathered the remnants of the food to bring them away. As they were about to go, Maildun's eldest foster brother asked him:

"Shall I bring one of those large torques away with me?"

"By no means," said Maildun; "it is well that we have got food and rest. Bring nothing away, for it is certain that this house is not left without some one to guard it."

The young man, however, disregarding Maildun's advice, took down one of the torques and brought it away. But the cat followed him, and overtook him in the middle of the court, and, springing on him like a blazing, fiery arrow, he went through his body, and reduced it in a moment to a heap of ashes. He then returned to the room, and, leaping up on one of the pillars, sat upon it.

Maildun turned back, bringing the torque with him, and, approaching the cat, spoke some soothing words; after which he put the torque back to the place from which it had been taken. Having done this, he collected the ashes of his foster brother, and, bringing them to the shore, cast them into the sea. They all then went on board the curragh, and continued their voyage, grieving for their lost companion, but thanking God for His many mercies to them.

After a time, they came to a sea like green crystal. It was so calm and transparent that they could see the sand at the bottom quite clearly, sparkling in the sunlight. And in this sea they saw neither monsters, nor ugly animals, nor rough rocks; nothing but the clear water and the sunshine and the bright sand. For a whole day they sailed over it, admiring its splendour and beauty.

After leaving this they entered on another sea, which seemed like a clear, thin cloud; and it was so transparent, and appeared so light, that they thought at first it would not bear up the weight of the curragh.

Looking down, they could see, beneath the clear water, a beautiful country, with many mansions surrounded by groves and woods. In one place was a single tree; and, standing on its branches, they saw an animal fierce and terrible to look upon.

Round about the tree was a great herd of oxen grazing, and a man stood near to guard them, armed with shield, and spear, and sword; but when he looked up and saw the animal on the tree, he turned anon and fled with the utmost speed. Then the monster stretched forth his neck, and, darting his head downward, plunged his fangs into the back of the largest ox of the whole herd, lifted him off the ground into the tree, and swallowed him down in the twinkling of an eye; whereupon the whole herd took to flight.

When Maildun and his people saw this, they were seized with great terror; for they feared they should not be able to cross the sea over the monster, on account of the extreme mist-like thinness of the water; but after much difficulty and danger they got across it safely.

The next thing they found after this was an immense silver pillar standing in the sea. It had eight sides, each of which was the width of an oar-stroke of the curragh, so that its whole circumference was eight oar-strokes. It rose out of the sea without any land or earth about it, nothing but the boundless ocean; and they could not see its base deep down in the water, neither were they able to see the top on account of its vast height.

A silver net hung from the top down to the very water, extending far out at one side of the pillar; and the meshes were so large that the curragh in full sail went through one of them. When they were passing through it, Diuran struck the mesh with the edge of his spear, and with the blow cut a large piece off it.

"Do not destroy the net," said Maildun; "for what we see is the work of great men."

"What I have done," answered Diuran, "is for the honour of my God, and in order that the story of our adventures may be more readily believed; and I shall lay this silver as an offering on the altar of Armagh, if I ever reach Erin."

That piece of silver weighed two ounces and a half, as it was reckoned afterwards by the people of the church of Armagh.

After this they heard someone speaking on the top of the pillar, in a loud, clear, glad voice; but they knew neither what he said, nor in what language he spoke.

They came now to a small island with a high wall of fire all round it, and there was a large open door in the wall at one side near the sea. They sailed backward and forward many times and always paused before the door; for whenever they came right in front of it, they could see almost the whole island through it.

And this is what they saw: A great number of people, beautiful and glorious-looking, wearing rich garments adorned and radiant all over; feasting joyously, and drinking from embossed vessels of red gold which they held in their hands. The voyagers heard also their cheerful, festive songs; and they marvelled greatly, and their hearts were full of gladness at all the happiness they saw and heard. But they did not venture to land.

A little time after leaving this, they saw something a long way off towards the south, which at first they took to be a large white bird floating on the sea, and rising and falling with the waves; but on turning their curragh towards it for a nearer view, they found that it was a man. He was very old, so old that he was covered all over with long, white hair, which grew from his body; and he was standing on a broad, bare rock, and kept continually throwing himself on his knees, and never ceased praying.

When they saw that he was a holy man, they asked and received his blessing; after which they began to converse with him; and they inquired who he was, and how he had come to that rock. Then the old man gave them the following account:

"I was born and bred in the island of Tory. When I grew up to be a man, I was cook to the brotherhood of the monastery; and a wicked cook I was; for every day I sold part of the food intrusted to me, and secretly bought many choice and rare things with the money. Worse even than this I did; I made secret passages underground into the church and into the houses belonging to it, and I stole from time to time great quantities of golden vestments, book-covers adorned with brass and gold, and other holy and precious things.

"I soon became very rich, and had my rooms filled with costly couches, with clothes of every colour, both linen and woollen, with brazen pitchers and caldrons, and with brooches and armlets of gold. Nothing was wanting in my house, of furniture and ornament, that a person in a high rank of life might be expected to have; and I became very proud and overbearing.

"One day I was sent to dig a grave for the body of a rustic that had been brought from the mainland to be buried on the island. I went and fixed on a spot in the little graveyard; but as soon as I had set to work, I heard a voice speaking down deep in the earth beneath my feet:

"'Do not dig this grave.'

"I paused for a moment, startled; but, recovering myself, I gave no further heed to the mysterious words, and again I began to dig. The moment I did so, I heard the same voice, even more plainly than before:

"'Do not dig this grave! I am a devout and holy person, and my body is lean and light; do not put the heavy, pampered body of that sinner down upon me!'

"But I answered, in the excess of my pride and obstinacy, 'I will certainly dig this grave; and I will bury this body down on you.'

"'If you put that body down on me, the flesh will fall off your bones, and you will die, and be sent to the infernal pit at the end of three days; and, moreover, the body will not remain where you put it.'

"'What will you give me?' I asked, 'if I do not bury the corpse on you?'

"'Everlasting life in heaven,' replied the voice.

"'How do you know this; and how am I to be sure of it?' I inquired.

"And the voice answered me, 'The grave you are digging is clay. Observe now whether it will remain so, and then you will know the truth of what I tell you. And you will see that what I say will come to pass, and that you cannot bury that man on me, even if you should try to do so.'

"These words were scarce ended, when the grave was turned into a mass of white sand before my face. And when I saw this I brought the body away, and buried it elsewhere.

"It happened, some time after, that I got a new curragh made, with the hides painted red all over; and I went to sea in it. As I sailed by the shores and islands, I was so pleased with the view of the land and sea from my curragh, that I resolved to live altogether in it for some time; and I brought on board all my treasures—silver cups, gold bracelets, and ornamented drinking horns, and everything else, from the largest to the smallest article.

"I enjoyed myself for a time, while the air was clear and the sea calm and smooth. But one day, the winds suddenly arose and a storm burst upon me, which carried me out to sea, so that I quite lost sight of land, and I knew not in what direction the curragh was drifting. After a time, the wind abated to a gentle gale, the sea became smooth, and the curragh sailed on as before, with a quiet, pleasant movement.

"But suddenly, though the breeze continued to blow, I thought I could perceive that the curragh ceased moving, and, standing up to find out the cause, I saw with great surprise an old man not far off, sitting on the crest of a wave.

"He spoke to me; and, as soon as I heard his voice, I knew it at once, but I could not at the moment call to mind where I had heard it before. And I became greatly troubled, and began to tremble, I knew not why.

"'Whither art thou going?' he asked.

"'I know not,' I replied; 'but this I know, I am pleased with the smooth, gentle motion of my curragh over the waves.'

"'You would not be pleased,' replied the old man, 'if you could see the troops that are at this moment around you.'

"'What troops do you speak of?' I asked. And he answered:

"'All the space round about you, as far as your view reaches over the sea, and upwards to the clouds, is one great towering mass of demons, on account of your avarice, your thefts, your pride, and your other crimes and vices.'

"He then asked, 'Do you know why your curragh has stopped?'

"I answered, 'No'; and he said, 'It has been stopped by me; and it will never move from that spot till you promise me to do what I shall ask of you.'

"I replied that perhaps it was not in my power to grant his demand.

"'It is in your power,' he answered; 'and if you refuse me the torments of hell shall be your doom.'

"He then came close to the curragh, and, laying his hands on me, made me swear to do what he demanded.

"'What I ask is this,' said he; 'that you throw into the sea this moment all the ill-gotten treasures you have in the curragh.'

"This grieved me very much, and I replied, 'It is a pity that all these costly things should be lost.'

"To which he answered, 'They will not go to loss; a person will be sent to take charge of them. Now do as I say.'

"So, greatly against my wishes, I threw all the beautiful precious articles overboard, keeping only a small wooden cup to drink from.

"'You will now continue your voyage,' he said; 'and the first solid ground your curragh reaches, there you are to stay.'

"He then gave me seven cakes and a cup of watery whey as food for my voyage; after which the curragh moved on, and I soon lost sight of him. And now I all at once recollected that the old man's voice was the same as the voice that I had heard come from the ground, when I was about to dig the grave for the body of the rustic. I was so astonished and troubled at this discovery, and so disturbed at the loss of all my wealth, that I threw aside my oars, and gave myself up altogether to the winds and currents, not caring whither I went; and for a long time I was tossed about on the waves, I knew not in what direction.

"At last it seemed to me that my curragh ceased to move; but I was not sure about it, for I could see no sign of land. Mindful, however, of what the old man had told me, that I was to stay wherever my curragh stopped, I looked round more carefully; and at last I saw, very near me, a small rock level with the surface, over which the waves were gently laughing and tumbling. I stepped on to the rock; and the moment I did so, the waves seemed to spring back, and the rock rose high over the level of the water; while the curragh drifted by and quickly disappeared, so that I never saw it after. This rock has been my abode from that time to the present day.

"For the first seven years, I lived on the seven cakes and the cup of whey given me by the man who had sent me to the rock. At the end of that time the cakes were all gone; and for three days I fasted, with nothing but the whey to wet my mouth. Late in the evening of the third day, an otter brought me a salmon out of the sea; but though I suffered much from hunger, I could not bring myself to eat the fish raw, and it was washed back again into the waves.

"I remained without food for three days longer; and in the afternoon of the third day, the otter returned with the salmon. And I saw another otter bring firewood; and when he had piled it up on the rock, he blew it with his breath till it took fire and lighted up. And then I broiled the salmon and ate till I had satisfied my hunger.

"The otter continued to bring me a salmon every day, and in this manner I lived for seven years longer. The rock also grew larger and larger daily, till it became the size you now see it. At the end of seven years, the otter ceased to bring me my salmon, and I fasted for three days. But at the end of the third day, I was sent half a cake of fine wheaten flour and a slice of fish; and on the same day my cup of watery whey fell into the sea, and a cup of the same size, filled with good ale, was placed on the rock for me.

"And so I have lived, praying and doing penance for my sins to this hour. Each day my drinking vessel is filled with ale, and I am sent half a wheat-flour cake and a slice of fish; and neither rain nor wind nor heat nor cold is allowed to molest me on this rock."

This was the end of the old man's history. In the evening of that day, each man of the crew received the same quantity of food that was sent to the old hermit himself, namely, half a cake and a slice of fish; and they found in the vessel as much good ale as served them all.

The next morning he said to them, "You shall all reach your own country in safety. And you, Maildun, you shall find in an island on your way, the very man that slew your father; but you are neither to kill him nor take revenge on him in any way. As God has delivered you from the many dangers you have passed through, though you were very guilty, and well deserved death at His hands; so you forgive your enemy the crime he committed against you."

After this they took leave of the old man and sailed away.

Soon after they saw a beautiful verdant island, with herds of oxen, cows, and sheep browsing all over its hills and valleys; but no houses nor inhabitants were to be seen. And they rested for some time on this island, and ate the flesh of the cows and sheep.

One day, while they were standing on a hill, a large falcon flew by; and two of the crew, who happened to look closely at him, cried out, in the hearing of Maildun:

"See that falcon! He is surely like the falcons of Erin!"

"Watch him closely," cried Maildun, "and observe exactly in what direction he is flying!"

And they saw that he flew to the south-east, without turning or wavering.

They went on board at once; and, having unmoored, they sailed to the south-east after the falcon. After rowing the whole day, they sighted land in the dusk of the evening, which seemed to them like the land of Erin.

On a near approach, they found it was a small island; and now they recognized it as the very same island they had seen in the beginning of their voyage, in which they had heard the man in the great house boast that he had slain Maildun's father, and from which the storm had driven them out into the great ocean.

They turned the prow of their vessel to the shore, landed, and went towards the house. It happened that at this very time the people of the house were seated at their evening meal; and Maildun and his companions, as they stood outside, heard a part of their conversation.

Said one to another, "It would not be well for us if we were now to see Maildun."

"As to Maildun," answered another, "it is very well known that he was drowned long ago in the great ocean."

"Do not be sure," observed a third; "perchance he is the very man that may waken you up some morning from your sleep."

"Supposing he came now," asks another, "what should we do?"

The head of the house now spoke in reply to the last question; and Maildun at once knew his voice:

"I can easily answer that," said he. "Maildun has been for a long time suffering great afflictions and hardships; and if he were to come now, though we were enemies once, I should certainly give him a welcome and a kind reception."

When Maildun heard this, he knocked at the door, and the doorkeeper asked who was there; to which Maildun made answer:—

"It is I, Maildun, returned safely from all my wanderings."

The chief of the house then ordered the door to be opened; and he went to meet Maildun, and brought himself and his companions into the house. They were joyfully welcomed by the whole household; new garments were given to them; and they feasted and rested, till they forgot their weariness and their hardships.

They related all the wonders God had revealed to them in the course of their voyage, according to the word of the sage who says, "It will be a source of pleasure to remember these things at a future time."

After they had remained here for some days, Maildun returned to his own country. And Diuran Lekerd took the five half-ounces of silver he had cut down from the great net at the Silver Pillar, and laid it, according to his promise, on the high altar of Armagh.

THE VOYAGE OF SAYNT BRANDON[1]

SAYNT BRANDON, the holy man, was a monke, and borne in Yrlonde, and there he was abbot of an house wherein were a thousand monkes, and there he ladde a full strayte and holy lyfe, in grete penaunce and abstynence, and he governed his monkes ful vertuously. And than within shorte tyme after, there came to hym an holy abbot that hyght Beryne to vysyte hym, and eche of them was joyfull of other; and than saynt Brandon began to tell the abbot Beryne of many wonders that he had seen in dyverse londes. And whan Beryne

---

[1]From "Saynt Brandon: A Medieval Legend of the Sea," in Wynkyn de Worde's edition of *The Golden Legend*.

herde that of saynt Brandon he began to sygh, and sore wepte. And saynt Brandon comforted him the best wyse he coude, sayenge,

"Ye come hyther for to be joyfull with me, and therefore for Goddes love leve your mournynge, and tell me what mervayles ye have seen in the grete see occean, that compasseth all the worlde aboute, and all other waters comen out of hym, whiche reneth in all the partyes of the erth."

And than Beryne began to tell saynt Brandon and to his monkes the mervaylles that he had seen, full sore wepynge, and sayd,

"I have a sonne, his name is Meruoke, and he was a monke of grete fame, whiche had grete desyre to seke aboute by shyppe in dyverse countrees, to fynde a solytary place wherein he myght dwell secretly out of the besynesse of the worlde, for to serve God quyetly with more devocyon; and I counseyled hym to sayle into an ylonde ferre in the see, besydes the Mountaynes of Stones, whiche is ful well knowen, and than he made hym redy and sayled thyder with his monkes. And when he came thyder, he lyked that place full well, where he and his monkes served our Lorde full devoutly."

And than Beryne sawe in a visyon that this monke Meruoke was sayled ryght ferre eestwarde into the see more than thre dayes saylynge, and sodeynly to hys semynge there came a derke cloude and overcovered them, that a grete parte of the daye they sawe no lyght; and as our Lorde wold, the cloude passed awaye, and they sawe a full fayr ylond, and thyderwarde they drewe. In that ylonde was joye and myrth ynough, and all the erth of that ylonde shined as bryght as the sonne, and there were the fayrest trees and herbes that ever ony man sawe, and there were many precyous stones shynynge bryght, and every herbe there was ful of fygures, and every tree ful of fruyte; so that it was a glorius sight, and an hevenly joye to abide there. And than there came to them a fayre yonge man, and full curtoysly he welcomed them all, and called every monke by his name, and sayd that they were much bounde to prayse the name of our Lorde Jesu, that wold of his grace shewe to them that glorious place, where is every day, and never night, and this place is called paradyse terrestre. But by this ylonde is an other ylonde wherin no man may come. And this yonge man sayd to them,

"Ye have ben here halfe a yere without meet, drynke, or slepe." And they supposed that they had not ben there the space of half an houre, so mery and joyfull they were there. And the yonge man tolde them that this is the place that Adam and Eve dwelte in fyrst, and ever should have dwelled here, yf that they had not broken the commaundment of God. And than the yonge man brought them to theyr shyppe agayn, and sayd they might no lenger abyde there; and when they were all shypped, sodeynly this yonge man vanysshed away out of theyr sight.

And than within shorte tyme after, by the purveyaunce of our Lorde Jesu, they came to the abbey where saint Brandon dwelled, and than he with his bretherne receyved them goodly, and demaunded where they had ben so longe, and they sayd,

"We have been in the Londe of Byheest, to-fore the gates of Paradyse, where as is ever daye, and never night."

And they sayd all that the place is full delectable, for yet all theyr clothes smelled of the swete and joyfull place.

And than saynt Brandon purposed soone after for to seke that place by Goddes helpe, and anone began to purvey for a good shyppe, and a stronge, and vytallyed it for vij. yere; and than he toke his leve of all his bretherne, and toke xij. monkes with him. But or they entred into the shyppe they fasted xl. dayes, and lyved devoutly, and eche of them receyved the sacrament. And whan saynt Brandon with his xij. monkes were entred into the shyppe, there came other two of his monkes, and prayed hym that they myght sayle with hym. And than he sayd, "Ye may sayle with me, but one of you shall go to hell, or ye come agayn." But not for that they wold go with hym.

And than saynt Brandon badde the shypmen to wynde up the sayle, and forth they sayled in Goddes name, so that on the morow they were out of syght of ony londe; and xl. dayes and xl. nightes after they sayled playn eest, and than they sawe an ylonde ferre fro them, and they sayled thyder-warde as fast as they coude, and they saw a grete roche of stone appere above all the water, and thre dayes they sayled aboute it or they coude gete in to the place. But at the last, by the purveyaunce of God, they founde a lytell haven, and there went a-londe everychone, and than sodeynly came a fayre hounde, and fell down at the feet of saynt Brandon, and made hym good chere in his maner. And than he badde his bretherne,

"Be of good chere, for our Lorde hath sente to us his messenger, to lede us into some good place."

And the hounde brought them into a fayre hall, where they founde the tables spredde redy, set full of good meet and drynke. And than saynt Brandon sayd graces, and than he and his bretherne sate down and ete and dranke of suche as they founde; and there were beddes redy for them, wherin they toke theyr rest after theyr longe labour.

And on the morrowe they returned agayne to theyr shyppe ande sayled a longe tyme to the see after or they coude fynde ony londe, tyll at the last, by the purveyaunce of God, they sawe ferre fro them a full fayre ylonde, ful of grene pasture, wherein were the whytest and gretest shepe that ever they sawe; for every shepe was as grete as an oxe. And soone after came to them a goodly olde man, whiche welcomed them, and made them good chere, and sayd,

"This is the Ylonde of Shepe, and here it is never colde weder, but ever sommer, and that causeth the shepe to be so grete and whyte; they ete of the best grasses and herbes that is ony where."

And than this olde man toke his leve of them, and bad them sayle forth ryght eest, and within shorte tyme, by Goddes grace, they sholde come into a place lyke paradyse, wherin they shold kepe theyr Eester-tyde.

And than they sayled forth, and came soone after to that lond; but bycause of lytell depthe in some place, and in some place were grete rockes, but at the last they wente upon an ylonde, wenynge to them they had ben safe, and made theron a fyre, for to dresse theyr dyner, but saynt Brandon abode styll in the shyppe. And whan the fyre was ryght hote, and the meet nigh soden, than this ylonde began to move; wherof the monkes were aferde, and fledde anone to the shyppe, and lefte the fyre and meet behynde them, and mervayled sore of the movyng. And saynt Brandon comforted them, and sayd that it was a grete fisshe named Jasconye, whiche laboureth nyght and day to put his tayle in his mouth, but for gretnes he may not.

And than anone they sayled west thre dayes and thre nyghtes or they sawe ony londe, wherfore they were ryght hevy. But soone after, as God wold, they saw a fayre ylonde, full of floures, herbes, and trees, wherof they thanked God of his good grace, and anone they went on londe. And whan they had gone longe in this, they founde a ful fayre well, and therby stode a fayre tree, full of bowes, and on every bough sate a fayre byrde, and they sate so thycke on the tree that unneth ony lefe myght be seen, the nombre of them was so grete, and they songe so meryly that it was an hevenly noyse to here. Wherfore saynt Brandon kneled down on his knees, and wepte for joye, and made his prayers devoutly unto our Lord God to knowe what these byrdes ment. And than anone one of the byrdes fledde fro the tree to saynt Brandon, and he with flykerynge of his wynges made a full mery noyse lyke a fydle, that hym semed he herde never so joyfull a melodye. And than saynt Brandon commaunded the byrde to tell hym the cause why they sate so thycke on the tree, and sange so meryly. And than the byrde sayd,

"Somtyme we were aungels in heven, but whan our mayster Lucyfer fell down into hell for his hygh pryde, we fell with hym for our offences, some hyther, and some lower, after the qualyté of theyr trespace; and bycause our trespace is but lytell, therfore our Lorde hath set us here out of all payne in full grete joye and myrth, after his pleasynge, here to serve hym on this tree in the best maner that we can. The Sonday is a day of rest fro all worldly occupacyon, and, therfore, that daye all we be made as whyte as ony snow, for to prayse our Lorde in the best wyse we may." And than this byrde sayd to saynt Brandon, "It is xij. monethes past that ye departed fro your abbey, and in the vij. yere hereafter ye shall se the place that ye desyre to come, and all this vij. yere ye shel kepe your Eester here with us every yere, and in the ende of the vij. yere ye shal come into the londe of Byhest."

And this was on Eester daye that the byrde sayd these wordes to saynt Brandon. And than this fowle flewe agayn to his felawes that sate on the tree. And than all the byrdes began to synge evensonge so meryly, that it was an hevenly noyse to here; and after souper saynt Brandon and his felawes wente to bedde, and slepte well, and on the morowe they arose betymes, and than those byrdes began matyns, pryme, and houres, and all suche service as Chrysten men use to synge.

And saynt Brandon with his felawes abode there viij. wekes, tyll Trinité Sonday was past; and they sayled agayne to the Ylonde of Shepe, and there they vytayled tham wel, and syth toke theyr leve of that olde man, and returned agayn to shyppe. And than the byrde of the tree came agayn to saynt Brandon, and sayd,

"I am come to tell you that ye shall sayle fro hens into an ylonde, wherein is an abbey of xxiiij. monkes, whiche is fro this place many a myle, and there ye shall holde your Chrystmasse, and your Eester with us, lyke as I tolde you."

And than this byrde flewe to his felawes agayn. And than saynt Brandon and his felawes sayled forth in the occyan; and soone after fell a grete tempest on them, in whiche they were gretely troubled longe tyme, and sore for-laboured. And after that, they founde by the purveyaunce of God, an ylonde whiche was ferre fro them, and than they full mekely prayed our Lord to sende them thyder in safeté, but it was xl. dayes after or they came thyder, wherfore all the monkes were so wery of that trouble that they set lytel pryce on theyr lyves, and cryed contynually to our Lord to have mercy on them and brynge them to that ylonde in safeté. And by the purveyaunce of God, they came at the last unto a lytell haven; but it was so strayte that unneth the shyppe might come in. And after they came to an ancre, and anone the monkes went to londe, and whan they had longe walked about, at the laste they founde two fayre welles; that one was fayre and clere water, and that other was somwhat troubly and thycke. And than they thanked our Lorde full humbly that had brought them thyder in safeté, and they wolde fayne have droken of that water, but saynt Brandon charged them that they sholde take none without lycence; "for yf we absteyne us a whyle, our Lord wyll purvey for us in the best wyse."

And anone after came to them a fayre old man, with hoor heer, and welcomed them ful mekely, and kyssed saynt Brandon, and ledde them by many a fayre welle tyll they came to a fayre abbey, where they were receyed with grete honour, and solempne processyon, with xxiiij. monkes all in ryal copes of cloth of golde, and a ryal crosse was before them. And than the abbot welcomed saynt Brandon and his felawashyp, and kyssed them full mekely, and toke saynt Brandon by the hande, and ledde hym with his monkes into a fayre hall, and set them downe a-rowe upon the benche; and the abbot of the place wasshed all theyr feet with fayre water of the well that they sawe before, and after ladde them into the fraytour, and there set them amonge his covent. And anone there came one by the purveyaunce of God, whiche served them well of meet and drynke. For every monke had set before hym a fayre whyte lofe and whyte rotes and herbes, whiche were ryght delycyous, but they wyst not what rotes they were; and they dranke of the water of the fayre clere welle that they sawe before whan they came fyrst a-londe, whiche saynt Brandon forbadde them. And than the abbot came and chered saynt Brandon and his monkes, and prayed them to ete and drinke for charité "for every day our Lorde sendeth a goodly olde man that covereth this table, and setteth our meet and drynke to-fore us; but we knowe not how it cometh, ne we ordeyne never ne meet ne drynke for us, and yet we have ben lxxx. yere here, and ever our Lorde (worshypped mote he be) fedeth us.

And than saynt Brandon wente to the chirche with the abbot of the place, and there they sayd evensonge togyder full devoutly.

And whan saynt Brandon had dwelled there fro Chrystmasse ever tyll the xij. daye was passed, than he toke his leve of the abbot and covent, and returned with his monkes to his shyppe, and sayled fro thens with his monkes to-warde the abbey of saynt Hylaryes but they had grete tempestes in the see fro that tyme tyll Palme Sondaye. And than they came to the Ylonde of Shepe, and there were receyved of the olde man, whiche brought them to a fayre hall and served them. And on Sher-Thursdaye after souper he wasshed theyr feet and kyssed them, lyke as our Lorde dyd to his discyples, and there abode tyll Saterdaye Eester even, and than they departed and sayled to the place where the grete fysshe lay, and anone they saw theyr caudron upon the fysshes backe whiche they had left there xij. monethes to-fore, and there they kepte the servyce of the resurreccyon on the fysshes backe, and after they sayled the same daye by the mornynge to the ylonde where as the tree of byrdes was, and than the sayd byrde welcomed saynt Brandon and all his felaw-shyp, and went agayn to the tree and sange full meryly. And there he and his monkes dwelled fro Eester tyll Trynité Sondaye, as they dyd the yere before, in full grete joye and myrth; and dayly they herde the mery servyce of the byrdes syttynge on the tree.

And than the byrde told to saynt Brandon that he sholde returne agayn at Chrystmasse to the abbey of monkes, and at Eester thyder agayn, and the other dele of the yere labour in the occean in full grete perylles, "and fro yere to yere tyll the vij. yere ben accomplysshed, and than shall ye come to the joyfull place of Paradyse, and dwell there xl. daye in full grete joye and myrth; and after ye shall returne home into your owne abbey in safeté, and there end your lyf and come to the blysse of heven, to whiche our Lorde bought you with his precyous blode."

And than the aungell of our Lorde ordeyned all thynges that was nedefull to saynt Brandon and to his monkes, in vytayles and all other thynges necessary. And than they thanked our Lorde of his grete good-nes that he had shewed to them ofte in theyr grete nede, and than sayled forth in the grete see occan abydynge the mercy of our Lord in grete trouble and tempestes, and soone after came to them an horryble fysshe, whiche folowed the shyppe long tyme, castynge so muche water out of his mouth into the shyppe, that they supposed to have ben drowned. Wherfore they devoutly prayed to God to delyver them of that grete peryll. And anone after came an other fysshe, greter than he, out of the west see, and faught with him, and at the laste clave him in thre places, and than returned agayne. And than they thanked mekely our Lord of theyr delyveraunce fro this grete peryll; but they were in grete hevynesse, because theyr vytayles were nygh spente. But, by the ordynaunce of our Lorde, there came a byrde and brought to them a grete braunche of a vine full of reed grapes, by whiche they lyved xiiij. dayes; and than they came to a lytell ylonde, wherin were many vynes full of grapes, and they there londed, and thanked God, and gadred as many grapes as they lyved by xl. dayes after, alwaye saylynge in the see in many a storme and tempest.

And as they thus sayled, sodeynly came fleynge towarde them a grete grype, whiche assayled them and was lyke to have destroyed them; wherfore they devoutly prayed for helpe, and ayde of our Lorde Jesu Chryst. And than the byrde of the tree of the ylonde where they had holden theyr Eester to-fore came to the gripe and smote out both his eyen, and after slewe hym; wherof they thanked our Lorde, and than sayled forth contynually tyll saynt Peters daye, and than songen they solempnely theyr servyce in the honour of the feest. And in that place the water was so clere, that they myght se all the fysshes that were aboute them, wherof they were full sore agast, and the monkes counseyled saynt Brandon to synge no more, for all the fysshes lay than as they had slepte. And than saynt Brandon sayd,

"Drede ye not, for ye have kepte by two Eesters the feest of the resurreccion upon the grete fysshes backe, and therfore drede ye not of these lytel fysshes."

And than saynt Brandon made hym redy, and wente to masse, and badde his monkes to synge the best wyse they coude. And than anone all the fysshes awoke and came aboute the shyppe so thicke, that unneth they myght se the water for the fysshes. And whan the masse was done, all the fysshes departed so that they were no more seen.

And seven dayes they sayled alwaye in that clere water. And than there came a south wynde and drove the shyppe north-warde where as they sawe an ylonde full derke and full of stenche and smoke; and there they herde grete blowynge and blastynge of belowes, but they myght se no thynge, but herde grete thondrynge, wherof they were sore aferde and blyssed them ofte. And soone after there came one stertynge out all brennynge in fyre, and stared full gastly on them with grete staryinge eyen, of whome the monkes were agast, and at his departyng from them he made the horryblest crys that myght be herde. And soone there came a grete nombre of fendes and assayled them with hokes and brennynge yren malles, whiche ranne on the water, folowyng fast theyr shyppe, in suche wyse that it semed all the see to be on fyre; but by the wyll of God they had no power to hurte ne to greve them, nr thyr shyppe. Wherfore the fendes began to rore and crye, and threwe theyr hokes and malles at them. And they than were sore aferde, and prayed to God for comforte and helpe; for they sawe the fendes all about the shyppe and them semed that all the ylonde and the see to be on a fyre. And with a sorowfull crye all the fendes departed fro them and returned to the place that they came fro. And than saynt Brandon tolde to them that this was a parte of hell, and therfore he charged them to be stedfast in the fayth, for they shold yet se many a dredefull place or they came home agayne.

And than came the south wynde and drove them ferther into the north, where they sawe an hyll all on fyre, and a foule smoke and stenche comyng from thens, and the fyre stode on eche syde of the hyll lyke a wall all brennynge. And than one of his monkes began to crye and wepe ful sore, and sayd that his ende was comen, and that he mught abyde no lenger in the shyppe, and anone he lepte out of the shyppe into the see, and than he cryed and rored full pyteously, cursynge the tyme that he was borne, and also fader and moder that bygate him, bycause they sawe no better to his correccyon in his yonge age, "for now I must go to per-petual payne." And than the sayenge of saynt Brandon was veryfyed that he sayd to hym whan he entred into the shyppe. Therfore it is good a man to do penaunce and forsake Synne, for the houre of deth is incer-tayne.

And than anone the wynde turned into the north, and drove the shyppe into the south, whiche sayled vij. dayes contynually; and they came to a grete rocke standynge in the see, and theron sate a naked man in full grete mysery and payne; for the wawes of the see had so beten his body that all the flesshe was gone of, and nothynge lefte but synewes and bare bones. And whan the wawes were gone, there was a canvas that henge over his heed whiche bette his body full sore with the blowynge of the wynde, and also there were two oxe tongues and a grete stone that he sate on, whiche dyd him full grete ease. And than saynt Brandon charged hym to tell hym what he was. And he sayd,

"My name is Judas, that solde our Lorde Jesu Chryst for xxx. pens, whiche sytteth here moche wretchedly, how be it I am worthy to be in the gretest payne that is; but our Lorde is so mercyfull that he hath re-warded me better than I have deserved, for of ryght my place is in the brennynge hell; but I am here but certayne tymes of the yere, that is, fro Chrystmasse to twelfth daye, and fro Eester tyll Whytsontyde be past, and every feestfull daye of our lady, and every Saterdaye at noone tyll Sonday that evensonge be done; but all other tymes I lye styll in hell in ful brennynge fyre with Pylate, Herode, and Cayphas; therfore accursed be the tyme that ever I knewe them."

And than Judas prayed saynt Brandon to abyde styll there all that nyght, and that he wolde kepe hym there styll that the fendes sholde not fetche hym to hell. And he sayd,

"With Goddes helpe thou shalt abyde here all this nyght."

And than he asked Judas what cloth that was that henge over his heed. And he sayd it was a cloth that he gave unto a lepre whiche was bought with the money that he stale fro our Lorde whan he bare his purse "wherfor it dothe to me grete payne now in betyng my face with the blowynge of the wynde; and these two oxe tongues that hange here above me, I gave them somtyme to two preestes to praye for me. I bought them wyth myne owne money, and therfore they ease me, bycause the fysshes of the see knawe on them and spare me. And this stone that I syt on laye somtyme in a desolate place where it eased no man; and I toke it thens and layd it in a foule waye, where it dyd moche ease to them that went by that waye, and therfore it easeth me now; for every good dede shall be rewarded, and every evyll dede shal be punysshed."

And the Sondaye agaynst even there came a grete multitude of fendes blastyng and rorynge, and badde saynt Brandon go thens, that they myght have theyr servaunt Judas, "for we dare not come in the presence of our mayster, but yf we brynge hym to hell with us."

And saynt Brandon sayd,

"I lette not you do your maysters commaundement, but by the power of our Lorde Jesu Chryst I charge you to leve hym this nyght tyll to morrow."

"How darest thou helpe hym that so solde his mayster for xxx. pens to the Jewes, and caused hym also to dye the moost shamefull deth upon the crosse?"

And than saynt Brandon charged the fendes by his passyon that they sholde not noy hym that nyght. And than the fendes went theyr way rorynge and cryenge towarde hell to theyr mayster, the grete devyll. And than Judas thanked saynt Brandon so rewfully that it was pité to se, and on the morowe the fendes came with an horyble noyse, sayenge that they had that nyght suffred grete payne bycause they brought not Judas, and sayd that he shold suffre double payne the six dayes folowynge. And they toke than Judas tremblynge for fere with them to payne.

And after saynt Brandon sayled south-warde thre dayes and thre nyghtes, and on the Frydaye they sawe an ylonde, and than saynt Brandon began to sygh and saye,

"I se the ylonde wherin saynt Poule the hermyte dwelleth, and hath dwelled here xl. yere, without meet and drynke ordeyned by mannes hande."

And whan they came to the londe, saynt Poule came and welcomed them humbly. He was olde and for-growen, so that no man myght se his body, of whom saynt Brandon sayd weepyng,

"Now I se a man that lyveth more lyke an aungell than a man, wherfore we wretches may be ashamed that we lyve not better."

Than saynt Poule sayd to saynt Brandon,

"Thou art better than I; for our Lorde hath shewed to the more of his prevytees than he hath done to me, wherfore thou oughtest to be more praysed than I."

To whome saynt Brandon sayd, "We ben monkes and must labour for our meet, but God hath provyded for the suche meet as thou holdest the pleased, wherfore thou art moche better than I."

To whome saynt Poule sayd, "Somtyme I was a monke of saynt Patrykes abbey in Yrelonde, and was wardeyn of the place where as men entre into saynt Patrikes purgatory. And on a day there came one to me, and I asked hym what he was, and he sayd I am your abbot Patryke, and charge the that thou departe from hens to morowe erly to the see syde, and there thou shalt fynde a shyppe, into the whiche thou must entre, whiche God hath ordeyned for the, whose wyll thou must accomplysshe. And so the nexte daye I arose, and went forth and founde the shyppe, in whiche I entred, and by the purveyaunce of God I was brought into this ylonde the seventh yere after, and than I lefte the shyppe and went to londe, and there I walked up and downe a good whyle, and than by the purveyaunce of God there came an otter goynge on his hynder feet and brought me a flynte stone, and an yren to smite fyre with, in his two fore clawes of his feet; and also he had aboute his necke grete plenté of fysshes, whiche he cast downe before me and went his waye, and I smote fyre, and made a fyre of styckes, and dyd sethe the fysshe, by whiche I lyved thre dayes. And than the otter came agayn, and brought me fysshe for other thre dayes; and thus he hath done lj. yere, through the grace of God. And there was a grete stone, out of whiche our Lorde made to sprynge fayre water, clere and swete, wherof I drynke dayly. And thus have I lyved this lj. yere, and I was lx. yere olde when I came hyther, and am now an hondred and xj. yere olde, and abyde tyll it please our Lorde to sende for me; and if it pleased hym, I wolde fayne be discharged of this wretched lyfe."

And then he bad saynt Brandon to take of the water of the welle, and to cary it into his shyppe, "for it is tyme that thou departe, for thou hast a grete journey to do; for thou shalt sayle to an ylonde whiche is xl. dayes saylynge hens, where thou shalt holde thyn Eester lyke as thou hast done to-fore, wher as the tree of byrdes is. And fro thens thou shalte sayle into the Londe of Byheest, and shalt abyde there xl. dayes, and after returne home into thy countree in safeté."

And than these holy men toke leve eche of other, and they wepte bothe full sore and kyssed eche other.

And than saynt Brandon entred into his shyppe, and sayled xl. dayes even southe, in full grete tempest. And on Eester even came to theyr procuratour, whiche made to them good chere, as he had before tyme.

And from thens they came to the grete fysshe, where they sayd matyns and masse on Eester daye. And whan the masse was done, the fysshe began to meve, and swamme forth fast into the see, wherof the monkes were sore agast which stode upon hym, for it was a grete mervayle to se suche a fysshe as grete as all a countree for to swymme so fast in the water; but by the wyll of our Lorde God this fysshe set all the monkes a-londe in the Paradise of Byrdes, all hole and sounde, and than returned to the place that he came fro. And than saynt Brandon and his monkes thanked our Lorde God of theyr delyveraunce of the grete fysshe, and kepte theyr Eestertyde tyll Trinité Sondaye, lyke as they had done before tyme.

And after this they toke theyr shyppe and sayled eest xl. dayes, and at the xl. dayes ende it began to hayle ryght fast, and therwyth came a derke myst, whiche lasted longe after, which fered saynt Brandon and his monkes, and prayed to our Lord to kepe and helpe them. And than anone came theyr procuratour, and badde them to be of good chere, for they were come into the Londe of Byheest. And soone after that myst passed awaye, and anone they sawe the fayrest countree eest-warde that ony man myght se, and was so clere and bryght that it was an hevenly syght to beholde; and all the trees were charged with rype fruyte and herbes full of floures; in whiche londe they walked xl. dayes, but they coude se none ende of that londe; and there was alwaye daye and never nyght, and the londe attemperate ne to hote ne to colde. And at last they came to a ryver, but they durst not go over. And there came to them a fayre yonge man, and welcomed them curtoysly, and called eche of them by his name, and dyd grete reverence to saynt Brandon, and sayd to them,

"Be ye now joyfull, for this is the londe that ye have sought; but our Lorde wyll that ye departe hens hastely, and he wyll shew to you more of his secretes whan ye come agayn into the see; and our Lorde wyll that ye lade your shyppe with the fruyte of this londe, and hye you hens, for ye may no lenger abyde here, but thou shalt sayle agyne into thyne owne countree, and soone after thou comest home thou shalt dye. And this water that thou seest here departeth the worlde assondre; for on that other syde of the water may no man come that is in this lyfe. And the fruyte that ye se is alwaye thus rype every tyme of the yere, and alwaye it is here lyght as ye now se; and he that kepeth our Lordes hestes at all tymes shall se this londe, or he passe out of this worlde."

And then saynt Brandon and his monkes tike of that fruyte as moche as they wolde, and also toke with them grete plenté of percyous stones; and than toke theyr leve and went to shyppe, wepynge sore bycause they myght no lenger abyde there. And than they toke theyr shyppe and came home into Yrelonde in safeté, whome theyr bretherne receyved with grete joye, gyvynge thankynges to our Lorde, whiche had kepte them all those seven yere fro many a peryll, and brought them home in safeté, to whome be gyven honour and glory worlde withouten ende. Amen.

And soone after, this holy man, saynt Brandon wexed feble and seke, and had but lytell joye of this worlde, but ever after his joye and mynde was in the joyes of heven. And in shorte tyme after, he, beynge full of vertues, departed out of this lyfe into everlastyng lyfe, and was worshypfully buryed in a fayre abbey, whiche he hym selfe founded, where our Lorde sheweth for this holy saynt many fayre myracles. Wherfore let us devoutly praye to this holy saynt that he praye for us unto our Lord, that he have mercy on us, to whom be gyven laude, honour, and empyre, world withouten ende. Amen.

GREAT BRITAIN

HOW SCYLD SET FORTH UPON HIS LAST VOYAGE[1]

AT HIS appointed time then Scyld departed, to go into the peace of the Lord; they then, his dear comrades, bore him out to the shore of the sea, as he himself requested, the while that he, the friend of the Scyldings, the beloved chieftain, had power with his words; long he owned it! There upon the beach stood the ring-prowed ship, the vehicle of the noble, shining like ice, and ready to set out. They then laid down the dear prince, the distributer of rings, in the bosom of the ship, the mighty one beside the mast; there was much of treasures, of ornaments, brought from afar. Never heard I of a comelier ship having been adorned with battle-weapons and with war-weeds, with bills and mailed coats. Upon his bosom lay a multitude of treasures which were to depart afar with him, into the possession of the flood. They furnished him not less with offerings, with mighty wealth, than those had done who in the beginning sent him forth in his wretchedness, alone over the waves. Moreover they set up over him a golden ensign, high over head; they let the deep-sea bear him; they gave him to the ocean. Sad was their spirit, mournful their mood. Men know not in sooth to say (men wise of counsel or any man under the heavens) who received the freight.

HOW BEOWULF FOR THE SPACE OF FIVE NIGHTS ABODE IN THE SEA[1]

HUNFERTH, the son of Eglaf, spake, he that sat at the feet of the Lord of the Scyldings.

"Art thou the Beowulf that didst contend with Brecca on the wide sea, in a swimming match, where ye for pride explored the fords, and out of vain glory ventured your lives upon the deep water? Nor might any man, friend or foe, blame your sorrowful expedition: there ye rode upon the sea, there ye two covered the ocean-stream with your arms, measured the sea-streets, whirled them with your hands, glided over the ocean; with the waves of the deep the fury of winter boiled; ye two on the realms of water laboured for a week: he overcame thee in swimming, he had more strength; then at the morning tide the deep sea bore him up on Heathoraemes, whence he sought his own paternal land, dear to his people, the land of the Brondings, where he owned a nation, a town and rings. All his promise to thee, the son of Beanstan truly performed."

Beowulf, the son of Ecgtheow, spake:

---

[1]From J. M. Kemble's translation of *Beowulf*.

"Lo! for a long while thou, my friend Hunferth, drunken with beer, hast spoken about Brecca, hast said respecting his journey; I tell thee the truth, that I have greater strength upon the sea, laboriousness upon the waves, than any other man. We two, when we were boys, had said and promised that (we were both of us as yet in early youth) that we could venture with our lives, out upon the ocean: and so we performed it. We had our naked swords, hard in our hands, when we two rode upon the sea; we two thought to defend ourselves against the whale-fishes. He could not float at all far away from me over the waves of the flood, more rapidly on the deep sea, I would not part from him; there were we two together, a space of five nights upon the sea, until the flood drove us asunder; the coldest of storms, darkening night, and a wind from the north, warlike, fierce, turned up the boiling fords; the waves were fierce. The pride of the sea-fishes was excited: there against my foes my body-shirt, hard, locked by the hand, gave help; my twisted war-dress lay upon my breast, adorned with gold. Me did the many coloured foe drag to the bottom of the sea, he had me fast, grim in his grip: nevertheless it was granted to me to reach the wretch with my point, with my war-bill: the mighty sea-beast received the war-rush through my hand.

"Thus often did my hated foes violently menace me; I served them with my dear sword, as it was fitting; they, the evil-doers, had no joy of the slaughter, in that they attacked me, that they set upon me all together, near the bottom of the sea. But in the morning wounded with knives, they lay aloft beside the leavings of the waves, put to sleep with swords; so that never since, about the boiling ford they have hindered the sea-sailers of their way. The light came from the East, the bright beacon of God, the fierce seas became calm, so that I might see the ocean-promontories, the windy walls. Fate often preserveth a warrior not yet doomed to die, when his valour availeth. Yet I had the fortune to slay with my sword nine nicors: never have I heard of a harder battle by night under the concave of heaven, nor of a man more wretched on the ocean-streams: nevertheless I continued my journey, I escaped with life; weary of my expedition: then did the sea bear me up on Finland, the flood upon the sand, the boiling fords.

HOW RICHARD CŒUR DE LION, SAILING TO THE HOLY LAND, CAPTURED A SARACEN SHIP[1]

Geoffrey de Vinsauf

KING RICHARD, having furnished himself with every thing necessary for the voyage, prepared, according to agreement, to follow after the king of France as quickly as he could; and appointed

[1] From *The Itinerary of Richard King of the English to the Holy Land.*

Robert de Torneham to conduct and take care of the fleet. He sent forward his betrothed, with his sister, the dowager queen of Sicily, in advance, in one of the ships which are commonly called dromons, keeping a course direct to the east; he had also placed some knights on board, and a numerous retinue of servants, for their comfort and safe-keeping. These kind of vessels are slower than others, on account of their burthern, but of stronger make. The multitude of the galleys remained immove-able, until the king, having dined, on account of the annoyances which had happened, bade farewell, with all his army, to the natives, and was on the point of setting out and committing himself to favourable winds and the waves of the sea. Then the whole multitude of ships was launched into the sea, impelled by numerous oarsmen. The city of Messina might justly boast that so great a fleet had never in past ages quitted these shores; and that they never will see there such a one again.

Therefore, on the seventeenth day after the departure of the king of France, *i.e.*, on the Wednesday after Palm Sunday, King Richard followed with a numerous fleet of ships, and passing amid the Faro with a fair breeze, some by sailing, some by rowing, they came out into the deep —the dromons, however, keeping them in the rear as Richard had planned, in order that, as far as it was possible to avoid it, they should not part company, unless they were accidently separated by the tides; while the galleys purposely relaxed their speed and kept pace with the ships of burthern, to guard their multitude, and protect the weaker.

The wind all at once began to fall gradually, so that the fleet was compelled to remain motionless at anchor between Calabria and Mount Gibello; but on the morrow, *i.e.* the day of the Lord's Supper, He who withdraws and sends forth the winds from his treasuries, sent us a wind which continued the whole day, not too strong, but impelling the fleet at a moderate speed; but after that it abated altogether on the following night. But on Holy Friday, a contrary wind arising, drove it back to the left, and the sea being very much agitated thereby, boiled up from the very depths, while the waves beat together, and the storm increased; the roar of the dashing waves, and the ships creaking with the violence of the wind, struck all with no small terror, and from the excessive fury of the latter, all management of the ships was at an end; for no pilot could steer them while tossing to and fro in such a manner. They were borne hither and thither; their line was broken, and they went different ways. The crews committed themselves to the guidance of the Lord, despairing of earthly aid; but as far as human weakness permitted, we determined to bear all things with patience, under the eye of our Saviour, who on that day had suffered so undeserved a death for our sakes. And as the ships were tossed to and fro, and dispersed divers ways, men's stomachs began to feel a qualm, and were affected by a violent nausea; and this feeling of sickness made them almost insensible to the dangers around; but towards evening, it grew by degrees calm, and the fury of the winds and waves abated. A favourable wind now springing up, according to our wishes, and the sailors having recovered their strength and confidence, we strove to keep a direct course for our voyage.

King Richard, unmoved amid this state of confusion, never ceased to animate those who were dispirited, and bid them take courage, and hope for better fortune; moreover, he had as usual a very large wax-light in a lantern, hoisted aloft in his ship to give light to the rest of the fleet and direct them in their way. He had on board most experienced sailors, who did every thing which human art could do to oppose the fury of the winds. All, therefore, as far as they could, followed the light burning in the king's ship. The king remained stationary some time to collect his fleet, which congregated together by seeing the light, so that the king resembled a hen gathering together her chickens. After that, we started with a favourable wind, and sailed along, without obstacle or injury, on the Saturday of the Passover, as well as on the day of the festival, and until the following Wednesday. That day we came in sight of Crete, where the king put in to repose and collect his fleet. When the ships had come together, twenty-five were found missing, at which the king was much grieved.

On the morrow, being Thursday, the king and all his army entered their ships; when the wind began to rise stronger, and though favourable, was very vehement in impelling us forward, for we moved rapidly along, with sails swelled out and mast slightly bent, not unlike the flight of birds. The wind, which slackened not all night, at dawn of day drove our fleet violently upon the island of Rhodes: there was no port, and the surf stretched along the shore; however, we enjoyed there our rest the better for having wished for it so earnestly, from that day until the following Monday, when we put in at Rhodes. Rhodes was anciently a very large city, not unlike Rome; though its extent can scarcely be estimated, there are so many ruins of houses and portions of fallen towers still standing, and such wonderful remains of walls and buildings of admirable workmanship. There are also a few monasteries still remaining out of so many ancient edifices, for the most part deserted, though formerly inhabited by such numerous societies of monks. The site of so great a city, though by time laid waste, proves the former existence of a large population; but very few inhabitants were found there now who could sell us food. But as the king was indisposed, we tarried there a few days, during which he waited the arrival of the ships that had wandered out of their course and lost us, and the galleys which followed him.

Having spent ten days at Rhodes, which is a very fertile and productive island, they went on board, and set out on their voyage on the 1st of May. They were borne on their course into that most dangerous place, called the Gulf of Satalia. There a mighty strife of currents formed by the junction of four seas, struggled violently together, each dashing against and resisting the other. We were on the point of entering it, when lo! as if apprehensive of our safety, a contrary current carried us back to the place from whence we had started. But in a short time, the wind, which in those parts is constantly shifting, drove us from behind back again into the gulf, with the more danger from its increased violence. Fearing the effects of its fury, we did all we could to guard against the dangers of the place, and pass over the waves that boiled and foamed around.

The royal ship was always in advance, and when the king lifted his eyes, he saw beneath a calm sky, a very large ship of the sort called a buss (*buza*) bearing down, which was returning from Jerusalem. The king, therefore, speedily sent men to inquire for intelligence concerning the siege of Acre, from those who were in the ship; who replied that the king of France had already arrived at Acre in safety, and was diligently employed in making machines, until the arrival of the king of England.

When King Richard heard all these things from the aforesaid sailors, the buss passed on its way, and he made all his arrangements in high spirits. . . .

By this time a report was spread that Acre was on the point of being taken, and when the king heard it, he sighed deeply and said,

"May God defer the taking of Acre till I come, after it has been so long besieged, and therefore the triumph will be the more glorious with the assistance of God."

Then getting ready with all speed, he went on board one of his largest and swiftest galleys, at Famagusta; and as was his wont, he moved forward in advance, impatient of delay, while the other ships followed in his wake as quickly as they could, and well prepared, for there is no power that might not justly have dreaded their hostility. As they ploughed across the sea, the Holy Land of Jerusalem was described for the first time the fort called Margat being the first spot that met the eye; afterwards Tortuosa, situated on the sea-shore; then Tripolis, Nephyn, and Bocion. And soon after appeared the lofty tower of Gibelath. Lastly, on this side of Sidon, opposite Baruth, there bore in sight a vessel filled with Saracens, chosen from all the Pagan empire, and destined by Saladin for the assistance of the besieged in Acre. They were not able to obtain a speedy entrance into the port, because of the Christian army that menaced them, and so were waiting a favourable moment for entering the port by surprise.

The king, observing the ship, called Peter des Barres, commander of one of his galleys, and ordered him to row quickly, and inquire who commanded the vessel. And when they answered that it belonged to the king of France, the king in his eager haste approached it; but it had no mark of being French, neither did it bear any Christian symbol or standard; and on looking at it near, the king began to wonder at its immense size and compact make, for it was crowned with three tall masts, and its sides were marked with streaks of red and yellow, and it was well furnished in all manner of equipments, so that nothing could exceed them, and it was abundantly supplied with all kinds of provisions. One of those on board said, that while at Baruth, he saw the vessel laden with all these things; viz. one hundred camel-loads of arms, slings, bows, darts, and arrows: it had also on board seven Saracen admirals, and eighty chosen Turks, besides a quantity of all kinds of provisions, exceeding computation. They had also on board a large quantity of Greek fire, in bottles, and two hundred most deadly serpents for the destruction of the Christians. Others were therefore sent to obtain more exact information who they were, and when, instead of their former answer, they replied that they were Genoese, bound for Tyre, our men began to doubt the truth at this change of reply; one of our galleymen persisted that they were Saracens, and on the king's questioning him, he said,

"I give you leave to cut off my head, or hang me on a tree, if I do not prove these men to be Saracens. Now let a galley be sent quickly after them, for they are making away, and let no kind of salute be given them by us, and in this way we shall have certain proof what their intention is, and how far they are to be believed."

At the king's command, therefore, a galley was sent at full speed after them, and on reaching their ship, and rowing by its side without giving a salute, they began to throw darts and arrows at our men. On seeing this, the king ordered the ship to be attacked forthwith, and after casting a shower of darts against each other, the ship relaxed its speed, for the wind carried it but slowly along. Though our galley men rowed repeatedly round the ship, to scrutinize the vessel, they could find no point of attack: it appeared so solid and so compact, and of such strong materials; and it was defended by a guard of warriors, who kept throwing darts at them. Our men, therefore, relished not the darts, nor the great height of the ship, for it was enough to strive against a foe on equal ground, whereas a dart thrown from above always tells upon those below, since its iron point falls downwards. Hence, their ardour relaxed, but the spirit of the king increased, and he exclaimed aloud,

"Will you allow the ship to get away untouched and uninjured? Shame upon you! are you grown cowards from sloth, after so many triumphs? The whole world knows that you engaged in the service of the Cross, and you will have to undergo the severest punishment, if you permit an enemy to escape while he lives, and is thrown in your way."

Our men, therefore, making a virtue of necessity, plunged eagerly into the water under the ship's side, and bound the rudder with ropes to turn and retard its progress, and some, catching hold of the cables, leapt on board the ship. The Turks receiving them manfully, cut them to pieces as they came on board, and lopping off the head of this one, and the hands of that, and the arms of another, cast their bodies into the sea. Our men seeing this, and glowing with anger, gained fresh courage from the thirst for vengence, and crossing over the bulwarks of the vessel, attacked the Turks in a body with great fierceness, who, though giving way a little, made an obstinate resistance. The Turks gathering boldness from despair, used all their efforts to repel those who threatened them, cutting off the arms, hands, and even heads of our men; but they, after a mighty struggle, drove the Turks back as far as the prow of the ship, while from the interior others rushed upon our men in a body, preparing to die bravely or repel the foe; they were the choice youth of the Turks, fitted for war, and suitably armed. The battle lasted a long time, and many fell on both sides; but at last, the Turks, pressing boldly on our men, drove them back, though they resisted with all their might, and forced them from the ship. Upon which our men retired to their galleys, and surrounding the vessel on all sides, tried to find a more easy mode of attacking it.

The king, seeing the danger his men were in, and that while the ship was uninjured it would not be easy to take the Turks with the arms and provisions therein, commanded that each of the galleys should attack the ship with its spur, *i.e.*, its iron beak. Then the galleys drawing back, were borne by rapid strokes of the oar against the ship's sides to pierce them, and thus the vessel was instantly broken, and becoming pervious to the waves, began to sink. When the Turks saw it, they leapt into the sea to die, and our men killed some of them and drowned the rest. The king kept thirty-five alive, namely, the admirals and men who were skilled in making machines, but the rest perished, the arms were abandoned, and the serpents sunk and scattered about by the waves of the sea. If that ship had arrived safely at the siege of Acre, the Christians would never have taken the city; but by the care of God it was converted into the destruction of the infidels, and the aid of the Christians, who hoped in Him, by means of King Richard, who by His help prospered in war.

THE BATTLE OF ESPAGNOLS–SUR–MER[1]

Sir John Froissart

(1313–1419)

ABOUT this period, there was much ill will between the king of England and the Spaniards, on account of some infractions and pillages committed at sea by the latter. It happened at this season, that the Spaniards who had been in Flanders with their merchandize, were informed they would not be able to return home, without meeting the English fleet. The Spaniards did not pay much attention to this in-

---

[1]From *The Chronicles of England.*

telligence: however, after they had disposed of their goods, they amply provided their ships from Sluys with arms and artillery, and all such archers, cross-bowmen, and soldiers as were willing to receive pay. The king of England hated these Spaniards greatly, and said publicly:

"We have for a long time spared these people; for which they have done us much harm; without amending their conduct; on the contrary they grow more arrogant; for which reason they must be chastised as they repass our coasts."

When the Spaniards had completed their cargoes, and laden their vessels with linen cloths, and whatever they imagined would be profitable in their own country, they embarked on board their fleet at Sluys. They knew they should meet the English, but were indifferent about it; for they had marvellously provided themselves with all sorts of warlike ammunition; such as bolts for cross-bows, cannon, and bars of forged iron to throw on the enemy, in hopes, with the assistance of great stones, to sink him. When they weighed anchor, the wind was favourable for them: there were forty large vessels of such a size, and so beautiful, it was a fine sight to see them under sail. Near the top of their masts were small castles, full of flints and stones, and a soldier to guard them; and there also was the flag-staff, from whence fluttered their streamers in the wind, that it was pleasant to look at them. If the English had a great desire to meet them, it seemed as if the Spaniards were still more eager for it, as will hereafter appear. The Spaniards were full ten thousand men, including all sorts of soldiers they had enlisted when in Flanders: this made them feel sufficient courage not to fear the combat with the king of England, and whatever force he might have at sea. Intending to meet the English fleet, they advanced with a favourable wind until they came opposite Calais.

The king of England being at sea, had very distinctly explained to all his knights the order of battle he would have them follow: he had appointed the lord Robert de Namur to the command of a ship called *La Salle du Roi*, on board of which was all his household. The king posted himself in the fore part of his own ship: he was dressed in a black velvet jacket, and wore on his head a small hat of beaver, which became him much. He was that day, as I was told by those who were present, as joyous as he ever was in his life, and ordered his minstrels to play before him a German dance which sir John Chandos had lately introduced. For his amusement, he made the same knight sing with his minstrels, which delighted him greatly. From time to time he looked up to the castle on his mast, where he had placed a watch to inform him when the Spaniards were in sight.

Whilst the king was thus amusing himself with his knights, who were happy in seeing him so gay, the watch, who had observed a fleet, cried out:

"Ho, I spy a ship, and it appears to me to be a Spaniard."

The minstrels were silenced; and he was asked if there were more than one: soon after he replied,

"Yes; I see two, three, four, and so many that, God help me, I cannot count them."

The king and his knights then knew they must be the Spaniards. The trumpets were ordered to sound, and the ships to form a line of battle for the combat; as they were aware that, since the enemy came in such force, it could not be avoided. It was, however, rather late, about the hour of vespers. The king ordered wine to be brought, which he and his knights drank; when each fixed their helmets on their heads. The Spaniards now drew near; they might easily have refused the battle, if they had chosen it, for they were well freighted, in large ships, and had the wind in their favour. They could have avoided speaking with the English, if they had willed, but their pride and presumption made them act otherwise. They disdained to sail by, but bore instantly down on them, and commenced the battle.

When the king of England saw from his ship their order of battle, he ordered the person who managed his vessel, saying:

"Lay me alongside the Spaniard who is bearing down on us; for I will have a tilt with him."

The master dared not disobey the king's order, but laid his ship ready for the Spaniard, who was coming full sail. The king's ship was large and stiff; otherwise she would have been sunk, for that of the enemy was a great one, and the shock of their meeting was more like the crash of a torrent or tempest; the rebound caused the castle in the king's ship to encounter that of the Spaniard: so that the mast of the latter was broken, and all in the castle fell with it into the sea, when they were drowned. The English vessel, however, suffered, and let in water, which the knights cleared, and stopped the leak, without telling the king any thing of the matter. Upon examining the vessel he had engaged lying before him, he said:

"Grapple my ship with that; for I will have possession of her."

His knights replied:

"Let her go her way; you shall have better than her."

That vessel sailed on, and another large ship bore down, and grappled with chains and hooks to that of the king. The fight now began in earnest, and the archers and cross-bows on each side were eager to shoot and defend themselves. The battle was not in one place, but in ten or twelve at a time. Whenever either party found themselves equal to the enemy, or superior, they instantly grappled, when grand deeds of arms were performed. The English had not any advantage; and the Spanish ships were much larger and higher than their opponents, which gave them a great superiority in shooting and casting stones and iron bars on board their enemy, which annoyed them exceedingly. The knights on board the king's ship were in danger of sinking, for the leak still admitted water: this made them more eager to conquer the vessel they were grappled to: many gallant deeds were done; and at last they gained the ship, and flung all they found in it overboard, having quitted their own ship. They continued the combat against the Spaniards, who fought valiantly, and whose cross-bowmen shot such bolts of iron as greatly distressed the English.

This sea-fight between the English and Spaniards was well and hardly fought: but, as night was coming on, the English exerted themselves to do their duty well, and discomfort their enemies. The Spaniards, who are used to the sea, and were in large ships, acquitted themselves to the utmost of their power.

The young Prince of Wales and his division were engaged apart: his ship was grappled by a great Spaniard, where he and his knights suffered much; for she had so many holes, that the water came in very abundantly, and they could not by any means stop the leaks, which gave the crew fears of her sinking, they therefore did all they could to conquer the enemy's ship, but in vain; for she was very large, and excellently well defended. During this danger of the prince, the duke of Lancaster came near, and, as he approached, saw he had the worst of the engagement, and that his crew had too much on their hands, for they were baling out water: he therefore fell on the other side of the Spanish vessel, with which he grappled, shouting,

"Derby to the rescue!"

The engagement was now very warm, but did not last long, for the ship was taken, and all the crew thrown overboard, not one being saved. The prince, with his men, instantly embarked on board the Spaniard; and scarcely had they done so when his own vessel sunk, which convinced them of the imminent danger they had been in.

The engagement was in other parts well contested by the English knights, who exerted themselves, and need there was of it, for they found those who feared them not. Late in the evening, the *Salle du Roi*, commanded by lord Robert de Namur, was grappled by a large Spaniard, and the fight was very severe. The Spaniards were determined to gain this ship; and, the more effectually to succeed in carrying her off, they set all their sails, took advantage of the wind, and in spite of what lord Robert and his crew could do, towed her out of the battle: for the Spaniard was of a more considerable size than the lord Robert's ship, and therefore she more easily conquered. As they were thus towed, they passed near the king's ship, to whom they cried out,

"Rescue the *Salle du Roi*!"

but were not heard; for it was dark; and, if they were heard, they were not rescued. The Spaniards would have carried away with ease this prize, if it had not been for a gallant act of one Hanequin, a servant to the lord Robert, who, with his drawn sword on his wrist, leaped on board the enemy, ran to the mast, and cut the large cable which held the main sail, by which it became unmanageable; and with great agility, he cut other four principal ropes, so that the sails fell on the deck, and the course of the ship was stopped. Lord Robert, seeing this, advanced with his men, and, boarding the Spaniard, sword in hand, attacked the crew so vigorously that all were slain or thrown overboard, and the vessel won.

I cannot speak of every particular circumstance of this engagement. It lasted a considerable time; and the Spaniards gave the king of England and his fleet enough to do. However, at last, victory declared for the English: the Spaniards lost fourteen ships; the others saved themselves by flight. When it was completely over, and the king saw he had none to fight with, he ordered his trumpets to sound a retreat, and made for England.

HOW SIR LAUNCELOT ENTERED INTO THE SHIP WHERE SIR PERCIVALE'S SISTER LAY DEAD: AND HOW HE MET WITH SIR GALAHAD HIS SON[1]

Sir Thomas Malory

(fl. 1470)

NOW saith the history, that when Launcelot was come to the water of Mortoise, he was in great peril, and so he laid him down and slept, and took the adventure that God would send him.

So when he was asleep, there came a vision unto him and said, Launcelot, arise up, and take thine armour, and enter into the first ship that thou shalt find. And when he had heard these words, he start up and saw great clearness about him. And then he lift up his hand and blessed him, and so took his arms, and made him ready; and so by adventure he came by a strand, and found a ship, the which was without sail or oar. And as soon as he was within the ship, there he felt the most sweetness that ever he felt; and he was fulfilled with all thing that he thought on or desired. Then said he,

Fair sweet Father Jesu Christ, I wot not in what joy I am, for this joy passeth all earthly joys that ever I was in.

And so in this joy he laid him down to the ship's board, and slept till day.

And when he awoke he found there a fair bed, and therein lying a gentlewoman dead, the which was Sir Percivale's sister. And as Launcelot devised her, he espied in her right hand a writ, the which he read, the which told him all the adventures that ye have heard tofore, and of what lineage she was come. So with this gentlewoman Sir Launcelot was a month and more. If ye would ask how he lived, He that fed the people

---

[1]From *Morte Darthur*.

of Israel with manna in the desert, so was he fed. For every day, when
he had said his prayers, he was sustained with the grace of the Holy
Ghost.

So on a night he went to play him by the water side, for he was somewhat weary of the ship. And then he listened, and heard an horse come,
and one riding upon him. And when he came nigh he seemed a knight.
And so he let him pass, and went there as the ship was, and there he
alight, and took the saddle and the bridle and put the horse from him,
and went into the ship.

And then Launcelot dressed unto him and said,

Ye be welcome.

And he answered and saluted him again, and asked him,

What is your name? for much my heart giveth unto you.

Truly, said he, my name is Launcelot du Lake.

Sir, said he, then be ye welcome, for ye were the beginner of me in
this world.

Ah, said he, are ye Galahad?

Yea forsooth, said he.

And so he kneeled down and asked him his blessing, and after took
off his helm and kissed him. And there was great joy between them,
for there is no tongue can tell the joy that they made either of other,
and many a friendly word spoken between, as kind would, the which is
no need here to be rehearsed. And there every each told other of their
adventures and marvels that were befallen to them in many journeys,
sith that they departed from the court. Anon as Galahad saw the gentlewoman dead in the bed, he knew her well enough, and told great worship
of her, and that she was the best maid living, and it was great pity of
her death.

So dwelled Launcelot and Galahad within that ship half a year, and
served God daily and nightly with all their power. And often they arrived in isles far from folk, where there repaired none but wild beasts;
and there they found many strange adventures and perilous, which they
brought to an end. But because the adventures were with wild beasts,
and not in the quest of the Sancgreal, therefore the tale maketh here no
mention thereof, for it would be too long to tell of all those adventures
that befell them.

So after, on a Monday, it befell that they arrived in the edge of a
forest, tofore a cross, and then saw they a knight, armed all in white,
and was richly horsed, and led in his right hand a white horse. And so
he came to the ship, and saluted the two knights on the high Lord's
behalf, and said,

Galahad, sir, ye have been long enough with your father, come out
of the ship and start upon this horse, and go where the adventures shall
lead thee in the quest of the Sancgreal.

Then he went to his father, and kissed him sweetly, and said,

Fair, sweet father, I wot not when I shall see you more, till I see the body of Jesu Christ.

I pray you, said Launcelot, pray ye to the nigh Father that He hold me in his service.

And so he took his horse; and there they heard a voice that said, Think for to do well, for the one shall never see the other before the dreadful day of doom.

Now, son Galahad, said Launcelot, since we shall depart, and never see other, I pray to the high Father to preserve both me and you both.

Sir, said Galahad, no prayer availeth so much as yours.

And therewith Galahad entered into the forest.

And the wind arose, and drove Launcelot more than a month throughout the sea, where he slept but little, but prayed to God that he might see some tidings of the Sancgreal. So it befell on a night, at midnight he arrived afore a castle, on the back side, which was rich and fair. And there was a postern opened towards the sea, and was open without any keeping, save two lions kept the entry; and the moon shone clear. Anon Sir Launcelot heard a voice that said,

Launcelot, go out of this ship, and enter into the castle, where thou shalt see a great part of thy desire.

Then he ran to his arms, and so armed him, and so he went to the gate, and saw the lions. Then set he hand to his sword, and drew it. Then there came a dwarf suddenly, and smote him on the arm so sore that the sword fell out of his hand. Then heard he a voice say,

Oh man of evil faith and poor belief, wherefore trowest thou more on thy harness than in thy Maker? for He might more avail thee than thine armour, in whose service thou art set.

Then said Launcelot,

Fair Father Jesu Christ, I thank thee of thy great mercy, that thou reprovest me of my misdeed. Now see I well that ye hold me for your servant.

Then took he again his sword, and put it up in his sheath, and made a cross in his forehead, and came to the lions, and they made semblant to do him harm. Notwithstanding he passed by them without hurt, and entered into the castle to the chief fortress, and there were they all at rest. Then Launcelot entered in so armed, for he found no gate nor door but it was open. And at the last he found a chamber whereof the door was shut, and he set his hand thereto to have opened it, but he might not.

Then he enforced him mickle to undo the door. Then he listened, and heard a voice which sang so swetly that it seemed none earthly thing; and him thought the voice said:

Joy and honour be to the Father of Heaven.

Then Launcelot kneeled down tofore the chamber, for well wist he that there was the Sancgreal within that chamber.

OF THE GREAT SEA FIGHT BETWEEN SIR ANDREW WOOD, KNIGHT, AND CAPTAIN STEPHEN BULL[1]

Robert Lindsay of Pitscottie

(1500(?)–1565(?))

THIS same year, certain English ships came in our Scottish firth, and spoiled our merchandise with all other passengers that came in their way. Of this the King and Council thought great ill, and desired effectuously to be revenged thereof; but they could get no man, neither captains, marriners, nor skippers, that would take in hand to pass forth upon them: till at the last, they sent for Sir Andrew Wood, knight of Largo, and desired him to pass forth upon the said Englishmen, and to that effect he should be well furnished with men, victuals and artillery, and he should have the King's favour therefor, and be rewarded richly for his travail.

Of this Sir Andrew Wood was well content, and passed forth of the Firth with two ships well manned and artilleried, to pass upon the said Englishmen, whom he foregathered with at the Castle of Dunbar, where they fought very cruelly on either side, with uncertain victory a long space, notwithstanding the Englishmen were five, and he but two, as said is, to wit, *The Yellow Carvel*, and the *Flower*. Yet the said Sir Andrew Wood prevailed by his singular manhood and wisdom, and brought all his five ships to Leith as prisoners, and delivered the Captains thereof to the King's Grace, for the which notable act, the said Captain Wood was well rewarded.

But incontinent, when the King of England heard tell of their news, that his ships were foughten and taken by Sir Andrew Wood, he was greatly displeased therewith, and made proclamations through all England, that whosoever would pass to the sea, and fight with Sir Andrew Wood, and if he happened to take him prisoner, and bring him to him, he should have for his reward, one thousand pound sterling to spend by year. There were many that refused, because they knew Sir Andrew Wood to be such a Captain upon the sea, and very fortunate in battle, wherefore they had no will to assail him.

Nevertheless, one captain of war, a gentleman called Stephen Bull, took in hand to pass to the sea and fight with Sir Andrew Wood, and bring him prisoner to the King of England, either quick or dead, whereat the King of England was greattumly rejoiced, and caused provide the said Captain three great ships well furnished with men and artillery. After this the Captain passed to the sea, and sailed till he came to the Scottish firth, that is to say, to the back of Inchmay, beyond the Bass, and took many of our boats that were travelling for fishes, to win their

[1]From *The Chronicles of Scotland.*

living: and took many of them to give him knowledge where Sir Andrew
Wood was, till at the last, a little before the day breaking, upon a Sunday
morning, one of the English ships perceived two ships coming under sail
by St Cobes head: then the English captain caused some of the Scottish prisoners pass to the tops of the ships that they might see or spy if
it was Sir Andrew Wood or not: but the Scottishmen dissembled, and
said they knew not who it was, till at the last, the Captain promised
their ransom free to tell the verity if it was Captain Wood or not, who
certified him that it was he indeed. Then the Captain was very blyth,
and gart fill the wine, and drink about to all the skippers and captains
that was under him, praying them to take good courage, for their enemies were at hand; for the which cause, he gart order his ships in fier of
war,[1] and set the quartermaster and captains, every one in his own
room, and caused the gunners to charge and put all in order like a good
and stout captain.

On the other side, Sir Andrew Wood came pertly forward, knowing
no impediment of enemies to be in his gait, till at the last, he perceived
two ships coming under sail, and making fast towards them in fier of
war. Then Captain Wood seeing this, exhorted his men to battle, beseeching them to be fierce against their enemies, who had sworn and
avowed to make them prisoners to the King of England.

"But, will God, they shall fail of their purpose. Therefore set yourselves in order, every man to his own room, and let your guns and cross-
bows be ready. But above all, use the fire balls well in the tops of the
ships, and let us keep our overlofts with two-handed swords, and every
good fellow do and remember on the welfare of the realm, and his own
honour, and, will God, for my own part, I shall show you good example."

So he caused pierce the wine, and every man drank to other.

By this the sun began to rise and shine bright on the sails, so the English ships appeared very awful in the sight of the Scots, by reason their
ships were great and strong, and well furnished with great artillery. Yet
the Scots affeared nothing, but cast them to windward of the English,
who seeing that, shot two great cannons at the Scots, thinking that they
should have stricken sail at their boast. But the Scottishmen, nothing
affeared therewith, came stoutly forward upon the wind side, upon
Captain Stephen Bull, and clipped from hand, and fought there from the
rising of the sun, till the going down of the same, in the long summer's
day, till all the men and women that dwelt near the coast side, stood and
beheld the fighting, which was terrible to see. Yet notwithstanding the
night severed them, that they were forced to depart from each other till
the morn that the day began to break and their trumpets blew on either
side, and made them again to the battle, who clipped and fought so
cruelly that neither skippers nor mariners took heed of their ships, but

---

[1] Order of battle.

fighting still till the ebb tide and south wind bore them to Inchcape, fornent the mouth of Tay.

The Scottishmen seeing this, they took such courage and hardiment, that they doubled on the strokes on the Englishmen, and there took Stephen Bull and his three ships, and had them up to the town of Dundee, and there remained till their hurt men were cured, and the dead buried; and thereafter took Stephen Bull, and had him to the King's Grace as a prisoner. And the King received him gladly, and thanked Sir Andrew Wood greatly, and rewarded him richly for his labours, and great proof of his manhood, and thereafter propyned the English Captain richly, and all his men, and sent them all safely home, their ships, and all their furnishing, because they had shown themselves so stout and hardy warriors.

So he sent them all back to the King of England, to let him understand that he had as manly men in Scotland as he had in England; therefore desired him to send no more of his Captains in time coming. But the King of England hearing of their news, was discontented, when as his men said to him, that the King of Scotland said to them, if they came again in such form to perturb his coasts, that it might be they would not be so well entertained, no loup home so dry shod. Always the King of England accounted himself obleist to the King of Scotland, for the safe deliverance of his men, and entertaining of them.

THE WORLD ENCOMPASSED BY SIR FRANCIS DRAKE[1]

Richard Hakluyt

(1553–1616)

THE 15. day of November, in the yeere of our Lord 1577. M. Francis Drake, with a fleete of five ships and barkes, and to the number of 164 men, gentlemen and sailers, departed from Plimmouth, giving out his pretended voyage for Alexandria: but the wind falling contrary, hee was forced the next morning to put into Falmouth haven in Cornewall, where such and so terrible a tempest tooke us, as few men have seene the like, and was in deed so vehement, that all our ships were like to have gone to wracke: but it pleased God to preserve us from that extremitie, and to afflict us onely for that present with these two particulars: The mast of our Admirall which was the *Pellican*, was cut over boord for the safegard of the ship, and the *Marigold* was driven ashore, and somewhat bruised: for the repairing of which damages wee returned againe to Plimmouth, and having recovered those harmes, and brought the ships againe to good state, we set forth the second time from Plimmouth, and set saile the 13. day of December following.

[1]From *The Principal Navigations, Voyages and Discoveries of the English Nation.*

The 25. day of the same moneth we fell with the Cape Cantin, upon the coast of Barbarie, and coasting along, the 27. day we found an Island called Mogador, lying one mile distant from the maine, betweene which Island and the maine, we found a very good and safe harbour for our ships to ride in, as also very good entrance, and voyde of any danger.

On this Island our Generall erected a pinnesse, whereof he brought out of England with him foure already framed.

Our pinnesse being finished, wee departed from this place the 30. and last day of December, and coasting along the shore, wee did descrie, not contrary to our expectation, certaine Canters which were Spanish fishermen, to whom we gave chase and tooke three of them, and proceeding further we met with 3. Caravels and tooke them also.

The 17. day of January we arrived at Cape Blanco, where we found a ship riding at anchor, within the Cape, and but two simple Mariners in her, which ship we tooke and caried her further into the harbour, where we remained 4. dayes, and in that space our General mustered, and trayned his men on land in warlike maner, to make them fit for all occasions.

In this place we tooke of the Fishermen such necessaries as wee wanted, and they could yeeld us, and leaving heere one of our litle barkes called the *Benedict*, wee tooke with us one of theirs which they called Canters, being of the burden of 40. tunnes or thereabouts.

All these things being finished, wee departed this harbour the 22. of Januarie, carying along with us one of the Portugall Caravels which was bound to the Islands of Cape Verde for salt, whereof good store is made in one of those Islands.

The master or Pilot of that Caravel did advertise our Generall that upon one of those Islands called Mayo, there was great store of dryed Cabritos, which a few inhabitants there dwelling did yeerly make ready for such of the kings Ships as did there touch, beeing bound for his countrey of Brasile or elsewhere. Wee fell with this Island the 27. of January, but the Inhabitants would in no case traffique with us, being thereof forbidden by the kings Edict: yet the next day our Generall sent to view the Island, and the likelihoodes that might be there of provision of victuals, about threescore and two men under the conduct and government of Master Winter and Master Doughtie, and having travailed to the mountaines the space of three miles, and arriving there somewhat before the day breake, we arrested our selves to see day before us, which appearing, we found the inhabitants to be fled: but the place, by reason that it was manured, wee found to be more fruitfull then the other part, especially the valleys among the hills.

Here we gave our selves a litle refreshing, as by very ripe and sweete grapes, which the fruitfulnesse of the earth at that season of the yeere yeelded us: and that season being with us the depth of Winter, it may seeme strange that those fruites were then there growing.

Being returned to our ships, our Generall departed hence the 31. of this moneth, and sayled by the Island of S. Iago, but farre enough from the danger of the inhabitants, who shot and discharged at us three peeces, but they all fell short of us, and did us no harme.

Being before this Island, we espied two ships under sayle, to the one of which wee gave chase, and in the end boorded her with a ship-boat without resistance, which we found to be a good prize, and she yeelded unto us good store of wine: which prize our Generall committed to the custodie of Master Doughtie, and reteining the Pilot, sent the rest away with his Pinnesse, giving them a Butte of wine and some victuals, and their wearing clothes, and so they departed.

The same night wee came with the Island called by the Portugals, Ilha del Fogo, that is, the burning Island: in the North side whereof is a consuming fire, the matter is sayde to be of Sulphure, but notwithstanding it is like to bee a commodious Island, because the Portugals have built, and doe inhabite there.

Upon the South side thereof lyeth a most pleasant and sweete Island, the trees whereof are always greene and faire to looke upon, in respect whereof they call it Ilha Brava, that is, the brave Island. From the bankes thereof into the sea doe run in many places reasonable streames of fresh waters easie to be come by, but there was no convenient roade for our ships: for such was the depth, that no ground could bee had for anchoring, and it is reported, that ground was never found in that place, so that the tops of Fogo burne not so high in the ayre, but the rootes of Brava are quenched as low in the sea.

Being departed from these Islands, we drew towards the line, where wee were becalmed the space of 3. weekes, but yet subject to divers great stormes, terrible lightnings and much thunder: but with this miserie we had the commoditie of great store of fish, as Dolphins, Bonitos, and flying fishes, whereof some fell into our shippes, wherehence they could not rise againe for want of moisture, for when their wings are drie, they cannot flie.

From the first day of our departure from the Islands of Cape Verde, wee sayled 54. dayes without sight of land, and the first land that we fell with was the coast of Brasil, which we saw the fift of April in ye height of 33. degrees towards the pole Antarctike, and being discovered at sea by the inhabitants of the countrey, they made upon the coast great fires for a sacrifice (as we learned) to the devils, about which they use conjurations, making heapes of sande and other ceremonies, that when any ship shall goe about to stay upon their coast, not onely sands may be gathered together in shoalds in every place, but also that stormes and tempests may arise, to the casting away of ships and men.

The seventh day in a mightie great storme both of lightning, rayne, and thunder, wee lost the Canter which we called the *Christopher:* but the eleventh day after, by our Generalls great care in dispersing his ships, we found her againe, and the place where we met, our Generall called the Cape of Joy, where every ship tooke in some water. Heere we found a good temperature and sweete ayre, a very faire and pleasant countrey with an exceeding fruitfull soyle, where were great store of large and mightie Deere, but we came not to the sight of any people: but traveiling further into the countrey, we perceived the footing of people in the clay-ground, shewing that they were men of great stature. Being returned to our ships, we wayed anchor, and ranne somewhat further, and harboured our selves betweene a rocke and the maine, where by meanes of the rocke that brake the force of the sea, we rid very safe, and upon this rocke we killed for our provision certaine sea-wolves, commonly called with us Seales,

From hence we went our course to 36. degrees, and entred the great river of Plate, and ranne into 54. and 55. fadomes and a halfe of fresh water, where wee filled our water by the ships side: but the Generall finding here no good harborough, as he thought he should, bare out againe to sea the 27. of April, and in bearing out we lost sight of our Flieboate wherein master Doughtie was, but we sayling along, found a fayre and reasonable good Bay wherein were many, and the same profitable Islands, one whereof had so many Seales, as would at the least have laden all our Shippes, and the rest of the Islands are as it were laden with foules which is wonderfull to see, and they of divers sortes. It is a place very plentifull of victuals, and hath in it no want of fresh water.

The eighteenth day of May our Generall thought it needfull to have a care of such Ships as were absent, and therefore indevouring to seeke the Flieboate wherein master Doughtie was, we espied her againe the next day: and whereas certaine of our ships were sent to discover the coast and to search an harbour, the *Marygold* and the Canter being imployed in that businesse, came unto us and gave us understanding of a safe harbour that they had found, wherewith all our ships bare, and entred it.

Heere our Generall in the Admiral, rid close aboord the Flieboate, and tooke out of her all the provision of victuals and what else was in her, and halling her to the Lande, set fire to her, and so burnt her to save the iron worke: which being a doing, there came downe of the countrey certaine of the people naked, saving only about their waste the skinne of some beast with the furre or haire on, and every man his bow which was an ell in length, and a couple of arrowes. These people would not of a long time receive any thing at our handes: yet at length our Generall being ashore, and they dauncing after their accustomed manner about him, and hee once turning his backe towards them, one leapt suddenly to him, and tooke his cap with his golde band off his head, and ran a litle distance from him and shared it with his fellow, the cap to the one, and the band to the other.

Having dispatched all our businesse in this place, wee departed and set sayle, and immediately upon our setting foorth we lost our Canter which was absent three or foure dayes: but when our General had her againe, he tooke out the necessaries, and so gave her over neere to the Cape of Good Hope.

The next day after being the twentieth of June, wee harboured our selves againe in a very good harborough, called by Magellan Port S. Julian, where we found a gibbet standing upon the maine, which we supposed to be the place where Magellan did execution upon some of his disobedient and rebellious company.

In this Port our Generall began to enquire diligently of the actions of M. Thomas Doughtie, and found them not to be such as he looked for, but tending rather to contention or mutinie, or some other disorder, whereby (without redresse) the successe of the voyage might greatly have bene hazarded: whereupon the company was called together and made acquainted with the particulars of the cause, which were found partly by master Doughties owne confession, and partly by the evidence of the fact, to be true: which when our Generall saw, although his private affection to M. Doughtie (as hee then in the presence of us all sacredly protested) was great, yet the care he had of the state of the voyage, of the expectation of her Majestie, and of the honour of his countrey did more touch him, (as indeede it ought) then the private respect of one man: so that the cause being throughly heard, and all things done in good order as neere as might be to the course of our lawes in England, it was concluded that M. Doughtie should receive punishment according to the qualitie of the offence: and he seeing no remedie but patience for himselfe, desired before his death to receive the Communion, which he did at the hands of M. Fletcher our Minister, and our Generall himselfe accompanied him in that holy action: which being done, and the place of execution made ready, hee having embraced our Generall and taken his leave of all the companie, with prayer for the Queenes majestie and our realme, in quiet sort laid his head to the blocke, where he ended his life.

The 17. day of August we departed the port of S. Julian, and the 20. day we fell with the streight or freat of Magellan going into the South Sea, at the Cape or headland whereof we found the body of a dead man, whose flesh was cleane consumed.

The 21. day we entred the streight, which we found to have many turnings, and as it were shuttings up, as if there were no passage at all, by meanes whereof we had the wind often against us, so that some of the fleete recovering a Cape or point of land, others should be forced to turne backe againe, and to come to an anchor where they could.

This streight is extreme cold, with frost and snow continually: the trees seeme to stoope with the burden of the weather, and yet are greene continually, and many good and sweete herbes doe very plentifully grow and increase under them. The bredth of the streight is in some place a league, in some other places 2 leagues, and 3 leagues, and in some other 4 leagues, but the narrowest place hath a league over.

The 6. day of September we entred the South sea at the Cape or head shore.

The seventh day we were driven by a great storme from the entring into the South sea two hundred leagues and odde in longitude, and one degree to the Southward of the Streight: in which height, and so many leagues to the Westward, the fifteenth day of September fell out the Eclipse of the Moone at the houre of sixe of the clocke at night: but neither did the Eclipticall conflict of the Moone impayre our state, nor her clearing againe amend us a whit, but the accustomed Eclipse of the Sea continued in his force, wee being darkened more then the Moone seven fold.

From the Bay (which we called The Bay of severing of friends) wee were driven backe to the Southward of the streights in 57. degrees and a terce: in which height we came to an anker among the Islands, having there fresh and very good water, with herbes of singular vertue. Not farre from hence we entred another Bay, where wee found people both men and women in their Canoas, naked, and ranging from one Island to another to seeke their meat, who entered traffique with us for such things as they had.

We returning hence Northward againe, found the 3. of October three Islands, in one of which was such plentie of birdes as is scant credible to report.

The 8. day of October we lost sight of one of our Consorts wherein M. Winter was, who as then we supposed was put by a storme into the streights againe, which at our returne home wee found to be true, and he not perished, as some of our company feared.

Thus being come into the height of the streights againe, we ran, supposing the coast of Chili to lie as the generall Maps have described it, namely Northwest, which we found to lie and trend to the Northeast and Eastwards, whereby it appeareth that this part of Chili hath not bene truely hitherto discovered, or at the least not truely reported for the space of 12. degrees at the least, being set downe either of purpose to deceive, or of ignorant conjecture.

We continuing our course, fell the 29. of November with an Island called la Mocha, where we cast anchor, and our Generall hoysing out our boate, went with ten of our company to shore, where wee found people, whom the cruell and extreme dealings of the Spaniards have forced for their owne safetie and libertie to flee from the maine, and to fortifie themselves in this Island. We being on land, the people came downe to us to the water side with shew of great courtesie, bringing to us potatoes, rootes, and two very fat sheepe, which our Generall received and gave them other things for them, and had promise to have water there: but the next day repayring againe to the shore, and sending two men aland with barrels to fill water, the people taking them for Spaniards (to whom they use to shew no favour if they take them) layde violent hands on them, and as we thinke, slew them.

Our Generall seeing this, stayed here no longer, but wayed anchor, and set sayle towards the coast of Chili, and drawing towards it, we mette neere to the shore an Indian in a Canoa, who thinking us to have bene Spaniards, came to us and tolde us, that at a place called S. Iago, there was a great Spanish ship laden from the kingdome of Peru: for which good newes our Generall gave him divers trifles, wherof he was glad, and went along with us and brought us to the place, which is called the port of Valparizo.

When we came thither, we found indeede the ship riding at anker, having in her eight Spaniards and three Negroes, who thinking us to have bene Spaniards and their friends, welcommed us with a drumme, and made ready a Bottija of wine of Chili to drinke to us: but as soone as we were entred, one of our company called Thomas Moone began to lay about him, and strooke one of the Spanyards, and sayd unto him, Abaxo Perro, that is in English, Goe downe dogge. One of these Spaniards seeing persons of that quality in those seas, all to crossed, and blessed himselfe: but to be short, wee stowed them under hatches all save one Spaniard, who suddenly and desperately leapt over boord into the sea, and swamme ashore to the towne of S. Iago, to give them warning of our arrivall.

They of the towne being not above 9. housholds, presently fled away and abandoned the towne. Our generall manned his boate, and the Spanish ships boate, and went to the Towne, and being come to it, we rifled it, and so being come aboord, we departed the Haven, having first set all the Spaniards on land, saving one John Griego a Greeke borne, whom our Generall caried with him for his Pilot to bring him into the haven of Lima.

When we were at sea, our Generall rifled the ship, and found in her good store of the wine of Chili, and 25000. pezoes of very pure and fine gold of Baldivia, amounting in value to 37000 ducats of Spanish money, and above. So going on our course, wee arrived next at a place called Coquimbo, where our Generall sent 14. of his men on land to fetch water: but they were espied by the Spaniards, who came with 300. horsemen and 200. footemen, and slewe one of our men with a piece, the rest came aboord in safetie, and the Spaniards departed: wee went on shore againe, and buried our man, and the Spaniards came down againe with a flag of truce, but we set sayle and would not trust them.

From hence we went to a certaine port called Tarapaza, where being landed, we found by the Sea side a Spaniard lying asleepe, who had lying by him 13 barres of silver, which weighed 4000. ducats Spanish; we tooke the silver, and left the man.

Not farre from hence going on land for fresh water, we met with a

Spaniard and an Indian boy driving 8. Llamas or sheepe of Peru which are as big as asses; every of which sheepe had on his backe 2. bags of leather. each bagge conteining 50. li. weight of fine silver: so that bringing both the sheepe and their burthen to the ships, we found in all the bags 800. weight of silver.

Here hence we sailed to a place called Arica, and being entred the port, we found there three small barkes which we rifled, and found in one of them 57 wedges of silver, each of them weighing about 20 pound weight, and every of these wedges were of the fashion and bignesse of a brickbat. In all these 3. barkes we found not one person: for they mistrusting no strangers, were all gone aland to the Towne, which consisteth of about twentie houses, which we would have ransacked if our company had bene better and more in number. But our Generall contented with the spoyle of the ships, left the Towne and put off againe to sea and set sayle for Lima, and by the way met with a small barke, which he boorded, and found in her good store of linnen cloth, whereof taking some quantitie, he let her goe.

To Lima we came the 13. day of February, and being entred the haven, we found there about twelve sayle of ships lying fast moored at an anker, having all their sayles caried on shore; for the masters and marchants were here most secure, having never bene assaulted by enemies, and at this time feared the approch of none such as we were. Our generall rifled these ships, and found in one of them a chest full of royals of plate, and good store of silkes and linnen cloth, and tooke the chest into his owne ship, and good store of the silkes and linnen. In which ship hee had newes of another ship called the *Cacafuego* which was gone towards Paita, and that the same shippe was laden with treasure: whereupon we staied no longer here, but cutting all the cables of the shippes in the haven, we let them drive whither they would, either to sea or to the shore, and with all speede we followed the *Cacafuego* toward Paita, thinking there to have found her: but before wee arrived there, she was gone from thence towards Panama, whom our Generall still pursued, and by the way met with a barke laden with ropes and tackle for ships, which he boorded and searched, and found in her 80 li. weight of golde, and a crucifixe of gold with goodly great Emerauds set in it which he tooke, and some of the cordage also for his owne ship.

From hence we departed, still following the *Cacafuego*, and our Generall promised our company, that whosoever could first descrie her, should have his chaine of gold for his good news. It fortuned that John Drake going up into the top, descried her about three of the clocke, and about sixe of the clocke we came to her and boorded her, and shotte at her three peeces of ordinance, and strake down her Misen, and being entered, we found in her great riches, as jewels and precious stones, thirteene chests full of royals of plate, foure score pound weight of golde, and sixe and twentie tunne of silver. The place where we tooke this prize, was called Cape de San Francisco, about 150. leagues from Panama.

The Pilots name of this Shippe was Francisco, and amongst other plate that our Generall found in this ship, he found two very faire guilt bowles of silver, which were the Pilots: to whom our Generall sayd: Senior Pilot, you have here two silver cups, but I must needes have one of them: which the Pilot because hee could not otherwise chuse, yeelded unto, and gave the other to the steward of our Generals ships.

When this Pilot departed from us, his boy sayde thus unto our Generall: Captaine, our ship shall be called no more the *Cacafuego*, but the *Cacaplata*, and your shippe shall bee called the *Cacafuego*: which pretie speach of the Pilots boy ministred matter of laughter to us, both then and long after.

When our Generall had done what hee would with this *Cacafuego*, hee cast her off, and wee went on our course still towards the West, and not long after met with a ship laden with linnen cloth and fine China-dishes of white earth, and great store of China-silks, of all which things wee tooke as we listed.

The owner himselfe of this ship was in her, who was a Spanish Gentleman, from whom our Generall tooke a Fawlcon of golde, with a great Emeraud in the breast thereof, and the Pilot of the ship he tooke also with him, and so cast the ship off.

This Pilot brought us to the haven of Guatulco, the towne whereof, as he told us, had but 17. Spaniards in it. As soone as we were entred this haven, wee landed, and went presently to the Towne, and to the Townehouse, where we found a Judge sitting in judgement, being associate with three other officers, upon three Negros that had conspired the burning of the Towne: both which Judges and prisoners we tooke, and brought them a shipboord, and caused the chief Judge to write his letter to the Towne, to command all the Townesmen to avoid, that we might safely water there. Which being done, and they departed, we ransacked the Towne, and in one house we found a pot of the quantitie of a bushell, full of reals of plate, which we brought to our ship.

And here one Thomas Moone one of our company, tooke a Spanish Gentleman as hee was flying out of the towne, and searching him, he found a chaine of golde about him, and other jewels, which he tooke, and so let him goe.

At this place our Generall among other Spaniards, set ashore his Portugall Pilote, which hee tooke at the Islands of Cape Verde, out of a ship of S. Mary port of Portugall: and having set them ashore, we departed hence, and sailed to the Island of Canno, where our Generall landed, and brought to shore his owne ship, and discharged her, mended, and graved her, and furnished our ship with water and wood sufficiently.

And while wee were here, we espied a shippe, and set saile after her, and tooke her, and found in her two Pilots, and a Spanish Governour, going for the Islands of the Philippinas: wee searched the shippe, and tooke some of her marchandizes, and so let her goe. Our Generall at this place and time, thinking himself both in respect of his private injuries received from the Spaniards, as also of their contempts and indignities offered to our countrey and Prince in generall, sufficiently satisfied, and revenged: and supposing that her Majestie at his returne would rest contented with this service, purposed to continue no longer upon the Spanish coasts, but began to consider and to consult of the best way for his Countrey.

He thought it not good to returne by the Streights, for two speciall causes: the one, lest the Spaniards should there waite, and attend for him in great number and strength, whose hands, hee being left but one ship, could not possibly escape. The other cause was the dangerous situation of the mouth of the streights in the South sea, where continuall stormes reigning and blustering, as he found by experience, besides the shoalds and sands upon the coast, he thought it not a good course to adventure that way: he resolved therefore to avoyde these hazards, to goe forward to the Islandes of the Malucos, and therehence to saile the course of the Portugals by the Cape of Buena Esperanza.

Upon this resolution, hee beganne to thinke of his best way to the Malucos, and finding himselfe where he now was becalmed, he saw that of necessitie hee must be forced to take a Spanish course, namely to sayle somewhat Northerly to get a winde. Wee therefore set saile, and sayled 600. leagues at the least for a winde, and thus much we sailed from the 16. of April, till the 3. of June.

The 5. day of June, being in 43. degrees towards the pole Arcticke, we found the ayre so colde, that our men being grievously pinched with the same, complained of the extremitie thereof, and the further we went, the more the colde increased upon us. Whereupon we thought it best for that time to seeke the land, and did so, finding it not mountainous, but low plaine land, till wee came within 38. degrees towards the line. In which height it pleased God to send us into a faire and good Baye, with a good winde to enter the same.

In this Baye wee anchored, and the people of the Countrey having their houses close by the waters side, shewed themselves unto us, and sent a present to our Generall.

When they came unto us, they greatly wondred at the things that wee brought, but our Generall (according to his naturall and accustomed humanitie) courteously intreated them, and liberally bestowed on them necessary things to cover their nakednesse, whereupon they supposed us to be gods, and would not be perswaded to the contrary: the presents which they sent to our Generall were feathers, and calles of net-worke.

Our Generall called this Countrey Nova Albion, and that for two causes: the one in respect of the white bankes and cliffes, which lie towards the sea: and the other, because it might have some affinitie with our Countrey in name, which sometime was so called.

At our departure hence our Generall set up a monument of our being there, as also of her Majesties right and title to the same, namely a plate, nailed upon a faire great poste, whereupon was ingraven her Majesties name, the day and yeere of our arrivall there, with the free giving up of the province and people into her Majesties hands, together with her hignesse picture and armes, in a peece of sixe pence of current English money under the plate, whereunder was also written the name of our Generall.

It seemeth that the Spaniards hitherto had never bene in this part of the Countrey, neither did ever discover the land by many degrees, to the Southwards of this place.

After we had set saile from hence, wee continued without sight of land till the 13. day of October following, which day in the morning wee fell with certaine Islands 8. degrees to the Northward of the line, from which Islands came a great number of Canoas, having in some of them 4. in some 6. and in some also 14. men, bringing with them cocos, and other fruites. Their Canoas were hollow within, and cut with great arte and cunning, being very smooth within and without, and bearing a glasse as it were a horne daintily burnished, having a prowe, and a sterne of one sort, yeelding inward circle-wise, being of a great height, and full of certaine white shels for a braverie, and on each side of them lie out two peeces of timber about a yard and a halfe long, more or lesse, according to the smalnesse, or bignesse of the boate.

Leaving this Island the night after we fell with it, the 18. of October, we lighted upon divers others, some whereof made a great shew of Inhabitants.

Wee continued our course by the Islands of Tagulada, Zelon, and Zewarra, being friends to the Portugals, the first whereof hath growing in it great store of Cinnamom.

The 14. of November we fell with the Islands of Maluco, which day at night (having directed our course to runne with Tydore) in coasting along the Island of Mutyr, belonging to the King of Ternate, his Deputie or Vice-king seeing us at sea, came with his Canoa to us without all feare, and came aboord, and after some conference with our Generall, willed him in any wise to runne in with Ternate, and not with Tydore, assuring him that the King would bee glad of his comming, and would be ready to doe what he would require, for which purpose he himselfe would that night be with the King, and tell him the newes, with whom if he once dealt, hee should finde that as he was a King, so his word should stand: adding further, that if he went to Tydore before he came to Ternate, the King would have nothing to doe with us, because hee held the Portugall as his enemie: whereupon our General resolved to runne with Ternate, where the next morning early we came to anchor, at which time our Generall sent a messenger to the king with a velvet cloke for a present, and token of his comming to be in peace, and that he required nothing but traffique and exchange of marchandize, whereof he had good store, in such things as he wanted.

In the meane time the Vice-king had bene with the king according to his promise, signifying unto him what good things he might receive from us by traffique: whereby the King was mooved with great liking towards us, and sent to our Generall with speciall message, that hee should have what things he needed, and would requite with peace and friendship, and moreover that hee would yeeld himselfe, and the right of his Island to bee at the pleasure and commandement of so famous a Prince as we served. In token whereof he sent to our Generall a signet, and within short time after came in his owne person, with boates, and Canoas to our ship, to bring her into a better and safer roade then she was in at present.

After that we had heere by the favour of the king received all necessary things that the place could yeeld us: our General considering the great distance, and how farre he was yet off from his Countrey, thought it not best here to linger the time any longer, but waying his anchors, set out of the Island, and sayled to a certaine litle Island to the Southwards of Celebes, where we graved our ship, and continued there in that and other businesses 26. dayes. This Island is throughly growen with wood of a large and high growth, very straight and without boughes, save onely in the head or top, whose leaves are not much differing from our broome in England. Amongst these trees night by night, through the whole land, did shew themselves an infinite swarme of fiery wormes flying in the ayre, whose bodies beeing no bigger then our common English flies, make such a shew and light, as if every twigge or tree had bene a burning candle.

When wee had ended our businesse here, we waied, and set saile to runne for the Malucos: but having at that time a bad winde, and being amongst the Islands, with much difficultie wee recovered to the North-ward of the Island of Celebes, where by reason of contrary winds not able to continue our course to runne Westwards, we were inforced to alter the same to the Southward againe, finding that course also to be very hard and dangerous for us, by reason of infinite shoalds which lie off, and among the Islands: whereof wee had too much triall to the hazard and danger of our shippe and lives. For of all other dayes upon the 9. of Januarie, in the yeere 1579, wee ranne suddenly upon a rocke, where we stucke fast from 8. of the clocke at night til 4. of the clocke in the afternoone the next day, being indeede out of all hope to escape the danger: but our Generall as hee had alwayes hitherto shewed himself couragious, and of a good confidence in the mercie and protection of God: so now he continued in the same, and lest he should seeme to perish wilfully, both he, and we did our best indevour to save our selves, which it pleased God so to blesse, that in the ende we cleared our selves most happily of the danger.

We lighted our ship upon the rockes of 3. tunne of cloves, 8. peeces of ordinance, and certaine meale and beanes; and then the winde (as it were in a moment by the speciall grace of God) changing from the starreboord to the larboord of the ship, we hoised our sailes, and the happy gale drove our ship off the rocke into the sea againe, to the no litle comfort of all our hearts, for which we gave God such prayse and thanks, as so great a benefite required.

The 8. of Februarie following, wee fell with the fruitfull Island of Barateve, having in the meane time suffered many dangers by windes and shoalds. The people of this Island are comely in body and stature, and of a civill behaviour, just in dealing, and courteous to strangers, whereof we had the experience sundry wayes, they being most glad of our presence, and very ready to releeve our wants in those things which their Countrey did yeelde.

At our departure from Barateve, we set our course for Java Major, where arriving, we found great courtesie, and honourable entertainment. This Island is governed by 5. Kings, whom they call Rajah: as Rajah Donaw, and Rajah Mang Bange, and Rajah Cabuccapollo, which live as having one spirite and one minde.

Of these five we had foure a shipboord at once, and two or three often. They are wonderfully delighted in coloured clothes, as red and greene: their upper parts of their bodies are naked, save their heads, whereupon they weare a Turkish roll as do the Maluccians: from the middle downward they weare a pintado of silke, trailing upon the ground, in colour as they best like. Not long before our departure, they tolde us, that not farre off there were such great Ships as ours, wishing us to beware: upon this our Captaine would stay no longer.

From Java Major we sailed for the cape of Good Hope, which was the first land we fell withall: neither did we touch with it, or any other land, untill we came to Sierra Leona, upon the coast of Guinea; notwithstanding we ranne hard aboord the Cape, finding the report of the Portugals to be most false, who affirme, that it is the most dangerous Cape of the world, never without intolerable stormes and present danger to travailers, which come neere the same.

This Cape is a most stately thing, and the fairest Cape we saw in the whole circumference of the earth, and we passed by it the 18. of June.

From thence we continued our course to Sierra Leona, on the coast of Guinea, where we arrived the 22. of July, and found necessarie provisions, great store of Elephants, Oisters upon trees of one kind, spawning and increasing infinitely, the Oister suffering no budde to grow. We departed thence the 24. day.

We arrived in England the third of November 1580, being the third yeere of our departure.

THE DEATH OF SIR HUMFREY GILBERT[1]

Edward Haie

UPON Tewsday the 27 of August, toward the evening, our Generall caused them in his frigat to sound, who found white sande at 35 fadome, being then in latitude about 44 degrees.

Wednesday toward night the wind came South, and wee bare with the land all that night, Westnorthwest, contrary to the mind of master Cox: nevertheless wee followed the Admirall, deprived of power to prevent a mischiefe, which by no contradiction could be brought to hold other course, alleaging they could not make the ship to worke better, nor to lie otherwaies.

The evening was faire and pleasant, yet not without token of storme to ensue, and most part of this Wednesday night, like the Swanne that singeth before her death, they in the Admiral, or *Delight*, continued in sounding of Trumpets, with Drummes, and Fifes: also winding the Cornets Haughtboyes: and in the end of their jolitie, left with the battell and ringing of dolefull knels.

Towards the evening also we caught in the *Golden Hinde* a very mighty Porpose, with a harping yron, having first striken divers of them, and brought away part of their flesh, sticking upon the yron, but could recover onely that one. These also passing through the Ocean, in heardes, did portend Storme. I omit to recite frivolous reportes by them in the Frigat, of strange voyces, the same night, which scarred some from the helme.

Thursday, the 29 of August, the wind rose, and blew vehemently at South and by East, bringing withal raine, and thicke mist, so that we could not see a cable length before us. And betimes in the morning we were altogether runne and folded in amongst flats and sands, amongst which we found shoale and deepe in every three or foure shippes length, after wee began to sound: but first we were upon them unawares, untill master Cox looking out, discerned (in his judgement) white cliffes, crying land withall, though we could not afterward descrie any land, it being very likely the breaking of the sea white, which seemed to be white cliffes, through the haze and thicke weather.

Immediately tokens were given unto the *Delight*, to cast about to seaward, which, being the greater ship, and of burden 120 tunnes, was yet formost upon the breach, keeping so ill watch, that they knew not the danger, before they felt the same, too late to recover it: for presently the Admirall strooke a ground, and had soone after her sterne and hinder partes beaten in pieces: whereupon the rest (that is to say, the Frigat in

---

[1]From Hakluyt's *Voyages*.

which was the Generall and the *Golden Hinde*) cast about Eastsoutheast, bearing to the South, even for our lives into the windes eye, because that way caried us to the seaward. Making out from this danger, wee sounded one while seven fadome, then five fadome, then foure fadome and lesse, againe deeper, immediately foure fadome, then but three fadome, the sea going mightily and high. At last we recovered (God be thanked) in some despaire, to sea roome enough.

In this distresse wee had vigilant eye unto the Admirall, whom wee sawe cast away, without power to give the men succour, neither could we espie any of the men that leaped overboord to save themselves, either in the same Pinnesse or Cocke, or upon rafters, and such like meanes, presenting themselves to men in those extremities: for we desired to save the men by every possible meanes. But all in vaine, sith God had determined their ruine: yet all that day, and part of the next, we beat up and downe as neere unto wracke as was possible for us, looking out, if by goodhap we might espie any of them.

After this heavie chance, we continued in beating the sea up and downe, expecting when the weather would cleere up, that we might yet beare in with the land, which we judged not farre off, either the continent or some Island. For we many times, and in sundry places found ground at 50, 45, 40 fadomes, and lesse. The ground comming upon our lead, being sometimes oozie sand, and otherwhile a broad shall, with a little sand about it.

Our people lost courage dayly after this ill successe, the weather continuing thicke and blustering, with increase of cold. Winter drawing on, which tooke from them all hope of amendement, setling an assurance of worse weather to growe upon us every day. The Leeside of us lay full of flats and dangers inevitable, if the wind blew hard at South. Some againe doubted we were ingulfed in the Bay of S. Laurence, the coast full of dangers, and unto us unknowen. But above all, provision waxed scant, and hope of supply was gone, with losse of our Admirall.

Those in the Frigat were already pinched with spare allowance, and want of clothes chiefly: Whereupon they besought the Generall to returne for England, before they all perished. And to them of the *Golden Hinde*, they made signes of their distresse, pointing to their mouthes, and to their clothes thinne and ragged: then immediately they also of the *Golden Hinde*, grew to be of the same opinion and desire to returne home.

The former reasons having also moved the Generall to have compassion of his poore men, in whom he saw no want of good will, but of meanes fit to performe the action they came for, resolved upon retire: and calling the Captaine and Master of the *Hinde*, he yeelded them many reasons, inforcing this unexpected returne, withall protesting himselfe, greatly satisfied with that hee had seene, and knew already.

Reiterating these words, Be content, we have seene enough, and take no care of expence past: I will set you foorth royally the next Spring, if God send us safe home. Therefore I pray you let us no longer strive here, where we fight against the elements.

Omitting circumstance, how unwillingly the Captaine and Master of the *Hinde* condescended to this motion, his owne company can testifie: yet comforted with the Generals promises of a speedie returne at Spring, and induced by other apparent reasons, proving an impossibilitie, to accomplish the action at that time, it was concluded on all hands to retire.

So upon Saturday in the afternoone the 31 of August, we changed our course, and returned backe for England, at which very instant, even in winding about, there passed along betweene us and towards the land which we now forsooke a very lion to our seeming, in shape, hair and colour, not swimming after the maner of a beast by mooving of his feete, but rather sliding upon the water with his whole body (excepting the legs) in sight, neither yet diving under, and againe rising above the water, as the maner is of Whales, Dolphins, Tunise, Porposes, and all other fish: but confidently shewing himselfe above water without hiding: Notwithstanding, we presented ourselves in open view and gesture to amase him, as all creatures will be commonly at a sudden gaze and sight of men. Thus he passed along turning his head to and fro, yawning, and gaping wide, with ougly demonstration of long teeth, and glaring eies, and to bidde us a farewell (comming right against the *Hinde*) he sent forth a horrible voyce, roaring or bellowing as doeth a lion, which spectacle wee all beheld so farre as we were able to discerne the same, as men prone to wonder at every strange thing, as this doubtlesse was, to see a lion in the Ocean sea, or fish in shape of a lion. What opinion others had thereof, and chiefly the Generall himselfe, I forbeare to deliver: But he tooke it for Bonum Omen, rejoycing that he was to warre against such an enemie, if it were the devill.

The wind was large for England at our returne, but very high, and the sea rough, insomuch as the Frigat wherein the Generall went was almost swalowed up.

Munday in the afternoone we passed in the sight of Cape Race, having made as much way in little more then two dayes and nights backe againe, as before wee had done in eight dayes from Cape Race, unto the place where our ship perished. Which hindrance thitherward, and speed back againe, is to be imputed unto the swift current, as well as to the winds, which we had more large in our returne.

This munday the Generall came aboord the *Hind* to have the Surgeon of the *Hind* to dresse his foote, which he hurt by treading upon a naile; At what time we comforted ech other with hope of hard successe to be all past, and of the good to come. So agreeing to cary out lights alwayes by night, that we might keepe together, he departed into his frigat, being by no meanes to be intreated to tarie in the *Hind*, which had bene more for his security. Immediately after followed a sharpe storme, which we overpassed for that time. Praysed be God.

The weather faire, the Generall came aboord the *Hind* againe, to make merrie together with the Captaine, Master, and company, which was the last meeting, and continued there from morning untill night. During which time there passed sundry discourses, touching affaires past, and to come, lamenting greatly the losse of his great ship, more of the men, but most of all of his bookes and notes, and what els I know not, for which hee was out of measure grieved, the same doubtles being some matter of more importance then his bookes, which I could not draw from him: yet by circumstance I gathered, the same to be ye Ore which Daniel the Saxon had brought unto him in the New found land. Whatsoever it was, the remembrance touched him so deepe, as not able to contain himselfe, he beat his boy in great rage, even at the same time, so long after the miscarying of the great ship, because upon a faire day, when wee were be-calmed upon the coast of the New found land, neere unto Cape Race, he sent his boy aboord the Admirall, to fetch certaine things: amongst which, this being chiefe, was yet forgotten and left behind. After which time he could never conveniently send againe aboord the great ship, much lesse hee doubted her ruine so neere at hand.

Herein my opinion was better confirmed diversly, and by sundry conjectures, which maketh me have the greater hope of this rich Mine. For where as the Generall had never before good conceit of these North parts of the world: now his mind was wholly fixed upon the New found land. And as before he refused not to grant assignements liberally to them that required the same into these North parts, now he became contrarily affected, refusing to make any so large grants, especially of S. Johns, which certaine English merchants made suite for.

Also laying downe his determination in the Spring following, for dis-posing of his voyage then to be reattempted: he assigned the Captaine and Master of the *Golden Hind*, unto the South discovery, and reserved unto himselfe the North, affirming that this voyage had wonne his heart from the South, and that he was now become a Northerne man alto-gether.

Last, being demanded what means he had at his arrivall in England, to compasse the charges of so great preparation as he intended to make the next Spring: having determined upon two fleetes, one for the South, an-other for the North: Leave that to mee (hee replied) I will aske a pennie of no man. I will bring good tidings unto her Majestie, who wil be so gracious, to lend me 10000 pounds, willing us therefore to be of good cheere: for he did thanke God (he sayd) with al his heart, for that he had seene, the same being enough for us all, and that we needed not to seeke any farther. And these last words he would often repeate, with demon-stration of great fervencie of mind, being himselfe very confident, and setled in beliefe of inestimable good by this voyage: which the greater number of his followers nevertheles mistrusted altogether, not being made partakers of those secrets, which the Generall kept unto himselfe.

Yet all of them that are living, may be witnesses of his words and pro-testations, which sparingly I have delivered.

Leaving the issue of this good hope unto God, who knoweth the trueth only, and can at his good pleasure bring the same to light: I will hasten to the end of this tragedie, which must be knit up in the person of our Generall. And as it was Gods ordinance upon him, even so the vehement perswasion and intreatie of his friends could nothing availe, to divert him from a wilfull resolution of going through in his Frigat, which was over-charged upon their deckes, with fights, nettings, and small artil-lerie, too cumbersome for so small a boate, that was to pass through the Ocean sea at that season of the yere, when by course we might expect much storme of foule weather, whereof indeed we had enough.

But when he was intreated by the Captaine, Master, and other his well wishers of the *Hinde,* not to venture in the Frigat, this was his answere: I will not forsake my little company going homeward, with whom I have passed so many stormes and perils. And in very trueth, hee was urged to be so over hard, by hard reports given of him, that he was afraid of the sea, albeit this was rather rashnes, then advised resolu-tion, to preferre the wind of a vaine report to the weight of his owne life.

Seeing he would not bend to reason, he had provision out of the *Hinde,* such as was wanting aboord his Frigat. And so we committed him to Gods protection, and set him aboord his Pinnesse, we being more than 300 leagues onward of our way home.

By that time we had brought the Islands of Açores South of us, yet wee then keeping much to the North, until we had got into the height and elevation of England: we met with very foule weather, and terrible seas, breaking short and high Pyramid wise. The reason whereof seemed to proceede either of hilly grounds high and low within the sea, (as we see hills and dales upon the land) upon which the seas do mount and fall: or else the cause proceedeth of diversitie of winds, shifting often in sundry points: al which having power to move the great Ocean, which againe is not presently setled, so many seas do encounter together, as there had bene diversitie of windes. Howsoever it commeth to passe, men which all their life time had occupied the Sea, never saw more outragious Seas. We had also upon our maine yard, an apparition of a little fire by night, which seamen doe call Castor and Pollux. But we had onely one, which they take an evill signe of more tempest: the same is usuall in stormes.

Munday the ninth of September, in the afternoone, the Frigat was neere cast away, oppressed by waves, yet at that time recovered: and giving foorth signes of joy, the Generall sitting abaft with a booke in his hand, cried out unto us in the *Hind* (so oft as we did approch within hearing): We are as neere to heaven by sea as by land. Reiterating the same speech, well beseeming a souldier, resolute in Jesus Christ, as I can testifie he was.

The same Munday night, about twelve of the clocke, or not long after, the Frigat being ahead of us in the *Golden Hinde*, suddenly her lights were out, whereof as it ere in a moment, we lost the sight, and withall our watch cryed, the Generall was cast away, which was too true. For in that moment, the Frigat was devoured and swallowed up of the Sea. Yet still we looked out all that night, and ever after, untill we arrived upon the coast of England: Omitting no small saile at sea, unto which we gave not the tokens betweene us, agreed upon, to have perfect knowledge of each other, if we should at any time be separated.

Thus have I delivered the contents of the enterprise and last action of sir Humfrey Gilbert knight, faithfully.

THE LAST FIGHT OF THE *REVENGE*

A REPORT OF THE TRUTH OF THE FIGHT ABOUT THE ACORES THIS LAST
SUMMER BETWIXT THE "REVENGE," ONE OF HER MAIESTIES
SHIPPES, AND AN ARMADA OF THE KING OF SPAINE[1]

Sir Walter Raleigh
(1552(?)–1618)

BECAUSE the rumours are diversely spred, as well in Englande as in the lowe countries and els where, of this late encounter between her maiesties ships and the Armada of Spain; and that the Spaniardes according to their usuall maner, fill the world with their vaine glorious vaunts, making great apparance of victories: when on the contrary, themselves are most commonly and shamefully beaten and dishonoured; thereby hoping to possesse the ignorant multitude by anticipating and forerunning false reports: It is agreeable with all good reason, for manifestation of the truth to overcome falsehood and untruth; that the beginning, continuance and successe of this late honourable encounter of Syr Richard Grinvile, and other her maiesties Captaines, with the Armada of Spaine; should be truely set downe and published without parialltie or false imaginations.

The L. Thomas Howard, with six of her Maiesties ships, six victualers of London, the barke *Ralegh*, and two or three Pinasses riding at anchor nere unto Flores, one of the Westerlie Islands of the Azores, the last of August in the after noone, had intelligence by one Captaine Midleton, of the approch of the Spanish Armada. Which Midleton being in a verie good Sailer, had kept them companie three daies before, of good purpose, both to discover their forces the more, as also to give advice to my L. Thomas of their approach. He had no sooner delivered the newes but the Fleet was in sight: manie of our shippes companies were

---

[1]From *The Last Fight of the "Revenge"* (Arber Reprints). By permission of **Constable & Co.**

on shore in the Iland; some providing balast for their ships; others filling of water and refreshing themselves from the land with such thinges as they coulde either for money, or by force recover. By reason whereof our ships being all pestered and romaging everie thing out of order, verie light for want of balast. And that which was most to our disadvantage, the one halfe part of the men of everie shippe sicke, and utterly unserviceable. For in the *Revenge* there were nintie diseased: in the *Bonaventure*, not so many in health as could handle her maine saile. For had not twentie men been taken out of a Barke of Sir George Caryes, his being commanded to be sunke, and those appointed to her, she had hardly ever recovered England. The rest for the most part were in little better state.

The names of her Maiesties shippes were these as followeth: the *Defiaunce*, which was Admirall, the *Revenge* Viceadmirall, the *Bonaventure* commanded by Captaine Crosse, the *Lion* by George Fenner, the *Foresight* by M. Thomas Vavisour, and the *Crane* by Duffield. The *Foresight* and the *Crane* being but small ships; onely the other were of the middle size; the rest, besides the Barke *Ralegh*. commanded by Captaine Thin, were victualers, and of small force or none.

The Spanish fleete having shrouded their approach by reason of the Iland; were now so soone at hand, as our ships had scarce time to waye their anchors, but some of them were driven to let slippe their Cables and set sayle. Sir Richard Grinvile was the last waied, to recover the men that were upon the Iland, which otherwise had been lost. The L. Thomas with the rest verie hardly recovered the winde, which Sir Richard Grinvile not being able to do, was perswaded by the maister and others to cut his maine saile, and cast about, and to trust to the sailing of his shippe: for the squadron of Sivill were on his wether bow. But Sir Richard utterly refused to turne from the enemie, alledging that he would rather chose to dye, then to dishonour him selfe, his countrie, and her Maiesties shippe, perswading his companie that he would passe through the two Squadrons, in despight of them: and enforce those of Sivill to give him way. Which he performed upon diverse of the formost, who as the Marriners terme it, sprang their luffe, and fell under the lee of the *Revenge*. But the other course had beene the better, and might right well have beene answered in so great an impossibilitie of prevailing. Notwithstanding out of the greatnesse of his minde, he could not bee perswaded,

In the meane while as hee attended those which were nearest him, the great *San Philip* being in the winde of him, and comming towards him, becalmed his sailes in such sort, as the shippe could neither way nor feele the helme: so huge and high carged was the Spanish ship, being of a thousand and five hundreth tuns. Who after laid the *Revenge* aboord. When he was thus bereft of his sailes, the ships that wer under his lee luffing up, also laid him aboorde: of which the next was the Admirall of the Biscaines, a verie mightie and puysant shippe commanded by Brittan Dona. The said *Philip* carried three tire of ordinance on a side, and eleven peeces in everie tire. She shot eight forth right out of her chase, besides those of her Sterne portes.

After the *Revenge* was intangled with this *Philip*, foure other boorded her; two on her larboord, and two on her starboord. The fight thus beginning at three of the clocke in the after noone, continued verie terrible all that evening. But the great *San Philip* having receyved the lower tire of the *Revenge*, discharged with crossebarshot, shifted hir selfe with all diligence from her sides, utterly misliking hir first entertainment. Some say that the shippe foundred, but wee cannot report it for truth, unlesse we were assured. The Spanish ships were filled with companies of souldiers, in some two hundred besides the Marriners; in some five, in others eight hundreth. In ours there were none at all, beside the Marriners, but the servants of the commanders and some fewe voluntarie Gentlemen only. After many enterchanged voleies of great ordinance and small shot, the Spaniards deliberated to enter the *Revenge*, and made divers attempts, hoping to force her by the multitudes of their armed souldiers and Musketiers, but were still repulse againe and againe, and at all times beaten backe, into their owne shippes, or into the seas.

In the beginning of the fight, the *George Noble* of London, having received some shot thorow her by the Armados, fell under the Lee of the *Revenge*, and asked Syr Richard what he would command him, being but one of the victulers and of small force: Syr Richard bid him save himselfe, and leave him to his fortune. After the fight had thus without intermission, continued while the day lasted and some houres of the night, many of our men were slaine and hurt, and one of the great Gallions of the Armada, and the Admirall of the Hulkes both sunke, and in many other of the Spanish ships great slaughter was made. Some write that sir Richard was verie dangerously hurt almost in the beginning of the fight, and laie speechlesse for a time ere he recovered. But two of the *Revenges* owne companie, brought home in a ship of Lime from the Ilandes, examined by some of the Lordes, and others: affirmed that he was never so wounded as that hee forsooke the upper decke, til an houre before midnight; and then being shot into the bodie with a Musket as hee was a dressing, was againe shot into the head, and withall his Chirugion wounded to death. This agreeth also with an examination taken by Syr Francis Godolphin, of 4 other Marriners of the same shippe being returned, which examination the said Syr Francis sent unto maister William Killigrue of her Maiesties privie Chamber.

But to return to the fight, the Spanish ships which attempted to board the *Revenge*, as they were wounded and beaten of, so alwaies others came in their places, she having never lesse then two mightie Gallions by her sides, and aboard her. So that ere the morning from three of the clocke the day before, there had fifteene severall Armados assailed her; and all so ill approved their entertainment, as they were by the break of day, far more willing to harken to a composition, then hastily to make any more assaults or entries. But as the day encreased, so our men decreased: and as the light grew more and more, by so much more grew our discomforts. For none appeared in sight but enemies, saving one small ship called the *Pilgrim*, commanded by Jacob Whiddon, who hovered all night to see the successe: but in the mornyng bearing with the *Revenge*, was hunted like a hare amongst many ravenous houndes but escaped.

All the powder of the *Revenge* to the last barrell was now spent, all her pikes broken, fortie of her best men slaine, and the most part of the rest hurt. In the beginning of the fight she had but one hundreth free from sicknes, and fourescore and ten sicke, laid in hold upon the Ballast. A small troupe to man such a ship, and a weake Garrison to resist so mighty an Army. By those hundred all was sustained, the voleis, bourdings, and entrings of fifteene shippes of warre, besides those which beat her at large. On the contrarie, the Spanish were alwaies supplied with souldiers brought from everie squadron: all maner of Armes and pouder at will. Unto ours there remained no comfort at all, no hope, no supply either of ships, men, or weapons; the mastes all beaten over board, all her tackle cut a sunder, her upper worke altogither rased, and in effect evened shee was with the water, but the very foundation or bottom of a ship, nothing being left over head either for flight or defence.

Syr Richard finding himselfe in this distresse, and unable anie longer to make resistance, having endured in this fifteene houres fight the assault of fifteene severall Armadoes, all by tornes aboorde him, and by estimation eight hundred shot of great artillerie, besides manie assaults and entries. And that himselfe and the shippe must needes be possessed by the enemie, who were now all cast in a ring round about him; The *Revenge* not able to move one way or other, but as she was moved with the waves and billow of the sea: commanded the maister Gunner, whom he knew to be a most resolute man, to split and sinke the shippe; that thereby nothing might remaine of glorie or victorie to the Spaniards: seeing in so many houres fight, and with so great a Navie they were not able to take her, having had fifteene houres time, fifteene thousand men, and fiftie and three saile of men of warre to performe it withall. And perswaded the companie, or as manie as he could induce, to yeelde themselves unto God, and to the mercie of none els; but as they had like valiant resolute men, repulsed so manie enimies, they should not now shorten the honour of their nation by prolonging their owne lives for a few houres, or a few daies.

The maister Gunner readilie condescended and divers others; but the Captaine and the Maister were of an other opinion, and besought Sir Richard to have care of them: alleaging that the Spaniard would be as readie to entertaine a composition as they were willing to offer the same: and that there being diverse sufficient and valiant men yet living, and whose woundes were not mortall, they might doe their countrie and prince acceptable service hereafter. And (that where Sir Richard had alleaged that the Spaniards should never glorie to have taken one shippe of her Maiesties, seeing that they had so long and so notably defended them selves) they answered, that the shippe had sixe foote water in hold, three shot under water which were so weakly stopped, as with the first working of the sea, she must needes sinke, and was besides so crusht and brused, as she could never be removed out of the place.

And as the matter was thus in dispute, and Sir Richard refusing to hearken to any of those reasons: the maister of the *Revenge* (while the Captaine wan unto him the greater part) was convoyde aborde the Generall Don Alfonso Bassan. Who finding none over hastie to enter the *Revenge* againe, doubting least Sir Richard would have blowne them up and himselfe, and perceiving by the report of the maister of the *Revenge* his daungerous disposition: yeelded that all their lives should be saved, the companie sent for England, and the better sorte to pay such reasonable ransome as their estate would beare, and in the meane season to be free from Gally or imprisonment. To this he so much the rather condescended as well as I have saide, for feare of further losse and mischiefe to them selves, as also for the desire hee had to recover Sir Richard Grinvile; whom for his notable valure he seemed greatly to honour and admire.

When this answer was returned, and that safetie of life was promised, the common sort being now at the end of their perill, the most drew backe from Sir Richard and the maister Gunner, being no hard matter to diswade men from death to life. The maister Gunner finding him selfe and Sir Richard thus prevented and maistered by the greater number, would have slain him selfe with a sword, had he not beene by force withheld and locked into his Cabben. Then the Generall sent manie boates abord the *Revenge*, and diverse of our men fearing Sir Richards disposition, stole away aboord the Generall and other shippes. Sir Richard thus overmatched, was sent unto by Alonso Bassan to remove out of the *Revenge*, the shippe being marvellous unsaverie, filled with bloud and bodies of deade, and wounded men like a slaughter house. Sir Richard answered that he might do with his bodie what he list, for he esteemed it not, and as he was carried out of the shippe he swounded, and reviving againe desired the companie to pray for him. The Generall used Sir Richard with all humanitie, and left nothing unattempted that tended to his recoverie, highly commending his valour and worthines, and greatly bewailed the daunger wherein he was, beeing unto them a rare spectacle, and a resolution sildome approved, to see one ship turne toward so many enemies, to endure the charge and boording of so many huge Armados, and to resist and repell the assaults and entries of so many souldiers. All which and more, is confirmed by a Spanish Captaine of the same Armada, and a present actor in the fight, who being severed from the rest in a storm, was by the *Lyon* of London a small ship taken, and is now prisoner in London.

The generall commander of the Armada, was Don Alphonsc Bassan, brother to the Marquesse of Santa Cruce. The Admirall of the Biscaine squadron, was Britan Dona. Of the squadron of Sivill, Marques of *Arumburch*. The Hulkes and Flybotes were commanded by Luis Cutino. There were slaine and drowned in this fight, well neere two thousand of the enemies, and two especiall commanders Don Luis de Sant John and Don George de Prunaria de Mallaga, as the Spanish Captaine confesseth, besides divers others of speciall account, whereof as yet report is not made.

The Admirall of the Hulkes and the Ascention of Sivill, were both suncke by the side of the *Revenge;* one other recovered the rode of Saint Michels, and suncke also there; a fourth ranne herselfe with the shore to save her men.

Sir Richard died as it is said, the second or third day aboard the Generall, and was by them greatly bewailed. What became of his bodie, whether it were buried in the sea or on the lande wee know not: the comfort that remaineth to his friendes is, that he hath ended his life honourably in respect of the reputation wonne to his nation and country, and of the same to his posteritie, and that being dead, he hath not outlived his owne honour.

A fewe daies after the fight was ended, and the English prisoners dispersed into the Spanish and Indy ships, there arose so great a storme from the West and Northwest, that all the fleet was dispersed, as well the Indian fleet which were then come unto them as the rest of the Armada that attended their arrivall, of which 14 saile togither with the *Revenge,* and her 200 Spaniards, were cast away upon the Isle of S. Michaels. So it pleased them to honor the buriall of that renowned ship the *Revenge,* not suffring her to perish alone for the great honour she achieved in her life time.

A TRUE REPORTORY OF THE WRACKE AND REDEMPTION OF SIR THOMAS GATES, KNIGHT[1]

William Strachy

(*fl.* 1609–18)

EXCELLENT Lady, known that upon Friday late in the evening, we brake ground out of the Sound of Plymouth, our whole Fleete then consisting of seven good Ships, and two Pinnaces, all which from the said second of June, unto the twenty three of July, kept in friendly

---

[1]From *Purchas His Pilgrimes.*

consort together, not a whole watch at any time loosing the sight each of
other. Our course when we came about the height of betweene 26. and
27. degrees, we declined to the North-ward, and according to our Gov-
ernours instructions altered the trade and ordinary way used heretofore
by Dominico, and Mevis, in the West Indies, and found the winde to
this course indeede as friendly, as in the judgement of all Sea-men, it is
upon a more direct line, and by Sir George Summers our Admirall had
bin likewise in former time sailed, being a Gentleman of approved assured-
nesse, and ready knowledge in Sea-faring actions, having often carried
command, and chiefe charge in many Ships Royall of her Majesties, and
in sundry Voyages made many defeats and attempts in the time of the
Spaniards quarrelling with us, upon the Ilands and Indies, etc. We had
followed this course so long, as now we were within seven or eight dayes
at the most, by Cap. Newports reckoning of making Cape Henry upon
the coast of Virginia: When on S. James his day, July 24. being Monday
(preparing for no lesse all the blacke night before) the cloudes gathering
thicke upon us, and the windes singing, and whistling most unusually,
which made us to cast off our Pinnace towing the same untill then
asterne, a dreadfull storme and hideous began to blow from out the North-
east, which swelling, and roaring as it were by fits, some houres with
more violence then others, at length did beate all light from heaven;
which like an hell of darkenesse turned blacke upon us, so much the more
fuller of horror, as in such cases horror and feare use to overrunne the
troubled, and overmastered sences of all, which (taken up with amazement) the eares lay so sensible to the terrible cries, and murmurs of the
windes, and distraction of our Company, as who was most armed, and
best prepared, was not a little shaken. For surely (Noble Lady) as death
comes not so sodaine nor apparant, so he comes not so elvish and pain-
full (to men especially even then in health and perfect habitudes of body)
as at Sea; who comes at no time so welcome, but our frailty (so weake
is the hold of hope in miserable demonstrations of danger) it makes
guilty of many contrary changes, and conflicts: For indeede death is
accompanied at no time, nor place with circumstances every way so
uncapable of particularities of goodnesse and inward comforts, as at
Sea. For it is most true, there ariseth commonly no such unmercifull
tempest, compound of so many contrary and divers Nations, but that it
worketh upon the whole frame of the body, and most loathsomely affect-
eth all the powers thereof: and the manner of the sicknesse it laies upon
the body, being so unsufferable, gives not the minde any free and quiet
time, to use her judgement and Empire: which made the Poet say:

> Hostium uxores, puerique cæcos
> Sentiant motus orientis Hædi, et
> Æquoris nigri fremitum, et trementes
> Verbere ripas.

For foure and twenty houres the storme in a restlesse tumult, had blowne so exceedingly, as we could not apprehend in our imaginations any possibility of greater violence, yet did wee still finde it, not onely more terrible, but more constant, fury added to fury, and one storme urging a second more outragious then the former; whether it so wrought upon our feares, or indeede met with new forces: Sometimes strikes in our Ship amongst women, and passengers, not used to such hurly and discomforts, made us looke one upon the other with troubled hearts, and panting bosomes: our clamours dround in the windes, and the windes in thunder. Prayers might well be in the heart and lips, but drowned in the outcries of the Officers: nothing heard that could give comfort, nothing seene that might incourage hope. It is impossible for me, had I the voyce of Stentor, and expression of as many tongues, as his throate of voyces, to expresse the outcries and miseries, not languishing, but wasting his spirits, and art constant to his owne principles, but not prevailing. Our sailes wound up lay without their use, and if at any time wee bore but a Hollocke, or halfe forecourse, to guide her before the Sea, six and sometimes eight men were not inough to hold the whipstaffe in the steerage, and the tiller below in the Gunner roome, by which may be imagined the strength of the storme: In which, the Sea swelled above the Clouds, and gave battell unto Heaven. It could not be said to raine, the waters like whole Rivers did flood in the ayre. And this I did still observe, that whereas upon the Land, when a storme hath powred it selfe forth once in drifts of raine, the winde as beaten downe, and vanquished therewith, not long after indureth: here the glut of water (as if throatling the winde ere while) was no sooner a little emptied and qualified, but instantly the windes (as having gotten their mouthes now free, and at liberty) spake more loud, and grew more tumultuous, and malignant. What shall I say? Windes and Seas were as mad, as fury and rage could make them; for mine owne part, I had bin in some stormes before, as well upon the coast of Barbary and Algeere, in the Levant, and once more distressfull in the Adriatique gulfe, in a bottome of Candy, so as I may well say. *Ego quid sit ater Adriæ novi sinus, et quid albus Peccet lapex.* Yet all that I had ever suffered gathered together, might not hold comparison with this: there was not a moment in which the sodaine splitting, or instant over-setting of the Shippe was not expected.

Howbeit this was not all; It pleased God to bring a greater affliction yet upon us; for in the beginning of the storme we had received likewise a mighty leake. And the Ship in every joynt almost, having spued out her Okam, before we were aware (a casualty more desparate then any other that a Voyage by Sea draweth with it) was growne five foote suddenly deepe with water above her ballast, and we almost drowned within, whilest we sat looking when to perish from above. This imparting no lesse terrour then danger, ranne through the whole Ship with much fright and amazement, startled and turned the bloud, and tooke downe the braves of the most hardy Marriner of them all, insomuch as he that before happily felt not the sorrow of others, now began to sorrow for himselfe, when he saw such a pond of water so suddenly broken in, and which he knew could not (without present avoiding) but instantly sinke him. So as joyning (onely for his owne sake, not yet worth the saving) in the publique safety; there might be seene Master, Masters Mate, Boateswaine, Quarter Master, Coopers, Carpenters, and who not, with candels in their hands, creeping along the ribs viewing the sides, searching every corner, and listening in every place, if they could heare the water runne. Many a weeping leake was this way found, and hastily stopt, and at length one in the Gunner roome made up with I know not how many peeces of Beefe: but all was to no purpose, the Leake (if it were but one) which drunke in our greatest Seas, and tooke in our destruction fastest, could not then be found, nor ever was, by any labour counsell, or search. The waters still increasing, and the Pumpes going, which at length choaked with bringing up whole and continuall Bisket (and indeede all we had, tenne thousand weight) it was conceived, as most likely, that the Leake might be sprung in the Bread-roome, whereupon the Carpenter went downe, and ript up all the roome, but could not finde it so.

I am not able to give unto your Ladiship every mans thought in this perplexity, to which we were now brought; but to me, this Leakage appeared as a wound given to men that were before dead. The Lord knoweth, I had as little hope, as desire of life in the storme, and in this, it went beyond my will; because beyond my reason, why we should labour to preserve life; yet we did, either because so deare are a few lingring houres of life in all mankinde, or that our Christian knowledges taught us, how much we owed to the rites of Nature, as bound, not to be false to our selves, or to neglect the meanes of our owne preservation; the most despairefull things amongst men, being matters of no wonder nor moment with him, who is the rich Fountaine and admirable Essence of all mercy.

Our Governour, upon the tuesday morning (at what time, by such who had bin below in the hold, the Leake was first discovered) had caused the whole Company, about one hundred and forty, besides women, to be equally divided into three parts, and opening the Ship in three places (under the forecastle, in the waste, and hard by the Bitacke) appointed each man where to attend; and thereunto every man came duely upon his watch, tooke the Bucket, or Pumpe for one houre, and rested another. Then men might be seene to labour, I may well say, for life, and the better sort, even our Governour, and Admirall themselves, not refusing their turne, and to spell each the other, to give example to other. The common sort stripped naked, as men in Gallies, the easier both to hold out, and to shrinke from under the salt water, which continually leapt in among them, kept their eyes waking, and their thoughts and hands working, with tyred bodies, and wasted spirits, three dayes and foure nights destitute of outward comfort, and desperate of any deliverance, testifying how mutually willing they were, yet by labour to keepe each other from drowning, albeit each one drowned whilest he laboured.

Once, so huge a Sea brake upon the poope and quarter, upon us, as it covered our Shippe from stearne to stemme, like a garment or a vast cloude, it filled her brimme full for a while within, from the hatches up to the sparre decke. This source or confluence of water was so violent, as it rusht and carried the Helm-man from the Helme, and wrested the Whip-staffe out of his hand, which so flew from side to side, that when he would have ceased the same againe, it so tossed him from Star-boord to Lar-boord, as it was Gods mercy it had not split him: It so beat him from his hold, and so bruised him, as a fresh man hazarding in by chance fell faire with it, and by maine strength bearing somewhat up, made good his place, and with much clamour incouraged and called upon others; who gave her now up, rent in pieces and absolutely lost. Our Governour was at this time below at the Capstone, both by his speech and authoritie heartening every man unto his labour. It strooke him from the place where hee sate, and groveled him, and all us about him on our faces, beating together with our breaths all thoughts from our bosomes, else, then that wee were now sinking. For my part, I thought her alreadie in the bottome of the Sea; and I have heard him say, wading out of the floud thereof, all his ambition was but to climbe up above hatches to dye in *Aperto cœlo,* and in the company of his old friends. It so stun'd the ship in her full pace, that shee stirred no more, then if shee had beene caught in a net, or then, as if the fabulous Remora had stucke to her fore-castle. Yet without bearing one inch of saile, even then shee was making her way nine or ten leagues in a watch. One thing, it is not without his wonder (whether it were the feare of death in so great a storme, or that it pleased God to be gracious unto us) there was not a passenger, gentleman, or other, after hee beganne to stirre and labour, but was able to relieve his fellow, and make good his course: And it is most true, such as in all their life times had never done houres worke before (their mindes now helping their bodies) were able twice fortie-eight houres together to toile with the best.

During all this time, the heavens look'd so blacke upon us, that it was not possible the elevation of the Pole might be observed: nor a Starre by night, not Sunne beame by day was to be seene. Onely upon the thursday night Sir George Summers being upon the watch, had an apparition of a little round light, like a faint Starre, trembling, and streaming along with a sparkeling blaze, halfe the height upon the Maine Mast, and shooting sometimes from Shroud to Shroud, tempting to settle as it were upon any of the foure Shrouds: and for three or foure houres together, or rather more, halfe the night it kept with us; running sometimes along the Maine-yard to the very end, and then returning. At which, Sir George Summers called divers about him, and shewed them the same, who observed it with much wonder, and carefulnesse: but upon a sodaine, towards the morning watch, they lost the sight of it, and knew not what way it made. The superstitious Sea-men make many constructions of this Sea-fire, which neverthelesse is usuall in stormes: the same (it may be) which the Graecians were wont in the Mediterranean to call Castor and Pollux, of which, if one onely apeared without the other, they tooke it for an evill signe of great tempest. The Italians, and such, who lye open to the Adriatique and Tyrrene Sea, call it (a sacred Body) *Corpo sancto:* the Spaniards call it Saint Elmo, and have an authentique and miraculous Legend for it. Be it what it will, we laid other foundations of safety or ruine, then in the rising or falling of it, could it have served us now miraculously to have taken our height by, it might have strucken amazement, and a reverence in our devotions, according to the due of a miracle. But it did not light us any whit the more to our knowne way, who ran now (as doe hoodwinked men) at all adventures, sometimes North, and North-east, then North and by West, and in an instant againe varying two or three points, and sometimes halfe the Compasse. East and by South we steered away as much as we could to beare upright, which was no small carefulnesse nor paine to doe, albeit we much unrigged our Ship, threw over-boord much luggage, many a Trunke and Chest (in which I suffered no meane losse) and staved many a Butt of Beere, Hogsheads of Oyle, Syder, Wine and Vinegar, and heaved away all our Ordnance on the Starboord side, and had now purposed to have cut downe the Maine Mast, the more to lighten her, for we were much spent, and our men so weary, as their strengths together failed them, with their hearts, having travailed now from Tuesday till Friday morning, day and night, without either sleepe or foode; for the leakeage taking up all the hold, wee could neither come by Beere nor fresh water; fire we could keepe none in the Cooke-roome to dresse any meate, and carefulnesse, griefe, and our turne at the Pumpe or Bucket, were sufficient to hold sleepe from our eyes.

And surely Madam, it is most true, there was not any houre (a matter of admiration) all these dayes, in which we freed not twelve hundred Barricos of water, the least whereof contained six gallons, and some eight, besides three deepe Pumpes continually going, two beneath at the Capstone, and the other above in the halfe Decke, and at each Pumpe foure thousand stroakes at the least in a watch; so as I may well say, every foure houres, we quitted one hundred tunnes of water: and from Tuesday noone till Friday noone, we bailed and pumped two thousand tunne, and yet doe what we could, when our Ship held least in her, (after tuesday night second watch) shee bore ten foote deepe, at which stay our extreame working kept her one eight glasses, forbearance whereof had instantly sunke us, and it being now Friday, the fourth morning, it wanted little, but that there had bin a generall determination, to have shut up hatches, and commending our sinfull soules to God, committed the Shippe to the mercy of the Sea: surely, that night we must have done it, and that night had we then perished: but see the goodnesse and sweet introduction of better hope, by our mercifull God given unto us. Sir George Summers, when no man dreamed of such happinesse, had discovered, and cried Land. Indeede the morning now three quarters spent, had wonne a little cleerenesse from the dayes before, and it being better surveyed, the very trees were seene to move with the winde upon the shoare side: whereupon our Governour commanded the Helme-man to beare up, the Boateswaine sounding at the first, found it thirteene fathome, and when we stood a little in seven fathome; and presently heaving his lead the third time, had ground at foure fathome, and by this, we had got her within a mile under the South-east point of the land, where we had somewhat smooth water. But having no hope to save her by comming to an anker in the same, we were inforced to runne her ashoare, as neere the land as we could, which brought us within three quarters of a mile of shoare, and by the mercy of God unto us, making out our Boates, we had ere night brought all our men, women, and children, about the number of one hundred and fifty, safe into the Iland.

We found it to be the dangerous and dreaded Iland, or rather Ilands of the Bermuda: which, because they be so terrible to all that ever touched on them, and such tempests, thunders, and other fearefull objects are seene and heard about them, be called commonly, The Devils Ilands, and are feared and avoyded of all sea travellers alive, above any other place in the world. Yet it pleased our mercifull God, to make even this hideous and hated place, both the place of our safetie, and means of our deliverance.

THE LAST VOYAGE OF HENRY HUDSON[1]

Abacuk Pricket

WE BEGAN our Voyage for the North-west passage; the seventeenth of April, 1610. Thwart of Shepey, our Master sent Master Colbert backe to the Owners with his Letter. The next day we weighed from hence, and stood for Harwich, and came thither the eight and twentieth of Aprill. From Harwich we set sayle the first of May, along the Coast to the North, till we came to the Iles of Orkney, from thence to the Iles of Faro, and from thence to Island: on which we fell in a fogge, hearing the Rut of the Sea, ashoare, but saw not the Land whereupon our Master came to an Anchor. Heere we were embayed in the South-east part of the Land. Wee weighed and stood along the Coast, on the West side towards the North: but one day being calme, we fell a fishing,

[1]From *Purchas His Pilgrimes.*

and caught good store of fish, as Cod and Ling, and Butte, with some other sorts that we knew not. The next day, we had a good gale of wind at South-west, and raysed the Iles of Westmonie, where the King of Denmarke hath a Fortresse, by which we passed to rayse the Snow Hill foot, a Mountayne so called on the North-west part of the Land. But in our course we saw that famous Hill, Mount Hecla, which cast out much fire, a signe of foule weather to come in short time. Wee leave Island a sterne of us, and met a Mayne of Ice, which did hang on the North part of Island, and stretched downe to the West, which when our Master saw, he stood backe for Island to find an Harbour, which we did on the North-west part, called Derefer,[1] where wee killed good store of Fowle. From hence wee put to Sea againe, but (neither wind nor weather serving) our Master stood backe for this Harbour againe, but could not reach it, but fell with another to the South of that, called by our Englishmen, Louise Bay: where on the shoare we found an hot Bath, and heere all our Englishmen bathed themselves: the water was so hot that it would scald a Fowle.

From hence the first of June we put to Sea for Groneland, but to the West wee saw Land as we thought, for which we beare the best part of a day, but it proved but a foggie bank. So wee gave it over, and made for Gronland, which we raysed the fourth of June. Upon the Coast thereof hung good store of Ice, so that our Master could not attayne to the shoare by any meanes. The Land in this part is very Mountaynous, and full of round Hils, like to Sugar-loaves, covered with snow. We turned the Land on the South side, as neere as the Ice would suffer us. Our course for the most part was betweene the West and North-west, till we raysed the Desolations, which is a great Iland in the West part of Groneland. On this Coast we saw store of Whales, and at one time three of them came close by us, so as wee could hardly shunne them: then two passing very neere, and the third going under our ship, wee received no harme by them, praysed bee God.

From the Desolations our Master made his way North-west, the wind being against him, who else would have gone more to the North: but in this course we saw the first great Iland or Mountayne of Ice, whereof after we saw store. About the latter end of June, we raysed Land to the North of us, which our Master tooke to bee that Iland which Master Davis setteth downe in his Chart. On the West side of his Streight, our Master would have gone to the North of it, but the wind would not suffer him: so we fell to the South of it, into a great Rippling or over-fall of current, the which setteth to the West. Into the current we went, and made our way to the North of the West, till we met with Ice which hung on this Iland. Wherefore our Master casting about, cleered himselfe of this Ice, and stood to the South, and then to the West, through store of

---

[1] Or Diraford.

floting Ice, and upon the Ice store of Seales. We gained a cleere Sea, and continued our course till wee meete Ice; first, with great Ilands, and then with store of the smaller sort. Betweene them we made our course North-west, till we met with Ice againe. But, in this our going betweene the Ice, we saw one of the great Ilands of Ice overturne, which was a good warning to us, not to come nigh them, nor within their reach. Into the Ice wee put ahead, as betweene two Lands. The next day we had a storme, and the wind brought the Ice so fast upon us, that in the end we were driven to put her into the chiefest of the Ice, and there to let her lie. Some of our men this day fell sicke, I will not say it was for feare, although I saw small signe of other griefe.

The storme ceasing, we stood out of the Ice, where wee saw any cleere Sea to goe to: which was sometime more, and sometime lesse. Our course was as the Ice did lye, sometime to the North, then to the North-west, and then to the West, and to the South-west: but still inclosed with Ice. Which when our Master saw, he made his course to the South, thinking to cleere himselfe of the Ice that way: but the more he strove, the worse he was, and the more inclosed, till we could goe no further. Here our Master was in despaire, and (as he told me after) he thought he should never have got out of this Ice, but there have perished. Therefore hee brought forth his Card, and shewed all the company, that hee was entred above an hundred leagues further than ever any English was: and left it to their choice, whether they would proceed any further; yea, or nay. Whereupon, some were of one minde, and some of another, some wishing themselves at home, and some not caring where, so they were out of the Ice: but there were some who then spake words, which were remembred a great while after.

There was one who told the Master, that if he had an hundred pounds, hee would give fourescore and ten to be at home: but the Carpenter made answere, that if hee had an hundred, hee would not give ten upon any such condition, but would thinke it to be as good money as ever he had any, and to bring it as well home, by the leave of God. After many words to no purpose, to worke we must on all hands, to get our selves out, and to cleere our ship. After much labour and time spent, we gained roome to turne our ship in, and so by little and little, to get cleere in the Sea a league or two off, our course being North and North-west.

In the end, we raysed Land to the South-west, high Land and covered with Snow. Our Master named this Land, Desire provokes. Lying here, wee heard the noyse of a great over-fall of a tyde, that came out of the Land: for now we might see well, that wee had beene embayed before, and time had made us know, being so well acquainted with the Ice, that when night, or foggie, or foule weather tooke us, we would seeke out the broadest Iland of Ice, and there come to anchor and runne, and sport, and fill water that stood on the Ice in Ponds, both sweete and good. But after we had brought this Land to beare South of us, we had the tyde and the current to open the Ice, as being carried first one way, and then another: but in Bayes they lye as in a pond without moving. In this Bay where wee were thus troubled with Ice, wee saw many of those Mountaynes of Ice aground, in sixe or sevenscore fathome water. In this our course we saw a Beare upon a piece of Ice by it selfe, to the which our men gave chase with their Boat: but before they came nigh her, the tyde had carried the Ice and the Beare on it, and joyned it with the other Ice: so they lost their labour, and came aboord againe.

We continued our course to the North-west, and raysed Land to the North of our course, toward which we made, and comming nigh it, there hung on the Eastermost point, many Ilands of floting Ice, and a Beare on one of them, which from one to another came towards us, till she was readie to come aboord. But when she saw us looke at her, she cast her head betweene her hinder legges, and then dived under the Ice: and so from one piece to another, till she was out of our reach. We stood along by the Land on the Southside ahead of us, wee met with Ice that hung on a point of Land that lay to the South, more than this that we came up by: which when our Master saw, he stood in for the shoare. At the West end of this Iland (for so it is) we found an Harbour, and came in (at a full Sea) over a Rocke, which had two fathome and an halfe on it, and was so much bare at a low water. But by the great mercie of God, we came to an Anchor cleere of it: and close by it, our Master named them, the Iles of Gods Mercie.

From hence we stood to the South-west, to double the Land to the West of us, through much floting Ice: In the end wee found a cleere Sea, and continued therein, till wee raysed Land to the North-west. Then our Master made his course more to the South then before: but it was not long ere we met with Ice which lay ahead of us. Our Master would have doubled this Ice to the North, but could not; and in the end put into it downe to the South-west through much Ice, and then to the South, where we were embayed againe. Our Master strove to get the shoare, but could not, for the great store of Ice that was on the coast. From out of this Bay, we stood to the North, and were soone out of the Ice: then downe to the South-west, and so to the West, where we were enclosed (to our sight) with Land and Ice. For wee had Land from the South to the North-west on one side, and from the East to the West on the other side: but the Land that was to the North of us, and lay by East and West, was but an Iland. On we went till we could goe no further for Ice: so we made our ship fast to the Ice which the tide brought upon us, but when the ebbe came, the Ice did open, and made way; so as in seven or eight houres we were cleere from the Ice, till we came to weather; but onely some of the great Ilands, that were carried along with us to the North-west.

Having a cleere Sea, our Master stood to the West along by the South shoare, and raysed three Capes or Head-lands, lying one above another.

The middlemost is an Iland, and maketh a Bay or Harbour, which (I take) will prove a good one. Our Master named them Prince Henries Cape, or Fore-land. When we had layd this we raised another, which was the extreme point of the Land, looking towards the North: upon it are two Hills, but one (above the rest) like an Hay-cocke; which our Master named, King James his Cape. To the North of this, lie certaine Ilands, which our Master named, Queene Annes Cape, or Fore-land. Wee followed the North shoare still. Beyond the Kings Cape there is a Sound or Bay, that hath some Ilands in it: and this is not to be forgotten, if need be. Beyond this, lieth some broken Land, close to the Mayne, but what it is I know not: because we passed by it in the night.

Wee stood to the North to double this Land, and after to the West againe, till wee fell with Land that stretched from the Mayne, like a shewer from the South to the North, and from the North to the West, and then downe to the South againe. Being short of this Land, a storme tooke us, the wind at West, we stood to the North, and raised Land: which when our Master saw, he stood to the South againe; for he was loath at any time that wee should see the North shoare. The storme continuing, and comming to the South shoare againe, our Master found himselfe shot to the West, a great way, which made him muse, considering his Leeward way. To the South-west of this Land, on the Mayne, there is an high Hill, which our Master named Mount Charles. To the North and beyond this, lieth an Iland, that to the East hath a faire head, and beyond it to the West other broken Land, which maketh a Bay within, and a good Road may be found there for ships. Our Master named the first, Cape Salsburie.

When we had left this to the North-east, we fell into a Rippling or Over-fall of a Current, which (at the first) we tooke to bee a Shoald: but the Lead being cast, wee had no ground. On we passed still in sight of the South shoare, till we raised Land lying from the Mayne some two leagues. Our Master tooke this to bee a part of the Mayne of the North Land; but it is an Iland, the North side stretching out to the West more then the South. This Iland hath a faire Head to the East, and very high Land, which our Master named Deepes Cape: and the Land on the South side, now falling away to the South, makes another Cape or Head-land, which our Master named, Worsenhams Cape. When wee were nigh the North or Iland Cape, our Master sent the Boat ashoare, with my selfe (who had the charge) and the Carpenter, and divers others, to discover to the West and North-west, and to the South-west: but we had further to it then we thought; for the Land is very high, and we were overtaken with a storme of Raine, Thunder, and Lightning. But to it we came on the North-east side, and up we got from one Rocke to another, till we came to the highest of that part. Here we found some plaine ground, and saw some Deere; as first, foure or five, and after a dozen or sixteene in an Herd, but could not come nigh them with a Musket shot.

Thus, going from one place to another, wee saw to the West of us an high Hill above all the rest, it being nigh us: but it proved further off then we made account; for, when wee came to it, the Land was so steepe on the East and North-east parts, that wee could not get unto it. To the South-west we saw that wee might, and towards that part wee went along by the side of a great Pond of water, which lieth under the East side of this Hill: and there runneth out of it a st=reame of water, as much as would drive an over-shot Mill: which falleth downe from an high Cliffe into the Sea on the South side. In this place great store of Fowle breed, and there is the best Grasse that I had seene since we came from England.

Our Master (in this time) came in betweene the two Lands, and shot off some Peeces to call us aboord; for it was a fogge. Wee came aboord, and told him what we had seene, and perswaded him to stay a day or two in this place, telling him what refreshing might there bee had: but by no meanes would he stay, who was not pleased with the motion. So we left the Fowle, and lost our way downe to the South-west, before they went in sight of the Land, which now beares to the East from us, being the same mayne Land that wee had all this while followed. Now, we had lost the sight of it, because it falleth away to the East, after some five and twenty or thirty leagues. Now we came to the shallow water, wherewith wee were not acquainted since we came from Island; now we came into broken ground and Rockes, through which we passed downe to the South. In this our course we had a storme, and the water did shoald apace. Our Master came to an anchor in fifteene fathoms water.

Wee weighed and stood to the South-east, because the Land in this place did lie so. When we came to the point of the West Land (for we now had Land on both sides of us) we came to an anchor. Our Master sent the Boat ashoare, to see what that Land was, and whether there were any way through. They soone returned, and shewed that beyond the point of Land to the South, there was a large Sea. This Land on the West side, was a very narrow Point. Wee weighed from hence, and stood in for this Sea betweene the two Lands, which (in this place) is not two leagues broad downe to the South, for a great way in sight of the East shoare. In the end we lost sight thereof, and saw it not till we came to the bottome of the Bay, into sixe or seven fathomes water. Hence we stood up to the North by the West shoare, till wee came to an Iland in 53. where we tooke in water and ballast.

From hence wee passed towards the North: but some two or three dayes after (reasoning concerning our comming into this Bay, and going out) our Master tooke occasion to revive old matters, and to displace Robert Juet from being his Mate, and the Boatswaine from his place, for words spoken in the first great Bay of Ice. Then hee made Robert Billet his Mate, and William Wilson our Boat-swaine. Up to the North wee stood, till we raised Land, then downe to the South, and up to the

North, then downe againe to the South: and on Michaelmasse day came in, and went out of certaine Lands: which our Master sets downe by the name of Michaelmasse Bay, because we came in and went out on that day. From hence wee stood to the North, and came into shoald water; and the weather being thicke and foule, wee came to an anchor in seven or eight fathome water, and there lay eight dayes: in all which time wee could not get one houre to weigh our anchor. But the eight day, the wind beginning to cease, our Master would have the anchor up, against the mind of all who knew what belonged thereunto. Well, to it we went, and when we had brought it to a peake, a Sea tooke her, and cast us all off from the Capstone, and hurt divers of us. Here wee lost our Anchor, and if the Carpenter had not beene, we had lost our Cable too: but he (fearing such a matter) was ready with his Axe, and so cut it.

From hence we stood to the South, and to the South-west, through a cleere Sea of divers sounding, and came to a Sea of two colours, one blacke, and the other white, sixteene or seventeene fathome water, betweene which we went foure or five leagues. But the night comming, we tooke in our Top-sayles, and stood afore the wind with our Maine-sayle and Fore-sayl, and came into five or sixe fathomes, and saw no Land for it was darke. Then we stood to the East, and had deepe water againe, then to the South and Southwest, and so came to our Westermost Bay of all, and came to an anchor neerest to the North shoare. Out went our Boat to the Land that was next us, when they came neere it, our Boat could not flote to the shoare it was so shallow: yet ashoare they got. Here our men saw the footing of a man and a Ducke in the snowy Rockes, and Wood good store, whereof they tooke some and returned aboord. Being at anchor in this place, we saw a ledge of Rockes to the South of us, some league of length; It lay North and South, covered at a full Sea; for a strong tide setteth in here. At mid-night wee weighed, and stood to goe out as we came in; and had not gone long, but the Carpenter came and told the Master, that if he kept that course he would be upon the Rockes: the Master conceived that he was past them, when presently wee ranne on them, and there stucke fast twelve houres: but (by the mercy of God) we got off unhurt, though not unscarred.

Wee stood up to the East and raysed three Hills, lying North and South: wee went to the furthermost, and left it to the North of us, and so into a Bay, where wee came to an anchor. Here our Master sent out our Boat, with my selfe and the Carpenter to seeke a place to winter in: and it was time; for the nights were long and cold, and the earth covered with Snow. Having spent three moneths in a Labyrinth without end, being now the last of October, we went downe to the East, to the bottome of the Bay: but returned without speeding of that we went for. The next day we went to the South, and the South-west, and found a place, whereunto we brought our ship, and haled her aground: and this was the first of November. By the tenth thereof we were frozen in: but now we were in, it behooved us to have care of what we had; for, that we were sure of; but what we had not, was uncertaine.

Wee were victualled for sixe moneths in good proportion, and of that which was good: if our Master would have had more, he might have had it at home and in other places. Here we were now, and therefore it behoved us so to spend, that wee might have (when time came) to bring us to the Capes where the Fowle bred, for that was all the hope wee had to bring us home. Wherefore our Master tooke order, first for the spending of that wee had, and then to increase it, by propounding a reward to them that killed either Beast, Fish, or Fowle. About the middle of this moneth of November, dyed John Williams our Gunner: God pardon the Masters uncharitable dealing with this man. Now for that I am come to speake of him, out of whose ashes (as it were) that unhappy deed grew which brought a scandall upon all that are returned home, and upon the action it selfe, the multitude (like the dog) running after the stone, but not at the caster: therefore, not to wrong the living, nor slander the dead, I will (by the leave of God) deliver the truth as neere as I can.

You shall understand, that our Master kept (in his house at London) a young man, named Henrie Greene, borne in Kent, of Worshipfull Parents, but by his leud life and conversation hee had lost the good will of all his friends, and had spent all that hee had. This man, our Master would have to Sea with him, because hee could write well: our Master gave him meate, and drinke, and lodging, and by meanes of one Master Venson, with much adoe got foure pounds of his mother to buy him clothes, wherewith Master Venson would not trust him: but saw it laid out himselfe. This Henrie Greene was not set downe in the owners booke, nor any wages made for him. Hee came first aboord at Gravesend, and at Harwich should have gone into the field, with one Wilkinson. At Island the Surgeon and hee fell out in Dutch, and hee beat him a shoare in English, which set all the company in a rage: so that wee had much adoe to get the Surgeon aboord. I told the Master of it, but hee bade mee let it alone, for (said hee) the Surgeon had a tongue that would wrong the best friend hee had. But Robert Juet (the Masters Mate) would needs burne his finger in the embers, and told the Carpenter a long tale (when hee was drunke) that our Master had brought in Greene to cracke his credit that should displease him: which words came to the Masters eares, who when hee understood it, would have gone backe to Island, when he was fortie leagues from thence, to have sent home his Mate Robert Juet in a Fisher-man. But, being otherwise perswaded, all was well. So Henry Greene stood upright, and very inward with the Master, and was a serviceable man every way for manhood: but for Religion he would say, he was cleane paper whereon he might write what hee would. Now, when our Gunner was dead, and (as the order is in such cases) if the company stand in need of any thing that belonged to the man deceased, then is it brought to the Mayne Mast, and there sold to them that will give most for the same: This Gunner had a gray cloth gowne, which Greene prayed the Master to friend him so much as to let him have it, paying for it as another would give: the Master saith hee should, and thereupon hee answered some, that sought to have it, that Greene should have it, and none else, and so it rested.

Now out of season and time, the Master calleth the Carpenter to goe in hand with an house on shoare, which at the beginning our Master would not heare, when it might have beene done. The Carpenter told him, that the Snow and Frost were such, as hee neither could, nor would goe in hand with such worke. Which when our Master heard, hee ferreted him out of his Cabbin to strike him, calling him by many foule names, and threatning to hang him. The Carpenter told him that hee knew what belonged to his place better than himselfe, and that hee was no House Carpenter. So this passed, and the house was (after) made with much labour, but to no end. The next day after the Master and the Carpenter fell out, the Carpenter tooke his Peece and Henry Greene with him, for it was an order that none should goe out alone, but one with a Peece, and another with a Pike. This did move the Master so much the more against Henry Greene, that Robert Billet his Mate must have the gowne, and had it delivered unto him; which when Henry Greene saw, he challenged the Masters promise: but the Master did so raile on Greene, with so many words of disgrace, telling him, that all his friends would not trust him with twenty shillings, and therefore why should he? As for wages he had none, nor none should have, if he did not please him well. Yet the Master had promised him to make his wages as good, as any mans in the ship; and to have him one of the Princess guard when we came home. But you shall see how the devil out of this so wrought with Green, that he did the Master what mischiefe hee could in seeking to discredit him, and to thrust him and many other honest men out of the Ship in the end. To speake of all our trouble in this time of Winter (which was so cold, as it lamed the most of our Company, and my selfe doe yet feele it) would bee too tedious.

But I must not forget to shew, how mercifully God dealt with us in this time; for the space of three moneths wee had such store of Fowle of one kinde (which were Partridges as white as milke) that wee killed above an hundred dozen, besides others of sundry sorts: for all was fish that came to the net. The Spring comming, this Fowle left us, yet they were with us all the extreame cold. Then in their places came divers sort of other Fowle, as Swanne, Geese, Duck, and Teale, but hard to come by. Our Master hoped they would have bred in those broken grounds, but they doe not: but came from the South, and flew to the North, further then we were this Voyage: yet if they be taken short with the wind at North, or North-west, or North-east, then they fall and stay till the winde serve them, and then flye to the North.

About this time, when the Ice began to breake out of the Bayes, there came a Savage to our Ship, as it were to see and to bee seene, being the first that we had seene in all this time: whom our Master intreated well, and made much of him, promising unto himselfe great matters by his meanes, and therefore would have all the Knives and Hatchets (which any man had) to his private use, but received none but from John King the Carpenter, and my selfe. To this Savage our Master gave a Knife, a Looking-glasse, and Buttons, who received them thankefully, and made signes that after hee had slept hee would come againe, which hee did. When hee came, hee brought with him a Sled, which hee drew after him, and upon it two Deeres skinnes, and two Beaver skinnes. Hee had a scrip under his arme, out of which hee drew those things which the Master had given him. Hee tooke the Knife and laid it upon one of the Beaver skinnes, and his Glasses and Buttons upon the other, and so gave them to the Master, who received them; and the Savage tooke those things which the Master had given him, and put them up into his script againe. Then the Master shewed him an Hatchet, for which hee would have given the Master one of his Deere skinnes, but our Master would have them both, and so hee had, although not willingly. After many signes of people to the North, and to the South, and that after so many sleepes he would come againe, he went his way, but never came more.

Now the Ice being out of the Sounds, so that our Boat might go from one place unto another, a company of men were appointed by the Master to go a fishing with our net; their names were as followeth: William Wilson, Henry Greene, Michael Perce, John Thomas, Andrew Moter, Bennet Matthewes, and Arnold Lodlo. These men, the first day they went, caught five hundred fish, as big as good Herrings, and some Troutes: which put us all in some hope to have our wants supplied, and our Commons amended: but these were the most that ever they got in one day, for many dayes they got not a quarter so many. In this time of their fishing, Henry Green and William Wilson, with some others plotted to take the net and the shallop, which the Carpenter had now set up, and so to shift for themselves. But the shallop being readie, our Master would goe in it himselfe, to the South and South-west, to see if hee could meete with the people; for, to that end was it set up, and (that way) wee might see the Woods set on fire by them. So the Master tooke the Sayve and the Shallop, and so much victuall as would serve for eight or nine dayes, and to the South hee went. They that remained aboord, were to take in water, wood and ballast, and to have all things in a readiness against hee came backe. But hee set no time of his returne; for he was perswaded, if he could meet with the people, hee should have flesh of them, and that good store; but he returned worse than hee went forth. For, hee could by no meanes meete with the people, although they were neere them, yet they would set the woods on fire in his sight.

Being returned, hee fitted all things for his returne, and first, delivered all the bread out of the bread roome (which came to a pound a piece for every mans share) and delivered also a Bill of Returne, willing them to have that to shew, if it pleased God, that they came home: and he wept when hee gave it unto them. But to helpe us in this poore estate with some reliefe, the Boate and Sayve went to worke on Friday morning, and stayed till Sunday noone: at which time they came aboord, and brought fourescore small Fish, a poore reliefe for so many hungry bellies. Then we wayed, and stood out of our wintering place, and came to an Anchor without, in the mouth of the Bay: from whence we wayed and came to an anchor without in the Sea, where our bread being gone, that store of cheese we had was to stop a gap, whereof there were five, whereat the company grudged, because they made account of nine. But those that were left, were equally divided by the Master, although he had counsell to the contrarie: for there were some who having it, would make hast to bee rid thereof, because they could not governe it. I knew when Henrie Greene gave halfe his bread, which hee had for fourteene dayes, to one to keepe, and prayed him not to let him have any untill the next Monday: but before Wednesday at night, hee never left till hee had it againe, having eaten up his first weeks bread before. So Wilson the Boatswaine hath eaten (in one day) his fortnights bread, and hath beene two or three dayes sicke for his labour. The cause that moved the Master to deliver all the Cheese, was because they were not all of one goodnesse, and therefore they should see that they had no wrong done them: but every man should have alike the best and the worst together, which was three pounds and a halfe for seven dayes.

The wind serving, we weighed and stood to the North-west, and on Munday at night (the eighteenth day of June) wee fell into the Ice, and the next day the wind being at West, we lay there till Sunday in sight of Land. Now being here, the Master told Nicholas Simmes, that there would be a breaking up of chests, and a search for bread, and willed him (if hee had any) to bring it to him, which hee did, and delivered to the Master thirty cakes in a bagge. This deed of the Master (if it bee true) hath made mee marvell, what should bee the reason that hee did not stop the breach in the beginning, but let it grow to that height, as that it overthrew himselfe and many other honest men: but there are many devices in the heart of man, yet the counsell of the Lord shall stand.

Being thus in the Ice on Saturday, the one and twentieth of June at night, Wilson the Boatswayne, and Henry Greene came to mee lying (in my Cabbin) lame, and told mee that they and the rest of their Associates, would shift the Company, and turne the Master, and all the sicke men into the shallop, and let them shift for themselves. For, there was not fourteen daies victual left for all the Company, at that poore allowance they were at, and that there they lay, the Master not caring to goe one way or other: and that they had not eaten any thing these three dayes, and therefore were resolute, either to mend or end, and what they had begun they would goe through with it, or dye. When I heard this, I told them I marvelled to heare so much from them, considering that they were married men, and had wives and children, and that for their sakes they should not commit so foule a thing in the sight of God and man, as that would bee; for why should they banish themselves from their native Countrie? Henry Greene bad me hold my peace, for he knew the worst, which was, to be hanged when hee came home, and therefore of the two he would rather he hanged at home then starved abroad: and for the good will they bare me, they would have mee stay in the Ship. I gave them thankes, and told them that I came into her, not to forsake her, yet not to hurt my selfe and others by any such deed. Henry Greene told me then, that I must take my fortune in the Shallop. If there bee no remedie (said I) the will of God bee done.

Away went Henry Greene in a rage, swearing to cut his throat that went about to disturbe them, and left Wilson by me, with whom I had some talke, but to no good: for he was so perswaded, that there was no remedie now, but to goe on while it was hot, least their partie should faile them, and the mischiefe they had intended to others, should light on themselves. Henry Greene came againe, and demanded of him what I said. Wilson answered, He is in his old song, still patient. Then I spake to Henry Greene to stay three dayes, in which time I would so deale with the Master, that all should be well. So I dealt with him to forbeare but two dayes, nay twelve houres; there is no way then (say they) but out of hand. Then I told them that if they would stay till Munday, I would joyne with them to share all the victuals in the ship, and would justifie it when I came home; but this would not serve their turnes. Wherefore I told them, it was some worse matter they had in hand then they made shew of, and that it was bloud and revenge hee sought, or else he would not at such a time of night undertake such a deed. Henry Greene (with that) taketh my Bible which lay before me, and sware that hee would doe no man harme, and what hee did was for the good of the voyage, and for nothing else; and that all the rest should do the like. The like did Wilson sweare.

Henry Greene went his way, and presently came Juet, who because hee was an ancient man, I hoped to have found some reason in him; but hee was worse than Henry Greene, for hee sware plainely that he would justifie this deed when he came home. After him came John Thomas, and Michel Perce, as birds of one feather: but because they are not living I will let them goe, as then I did. Then came Moter and Bennet, of whom I demanded, if they were well advised what they had taken in hand. They answered, they were, and therefore came to take their oath.

Now, because I am much condemned for this oath, as one of them that plotted with them, and that by an oath I should bind them together to performe what they had begun, I thought good heere to set downe to the view of all, how well their oath and deedes agreed: and thus it was. You

shall sweare truth to God, your Prince and Countrie: you shall doe nothing, but to the glory of God, and the good of the action in hand, and
harme to no man. This was the oath, without adding or diminishing. I
looked for more of these companions (although these were too many)
but there came no more. It was darke, and they in a readinesse to put
this deed of darknesse in execution. I called to Henry Greene and Wilson,
and prayed them not to goe in hand with it in the darke, but to stay till
the morning. Now, everie man (I hope) would goe to his rest, but wicked-
nesse sleepeth not; for Henry Greene keepeth the Master company all
night (and gave mee bread, which his Cabbin-mate gave him) and others
are as watchfull as he. Then I asked Henrie Greene, whom he would put
out with the Master? he said, the Carpenter, John King, and the sicke
men. I said, they should not doe well to part with the Carpenter, what
need soever they should have. Why the Carpenter was in no more regard
amongst them, was; first, for that he and John King were condemned for
wrong done in the victuall. But the chiefest cause was, for that the Master loved him, and made him his Mate, upon his returne out of our wintering place, thereby displacing Robert Billet, whereat they did grudge,
because hee could neither write nor read. And therefore (said they) the
Master and his ignorant Mate would carry the Ship whither the Master
pleased: the Master forbidding any man to keepe account or reckoning,
having taken from all men whatsoever served for that purpose. Well, I
obtained of Henrie Greene and Wilson, that the Carpenter should stay,
by whose meanes I hoped (after they had satisfied themselves) that the
Master, and the poore man might be taken into the Ship againe. Or, I
hoped, that some one or other would give some notice, either to the
Carpenter John King, or the Master; for so it might have come to passe
by some of them that were the most forward.

Now, it shall not bee amisse to shew how we were lodged, and to begin
in the Cooke roome; there lay Bennet and the Cooper lame; without the
Cooke roome, on the steere-board side, lay Thomas Wydhouse sicke;
next to him lay Sydrack Funer lame, then the Surgeon, and John Hudson
with him; next to them lay Wilson the Boatswaine, and then Arnold
Lodlo next to him: in the Gun-roome lay Robert Juet and John Thomas;
on the Larboord side, lay Michael Bute and Adria Moore, who had never
beene well since wee lost our anchor; next to them lay Michael Perce and
Andrew Moter. Next to them without the Gun-roome, lay John King,
and with him Robert Billet: next to them my selfe, and next to me Francis Clements: In the mid-ship, betweene the Capstone and the Pumpes,
lay Henrie Greene and Nicholas Simmes. This night John King was late
up, and they thought he had been with the Master, but he was with the
Carpenter, who lay on the Poope, and comming downe from him, was
met by his Cabbin-mate, as it were by chance, and so they came to their
Cabbin together. It was not long ere it was day: then came Bennet for
water for the Kettle, hee rose and went into the Hold: when hee was in,

they shut the Hatch on him (but who kept it downe I know not) up upon the Deck went Bennet.

In the meane time Henrie Greene, and another went to the Carpenter, and held him with a talke, till the Master came out of his Cabbin (which hee soone did) then came John Thomas and Bennet before him, while Wilson bound his armes behind him. He asked them what they meant? they told him, he should know when he was in the Shallop. Now Juet, while this was a doing, came to John King into the Hold, who was provided for him, for he had got a sword of his own, and kept him at a bay, and might have killed him, but others came to helpe him: and so he came up to the Master. The master called to the Carpenter, and told him that he was bound; but, I heard no answere he made. Now Arnold Lodlo, and Michael Bute rayled at them, and told them their knaverie would shew it selfe. Then was the Shallop haled up to the Ship side, and the poore, sicke, and lame men were called upon to get them out of their Cabbins into the Shallop. The Master called to me, who came out of my Cabbin as well as I could, to the Hatch way to speake with him: where, on my knees I besought them, for the love of God, to remember themselves, and to doe as they would be done unto. They bad me keepe my selfe well, and get me into my Cabbin; not suffering the Master to speake with me. But when I came into my Cabbin againe, hee called to me at the Horne, which gave light into my Cabbin, and told mee that Juet would overthrow us all; nay (said I) it is that villaine Henry Greene, and I spake it not softly.

Now was the Carpenter at libertie, who asked them, if they would bee hanged when they came home: and as for himselfe, hee said, hee would not stay in the Ship unlesse they would force him: they bad him goe then, for they would not stay him: I will (said hee) so I may have my chest with mee, and all that is in it: they said, hee should, and presently they put it into the Shallop. Then hee came downe to mee, to take his leave of mee, who perswaded him to stay, which if he did, he might so worke that all should bee well: hee said, hee did not thinke, but they would be glad to take them in againe. For he was so perswaded by the Master, that there was not one in all the ship, that could tell how to carrie her home; but (saith he) if we must part (which wee will not willingly doe, for they would follow the ship) hee prayed me, if wee came to the Capes before them, that I would leave some token that wee had beene there, neere to the place where the Fowles bred, and hee would doe the like for us: and so (with teares) we parted. Now were the sicke men driven out of their Cabbins into the Shallop; but John Thomas was Francis Clements friend, and Bennet was the Coopers, so as there were words betweene them and Henrie Greene, one saying, that they should goe, and the other swearing that they should not goe, but such as were in the shallop should returne. When Henrie Greene heard that, he was compelled to give place, and to put out Arnold Lodlo, and Michael Bute, which with much adoe they did.

In the meane time, there were some of them that plyed their worke, as if the Ship had beene entred by force, and they had free leave to pillage, breaking up Chests, and rifling all places. One of them came by me, who asked me, what they should doe. I answered, hee should make an end of what hee had begun; for I saw him doe nothing but sharke up and downe. Now, were all the poore men in the Shallop, whose names are as followeth; Henrie Hudson, John Hudson, Arnold Lodlo, Sidrack Faner, Phillip Staffe, Thomas Woodhouse, or Wydhouse, Adam Moore, Henrie King, Michael Bute. The Carpenter got of them a Peece, and Powder, and Shot, and some Pikes, an Iron Pot, with some meale, and other things. They stood out of the Ice, the Shallop being fast to the Sterne of the Shippe, and so (when they were nigh out, for I cannot say, they were cleane out) they cut her head fast from the Sterne of our Ship, then out with their Top-sayles, and towards the East they stood in a cleere Sea. In the end they tooke in their Top-sayles, righted their Helme, and lay under their Fore-sayle till they had ransacked and searched all places in the Ship. In the Hold they found one of the vessels of meale whole, and the other halfe spent, for wee had but two; wee found also two firkins of Butter, some twentie seven piece of Porke, halfe a bushell of Pease, but in the Masters Cabbin we found two hundred of bisket Cakes, a pecke of Meale, of Beere to the quantitie of a Butt, one with another. Now, it was said, that the Shallop was come within sight, they let fall the Main-sayle, and out with their Top-sayles, and flye as from an Enemy.

Then I prayed them yet to remember themselves: but William Wilson (more then the rest) would heare of no such matter. Comming nigh the East shoare they cast about, and stood to the West and came to an Iland, and anchored in sixteene or seventeene fathome water. So they sent the Boat, and the Net ashoare to see if they could have a Draught: but could not for Rocks and great stones. Michael Perse killed two Fowle, and heere they found good store of that Weede, which we called Cockle grasse in our wintering place, whereof they gathered store, and came aboard againe. Heere we lay that night, and the best part of the next day, in all which time we saw not the shallop, or ever after.

THE DANGEROUS VOYAGE OF CAPT. THOMAS JAMES, 1631[1]

Told by Himself

I

How He Made Preparation

HAVING been many Years importun'd, by my honourable and worthy Friends, to undertake the Discovery of that Part of the World, which is commonly called The North West Passage into the

[1]From *The Dangerous Voyage of Capt. Thomas James* (1631).

South Sea, and so to proceed to Japan, and to round the World to the Westward; being press'd forward withal, by the earnest Desire of the King's most excellent Majesty had, to be satisfied thereof; I acquainted my good Friends, the Merchants of Bristol with my Design, who freely offer'd to be at the Charge of furnishing Shipping for that Purpose. And being thus enabled, I address'd myself to the Honourable Sir Thomas Roe, Kt. (as the most learned, and the greatest Traveller by Sea or Land, this Day in England) who most graciously accepted of the Offer, and encourag'd me by many Favours in my Undertaking. Therefore with all Speed I contriv'd in my Mind, the best Model I could; whereby I might effect my Design. The Adventurers Money was instantly ready, and put into a Treasurer's Hand, that there might be no Want of present Pay, for any Thing I thought necessary for the Voyage.

I was ever of Opinion, that this particular Action might be better effected by one Ship, than more; because in those icy Seas, so much subject to Fogs, they might be easily separated; I forbear to speak of Storms and other Accidents, as a Rendezvous in Discoveries, cannot surely or without much Hinderance be appointed; and that speedy Perseverence is the Life of such a Business: Therefore I resolv'd to have but one Ship, the Ship-boat, and a Shallop.

A great Ship, as by former Experience I had found, was unfit to be forc'd through the Ice; therefore I made Choice of a well condition'd, strong Ship, of the Burthen of 70 Tons and in God and that only Ship, to put the Hope of my future Fortune.

The Ship being resolv'd upon, and that in less Time than Eighteen Months our Voyage could not be effected; I next consider'd how our Ship of 70 Tons in Bulk and Weight might be proportioned; in Victuals, and other Necessaries: This was all done, as soon as we could; and the Number of Men it would serve, at ordinary Allowance, for the forementioned Time, was found to be, twenty two, a small Number to perform such a Business, yet double the Number sufficient to sail the Ship.

The Baker, Brewer, Butcher, and others, undertake their Offices upon their Credit; knowing it to be a general Business, and their utter undoing if they fail'd in the Performance, but truly they prov'd themselves Masters in their Arts; and have my Praise for their honest Care: In them consisted great part of the Performance of the Voyage.

The Carpenters go in Hand with the Ship, to make her as strong and as serviceable as possibly they could.

Every Thing being duly proportion'd, and my small Number of Men known. I began to think of the Quality and Ability they should be of.

Voluntary Loiterers I at first Disclaim'd, and publish'd I would have all unmarried, approved, able, and healthy Seamen: In a few Days an abundant Number presented themselves; furnished with experience in Marine Affairs. I first made choice of a Boatswain; and some to work with him, for fitting the Rigging of the Ship; and as Things went forward shipp'd the Subordinate Crew; and all Things being perfectly ready, I shipp'd the Master's Mates; and last of all, the Master of my Ship, and my Lieutenant. The whole Company were Strangers to me, and to each other; but yet privately recommended by worthy Merchants, for their Ability and Fidelity. I was sought to by divers, that had been in Places of the chief Command in this Action formerly; and others also that had us'd the Northerly Icy Seas; but I utterly refus'd them all; and would by no Means have any with me that had been in the like Voyage, or Adventure, for some private Reasons unnecessary here to be related; keeping thus the Power in my own Hands I had all the Men to acknowledge immediate Dependance upon myself alone, both for Direction and Disposing of all, as well of the Navigation, as all other Things whatsoever.

In the mean Time, the better to strengthen my former Studies in this Business, I sought after Journals, Charts, Discourses, or whatever else might help my understanding.

I set skilful workmen to make me Quadrants, Staves, Semi-circles, etc. as much, namely, as concern the Fabrick of them; not trusting to their mechanick hands to divide them; but had them divided by an ingenious Practitioner in the Mathematicks. I likewise had Compass Needles made after the most reasonable and truest Way that could be thought of; and by the First of April, every Thing was ready to be put together into our hopeful Ship.

In the Mean Time, I made a Journey to London, to know His Majesty's further Pleasure, and to make known to him my Readiness; who calculating for the foremention'd Honourable Knight, (Sir Thomas Roe,) I speedily after receiv'd His Majesty's Royal Letters, with Directions for proceeding in my Voyage, and my Discharge: Whereupon, I had forth the Ship into the Road, expecting a fair Wind to begin the Voyage.

II

The Ship Encompassed with Ice

The 3rd of May (After Prayer for good Success on our Endeavours) about three in the Afternoon, we sail'd down the Severn, with little Wind, to the Westward of Lundy; where the Wind opposed us so strongly that we were obliged to anchor in Lundy Road, the 5th in the Evening; where we remain'd till the 8th in the Morning. Now hoping the Wind would favour us, we sail'd; but were forc'd to put into Melford, where we anchor'd about Midnight. Here we remain'd till the 17th in the Morning; when with the first fair Wind, we proceeded and doubled about Cape Cleer off Ireland. The 22nd we were in Lat. 51:26, and the Blaskes did beat off us North-East, about twelve Leagues off; which Blaskes is in Lat. 52:4. Here I order'd the Course that should be kept, which was generally W.N.W. as the Wind would permit; which in this Course and Distance is very variable. The 4th of June we made the Land of Greenland; standing in with it to have Knowledge of the trending of it; it prov'd very foul Weather; and the next Day, by two in the Morning, we found ourselves encompassed with Ice, and endeavouring to clear ourselves of it (by Reason we could not see far about us) we were the more engag'd, and struck many fearful Blows against it: At length we made fast to a great Piece, (it blowing very hard) and with Poles wrought Day and Night to keep off the Ice; in which Labour we broke all our Poles. The 6th about two in the Morning, we were beset with many extraordinary great Pieces of Ice, that came upon us, as it were with Violence, and doubtless would have crushed us to Pieces, if we had not let fall some Sail, which the Ship presently felt. In escaping that Danger, we ran against another great Piece, that we doubted whether our Ship had not been stav'd to Pieces: But pumping, we found she made no Water. The former Pieces of Ice, had crush'd our Shallop all to Pieces; wherefore I caus'd our Long Boat speedily to be had up from betwixt the Decks, and put over Board: By the Help whereof we recover'd our broken Shallop; and had her upon the Deck, intending to new build her. All this Day, we beat, and were beaten fearfully, amongst the Ice; it blowing a very Storm. In the Evening, we were inclosed among great Pieces, as high as our Poop: and some of the sharp blue Corners of them, reach'd quite under us. All these great Pieces, by Reason it was the outside of the Ice, did heave and set, and so beat us, that it was wonderfull how the Ship could indure one Blow of it; (*but it was only God's preservation of us, to whom be all Honour and Glory.*) In this Extremity I made the Men let fall. and make what Sail they could; and the Ship forc'd herself through it, though so toss'd and beaten, as I think never Ship was. When we were clear, we tried the Pumps, and found them stanch: Upon which we went instantly to Prayer, *to praise God for his merciful Delivery of us.*

III

She Runs Ashore

The 12th in the Morning, it began to blow hard at S. E. which was partly of the Shore; and the Ship began to drive; it being soft oozy Ground. We heav'd in our Anchor thereupon, and came to Sail under two Courses. Whilst the most were busy in heaving out of Top-sails: Some, that should have had special Care of the Ship, ran her ashore upon the Rocks, out of mere Carelessness, in looking out and about, or heaving of the Lead, after they had seen the Land all Night long, and might even then have seen it, if they had not been blind with Self-conceit; and been enviously opposite in Opinion. The first Blow, struck me out of a deep Sleep, and I running out of my Cabbin, thought no other at first, but I had been waken'd, when I saw our Danger, to provide myself for another World.

After I had controul'd a little Passion in myself, and had check'd some bad Counsel that was given me, to revenge myself upon those that had committed this Error; I order'd what should be done to get off these Rocks and ·Stones. First, we hal'd all our Sails aback; but that did no Good, but made her Beat the harder. Whereupon we struck all our Sails amain, and furl'd them up close, tearing down our Stern, to bring the Cable thro' the Cabbin to Capstang; and so laid out an Anchor to heave her astern. I made all the Water in Hold to be stav'd; and set some to the Pumps to pump it out, and intended to do the like with our Beer; Others I put to throw out all our Coals, which was soon and readily done. We coil'd out our Cables into our Long-Boat; all this While, the Ship beating so furiously that we saw some of the Sheathing swim by us. Then stood we, as many as could, to the Capstang; and heav'd with such a good Will, that the Cable broke, and we lost our Anchor. Out, with all Speed, therefore, we put another. We could not now perceive whether she leak'd or no; and that by Reason we were employ'd in pumping out the Water, which we had bulg'd in Hold, tho' we much doubted, but she had re-ceiv'd her Death's Wound: Therefore we put into the Boat the Carpen-ter's Tools, a Barrel of Bread, a Barrel of Powder, six Muskets, with some Match; and a Tinder-box, Fish Hooks and Lines, Pitch and Oakum: And to be brief, whatever could be thought on in such an Extremity. All this we sent ashore, to prolong a miserable Life for a few Days. We were five Hours thus beating, in which Time she struck 100 Blows; insomuch that we thought every Stroke had been the last that it was possible she could have endur'd. The Water, we could not perceive, in all this Time to flow any Thing at all. At length, *it pleas' God*, she beat over all the Rocks, tho' yet we knew not whether she was stanch. Whereupon to pumping we go on all Hands, till we made the Pumps suck; and then we saw how much Water she made in a Glass. We found her to be very leaky; but we went to Prayer, and *gave God Thanks it was no worse*; and so fitted all Things again, and got further off and came to an Anchor.

IV

And Is Forsaken

I lay ashore till the 17th; all which Time our Miseries incresd'd. It snow'd and froze extremely. At which Time, we looking from the Shore towards the Ship, she look'd like a Piece of Ice, in the Fashion of a Ship; or a Ship resembling a Piece of Ice. The Snow was all frozen about her, and all her Fore-part firm Ice; and so she was on both Sides also. Our Cables froze in the Hawse, wonderful to behold. I got me aboard, where the long Nights I spent, with tormenting Cogitations; and in the Day-time, I could not see any Hope of saving the Ship. This I was assur'd of, that it was impossible to endure these Extremities long. Every Day the Men must beat the Ice off the Cables, while some within Board, with the Carpenter's long Calking Iron, digg'd the Ice out of the Hawses: In which Work, the Water would freeze on their Cloaths and Hands, and would so benumb them, that they could hardly get into the Ship, without being heav'd in with a rope.

The 23rd, the Ice incresd'd extraordinarily; and the Snow lay on the Water in Flakes, as it fell; much Ice also drove by us: yet nothing hard all this while. In the Evening, after the Watch was set, a great Piece came athwart our Hawse; and four more followed after him; the least of them a Quarter of a Mile broad, which in the Dark very much astonish'd us, thinking it would carry us out of the Harbour, upon the Shoal's Eastern Point, which was full of Rocks. It was newly congeal'd, a Matter of two Inches thick; and we broke thro' it, the Cable and Anchor enduring an incredible Stress, sometimes stopping the whole Ice. We shot off three Muskets, signifying to our Men ashore, that we were in Distress; who answer'd us again, but could not help us. By 10 o'Clock it was all pass'd; nevertheless we watched carefully; and the Weather was warmer than we had felt it any Time this Month. In the Morning by Break of Day, I sent for our Men aboard, who made up the House and arriv'd by 10, being driven by the Way to wade thro' the congeal'd Water; so that they recover'd the Boat with Difficulty. There drove by the Ship many Pieces of Ice, tho' not so large as the former, yet much thicker: One Piece came foul of the Cable, and made the Ship drive.

As soon as we were clear of it, we join'd our Strengths together, and had up our Eastermost Anchor; and now I ressolved to bring the Ship aground; for no Cables nor Anchors would hold her.

With the Flood, we weigh'd our Westermost Anchor, *perceiving God's assistance manifestly;* because it happen'd to be fine warm Weather, otherwise we had not been able to work. The Wind was now S. which blew in upon the Shoar, and made the lowest Tides. We brought the Ship into 12 foot Water, and laid out one Anchor in an Offing, and another in Shoal Water, to draw her on Land at Command. Our Hope also was, that some Stones that were to the Westward of us, would fend off some of the Ice. We then being about a Mile from the Shore, about 10 o'Clock in the dark night, the Ice came driving upon us, and our Anchors came Home. She drove some 2 Cable's length, and the Wind blowing on the Shore, by 2 o'Clock she came aground, and stopt much Ice; yet she lay well all Night, and we took some Rest.

The 25th, the Wind shifted Easterly; and put Abundance of Ice on us. When the Flood was made we encourag'd one another, and to work we go; drawing home our Anchor by main Force, under great Pieces of Ice, our Endeavour being to put the Ship to the Shore. But to our great Discomfort, when the half Tide was made; (which was two Hours before High Water) the Ship drove among the Ice to the Eastward, do what we could, and so would have on the Shoal Rocks. As I have said before, these two Days and this Day was very warm Weather; and it rain'd, which it had not yet but once done, since we came hither; otherwise, it had been impossible we could have wrought. Withal, the Wind shifted also to the S. and at the very Instant blew a hard Puff, which so continu'd half an Hour. I caus'd the two Topsails to be had up from betwixt Decks, and we hoist'd them up with Ropes in all Haste, and we forc'd the Ship ashore, when she had not half a Cable's Length to drive on the rocky Shoals. In the Evening, we broke Way thro' the Ice, and put an Anchor to Shoreward in 5 Foot Water, to keep her to the Shore, if possible. Here Sir Hugh Willoughby came into my Mind, who, without Doubt, was driven out of his Harbour in this Manner, and so starv'd at Sea. *But God was more merciful to us.* About 9 at Night, the Wind came up at N. W. and blew a very Storm. This Wind was of the Shore, which blew away all the Ice from about us, long before we were afloat. There came in a great rolling Sea withall, about the Point; accompanied with a great Surf on the Shore. And now were we left to the mercy of the Sea, on the Ground. By 10, she began to roll in her Dock, and soon after began to beat against the Ground. We stood at the Capstang, as many as could; others at the Pumps, for we thought that every fifth or sixth Blow would have stav'd her to Pieces. We heav'd to the uttermost of our Strengths, to keep her as near the Ground as we could. By Reason of this Wind, it flow'd very much Water, and we drew her up so high, that it was doubtful, if ever we should get her off again. She continu'd thus beating, till two o'Clock the next Morning, and then she settled again. Where upon we went to Sleep, to restore Nature; seeing the next Tide we expected to be again tormented.

The 26th, in the Morning Tide, our Ship did not float, whereby we had some Quietness. After Prayers, I call'd a Consultation of the Master, my Lieutenant, the Mates, Carpenter, and Boatswain; to whom I propos'd, that now we were put to our last Shifts; and therefore they should tell me what they thought of it: Namely, whether it were not best, to carry all our Provision ashore; and when the Wind should come Northerly, it were not safest to draw her further off, and sink her. After many Reasonings they allow'd of my Purpose, and so I communicated it to the Company, who all willingly agreed to it. And so we fell to getting up of our Provisions: First, our Bread, of which we landed this Day two Dryfats with a Hogshead of Beef; having much ado to get the Boat thro' the thick, congeal'd Water. In the Evening, the Wind came up at N. E. and E. and fill'd the Bay full of Ice.

The 27th, the Bay continu'd full of Ice, which I hop'd would so continue and freeze, that we should not be forc'd to sink our Ship. This Day we could land nothing.

The 28th, at Break of Day, three of our Men went ashore over the Ice, unknown to me; and the Wind coming up at W. drove the Ice from betwixt us and the Shore, and most Part of the Bay also: And yet not so, but the Boat could go ashore for any Thing. I made the Carpenter fit a Place against all sudden Extremities; for that with the N. W. or Northerly Wind, I meant to effect our last Project. In the Run of her, on the Starboard Side; he cut away the Ceiling and the Plank to the Sheathing, some 4 or 5 Inches square; some 4 foot high from the Keel of her, that so it might be bor'd out, at an Instant. We brought our Bread, which was remaining in the Bread-Room, up in to the great Cabbin; and likewise all our Powder, fitting much of our light, dry Things betwixt Decks.

The 29th, at 5 in the Morning, the Wind came up at W. N. W. and began to Blow very hard. It was ordinary for the Wind to shift from the W. by the N. round about. So first, I order'd the Cooper to go down in Hold, and look to all our Casks; those that were full, to mawl in the Bungs of them; those that were empty, to get up, or if they could not be gotten up, to stave them. Then to coil all our Cables upon our lower Tire, and to lay on our spare Anchors, and any Thing that was weighty, to keep it down from rising. By 7 o'Clock, it blew a Storm at N. W. our bitter Enemy. The Ship was already bedded some two Foot in the Sand, and whilst that was flowing, she must beat. This I before had in my Consideration; for I thought she was so far driven up, that we should never get her off. Yet we had been so ferrited by her last beating, that I resolv'd to sink her right down, rather than run that Hazard. By 9, she began to roll in her Dock, with a most extraordinary great Sea that was come; which I found to be occasion'd by the foremention'd Overfall. And this was the fatal Hour that put us to our Wits End. Wherefore I went down into the Hold with the Carpenter, and took his Auger and bor'd a Hole in the Ship, and let in the Water. Thus, with all Speed, we began to cut out other Places, to bore through, but every Place was full of Nails. By 10, notwithstanding, the lower Tire was cover'd with Water, for all which, she began so to beat in her Dock more and more, that we could nor work, nor stand to do and Thing in her. Nor would she sink so fast as we would have her, but continu'd beating double Blows; first abaft, and then before, that it was wonderful, how she could endure a Quarter of an Hour with it. By 12, her lower Tire rose, and that did so counterbeat on the Inside, that it beat the Bulk-Heads of the Bread-room, Powder-room, and Fore-piece, all to Pieces; and when it came be-twixt Decks, the Chests fled wildly about, and the Water did flash and fly wonderfully; so that now we expected every Minute, when the Ship would open and break to Pieces. At one, she beat off her Rudder, and that was gone, we knew not which Way. Thus she continu'd beating till 3; and then the Sea came up on the Upper Deck; and soon after, she began to settle. In her, we were fain to sink the most Part of our Bedding and Cloaths; and the Chirugeon's Chest with the rest. Our Men that were ashore, stood looking upon us, almost dead with Cold, and Sor-rows to see our Misery, and their own. We look'd upon them again, and both upon each other with woful Hearts. Dark Night drew on, and I order'd the Boat to be hal'd up, and commanded my loving Companions to go all into her; who express'd their faithful Affections to me, as loath to part from me. I told them, that my Meaning was to go ashore with them. And thus, lastly, I forsook the Ship.

V

And Again Recovered

April 1632. The 1st of this month being Easter-Day, we solemniz'd it as religiously as God gave us Grace to do. And now sitting all about the Fire, we reason'd and considered together upon our Estate: We had five Men, whereof the Carpenter was one, not able to do any Thing. The Boatswain and many more, were very infirm; and of all the rest, we had but five, that could eat of their ordinary Allowance. The Time and Season of the Year came forwards apace; and the Cold very little abated: Our Pinnace was in an indifferent Forwardness; but the Carpenter grew worse and worse: The Ship, as we then thought, lay all full of solid Ice, which was Weight enough to open the Seams of any new and sound Vessel; especially of one that had lain so long upon the Ground as she had done. In short, after many Disputations, and laying open of our miserable and hopeless Estates, I resolv'd upon this Course; that notwithstanding it was more Labour, and we weaker and weaker; yet with the firm warm Weather, we would begin to clear the Ship; that we might have the Time before us, to think of some other Course. This being order'd, we look'd to those Tools we had, to dig the Ice out of her; we had but two Iron Bars ashore; the rest were sunk in the Ship, and one of them was broken too. We fell to fitting of those Bars, and four broken Shovels that we had: which we intended, as afterwards we did, to dig the Ice out of her; and to lay that Ice on a Heap, upon the Larboard Bow, and to sink it down to the Ground so fast, that it should be a Barricado to us, when the Ice broke up, which we fear'd would tear us to Pieces.

The 16th, was the most comfortable Sunshine Day, that came this Year; and I put some to clear off the Snow from the upper Decks of the Ship; and to clear and dry the great Cabbin, by making Fire in it. Others I put to dig down thro' the Ice, to come by our Anchor, that was in Shoal Water, which the 17th, in the Afternoon we got up, and carried aboard.

The 18th, I put them to dig down thro' the Ice, near the Place where we thought our Rudder might be. They digg'd down, and came to Water; but no Hopes of finding of it; we had many Doubts that it might be sanded: Or that the Ice might have carried it away already, the last Year: Or if we could not recover it by digging before the Ice broke up, and drove, there was little Hopes of it.

By the 21st, we had labour'd so hard, that we came to the sight of a Cask; and could likewise perceive, that there was some Water in the Hold. This we knew could not be thaw'd Water; because it froze Night and Day very hard aboard the Ship, and on the Land also.

By the 23rd, in the Evening, we came to pierce the forementioned Cask; and found it full of very good Beer, which much rejoic'd us all; especially the sick Men, notwithstanding it tasted a little of the bulg'd Water. By this we thought that the Holes we had cut to sink the Ship were frozen, and that this Water had stood in the Ship all the Winter.

The 24th, we went betimes in the Morning to work; but we found that the Water was risen above the Ice where we had left Work, about two Foot; for the Wind had blown very hard at N. the Night before. In the Morning, the Wind came about at S. and blew hard, and altho' we had little Reason for it, we yet expected a low veer of the Water. I thereupon put them to work on the Outside of the Ship, that we might come to the lower Hole, which we had cut in the Stern-Shoots. With much Labour by Night, we digg'd down thro' the Ice to it; and found it unfrozen, as it had been all the Winter, and to our great Comforts, we found that on the Inside, the Water was ebb'd within the Hole, and that on the Outside, it was ebb'd a Foot lower. Hereupon I caus'd a Shot-board to be nail'd upon it, and to be made as tight as might be, to try if the Water came in any other Way. To the other two Holes, we had digg'd on the Inside, and found them frozen. Now I did this betimes, that if we found the Ship founder'd, we might resolve on some Course to save or prolong our Lives, by getting to the Main before the Ice were broken up. As for our Boat it was too little, and bulg'd besides that. Our Carpenter was by this Time past Hopes, and therefore little Hope had we of our Pinnace. But which was worst of all, we had not four Men able to travel thro' the Snow over the Ice, and in this miserable State were we at this Present.

The 25th, we satisfied our Longing; for the Wind now coming about Northerly, the Water rose by the Ship's Side, where we had digg'd down, a Foot and more above the Hold: and yet did not rise within Board. This so incouraged us, that we fell lustily to digging, and to heave the Ice, out of the Ship. I put the Cook and some others, to thaw the Pumps; who by continual pouring of hot Water into them; by the 27th, in the Morning they had clear'd one of them: Which, we proving, found it delivered Water very sufficiently. Thus we fell to pumping, and having clear'd two Foot Water, we left the other to a second Trial. Continuing our Work thus, in digging the Ice; by the 28th, we had clear'd our other Pump; which we also found to deliver Water very well. We found Likewise, that the Water did not rise any Thing in the Hold.

The 29th, it rain'd all Day long, a sure Sign to us, that Winter was broken up.

The 30th, we were betimes aboard at our Work: Which Day, and the 31st, were very cold, with Snow and Hail; which pinch'd our sick Men more than any Time this Year. This Evening being *May* Eve; we re-turn'd late from our Work to the House, and made a good Fire, and chose ladies, and ceremoniously wore their Names in our Caps; endeavouring to revive ourselves by any Means.

May 1632. The first, we went aboard betimes to heave out the Ice.

The 2nd, it did snow and blow, and was so could, that we were forc'd to keep House all Day.

By the 9th, we were come to, and got up our five Barrels of Beef and Pork, and had found four Buts of Beer, and one of Cider, which God had preserv'd for us: It had lain under Water all the Winter; yet we could not perceive that it was any Thing the worse. God make us ever thankful for the Comfort it gave us.

The 10th, it snow'd and blew so cold, that we could not stir out of the House; yet nevertheless by Day the Snow vanisheth away apace on the Land.

The 11th, we were aboard betimes, to heave out Ice. By the 12th, at Night we had cleared out all the Ice, out of the Hold, and found likewise our Store-Shooes, which had lain soak'd in the Water all the Winter; but we dried them by the Fire, and fitted ourselves with them. We struck again our Cables into the Hold; there stood a But of Wine also, which had been all the Winter on the upper Deck, and continu'd as yet, all firm frozen. We fitted the Ship also, making her ready to sink again, when the Ice broke up. We could hitherto find no Defect in her; and therefore well hop'd that she was stanch. The Carpenter, nevertheless, argu'd to the contrary; alledging that now she lay on the Ground, in her Dock, the Ice had fill'd her Defects, and that the Ice was the Thing that kept out the Water; but when she should come to labour in the Sea, she would certainly open. And indeed we could now see quite thro' her Seams, betwixt Wind and Water. But that which troubl'd us most, was the Loss of her Rudder, and she now lay in the very Strength of the Tide: Which, whenever the Ice drove, might tear her in Pieces. But we still hop'd the best.

The 14th, we began a new Sort of Work. The Boatswain, and a convenient Number sought ashore the rest of our Rigging, which was much spoil'd by the pecking it out of the Ice, and this they now fell to fitting. I set the Cooper to fit our Cask, altho', poor Man, he was very infirm; my Intent being, to pass some Cables under the Ship, and so to buoy her up with these Casks; if we could not get her off otherwise.

The 18th, our Carpenter William Cole died, a Man belov'd of us all; as much for his inate Goodness, as for the present necessity we had of a Man of his Quality. He had indur'd a long Sickness, with much Patience, and made a very godly End. And now were we in the most miserable State, that we were in all the Voyage. Before his extreme Weakness, he had brought the Pinnace to that pass, that she was ready to be boulted, etc. and to be joyn'd to receive the Plank; so that we were not so discourag'd by his Death, but that we hop'd ourselves to finish her; if the Ship prov'd unserviceable.

This Pinnace was 27 Foot by the Keel, 10 Foot by the Beam, and 5 Foot in the Hold: She had 17 Ground Timbers, 34 Principal Staddles, and 8 short Staddles. He had contriv'd her with a round Stern, to save Labour; and indeed she was a well proportion'd Vessel. Her Burthen was 12 or 14 Tons.

The 21st, was the warmest Sunshine Day, that came this Year. I sent two a fowling, and myself, the Master, Surgeon, and one more, with our Pieces and Dogs, we went into the Woods to see what we could find. We wandered from the House 8 miles, and search'd with all Diligence; but return'd comfortless, not an Herb nor Leaf eatable could we find. Our Fowlers had as bad Success. In the Woods, we found the Snow partly wasted away, so that it was passable. The Ponds were almost unthaw'd, but the Sea we could see firm frozen.

The 22nd, we went aboard the Ship, and found she had made so much Water, that it was risen above the Ballast, which made us doubt again of her Soundness. We fell to pumping, and pump'd her quite dry. And now by Day sometimes, we have such hot Glooms, that we cannot endure in the Sun, and yet in the Night it would freeze very hard. This Unnaturalness of the Season tormented our Men, that they now grew worse and worse daily.

The 23rd, our Boatswain, a painful Man, having been long sick, which he had heartily resisted, was taken with such a painful Ach in one of his Thighs, that we verily thought he would have died presently. He kept his Bed all Day in great Extremity, and it was a maxim among us, that if anyone kept his Bed two Days, he could rise no more. This made every Man to strive to keep up, for Life.

The 24th, was very warm Sun-shine, and the Ice consum'd by the Shore's Side, and crack'd all over the Bay, with a fearful Noise. About three in the After noon, we could perceive the Ice with the Ebb, to drive by the Ship. Whereupon I sent two, with all Speed to the Master, with Order, to beat out the Hole, and to sink the Ship; as likewise to look for the Rudder betwixt the Ice. This he presently perform'd, and a happy fellow, one David Hammon pecking betwixt the Ice, struck upon it, and it came up with his Lance; who crying that he had found it, the rest came and got it up on the Ice, and so into the Ship. In the mean Time, with the little Drift that the Ice had, it began to rise and mount into high Heaps against the Shoal Shores, and Rocks, and likewise against the Heap of Ice, which we had put for a Barricado to our Ship; but with little Harm to us; yet we were forc'd to cut away the 20 Fath. of Cable, which was frozen in the Ice. After an Hour, the Ice settled again, not having any Vent outwards. Oh! this was a joyful Day to us all, and we gave God Thanks for the Hopes we had of it.

The 25th, was a fine warm Day, and with the Ebb the Ice drove against the Ship, and shook her soundly.

By the 28th, it was pretty clear, betwixt the Ship and the Shore, and

I hop'd the Ice would no more dangerously oppress us. Wherefore I caus'd the lower Hole to be firmly stopt; the Water then remaining three Foot above the Ballast.

The 29th, being Prince Charles's Birth Day, we kept Holy Day, and display'd His Majesty's Colours, both on Land and Aboard, and nam'd our Habitation, Charles Town; by Contraction, Charlton: and the Island Charlton Island.

The 30th, we lanch'd our Boat, and had intercourse sometimes betwixt the Ship and the Shore by Boat which was News to us.

The last of this Month, we found on the Beach some Vetches, to appear out of the Ground; which I made Men to pick up, and boil for our sick Men.

This Day we made an end of fitting all our Rigging and Sails; and it being a very hot Day, we dried, etc. our Fish in the Sun, and air'd all our other Provisions.

June 1632. The four first Days, it snow'd, hail'd, and blew very hard, and it was so cold, that the Ponds of Water froze over, and the Water in our Cans froze in the very House; and Cloaths also that had been wash'd and hung out to dry, did not thaw all Day.

The 5th, it continu'd blowing very hard on the Broad Side of the Ship, which made her swag and wallow in her Dock, notwithstanding she was sunk, which shook her very much. The Ice withal drove against her, and gave her many fearful Blows. I resolv'd to endeavour to hang the Rudder; and when God sent us Water, notwithstanding the Abundance of Ice that was yet about us, to have her further off: In the Afternoon, we under run our small Cable to our Anchor, which lay astern in deep Water; and so with some Difficulty got up our Anchor. This Cable had lain slack under Foot, and under the Ice, all the Winter; and we could never have a clear Slatch from Ice, to have it up, before now; we found it not a Jot the worse. I put some to make Colrakes, that they might go into the Water, and rake a Hole in the Sands to let down our Rudder.

The 6th, we went about to hang it, and our young lustiest Men took it by Turns, to go into the Water, and to rake away the Sand, but they were not able to indure the Cold half a Quarter of an Hour, it was so mortifying; yea, use what Comforts we could, it would make them swoon and die away. We brought it to the Stern Post; but were then forc'd to give it over, being able to work at it no longer. Then we plugg'd up the upper Holes aboard, and fell to pumping the Water out of her again.

The 7th, we wrought about our Rudder, but were again forc'd to give over; and to put our Cables over-board, with Messengers unto them, the Anchor lying to that Pass, that we might keep her right in her Dock, when we had brought her light.

By the 8th, at Night, we had pump'd all the Water out of her; and she a high Water would float in her Dock, tho' she were still dock'd in the Sands, almost 4 Foot. This made us confident what was to be done. I resolv'd to heave out all the Ballast, for the Bottom of her being so saok'd all the Winter, I hop'd was so heavy, that it would bear her. If we could not get her off that way, I then thought to cut her down to the lower Deck, and take out her Masts; and so with our Casks to buoy her off.

The 9th, betimes in the Morning, we fell to Work. We hoisted out our Beer and Cyder, and made a Raft of it, fastening it to our Shore-Anchor. The Beer and Cyder sunk presently to the Ground, which was nothing strange to us; for any Wood or Pipe Staves that had lain under the Ice all the Winter, would also sink down as soon as ever it was heav'd overboard; This Day we heav'd out 10 Ton of Ballast.

The 11th, was very warm Weather, and we hung our Rudder. The Tides now very much deceiv'd us; for a Northerly Wind would very little raise the Water. This made us Doubt of getting off our Ship.

The 15th, This Day, I went to our Watch-Tree; but the Sea, for anything I could perceive to the contrary, was still firm frozen, and the Bay we were in, full of Ice; having no Way to vent it.

The 17th, the wind came Northerly, and we expecting a high Tide, in the Morning betimes, put out our small Cable astern, out at the Gun Room Port; but the Morning Tide we had not Water by a Foot. In the Evening, I had laid Marks, by Stones, etc. and I thought the Water flow'd apace. Making Signs, therefore for the Boat to come ashore, I took all that were able to do any Thing with me aboard; and at High Water, altho' she wanted something to rise clear out of her Dock, yet we heav'd with such a good Will, that we heav'd her thro' the Sand into a Foot and a half deeper Water; and further we durst not yet bring her, for the Ice was all thick about us. After we had moor'd her, we went all to Prayers; and gave God Thanks, that he had given us our Ship again.

The 18th, we were up betimes; the Cooper, and some with him, to fill fresh Water; myself, with others to gather Stones at Low Water; which we piling up in a Heap, at High Water, the Cockswain and his Gang, fetch'd them aboard; where the Master with the rest stow'd them. The Ship at Low Water had a great Lust to the Offing; by which Means we could the better come and stop the two upper Holes firmly: After which, we fitted other convenient Places, to make others to sink her, if Occasion were.

The 19th, we were all up betimes to work; as afore specified: These two Days, our Ship did not float; and it was a Happy Hour, when we got her off, for we never had such a high Tide all the Time we were here. In the Evening, I went up to our Watch-Tree; and this was the first Time I could see any open Water, any way, except that little by the Shore Side, where we were. This put us in some Comfort, that the Sea would shortly break up, which we knew must be to the Northward; seeing that Way we were certain, there were about 200 leagues of Sea.

The 20th, we labour'd as aforesaid. The Wind at N. N. W. The Tide rose so high, that our Ship floated, and we drew her further off, into a Foot and a half deeper Water. Thus we did it by little and little; for the Ice was still wonderful thick round about us.

The 22nd, there drove much Ice about us, and within us, and brought Home our Stern-Anchor. At High Water, notwithstanding all the Ice, we heav'd our Ship further off; that so she may lie afloat at Low Water.

The next Low Water, we sounded all about the Ship; and found it very foul Ground, we discover'd Stones 3 Foot high, above the Ground, and two of them within a Ship's Breadth of the Ship; whereby did more manifestly appear God's Mercies to us; for if when we forc'd her ashore, she had struck one Blow against those Stones, it had bulg'd her. Many such Dangers were there in this Bay; which we now first perceiv'd, by the Ice's grounding and rising against them. In the Evening, we tow'd off the Ship, unto the Place she rid last Year, and there moor'd her. Steering the Ship, Night and Day, Flood and Ebb, among the dispers'd Ice that came athwart of us.

The 23rd, we labour'd in fetching our provisions aboard; Which to do, we were forc'd to wade to carry it to the Boat a full Flight Shot; and all by Reason the Wind was Southerly.

The 24th, I took an observation of the Moon's coming to the Meridian. I had formerly cut down a very high Tree, and made a cross of it: To it, I now fasten'd upermost the King and Queen's Pictures, drawn to the Life; and doubly wrapt in Lead, and so close, that no Weather could hurt them. Betwixt both these, I affix'd His Majesty's Royal Title: *viz.* Charles *the First, King of* England, Scotland, France *and* Ireland. *As also of* Newfoundland, *and of these Territories, and to the Westward, as far as to* Nova Albion, *and to the Northward to the Lat. of* 80 *Deg. etc.*

On the Outside of the Lead, I fasten'd a Shilling, and a Six Pence of His Majesty's Coin: Under that, we fasten'd the King's Arms, fairly cut in Lead; and under that, the Arms of the City of Bristol. And this being Midsummer-Day, we rais'd it on the top of the bare Hill, where we had buried our dead Fellows; formerly by this Ceremony taking Possession of these Territories, to His Majesty's Use.

The Wind continuing Southerly, and blowing hard, put all the Ice upon us; so that the Ship now rid among it, in such apparent Danger, that I thought verily we should have lost her. We labour'd, Flood and Ebb, both with Poles and Oars, to heave away and part the Ice from her. But it was God that protected and preserved us; for it was past any Man's Understanding, how the Ship could endure it, or we by our Labour save her. In the Night, the Wind shifted to the Westward, and blew the Ice from us; whereby we had some Rest.

The 25th, in the Morning, the Boatswain with a convenient Crew with him, began to rig the Ship; the Rest fetching our Provisions aboard. About 10 o'clock, when it was something dark, I took a Lance in my

Hand; and one with me with a Musket and some Fire, and went to our Watch-Tree, to make a Fire on the eminentest Place of the Island; to see if it would be answered: Such Fires I had formerly made to have Knowledge, if there were any Savages on the Main, or the Islands about us. Had there been any, my Purpose was to have gone to them, to get some Intelligence of some Christians, or some Ocean Seas, thereabouts. When I was come to the Tree, I laid down my Lance, and so did my Consort his Musket; whilst I myself climbed up to the Top of the Tree, I order'd him to put Fire to some low Tree thereabouts. He, unadvisedly put Fire to some Trees that were to Windward; so that they, and all the Rest too, by Reason it had been very hot Weather, being dry, took Fire like Flax or Hemp; and the Wind blowing the Fire towards me, I made haste down the Tree. But before I was half Way down, the Fire took in the Bottom of it, and blaz'd so fiercely upwards, that I was forc'd to leap off the Tree, and down a steep Hill; and, in short, with much ado, escap'd burning. The Moss on the Ground was as dry as Flax, and it ran most strangely, like a Train along the Earth. The Musket and Lance were both burnt. My Consort at last came to me, and was joyful to see me; for he thought verily I had been burnt. And thus we went Homeward together, leaving the Fire increasing and burning most furiously. I slept but little all Night after; and at Break of Day, I made all our Powder and Beef to be carried aboard. This Day, I went to the Hills, to look at the Fire; where I saw it still burn most furiously, both to Westward and Northward: Leaving one upon the Hills to watch it, I came home immediately, and made them take down our new Suit of Sails, and carry them to the Sea Side, ready to be cast in, if Occasion were, and to make haste to take down our Houses. About Noon, the Wind shifted Northerly; and our Sentinel came running Home, bringing us Word that the Fire follow'd him at his Heels, like a Train of Powder. There was no Occasion to bid us to take down and carry all to the Sea Side. The Fire came towards us with a most terrible rattling Noise; bearing a full Mile in Breadth; and by that Time we had uncover'd our Houses and going to carry away our last Things, the Fire was come to our Town, and siez'd it; and, in a trice burnt it down to the Ground. This Night we lay all together aboard the Ship, and gave God Thanks, who had been thus merciful to us.

The 27th, 28th, and 29th, we wrought hard, in fetching our Things aboard, and likewise our Water, which we must tow off with the Ebb, and bring it to the Ship with the Flood.

The 30th, we most earnestly continu'd our Labour, and brought our Sails to Yard: and by 11 o'clock at Night had made a pretty Ship; meaning to have finish'd our Business with the Week and the Month, that so we might the better solemnize the Sabbath ashore to Morrow, and so take leave of our wintering Island.

The Wind had been variable a great While, and the Bays so clear of

Ice, that we could not see a Piece of it; for it was all gone to the North-ward.

July 1632. The 1st of this Month being *Sunday* we were up betimes. And I caus'd our Ship to be adorn'd, the best we could; our Flag on the Poop, and the King's Colours in the main Top. I had provided a short account of all the Passages of our Voyage to this Day: I likewise wrote in what State we were at present, and how I intended to prosecute the Discovery, both to the Westward and to the Southward, about this Island. This brief Discourse I had concluded, with a Request to any noble-minded Traveller that should take it down, or come to the Notice of it; that if we should perish in the Action, then to make our Endeavours known to our Soverign Lord and King. And thus with our Arms, Drums and Colours, Cook and Kettle, we went ashore, and first we march'd up to our eminent Cross, adjoining to which we had buried our dead Fellows. There we read Morning Prayer, and then walk'd up and down till Dinner Time. After Dinner, we walk'd to the highest Hills, to see which Way the Fire had wafted. We descried, that it had consum'd to the Westward, 16 Miles at least, and the whole Breadth of the Island: Near our Cross and Dead, it could not come; by Reason it was a bare sandy Hill. After Evening Prayer, I happen'd to walk along the Beach Side; where I found an Herb, resembling Scurvy Grass. I had some gathered, which we boil'd with our Meat to Supper. It was most excellent good, and far better than our Vetches. After Supper we all went to seek for more of it; which we did, to the Quantity of two Bushels, which did afterwards much refresh us: And now the Sun was set, and the Boat come ashore for us: Whereupon we assembl'd ourselves together, and went up to take the last View of our Dead, and to look unto their Tombs, and other Things.

So fastening my Brief, which was securely wrapp'd up in lead, to the Cross, we presently took boat and departed, and never put Foot more on that Island.

Monday, being the Second of *July* 1632, we were up betimes, about Stowing and Fitting our Ship, and Weighing of our Anchors, which when the last was a-trip, we went to Prayer, beseeching God to continue His Mercies to us, and rendering Him Thanks for having thus restor'd us. Our Ship we found no Defect in; we had Abundance of such Provisions as we brought out of England; and we were in indifferent Health, and gather'd Strength daily. This being done, we weighed, and came chear-fully to sail.

PRINCE RUPERT'S EXPLOITS AT SEA[1]

Captain Valentine Pyne
(1603–1677)

I

How Prince Rupert's Men Saved Him in Despite of Himself

HIS HIGHNESS, in pursuance of his former resolves, having refreshed his man and taken in provisions, stood away for the Canary Islands, where he spent much time in visiting the Roads; but finding no ships, and judging if that we might take any, it would not countervail the expense of time and provisions, called a Council of War, to communicate his intentions unto them of going more southwards, thereby to demonstrate his will that all actions might be managed by general consent, lest some pertinacious minds should deprave his worth by imputing all casualties to his improvidence.

This precaution was advised, yet succeeded ill, for they being forewarned of his intents, resolved to undo his design by all the means they could. It being proposed in council to sail to the Cape de Verde Islands, to new victual, secure from storms or enemies, it was carried by the negative, alleging many frivolous arguments to the contrary; the major part siding with it because few of them knew the place or had been so far southward.

His Highness, not being advertised of this combination, was surprised to find such a sudden change in the resolution of his Council, and fearing the affects that this averseness might produce in the giddy multitude, consented to their vote, which was declared for the Isles of Azores, concluding that to be the fittest place to victual in, giving out likewise that there we might meet with the English East India Fleet.

But they neither considered the extremity of the weather subject to those places, nor the time we were to consume in victualling, for we must of necessity receive it as a courtesy from others. Yet to avoid the censure of self-will and rashness His Highness stood for those Islands, although he foresaw part of his ensuing disasters.

The first land we fell in with was the Island of St Mary, and, the weather being slacked, from thence we stood for St Michael's where we began to take order for our victuals. As soon as we were at anchor in the Ponta Del Gada Road, and had saluted their fort, they returned us thanks, and the Governor sent some officers to welcome his Highness, who brought with them a present of refreshings according to the custom of the country. The next day his Highness sent one of his gentlemen to give him thanks, and to present him a considerable quantity of such

[1]From Eliot Warburton's *Memoirs of Prince Rupert and the Cavaliers.*

goods as our prizes could afford. His Highness having spent some time in that Road, the Governor came in person aboard to visit him, and at his departure the Prince gave him nineteen guns, and the fleet proportionably as he passed.

Being thus assured of the Governor's friendship and assistance, his Highness left such persons ashore as were necessary for his victualling and stood away for the island of Terceira. As soon as we were freed of the land, we descried a Spanish galleon about three leagues' distance from us, and the sea being calm, we put forth our galleries and towed our ships toward her. At length by force of hands we fetched her up, who at first summons surrendered. She was bound from the West Indies to St Lucar, but by extremity of weather and losing her mast was forced into Porto Rico, being now in the Road of Angra in the Island of Terceira. His Highness received a compliment from the Governor by which he offered him the assistance of the island, but standing on his gravity, came not aboard himself to pay that respect which was due to so great a person. Nevertheless his Highness made use of his proffer, and having treated with some English merchants about victualling his fleet, both with wine and flesh, stood again for St Michael's.

Being athwart the opening of the Island, we met with such foul weather as we could hardly bear our course, yet, fearing the land, we strained hard to keep the seaboard. In this unfortunate gust, the Admiral[1] sprung a leak, that they could not keep her clear with one chain-pump. The next day, the wind slacking, we stood into St Michael's Road, and as soon as we were at anchor, strove by stitching of bonnets to stop the leak, but could not, by reason we knew not certainly where it was. The Governor sent a diver aboard his Highness to search for it, but to no purpose, for there being no harbours we could not unload our ship, nor trench the bales so low as to find it out.

Then his Highness stood for Terceira, to hasten his business there, that being the greatest part of his victual which he was to expect, resolving once more to propose the southern voyage to his Council, hoping they would consider the necessity of the fleet as well as their own interests, and tracing the divisions to the very centre whence they derived, endeavoured to smother them.

But they whose souls were seized with a fatal cancer, suffered their undigested venom to overflow like a raging billow, to the destruction of us all. So high was their insolence that they infected his very domestics, and so public their improvidence that they concealed not their intentions in their cups, making private meetings in their cabins, where they conceived it convenient to engage any man to their faction, until his Highness, full freighted with such contempt of their audacious proceedings and actions, commanded some of their cabins to be pulled down, with

---

[1]The *Constant Reformation*.

further order to the captain of his guards not to suffer any meetings after setting the watch, nor candle to be lighted betwixt decks, but in such places as were appointed for the ship's use. So great and violent was their distemper that he feared the private communication of his men.

Our provisions not yet being made, we were forced out of the harbour by stormy weather; being clear of the land, we lay a try under our main course, hoping that the weather slacking, we might stand into the Road to ship our provisions. But the wind increasing, and our ships labouring in a ground sea, the Admiral's leak increased so much that both the pumps could hardly keep her free, which forced them to bear up before the wind, hoping thereby to ease the ship; but the leak being far under the holdings, strained the more.

The Vice-Admiral[1] and the *Honest Seaman* bore up with them, and kept as close as the water would permit, the Spanish prize being far in our weather-quarter; the *Revenge*, having more care of her than the Admiral, kept her wind. While we thus stood before it, we gave her over, and took in our mainsail as before. Whilst we thus laboured with disturbed winds, as well as distempered seas, heaven frowning on our disorders, suffered us to fall into that fatality which we strove to prevent. Men may propose, but God will dispose; for the Admiral's pinnace, being too large to be hoisted in, was moored astern with two halsers, and was forced from the ship by rage of the weather. The Vice-Admiral being likewise surprised by the storm, and endeavouring to hoist in her boat, sunk it by the ship's side.

These were sad presages; for three days after, the wind being rather enraged than abated, the ship straining hard, started a butt-head, which added so much water as no pumping could keep her free. They continued firing off guns, to give the other ships notice to keep near them. This disaster befell them about six in the morning, keeping that rate until about ten. By force of hands they gained upon the leak; and, endeavouring to stop it within board, thrust down one hundred and twenty pieces of raw beef into it, and stanchioned them down. This gave them some hopes of life; but it lasted not long, for the ship setting hard, drove in the stanchion, and sprang the plank; so that now, being past hopes of recovery, they made a waft with the standard at the flagstaff-head to let us know their condition, and began to heave their guns overboard to lighten their ship; but all in vain, for the water gained so fast upon them that they could not stand in the hold to bale; the casks rolling to and fro, beat them from their work.

Notwithstanding all this they strove with cheerful resolution to the last, without hope. For the wind was so high, and the sea so overgrown that no ship dare to approach near for our assistance, lest they should perish together. The Admiral's mainmast being cut by the board, the

---

[1] The *Swallow*, commanded by Rupert's brother, Maurice.

Honest Seaman ran aboard on the weather-bow, expecting some of them would save themselves upon it, that he might be ready to take them up; but their resolution being to die together, not one endeavoured to escape.

His Highness waved his brother, Prince Maurice, under his stern, desiring to commit such things to his knowledge as was fitting to declare before his death, resolving to perish among his men. Prince Maurice, bearing under his stern, and being sadly sensible of his brother's ruin, was not apprehensive of his own, but commanded his master to lay him aboard, resolving to save his brother or perish with him. But the officers in mutinous words, refused to obey him in such a case, and not without reason, declaring to him the certainty of their own destruction, without any hopes of assisting his brother. The Princes endeavoured to speak one to another, but the hideous noise of the winds and seas overnoised their voices.

Prince Maurice, seeing himself deprived of his interest, persuaded his officers to fit a small boat which he had aboard to procure his brother's safety; which they seemed to do, but were long about it. During which the Admiral's men, perceiving the Prince's resolution to perish with them, were not only content to die, but to do some brave act that might eternize their fame, by outdoing all that ever was done in the like exigent; and like souls of a new stamp, preferring the General's safety before so many lives of theirs, having a small boat left, beseeched his Highness to secure them, by preserving, if possible, himself.

But he, unwilling not to share in so eminent a death, and scorning to be outdone by inferiors, thanked them for their care, yet refused their offer, although his fate were clothed in a more horrid shape; assuring them, as they had run all fortunes with him, so in this last he would participate with them. Thus did either strive to breathe their last in unspeakable magnanimity.

His men, seeing supplications would not prevail, having selected a crew of undaunted lads, hoisted out their boat, and by force put him into it, desiring him at parting to remember they died his true servants.

Being from the side, they rowed aboard the *Honest Seaman*, which was the nearest ship. His Highness being aboard, sent back the skiff to save as many as they could, only nominating Monsieur Mortaigne, Captain Fearnes, and Captain Billingsley. Fearnes accepted the offer, and was saved aboard the Vice-Admiral with Mr Galloway, his Highness's servant. No sooner were they put aboard but the skiff sunk by the ship's side. The other two, choosing rather to die among their soldiers than save themselves.

This fatal divorce from faithful friends and servants touched his Highness very passionately, who, endeavouring their safety, although with hazard of his own, commanded the men at the helm to edge towards the Blake, hoping thereby to enter their men on his bowsprit. But she was so full of water that she could not stir a-head; so that, being past all hopes of having means to escape death, they prepared themselves for it, taking a sad farewell of their friends, by making sorrowful signs one to another. Yet all this could not move the Vice-Admiral's men to so much charity to hoist out their boat to save any of the rest; which savoured more of malice than excusable judgment, although they pretended several excuses.

Thus these distressed persons kept the ship above water until nine at night, and then, burning two fire-pikes, to give us notice of their departure, took leave of the world, being at that instant one hundred leagues south and by east from the island of Terceira. In this wreck perished 333 men, whose actions speak their merit. The severest censurers will confess it a hard matter to set a full value upon so generous a crew. The wealth in her was very considerable, yet made little impression in his Highness to the loss of the men. The next day, the wind beginning to slack, Prince Maurice fetched his brother from aboard the *Honest Seaman* unto the *Swallow*, when, overladen with the grief of so inestimable a loss, he returned from the Western Islands. The first land we made was the island of Pico, bearing N. N. E. from us. We stood into the road of Fayal, where, to welcome his Highness after his sad loss, he saw the ruin of another of his ships, called the *Loyal Subject*, which by storm was driven from her anchors and cast upon a rock, where she staved. Thus was his spirit alarmed with misfortunes and kept waking with new troubles.

II

And How, after Four Years, He Came Home with but One Ship

Having finished our business, we sailed to the Virgin Islands to careen our ships, where we came to an anchor in "Dixon's Hole," otherwise named "Cavaliers' Harbour,"[1] where we unloaded the Admiral,[2] and fitted her for the careen. We were here three days before we could find fresh water; and fearing the want thereof, his Highness sent the *Sarah* to Santa Cruz to water the fleet, where she met the pink we lost off St Lucia, which by foul weather was driven so low: they returned together to our harbour. Her officer, having given an account of his voyage, was employed back to the same place to procure cassava-roots out of the ruined plantations to help our victuals; but the ground being overgrown, he could find but few. While we were fitting to careen the Admiral, the carpenters were sent ashore to cut stanchions and bars to haul down by: some of them, being new men, got possession of the pinnace, and leaving the others ashore, ran away with her to Porto Rico, an island inhabited by Spanish, near the place where we were. His Highness knowing their intelligence might do us injury, provisions growing very short, was en-

---

[1] Now Rupert's Bay.

[2] The *Swallow*.

forced to retrench our provisions, allowing to each man four ounces of bread *per diem;* and the like of all other viands, and himself no more; which abstinence of his made every one undergo their hardship with alacrity.

Our business finished here, we burnt the *Sarah*, the *John*, and the *Mary*, being all unserviceable; and disposed of their goods into other ships, and passed betwixt two islands to west of it, called the Passages: hauling close by the wind, we stood into twelve degrees, the wind blowing trade at east-north-east: betwixt that and the north-east, we tacked to weather those islands. We stood to the southward until by computation we were within twelve leagues of the island Anguila, bearing south and by east from us.

There began a stress of wind at north, which they call in those parts a hierecane; it forced us to take in all our sails, except the main-course, with which we tried until eight of the clock; but then the storm increasing tore our sail from the yard, though of new double canvas. Rolling now in the trough of the sea, we strove to set our mizen to keep her up, but as soon as the foot was open the sails blew quite away, so that being destitute of all human help, we lay at the mercy of God. Being near a lee shore, and the weather so thick we could not discern our ship's length before us, the bolt-ropes and running rigging keeping our men from the deck, so as they could not stand to any labour; but the Divine Providence taking compassion on us in this helpless and deplorable condition; being twelve of the night, within half a league of a high rock, called Sombrero; we guessed afterwards that we drove betwixt that and an island called Anguilita (where never ships were known to sail before) without seeing or knowing anything but the general calamity and danger; being between the land about one in the morning, although unknown to any man. The wind shifted to eastward, and we drove until day, when not seeing any of our fleet, we set our sprit-sail to bring her head about to seek some land before night, or know, if possible, where we were.

Having cast our ship, the master commanded to take in the sail; but Heaven, which never left us, made use of weak instruments to manifest his mercy, for as they were taking it in, it blew out of the bolt-ropes, so that being past recovery, let it stand: this hastened our way so much as it brought us within sight of danger by three in the morning, we standing directly on a ledge of rocks that are in length ten leagues which lies between Æregados[1] and the Virgins, so that if we had been benighted, we had undoubtedly all perished, without a miracle, which in part was declared; for having cut the balancing of our fore-yardarm, and set that with much ado, we brought another sprit-sail to the yard by force of hands, endeavouring (though with small hopes) to weather the ledge. As we drew near to it, the wind scanted upon us; yet it pleased God to pre-

---

[1] The Anagadas.

serve us in this extremity; for being within half a league of our ruin, the wind veered two points to the eastward, so that we weathered to the rocks, and got sight of the Virgin Islands, where we came to an anchor in the sound in twelve fathom water.

The next day the hurricane ceased, and we sailed to our former harbour, where we spent three days to fit ourselves for sea again, both our topmasts being spent, and our ship left like a wreck, without rigging or sails. In this dismal storm we lost the Vice-Admiral, and the fly boat, who by all probability perished on those lands which we escaped in the night, being a league to the windward of us. When the hurricane began, the *Honest Seaman* was driven to leeward as far as Hispaniola, where she was afterwards cast ashore, and lost in Porto Pina, by the ill-working of the master.

If my memory had been so treacherous as to have forgotten my duty, I should condemn myself of a crime unpardonable; therefore give me leave to make a contracted value of what we lost in this disaster; and having read it, confess with me it was inestimable. In this fatal wreck,— besides a great many brave gentlemen, and others—the sea, to glut itself, swallowed Prince Maurice, whose fame the mouth of detraction cannot blast, his very enemies bewailing his loss. Many had more power, few more merit; he was snatched from us in obscurity, lest, beholding his loss would have prevented some from endeavouring their own safety: —so much he lived beloved, and died bewailed.

Our ships being fitted, we left the harbour, endeavouring to ply to windward, and either to procure provisions or perish in the acquisition; but being to the eastward of those islands, we met with a south-west wind, which never left us until we were within sight of Montserrat, so that we were not long in bearing up. We were six days becalmed, ten leagues distant from thence, and could gain no nearer, between the current and Guadaloupe heaving and setting us to and fro, until at length the wind freshing upon us, we got up with it. We stood into the road by night, and having made a small vessel at anchor (which we hoped was a New Englandman laden with provisions), by reason it was dark, we stood off till day; when making her under sail, we gave chase, and took her before she could get free of the point of the island called Brambsbies Island Point. This done, we stood along the shore to the northward, and being open off Antigua, we descried a Spanish galeon off Five Island Harbour, to whom we gave chase; but she sailing better than we, we gave her over, and tacked and stood for Guadaloupe, where we came to an anchor next day, and were kindly welcomed. The Governor sent the Major of the Island aboard his Highness to assure him of what assistance the island could afford, which he worthily performed, for a speedy course was taken to replenish us with provisions, their storehouses having order to sell their wine unto us, which must be acknowledged a great favour. Two days after the Governor sent his brother to wait on his Highness, who, with an expression of zeal, offered his utmost power to serve the Prince.

While we were here arrived a Dutch ship bound for Antigua, who having received some affront (to revenge himself) told us of two English ships that were in Five Island Harbour, which invited the Prince to make speedy sail thither: where arriving, he landed fifty men under command of a gentleman, Sir Robert Holmes, who, upon landing, beat them off from the fort, upon which the ships surrendered. One of them by disaster was sunk before our arrival; her goods we took out, and brought the other to Guadaloupe, a little harbour that lies to the north of the corner road. While we lay in that road, we saw a New Englandman, laden with provisions in the offing, and so took him, and brought him into the little harbour again, which (like manna from heaven) fell into our hands, supplying us at such a season when our necessities were greatest, being homeward bound.

The Admiral being alone, his prizes took up many of his men, which disenabled him from undertaking any design but to return northward, having small hopes to recover any of those ships which were separated from him by the hurricane. Yet, resolving to visit the English islands once more, he sailed to Montserrat, where, arriving as soon as it was light, he stood close under the land, until he came to the Indian bay, where he took two shallops, and kept them from giving intelligence. Coasting along the islands, he came to Meirs,[1] where they had raised two new batteries, and from them discharged many shots at us. His Highness thought it not convenient to hazard all for small gains, and so departed from thence to the island of Statius,[2] inhabited by the Dutch. He came to an anchor, and stayed there some days to take in fresh water; from thence he stood for the Virgin Islands, where he disembarked, directing his course for the northward. We were, by computation, within twelve leagues of the Bermudas, but, being foggy weather, could not discern it: from thence, meeting with westerly winds, we sailed for the Azores.

The first land we fell in with was the islands of Flores and Corvo: from thence we stood for Fayal, thinking to refresh our people, and inform ourselves how affairs went; but when in the road, and expecting nothing less than friendship, we saluted the forts, they, instead of thanks, returned a shot which struck the Admiral in her bow. The Prince wondering at such rude treatment, sent his boat ashore to inform the governor of his being there, and to know a reason why that shot was made; but his boat rowing towards the landing-place, was waved to keep off, and not suffered to come within speech. The Prince having put some Portuguese in on whom he had relied—their ship being cast away—sent the

---

[1] St Christopher?
[2] St Eustatius?

boat again; notwithstanding whose relation of their kind usage, our men were not permitted to land, but received answer that there was no reception for us, without any reason showed. His Highness, being unsatisfied with that abrupt answer, sailed to St Michael's, hoping there to receive a better welcome from that governor, whose friendship he had obliged by former civilities; but coming there, within half-shot of their fort, they fired two guns, whose shot passed over the ships, as advice for us not to anchor there. At the same instant appeared a ship in the offing, to whom we gave chase, she was a Frenchman, with whom having spoken, we stood to the northward, betwixt St Michael's and Terceira, where we met foul weather.

The gust being past, we directed our course for the coast of Brittany, intending for the river of Nantes, there to put off our merchandize. Being, by computation, in the height of Cape Finesterre, having men at topmast-head to descry land, they made two ships under the lee-bow, to whom the Prince gave chase; but by the ill conning of the mates, the ship was brought to leeward, which caused the Prince to conn her himself, until he came within shot of the leewardmost; but by reason of a ground-sea, and the discovery of seven or eight sail more, his Highness was persuaded not to lay her aboard, for fear of disabling his own ship from working, in case the rest should bear up with him, and so giving over his chase, stood all night under a pair of courses, the prizes being with them, commanded by Sir Robert Holmes, contemning their chase, in case they intended it. Next day, expecting to hear further from them, he found a clear sea, and not a ship to be seen. Having made the Cape, he stood for his intended port. Being far within the bay, he caused the lead to be heaved, and found sixty fathoms water, which proved to be sounding of rock Bon, a sunk rock that lieth off the river of Nantes, and is very dangerous, by reason there is no mark for it.

Two days after, about nine at night, we saw the island of Belleisle right a-head, which we no sooner made, than we tacked the ship for fear of broken ground which lieth off that island; but the moon was so foully eclipsed, as the ships could hardly see one the other. In this haven Providence is to be remembered, that we should so fortunately make that island before that darkness, for otherwise this last adventure might prove as perilous as any of the former, that coast being very rugged. We stood to sea all night; next day came into the river of Nantes, where we anchored against St Lazar, and continued there that night; next day we weighed anchor, to get higher up the river to Pameboeuf; but as soon as he was under sail, the pilots of the country, who, according to custom, were taken in, brought the ship on ground upon a bank, which lieth about the middle of the channel, where she was in danger of wreck, for the tide of ebb being long spent, and the bank steep, she had like to have overset. The men, despairing of getting her off, were desirous to quit her, as they were able to shift for themselves; nevertheless, through the industry and care of his Highness, the guns were brought over to the grounded side, and so kept her to rights, until, at half-flood, the tide setting very strong, she began to cast and heel, insomuch as the water came into her ports, when, shifting her guns, they righted her again, and at high-water brought her off safe to an anchor before Pameboeuf.

Thus having overcome all misfortunes, the Prince ended his voyage; and having taken order for the security of his prizes, he sent his own ship to Crosiack, on the north side, without the river's mouth; thinking to repair and fit her for sea again. Here, however, like a grateful servant, having brought her princely master through so many dangers, she consumed herself; scorning, after being quitted by him, that any inferior person should command her; so as he might, with Cæsar, say to his men, they carried Rupert and his fortune.

THE ENGLISH STORY OF THE FOUR DAYS' BATTLE

I[1]

HIS Highness[2] and the Duke of Albemarle being made joynt Generals at Sea for the Summers Expedition, 1666, April 23. they set forward towards the Fleet, in order to their entring upon their Commands; they divided the Fleet, the Prince Commanding the Blew Squadron, wherewith he Sailed towards France to seek the French Fleet, which they suspected was coming to joyn with the Dutch; and the Duke the other two, wherewith meeting with the Dutch Fleet on Friday, about four or five Leagues from the North Foreland, consisting of an Hundred Sail, he couragiously Attackt them, although he had but half that number, bravely maintaining the Fight two days, and part of the third; but they overnumbring him, he had been hardly put to it if the Prince (who hearing the Guns tact about and made towards the Duke) had not in the afternoon come in to his assistance: upon his approach, de Ruyter sent out Thirty stout Ships to intercept him, and prevent his joyning with the Duke; but avoiding them, he made towards him, sending him word, that if he approved of it, he would keep the wind of them, and Ingage the Thirty Ships that were sent out to him: the Duke advised him rather to joyn the Fleet; which being done, night put an end to their further proceedings.

On Munday morning, as soon as it grew light, they perceived the Dutch to be fled, and gotten almost out of sight, St Georges Channel having proved too dangerous and stormy for them. But making all the Sail they could, they quickly got up with them, and the Prince with his

---

[1]From *Historical Memoires of the Life and Death of That Wise and Valiant Prince Rupert, Prince Palatine of the Rhine* (1683).

[2]Prince Rupert.

fresh Squadron fell in with them with an undaunted Courage and Bravery, passing five times through the whole Body of their Fleet, doing them incredible damage; so that not able longer to endure it, with all the Sail they could make, they began to run, being pursued by the English for some time, and had been longer, had not the four days Ingagement occasioned a scarcity of Powder, and the Princes receiving two shots in his Powder-room, in his last passing through their Fleet, and finding his Masts disabled, prevented it, and occasioned them to repair to the Buoy in the Nore; but having repaired and rigged, they stood out to Sea again, as did likewise the Dutch; and both Fleets meeting, they began a second Fight, no less bloody than the former, both sides fighting with all the Courage and Valour that could be expected, from the most inveterate and inraged Enemies; de Ruyter resolving to revenge his last disgrace, and the Prince resolving nothing less than maintaining his former Victory, and acquire new Honour by obtaining a fresh one.

They began to Fight about Nine in the Morning, and the Prince to make good his resolution, charged with a Courage like himself, and de Ruyter made a suitable retaliation, powring broad sides upon each other with such fury, that the roaring of the Cannon seemed to outvye the thundring of the Heavens, and the smoak clowded the Sun, and rendred the Air more dark and dismal than black Munday; there you might see the Heads of some, the Arms, Legs, or Thighs of others shot off, and others who were cut off by the middle with a Chain-shot, breathing out their last in anguish and pain; some burning in ships fired, and others exposed to the mercy of the liquid Element, some of them sinking, whilst others who learned the Art of Swimming, lift up their heads above water, and implore pity from their very Enemies, intreating them to save their lives, although with the loss of their Liberties: and yet in the midst of all these deplorable calamities, those that survive fight with as much resolution and fury as ever, their Courage and Valour being rather heightned and increased than daunted or diminished thereby. At last de Ruyter made all the Sail he could, and run for it, being pursued by the English that night, and the next day, over several Flats and Banks, till they could go no farther without stranding, shamefully chasing them into their Harbours. Yet they speedily took the Sea again, and passing by the back of the Goodwin Sands, they made for the French Coast, in hope to joyn the French Fleet; but the English discovering them, followed them close, the Dutch halling close to the shore for fear: but the weather was so tempestuous, the Prince was forced to forsake the Chace, and stand for St Helens Bay, the place of Rendezvous, and the properest station for his hindring the conjunction of the Dutch and French Fleets.

II[1]

John Campbell

(1708–1775)

Prince Rupert and the duke of Albemarle went on board the fleet on the 23rd of April, 1666, and sailed with it in the beginning of May. Towards the latter end of that month, the court was informed that the French fleet, under the command of the duke of Beaufort, were coming out to the assistance of the Dutch. But this rumour of their joining the Dutch, was spread by the court of France, in order to deceive us, and distress the Dutch; they in reality having no such intention. Upon the receiving this news, the court sent positive orders to Prince Rupert to sail with the white squadron to look out and fight the French; which command that brave prince obeyed, but found it, what many wise people before thought it, a mere gasconade, intended to hurt us, and to raise the courage of their new allies, in order to bring them into still greater dangers.

At the same time Prince Rupert sailed from the Downs, the Dutch with their whole force put to sea, the wind at north-east, and having a fresh gale. This brought the Dutch fleet on the coasts of Dunkirk, and carried away his highness towards the Isle of Wight; but the wind suddenly shifting to the south-west, and blowing hard, brought both the Dutch and the duke of Albemarle with his two squadrons to an anchor. Captain Bacon in the *Bristol* first discovered the enemy, and, by firing his guns, gave notice of it to the English fleet. Upon this a council of war was called, wherein, without much debate, it was resolved to fight the enemy, notwithstanding their great superiority.

After the departure of Prince Rupert, the duke of Albemarle had with him only sixty sail; whereas the Dutch fleet consisted of ninety one men of war, carrying four thousand seven hundred and sixteen guns, and twenty-two thousand four hundred and sixty-two men. It was the first of June when they were discerned, and the duke was so warm for engaging, that he attacked the enemy before they had time to weigh anchor; and, as De Ruyter himself says in his letter, they were obliged to cut their cables; and in the same letter he also owns, that, to the last, the English were the aggressors, notwithstanding their inferiority and other disadvantages. The English fleet had the weather-gage, but the wind bowed their ships so much, that they could not use their lowest tier. Sir William Berkley's squadron led the van. The duke of Albemarle, when he came on the coast of Dunkirk, to avoid running full on a sand, made a sudden tack, and this brought his top-mast by the board, which compelled him to lie by four or five hours, till another could be set up.

[1]From *The Naval History of Great Britain*.

The blue squadron knowing nothing of this, sailed on, charging through the Dutch fleet, though they were five to one.

In this engagement fell the brave Sir William Berkley, and his ship, the *Swiftsure*, a second rate, was taken; so was the *Essex*, a third rate; and Sir John Harman, in the *Henry*, had the whole Zealand squadron to deal with. His ship being disabled, the Dutch admiral, Cornelius Evertz, called to Sir John, and offered him quarter, who answered, "No, Sir! it is not come to that yet;" and immediately discharged a broadside, by which Evertz was killed, and several of his ships damaged; which so discouraged their captains, that they quitted the *Henry*, and sent three fire-ships to burn her. The first grappled on her starboard quarters, and there began to raise so thick a smoke, that it was impossible to perceive where the irons were fixed. At last, when the ship began to blaze, the boatswain of the *Henry* threw himself on board, and having, by its own light, discovered and removed the grappling irons, in the same instant jumped back on board his own ship. He had scarcely done this, before another fire-ship was fixed on the larboard, which did its business so effectually, that the sails being quickly on fire, frighted the chaplain and fifty men overboard. Upon this, Sir John drew his sword, and threatened to kill any man who should attempt to provide for his own safety by leaving the ship. This obliged them to endeavour to put out the fire, which in a short time they did; but the cordage being burnt, the cross-beam fell, and broke Sir John's leg, at which instant, the third fire-ship bore down; but four pieces of cannon loaded with chain-shot, disabled her: so that, after all, Sir John brought his ship into Harwich, where he repaired her as well as he could, and, notwithstanding his broken leg, put to sea again to seek the Dutch. The battle ended on the first day about ten in the evening.

The following night was spent in repairing the damage suffered on both sides, and next morning the attack was renewed by the English with fresh vigour. Admiral Van Tromp, with Vice-admiral Vander Hulst, being on board one ship, rashly engaged it among the English, and their vessel was in the utmost danger of being either taken or burnt. The Dutch affairs, according to their own account, were now in a desperate condition; but Admiral De Ruyter at last disengaged them, though not till his ship was disabled, and Vice-admiral Vander Hulst killed. This only changed the scene; for De Ruyter was now as hard pressed as Tromp had been before. However, a reinforcement arriving preserved him also; and so the second day's fight ended earlier than the first.

The third day, the duke of Albemarle found it necessary to retreat; and he performed it with wonderful courage and conduct. He first burnt three ships that were absolutely disabled: he next caused such as were most torn to sail before; and, with twenty-eight men of war that were in a pretty good condition, brought up the rear. Sir John Harman, indeed, says he had but sixteen ships that were able to fight. Yet, in the evening, his grace, discovering the white squadron coming to his assistance, resolved to engage the enemy again. In joining Prince Rupert, a very unlucky accident happened; for Sir George Ayscue, who was on board the *Royal Prince*, the largest and heaviest ship in the whole fleet, ran upon the *Gallopper*; and being there in danger of burning, and out of all hopes of relief, was forced to surrender; and night then falling, ended this day's engagement.

On the 4th of June, the Dutch, who were still considerably stronger than the English, were almost out of sight; but the duke of Albemarle, having prevailed on the Prince to follow them, about eight in the morning they engaged again, and the English fleet charged five times through the Dutch; till Prince Rupert's ship being disabled, and that of the duke of Albemarle very roughly handled, about seven in the evening the fleets separated, each side being willing enough to retire. In this day's engagement fell that gallant admiral Sir Christopher Myngs, who having a shot in the neck, remained upon deck, and gave orders, keeping the blood from flowing, with his fingers, above an hour, till another shot pierced his throat, and put an end to his pain.

This was the most terrible battle fought in this, or perhaps in any other war, as the Dutch admirals themselves say; and the pensioner De Witte, who was no flatterer of our nation, yet too quick a man not to discern, and of too great a spirit to conceal the truth, said roundly upon the occasion, "If the English were beat, their defeat did them more honour than all their former victories; their own fleet could never have been brought on after the first day's fight, and he believed none but theirs could; and all the Dutch had discovered was, that Englishmen might be killed, and English ships burnt; but that the English courage was invincible."

SOME ADVENTURES OF CRUSOE[1]

Daniel Defoe
(1661(?)–1731)

I

He Is Saved from the Wreck

THE ship being fitted out, and the cargo furnished, and all things done, as by agreement, by my partners in the voyage, I went on board in an evil hour, the 1st of September, 1659, being the same day eight years that I went from my father and mother at Hull, in order to act the rebel to their authority, and the fool to my own interests.

Our ship was about one hundred and twenty tons burden, carried

---

[1]From *Robinson Crusoe*.

six guns, and fourteen men, besides the master, his boy, and myself. We had on board no large cargo of goods, except of such toys as were fit for our trade with the Negroes, such as beads, bits of glass, shells, and other trifles, especially little looking-glasses, knives, scissors, hatchets and the like.

The same day I went on board we set sail, standing away to the northward upon our own coast, with design to stretch over for the African coast when we came about ten or twelve degrees of northern latitude, which, it seems, was the manner of course in those days. We had very good weather, only excessively hot, all the way upon our own coast, till we came to the height of Cape St Augustino; from whence, keeping further off at sea, we lost sight of land, and steered as if we were bound for the isle Fernando de Noronha, holding our course N. E. by N., and leaving those isles on the east. In this course we passed the line in about twelve days' time, and were, by our last observation, in seven degrees twenty-two minutes northern latitude, when a violent tornado, or hurricane, took us quite out of our knowledge. It began from the south-east, came about to the north-west, and then settled in the north-east; from whence it blew in such a terrible manner, that for twelve days together we could do nothing but drive, and, scudding away before it, let it carry us whither ever fate and the fury of the winds directed; and, during these twelve days, I need not say that I expected every day to be swallowed up; nor, indeed, did any in the ship expect to save their lives.

In this distress we had, besides the terror of the storm, one of our men die of the calenture, and one man and the boy washed overboard. About the twelfth day, the weather abating a little, the master made an observation as well as he could, and found that he was in about eleven degrees north latitude, but that he was twenty-two degrees of longitude difference west from Cape St Augustino; so that he found he was upon the coast of Guiana, or the north part of Brazil, beyond the river Amazons, towards that of the river Oroonoque, commonly called the Great River; and began to consult with me what course he should take, for the ship was leaky, and very much disabled, and he was going directly back to the coast of Brazil.

I was positively against that; and looking over the charts of the seacoast of America with him, we concluded there was no inhabited country for us to have recourse to, till we came within the circle of the Caribbee Islands, and therefore resolved to stand away for Barbadoes; which, by keeping off at sea, to avoid the indraft of the Bay or Gulf of Mexico, we might easily perform, as we hoped, in about fifteen days' sail; whereas we could not possibly make our voyage, to the coast of Africa without some assistance both to our ship and to ourselves.

With this design we changed our course, and steered away N. W. by W., in order to reach some of our English islands, where I hoped for relief. But our voyage was otherwise determined; for, being in the latitude of twelve degrees eighteen minutes, a second storm came upon us, which carried us away with the same impetuosity westward, and drove us so out of the way of all human commerce, that, had all our lives been saved as to the sea, we were rather in danger of being devoured by savages than ever returning to our own country.

In this distress, the wind still blowing very hard, one of our men early in the morning cried out, "Land!" and we had no sooner run out of the cabin to look out, in hopes of seeing whereabouts in the world we were, than the ship struck upon a sand, and in a moment, her motion being so stopped, the sea broke over her in such a manner, that we expected we should all have perished immediately; and we were immediately driven into our close quarters, to shelter us from the very foam and spray of the sea.

It is not easy for any one who has not been in the like condition to describe or conceive the consternation of men in such circumstances. We knew nothing where we were, or upon what land it was we were driven—whether an island or the main, whether inhabited or not inhabited. As the rage of the wind was still great, though rather less than at first, we could not so much as hope to have the ship hold many minutes without breaking into pieces, unless the winds, by a kind of miracle, should turn immediately about. In a word, we sat looking upon one another, and expecting death every moment, and every man, accordingly, preparing for another world; for there was little or nothing more for us to do in this. That which was our present comfort, and all the comfort we had, was that, contrary to our expectation, the ship did not break yet, and that the master said the wind began to abate.

Now, though we thought that the wind did a little abate, yet the ship having thus struck upon the sand, and sticking too fast for us to expect her getting off we were in a dreadful condition indeed and had nothing to do but to think of saving our lives as well as we could. We had a boat at our stern just before the storm, but she was first staved by dashing against the ship's rudder, and in the next place, she broke away, and either sunk, or was driven off to sea; so there was no hope from her. We had another boat on board, but how to get her off into the sea was a doubtful thing. However, there was no time to debate, for we fancied the ship would break in pieces every minute, and some told us she was actually broken already.

In this distress, the mate of our vessel laid hold of the boat, and with the help of the rest of the men, got her slung over the ship's side; and getting all into her, let go, and committed ourselves, being eleven in number, to God's mercy and the wild sea; for though the storm was abated considerably, yet the sea ran dreadfully high upon the shore, and might be well called *den wild zee*, as the Dutch call the sea in a storm.

And now our case was very dismal indeed; for we all saw plainly, that the sea went so high that the boat could not live, and that we should be inevitably drowned. As to making sail, we had none, nor, if we had, could we have done anything with it; so we worked at the oar towards the land, though with heavy hearts, like men going to execution; for we all knew that when the boat came nearer the shore, she would be dashed in a thousand pieces by the breach of the sea. However, we committed our souls to God in the most earnest manner; and the wind driving us towards the shore, we hastened our destruction with our own hands, pulling as well as we could towards land.

What the shore was, whether rock or sand, whether steep or shoal, we knew not. The only hope that could rationally give us the least shadow of expectation, was, if we might find some bay or gulf, or the mouth of some river, where by great chance we might have run our boat in, or got under the lee of the land, and perhaps made smooth water. But there was nothing like this appeared; but as we made nearer and nearer the shore, the land looked more frightful than the sea.

After we had rowed or rather driven about a league and a half, as we reckoned it, a raging wave, mountain-like, came rolling astern of us, and plainly bade us expect the *coup de grace*. In a word, it took us with such a fury, that it overset the boat at once; and separating us, as well from the boat as from one another, gave us not time to say, "O God!" for we were all swallowed up in a moment.

Nothing can describe the confusion of thought which I felt, when I sunk into the water; for though I swam very well, yet I could not deliver myself from the waves so as to draw breath, till that wave having driven me, or rather carried me, a vast way on towards the shore, and having spent itself, went back, and left me upon the land almost dry, but half dead with the water I took in. I had so much presence of mind, as well as breath left, that seeing myself nearer the main land than I expected, I got upon my feet, and endeavoured to make on towards the land as fast as I could, before another wave should return and take me up again; but I soon found it was impossible to avoid it; for I saw the sea come after me as high as a great hill, and as furious as an enemy, which I had no means or strength to contend with; my business was to hold my breath, and raise myself upon the water, if I could; and so, by swimming, to preserve my breathing and pilot myself towards the shore, if possible, my greatest concern now being, that the sea, as it would carry me a great way towards the shore when it came on, might not carry me back again with it when it gave back towards the sea.

The wave that came upon me again, buried me at once twenty or thirty feet deep in its own body, and I could feel myself carried with a mighty force and swiftness towards the shore a very great way; but I held my breath, and assisted myself to swim still forward with all my might. I was ready to burst with holding my breath, when as I felt myself raising up, so, to my immediate relief, I found my head and hands shoot out above the surface of the water; and though it was not two seconds of time that I could keep myself so, yet it relieved me greatly, gave me breath and new courage. I was covered again with water a good while, but not so long but I held it out; and, finding the water had spent itself and began to return, I struck forward against the return of the waves, and felt ground again with my feet. I stood still a few moments to recover breath and till the waters went from me, and then took to my heels and ran, with what strength I had, further towards the shore. But neither would this deliver me from the fury of the sea, which came pouring in after me again; and twice more I was lifted up by the waves and carried forwards as before, the shore being very flat.

The last time of these two had well-nigh been fatal to me, for the sea having hurried me along, as before, landed me, or rather dashed me, against a piece of rock, and that with such force, that it left me senseless, and indeed helpless, as to my own deliverance; for the blow taking my side and breast, beat the breath, as it were, quite out of my body; and had it returned again immediately, I must have been strangled in the water; but I recovered a little before the return of the waves, and seeing I should be covered again with the water, I resolved to hold fast by a piece of the rock, and so to hold my breath, if possible, till the wave went back. Now, as the waves were not so high as at first, being nearer land, I held my hold till the wave abated, and then fetched another run, which brought me so near the shore, that the next wave, though it went over me, yet did not so swallow me up as to carry me away; and the next run I took, I got to the main land, where, to my great comfort, I clambered up the cliffs of the shore, and sat me down upon the grass, far from danger and quite out of the reach of the water.

II

And Attempts to Escape from the Island

My thoughts ran many times upon the prospect of land which I had seen from the other side of the island; and I was not without secret wishes that I were on shore there, fancying that, seeing the main land, and an inhabited country, I might find some way or other to convey myself farther, and perhaps at last find some means of escape.

But all this while I made no allowance for the dangers of such an undertaking, and how I might fall into the hands of savages, and perhaps such as I might have reason to think far worse than the lions and tigers of Africa: that if I once came in their power, I should run a hazard of more than a thousand to one of being killed, and perhaps of being eaten, for I had heard that the people of the Caribbean coast were cannibals, or man-eaters, and I knew by the latitude that I could not be far from that shore.

Now I wished for my boy Xury, and the long-boat with the shoulder-of-mutton sail, with which I sailed above a thousand miles on the coast of Africa; but this was in vain: then I thought I would go and look at our ship's boat, which, as I have said, was blown up upon the shore a great way, in the storm, when we were first cast away. She lay almost where she did at first, but not quite; and was turned, by the force of the waves and the winds, almost bottom upward, against a high ridge of beachy rough sand, but no water about her. If I had had hands to have refitted her, and to have launched her into the water, the boat would have done well enough, and I might have gone back into the Brazils with her easily enough; but I might have foreseen that I could no more turn her and set her upright upon her bottom, than I could remove the island; however, I went to the woods, and cut levers and rollers, and brought them to the boat, resolving to try what I could do; suggesting to myself, that if I could but turn her down, I might repair the damage she had received, and she would be a very good boat, and I might go to sea in her very easily.

I spared no pains, indeed, in this piece of fruitless toil, and spent, I think, three or four weeks about it; at last, finding it impossible to heave it up with my little strength, I fell to digging away the sand, to undermine it, and so to make it fall down, setting pieces of wood to thrust and guide it right in the fall.

But when I had done this I was unable to stir it up again, or to get under it, much less to move it forward towards the water; so I was forced to give it over; and yet, though I gave over the hopes of the boat, my desire to venture over for the main increased, rather than decreased, as the means for it seemed impossible.

This at length put me upon thinking whether it was not possible to make myself a canoe, or periagua, such as the natives of those climates make, even without tools, or, as I might say, without hands, of the trunk of a great tree. This I not only thought possible, but easy, and pleased myself extremely with the thoughts of making it, and with my having much more convenience for it than any of the Negroes or Indians; but not at all considering the particular inconveniences which I lay under more that the Indians did, viz. want of hands to move it, when it was made, into the water—a difficulty much harder for me to surmount than all the consequences of want of tools could be to them; for what was it to me, if when I had chosen a vast tree in the woods, and with much trouble cut it down, if I had been able with my tools to hew and dub the outside into the proper shape of a boat, and burn or cut out the inside to make it hollow, so as to make a boat of it—if, after all this, I must leave it just there where I found it, and not be able to launch it into the water?

One would have thought I could not have had the least reflection upon my mind of my circumstances while I was making this boat, but I should have immediately thought how I should get it into the sea; but my thoughts were so intent upon my voyage over the sea in it, that I never once considered how I should get it off the land: and it was really, in its own nature, more easy for me to guide it over forty-five miles in sea, than about forty-five fathoms of land, where it lay, to set it afloat in the water.

I went to work on this boat the most like a fool that ever man did, who had any of his senses awake. I pleased myself with the design, without determining whether I was ever able to undertake it; not but that the difficulty of launching my boat came often into my head; but I put a stop to my inquiries into it, by this foolish answer, which I gave myself: "Let me first make it; I warrant I will find some way or other to get it along when it is done."

This was a most preposterous method; but the eagerness of my fancy prevailed, and to work I went. I felled a cedar tree, and I question much whether Solomon ever had such a one for the building of the Temple of Jerusalem; it was five feet ten inches diameter at the lower part next the stump, and four feet eleven inches diameter at the end of twenty-two feet; after which it lessened for a while, and then parted into branches. It was not without infinite labour that I felled this tree; I was twenty days hacking and hewing at it at the bottom; I was fourteen more getting the branches and limbs, and the vast spreading head cut off, which I hacked and hewed through with axe and hatchet, and inexpressible labour: after this, it cost me a month to shape it and dub it to a proportion, and to something like the bottom of a boat, that it might swim upright as it ought to do. It cost me near three months more to clear the inside, and work it out so as to make an exact boat of it; this I did, indeed, without fire, by mere mallet and chisel, and by the dint of hard labour, till I had brought it to be a very handsome periagua, and big enough to have carried six and twenty men, and consequently big enough to have carried me and all my cargo.

When I had gone through this work, I was extremely delighted with it. The boat was really much bigger than ever I saw a canoe or periagua, that was made of one tree in my life. Many a weary stroke it had cost, you may be sure; and had I gotten it into the water, I make no question but I should have begun the maddest voyage, and the most unlikely to be performed that ever was undertaken.

But all my devices to get it into the water failed me; though they cost me infinite labour too. It lay about one hundred yards from the water, and not more; but the first inconvenience was, it was uphill towards the creek. Well, to take away this discouragement, I resolved to dig into the surface of the earth, and so make a declivity: this I began, and it cost me a prodigous deal of pains (but who grudge pains that have their deliverance in view?); but when this was worked through, and this difficulty managed, it was still much the same, for I could no more stir the canoe than I could the other boat. Then I measured the distance of ground, and resolved to cut a dock or canal, to bring the water up to the canoe, seeing I could not bring the canoe down to the water. Well, I began this work; and when I began to enter upon it, and calculate how deep it was to be dug, how broad, how the stuff was to be thrown out, I found that, by the number of hands I had, being none but my own, it must have been ten or twelve years before I could have gone through with it; for the shore lay so high, that at the upper end it must have been at least twenty feet deep; so at length, though with great reluctancy, I gave this attempt over also.

In the middle of this work, I finished my fourth year in this place, and kept my anniversary with the same devotion, and with as much comfort as ever before; for, by a constant study and serious application to the Word of God, and by the assistance of His grace, I gained a different knowledge from what I had before. I entertained different notions of things. I looked now upon the world as a thing remote, which I had nothing to do with, no expectation from, and, indeed, no desires about: in a word, I had nothing indeed to do with it, nor was ever likely to have.

I cannot say, after this, for five years, any extraordinary thing happened to me, but I lived on in the same course, in the same posture and place, as before; the chief things I was employed in, besides my yearly labour of planting my barley and rice, and curing my raisins, of both which I always kept up just enough to have sufficient stock of one year's provision beforehand; I say, besides this yearly labour, and my daily pursuit of going out with my gun, I had one labour, to make a canoe, which at last I finished: so that, by digging a canal to it of six feet wide and four feet deep, I brought it into the creek, almost half a mile. As for the first, which was so vastly big, for I made it without considering beforehand, as I ought to have done, how I should be able to launch it, so, never being able to bring it into the water, or bring the water to it, I was obliged to let it lie where it was as a memorandum to teach me to be wiser the next time: indeed, the next time, though I could not get a tree proper for it, and was in a place where I could not get the water to it at any less distance than, as I have said, near half a mile, yet, as I saw it was practicable at last, I never gave it over; and though I was near two years about it, yet I never grudged my labour, in hopes of having a boat to go off to sea at last.

However, though my little periagua was finished, yet the size of it was not at all answerable to the design which I had in view when I made the first; I mean of venturing over to the *terra firma*, where it was above forty miles broad; accordingly, the smallness of my boat assisted to put an end to that design, and now I thought no more of it. As I had a boat, my next design was to make a cruise round the island; for as I had been on the other side in one place, crossing, as I have already described it, over the land, so the discoveries I made in that little journey made me very eager to see other parts of the coast; and now I had a boat, I thought of nothing but sailing round the island.

For this purpose, that I might do everything with discretion and consideration, I fitted up a little mast in my boat, and made a sail too out of some of the pieces of the ship's sails which lay in store, and of which I had a great stock by me. Having fitted my mast and sail, and tried the boat, I found she would sail very well: then I made little lockers, or boxes, at each end of my boat, to put provisions, necessaries, ammunition, etc. into, to be kept dry, either from rain or the spray of the sea; and a little, long, hollow place I cut in the inside of the boat, where I could lay my gun, making a flap to hang down over it, to keep it dry.

I fixed my umbrella also in a step at the stern, like a mast, to stand over my head, and keep the heat of the sun off me, like an awning; and thus I ever now and then took a little voyage upon the sea; but never went far out, nor far from the little creek. At last, being eager to view the circumference of my little kingdom, I resolved upon my cruise; and accordingly I victualled my ship for the voyage, putting in two dozen of loaves (cakes I should rather call them) of barley bread, an earthen pot full of parched rice (a food I ate a great deal of) a little bottle of rum, half a goat, and powder and shot for killing more, and two large watchcoats, of those which, as I mentioned before, I had saved out of the seamen's chests; these I took, one to lie upon, and the other to cover me in the night.

It was the 6th of November, in the sixth year of my reign, or my captivity, which you please, that I set out on this voyage, and I found it much longer than I expected; for though the island itself was not very large, yet when I came to the east side of it, I found a great ledge of rocks lie out about two leagues into the sea, some above water, some under it; and beyond that a shoal of sand, lying dry half a league more, so that I was obliged to go a great way out to sea to double the point.

When I first discovered them, I was going to give over my enterprise, and come back again, not knowing how far it might oblige me to go out to sea: and, above all, doubting how I should get back again: so I came to an anchor; for I had made a kind of an anchor with a piece of a broken grappling which I got out of the ship.

Having secured my boat, I took my gun and went on shore, climbing up a hill, which seemed to overlook that point where I saw the full extent of it, and resolved to venture.

In my viewing the sea from that hill where I stood, I perceived a strong and, indeed, a most furious current, which ran to the east, and even came clost to the point; and I took the more notice of it, because I saw there might be some danger, that when I came into it, I might be carried out to sea by the strength of it, and not be able to make the island again; and, indeed, had I not got first upon this hill, I believe it would have been so; for there was the same current on the other side of the island, only that it set off at a farther distance, and I saw there was a strong eddy under the shore; so I had nothing to do but to get out of the first current, and I should presently be in an eddy.

I lay here, however, two days, because the wind blowing pretty fresh at E. S. E., and that being just contrary to the current, made a great breach of the sea upon the point; so that it was not safe for me to keep too close to the shore for the beach, nor to go too far off, because of the stream.

The third day, in the morning, the wind having abated overnight, the sea was calm, and I ventured: but I am a warning to all rash and ignorant pilots; for no sooner was I come to the point, when I was not even my boat's length from the shore, but I found myself in a great depth of water, and a current like the sluice of a mill: it carried my boat along with it with such violence that all I could do could not keep her so much as on the edge of it; but I found it hurried me farther and farther out from the eddy which was on my left hand. There was no wind stirring to help me, and all I could do with my paddles signified nothing: and now I began to give myself over for lost; for as the current was on both sides of the island, I knew in a few leagues' distance they must join again, and then I was irrecoverably gone; nor did I see any possibility of avoiding it; so that I had no prospect before me but of perishing, not by the sea, for that was calm enough, but of starving from hunger. I had indeed, found a tortoise on the shore, as big almost as I could lift, and had tossed it into the boat; and I had a great jar of fresh water, that is to say, one of my earthen pots; but what was all this to being driven into the vast ocean, where, to be sure, there was no shore, no main land or island, for a thousand leagues at least?

And now I saw how easy it was for the providence of God to make even the most miserable condition of mankind worse. Now I looked back upon my desolate, solitary island, as the most pleasant place in the world, and all the happiness my heart could wish for was to be but there again. I stretched out my hands to it, with eager wishes: "O happy desert!" said I, "I shall never see thee more. O miserable creature! Whither am I going? Then I reproached myself with my unthankful temper, and that I had repined at my solitary condition; and now what would I give to be on shore there again! Thus, we never see the true state of our condition till it is illustrated to us by its contraries, nor know how to value what we enjoy, but by the want of it. It is scarcely possible to imagine the consternation I was now in, being driven from my beloved island (for so it appeared to me now to be) into the wide ocean, almost two leagues, and in the utmost despair of ever recovering it again. However, I worked hard till indeed my strength was almost exhausted, and kept my boat as much to the northward, that is, towards the side of the current which the eddy lay on, as possible I could; when about noon, as the sun passed the meridian I thought I felt a little breeze of wind in my face, springing up from S. S. E. This cheered my heart a little, and especially when, in about half an hour more, it blew a pretty gentle gale. By this time, I had got at a frightful distance from the island, and had the least cloudy or hazy weather intervened, I had been undone another way, too; for I had no compass on board, and should never have known how to have steered towards the island, if I had but once lost sight of it; but the weather continuing clear, I applied myself to get up my mast again, and spread my sail, standing away to the north as much as possible, to get out of the current.

Just as I had set my mast and sail, and the boat began to stretch away, I saw even by the clearness of the water some alteration of the current was near; for where the current was so strong the water was foul; but perceiving the water clear, I found the current abate; and presently I found to the east, at about half a mile, a breach of the sea upon some rocks: these rocks I found caused the current to part again, and as the main stress of it ran away more southerly, leaving the rocks to the northeast, so the other returned by the repulse of the rocks, and made a strong eddy, which ran back again to the north-west, with a very sharp stream.

They who know what it is to have a reprieve brought to them upon the ladder, or to be rescued from thieves just going to murder them, or who have been in such extremities, may guess what my present surprise of joy was, and how gladly I put my boat into the stream of the eddy; and the wind also freshening, how gladly I spread my sail to it, running cheerfully before the wind, and with a strong tide or eddy under foot.

This eddy carried me about a league in my way back again, directly towards the island, but about two leagues more to the northward than the current which carried me away at first; so that when I came near the island, I found myself open to the northern shore of it, that is to say, the other end of the island, opposite to that which I went out from.

When I had made something more than a league of way by the help of this current or eddy, I found it was spent, and served me no farther. However, I found that being between two great currents, viz. that on the south side, which had hurried me away, and that on the north, which lay about a league on the other side; I say, between these two, in the wake of the island, I found the water at least still, and running no way; and having still a breeze of wind fair for me, I kept on steering directly for the island, though not making such fresh way as I did before.

About four o'clock in the evening, being then within a league of the island, I found the point of the rocks which occasioned this disaster, stretching out, as is described before, to the southward, and casting off the current more southerly, had, of course, made another eddy to the north; and this I found very strong, but not directly setting the way my course lay, which was due west, but almost full north. However, having a fresh gale, I stretched across this eddy, slanting north-west; and in about an hour came within about a mile of the shore, where, it being smooth water, I soon got to land.

When I was on shore, I fell on my knees, and gave God thanks for my deliverance, resolving to lay aside all thoughts of my deliverance by my boat; and refreshing myself with such things as I had, I brought my boat close to the shore, in a little cove that I had spied under some trees, and laid me down to sleep, being quite spent with the labour and fatigue of the voyage.

I was now at a great loss which way to get home with my boat! I had run so much hazard, and knew too much of the case, to think of attempting it by the way I went out; and what might be at the other side (I mean the west side) I knew not, nor had I any mind to run any more ventures: so I resolved on the next morning to make my way westward along the shore, and to see if there was no creek where I might lay up my frigate in safety, so as to have her again, if I wanted her. In about three miles, or thereabouts, coasting the shore, I came to a very good inlet or bay, about a mile over, which narrowed till it came to a very little rivulet or brook, where I found a very convenient harbour for my boat, and where she lay as if she had been in a little dock made on purpose for her. Here I put in, and having stowed my boat very safe, I went on shore to look about me, and see where I was.

I soon found I had but a little passed by the place where I had been before, when I travelled on foot to that shore; so taking nothing out of my boat but my gun and umbrella, for it was exceedingly hot, I began my march. The way was comfortable enough after such a voyage as I had been upon, and I reached my old bower in the evening, where I found every thing standing as I left it; for I always kept it in good order, being, as I said before, my country-house.

I got over the fence, and laid me down in the shade to rest my limbs, for I was very weary, and fell asleep; but judge you, if you can, that read my story, what a surprise I must be in when I was awaked out of my sleep by a voice, calling me by my name several times, "Robin, Robin, Robin Crusoe: poor Robin Crusoe! Where are you, Robin Crusoe? Where are you? Where have you been?"

I was so dead asleep at first, being fatigued with rowing, or paddling as it is called, the first part of the day, and with walking the latter part that I did not wake thoroughly; but dozing between sleeping and waking, thought I dreamed that somebody spoke to me; but as the voice continued to repeat, "Robin Crusoe, Robin Crusoe," at last I began to wake more perfectly and was at first dreadfully frightened, and started up in the utmost consternation; but no sooner were my eyes open, but I saw my Poll sitting on the top of the hedge; and immediately knew that it was he that spoke to me; for just in such bemoaning language I had used to talk to him, and teach him; and he had learned it so perfectly that he would sit upon my finger, and lay his bill close to my face, and cry, "Poor Robin Crusoe! Where are you? Where have you been? How came you here?" and such things as I had taught him.

However, even though I knew it was the parrot, and that indeed it could be nobody else, it was a good while before I could compose myself.

First, I was amazed how the creature got thither; and then, how he should just keep about the place, and nowhere else; but as I was well satisfied it could be nobody but honest Poll, I got over it; and holding out my hand, and calling him by his name, "Poll," the sociable creature came to me, and sat upon my thumb, as he used to do, and continued talking to me, "Poor Robin Crusoe! And how did I come here? and where had I been?" just as if he had been overjoyed to see me again; and so I carried him home along with me.

GULLIVER AT LILLIPUT AND BROBDINGNAG[1]

Jonathan Swift

(1667–1745)

I

How He Was Wrecked upon the Shores of Lilliput

MY FATHER had a small estate in Nottinghamshire; I was the third of five sons. He sent me to Emanuel college in Cambridge, at fourteen years old, where I resided three years, and applied myself close to my studies; but the charge of maintaining me, although I had a very scanty allowance, being too great for a narrow fortune, I was bound apprentice to Mr James Bates, an eminent surgeon in London, with whom I continued four years; and my father now and then sending me small sums of money, I laid them out in learning navigation, and other parts of the mathematics, useful to those who intend to travel, as I always believed it would be, some time or other, my fortune to do. When I left Mr Bates, I went down to my father; where, by the assistance of him and my uncle John, and some other relations, I got forty pounds, and a promise of thirty pounds a year to maintain me at Leyden; there I studied physic two years and seven months, knowing it would be useful in long voyages.

Soon after my return from Leyden, I was recommended by my good master, Mr Bates, to be surgeon to the *Swallow*, Captain Abraham Pannell, commander: with whom I continued three years and a half, making a voyage or two into the Levant, and some other parts. When I came back I resolved to settle in London: to which Mr Bates, my master, encouraged me, and by him I was recommended to several patients. I took part of a small house in the Old Jewry; and being advised to alter my condition, I married Mrs Mary Burton, second daughter to Mr Edmund Burton, hosier, in Newgate-street, with whom I received four hundred pounds for a portion.

---

[1]From *Gulliver's Travels.*

But my good master Bates dying in two years after, and I having few friends, my business began to fail; for my conscience would not suffer me to imitate the bad practice of too many among my brethren. Having therefore consulted with my wife, and some of my acquaintance, I determined to go again to sea. I was surgeon successively in two ships, and made several voyages, for six years, to the East and West Indies, by which I got some addition to my fortune. My hours of leisure I spent in reading the best authors, ancient and modern, being always provided with a good number of books; and when I was ashore, in observing the manners and dispositions of the people, as well as learning their language; wherein I had a great facility, by the strength of my memory.

The last of these voyages not proving very fortunate, I grew weary of the sea, and intended to stay at home with my wife and family. I removed from the Old Jewry to Fetter-lane, and from thence to Wapping, hoping to get business among the sailors, but it would not turn to account. After three years' expectation that things would mend, I accepted an advantageous offer from Captain William Prichard, master of the *Antelope*, who was making a voyage to the South Sea. We set sail from Bristol, May 4, 1699, and our voyage at first was very prosperous.

It would not be proper, for some reasons, to trouble the reader with the particulars of our adventures in those seas; let it suffice to inform him, that in our passage from thence to the East Indies, we were driven by a violent storm to the north-west of Van Diemen's Land. By an observation, we found ourselves in the latitude of 30 degrees 2 minutes south. Twelve of our crew were dead by immoderate labour and ill food; the rest were in a very weak condition. On the 5th of November, which was the beginning of summer in those parts, the weather being very hazy, the seamen spied a rock within half a cable's length of the ship; but the wind was so strong, that we were driven directly upon it, and split. Six of the crew, of whom I was one, having let down the boat into the sea, made shift to get clear of the ship and the rock. We rowed, by my computation, about three leagues, till we were able to work no longer, being already spent with labour while we were in the ship. We therefore trusted ourselves to the mercy of the waves, and in about half an hour the boat was overset by a sudden flurry from the north. What became of my companions in the boat, as well as of those who escaped on the rock, or were left in the vessel, I cannot tell; but conclude they were all lost.

For my own part, I swam as fortune directed me, and was pushed forward by the wind and tide. I often let my legs drop, and could feel no bottom; but when I was almost gone, and able to struggle no longer, I found myself within my depth; and by this time the storm was so much abated. The declivity was so small, that I walked near a mile before I got to the shore, which I conjectured was about eight o'clock in the evening. I then advanced forward near half a mile, but could not discover any sign of houses or inhabitants; at least I was in so weak a condition, that I did not observe them. I was extremely tired, and with that, and the heat of the weather, and about half a pint of brandy that I drank as I left the ship, I found myself much inclined to sleep. I lay down on the grass, which was very short and soft, where I slept sounder than I ever remembered to have done in my life, and, as I reckoned, about nine hours; for when I awaked, it was just day-light. I attempted to rise, but was not able to stir; for as I happened to lie on my back, I found my arms and legs were strongly fastened on each side to the ground; and my hair, which was long and thick, tied down in the same manner. I likewise felt several slender ligatures across my body, from my arm-pits to my thighs. I could only look upwards, the sun began to grow hot, and the light offended my eyes. I heard a confused noise about me; but in the posture I lay, could see nothing except the sky. In a little time I felt something alive moving on my left leg, which advancing gently forward over my breast came almost up to my chin; when bending my eyes downward as much as I could, I perceived it to be a human creature not six inches high, with a bow and arrow in his hands, and a quiver at his back. In the mean time, I felt at least forty more of the same kind (as I conjectured) following the first. I was in the utmost astonishment, and roared so loud, that they all ran back in a fright; and some of them, as I was afterwards told, were hurt with the falls they got by leaping from my sides upon the ground. However, they soon returned, and one of them, who ventured so far as to get a full sight of my face, lifting up his hands and eyes by way of admiration, cried out in a shrill but distinct voice, *Hekinah degul!*

II

How He Captured the Blefuscu Fleet

The Empire of Blefuscu is an island situated to the north-east of Lilliput, from which it is parted only by a channel of eight hundred yards wide. I had not yet seen it, and upon this notice of an intended invasion, I avoided appearing on that side of the coast, for fear of being discovered by some of the enemy's ships, who had received no intelligence of me; all intercourse between the two empires having been strictly forbidden during the war, upon pain of death, and an embargo laid by our emperor upon all vessels whatsoever. I communicated to his majesty a project I had formed, of seizing the enemy's whole fleet; which, as our scouts assured us lay at anchor in the harbour, ready to sail with the first fair wind. I consulted the most experienced seamen upon the depth of the channel, which they had often plumbed; who told me, that in the middle at high water it was seventy *glumgluffs* deep, which is about six feet of European measure; and the rest of it fifty *glumgluffs* at most.

I walked towards the north-east coast, over against Blefuscu; where, lying down behind a hillock, I took out my small perspective glass, and viewed the enemy's fleet at anchor, consisting of about fifty men of war, and a great number of transports: I then came back to my house, and gave orders (for which I had a warrant) for a great quantity of the strongest cable and bars of iron. The cable was about as thick as pack-thread, and the bars of the length and size of a knitting-needle. I trebled the cable to make it stronger, and for the same reason I twisted three of the iron bars together, bending the extremities into a hook. Having thus fixed fifty hooks to as many cables, I went back to the north-east coast, and putting off my coat, shoes, and stockings, walked into the sea, in my leathern jerkin, about half an hour before high water. I waded with what haste I could, and swam in the middle about thirty yards, till I felt ground. I arrived at the fleet in less than half an hour. The enemy were so frightened when they saw me, that they leaped out of their ships and swam to shore, where there could not be fewer than thirty thousand souls: I then took my tackling, and fastening a hook to the hole at the prow of each, I tied all the cords together at the end.

While I was thus employed, the enemy discharged several thousand arrows, many of which stuck in my hands and face; and, besides the excessive smart, gave me much disturbance in my work. My greatest apprehension was for mine eyes, which I should have infallibly lost, if I had not suddenly thought of an expedient. I kept, among other little necessaries, a pair of spectacles, in a private pocket, which, as I observed before, had escaped the emperor's searchers. These I took out, and fas-tened as strongly as I could upon my nose, and thus armed, went on boldly with my work, in spite of the enemy's arrows, many of which struck against the glasses of my spectacles, but without any other effect than a little to discompose them. I had now fastened all the hooks, and taking the knot in my hand, began to pull; but not a ship would stir, for they were all too fast held by their anchors; so that the boldest part of my enterprise remained. I therefore let go the cord, and leaving the hooks fixed to the ships, I resolutely cut with my knife the cables that fastened the anchors, receiving about two hundred shots in my face and hands; then I took up the knotted end of the cables, to which my hooks were tied, and with the greatest ease drew fifty of the enemy's largest men-of-war after me.

The Blefuscudians, who had not the least imagination of what I in-tended, were at first confounded with astonishment. They had seen me cut the cables, and thought my design was only to let the ships run adrift, or fall foul of each other, but when they perceived the whole fleet moving in order, and saw me pulling at the end, they set up such a scream of grief and despair as it is almost impossible to describe or conceive. When I had got out of danger, I stopped awhile to pick out the arrows that stuck in my hands and face; and rubbed on some of the same ointment that was given me on my first arrival, as I have formerly mentioned. I then took off my spectacles, and waiting about an hour, till the tide was a little fallen, I waded through the middle with my cargo, and arrived safe at the royal port of Lilliput.

The emperor and his whole court stood on the shore, expecting the issue of this great adventure. They saw the ships move forward in a large half-moon, but could not discern me, who was up to my breast in water. When I advanced to the middle of the channel, they were yet in pain, because I was under water to my neck. The emperor concluded me to be drowned, and that the enemy's fleet was approaching in a hostile manner; but he soon eased of his fears; for the channel growing shallower every step I made, I came in a short time within hearing, and holding up the end of the cable, by which the fleet was fastened, I cried in a loud voice, "Long live the most puissant king of Lilliput!" This great prince received me at my landing with all possible encomiums, and created me a *nardac* upon the spot, which is the highest title of honour among them.

III

How He Voyaged to Brobdingnag

Having been condemned, by nature and fortune, to an active and restless life, in two months after my return, I again left my native country, and took shipping in the Downs, on the 20th day of June, 1702, in the *Adventure*, captain John Nicholas, a Cornishman, commander, bound for Surat. We had a very prosperous gale, till we arrived at the Cape of Good Hope, where we landed for fresh water; but discovering a leak, we unshipped our goods, and wintered there; for the captain falling sick of an ague, we could not leave the Cape till the end of March. We then set sail, and had a good voyage till we passed the Straits of Madagascar; but having got northward of that island, and to about five degrees south latitude, the winds, which in those seas are observed to blow a constant equal gale between the north and west, from the beginning of December to the beginning of May, on the 19th of April began to blow with much greater violence, and more westerly than usual, continuing so for twenty days together: during which time, we were driven a little to the east of Molucca Islands, and about three degrees northward of the line, as our captain found by an observation he took the 2nd of May, at which time the wind ceased, and it was a perfect calm, whereat I was not a little rejoiced. But he, being a man well experienced in the navigation of those seas, bid us all prepare against a storm, which accordingly happened the day following; for the southern wind, called the southern monsoon, began to set in.

Finding it was likely to overblow, we took in our sprit-sail, and stood by to hand the fore-sail, but, making foul weather, we looked the guns were all fast and handed the mizen. The ship lay very broad off, so we thought it better spooning before the sea, than trying or hulling. We reefed the foresail, and set him, and hauled aft the fore-sheet; the helm was hard a-weather. The ship wore bravely. We belayed the fore down-haul; but the sail was split, and we hauled down the yard, and got the sail into the ship, and unbound all the things clear of it. It was a very fierce storm; and the sea broke strange and dangerous. We hauled off upon the laniard of the whip-staff, and helped the man at the helm. We would not get down our top-mast, but let all stand, because she scudded before the sea very well, and we knew that the top-mast being aloft, the ship was the wholesomer, and made better way through the sea, seeing we had sea-room. When the storm was over, we set fore-sail and main-sail, and brought the ship to. Then we set the mizen, main-top-sail, and the fore-top-sail. Our course was east-north-east, the wind was at south-west. We got the starboard tacks aboard; we cast off our weather-bowlings, weather-braces and lifts; we set in the lee-braces, and hauled them tight, and belayed them; and hauled over the mizen and hauled forward by tack to windward, and kept her full and by as near as she would lie.

During this storm, which was followed by a strong wind west-south-west, we were carried, by my computation, about five hundred leagues to the east, so that the oldest sailor on board could not tell in what part of the world we were. Our provisions held out well; our ship was staunch, and our crew all in good health; but we lay in the utmost distress for water. We thought it best to hold on the same course, rather than turn more northerly, which might have brought us to the north-west part of great Tartary, and into the Frozen Sea.

On the 16th day of June, 1703, a boy on the topmast discovered land. On the 17th, we came in full view of a great island or continent (for we knew not whether); on the south side whereof was a small neck of land jutting out into the sea, and a creek too shallow to hold a ship of above one hundred tons. We cast anchor within a league of this creek, and our captain sent a dozen of his men well armed in the long boat, with vessels for water, if any could be found. I desired his leave to go with them, that I might see the country, and make what discoveries I could. When we came to land, we saw no river, or spring, nor any sign of inhabitants. Our men therefore wandered on the shore to find out some fresh water near the sea, and I walked alone about a mile on the other side, where I ob-served the country all barren and rocky. I now began to be weary, and seeing nothing to entertain my curiosity, I returned gently down towards the creek; and the sea being full in my view, I saw our men already got into the boat, and rowing for life to the ship. I was going to holla after them, although it had been to little purpose, when I observed a huge creature walking after them in the sea, as fast as he could: he waded not much deeper than his knees, and took prodigious strides: but our men had the start of him half a league, and the sea thereabouts being full of sharp-pointed rocks, the monster was not able to overtake the boat. This I was afterwards told, for I durst not stay to see the issue of the adventure; and ran as fast as I could the way I first went, and then climbed up a steep hill, which gave me some prospect of the country. I found it fully cultivated; but that which first surprised me was the length of the grass, which, in those grounds that seemed to be kept for hay, was about twenty feet high.

I fell into a high road, for so I took it to be, though it served to the inhabitants only as a foot-path, through a field of barley. Here I walked on for some time, but could see little on either side, it being now near harvest, and the corn rising at least forty feet. I was an hour walking to the end of this field, which was fenced in with a hedge of at least one hundred and twenty feet high, and the trees so lofty that I could make no computation of their altitude. There was a stile to pass from this field into the next. It had four steps, and a stone to cross over when you came to the uppermost. It was impossible for me to climb this stile, because every step was six feet high, and the upper stone about twenty.

I was endeavouring to find some gap in the hedge, when I discovered one of the inhabitants in the next field, advancing towards the stile, of the same size with him whom I saw in the sea pursuing our boat. He appeared as tall as an ordinary spire steeple, and took about ten yards at every stride, as near as I could guess. I was struck with the utmost fear and astonishment, and ran to hide myself in the corn, whence I saw him at the top of the stile, looking back into the next field on the right hand, and heard him call in a voice many degrees louder than a speaking trumpet; but the noise was so high in the air, that at first I certainly thought it was thunder. Whereupon seven monsters, like himself, came towards him, with reaping hooks in their hands, each hook about the largeness of six scythes. These people were not so well clad as the first, whose servants or labourers they seemed to be; for, upon some words he spoke, they went to reap the corn in the field where I lay. I kept from them at as great a distance as I could, but was forced to move with extreme difficulty, for the stalks of the corn were sometimes not above a foot distant, so that I could hardly squeeze my body betwixt them. However I made a shift to go forward, till I came to a part of the field where the corn had been laid by the rain and wind. Here it was impossible for me to advance a step; for the stalks were so interwoven, that I could not creep through, and the beards of the fallen ears so strong and pointed, that they pierced through my clothes into my flesh. At the same time I heard the reapers not above a hundred yards behind me.

Being quite dispirited with toil, and wholly overcome by grief and despair, I lay down between two ridges, and heartily wished I might there end my days. I bemoaned my desolate widow and fatherless children. I lamented my own folly and wilfulness, in attempting a second voyage, against the advice of all my friends and relations. In this terrible agitation of mind, I could not forbear thinking of Lilliput, whose inhabitants looked upon me as the greatest prodigy that ever appeared in the world; where I was able to draw an imperial fleet in my hand, and perform those other actions which will be recorded for ever in the chronicles of that empire; while posterity shall hardly believe them, although attested by millions. I reflected what a mortification it must prove to me to appear as inconsiderable in this nation, as one single Lilliputian would be among us. But this I conceived was to be the least of my misfortunes; for, as human creatures are observed to be more savage and cruel in proportion to their bulk, what could I expect but to be a morsel in the mouth of the first among these enormous barbarians who should happen to seize me? Undoubtedly philosophers are in the right, when they tell us nothing is great or little otherwise than by comparison. It might have pleased fortune, to have let the Lilliputians find some nation where the people were as diminutive with respect to them, as they were to me. And who knows but that even this prodigious race of mortals might be equally overmatched in some distant part of the world, whereof we have yet no discovery.

Feared and confounded as I was, I could not forbear going on with these reflections, when one of the reapers approaching within ten yards of the ridge where I lay, made me apprehend that with the next step I should be squashed to death under his foot, or cut in two with his reaping hook. And therefore, when he was again about to move, I screamed as loud as fear could make me; whereupon the huge creature trod short, and looking round about under him for some time, at last espied me as I lay on the ground. He considered awhile, with the caution of one who endeavours to lay hold on a small dangerous animal in such a manner that it shall not be able either to scratch or bite him, as I myself had sometimes done with a weasel in England. At length he ventured to take me behind, by the middle, between his fore-finger and thumb, and brought me within three yards of his eyes, that he might behold my shape more perfectly. I guessed his meaning, and my good fortune gave me so much presence of mind, that I resolved not to struggle in the least as he held me in the air, above sixty feet from the ground, although he grievously pinched my sides, for fear I should slip through his fingers. All I ventured was to raise mine eyes towards the sun, and place my hands together in a supplicating posture, and to speak some words in an humble melancholy tone, suitable to the condition I then was in: for I apprehended every moment that he would dash me against the ground, as we usually do any little hateful animal which we have a mind to destroy. But my good star would have it, that he appeared pleased with my voice and gestures, and began to look upon me as a curiosity, much wondering to hear me pronounce articulate words, although he could not understand them. In the mean time I was not able to forbear groaning and shedding tears, and turning my head towards my sides; letting him know, as well as I could, how cruelly I was hurt by the pressure of his thumb and finger. He seemed to apprehend my meaning; for, lifting up the lappet of his coat, he put me gently into it.

IV

And of His Escape Therefrom

The king thought proper to pass a few days at a palace he has near Flanflasnic, a city within eighteen English miles of the seaside. Glumdalclitch and I were much fatigued, I had gotten a small cold, but the poor girl was so ill as to be confined to her chamber. I longed to see the ocean, which must be the only scene of my escape, if ever it should happen. I pretended to be worse than I really was, and desired leave to take the fresh air of the sea, with a page whom I was very fond of, and who had sometimes been trusted with me. I shall never forget with what unwillingness Glumdalclitch consented, nor the strict charge she gave the page to be careful of me, bursting at the same time into a flood of tears, as if she had some foreboding of what was to happen. The boy took me out in my box, about half an hour's walk from the palace, towards the rocks on the sea-shore. I ordered him to set me down, and lifting up one of my sashes, cast many a wistful melancholy look towards the sea. I found myself not very well, and told the page that I had a mind to take a nap in my hammock, which I hoped would do me good. I got in, and the boy shut the window close down to keep out the cold. I soon fell asleep, and all I conjecture is, while I slept, the page, thinking no danger could happen, went among the rocks to look for birds' eggs, having before observed him from my window searching about, and picking up one or two in the clefts. Be that as it will, I found myself suddenly awaked with a violent pull upon the ring, which was fastened at the top of my box, for the convenience of carriage. I felt my box raised very high in the air, and then borne forward with prodigious speed. The first jolt had like to have shaken me out of my hammock, but afterward the motion was easy enough. I called out several times as loud as I could raise my voice, but all to no purpose. I looked towards my windows, and could see nothing but the clouds and sky. I heard a noise just over my head, like the clapping of wings, and then began to perceive the woeful condition I was in; that some eagle had got the ring of my box in his beak, with an intent to let it fall on a rock, like a tortoise in a shell, and then pick out my body, and devour it: for the sagacity and smell of this bird enables him to discover his quarry at a great distance, though better concealed than I could be within a two-inch board.

In a little time, I observed the noise and flutter of wings to increase very fast, and my box was tossed up and down like a sign on a windy day. I heard several bangs or buffets, as I thought, given to the eagle (for such I am certain it must have been that held the ring of my box in his beak), and then, all on a sudden, felt myself falling perpendicularly down, for above a minute, but with such incredible swiftness that I almost lost my breath. My fall was stopped by a terrible squash, that sounded louder to my ears than the cataract of Niagara; after which, I was quite in the dark for another minute, and then my box began to rise so high, that I could see light from the tops of the windows. I now perceived I was fallen into the sea. My box, by the weight of my body, the goods that were in, and the broad plate of iron fixed for strength at the four corners of the top and bottom, floated about five feet deep in water. I did then, and do now suppose that the eagle which flew away with my box was pursued by two or three others, and forced to let me drop, while he defended himself against the rest, who hoped to share in the prey. The plates of iron fastened at the bottom of the box (for those were the strongest) preserved the balance while it fell, and hindered it from being broken on the surface of the water. Every joint of it was well grooved; and the door did not move on hinges, but up and down like a sash, which kept my closet so tight that very little water came in. I got with much difficulty out of my hammock, having first ventured to draw back the slip-board on the roof already mentioned, contrived on purpose to let in air, for want of which I found myself almost stifled.

How often did I then wish myself with my dear Glumdalclitch, from whom one single hour had so far divided me! And I may say with truth, that in the midst of my own misfortunes, I could not forbear lamenting my poor nurse, the grief she would suffer for my loss, the displeasure of the queen, and the ruin of her fortune. Perhaps many travellers have not been under greater difficulties and distress than I was at this juncture, expecting every moment to see my box dashed to pieces, or at least overset by the first violent blast, or rising wave. A breach in one pane of glass would have been immediate death: nor could anything have preserved the windows, but the strong lattice wires on the outside, against accidents in travelling. I saw the water ooze in at several crannies, although the leaks were not considerable, and I endeavoured to stop them as well as I could. I was not able to lift up the roof of my closet, which otherwise I certainly should have done, and sat on the top of it; where I might at least preserve myself some hours longer, than by being shut up (as I may call it) in the hold. Or if I escaped these dangers for a day or two, what could I expect but a miserable death of cold and hunger? I was four hours under these circumstances, expecting and indeed wishing, every moment to be my last.

I have already told the reader that there were two strong staples fixed upon that side of my box which had no window, and into which the servant who used to carry me on horseback would put a leathern belt, and buckle it about his waist. Being in this disconsolate state, I heard, or at least thought I heard, some kind of grating noise on that side of my box where the staples were fixed; and soon after I began to fancy that the box was pulled or towed along the sea; for I now and then felt a sort of tugging, which made the waves rise near the tops of my windows, leaving me almost in the dark. This gave me some faint hopes of relief, although I was not able to imagine how it could be brought about. I ventured to unscrew one of my chairs, which were always fastened to the floor; and having made a hard shift to screw it down again, directly under the slipping-board that I had lately opened, I mounted on the chair, and putting my mouth as near as I could to the hole, I called for help in a loud voice, and in all the languages I understood. I then fastened my handkerchief to a stick I usually carried, and thrusting it up the hole, waved it several times in the air, that if any boat or ship were near, the seamen might conjecture some unhappy mortal to be shut up in the box.

I found no effect from all I could do, but plainly perceived my closet to be moved along; and in the space of an hour, or better, that side of the box where the staples were, and had no windows, struck against something that was hard. I apprehended it to be a rock, and found myself tossed more than ever. I plainly heard a noise upon the cover of my closet, like that of a cable, and the grating of it as it passed through the ring. I then found myself hoisted up, by degrees, at least three feet higher than I was before. Whereupon I again thrust up my stick and handkerchief, calling for help till I was almost hoarse. In return to which, I heard a great shout repeated three times, giving me such transports of joy, as are not to be conceived but by those who feel them. I now heard a trampling over my head, and somebody calling through the hole with a loud voice, in the English tongue, "If there be anybody below, let them speak." I answered, "I was an Englishman drawn by ill-fortune into the greatest calamity that ever any creature underwent, and begged, by all that was moving, to be delivered of the dungeon I was in." The voice replied, "I was safe, for my box was fastened to their ship; and the carpenter should immediately come and saw a hole in the cover, large enough to pull me out." I answered, "that was needless, and would take up too much time; for there was no more to be done, but to let one of the crew put his finger into the ring, and take the box out of the sea into the ship, and so into the captain's cabin." Some of them, upon hearing me talk so wildly, thought I was mad; others laughed; for indeed it never came into my head, that I was now got among people of my own stature and strength. The carpenter came, and in a few minutes sawed a passage of about four feet square, then let down a small ladder, upon which I mounted, and thence was taken into the ship in a very weak condition.

The sailors were all in amazement, and asked me a thousand questions which I had no inclination to answer. I was equally confounded at the sight of so many pigmies, for such I took them to be, after having so long accustomed mine eyes to the monstrous objects I had left. But the Captain, Mr. Thomas Wilcocks, an honest, worthy Shropshire man, observing I was ready to faint, took me into his cabin, gave me a cordial to comfort me, and made me turn in upon his own bed, advising me to take a little rest, of which I had great need.

I slept some hours, but perpetually disturbed with dreams of the place I had left, and the dangers I had escaped. However, upon waking, I found myself much recovered. It was now about eight o'clock at night, and the captain ordered supper immediately, thinking I had already fasted too long. He entertained me with great kindness, observing me not to look wildly, or talk inconsistently; and, when we were left alone, desired I would give him a relation of my travels, and by what accident I came to be set adrift, in that monstrous wooden chest. He said, "that about twelve o'clock at noon, as he was looking through his glass, he espied it at a distance, and thought it was a sail, which he had a mind to make, being not much out of his course, in hopes of buying some biscuit, his own beginning to fall short. That upon coming nearer and finding his error, his sent out his long boat, to discover what it was; that his men came back in a fright, swearing they had seen a swimming house. That he laughed at their folly, and went himself in the boat, ordering his men to take a strong cable along with them. That the weather being calm, he rowed round me several times, observed my windows and wire lattices that defended them. That he discovered two staples upon one side, which was all of boards, without any passage for light. He then commanded his men to row up to that side, and fastening a cable to one of the staples, ordered them to tow my chest, as they called it, towards the ship. When it was there, he gave directions to fasten another cable to the ring fixed in the cover, and to raise up my chest with pulleys, which all the sailors were not able to do above two or three feet. He said, they saw my stick and handkerchief thrust out of the hole, and concluded that some unhappy man must be shut up in the cavity."

I asked "whether he or the crew had seen any prodigious birds in the air, about the time he first discovered me." To which he answered, "that discoursing this matter with the sailors while I was asleep, one of them said, he had observed three eagles flying towards the north, but remarked nothing of their being larger than the usual size"; which I suppose must be imputed to the great height they were at; and he could not guess the reason of my question. I then asked the captain "how far he reckoned we might be from land?" He said, "by the best computation he could make, we were at least a hundred leagues." I assured him he must be mistaken by almost half, for I had not left the country from whence I came above two hours before I dropped into the sea. Whereupon he began to think that my brain was disturbed, of which he gave me a hint and advised me to go to bed in a cabin he had provided. I assured him, "I was well refreshed with his good entertainment and company, and as much in my senses as ever I was in my life." He then grew serious, and desired to ask me freely, whether I were not troubled in my mind by the consciousness of some enormous crime, for which I was punished, at the command of some prince, by exposing me in that chest; as great criminals, in other countries, have been forced to sea in a leaky vessel, without provisions: for although he would be sorry to have taken so ill a man into his ship, yet he would engage his word to set me safe ashore, in the first port where we arrived. He added, "that his suspicions were much increased by some very absurd speeches I had delivered at first to his sailors, and afterwards to himself, in relation to my closet or chest, as well as by my odd looks and behaviour while I was at supper."

I begged his patience to hear me tell my story, which I faithfully did, from the last time I left England to the moment he first discovered me. And as truth always forces its way into rational minds, so this honest, worthy gentleman, who had some tincture of learning, and very good sense, was immediately convinced of my candour and veracity and said, "he hoped when we returned to England, I would oblige the world by putting it on paper, and making it public." My answer was, "that I thought we were overstocked with books of travels: that nothing could now pass which was not extraordinary; wherein I doubted some authors less consulted truth than their own vanity, or interest, or the diversion of ignorant readers; that my story could contain little beside common events, without those ornamental descriptions of strange plants, trees, birds, and other animals; or of the barbarous customs and idolatry of savage people, with which most writers abound." However, I thanked him for his good opinion, and promised to take the matter into my thoughts.

The captain having been at Tonquin, was, in his return to England, driven north-eastward to the latitude of 44 degrees, and longitude of 143. But meeting a trade wind two days after I came on board him, we sailed southward a long time, and coasting New-Holland kept our course west-south-west, and then south-south-west, till we doubled the Cape of Good Hope. Our voyage was very prosperous, and I shall not trouble the reader with a journal of it. The captain called in at one or two ports, and sent in his long-boat for provisions and fresh water; but I never went out of the ship till we came into the Downs, which was on the third day of June 1706, about nine months after my escape. I offered to leave my goods in security for payment of my freight, but the captain protested he would not receive one farthing. We took a kind leave of each other, and I made him promise he would come and see me at my house in Redriff. I hired a horse and guide for five shillings, which I borrowed of the captain.

As I was on the road, observing the littleness of the houses, the trees, the cattle, and the people, I began to think myself in Lilliput. I was afraid of trampling upon every traveller I met, and often called aloud to have them stand out of the way, so that I had liked to have gotten one or two broken heads for my impertinence.

When I came to my own house, for which I was forced to inquire, one of the servants opening the door, I bent down to go in (like a goose under a gate), for fear of striking my head. My wife ran out to embrace me, but I stooped lower than her knees, thinking she could otherwise never be able to reach my mouth. My daughter kneeled to ask my blessing, but I could not see her till she rose, having been so long used to stand with my head and eyes erect to above sixty feet; and then I went to take her up with one hand by the waist. I looked down upon the servants, and one or two friends who were in the house, as if they had been pigmies, and I a giant. I told my wife, "she had been too thrifty, for I found she had starved herself and her daughter to nothing." In short, I behaved myself so unaccountably, that they were all of the Captain's opinion when he first saw me and concluded I had lost my wits. This I mention as an instance of the great power of habit and prejudice.

In a little time, I and my family and friends came to a right understanding: but my wife protested I should never go to sea any more.

HOW COMMODORE ANSON CAME TO JUAN FERNANDES[1]

Richard Walter

(1716(?)–1785)

BEING arrived, on the 8th of May, off the Island of Socoro, which was the first rendezvous appointed for the squadron, and where we hoped to have met with some of our companions, we cruised for them in that station several days. But here we were not only disappointed in our expectations of being joined by our friends, and were thereby induced to favour the gloomy suggestions of their having all perished; but we were likewise perpetually alarmed with the fears of being driven on shore upon this coast which appeared too craggy and irregular to give us the least prospect, that in such a case any of us could possibly escape immediate destruction. For the land had indeed a most tremendous aspect: The most distant part of it, and which appeared far within the country, being the mountains usually called the Andes or Cordilleras, was extremely high, and covered with snow; and, the coast itself seemed quite rocky and barren, and the water's edge skirted with precipices. In some places indeed we discerned several deep bays running into the land, but the entrance into them was generally blocked up by numbers of little islands; and thought it was not improbable but there might be convenient shelter in some of those bays, and proper channels leading thereto; yet, as we were utterly ignorant of the coast, had we been driven ashore by the western winds which blew almost constantly there, we did not expect to have avoided the loss of our ship, and of our lives.

[1]From Anson's *Voyage Round the World* (1740–1744).

This continued peril, which lasted for above a fortnight, was greatly aggravated by the difficulties we found in working the ship; as the scurvy had by this time destroyed so great a part of our hands, and had in some degree affected almost the whole crew. Nor did we, as we hoped, find the winds less violent, as we advanced to the northward; for we had often prodigious squalls which split our sails, greatly damaged our rigging, and endangered our masts. Indeed, during the greatest part of the time we were up on this coast, the wind blew so hard, that in another situation, where we had sufficient sea-room, we should certainly have lain-to; but in the present exigency, we were necessitated to carry both our courses and top-sails, in order to keep clear of this lee-shore. In one of these squalls, which was attended by several violent claps of thunder, a sudden flash of fire darted along our decks, which, dividing, exploded with a report like that of several pistols, and wounded many of our men and officers as it passed, marking them in different parts of the body: This flame was attended with a strong sulphureous stench, and was doubtless of the same nature with the larger and more violent blasts of lightning which then filled the air.

It were endless to recite minutely the various disasters, fatigues, and terrors, which we encountered on this coast; all these went on increasing till the 22nd of May, at which time, the fury of all the storms which we had hitherto encountered, seemed to be combined, and to have conspired our destruction. In this hurricane almost all our sails were split, and great part of our standing rigging broken; and, about eight in the evening, a mountainous over-grown sea took us upon our starboard quarter, and gave us so prodigious a shock, that several of our shrouds broke with the jerk, by which our masts were greatly endangered; our ballast and stores too were so strangely shifted, that the ship heeled afterwards two streaks to port. Indeed it was a most tremendous blow, and we were thrown into the utmost consternation from the apprehension of instantly foundering; and though the wind abated in a few hours, yet, as we had no more sails left in a condition to bend to our yards, the ship laboured very much in a hollow sea, rolling gunwale to, for want of sail to steady her: So that we expected our masts, which were now very slenderly supported, to come by the board every moment. However, we exerted ourselves the best we could to stirrup out shrouds, to reeve new landyards, and to mend our sails; but while these necessary operations were carrying on, we ran great risque of being driven on shore on the Island on Chloe, which was not far distant from us; but in the midst of our peril the wind happily shifted to the southward, and we steered off the land with the main-sail only, the Master and myself undertaking the management of the helm, while every one else on board was busied in securing the masts, and bending the sails as fast as they could be repaired.

This was the last effort of that stormy climate; for in a day or two after we got clear of the land, and found the weather more moderate than we had yet experienced since our passing Streights Le Maire.

And now having cruised in vain for more than a fortnight in quest of the other ships of the squadron, it was resolved to take the advantage of the present favourable season, and the offing we had made from this terrible coast, and to make the best of our way for the Island of Juan Fernandes. For though our next rendezvous was appointed off the harbour of Baldivia, yet as we had hitherto seen none of our companions at this first rendezvous, it was not to be supposed that any of them would be found at the second: Indeed we had the greatest reason to suspect, that all but ourselves had perished. Besides, we were by this time reduced to so low a condition, that instead of attempting to attack the places of the enemy, our utmost hopes could only suggest to us the possibility of saving the ship, and some part of the remaining enfeebled crew, by our speedy arrival at Juan Fernandes; for this was the only road in that part of the world where there was any probability of our recovering our sick, or refitting our vessel, and consequently our getting thither was the only chance we had left to avoid perishing at sea.

Our deplorable situation then allowing no room for deliberation, we stood for the Island of Juan Fernandes; and to save time, which was now extremely precious (our men dying four, five, and six in a day), and likewise to avoid being engaged again with a lee-shore, we resolved, if possible, to hit the Island upon a meridian. And, on the 28th of May, being nearly in the parallel upon which it is laid down, we had great expectations of seeing it: But not finding it in the position in which the charts had taught us to expect it, we began to fear that we had gone too far to the westward; and therefore, though the Commodore himself was strongly persuaded, that he saw it on the morning of the 28th, yet his Officers believing it to be only a cloud, to which opinion the haziness of the weather gave some kind of countenance, it was, on a consultation, resolved to stand to the eastward, in the parallel of the Island; as it was certain, that by this course we should either fall in with the Island, if we were already to the westward of it; or should at least make the main land of Chili, from whence we might take a new departure, and assure ourselves, by running to the westward afterwards, of not missing the Island a second time.

On the 30th of May we had a view of the Continent of Chili, distant about twelve or thirteen leagues; the land made exceeding high, and uneven, and appeared quite white; what we saw being doubtless a part of the Cordilleras, which are always covered with snow. Though by this view of the land we ascertained our position, yet it gave us great uneasiness to find that we had so needlessly altered our course, when we were, in all probability, just upon the point of making the Island; for the mortality amongst us was now increased to a most dreadful degree, and those who remained alive were utterly dispirited by this new dis-

appointment, and the prospect of their longer continuance at sea: Our
water too began to grow scarce; so that a general dejection prevailed
amongst us, which added much to the virulence of the disease, and
destroyed numbers of our best men; and to all these calamities there was
added this vexatious circumstance, that when, after having got a sight
of the Main, we tacked and stood to the westward in quest of the Island,
we were so much delayed by calms and contrary winds, that it cost us
nine days to regain the westing, which, when we stood to the eastward,
we ran down in two. In this desponding condition, with a crazy ship, a
great scarcity of fresh water, and a crew so universally diseased, there
were not above ten fore-mast men in a watch capable of doing duty, and
even some of these lame, and unable to go aloft: Under these dishearten-
ing circumstances, we stood to the westward; and, on the 9th of June,
at daybreak, we at last discovered the long-wished-for Island of Juan
Fernandes, bearing N. by E. $\frac{1}{2}$ E, at eleven or twelve leagues distance.
And though, on this first view, it appeared to be a very mountainous
place, extremely ragged and irregular; yet as it was land, and the land we
sought for, it was to us a most agreeable sight: Because at this place only
could we hope to put a period to those terrible calamities we had so
long struggled with, which had already swept away above half our crew,
and which, had we continued a few days longer at sea, would inevitably
have completed our destruction. For we were by this time reduced to so
helpless a condition, that out of two hundred and odd men which remained alive, we could not, taking all our watches together, muster
hands enough to work the ship on an emergency, though we included the
officers, their servants, and the boys.

The wind being northerly when we first made the Island, we kept
plying all that day, and the next night, in order to get in with the land;
and wearing the ship in the middle watch, we had a melancholy instance
of the almost incredible debility of our people; for the Lieutenant could
muster no more than two Quarter-masters, and six Fore-mast men capable of working; so that without the assistance of the officers, servants,
and the boys, it might have proved impossible for us to have reached
the Island, after we had got sight of it; and even with this assistance
they were two hours in trimming the sails: To so wretched a condition
was a sixty gun ship reduced, which had passed Streights Le Maire but
three months before, with between four and five hundred men, almost
all of them in health and vigour.

However, on the 10th in the afternoon, we got under the lee of the
Island, and kept ranging along it, at about two miles distance, in order
to look out for the proper anchorage, which was described to be in a
bay on the North-side. Being now nearer in with the shore, we could discover that the broken craggy precipices, which had appeared so un-
promising at a distance, were far from barren, being in most places
covered with woods, and that between them there were every where in-

terspersed the finest vallies, clothed with a most beautiful verdure, and watered with numerous streams and cascades, no valley, of any extent, being unprovided of its proper rill. The water too, as we afterwards found, was not inferior to any we had ever tasted, and was constantly clear. The aspect of this country thus diversified, would, at all times, have been extremely delightful; but in our distressed situation, languishing as we were for the land and its vegetable productions (an inclination constantly attending every stage of the sea-scurvy), it is scarcely credible with what eagerness and transport we viewed the shore, and with how much impatience we longed for the greens and other refreshments which were then in sight; and particularly the water, for of this we had been confined to a very sparing allowance a considerable time, and had then but five ton remaining on board. Those only who have endured a long series of thirst, and who can readily recall the desire and agitation which the ideas alone of springs and brooks have at that time raised in them, can judge of the emotion with which we eyed a large cascade of the most transparent water, which poured itself from a rock near a hundred feet high into the sea, at a small distance from the ship. Even those amongst the diseased who were not in the very last stages of the distemper, though they had been long confined to their hammocks, exerted the small remains of strength that were left them, and crawled up to the deck to feast themselves with this reviving prospect. Thus we coasted the shore, fully employed in the contemplation of this enchanting landskip, which still improved upon us the farther we advanced. But at last the night closed upon us, before we had satisfied ourselves which was the proper bay to anchor in; and therefore we resolved to keep in soundings all night (we having then from sixty-four to seventy fathom), and to send our boat next morning to discover the road. However, the current shifted in the night, and set us so near the land that we were obliged to let go the best bower in fifty-six fathom, not half a mile from the shore.

At four in the morning, the cutter was dispatched with our third Lieutenant to find out the bay we were in search of, who returned again at noon with the boat laden with seals and grass; for though the Island abounded with better vegetables, yet the boat's crew, in their short stay, had not met with them; and they well knew, that even grass would prove a dainty, as indeed it was all soon and eagerly devoured. The seals too were considered as fresh provision, but as yet were not much admired, though they grew afterwards into more repute. For what rendered them less valuable at this juncture, was the prodigious quantity of excellent fish, which the people on board had taken, during the absence of the boat.

The Cutter, in this expedition, had discovered the bay where we intended to anchor, which we found was to the westward of our present station; and, the next morning, the weather proving favourable, we endeavoured to weigh, in order to proceed thither; but though, on this occasion, we mustered all the strength we could, obliging even the sick, who were scarce able to keep on their legs, to assist us; yet the capstan was so weakly manned, that it was near four hours before we hove the cable right up and down: After which, with our utmost efforts, and with many surges and some purchases we made use of to increase our power, we found ourselves incapable of starting the anchor from the ground. However, at noon, as a fresh gale blew towards the bay, we were induced to set the sails, which fortunately tripped the anchor; and then we steered along shore, till we came abreast of the point that forms the eastern part of the bay. On the opening of the bay, the wind that had befriended us thus far, shifted, and blew from thence in squalls; but by means of the head way we had got, we loofed close in, till the anchor brought us up in fifty-six fathom.

Soon after we had thus got to our new berth, we discovered a sail, which we made no doubt was one of our squadron; and on its nearer approach we found it to be the *Tryal* Sloop. We immediately sent some of our hands on board her, by whose assistance she was brought to an anchor between us and the land. We soon found that the Sloop had not been exempted from the same calamities which we had so severely felt; for her Commander, Captain Saunders, waiting on the Commodore, informed him, that out of his small complement, he had buried thirty-four of his men; and those that remained were so universally afflicted with the scurvy, that only himself, his Lieutenant, and three of his men, were able to stand by the sails. The *Tryal* came to an anchor within us, on the 12th, about noon, and we carried our hawsers on board her, in order to moor ourselves nearer in shore; but the wind coming off the land in violent gusts, prevented our mooring in the berth we intended.

Indeed, our principal attention was employed in business rather of more importance: For we were now extremely occupied in sending on shore materials to raise tents for the reception of the sick, who died apace on board, and doubtless the distemper was considerably augmented, by the stench and filthiness in which they lay; for the number of the diseased was so great, and so few could be spared from the necessary duty of the sails to look after them, that it was impossible to avoid a great relaxation in the article of cleanliness, which had rendered the ship extremely loathsome between decks. Notwithstanding our desire of freeing the sick from their hateful situation, and their own extreme impatience to get on shore, we had not hands enough to prepare the tents for their reception before the 16th; but on that and the two following days we sent them all on shore, amounting to a hundred and sixty-seven persons, besides twelve or fourteen who died in the boats, on their being exposed to the fresh air. The greatest part of our sick were so infirm, that we were obliged to carry them out of the ship in their hammocks, and to convey them afterwards in the same manner from the water side to their tents.

over a stony beach. This was a work of considerable fatigue to the few who were healthy; and therefore the Commodore, according to his accustomed humanity, not only assisted herein with his own labour, but obliged his Officers, without distinction, to give their helping hand. The extreme weakness of our sick may in some measure be collected from the numbers who died after they had got on shore; for it had generally been found, that the land, and the refreshments it produces, very soon recover most stages of the sea-scurvy; and we flattered ourselves, that those who had not perished on this first exposure to the open air, but had lived to be placed in their tents, would have been speedily restored to their health and vigour. Yet, to our great mortification, it was near twenty days after their landing, before the mortality was tolerably ceased; and for the first ten or twelve days, we buried rarely less than six each day, and many of those who survived, recovered by very slow and insensible degrees. Indeed, those who were well enough, at their first getting on shore, to creep out of their tents, and crawl about, were soon relieved, and recovered their health and strength in a very short time; but, in the rest, the disease seemed to have acquired a degree of inveteracy, which was altogether without example.

The arrival of the *Tryal* Sloop at this Island so soon after we came there ourselves, gave us great hopes of being speedily joined by the rest of our squadron; and we were for some days continually looking out, in expectation of their coming in sight. But near a fortnight being elapsed, without any of them having appeared, we began to despair of ever meeting them again; as we knew, that had our ship continued so much longer at sea, we should every man of us have perished, and the vessel, occupied by dead bodies only, would have been left to the caprice of the winds and waves. And this we had great reason to fear was the fate of our consorts, as each hour added to the probability of these desponding suggestions.

But on the 21st of June, some of our people, from an eminence on shore, discerned a ship to leeward, with her courses even with the horizon; and they, at the same time, particularly observed that she had no sail abroad except her courses and her main top-sail. This circumstance made them conclude that it was one of our squadron, which had probably suffered in her sails and rigging as severely as we had done: But they were prevented from forming more definite conjectures about her; for, after viewing her for a short time, the weather grew thick and hazy, and they lost sight of her. On this report, and no ship appearing for some days, we were all under the greatest concern, suspecting that her people were in the utmost distress for want of water, and so diminished and weakened by sickness, as not to be able to ply up to windward; so that we feared that, after having been in sight of the Island, her whole crew would notwithstanding perish at sea. However, on the 26th towards noon, we discerned a sail in the North-East quarter, which we conceived to be the very same ship that had been seen before, and our conjectures proved true: And about one o'clock she approached so near, that we could distinguish her to be the *Gloucester*. As we had no doubt of her being in great distress, the Commodore immediately ordered his boat to her assistance, laden with fresh water, fish, and vegetables, which was a very seasonable relief to them; for our apprehensions of their calamities appeared to be but too well grounded, as perhaps there never was a crew in a more distressed situation. They had already thrown overboard two-thirds of their complement, and of those which remained alive, scarcely any were capable of doing duty except the officers and their servants. They had been a considerable time at the small allowance of a pint of fresh water to each man for twenty-four hours, and yet they had so little left, that, had it not been for the supply we sent them, they must soon have died of thirst.

The ship plied in within three miles of the bay; but, the winds and currents being contrary, she could not reach the road. However, she continued in the offing the next day; but as she had no chance of coming to an anchor, unless the winds and currents shifted, the Commodore repeated his assistance, sending to her the *Tryal's* boat manned with the *Centurian's* people, and a farther supply of water and other refreshments. Captain Mitchel, the Captain of the *Gloucester*, was under the necessity of detaining both this boat and that sent the preceding day; for without the help of their crews, he had no longer strength enough to navigate the ship.

In this tantalizing situation the *Gloucester* continued for near a fortnight, without being able to fetch the road, though frequently attempting it, and at some times bidding very fair for it. On the 9th of July, we observed her stretching away to the eastward at a considerable distance, which we supposed was with a design to get to the southward of the Island but as we soon lost sight of her, and she did not appear for near a week, we were prodigiously concerned, knowing that she must be again in extreme distress for want of water. After great impatience about her, we discovered her again on the 16th, endeavouring to come round the eastern point of the Island: but the wind, still blowing directly from the bay, prevented her getting nearer than within four leagues of the land. On this, Captain Mitchel made signals of distress, and our long-boat was sent to him with a store of water and plenty of fish and other refreshments. And the long-boat being not to be spared, the Cockswain had positive orders from the Commodore to return again immediately; but the weather proving stormy the next day, and the boat not appearing, we much feared she was lost, which would have proved an irretrievable misfortune to us all: However, the third day after, we were relieved from this anxiety, by the joyful sight of the long-boat's sails upon the water; on which we sent the Cutter immediately to her assistance, who towed her along-side in a few hours; when we found that the crew of our long-boat had taken in six of the *Gloucester's* sick men to bring them on shore, two of which had died in the boat.

We now learnt that the *Gloucester* was in a most dreadful condition, having scarcely a man in health on board, except those they received from us: and, numbers of their sick dying daily, it appeared that, had it not been for the last supply sent by our long-boat, both the healthy and diseased must have all perished together for want of water. These calamities were the more terrifying, as they appeared to be without remedy: for the *Gloucester* had already spent a month in her endeavours to fetch the bay, and she was now no farther advanced than at the first moment she made the Island; on the contrary, the people on board her had worn out all their hopes of ever succeeding in it, by the many experiments they had made of its difficulty. Indeed, the same day her situation grew more desperate than ever, for after she had received our last supply of refreshments, we again lost sight of her; so that we in general despaired of her ever coming to an anchor.

Thus was this unhappy vessel bandied about within a few leagues of her intended harbour, whilst the neighbourhood of that place and of those circumstances, which could alone put an end to the calamities they laboured under, served only to aggravate their distress, by torturing them with a view of the relief it was not in their power to reach. But she was at last delivered from this dreadful situation, at a time when we least expected it; for after having lost sight of her for several days, we were pleasingly surprised, on the morning of the 23rd of July, to see her open the N. W. point of the bay with a flowing sail; when we immediately dispatched what boats we had to her assistance, and in an hour's time from our first perceiving her, she anchored safe within us in the bay.

I have thus given an account of the principal events, relating to the arrival of the *Gloucester*, in one continued narration. I shall only add, that we never were joined by any other of our ships, except our Victualler, the *Anna Pink*, who came in about the middle of August, and whose history I shall defer for the present; as it is now high time to return to the account of our own transactions on board and on shore, during the interval of the *Gloucester's* frequent and ineffectual attempts to reach the Island.

Our next employment, after sending our sick on shore from the *Centurian*, was cleansing our ship and filling our water. The first of these measures was indispensably necessary to our future health; as the numbers of sick, and the unavoidable negligence arising from our deplorable situation at sea, had rendered the decks most intolerably loathsome. And the filling our water was a caution that appeared not less essential to our security, as we had reason to apprehend that accidents might intervene, which would oblige us to quit the Island at a very short warning; for some appearances we had discovered on shore upon our first landing, gave us grounds to believe, that there were Spanish cruisers in these seas, which had left the Island but a short time before our arrival, and might possibly return thither again, either for a recruit of water, or in search of us; since we could not doubt, but that the sole business they had at sea was to intercept us, and we knew that this Island was the likeliest place, in their own opinion, to meet with us. The circumstances which gave rise to these reflections were, our finding on shore several pieces of earthern jars, made use of in those seas for water and other liquids, which appeared to be fresh broken: We saw, too, many heaps of ashes, and near them fish-bones and pieces of fish, besides whole fish scattered here and there, which plainly appeared to have been but a short time out of the water, as they were but just beginning to decay.

However, our fears on this head proved imaginary, and we were not exposed to the disgrace, which might have been expected to have befallen us, had we been necessitated (as we must have been, had the enemy appeared) to fight our sixty gun ship with no more than thirty hands.

Whilst the cleaning of our ship and the filling our water went on, we set up a large copper-oven on shore near the sick tents, in which we baked bread every day for the ship's company; for being extremely desirous of recovering our sick as soon as possible, we conceived that new bread, added to their greens and fresh fish, might prove a powerful article in their relief. Indeed, we had all imaginable reason to endeavour at the augmenting our present strength, as every little accident which to a full crew would be insignificant, was extremely alarming in our present helpless situation: Of this, we had a troublesome instance on the 30th of June; for at five in the morning, we were astonished by a violent gust of wind directly off shore, which instantly parted our small bower cable about ten fathom from the ring of the anchor: the ship at once swung off to the best bower, which happily stood the violence of the jerk, and brought us up with two cables an end in eighty fathom. At this time we had not above a dozen seamen in the ship, and we were apprehensive, if the squall continued, that we should be driven to sea in this wretched condition. However, we sent the boat on shore, to bring off all who were capable of acting; and the wind, soon abating of its fury, gave us an opportunity of receiving the boat back again with a reinforcement. With this additional strength we immediately went to work, to heave in what remained of the cable, which we suspected had received some damage from the foulness of the ground before it parted; and agreeable to our conjecture, we found that seven fathom and a half of the outer end had been rubbed, and rendered unserviceable. In the afternoon, we bent the cable to the spare anchor, and got it over the ship's side; and the next morning, July 1, being favoured with the wind in gentle breezes, we warped the ship in again, and let go the anchor in forty-one fathom; the eastermost point now bearing from us E. $\frac{1}{2}$ S; the westermost N. W. by W; and the bay as before, S. S. W; a situation in which we remained secure for the future. However, we were much concerned for the loss of our anchor, and swept frequently for it, in hopes to have recovered it; but the buoy having sunk at the very instant that the cable parted, we were never able to find it.

And now as we advanced in July, some of our men being tolerably recovered, the strongest of them were put upon cutting down trees, and splitting them into billets: while others, who were too weak for this employ, undertook to carry the billets by one at a time to the water-side: This they performed, some of them with the help of crutches, and others supported by a single stick. We next sent the forge on shore, and employed our smiths, who were but just capable of working, in mending our chain-plates, and our other broken and decayed iron-work. We began too the repairs of our rigging; but as we had not junk enough to make spun-yarn, we deferred the general overhale, in hopes of the daily arrival of the *Gloucester*, who we knew had a great quantity of junk on board. However, that we might dispatch as fast as possible in our refitting, we set up a large tent on the beach for the sail-makers; and they were immediately employed in repairing our old sails, and making us new ones. These occupations, with our cleansing and watering the ship (which was by this time pretty well completed), the attendance on our sick, and the frequent relief sent to the *Gloucester*, were the principal transactions of our infirm crew, till the arrival of the *Gloucester* at an anchor in the bay.

And now, after the *Gloucester's* arrival, we were employed in earnest in examining and repairing our rigging: but in the stripping our foremast, we were alarmed by discovering it was sprung just above the partners of the upper deck. The spring was two inches in depth, and twelve in circumference; however, the Carpenters, on inspecting it, gave it as their opinion, that fishing it with two leaves of an anchor-stock, would render it as secure as ever. But, besides this defect in our mast, we had other difficulties in refitting, from the want of cordage and canvas; for though we had taken to sea much greater quantities of both, than had ever been done before, yet the continued bad weather we met with had occasioned such a consumption of these stores, that we were driven to great straits: As after working up all our junk and old shrouds, to make twice-laid cordage, we were at last obliged to unlay a cable to work into running rigging. And with all the canvas, and remnants of old sails that could be mustered, we could only make up one complete suit.

Towards the middle of August our men being indifferently recovered, they were permitted to quit their sick tents, and to build separate huts for themselves, as it was imagined, that by living apart, they would be much cleanlier, and consequently likely to recover their strength the sooner; but at the same time particular orders were given, that, on the firing of a gun from the ship, they would instantly repair to the water-side. Their employment on shore was now either the procuring of refreshments, the cutting of wood, or the making of oil from the blubber of the sea-lions. This oil served us for several purposes, as burning in lamps, or mixing with pitch to pay the ship's sides, or, when worked up with wood ashes, to supply the use of tallow (of which we had none left) to give the ship boot-hose tops. Some of the men too were occupied in salting of cod; for there being two *Newfoundland* fishermen in the *Centurian*, the Commodore set them about laying in a considerable quantity of salted cod for a sea-store, though very little of it was used, as it was afterwards thought to be as productive of the scurvy, as any other kind of salt provisions.

I have before mentioned, that we had a copper-oven on shore to bake bread for the sick; but it happened that the greatest part of the flour, for the use of the squadron, was embarked on board our Victualler the *Anna Pink:* And I should have mentioned, that the *Tryal* Sloop, at her arrival, had informed us, that on the 9th of May, she had fallen in with our Victualler, not far distant from the Continent of Chili; and had kept company with her for four days, when they were parted in a hard gale of wind. This afforded us some room to hope that she was safe, and that she might join us; but all June and July being past, without any news of her, we then gave her over for lost, and at the end of July, the Commodore ordered all the ships to a short allowance of bread. Nor was it in our bread only, that we feared a deficiency; for since our arrival at this Island, we discovered that our former Purser had neglected to take on board large quantities of several kinds of provisions, which the Commodore had expressly ordered him to receive; so that the supposed loss of our Victualler was on all accounts a mortifying consideration. However, on Sunday, the 16th of August, about noon, we espied a sail in the northern quarter, and a gun was immediately fired from the *Centurian*, to call off the people from shore; who readily obeyed the summons, repairing to the beach, where the boats waited to carry them on board. And being now prepared for the reception of this ship in view, whether friend or enemy, we had various speculations about her; some judging it to be the *Severn*, others the *Pearl*, and several affirming that it did not belong to our squadron: But about three in the afternoon our disputes were ended, by an unanimous persuasion that it was our Victualler the *Anna Pink*. This ship though, like the *Gloucester*, she had fallen in to the northward of the Island, had yet the good fortune to come to an anchor in the bay, at five in the afternoon. Her arrival gave us all the sincerest joy; for each ship's company was immediately restored to their full allowance of bread, and we were now freed from the apprehensions of our provisions falling short, before we could reach some amicable port; a calamity, which in these seas is of all others the most irretrievable.

TRAFALGAR[1]

Robert Southey

(1774–1843)

THE station which Nelson had chosen was some fifty or sixty miles to the west of Cadiz, near Cape St Mary. At this distance he hoped to decoy the enemy out, while he guarded against the danger of being caught with a westerly wind near Cadiz, and driven within the Straits. The blockade of the port was rigorously enforced, in hopes that the combined fleets might be forced to sea by want. The Danish vessels therefore, which were carrying provisions from the French ports in the bay, under the name of Danish property, to all the little ports from Ayamonte to Algeziras, from whence they were conveyed in coasting boats to Cadiz, were seized. Without this proper exertion of power the blockade would have been rendered nugatory by the advantage thus taken of the neutral flag. The supplies from France were thus effectually cut off. There was now every indication that the enemy would speedily venture out; officers and men were in the highest spirits at the prospect of giving them a decisive blow—such, indeed, as would put an end to all further contests upon the seas.

On the 9th Nelson sent Collingwood what he called in his diary the "Nelson touch." "I send you," said he, "my plan of attack, as far as a man dare venture to guess at the very uncertain position the enemy may be found in; but it is to place you perfectly at ease respecting my intentions, and to give full scope to your judgment for carrying them into effect. We can, my dear Coll, have no little jealousies. We have only one great object in view, that of annihilating our enemies, and getting a glorious peace for our country. No man has more confidence in another than I have in you, and no man will render your services more justice than your very old friend, Nelson and Bronte."

The order of sailing was to be the order of battle—the fleet in two lines, with an advanced squadron of eight of the fastest sailing two-deckers. The second in command, having the entire direction of his line, was to break through the enemy, about the twelfth ship from their rear; he would lead through the centre, and the advanced squadron was to cut off three or four ahead of the centre. This plan was to be adapted to the strength of the enemy, so that they should always be one-fourth superior to those whom they cut off. Nelson said that "his admirals and captains, knowing his precise object to be that of a close and decisive action, would supply any deficiency of signals and act accordingly. In case signals cannot be seen or clearly understood, no captain can do wrong if he places his ship alongside that of an enemy."

[1]From *The Life of Nelson.*

About half-past nine in the morning of the 19th the *Mars*, being the nearest to the fleet of the ships which formed the line of communication with the frigates inshore, repeated the signal that the enemy were coming out of port. The wind was at this time very light, with partial breezes, mostly from the S. S. W. Nelson ordered the signal to be made for a chase in the south-east quarter. About two the repeating ships announced that the enemy were at sea. All night the British fleet continued under all sail, steering to the south-east. At daybreak they were in the entrance of the Straits, but the enemy were not in sight. About seven, one of the frigates made signal that the enemy were bearing north. Upon this the *Victory* hove to, and shortly afterwards Nelson made sail again to the northward. In the afternoon the wind blew fresh from the south-west, and the English began to fear that the foe might be forced to return to port.

A little before sunset, however, Blackwood, in the *Euryalus*, telegraphed that they appeared determined to go to the westward. "And that," said the Admiral in his diary, "they shall not do, if it is the power of Nelson and Bronte to prevent them." Nelson had signified to Blackwood that he depended upon him to keep sight of the enemy. They were observed so well that all their motions were made known to him, and as they wore twice, he inferred that they were aiming to keep the port of Cadiz open, and would retreat there as soon as they saw the British fleet; for this reason he was very careful not to approach near enough to be seen by them during the night. At daybreak the combined fleets were distinctly seen from the *Victory's* deck, formed in a close line of battle ahead, on the starboard tack, about twelve miles to leeward, and standing to the south. Our fleet consisted of twenty-seven sail of the line and four frigates; theirs of thirty-three and seven large frigates. Their superiority was greater in size and weight of metal than in numbers. They had four thousand troops on board, and the best riflemen that could be procured, many of them Tyrolese, were dispersed through the ships.

Soon after daylight Nelson came upon deck. The 21st of October was a festival in his family, because on that day his uncle, Captain Suckling, in the *Dreadnought*, with two other line-of-battle ships, had beaten off a French squadron of four sail of the line and three frigates. Nelson, with that sort of superstition from which few persons are entirely exempt, had more than once expressed his persuasion that this was to be the day of his battle also, and he was well pleased at seeing his prediction about to be verified. The wind was now from the west—light breezes, with a long heavy swell. Signal was made to bear down upon the enemy in two lines, and the fleet set all sail. Collingwood, in the *Royal Sovereign*, led the lee line of thirteen ships; the *Victory* led the weather line of fourteen. Having seen that all was as it should be, Nelson retired to his cabin, and wrote the following prayer—

"May the great God whom I worship, grant to my country, and for the benefit of Europe in general, a great and glorious victory, and may no misconduct in any one tarnish it, and may humanity after victory be the predominant feature in the British fleet! For myself individually, I commit my life to Him that made me, and may His blessing alight on my endeavours for serving my country faithfully! To Him I resign myself, and the just cause which is entrusted to me to defend. Amen, Amen, Amen."

Blackwood went on board the *Victory* about six. He found him in good spirits, but very calm; not in that exhilaration which he felt upon entering into battle at Aboukir and Copenhagen; he knew that his own life would be particularly aimed at, and seems to have looked for death with almost as sure an expectation as for victory. His whole attention was fixed upon the enemy. They tacked to the northward, and formed their line on the larboard tack; thus bringing the shoals of Trafalgar and St. Pedro under the lee of the British, and keeping the port of Cadiz open for themselves. This was judiciously done; and Nelson, aware of all the advantages which he gave them, made signal to prepare to anchor.

Villeneuve was a skilful seaman, worthy of serving a better master and a better cause. His plan of defence was as well conceived and as original as the plan of attack. He formed the fleet in a double line, every alternate ship being about a cable's length to windward of her second ahead and astern. Nelson, certain of a triumphant issue to the day, asked Blackwood what he should consider as a victory. That officer answered that, considering the handsome way in which battle was offered by the enemy, their apparent determination for a fair trial of strength, and the situation of the land, he thought it would be a glorious result if fourteen were captured. He replied: "I shall not be satisfied with less than twenty." Soon afterwards he asked him if he did not think there was a signal wanting. Captain Blackwood made answer that he thought the whole fleet seemed very clearly to understand what they were about. These words were scarcely spoken before that signal was made which will be remembered as long as the language or even the memory of England shall endure—"ENGLAND EXPECTS EVERY MAN WILL DO HIS DUTY!" It was received throughout the fleet with a shout of answering acclamation, made sublime by the spirit which it breathed and the feeling which it expressed. "Now," said Lord Nelson, "I can do no more. We must trust to the great Disposer of all events and the justice of our cause. I thank God for this great opportunity of doing my duty."

He wore that day, as usual, his admiral's frock-coat, bearing on the left breast four stars of the different orders with which he was invested. Ornaments which rendered him so conspicuous a mark for the enemy were beheld with ominous apprehension by his officers. It was known that there were riflemen on board the French ships, and it could not be doubted but that his life would be particularly aimed at. They communicated their fears to each other, and the surgeon, Mr Beatty, spoke to the chaplain, Dr Scott, and to Mr Scott, the public secretary, desiring that some person would entreat him to change his dress or cover the stars; but they knew that such a request would highly displease him. "In honour I gained them," he had said when such a thing had been hinted to him formerly, "and in honour I will die with them." Mr Beatty, however, would not have been deterred by any fear of exciting his displeasure from speaking to him himself upon a subject in which the weal of England, as well as the life of Nelson, was concerned; but he was ordered from the deck before he could find an opportunity. This was a point upon which Nelson's officers knew that it was hopeless to remonstrate or reason with him; but both Blackwood and his own captain, Hardy, represented to him how advantageous to the fleet it would be for him to keep out of action as long as possible, and he consented at last to let the *Leviathan* and the *Temeraire*, which were sailing abreast of the *Victory* be ordered to pass ahead.

Yet even here the last infirmity of this noble mind was indulged, for these ships could not pass ahead if the *Victory* continued to carry all her sail; and so far was Nelson from shortening sail, that it was evident he took pleasure in pressing on, and rendering it impossible for them to obey his own orders. A long swell was setting into the Bay of Cadiz. Our ships, crowding all sail, moved majestically before it, with light winds from the south-west. The sun shone on the sails of the enemy, but their well-formed line, with their numerous three-deckers, made an appearance which any other assailants would have thought formidable, but the British sailors only admired the beauty and the splendour of the spectacle, and in full confidence of winning what they saw, remarked to each other what a fine sight yonder ships would make at Spithead!

The French admiral, from the *Bucentaure*, beheld the new manner in which his enemy was advancing—Nelson and Collingwood, each leading his line; and pointing them out to his officers, he is said to have exclaimed that such conduct could not fail to be successful. Yet Villeneuve had made his own dispositions with the utmost skill, and the fleets under his command waited for the attack with perfect coolness. Ten minutes before twelve they opened their fire. Eight or nine of the ships immediately ahead of the *Victory*, and across her bows, fired single guns at her to ascertain whether she was yet within their range. As soon as Nelson perceived that their shot passed over him, he desired Blackwood and Captain Prowse, of the *Sirius*, to repair to their respective frigates, and on their way to tell all the captains of the line-of-battle ships that he depended on their exertions, and that, if by the prescribed mode of attack they found it impracticable to get into action immediately, they might adopt whatever they thought best, provided it led them quickly and closely alongside an enemy. As they were standing on the poop,

Blackwood took him by the hand, saying he hoped soon to return and find him in possession of twenty prizes. He replied, "God bless you, Blackwood; I shall never see you again."

Nelson's column was steered about two points more to the north than Collingwood's, in order to cut off the enemy's escape into Cadiz. The lee line, therefore, was first engaged. "See," cried Nelson, pointing to the *Royal Sovereign*, as she steered right for the centre of the enemy's line, cut through it astern of the *Santa Anna*, three-decker, and engaged her at the muzzle of her guns on the starboard side; "see how that noble fellow Collingwood carries his ship into action!" Collingwood, delighted at being first in the heat of the fire, and knowing the feelings of his commander and old friend, turned to his captain and exclaimed: "Rotherham, what would Nelson give to be here!" Both these brave officers, perhaps, at this moment thought of Nelson with gratitude for a circumstance which had occurred on the preceding day. Admiral Collingwood, with some of the captains, having gone on board the *Victory* to receive instructions, Nelson inquired of him where his captain was, and was told in reply that they were not upon good terms with each other. "Terms!" said Nelson; "good terms with each other!" Immediately he sent a boat for Captain Rotherham, led him, so soon as he arrived, to Collingwood, and saying, "Look, yonder are the enemy!" bade them shake hands like Englishmen.

The enemy continued to fire a gun at a time at the *Victory* till they saw that a shot had passed through her main-topgallant sail; then they opened their broadsides, aiming chiefly at her rigging, in the hope of disabling her before she could close with them. Nelson as usual had hoisted several flags, lest one should be shot away. The enemy showed no colours till late in the action, when they began to feel the necessity of having them to strike. For this reason the *Santissima Trinidad*, Nelson's old acquaintance, as he used to call her, was distinguishable only by her four decks, and to the bow of this opponent he ordered the *Victory* to be steered. Meantime an incessant raking fire was kept up upon the *Victory*. The Admiral's secretary was one of the first who fell; he was killed by a cannon shot while conversing with Hardy. Captain Adair, of the marines, with the help of a sailor, endeavoured to remove the body from Nelson's sight, who had a great regard for Mr Scott, but he anxiously asked, "Is that poor Scott that's gone?" and being informed that it was indeed so, exclaimed, "Poor fellow!"

Presently a double-headed shot struck a party of marines who were drawn up on the poop, and killed eight of them, upon which Nelson immediately desired Captain Adair to disperse his men round the ship, that they might not suffer so much from being together. A few minutes afterwards a shot struck the fore-brace bits on the quarter-deck, and passed between Nelson and Hardy, a splinter from the bit tearing off Hardy's buckle and bruising his foot. Both stopped, and looked anxiously at each other: each supposed the other to be wounded. Nelson then smiled, and said: "This is too warm work, Hardy, to last long."

The *Victory* had not yet returned a single gun; fifty of her men had by this time been killed or wounded, and her maintopmast, with all her studding sails and their booms, shot away. Nelson declared that in all his battles he had seen nothing which surpassed the cool courage of his crew on this occasion. At four minutes after twelve she opened her fire from both sides of her deck. It was not possible to break the enemy's lines without running on board one of their ships; Hardy informed him of this, and asked him which he would prefer. Nelson replied: "Take your choice, Hardy; it does not signify much." The master was ordered to put the helm to port, and the *Victory* ran on board the *Redoubtable* just as her tiller-ropes were shot away. The French ship received her with a broadside, then instantly let down her lower-deck ports for fear of being boarded through them, and never afterwards fired a great gun during the action. Her tops, like those of all the enemy's ships, were filled with riflemen. Nelson never placed musketry in his tops; he had a strong dislike to the practice, not merely because it endangers setting fire to the sails, but also because it is a murderous sort of warfare, by which individuals may suffer and a commander now and then be picked off, but which never can decide the fate of a general engagement.

Captain Harvey, in the *Temeraire*, fell on board the *Redoubtable* on the side; another enemy was in like manner on board the *Temeraire;* so that these four ships formed as compact a tier as if they had been moored together, their heads all lying the same way. The lieutenants of the *Victory* seeing this, depressed their guns of the middle and lower decks, and fired with a diminished charge, lest the shot should pass through and injure the *Temeraire;* and because there was danger that the *Redoubtable* might take fire from the lower deck guns, the muzzles of which touched her side when they were run out, the fireman of each gun stood ready with a bucket of water, which, as soon as the gun was discharged, he dashed into the hole made by the shot. An incessant fire was kept up from the *Victory* from both sides, her larboard guns playing upon the *Bucentaure* and the huge *Santissima Trinidad*.

It had been part of Nelson's prayer that the British fleet should be distinguished by humanity in the victory he expected. Setting an example himself, he twice gave orders to cease firing upon the *Redoubtable*, supposing that she had struck, because her great guns were silent; for, as she carried no flag, there was no means of instantly ascertaining the fact. From this ship, which he had thus twice spared, he received his death. A ball fired from her mizzen-top, which in the then situation of the two vessels was not more than fifteen yards from that part of the deck where he was standing, struck the epaulette on his left shoulder, about a quarter after one, just in the heat of action. He fell upon his face, on the spot which was covered with his poor secretary's blood. Hardy, who was a few steps from him, turning round, saw three men raising him up. "They have done for me at last, Hardy!" said he. "I hope not!" cried Hardy. "Yes," he replied, "my backbone is shot through!"

Yet even now, not for a moment losing his presence of mind, he observed as they were carrying him down the ladder, that the tiller-ropes, which had been shot away, were not yet replaced, and ordered that new ones should be rove immediately. Then, that he might not be seen by the crew, he took out his handkerchief and covered his face and his stars. Had he but concealed these badges of honour from the enemy, England perhaps would not have cause to receive with sorrow the news of the battle of Trafalgar. The cockpit was crowded with wounded and dying men, over whose bodies he was with some difficulty conveyed, and laid upon a pallet in the midshipmen's berth. It was soon perceived, upon examination, that the wound was mortal. This, however, was concealed from all except Captain Hardy, the chaplain, and the medical attendants. He himself being certain, from the sensation in his back and the gush of blood he felt momently within his breast, that no human care could avail him, insisted that the surgeon should leave him, and attend to those to whom he might be useful, "for," said he, "you can do nothing for me."

All that could be done was to fan him with paper, and frequently give him lemonade to alleviate his intense thirst. He was in great pain, and expressed much anxiety for the event of the action, which now began to declare itself. As often as a ship struck, the crew of the *Victory* hurrahed, and at every hurrah a visible expression of joy gleamed in the eyes and marked the countenance of the dying hero. But he became impatient to see Captain Hardy, and as that officer, though often sent for, could not leave the deck, Nelson feared that some fatal cause prevented him, and repeatedly cried, "Will no one bring Hardy to me? He must be killed! He is surely dead!"

An hour and ten minutes elapsed from the time when Nelson received his wound before Hardy could come to him. They shook hands in silence; Hardy in vain struggling to express the feelings of that most painful and yet sublimest moment. "Well, Hardy," said Nelson, "how goes the day with us?"—"Very well," replied Hardy; "ten ships have struck, but five of the van have tacked, and show an intention to bear down upon the *Victory*. I have called two or three of our fresh ships round, and have no doubt of giving them a drubbing."—"I hope," said Nelson, "none of our ships have struck." Hardy answered, "There was no fear of that." Then, and not till then, Nelson spoke of himself. "I am a dead man, Hardy," said he; "I am going fast; it will be all over with me soon. Come nearer to me." Hardy observed that he hoped Mr Beatty could yet hold out some prospect of life. "Oh no!" he replied, "it is impossible; my back is shot through. Beatty will tell you so." Captain Hardy then once more shook hands with him, and with a heart almost bursting hastened upon deck.

By this time, all feeling below the breast was gone; and Nelson, having made the surgeon ascertain this, said to him: "You know I am gone. I know it. I feel something rising in my breast"—putting his hand on his left side—"which tells me so." And upon Beatty's inquiring whether his pain was very great, he replied, "So great that he wished he was dead." "Yet," said he in a lower voice, "one would like to live a little longer too!" Captain Hardy, some fifty minutes after he had left the cockpit, returned, and again taking the hand of his dying friend and commander, congratulated him on having gained a complete victory. How many of the enemy were taken he did not know, as it was impossible to perceive them distinctly; but fourteen or fifteen at least. "That's well!" cried Nelson; "but I bargained for twenty." And then in a stronger voice he said, "Anchor, Hardy, anchor." Hardy upon this hinted that Admiral Collingwood would take upon himself the direction of affairs. "Not while I live, Hardy," said the dying Nelson, ineffectually endeavouring to raise himself from the bed; "Do you anchor."

His previous order for preparing to anchor had shown how clearly he foresaw the necessity of this. Presently calling Hardy back, he said to him in a low voice: "Don't throw me overboard"; and he desired that he might be buried by his parents, unless it should please the king to order otherwise. Then turning to Hardy: "Kiss me, Hardy," said he. Hardy knelt down and kissed his cheek, and Nelson said: "Now I am satisfied. Thank God, I have done my duty!" Hardy stood over him in silence for a moment or two, then knelt again and kissed his forehead. "Who is that?" said Nelson; and being informed, he replied: "God bless you, Hardy." And Hardy then left him for ever.

Nelson now desired to be turned upon his right side, and said: "I wish I had not left the deck, for I shall soon be gone." Death was indeed rapidly approaching. He said to the chaplain: "Doctor, I have *not* been a *great* sinner." His articulation now became difficult, but he was distinctly heard to say: "Thank God, I have done my duty!" These words he repeatedly pronounced. And they were the last words that he uttered. He expired at thirty minutes after four, three hours and a quarter after he had received his wound.

MR MIDSHIPMAN EASY[1]

Captain Frederick Marryat

(1792–1848)

THE *Aurora* sailed on the second day, and with a fine breeze stood across, making as much northing as easting; the consequence was, that one fine morning they saw the Spanish coast before they saw the

---

[1]From *Mr Midshipman Easy*.

Toulon fleet. Mr Pottyfar took his hands out of his pockets, because he could not examine the coast through a telescope without so doing; but this, it is said, was the first time that he had done so on the quarter-deck from the day that the ship had sailed from Port Mahon. Captain Wilson was also occupied with his telescope, so were many of the officers and midshipmen, and the men at the mastheads used their eyes, but there was nothing but a few small fishing-boats to be seen. So they all went down to breakfast, as the ship was hove-to close in with the land.

"What will Easy bet," said one of the midshipmen, "that we don't see a prize to-day?"

"I will not bet that we do not see a vessel—but I'll bet you what you please, that we do not take one before twelve o'clock at night."

"No, no, that won't do—just let the tea-pot travel over this way, for it's my forenoon watch."

"It's a fine morning," observed one of the mates, of the name of Martin; "but I've a notion it won't be a fine evening."

"Why not?" inquired another.

"I've now been eight years in the Mediterranean, and know something about the weather. There's a watery sky, and the wind is very steady. If we are not under double-reefed top-sails to-night, say I'm no conjuror."

"That you will be, all the same, if we are under bare poles," said another.

"You're devilish free with your tongue, my youngster. Easy, pull his ears for me."

"Pull them easy, Jack then," said the boy laughing.

"All hands make sail!" now resounded at the hatchways.

"There they are, depend upon it," cried Gascoigne, catching up his hat and bolting out of the berth, followed by all the others except Martin, who had just been relieved, and thought that his presence in the waist might be dispensed with for the short time, at least, which it took him to swallow a cup of tea.

It was very true; a galliot and four latteen vessels had just made their appearance round the eastern most point, and as soon as they observed the frigate, had hauled their wind. In a minute the *Aurora* was under a press of canvas, and the telescopes were all directed to the vessels.

"All deeply laden, sir," observed Mr Hawkins, the chaplain; "how the topsail of the galliot is scored!"

"They have a fresh breeze just now," observed Captain Wilson, to the first lieutenant.

"Yes sir, and it's coming down fast."

"Hands by the royal halyards, there."

The *Aurora* careened with the canvas to the rapidly-increasing breeze.

"Top-gallant sheet and halyards."

"Luff you may, quarter-master; luff, I tell you. A small pull of that weather maintop-gallant brace—that will do," said the master.

"Top-men aloft there;—stand by to clew up the royals—and Captain Wilson, shall we take them in?—I'm afraid of that pole—it bends now like a coach-whip," said Mr Pottyfar, looking up aloft, with his hands in both pockets.

"In royals—lower away."

"They are going about sir," said the second lieutenant, Mr Haswell.

"Look out," observed the chaplain, "it's coming."

Again the breeze increases, and the frigate was borne down.

"Hands reef topsails in stays, Mr Pottyfar."

"Ay, ay, sir—'bout ship."

The helm was put down and the topsails lowered and reefed in stays.

"Very well, my lads, very well indeed," said Captain Wilson.

Again the topsails were hoisted and the top-gallant sheets home. It was a strong breeze, although the water was smooth, and the *Aurora* dashed through at the rate of eight miles an hour, with her weather leeches lifting.

"Didn't I tell you so?" said Marin to his messmates on the gangway; "but there's more yet, my boys."

"We must take the top-gallant sails off her," said Captain Wilson, looking-aloft—for the frigate now careened to her bearings and the wind was increasing and squally. "Try them a little longer"; but another squall came suddenly—the halyards were lowered, and the sails clewed up and furled.

In the meantime the frigate had rapidly gained upon the vessels, which still carried on every stitch of canvas, making short tacks in-shore. The *Aurora* was again put about with her head towards them, and they were not two points on her weather-bow. The sky, which had been clear in the morning, was now overcast, the sun was obscured with opaque white clouds, and the sea was rising fast. Another ten minutes, and then they were under double-reefed topsails and the squalls were accompanied with heavy rain. The frigate now dashed through the waves, foaming in her course, and straining under the press of sail. The horizon was so thick that the vessels ahead were no longer to be seen.

"We shall have it, I expect," said Captain Wilson.

"Didn't I say so?" observed Martin to Gascoigne. "We take no prizes this day, depend upon it."

"We must have another hand to the wheel, sir, if you please," said the quarter-master, who was assisting the helmsman.

Mr Pottyfar, with his hands concealed as usual, stood by the capstern. "I fear, sir, we cannot carry the mainsail much longer."

"No," observed the chaplain, "I was thinking so."

"Captain Wilson, if you please, we are very close in," said the master; "don't you think we had better go about?"

"Yes, Mr Jones.—Hands about ship—and—yes, by heavens we must! —up mainsail."

The mainsail was taken off, and the frigate appeared to be immediately relieved. She no longer jerked and plunged as before.

"We're very near the land, Captain Wilson; thick as it is, I think I can make out the loom of it—shall we wear round, sir?" continued the master.

"Yes, hands wear ship—put the helm up."

It was but just in time, for as the frigate flew round, describing a circle, as she payed off before the wind, they could perceive the breakers lashing the precipitous coast, not two cables' length from them.

"I had no idea we were so near," observed the captain, compressing his lips; "can they see anything of those vessels?"

"I have not seen them this quarter of an hour, sir," replied the signal-man, protecting his glass from the rain under his jacket.

"How's her head now, quarter-master?"

"South south-east, sir."

The sky now assumed a different appearance—the white clouds had been exchanged for others dark and murky, the wind roared at intervals, and the rain came down in torrents. Captain Wilson went down into the cabin to examine the barometer.

"The barometer has risen," said he, on his return on deck. "Is the wind steady?"

"No, sir, she's up and off three points."

"This will end in a south-wester."

The wet and heavy sails now flapped from the shifting of the wind.

"Up with the helm, quarter-master."

"Up it is—she's off to the south-by-west."

The wind lulled, the rain came down in a deluge—for a minute it was quite calm, and the frigate was on an even keel.

"Man the braces. We shall be taken aback directly, depend upon it."

The braces were hardly stretched along before this was the case. The wind flew round to the south-west with a loud roar, and it was fortunate that they were prepared—the yards were braced round, and the master asked the captain what course they were to steer.

"We must give it up," observed Captain Wilson, holding on by the belaying pin. "Shape our course for Cape Sicie, Mr Jones."

And the *Aurora* flew before the gale, under her foresail and topsails close reefed. The weather was now so thick that nothing could be observed twenty yards from the vessel; the thunder pealed, and the lightning darted in every direction over the dark expanse. The watch was called as soon as the sails were trimmed, and all who could went below, wet, uncomfortable, and disappointed.

"What an old Jonah you are, Martin," said Gascoigne.

"Yes, I am," replied he; "but we have the worst to come yet, in my opinion. I recollect, not two hundred miles from where we are now, we had just such a gale in the *Favourite*, and we as nearly went down, when——"

At this moment a tremendous noise was heard above, a shock was felt throughout the whole ship, which trembled fore and aft as if it was about to fall in to pieces; loud shrieks were followed by plaintive cries, the lower deck was filled with smoke, and the frigate was down on her beam ends. Without exchanging a word, the whole of the occupants of the berth flew out, and were up the hatchway, not knowing what to think, but convinced that some dreadful accident had taken place.

On their gaining the deck it was at once explained; the foremast of the frigate had been struck by lightning, had been riven into several pieces, and had fallen over the larboard bow, carrying with it the main topmast and jib-boom. The jagged stump of the foremast was in flames, and burnt brightly, notwithstanding the rain fell in torrents. The ship, as soon as the foremast and main topmast had gone overboard, broached-to furiously, throwing the men over the wheel and dashing them senseless against the carronades; the forecastle, the forepart of the main deck, and even the lower deck, were spread with men, either killed or seriously wounded, or insensible from the electric shock. The frigate was on her beam ends, and the sea broke furiously over her; all was dark as pitch, except the light from the blazing stump of the foremast, appearing like a torch held up by the wild demons of the storm, or when occasionally the gleaming lightning cast a momentary glare, threatening every moment to repeat its attack upon the vessel, while the deafening thunder burst almost on their devoted heads. All was dismay and confusion for a minute or two; at last Captain Wilson, who had himself lost his sight for a short time, called for the carpenter and axes. They climbed up, that is, two or three of them, and he pointed to the mizenmast; the master was also there, and he cut loose the axes for the seamen to use; in a few minutes the mizenmast fell over the quarter, and the helm being put hard up, the frigate payed off and slowly righted. But the horror of the scene was not yet over. The boatswain, who had been on the forecastle, had been let below, for his vision was gone for ever. The men who lay scattered about had been examined, and they were assisting them down to the care of the surgeon, when the cry of "Fire!" issued from the lower deck. The ship had taken fire at the coal-hole and carpenter's store-room and the smoke that now ascended was intense.

"Call the drummer," said Captain Wilson, "And let him beat to quarters—all hands to their stations—let the pumps be rigged and the buckets passed along. Mr Martin, see that the wounded men are taken down below. Where's Mr Haswell? Mr Pottyfar, station the men to pass the water on by hand on the lower deck. I will go there myself. Mr Jones, take charge of the ship."

Pottyfar, who actually had taken his hands out of his pockets, hastened down to comply with the captain's orders on the main deck, as Captain Wilson descended to the deck below.

"I say, Jack, this is very different from this morning," observed Gascoigne.

"Yes," replied Jack, "so it is, but I say, Gascoigne, what's the best thing to do?—when the chimney's on fire on shore, they put a wet blanket over it."

"Yes," replied Gascoigne, "but when the coal-hole's on fire on board, they will not find that sufficient."

"At all events, wet blankets must be a good thing, Ned, so let us pull out the hammocks; cut the landyards and get some out—we can but offer them, you know, and if they do no good, at least it will show our zeal."

"Yes Jack, and I think when they turn in again, those whose blankets you take will agree with you, that zeal makes the service very uncomfortable. However, I think you are right."

The two midshipmen collected three or four hands, and in a very short time they had more blankets than they could carry—there was no trouble in wetting them, for the main deck was afloat—and followed by the men they had collected, Easy and Gascoigne went down with large bundles in their arms to where Captain Wilson was giving directions to the men.

"Excellent, Mr Easy, excellent Mr Gascoigne!" said Captain Wilson. "Come my lads, throw them over now, and stamp upon them well"; the men's jackets and the captain's coat had already been sacrificed to the same object.

Easy called the other midshipmen, and they went up for a further supply; but there was no occasion, the fire had been smothered; still the danger had been so great that the fore magazine had been floated. During all this, which lasted perhaps a quarter of an hour, the frigate had rolled gunwale under, and many were the accidents which occurred. At last all danger from fire had ceased, and the men were ordered to return to their quarters, when three officers and forty-seven men were found absent—seven of them were dead, most of them were already under the care of the surgeon, but some were still lying in the scuppers.

No one had been more active or more brave during this time of danger, than Mr Hawkins, the chaplain. He was everywhere, and when Captain Wilson went down to put out the fire he was there, encouraging the men, and exerting himself most gallantly. He and Mesty came aft when all was over, one just as black as the other. The chaplain sat down and wrung his hands—"God forgive me!" said he, "God forgive me!"

"Why so, sir?" said Easy, who stood near. "I am sure you need not be ashamed of what you have done."

"No, no, not ashamed of what I've done; but, Mr Easy, I have sworn so, sworn such oaths at the men in haste—I, the chaplain! God forgive me!—I meant nothing." It was very true that Mr Hawkins had sworn a great deal during his exertions but he was at that time the quarter-deck officer and not the chaplain; the example to the men and his gallantry had been most serviceable.

"Indeed, sir," said Easy, who saw the chaplain was in great tribulation, and hoped to pacify him, "I was certainly not there all the time, but I only heard you say, 'God bless you, my men! be smart,' and so on; surely that is not swearing."

"Was it that I said, Mr Easy—are you sure? I really had an idea that I had D—d them all in heaps, as some of them deserved—no, no, not deserved. Did I really bless them—nothing but bless them?"

"Yes, sir," said Mesty, who perceived what Jack wanted; "it was nothing, I assure you, but 'God bless you, Captain Wilson!—Bless your heart, my good men!—Bless the king!' and so on. You do nothing but shower down blessing and wet blanket."

"I told you so," said Jack.

"Well, Mr Easy, you've made me very happy," replied the chaplain; "I was afraid it was otherwise."

So indeed it was, for the chaplain had sworn like a boatswain; but as Jack and Mesty had turned all his curses into blessings, the poor man gave himself absolution, and shaking hands with Jack, hoped he would come down into the gunroom and take a glass of grog—nor did he forget Mesty, who received a good allowance at the gun-room door—to which Jack gladly consented, as the rum in the middies' berth had all been exhausted after the rainy morning; but Jack was interrupted in his third glass, by somebody telling him the captain wanted to speak with Mr Hawkins and with him.

Jack went up, and found the captain on the quarter-deck with the officers.

"Mr Easy," said Captain Wilson, "I have sent for you, Mr Hawkins, and Mr Gascoigne, to thank you on the quarter-deck, for your exertions and presence of mind on this trying occasion." Mr Hawkins made a bow. Gascoigne said nothing, but he thought of having extra leave when they arrived at Malta. Jack felt inclined to make a speech, and began something about when there was danger that it levelled every one to an equality even on board of a man-of-war.

"By no means, Mr Easy," replied Captain Wilson; "it does the very contrary; for it proves which is the best man, and those who are the best raise themselves at once above the rest."

Jack was very much inclined to argue the point, but he took the compliment and held his tongue, which was the wisest thing he could have done; so he made his bow, and was about to go down into the midshipmen's berth when the frigate was pooped by a tremendous sea, which washed all those who did not hold on down into the waist. Jack was among the number, and naturally catching at the first object which touched him, he caught hold of the chaplain by the leg, who commenced swearing most terribly; but before he could finish the oath, the water which had burst into the cabin through the windows—for the dead lights, in the confusion, had not yet been shipped—burst out of the cross bulk-heads, sweeping like a torrent the marine, the cabin door, and everything else in its force, and floating Jack and the chaplain with several others down the main hatchway on to the lower deck. The lower deck being also full of water, men and chests were rolling and tossing about, and Jack was sometimes in company with the chaplain, and at other times separated; at last they both recovered their legs, and gained the midshipmen's berth, which, although afloat, was still a haven of security. Mr Hawkins spluttered and spit, and so did Jack, until he began to laugh.

"This is very trying, Mr Easy," said the chaplain; "very trying indeed to the temper. I hope I have not sworn—I hope not."

"Not a word," said Jack—"I was close to you all the time—you only said, 'God preserve us!'"

"Only that? I was afraid that I said 'God d—m it!'"

"Quite a mistake, Mr Hawkins. Let's go into the gunroom, and try to wash this salt water out of our mouths, and then I will tell you all you said, as far as I could hear it, word for word."

So Jack by this means got another glass of grog, which was very acceptable in his wet condition, and made himself very comfortable, while those on deck were putting on the dead lights, and very busy setting the goose wings of the main-sail, to prevent the frigate from being pooped a second time.

THE PHANTOM SHIP[1]

Captain Frederick Marryat

(1792–1848)

A BANK of clouds rose up from the eastward, with a rapidity that to the seamen's eyes was unnatural, and it soon covered the whole firmament; the sun was obscured, and all was one deep and unnatural gloom; the wind subsided; and the ocean was hushed. It was not exactly dark, but the heavens were covered with one red haze, which gave an appearance as if the world was in a state of conflagration.

In the cabin the increased darkness was first observed by Philip, who went on deck; he was followed by the captain and passengers, who were in a state of amazement. It was unnatural and incomprehensive.

"Now, Holy Virgin, protect us! what can this be?" exclaimed the captain, in a fright. "Holy Saint Antonio, protect us! but this is awful."

"There—there!" shouted the sailors, pointing to the beam of the vessel. Every eye looked over the gunnel to witness what had occasioned such exclamations. Philip, Schriften, and the captain were side by side.

---

[1]From *The Phantom Ship*.

On the beam of the ship, not more than two cables' length distant, they beheld slowly rising out of the water the tapering masthead and spars of another vessel. She rose, and rose, gradually; her top-masts and top-sail yards, with the sails set, next made their appearance; higher and higher she rose up from the element. Her lower masts and rigging, and, lastly, her hull showed itself above the surface. Still she rose up, till her ports, with her guns, and at last the whole of her floatage was above water, and there she remained close to them, with her main yard squared, and hove to.

"Holy Virgin!" exclaimed the captain, breathless. "I have known ships to *go down*, but never to *come up* before. Now will I give one thousand candles, of ten ounces each, to the shrine of the Virgin, to save us in this trouble. One thousand wax candles! Hear me, blessed lady, ten ounces each! Gentlemen," cried the captain to the passengers, who stood aghast, "why don't you promise?—promise, I say *promise*, at all events."

"The Phantom Ship—the *Flying Dutchman*," shrieked Schriften. "I told you so, Philip Vanderdecken. There is your father. He, he!"

Philip's eyes had remained fixed on the vessel; he perceived that they were lowering down a boat from her quarter. "It is possible," thought he, "I shall now be permitted," and put his hand into his bosom and grasped the relic.

The gloom now increased, so that the strange vessel's hull could but just be discovered through the murky atmosphere. The seamen and passengers threw themselves down on their knees, and invoked their saints. The captain ran down for a candle, to light before the image of St Antonio, which he took out of its shrine and kissed with much apparent affection and devotion, and then replaced.

Shortly afterwards, the splash of oars was heard alongside, and a voice calling out, "I say, my good people, give us a rope from forward."

No one answered, or complied with the request. Schriften only went up to the captain, and told him that if they offered to send letters they must not be received, or the vessel would be doomed, and all would perish.

A man now made his appearance from over the gunnel, at the gangway. "You might as well have let me have a side-rope, my hearties," said he, as he stepped on deck. "Where is the captain?"

"Here," replied the captain, trembling from head to foot. The man who accosted him appeared a weather-beaten seaman, dressed in a fur cap and canvas petticoats; he held some letters in his hand.

"What do you want?" at last screamed the captain.

"Yes—what do you want?" continued Schriften. "He! he!"

"What, you here, pilot?" observed the man. "Well—I thought you had gone to Davy's locker long enough ago."

"He! he!" replied Schriften, turning away.

"Why, the fact is, captain, we have had very foul weather, and we wish to send letters home; I do believe that we shall never get round this cape."

"I can't take them," cried the captain.

"Can't take them! well, it's very odd, but every ship refuses to take our letters. It's very unkind; seamen should have a feeling for brother seamen, especially in distress. God knows, we wish to see our wives and families again; and it would be a matter of comfort to them if they only could hear from us."

"I cannot take your letters—the saints preserve us!" replied the captain.

"We have been a long while out," said the seaman, shaking his head.

"How long?" inquired the captain, not knowing what to say.

"We can't tell; our almanack was blown overboard, and we have lost our reckoning. We never have our latitude exact now, for we cannot tell the sun's declination for the right day."

"Let *me* see your letters," said Philip, advancing and taking them out of the seaman's hands.

"They must not be touched," screamed Schriften.

"Out, monster!" replied Philip, "who dares interfere with me?"

"Doomed—doomed—doomed!" shrieked Schriften, running up and down the deck, and then breaking into a wild fit of laughter.

"Touch not the letters," said the captain, trembling as if in an ague fit.

Philip made no reply, but held his hand out for the letters.

"Here is one from our second mate to his wife at Amsterdam, who lives on Waser Quay."

"Waser Quay has long been gone, my good friend; there is now a large dock for ships where it once was," replied Philip.

"Impossible!" replied the man. "Here is another from the boatswain to his father, who lives in the old market-place."

"The old market-place has long been pulled down, and there now stands a church upon the spot."

"Impossible!" replied the seaman. "Here is another from myself to my sweetheart, Vrow Ketser—with money to buy her a new brooch."

Philip shook his head. "I remember seeing an old lady of that name buried some thirty years ago."

"Impossible! I left her young and blooming. Here's one for the house of Slutz and Co., to whom the ship belongs."

"There's no such house now," replied Philip, "but I have heard that, many years ago, there was a firm of that name."

"Impossible! you must be laughing at me. Here is a letter from our captain to his son——"

"Give it me," cried Philip, seizing the letter.

He was about to break the seal, when Schriften snatched it out of his hand, and threw it over the lee gunnel.

"That's a scurvy trick for an old shipmate," observed the seaman.

Schriften made no reply, but catching up the other letters, which Philip had laid down on the capstan, he hurled them after the first. The strange seaman shed tears, and walked again to the side.

"It's very hard—very unkind," observed he, as he descended; "the time may come when you may wish that your family should know your situation."

So saying, he disappeared. In a few seconds was heard the sound of the oars, retreating from the ship.

"Holy Saint Antonio!" exclaimed the captain. "I am lost in wonder and fright. Steward, bring me up the arrack."

The steward ran down for the bottle; being so much alarmed as his captain, he helped himself before he brought it up to his commander.

"Now," said the captain, after keeping his mouth for two minutes to the bottle, and draining it to the bottom, "what is to be done next?"

"I'll tell you," said Schriften, going up to him. "That man there has a charm hung round his neck. Take it from him, and throw it overboard, and your ship will be saved. If not, it will be lost, with every soul on board."

"Yes, yes, it's all right, depend upon it," cried the sailors.

"Fools!" replied Philip, "do you believe that wretch? Did you not hear the man who came on board recognize him, and call him shipmate? He is the party whose presence on board will prove so unfortunate."

"Yes, yes," cried the sailors, "it's all right; the man did call him shipmate."

"I tell you it's all wrong," cried Schriften. "That is the man. Let him give up the charm."

"Yes, yes; let him give up the charm," cried the sailors, and they rushed upon Philip.

Philip started back to where the captain stood.

"Madmen, know ye what ye are about? It is the holy cross that I wear round my neck. Throw it overboard if you dare, and your souls are lost for ever," and he took the relic from his bosom and showed it to the captain.

"No, no, men," exclaimed the captain, who was now more settled in his nerves, "that won't do—the saints protect us."

The seamen, however, became clamorous; one portion were for throwing Schriften overboard, the other for throwing Philip. At last, the point was decided by the captain, who directed the small skiff hanging astern to be lowered down, and ordered both Philip and Schriften to get into it. The seamen approved of this arrangement, as it satisfied both parties. Philip made no objection; Schriften screamed and fought, but he was tossed into the boat. There he remained trembling in the stern-sheets, while Philip, who had seized the sculls, pulled away from the vessel in the direction of the Phantom Ship.

In a few minutes, the vessel which Philip and Schriften had left was no longer to be discerned through the thick haze; the Phantom Ship was still in sight, but at a much greater distance from them than she was before. Philip pulled hard towards her, but although hove to, she appeared to increase her distance from the boat. For a short time he paused on his oars, to regain his breath, when Schriften rose up and took his seat in the stern-sheets of the boat.

"You may pull and pull, Philip Vanderdecken," observed he, "but you will not gain that ship. No, no, that cannot be. We may have a long cruise together, but you will be as far from your object at the end of it, as you are now at the commencement. Why don't you throw me overboard again? You would be all the lighter. He! he!"

"I threw you overboard in a state of frenzy," replied Philip, "when you attempted to force from me my relic."

"And have I not endeavoured to make others take it from you this very day? Have I not? He! he!"

"You have," rejoined Philip, "but I am now convinced that you are as unhappy as myself, and that in what you are doing, you are only following your destiny, as I am mine. Why and wherefore I cannot tell, but we are both engaged in the same mystery; if the success of my endeavours depends upon guarding the relic, the success of yours depends upon your obtaining it, and defeating my purpose by so doing. In this matter we are both agents, and you have been, as far as my mission is concerned, my most active enemy. But, Schriften, I have not forgotten, and never will, that you kindly *did advise* my poor Amine; that you prophesied to her what would be her fate, if she did not listen to your counsel; that you were no enemy of hers, although you have been and are still mine. Although my enemy, for her sake I *forgive you*, and will not attempt to harm you."

"You do then forgive your enemy, Philip Vanderdecken?" replied Schriften, mournfully, "for such I acknowledge myself to be."

"I do, *with all my heart, with all my soul*," replied Philip.

"Then have you conquered me, Philip Vanderdecken; you have now made me your friend, and your wishes are about to be accomplished. You would know who I am. Listen. When your father, defying the Almighty's will, in his rage took my life, he was vouchsafed a chance of his doom being cancelled, through the merits of his son. I had also my appeal, which was for *vengeance*. It was granted that I should remain on earth, and thwart your will. That as long as we were enemies, you should not succeed; but that when you had conformed to the highest attribute of Christianity, proved on the holy cross, that of *forgiving your enemy*, your task should be fulfilled. Philip Vanderdecken, you have forgiven your enemy, and both our destinies are now accomplished."

As Schriften spoke, Philip's eyes were fixed on him. He extended his hand to Philip—it was taken; and as it was pressed, the form of the pilot wasted as it were into the air, and Philip found himself alone.

"Father of mercy, I thank thee," said Philip, "that my task is done, and that I again may meet my Amine."

Philip then pulled towards the Phantom Ship, and found that she no longer appeared to leave: on the contrary, every minute he was nearer and nearer, and, at last, he threw in his oars, climbed up her side and gained her deck.

The crew of the vessel crowded round him.

"Your captain," said Philip, "I must speak with your captain."

"Who shall I say, sir?" demanded one who appeared to be the first mate.

"Who?" replied Philip. "Tell him his son would speak to him, his son, Philip Vanderdecken."

Shouts of laughter from the crew followed this answer of Philip's; and the mate, as soon as they ceased, observed, with a smile.

"You forget, sir; perhaps you would say his father."

"Tell him his son, if you please," replied Philip. "Take no note of grey hairs."

"Well, sir, here he is coming forward," replied the mate, stepping aside, and pointing to the captain.

"What is all this?" inquired the captain.

"Are you Philip Vanderdecken, the captain of this vessel?"

"I am, sir," replied the other.

"You appear not to know me! But how can you? You saw me but when I was only three years old; yet may you remember a letter which you gave to your wife."

"Ha!" replied the captain; "and who, then, are you?"

"Time has stopped with you, but with those who live in the world he stops not; and for those who pass a life of misery, he hurries on still faster. In me behold your son, Philip Vanderdecken, who has obeyed your wishes; and, after a life of such peril and misery as few have passed, has at last fulfilled his vow, and now offers to his father the precious relic that he required to kiss."

Philip drew out the relic, and held it towards his father. As if a flash of lightning had passed through his mind, the captain of the vessel started back, clasped his hands, fell on his knees, and wept.

"My son, my son!" exclaimed he, rising and throwing himself into Philip's arms; "my eyes are opened—the Almighty knows how long they have been obscured."

Embracing each other, they walked aft, away from the men, who were still crowded at the gangway.

"My son, my noble son, before the charm is broken—before we resolve, as we must, into the elements, oh! let me kneel in thanksgiving and contrition; my son, my noble son, receive a father's thanks," exclaimed Vanderdecken. Then with tears of joy and penitence he humbly addressed himself to that Being whom he once so awfully defied.

The elder Vanderdecken knelt down; Philip did the same; still embracing each other with one arm, while they raised on high the other, and prayed.

For the last time the relic was taken from the bosom of Philip and handed to his father—and his father raised his eyes to heaven and kissed it. And as he kissed it, the long tapering upper spars of the Phantom vessel, the yards and sails that were set, fell into dust, fluttered in the air, and sank upon the wave. The mainmast, foremast, bowsprit, everything above the deck, crumbled into atoms and disappeared.

Again he raised the relic to his lips, and the work of destruction continued—the heavy iron guns sank through the decks and disappeared; the crew of the vessel (who were looking on) crumbled down into skeletons, and dust, and fragments of ragged garments; and there were none left on board the vessel in the semblance of life but the father and son.

Once more did he put the sacred emblem to his lips, and the beams and timbers separated, the decks of the vessel slowly sank, and the remnants of the hull floated upon the water; and as the father and son—the one young and vigorous, the other old and decrepit—still kneeling, still embracing, with their hands raised to heaven, sank slowly under the deep blue wave, the lurid sky was for a moment illuminated by a lightning cross.

Then did the clouds which obscured the heavens roll away swift as thought—the sun again burst out in all its splendour—the rippling waves appeared to dance with joy. The screaming sea-gull again whirled in the air, and the scared albatross once more slumbered on the wing. The porpoise tumbled and tossed in his sportive play, the albicore and dolphin leaped from the sparkling sea. All nature smiled as if it rejoiced that the charm was dissolved for ever, and that THE PHANTOM SHIP WAS NO MORE.

WHITBY WHALERS[1]

Elizabeth Gaskell

(1810–1865)

I

The Press Gang

SYLVIA scampered across the rough farm-yard in the wetting, drizzling rain to the place where she expected to find Kester; but he was not there, so she had to retrace her steps to the cow-house, and, making her way up a rough kind of ladder-staircase fixed against the wall

---

[1] From *Sylvia's Lovers*.

she surprised Kester as he sat in the wool-loft, looking over the fleeces reserved for the home-spinning.

"Kester, feyther's just tiring hissel' wi' weariness an' vexation, sitting by t' fireside wi' his hands afore him, an' nought to do. An' mother and me can't think on aught as'll rouse him up to a bit of a laugh, or aught more cheerful than a scolding. Now, Kester, thou mun just be off, and find Harry Donkin th' tailor, and bring him here; it's gettin' on for Martinmas, an' he'll be coming his rounds, and he may as well come here first as last, and feyther's clothes want a deal o' mending up, and Harry's always full of his news, and anyhow he'll do for feyther to scold, and be a new person too, and that's somewhat for all on us. Now go, like a good old Kester as yo' are." . . .

The next morning Sylvia's face was a little redder than usual when Harry Donkin's bow-legs were seen circling down the path to the house door.

"Here's Donkin, for sure!" exclaimed Bell, when she caught sight of him a minute after her daughter. "Well, I just call that lucky! for he'll be company for thee while Sylvia and me has to turn th' cheeses."

"That's all t' women know about it. Wi' them it's 'coompany, coompany, coompany,' an' they think a man' s no better than theirsels. A'd have yo' to know a've a vast o' thoughts in mysel', as I'm noane willing to lay out for t' benefit o' every man. A've niver gotten time for meditation sin' a were married; leastways, sin' a left t' sea. Aboard ship, wi' niver a woman we' in leagues o' hail, and upo' t' masthead, in special, a could. . . . Come in, Harry, come in, and talk a bit o' sense to me, for a've been shut up wi' women these four days, and a'm a'most a nateral by this time."

So Harry took off his coat, and seated himself professional-wise on the hastily cleared dresser, so that he might have all the light afforded by the long, low casement window. Then he blew in his thimble, sucked his finger, so that they might adhere tightly together, and looked about for a subject for opening conversation, while Sylvia and her mother might be heard opening and shutting drawers and box-lids before they could find the articles that needed repair, or that were required to mend each other.

"Women's well enough i' their way," said Daniel. . . . He had taken his pipe out of the square hollow in the fireside wall, where he usually kept it, and was preparing to diversify his remarks with satisfying interludes of puffing. "Why, look ye; this very baccy . . . came ashore sewed up neatly enough i' a woman's stays, as was wife to a fishing-smack down at t' bay yonder. She were a lean thing as iver you saw when she went for t' see her husband aboard t' vessel; but she coom back lustier by a deal, and wi' many a thing on her, here and theere, beside baccy. An' that were i' t' face o' coast-guard and yon tender, an' a'."

"Speaking of t' tender, there's been a piece o' wark i' Monkshaven this week wi' t' press-gang," said Harry. "Folk had gotten to think nought o' t' tender, she lay so still, an' t' leftenant paid such a good price for all he wanted for t' ship. But o' Thursday t' *Resolution*, first whaler back this season, came in port, and t' press gang showed their teeth, and carried off four as good able-bodied seamen as iver I made trousers for; and t' place were all up like a nest o' wasps, when yo've set your foot in t' midst. They were so mad, they were ready for t' fight t' very pavin' stones."

"A wish a'd been there! A just wish a had! A've a score for t' reckon up wi' t' press-gang!"

And the old man lifted up his right hand—his hand on which the forefinger and thumb were maimed and useless—partly in denunciation, and partly as a witness of what he had endured to escape from the service, abhorred because it was forced. His face became a totally different countenance with the expression of settled and unrelenting indignation, which his words called out.

"G'on, man, g'on," said Daniel, impatient with Donkin for the little delay occasioned by the necessity of arranging his work more fully.

"Ay! ay! all in good time; for a've a long tale to tell yet, an' a mun have some'un to iron out my seams, and look me out my bits, for there's none here fit for my purpose."

"Dang thy bits! Here, Sylvie! Sylvie! come and be tailor's man, and let t' chap get settled sharp, for a'm fain t' hear his story."

Sylvia took her directions, and placed her irons in the fire, and ran upstairs for the bundle which had been put aside by her careful mother for occasions like the present. Daniel grew angry before Donkin had selected his patterns and settled the work to his own mind.

"Well," said he at last; "a mought be a young man a-goin' a-wooin', by t' pains thou'st taken for t' match my oud clothes. I don't care if they're patched wi' scarlet, a tell thee; so as thou'lt work away at thy tale wi' thy tongue, same time as thou works at thy needle wi' thy fingers."

"Then, as a were saying, all Monkshaven were like a nest o' wasps, flyin' hither and thither, and makin' sich a buzzin' and a talkin' as niver were; and each wi' his sting out ready for t' vent his venom o' rage and revenge. And women cryin' and sobbin' i' t' streets—when, Lord help us! o' Saturday came a worse thing than iver! for all Friday there had been a kind o' expectation an' dismay about t' *Good Fortune*, as t' mariners had said was off St Abb's Head o' Thursday, when t' *Resolution* came in! and there was wives and maids wi' husbands an' sweethearts aboard t' *Good Fortune* ready to throw their eyes out on their heads wi' gazin', gazin', nor'ards over t' sea, as were all one haze o' blankness wi' t' rain; and when t' afternoon tide comed in, an' niver a line on her to be seen, folk were oncertain as t' whether she were holding off for fear o'

t' tender—as were out o' sight, too—or what were her mak' o' goin' on.
An' t' poor, wet, draggled women folk came up t' town, some slowly
cryin', as if their hearts was sick, an' others just bent their heads to t'
wind, and went straight to their homes, nother looking nor speaking to
ony one; but barred their doors, and stiffened theirsels up for a night o'
waiting. Saturday morn—yo'll mind Saturday morn, it were stormy
and gusty, downreet dirty weather—there stood t' folk again by daylight,
a-watching an', a-straining, and by that tide t' *Good Fortune* came o'er
t' bar. But t' excisemen had sent back her news by t' boat as took 'em
there. They'd a deal of oil, and a vast o' blubber. But for all that her
flag was drooping i' t' rain, half mast high, for mourning and sorrow,
an' they'd a dead man aboard—a dead man as was living and strong
last sunrise. An' there was another as lay between life an' death, and
there was seven more as should ha' been there as wasn't, but was carried off by t' gang. T' frigate as we'n a' heard tell on, as lying off Hartle-
pool, got tidings fra' t' tender as captured t' seamen o' Thursday: and
t' *Aurora*, as they ca'ed her, made off for t' nor'ard; and nine leagues
off St Abb's Head, t' *Resolution* thinks she were, she seed t' frigate, and
knowed by her build she were a man-o'-war, and guessed she were bound
on king's kidnapping. I seen t' wounded man mysen wi' my own eyes;
and he'll live! he'll live! Niver a man died yet, wi' such a strong purpose
o' vengeance in him. He could barely speak, for he were badly shot,
but his colour coome and went, as t' master's mate an' t' captain telled
me and some others how t' *Aurora* fired at 'em and how t' innocent
whaler hoisted her colours, but afore they were fairly run up, another
shot coome close in t' shrouds, and then t' Greenland ship being t' windward, bore down on t' frigate; but as they knew she were an oud fox,
and bent on mischief, Kinraid (that's he who lies a-dying, only he'll
noane die, a'se bound), the specksioneer, bade t' men go down between
decks, and fasten t' hatches well, and he'd stand guard, he an' captain,
and t' oud master's mate being left upo' deck for t' give a welcome just
skin-deep to t' boat's crew fra' t' *Aurora*, as they could see coming
t'wards them o'er t' watter, wi' their reg'lar man-o'-war's rowing——"

"Damn 'em!" said Daniel in soliloquy, and under his breath.

Sylvia stood, poising her iron, and listening eagerly, afraid to give
Donkin the hot iron for fear of interrupting the narrative, unwilling to
put it into the fire again, because that action would perchance remind
him of his work, which now the tailor had forgotten, so eager was he in
telling his story.

"Well, they coome on over t' watters wi' great bounds, and up t'
sides they coome like locusts, all armed men; an' t' captain says he saw
Kinraid hide away his whaling-knife under some tarpaulin, an' he knew
he meant mischief, an' he would no more ha' stopped him wi' a word
nor he would ha' stopped him fra' killing a whale. And when t' *Aurora's*
men were aboard, one on 'em runs to t' helm; and at that t' captain

says he felt as if his wife were kissed afore his face; but says he, 'I bethought me on t' men as were shut up below hatches, an' I remembered t' folk at Monkshaven as were looking out for us even then; an' I said to mysel', I would speak fair as long as I could, more by token o' the whaling-knife, as I could see glinting bright under t' black tarpaulin.' So he spoke quite fair and civil though he see'd they was nearing t' *Aurora* and t' *Aurora* was nearing them. Then t' navy captain hailed him thro' t' trumpet, wi' a great rough blast, and, says he, 'Order your men to come on deck.' And t' captain o' t' whaler says, his men cried up from under t' hatches as they'd niver be gi'en up wi'out bloodshed, and he sees Kinraid take out his pistol, and look well to t' priming; so he says to t' navy captain, 'We're protected Greenlandmen, and you have no right t' meddle wi' us.' But t' navy captain only bellows t' more, 'Order your men t' come on deck. If they won't obey you, and you have lost the command of your vessel, I reckon you're in a state of mutiny, and you may come aboard t' *Aurora* and such men as are willing t' follow you, and I'll fire int' the rest.' Yo' see, that were t' depth o' the man: he were for pretending and pretexting as t' captain could na manage his own ship, and as he'd help him. But our Greenland captain were none so poor-sighted, and says he, 'She's full of oil, and I ware you of consequences if you fire into her. Anyhow, pirate or no pirate' (for word pirate stuck in his gizzard), 'I'm an honest Monkshaven man, an' I come fra' a land where there's great icebergs and many a deadly danger, but niver a press-gang, thank God! and that's what you are, I reckon.' Them's the words he told me, but whether he spoke 'em out so bold at t' time, I'se not so sure; they were in his mind for t' speak, only maybe prudence got t' better on him, for he said he prayed i' his heart to bring his cargo safe to t' owners, come what might. Well t' *Aurora's* men aboard t' *Good Fortune* cried out, 'might they fire down t' hatches, and bring t' men out that a way?' and then t' specksioneer, he speaks, an' he says he stands ower t' hatches, and he has two good pistols, an' summut besides, and he don't care for his life, bein' a bachelor, but all below are married men, yo' see, and he'll put an end to t' first two chaps as come near t' hatches. An' they say he picked two off as made for t' come near, and then just as he were stooping for t' whaling-knife, an' it's as big as a sickle——"

"Teach folk as don't know a whaling-knife," cried Daniel. "I were a Greenland man mysel'."

"They shot him through t' side, and dizzied him, and kicked him aside for dead; and fired down t' hatches, and killed one man, and disabled two, and then t' rest cried for quarter, for life is sweet, e'en aboard a king's ship; and t' *Aurora* carried 'em off, wounded men, an' able men, an' all; leaving Kinraid for dead, as wasn't dead, and Darley for dead, as was dead, an' t' captain and master's mate as were too old for work; and t' captain, as loves Kinraid like a brother, poured rum down his

throat, and bandaged him up, and has sent for t' first doctor in Monkshaven for to get t' slugs out; for they say there's niver such a harpooner
in a' t' Greenland Seas; an' I can speak fra' my own seeing he's a fine
young fellow where he lies theere, all stark and wan for weakness and
loss o' blood. But Darley's dead as a door-nail; and there's to be such
a burying of him as niver was seen afore i' Monkshaven, come Sunday.
And now gi' us t' iron, wench, and let's lose no more time a-talking."

"It's noane loss o' time," said Daniel, moving himself heavily in his
chair, to feel how helpless he was once more. "If a were as young as
once a were—nay, lad, if a had na these sore rheumatics, now—a
reckon as t' press-gang 'ud find out as 't shouldn't do such things for
nothing. Bless thee, man! it's waur nor i' my youth i' th' Ameriky war,
and then 't were bad enough."

"And Kinraid?" said Sylvia, drawing a long breath, after the effort
of realising it all; her cheeks had flushed up, and her eyes had glittered
during the progress of the tale.

"Oh, he'll do. He'll not die. Life's stuff is in him yet."

II

The Manners of Whales

Farmer Robson left Haytersbank betimes, on a longish day's journey,
to purchase a horse. Sylvia and her mother were busied with a hundred
household things, and the early winter's evening closed in upon them
almost before they were aware.

The mother and daughter hardly spoke at all when they sat down
at last. The cheerful click of the knitting-needles made a pleasant home
sound; and in the occasional snatches of slumber that overcame her
mother, Sylvia could hear the long-rushing boom of the waves, down
below the rocks, for the Haytersbank gulley allowed the sullen roar to
come up so far inland. It might have been about eight o'clock—though
from the monotonous course of the evening it seemed much later—when
Sylvia heard her father's heavy step cranching down the pebbly path.
More unusual, she heard his voice talking to some companion.

Curious to see who it could be, with a lively instinctive advance towards any event which might break the monotony she had begun to
find somewhat dull, she sprang up to open the door. Half a glance
into the grey darkness outside made her suddenly timid, and she drew
back behind the door as she opened it wide to admit her father and Kinraid.

Daniel Robson came in bright and boisterous. He was pleased with
his purchase, and had had some drink to celebrate his bargain. He had
ridden the new mare into Monkshaven, and left her at the smithy there
until morning, to have her feet looked at, and to be new shod. On his
way from the town he had met Kinraid wandering about in search of

Haytersbank Farm itself, so he had just brought him along with him; and here they were, ready for bread and cheese, and aught else the mistress would set before them.

To Sylvia the sudden change into brightness and bustle occasioned by the entrance of her father and the specksioneer was like that which you may effect any winter's night, when you come into a room where a great lump of coal lies hot and slumbering on the fire; just break it up with a judicious blow from the poker, and the room, late so dark, and dusk, and lone, is full of life, and light, and warmth.

She moved about with pretty, household briskness, attending to all her father's wants. Kinraid's eyes watched her as she went backwards and forwards, to and fro, into the pantry, the back-kitchen, out of light into shade, out of the shadow into the broad firelight where he could see and note her appearance. She wore the high-crowned, linen cap of that day, surmounting her lovely masses of golden brown hair, rather than concealing them, and tied firm to her head by a broad blue ribbon. A long curl hung down on each side of her neck—her throat rather, for her neck was concealed by a little spotted handkerchief carefully pinned across at the waist of her brown stuff gown. . . .

By the time she could sit down, her father and Kinraid had their glasses filled, and were talking of the relative merits of various kinds of spirits; that led on to tales of smuggling, and the different contrivances by which they or their friends had eluded the preventive service; the nightly relays of men to carry the goods inland; the kegs of brandy found by certain farmers whose horses had gone so far in the night that they could do no work the next day. . . .

From smuggling adventures it was easy to pass on to stories of what had happened to Robson, in his youth a sailor in the Greenland seas, and to Kinraid, now one of the best harpooners in any whaler that sailed off the coast.

"There's three things to be afeared on," said Robson, authoritatively: "there's t' ice, that's bad; there's dirty weather, that's worse; and there's whales theirselves, as is t' worst of all; leastways, they was i' my days; t' darned brutes may ha' larnt better manners sin'. When I were young, they could niver be got to let theirsels be harpooned wi'out flounderin' and makin' play wi' their tails and their fins, till t' say were all in a foam, and t' boats' crews as all o'er wi' spray, which i' them latitudes is a kind o' shower-bath not needed."

"Th' whales hasn't mended their manners, as you call it," said Kinraid; "but th' ice is not to be spoken lightly on. I were once in th' ship *John*, of Hull, and we were in good green water, and were keen after whales; and ne'er thought harm of a great grey iceberg as were on our lee-bow, a mile or so off; it looked as if it had been there from the days of Adam, and were likely to see th' last man out, and it ne'er a bit bigger nor smaller in all them thousands and thousands o' years. Well, the fast-

boats were out after a fish, and I were specksioneer in one; and we were
so keen after capturing our whale, that none on us ever saw that we were
drifting away from them right into deep shadow o' th' iceberg. But we
were set upon our whale, and I harpooned it; and as soon as it were dead
we lashed its fins together, and fastened its tail to our boat; and then we
took breath and looked about us, and away from us a little space were
th' other boats, wi' two other fish making play, and as likely as not to
break loose, for I may say as I were th' best harpooner on board the
John, wi'out saying great things o' mysel'. So I says, 'My lads, one o'
you stay i' th' boat by this fish,' the fins o' which, as I said, I'd reeved a
rope through mysel', and which was as dead as Noah's grandfather—
'and th' rest on us shall go off and help th' other boats wi' their fish.'
For, you see, we had another boat close by in order to sweep th' fish.
(I suppose they swept fish i' your time, master?)"

"Ay, ay!" said Robson; "one boat lies still holding t' end o' t' line;
t' other makes a circuit round t' fish."

"Well! luckily for us we had our second boat, for we all got into it,
ne'er a man on us was left i' th' fast-boat. And says I, 'But who's to
stay by t' dead fish?' And no man answered, for they were all as keen
as me for to go and help our mates; and we thought as we could come back
to our dead fish, as had a boat for a buoy, once we had helped our mate.
So off we rowed, every man Jack on us, out o' the black shadow o' th'
iceberg, as looked as steady as th' pole-star. Well! We had na' been a
dozen fathoms away fra th' boat as we had left, when crash! down wi' a
roaring noise, and then a gulp of the deep waters, and then a shower o'
blinding spray; and when we had wiped our eyes clear, and getten our
hearts down agen fra our mouths, there were never a boat nor a glittering
belly o' e'er a great whale to be seen; but th' iceberg were there, still and
grim, as if a hundred ton or more had fallen off all in a mass, and crushed
down boat, and fish, and all, into th' deep water, as goes half through the
earth in them latitudes. Th' coal-miners round about Newcastle way
may come upon our good boat if they mine deep enough, else ne'er
another man will see her. And I left as good a clasp-knife in her as ever
I clapt eyes on."

"But what a mercy no man stayed in her," said Bell.

"Why, mistress, I reckon we a' must die some way; and I'd as soon
go down into the deep waters as be choked up wi' moulds."

"But it must be so cold," said Sylvia, shuddering and giving a little
poke to the fire to warm her fancy.

"Cold!" said her father, "what do ye stay-at-homes know about cold,
a should like to know? If yo'd been where a were once, north latitude 81,
in such a frost as ye ha' niver known, no, not i' deep winter, and it were
June i' them seas, and a whale i' sight, and a were off in a boat after her;
an' t' ill-mannered brute, as soon as she were harpooned, ups wi' her big,
awkward tail, and struck th' boat i' her stern, and chucks me out into t'

watter. That were cold, a can tell the'! First, I smarted all ower me, as if my skin were suddenly stript off me; and next, ivery bone i' my body had getten t' toothache, and there were a great roar i' my ears, an' a great dizziness i' my eyes; an' t' boat's crew kept throwin' out their oars, an' a kept clutchin' at 'em, but a could na' make out where they was, my eyes dazzled so wi' t' cold, an' I thought I were bound for 'kingdom come,' an' a tried to remember t' Creed, as a might die a Christian. But all a could think on was, 'What is your name, M. or N?' an' just as a were giving up both words and life, they heaved me aboard. But, bless ye, they had but one oar; for they'd thrown a' t' others after me; so yo' may reckon it were some time afore we could reach t' ship; an', a've heard tell, a were a precious sight to look on, for my clothes was just hard frozen to me, an' my hair a'most as big a lump o' ice as yon iceberg he was a-telling us on; they rubbed me as missus theere was rubbing t' hams yesterday, and gav' me brandy; an' a've niver getten t' frost out o' my bones for a' their rubbin', and a deal o' brandy as I 'ave ta'en sin'. Talk o' cold! it's little yo' women known o' cold!"

"But there's heat, too, i' some places," said Kinraid. "I was once a voyage i' an American. They goes for th' most part south, to where you come round to th' cold again; and they'll stay there for three year at a time, if need be, going into winter harbour i' some o' th' Pacific Islands. Well, we were i' th' southern seas, a-seeking for good whaling-ground; and, close on our larboard beam, there were a great wall o' ice, as much as sixty feet high. And says our captain—as were a dare-devil, if ever a man were—'There'll be an opening in yon dark grey wall, and into that opening I'll sail, if I coast along it till th' day o' judgment.' But, for all our sailing, we never seemed to come nearer to th' opening. The waters were rocking beneath us, and the sky were steady above us; and th' ice rose out o' the waters, and seemed to reach up into the sky. We sailed on, and we sailed on, for more days nor I could count. Our captain were a strange, wild man, but once he looked a little pale when he came upo' deck after his turn-in, and saw the green-grey ice going straight up on our beam. Many on us thought as the ship were bewitched for th' captain's words; and we got to speak low, and to say our prayers o' nights, and a kind o' dull silence came into th' very air; our voices did na' rightly seem our own. And we sailed on, and we sailed on. All at once, th' man as were on watch gave a cry; he saw a break in the ice, as we'd begun to think were everlasting; and we all gathered towards the bows, and the captain called to th' man at the helm to keep her course, and cocked his head, and began to walk the quarter-deck, jaunty again. And we came to a great cleft in th' long, weary rock of ice; and the sides o' th' cleft were not jagged, but went straight sharp down into th' foaming waters. But we took but one look at what lay inside, for our captain, with a loud cry to God, bade the helmsman steer nor'ards away fra' th' mouth o' hell. We all saw wi' our own eyes, inside that fearsome wall o' ice—seventy mile long, as we could swear to—inside that grey, cold ice, came leaping flames, all red and yellow wi' heat o' some unearthly kind out o' th' very waters o' the sea; making our eyes dazzle wi' their scarlet blaze, that shot up as high, nay, higher than th' ice around, yet never so much as shred on 't was melted. They did say that some beside our captain saw the black devils dart hither and thither, quicker than the very flames themselves; anyhow, *he* saw them. And as he knew it were his own daring as had led him to have that peep at terrors forbidden to any on us afore our time, he just dwined away, and we hadn't taken but one whale afore our captain died, and first mate took th' command. It were a prosperous voyage; but, for all that, I'll never sail those seas again, nor ever take wage aboard an American again."

"Eh, dear! but it's awful t' think o' sitting wi' a man that has seen th' doorway into hell," said Bell aghast.

Sylvia had dropped her work, and sat gazing at Kinraid with fascinated wonder.

Daniel was just a little annoyed at the admiration which his own wife and daughter were bestowing on the specksioneer's wonderful stories, and he said—

"Ay, ay. If a'd been a talker, ye'd ha' thought a deal more on me nor ye've iver done yet. A've seen such things, and done such things."

"Tell us, father!" said Sylvia, greedy and breathless.

"Some on 'em is past telling," he replied, "an some is not to be had for t' asking, seeing as how they might bring a man into trouble. But, as a said, if a had a fancy to reveal all as is on my mind a could make t' hair on your heads lift up your caps—well, we'll say an inch, at least. Thy mother, lass, has heerd one or two on 'em. Thou minds the story o' my ride on a whale's back, Bell? That'll maybe be within this young fellow's comprehension o' t' danger; thou's heerd me tell it, hastn't ta?"

"Yes," said Bell; "but it's a long time ago; when we was courting."

"An' that's afore this young lass were born, as is a'most up to woman's estate. But sin' those days a ha' been o'er busy to tell stories to my wife, an' as a'll warrant she's forgotten it; an' as Sylvia here niver heerd it, if yo'll fill your glass, Kinraid, yo' shall ha' t' benefit o't.

"A were a specksioneer mysel', though, after that, a rayther directed my talents int' t' smuggling branch o' my profession; but a were once a-whaling aboard t' *Aimwell* of Whitby. An' we was anchored off t' coast o' Greenland one season; an we'd getten a cargo o' seven whales; but our captain he were a keen-eyed chap, an' niver above doin' any man's work; an' once seein' a whale he throws himself int' a boat an' goes off to it, makin' signals to me, an' another specksioneer as were off for diversion i' another boat, for to come after him sharp. Well, afore we comes alongside, captain had harpooned t' fish; an' says he, 'Now, Robson, all ready! give into her again when she comes to t' top;' an' I stands up, right leg foremost, harpoon all ready, as soon as iver I cotched a sight o' t' whale, but niver a fin could a see. 'Twere no wonder, for she were right below t' boat in which a were; and when she wanted to rise, what does t' great, ugly brute do but come wi' her head, as is like cast iron, up bang again t' bottom o' t' boat. I were thrown up in t' air like a shuttle-cock, me an' my line an' my harpoon—up we goes, an' many a good piece o' timber wi' us, an' many a good fellow too; but I had t' look after mysel', an' a were up high i' t' air, afore I could say Jack Robinson, an' a thowt a were safe for another dive int' saut water; but i'stead a comes down plump on t' back o' t' whale. Ay! yo' may stare, master, but theere a were, an' main an' slippery it were, only a sticks my harpoon intil her, an' steadies mysel', an' looks abroad o'er t' vast o' waves, and gets sea-sick in a manner, an' puts up a prayer as she mayn't dive, and it were as good a prayer for wishin' it might come true as iver t' clergyman an' t' clerk too puts up i' Monkshaven Church. Well, a reckon it were heerd, for all a were i' them north latitudes, for she keeps steady, an' a does my best for t' keep steady; an' 'deed a was too steady, for a was fast wi' t' harpoon line, all knotted and tangled about me. T' captain, he sings out for me to cut it; but it's easy singin' out, and it's noane so easy fumblin' for your knife i' t' pocket o' your drawers, when yo've t' hold hard wi' t' other hand on t' back of a whale, swimmin' fourteen knots an hour. At last a thinks to mysel' a can't get free o' t' line, and t' line is fast to t' harpoon, and t' harpoon is fast to t' whale; and t' whale may go down fathoms deep wheniver t' maggot stirs i' her head; and t' watter's cold, an' noane good for drownin' in; a can't get free o' t' line, and a cannot get my knife out o' my breeches pocket, though t' captain should ca' it mutiny to disobey orders, and t' line's fast to t' harpoon—let's see if t' harpoon's fast to t' whale. So a tugged, an' a lugged, and t' whale didn't mistake it for ticklin', but she cocks up her tail, and throws out showers o' water as were ice or iver it touched me; but a pulls on at t' shank, an' a were only afeard as she wouldn't keep at t' top wi' it sticking in her; but at last t' harpoon broke, an' just i' time, for a reckon she was near as tired o' me as a were on her, and down she went; and a had hard work to make for t' boats as was near enough to catch me; for what wi' t' whale's being but slippery an' t' watter being cold, an' me hampered wi' t' line an' t' piece o' harpoon, it's a chance, missus, as thou had stopped an oud maid."

"Eh dear a' me!" said Bell, "how well I mind yo'r telling me that tale! It were twenty-four year ago come October. I thought I never could think enough on a man as had rode on a whale's back."

"Yo' may learn t' way of winnin' t' women," said Daniel, winking at the specksioneer.

And Kinraid immediately looked at Sylvia.

IN THE STEERAGE[1]

Charles Dickens

(1812–1870)

A DARK and dreary night; people nestling in their beds, or circling late about the fire; Want, colder than Charity, shivering at the street corners; church-towers humming with the faint vibration of their own tongues, but newly resting from the ghostly preachment "One!" The earth covered with a sable pall as for the burial of yesterday; the clumps of dark trees, its giant plumes of funeral feathers, waving sadly to and fro: all hushed, all noiseless, and in deep repose, save the swift clouds that skim across the moon, and the cautious wind, as, creeping after them upon the ground, it stops to listen, and goes rustling on, and stops again, and follows, like a savage on the trail.

Whither go the clouds and wind so eagerly? If, like guilty spirits, they repair to some dread conference with powers like themselves, in what wild regions do the elements hold council, or where unbend in terrible disport?

Here! Free from that cramped prison called the earth, and out upon the waste of waters. Here, roaring, raging, shrieking, howling, all night long. Hither come the sounding voices from the caverns on the coast of that small island, sleeping, a thousand miles away, so quietly in the midst of angry waves; and hither, to meet them, rush the blasts from unknown desert places of the world. Here, in the fury of their unchecked liberty, they storm and buffet with each other, until the sea, lashed into passion like their own, leaps up, in ravings mightier than theirs, and the whole scene is madness.

On, on, on, over the countless miles of angry space roll the long heaving billows. Mountains and caves are here, and yet are not; for what is now the one, is now the other; then all is but a boiling heap of rushing water. Pursuit, and flight, and mad return of wave on wave, and savage struggle ending in a sporting-up of foam that whitens the black night; incessant change of place, and form, and hue; constancy in nothing, but eternal strife; on, on, on, they roll, and darker grows the night, and louder howls the wind, and more clamorous and fierce become the million voices in the sea, when the wild cry goes forth upon the storm "A ship!"

Onward she comes, in gallant combat with the elements, her tall masts trembling, and her timbers starting on the strain; onward she comes, now high upon the curling billows, now low down in the hollows of the sea, as hiding for the moment from its fury; and every storm-voice in the air and water cries more loudly yet, "A ship!"

Still she comes striving on: and at her boldness and the spreading

---

[1] From *Martin Chuzzlewit*.

cry, the angry waves rise up above each other's hoary heads to look; and round about the vessel, far as the mariners on the decks can pierce into the gloom, they press upon her, forcing each other down, and starting up, and rushing forward from afar, in dreadful curiosity. High over her they break; and round her surge and roar; and giving place to others, moaningly depart, and dash themselves to fragments in their baffled anger. Still she comes onward bravely. And though the eager multitude crowd thick and fast upon her all the night, and dawn of day discovers the untiring train yet bearing down upon the ship in an eternity of troubled water, onward she comes, with dim lights burning in her hull, and people there, asleep; as if no deadly element were peering in at every seam and chink, and no drowned seaman's grave, with but a plank to cover it, were yawning in the unfathomable depths below.

Among these sleeping voyagers were Martin and Mark Tapley, who, rocked into a heavy drowsiness by the unaccustomed motion, were as insensible to the foul air in which they lay, as to the uproar without. It was broad day, when the latter awoke with a dim idea that he was dreaming of having gone to sleep in a four-post bedstead which had turned bottom upwards in the course of the night. There was more reason in this too, than in the roasting of eggs; for the first objects Mr Tapley recognized when he opened his eyes were his own heels—looking down to him, as he afterwards observed, from a nearly perpendicular elevation.

"Well!" said Mark, getting himself into a sitting posture, after various ineffectual struggles with the rolling of the ship. "This is the first time as ever I stood on my head all night."

"You shouldn't go to sleep upon the ground with your head to leeward then," growled a man in one of the berths.

"With my head to *where?*" asked Mark.

The man repeated his previous sentiment.

"No, I won't another time," said Mark, "when I know whereabouts on the map that country is. In the meanwhile I can give you a better piece of advice. Don't you nor any other friend of mine never go to sleep with his head in a ship any more."

The man gave a grunt of discontented acquiescence, turned over in his berth, and drew his blanket over his head.

"—For," said Mr Tapley, pursuing the theme by way of soliloquy, in a low tone of voice: "the sea is as nonsensical a thing as any going. It never knows what to do with itself. It hasn't got no employment for its mind, and is always in a state of vacancy. Like them Polar bears in the wild-beast shows as is constantly a-nodding their heads from side to side, it never *can* be quiet. Which is entirely owing to its uncommon stupidity."

"Is that you, Mark?" asked a faint voice from another berth.

"It's as much of me as is left, sir, after a fortnight of this work," Mr Tapley replied. "What with leading the life of a fly, ever since I've been aboard—for I've been perpetually holding-on to something or other, in a upside-down position—what with that, sir, and putting a very little into myself, and taking a good deal out of myself, there an't too much of me to swear by. How do *you* find yourself this morning, sir?"

"Very miserable," said Martin, with a peevish groan. "Ugh! This is wretched, indeed!"

"Creditable," muttered Mark, pressing one hand upon his aching head and looking round him with a rueful grin. "That's the great comfort. It *is* creditable to keep up one's spirits here. Virtue's its own reward. So's jollity."

Mark was so far right, that unquestionably any man who retained his cheerfulness among the steerage accommodations of that noble and fast-sailing line-of-packet ship, *The Screw*, was solely indebted to his own resources, and shipped his good humour, like his provisions, without any contribution or assistance from the owners. A dark, low, stifling cabin, surrounded by berths all filled to overflowing with men, women, and children, in various stages of sickness and misery, is not the liveliest place of assembly at any time; but when it is so crowded (as the steerage cabin of *The Screw* was, every passage out), that mattresses and beds are heaped upon the floor, to the extinction of everything like comfort, cleanliness, and decency, it is liable to operate not only as a pretty strong barrier against amiability of temper, but as a positive encourager of selfish and rough humours. Mark felt this, as he sat looking about him; and his spirits rose proportionately.

There were English people, Irish people, Welsh people, and Scotch people there; all with their little store of coarse food and shabby clothes; and nearly all with their families of children. There were children of all ages; from the baby at the breast, to the slattern-girl who was as much a grown woman as her mother. Every kind of domestic suffering that is bred in poverty, illness, banishment, sorrow, and long travel in bad weather, was crammed into the little space; and yet was there infinitely less of complaint and querulousness, and infinitely more of mutual assistance and general kindness to be found in that unwholesome ark, than in many brilliant ball-rooms.

Mark looked about him wistfully, and his face brightened as he looked. Here an old grandmother was crooning over a sick child, and rocking it to and fro, in arms hardly more wasted than its own young limbs; here a poor woman with an infant in her lap, mended another little creature's clothes, and quieted another who was creeping up about her from their scanty bed upon the floor. Here were old men awkwardly engaged in little household offices, wherein they would have been ridiculous but for their good-will and kind purpose; and here were swarthy fellows—giants in their way—doing such little acts of tenderness for those about them, as might have belonged to gentlest-hearted dwarfs. The very idiot in the corner who sat mowing there, all day, had his faculty of imitation roused by what he saw about him; and snapped his fingers to amuse a crying child.

"Now, then," said Mark, nodding to a woman who was dressing her three children at no great distance from him: and the grin upon his face had by this time spread from ear to ear: "Hand over one of them young uns according to custom."

"I wish you'd get breakfast, Mark, instead of worrying with people who don't belong to you," observed Martin, petulantly.

"All right," said Mark. "*She'll* do that. It's a fair division of labour, sir. I wash her boys, and she makes our tea. I never *could* make tea, but any one can wash a boy."

The woman, who was delicate and ill, felt and understood his kindness, as well she might, for she had been covered every night with his great-coat, while he had had for his own bed the bare boards and a rug. But Martin, who seldom got up or looked about him, was quite incensed by the folly of this speech, and expressed his dissatisfaction by an impatient groan.

"So it is, certainly," said Mark, brushing the child's hair as coolly as if he had been born and bred a barber.

"What are you talking about, now?" asked Martin.

"What you said," replied Mark; "or what you meant, when you gave that there dismal vent to your feelings. I quite go along with it, sir. It *is* very hard upon her."

"What is?"

"Making this voyage by herself along with these young impediments here, and going such a way at such a time of the year to join her husband. If you don't want to be driven mad with yellow soap in your eye, young man," said Mr Tapley to the second urchin, who was by this time under his hands at the basin, "you'd better shut it."

"Where does she join her husband?" asked Martin, yawning.

"Why, I'm very much afraid," said Mr Tapley, in a low voice, "that she don't know. I hope she mayn't miss him. But she sent her last letter by hand, and it don't seem to have been very clearly understood between 'em without it, and if she don't see him a-waving his pocket-handkerchief on the shore, like a pictur out of a song-book, my opinion is she'll break her heart."

"Why, how, in Folly's name, does the woman come to be on board ship on such a wild-goose venture!" cried Martin.

Mr Tapley glanced at him for a moment as he lay prostrate in his berth, and then said, very quietly:

"Ah! How indeed! I can't think! He's been away from her for two year: she's been very poor and lonely in her own country; and has always been a-looking forward to meeting him. It's very strange she should be here. Quite amazing! A little mad perhaps! There can't be no other way of accounting for it."

Martin was too far gone in the lassitude of sea-sickness to make any reply to these words, or even to attend to them as they were spoken. And the subject of their discourse returning at this crisis with some hot tea, effectually put a stop to any resumption of the theme by Mr Tapley; who, when the meal was over and he had adjusted Martin's bed, went up on deck to wash the breakfast service, which consisted of two half-pint tin mugs, and a shaving-pot of the same metal.

It is due to Mark Tapley to state that he suffered at least as much from sea-sickness as any man, woman, or child, on board; and that he had a peculiar faculty of knocking himself about on the smallest provocation, and losing his legs at every lurch of the ship. But resolved, in his usual phrase, to "come out strong" under disadvantageous circumstances, he was the life and soul of the steerage, and made no more of stopping in the middle of a facetious conversation to go away and be excessively ill by himself, and afterwards come back in the very best and gayest of tempers to resume it, than if such a course of proceeding had been the commonest in the world.

It cannot be said that as his illness wore off, his cheerfulness and good nature increased, because they would hardly admit of augmentation; but his usefulness among the weaker members of the party was much enlarged; and at all times and seasons there he was exerting it. If a gleam of sun shone out of the dark sky, down Mark tumbled into the cabin, and presently up he came again with a woman in his arms, or half-a-dozen children, or a man, or a bed, or a saucepan, or a basket, or something animate or inanimate, that he thought would be the better for the air. If an hour or two of fine weather in the middle of the day tempted those who seldom or never came on deck at other times to crawl into the long-boat, or lie down upon the spare spars, and try to eat, there, in the centre of the group, was Mr Tapley, handing about salt beef and biscuit, or dispensing tastes of grog, or cutting up the children's provisions with his pocket-knife, for their greater ease and comfort, or reading aloud from a venerable newspaper, or singing some roaring old song to a select party, or writing the beginnings of letters to their friends at home for people who couldn't write, or cracking jokes with the crew, or nearly getting blown over the side, or emerging, half-drowned, from a shower of spray, or lending a hand somewhere or other: but always doing something for the general entertainment. At night, when the cooking-fire was lighted on the deck, and the driving sparks that flew among the rigging, and the cloud of sails, seemed to menace the ship with certain annihilation by fire, in case the elements of air and water failed to compass her destruction; there, again, was Mr Tapley, with his coat off and his shirt sleeves turned up to his elbows, doing all kinds of culinary offices; compounding the strangest dishes; recognized by every one as an established authority; and helping all parties to achieve something which, left to themselves, they never could have done, and never would have dreamed of. In short, there never was a more popular character than Mark Tapley became, on board that noble and fast-sailing line-of-packet ship, *The Screw;* and he attained at last to such a pitch of universal admiration that he began to have grave doubts within himself whether a man might reasonably claim any credit for being jolly under such exciting circumstances.

"If this was going to last," said Tapley, "there'd be no great difference as I can perceive, between *The Screw* and the Dragon. I never *am* to get credit, I think. I begin to be afraid that the Fates is determined to make the world easy to me."

"Well, Mark," said Martin, near whose berth he had ruminated to this effect. "When will this be over?"

"Another week, they say, sir," returned Mark, "will most likely bring us into port. The ship's a-going along at present, as sensible as a ship can, sir; though I don't mean to say as that's any very high praise."

"I don't think it is, indeed," groaned Martin.

"You'd feel all the better for it, sir, if you was to turn out," observed Mark.

"And be seen by the ladies and gentlemen on the after-deck," returned Martin, with a scornful emphasis upon the words, "mingling with the beggarly crowd that are stowed away in this vile hole. I should be greatly the better for that, no doubt!"

"I'm thankful that I can't say from my own experience what the feelings of a gentleman may be," said Mark, "but I should have thought, sir, as a gentleman would feel a deal more uncomfortable down here than up in the fresh air, especially when the ladies and gentlemen in the after-cabin know just as much about him as he does about them, and are likely to trouble their heads about him in the same proportion. I should have thought that, certainly."

"I tell you, then," rejoined Martin, "you would have thought wrong, and do think wrong."

"Very likely, sir," said Mark, with imperturbable good temper. "I often do."

"As to lying here," cried Martin, raising himself on his elbow, and looking angrily at his follower. "Do you suppose it's a pleasure to lie here?"

"All the madhouses in the world," said Mr Tapley, "couldn't produce such a maniac as the man must be who could think that."

"Then why are you for ever goading and urging me to get up?" asked Martin. "I lie here because I don't wish to be recognized, in the better days to which I aspire, by any purse-proud citizen, as the man who came over with him among the steerage passengers. I lie here because I wish to conceal my circumstances and myself, and not to arrive in a new world badged and ticketed as an utterly poverty-stricken man. If I could have afforded a passage in the after-cabin, I should have held up my head with the rest. As I couldn't, I hide it. Do you understand that?"

"I am very sorry, sir," said Mark. "I didn't know you took it so much to heart as this comes to."

"Of course you didn't know," returned his master. "How should you know, unless I told you? It's no trial to *you*, Mark, to make yourself comfortable, and to bustle about. It's as natural for you to do so under the circumstances as it is for me not to do so. Why, you don't suppose there is a living creature in this ship who can by possibility have half so much to undergo on board of her as I have? Do you?" he asked, sitting upright in his berth and looking at Mark, with an expression of great earnestness not unmixed with wonder.

Mark twisted his face into a tight knot, and with his head very much on one side pondered upon this question as if he felt it an extremely difficult one to answer. He was relieved from his embarrassment by Martin himself, who said, as he stretched himself upon his back again and resumed the book he had been reading:

"But what is the use of my putting such a case to you, when the very essence of what I have been saying is, that you cannot by possibility understand it! Make me a little brandy-and-water, cold and very weak, and give me a biscuit, and tell your friend, who is a nearer neighbour of ours than I could wish, to try and keep her children a little quieter to-night than she did last night; that's a good fellow."

Mr Tapley set himself to obey these orders with great alacrity, and pending their execution, it may be presumed his flagging spirits revived: inasmuch as he several times observed, below his breath, that in respect of its power of imparting a credit to jollity, *The Screw* unquestionably had some decided advantages over the Dragon. He also remarked that it was a high gratification to him to reflect that he would carry its main excellence ashore with him, and have it constantly beside him wherever he went; but what he meant by these consolatory thoughts he did not explain.

And now a general excitement began to prevail on board; and various predictions relative to the precise day, and even the precise hour at which they would reach New York, were freely broached. There was infinitely more crowding on deck and looking over the ship's side than there had been before; and an epidemic broke out for packing up things every morning, which required unpacking again every night. Those who had any letters to deliver, or any friends to meet, or any settled plans of going anywhere or doing anything, discussed their prospects a hundred times a day; and as this class of passengers was very small, and the number of those who had no prospects whatever was very large, there were plenty of listeners and few talkers. Those who had been ill all along, got well now, and those who had been well, got better. An American gentleman in the after-cabin, who had been wrapped up in fur and oilskin the whole passage, unexpectedly appeared in a very shiny, tall, black hat, and constantly overhauled a very little valise of pale leather, which contained his clothes, linen, brushes, shaving apparatus, books, trinkets, and other baggage. He likewise stuck his hands deep into his pockets, and walked the deck with his nostrils dilated, as already inhaling the air of Freedom which carries death to all tyrants, and can never (under any circumstances worth mentioning) be breathed by slaves. An English gentleman who was strongly suspected of having run away from a bank, with something in his possession belonging to its strong-box besides the key, grew eloquent upon the subject of the rights of man, and hummed the Marseillaise Hymn constantly. In a word, one great sensation pervaded the whole ship, and the soil of America lay close before them: so close at last, that, upon a certain starlight night, they took a pilot on board, and within a few hours afterwards lay to until the morning, awaiting the arrival of a steamboat in which the passengers were to be conveyed ashore.

Off she came, soon after it was light next morning, and lying alongside an hour or more—during which period her very firemen were objects of hardly less interest and curiosity than if they had been so many angels, good or bad—took all her living freight aboard. Among them Mark, who still had his friend and her three children under his close protection: and Martin, who had once more dressed himself in his usual attire, but wore a soiled, old cloak above his ordinary clothes, until such time as he should separate for ever from his late companions.

The steamer—which, with its machinery on deck, looked, as it worked its long slim legs, like some enormously magnified insect or antediluvian monster—dashed at great speed up a beautiful bay; and presently they saw some heights, and islands, and a long, flat, straggling city.

"And this," said Mr Tapley, looking far ahead, "is the Land of Liberty, is it? Very well. I'm agreeable. Any land will do for me, after so much water!"

HOW GERARD WAS SAVED FROM THE WRECK[1]

Charles Reade

(1814–1884)

ABOUT two months before this scene in Eli's home,[2] the natives of a little maritime place between Naples and Rome might be seen flocking to the sea beach, with eyes cast seaward at a ship, that laboured against a stiff gale blowing dead on the shore.

At times she seemed likely to weather the danger, and then the specta-

[1] From *The Cloister and the Hearth.*

[2] The preceding chapter tells how Margaret read Gerard's letter to her to his family.

tors congratulated her aloud: at others the wind and sea drove her visibly
nearer, and the lookers-on were not without a secret satisfaction they
would not have owned even to themselves.

Non quia vexari quemquam est jucunda voluptas
Sed quibus ipse malis careas quia cernere suave est.

And the poor ship, though not scientifically built for sailing, was ad-
mirably constructed for going ashore, with her extravagant poop that
caught the wind, and her lines like a cocked hat reversed. To those on
the beach that battered labouring frame of wood seemed alive, and
struggling against death with a panting heart. But could they have
been transferred to her deck they would have seen she had not one beating heart but many, and not one nature but a score were coming out
clear in that fearful hour.

The mariners stumbled wildly about the deck, handling the ropes as
each thought fit, and cursing and praying alternately.

The passengers were huddled together round the mast, some sitting,
some kneeling, some lying prostrate, and grasping the bulwarks as the
vessel rolled and pitched in the mighty waves. One comely young man,
whose ashy cheek, but compressed lips, showed how hard terror was
battling in him with self-respect, stood a little apart, holding tight by a
shroud, and wincing at each sea. It was the ill-fated Gerard.

Meantime prayers and vows rose from the trembling throng amidships, and to hear them, it seemed there were almost as many gods about
as men and women. The sailors, indeed, relied on a single goddess. They
varied her titles only, calling on her as "Queen of Heaven," "Star of the
Sea," "Mistress of the World," "Haven of Safety." But among the landsmen Polytheism raged. Even those who by some strange chance hit on
the same divinity did not hit on the same edition of that divinity.

An English merchant vowed a heap of gold to our lady of Walsing-
ham. But a Genoese merchant vowed a silver collar of four pounds to
our lady of Loretto; and a Tuscan noble promised ten pounds of wax
lights to our lady of Ravenna; and with a similar rage for diversity they
pledged themselves, not on the true Cross, but on the true Cross in this,
that, or the other modern city.

Suddenly a more powerful gust than usual catching the sail at a disadvantage, the rotten shrouds gave way, and the sail was torn out with a
loud crack, and went down the wind smaller and smaller, blacker and
blacker, and fluttered into the sea, half a mile off, like a sheet of paper,
and ere the helmsman could put the ship's head before the wind, a
wave caught her on the quarter, and drenched the poor wretches to the
bone, and gave them a fore-taste of chill death. Then one vowed aloud
to turn Carthusian monk, if St Thomas would save him. Another would
go a pilgrim to Compostella, bareheaded, barefooted, with nothing but a

coat of mail on his naked skin, if St James would save him. Others invoked Thomas, Dominic, Denys, and above all, Catherine of Sienna.

Two petty Neapolitan traders stood shivering.

One shouted at the top of his voice—

"I vow to St Christopher at Paris a waxen image of his own weight, if I win safe to land."

On this the other nudged him, and said:

"Brother, brother, take heed what you vow. Why, if you sell all you have in the world by public auction, 'twill not buy his weight in wax."

"Hold your tongue, you fool," said the vociferator.

Then in a whisper:

"Think ye I am in earnest? Let me but win safe to land, I'll not give him a rush dip."

Others lay flat and prayed to the sea.

"Oh, most merciful sea! oh, sea most generous! oh, bountiful sea! oh, beautiful sea! be gentle, be kind, preserve us in this hour of peril."

And others wailed and moaned in mere animal terror each time the ill-fated ship rolled or pitched more terribly than usual; and she was now a mere plaything in the arms of the tremendous waves.

A Roman woman of the humbler class sat with her child at her half-bared breast, silent amid that wailing throng: her cheek ashy pale; her eye calm; and her lips moved at times in silent prayer, but she neither wept, nor lamented, nor bargained with the gods. Whenever the ship seemed really gone under their feet, and bearded men squeaked, she kissed her child; but that was all. And so she sat patient, and suckled him in death's jaws; for why should he lose any joy she could give him; *moribundo?* Ay, there I do believe, sat Antiquity among those mediævals. Sixteen hundred years had not tainted the old Roman blood in her veins; and the instinct of a race she had perhaps scarce heard of taught her to die with decent dignity.

A gigantic friar[1] stood on the poop with feet apart, like the Colossus of Rhodes, not so much defying, as ignoring, the peril that surrounded him. He recited verses from the Canticles with a loud unwavering voice; and invited the passengers to confess to him. Some did so on their knees, and he heard them, and laid his hands on them, and absolved them as if he had been in a snug sacristy, instead of a perishing ship. Gerard got nearer and nearer to him, by the instinct that takes the wavering to the side of the impregnable. And in truth, the courage of heroes facing fleshly odds might have paled by the side of that gigantic friar, and his still more gigantic composure. Thus, even here, two were found who maintained the dignity of our race; a woman, tender, yet heroic, and a monk steeled by religion against mortal fears.

---

[1] Brother Jerome.

And now, the sail being gone, the sailors cut down the useless mast a foot above the board, and it fell with its remaining hamper over the ship's side. This seemed to relieve her a little.

But now the hull, no longer impelled by canvas, could not keep ahead of the sea. It struck her again and again on the poop, and the tremendous blows seemed given by a rocky mountain, not by a liquid.

The captain left the helm and came amidships pale as death.

"Lighten her," he cried. "Fling all overboard, or we shall founder ere we strike, and lose the one little chance we have of life."

While the sailors were executing this order, the captain, pale himself, and surrounded by pale faces that demanded to know their fate, was talking as unlike an English skipper in like peril as can well be imagined.

"Friends," said he, "last night when all was fair, too fair, alas! there came a globe of fire close to the ship. When a pair of them come it is good luck, and nought can drown her that voyage. We mariners call these fiery globes Castor and Pollux. But if Castor come without Pollux, or Pollux without Castor, she is doomed. Therefore, like good Christians, prepare to die."

These words were received with a loud wail.

To a trembling inquiry how long they had to prepare, the captain replied—

"She may, or may not, last half-an-hour; over that, impossible; she leaks like a sieve; bustle, men, lighten her."

The poor passengers seized on everything that was on deck and flung it overboard. Presently they laid hold of a heavy sack; an old man was lying on it, seasick. They lugged it from under him. It rattled. Two of them drew it to the side; up started the owner, and with an unearthly shriek, pounced on it.

"Holy Moses! what would you do? 'Tis my all; 'tis the whole fruits of my journey; silver candlesticks, silver plates, brooches, hanaps——"

"Let go, thou hoary villain," cried the others; "shall all our lives be lost for thy ill-gotten gear?"

"Fling him in with it," cried one; "'tis this Ebrew we Christian men are drowned for."

Numbers soon wrenched it from him, and heaved it over the side. It splashed into the waves. Then its owner uttered one cry of anguish, and stood glaring, his white hair streaming in the wind, and was going to leap after it, and would, had it floated. But it sank, and was gone for ever; and he staggered to and fro, tearing his hair, and cursed them and the ship, and the sea, and all the powers of heaven and hell alike.

And now the captain cried out—

"See, there is a church in sight. Steer for that church, mate, and you, friends, pray to the saint, whoe'er he be."

So they steered for the church and prayed to the unknown god it was named after. A tremendous sea pooped them, broke the rudder, and jammed it immovable, and flooded the deck.

Then wild with superstitious terror some of them came round Gerard. "Here is the cause of all," they cried; "He has never invoked a single saint. He is a heathen; here is a pagan aboard."

"Alas, good friends, say not so," said Gerard, his teeth chattering with cold and fear. "Rather call these heathens, that lie a praying to the sea. Friends, I do honour the saints—but I dare not pray to them now—there is no time—(oh!) what avail me Dominic, and Thomas, and Catherine? Nearer God's throne than these St Peter sitteth; and if I pray to him, it's odd, but I shall be drowned ere he has time to plead my cause with God. Oh! oh! oh! I must need go straight to Him that made the sea, and the saints, and me. Our Father, which art in heaven, save these poor souls and me that cry for the bare life! Oh, sweet Jesus, pitiful Jesus, that didst walk Genezaret when Peter sank, and wept for Lazarus dead when the apostles' eyes were dry, oh, save poor Gerard—for dear Margaret's sake!"

At this moment the sailors were seen preparing to desert the sinking ship in the little boat, which even at that epoch every ship carried; then there was a rush of egotists; and thirty souls crowded into it. Remained behind three who were bewildered, and two who were paralysed, with terror. The paralysed sat like heaps of wet rags, the bewildered ones ran to and fro, and saw the thirty egotists put off, but made no attempt to join them: only kept running to and fro, and wringing their hands.

Besides these there was one on his knees, praying over the wooden statue of the Virgin Mary, as large as life, which the sailors had reverently detached from the mast. It washed about the deck, as the water came slushing in from the sea, and pouring out at the scuppers; and this poor soul kept following it on his knees, with his hands clasped at it, and the water playing with it. And there was the Jew palsied, but not by fear. He was no longer capable of so petty a passion. He sat cross-legged bemoaning his bag, and whenever the spray lashed him, shook his fist at where it came from, and cursed the Nazarenes, and their gods, and their devils, and their ships, and their waters, to all eternity.

And the gigantic Dominican, having shriven the whole ship, stood calmly communing with his own spirit. And the Roman woman sat pale and patient, only drawing her child closer to her bosom as death came nearer.

Gerard saw this, and it awakened his manhood.

"See! see!" he said, "they have ta'en the boat and left the poor woman and her child to perish."

His heart soon set his wit working.

"Wife, I'll save thee yet, please God."

And he ran to find a cask or a plank to float her. There was none.

Then his eye fell on the wooden image of the Virgin. He caught it up in his arms, and heedless of a wail that issued from its worshipper like a child robbed of its toy, ran aft with it.

"Come, wife," he cried. "I'll lash thee and the child to this. 'Tis sore worm eaten, but 'twill serve."

She turned her great dark eye on him and said a single word—
"Thyself?"

But with wonderful magnanimity and tenderness.

"I am a man, and have no child to take care of."

"Ah!" said she, and his words seemed to animate her face with a desire to live. He lashed the image to her side. Then with the hope of life she lost something of her heroic calm; not much: her body trembled a little, but not her eye.

The ship was now so low in the water that by using an oar as a lever he could slide her into the waves.

"Come," said he, "while yet there is time."

She turned her great Roman eyes, wet now, upon him.

"Poor youth!—God forgive me!—My child!"

And he launched her on the surge, and with his oar kept her from being battered against the ship.

A heavy hand fell on him; a deep sonorous voice sounded in his ear:
" 'Tis well. Now come with me."

It was the gigantic friar.

Gerard turned, and the friar took two strides, and laid hold of the broken mast. Gerard did the same, obeying him instinctively. Between them, after a prodigious effort, they hoisted up the remainder of the mast, and carried it off.

"Fling it in," said the friar, "and follow it."

They flung it in; but one of the bewildered passengers had run after them, and jumped first and got on one end. Gerard seized the other, the friar the middle.

It was a terrible situation. The mast rose and plunged with each wave like a kicking horse, and the spray flogged their faces mercilessly, and blinded them: to help knock them off.

Presently was heard a long grating noise ahead. The ship had struck, and soon after, she being stationary now, they were hurled against her with tremendous force. Their companion's head struck against the upper part of the broken rudder with a horrible crack, and was smashed like a cocoa-nut by a sledgehammer. He sank directly, leaving no trace but a red stain on the water, and a white clot on the jagged rudder, and a death cry ringing in their ears, as they drifted clear under the lee of the black hull. The friar uttered a short Latin prayer for the safety of his soul, and took his place composedly. They rolled along ὕπεκ θανάτοιο; one moment they saw nothing, and seemed down in a mere basin of watery hills: the next they caught glimpses of the shore speckled bright with people, who kept throwing up their arms with wild Italian gestures to encourage them, and the black boat driving bottom upwards, and between it and them the woman rising and falling like themselves. She had come across a paddle, and was holding her child tight with her left arm, and paddling gallantly with her right.

When they had tumbled along thus a long time, suddenly the friar said quietly:

"I touched the ground."

"Impossible, father," said Gerard; "we are more than a hundred yards from shore. Prithee, prithee, leave not our faithful mast."

"My son," said the friar, "you speak prudently. But know that I have business of Holy Church on hand, and may not waste time floating when I can walk, in her service. There, I felt it with my toes again; see the benefit of wearing sandals, and not shoon. Again; and sandy. Thy stature is less than mine: keep to the mast! I walk."

He left the mast accordingly, and extending his powerful arms, rushed through the water. Gerard soon followed him. At each overpowering wave the monk stood like a tower, and closing his mouth, threw his head back to encounter it, and was entirely lost under it awhile: then emerged and ploughed lustily on. At last they came close to the shore; but the suction outward baffled all their attempts to land. Then the natives sent stout fishermen into the sea, holding by long spears in a triple chain; and so dragged them ashore.

The friar shook himself, bestowed a short paternal benediction on the natives, and went on to Rome, with eyes bent on earth according to his rule, and without pausing. He did not even cast a glance back upon that sea, which had so nearly engulfed him, but had no power to harm him, without his Master's leave.

While he stalks on alone to Rome without looking back, I who am not in the service of Holy Church, stop a moment to say that the reader and I were within six inches of this giant once before; but we escaped him that time. Now I fear we are in for him. Gerard grasped every hand upon the beach. They brought him to an enormous fire, and with a delicacy he would hardly have encountered in the north, left him to dry himself alone; on this he took out of his bosom a parchment, and a paper, and dried them carefully. When this was done to his mind, and not till then, he consented to put on a fisherman's dress and leave his own by the fire, and went down to the beach. What he saw may be briefly related.

The captain stuck by the ship, not so much from gallantry, as from a conviction that it was idle to resist Castor or Pollux, whichever it was that had come for him in a ball of fire.

Nevertheless the sea broke up the ship and swept the poop, captain and all, clear of the rest, and took him safe ashore. Gerard had a principal hand in pulling him out of the water.

The disconsolate Hebrew landed on another fragment, and on touching earth, offered a reward for his bag, which excited little sympathy, but some amusement. Two more were saved on pieces of the wreck. The thirty egotists came ashore, but one at a time, and dead; one breathed still. Him the natives, with excellent intentions, took to a hot fire. So then he too retired from this shifting scene.

As Gerard stood by the sea, watching, with horror and curiosity mixed, his late companions washed ashore, a hand was laid lightly on his shoulder. He turned. It was the Roman matron, burning with womanly gratitude. She took his hand gently, and raising it slowly to her lips, kissed it; but so nobly, she seemed to be conferring an honour on one deserving hand. Then with face all beaming and moist eyes, she held her child up and made him kiss his preserver.

Gerard kissed the child more than once. He was fond of children. But he said nothing. He was much moved; for she did not speak at all, except with her eyes, and glowing cheeks, and noble antique gesture, so large and stately. Perhaps she was right. Gratitude is not a thing of words. It was an ancient Roman matron thanking a modern from her heart of hearts.

Next day towards afternoon, Gerard—twice as old as last year, thrice as learned in human ways, a boy no more, but a man who had shed blood in self-defence, and grazed the grave by land and sea—reached the Eternal City; *post tot naufragia tutus.*

HOW AMYAS THREW HIS SWORD INTO THE SEA[1]

Charles Kingsley
(1819-1875)

YES, it is over; and the great Armada is vanquished.

Yes, as the medals struck on the occasion said, "It came, it saw, and it fled." And whither? Away and northward, like a herd of frightened deer, past the Orkneys and Shetlands, catching up a few hapless fishermen as guides, past the coast of Norway, there, too, refused water and food by the brave descendants of the Vikings; and on northward ever towards the lonely Faroes, and the everlasting dawn which heralds round the Pole the midnight sun.

Their water is failing; the cattle must go overboard; and the wild northern sea echoes to the shrieks of drowning horses. They must homeward at least, somehow, each as best he can. Let them meet again at Cape Finisterre, if indeed they ever meet. Medina Sidonia, with some five-and-twenty of the soundest and best victualled ships, will lead the way, and leave the rest to their fate. He is soon out of sight; and forty

[1] From *Westward Ho!*

more, the only remnant of that mighty host, come wandering wearily behind, hoping to make the south-west coast of Ireland, and have help, or, at least, fresh water there, from their fellow Romanists. Alas from them!—

> Make Thou their way dark and slippery,
> And follow them up ever with Thy storm.

For now comes up from the Atlantic, gale on gale; and few of that hapless remnant reached the shoes of Spain.

And where are Amyas and the *Vengeance* all this while?

At the fifty-seventh degree of latitude, the English fleet, finding themselves growing short of provisions, and having been long since out of powder and ball, turn southward toward home, "thinking it best to leave the Spaniard to those uncouth and boisterous northern seas." A few pinnaces are still sent onward to watch their course; and the English fleet, caught in the same storms which scattered the Spaniards, "with great danger and industry reached Harwich port, and there provide themselves of victuals and ammunition," in case the Spaniard should return; but there is no need for that caution. Parma, indeed, who cannot believe that the idol at Halle, after all his compliments to it, will play him so scurvy a trick, will watch for weeks on Dunkirk dunes, hoping against hope for the Armada's return, casting anchors, and spinning rigging to repair their losses.

> But lang, lang may his ladies sit,
> With their fans intill their hand,
> Before they see Sir Patrick Spens
> Come sailing to the land.

The Armada is away on the other side of Scotland, and Amyas is following in its wake.

For when the Lord High Admiral determined to return, Amyas asked leave to follow the Spaniard; and asked, too, of Sir John Hawkins, who happened to be at hand, such ammunition and provision as could be afforded him, promising to repay the same like an honest man, out of his plunder if he lived, out of his estate if he died; lodging for that purpose bills in the hands of Sir John, who, as a man of business, took them, and put them in his pocket among the thimbles, string, and tobacco; after which Amyas, calling his men together, reminded them once more of the story of the Rose of Torridge and Don Guzman de Soto, and then asked:

"Men of Bideford, will you follow me? There will be plunder for those who love plunder; revenge for those who love revenge; and for all of us (for we all love honour) the honour of having never left the chase as long as there was a Spanish flag in English seas."

And every soul on board replied, that they would follow Sir Amyas Leigh around the world.

There is no need for me to detail every incident of that long and weary chase; how they found the *Sta Catharina*, attacked her, and had to sheer off, she being rescued by the rest; how when Medina's squadron left the crippled ships behind, they were all but taken or sunk, by thrusting into the midst of the Spanish fleet to prevent her escaping with Medina; how they crippled her, so that she could not beat to windward out into the ocean, but was fain to run south, past the Orkneys, and down through the Minch, between Cape Wrath and Lewis; how the younger hands were ready to mutiny, because Amyas, in his stubborn haste, ran past two or three noble prizes which were all but disabled, among others one of the great galliasses, and the two great Venetians, *La Ratta* and *La Belanzaza*—which were afterwards, with more than thirty other vessels, wrecked on the west coast of Ireland; how he got fresh water, in spite of certain "Hebridean Scots" of Skye, who, after reviling him in an unknown tongue, fought with him a while, and then embraced him and his men, with howls of affection, and were not much more decently clad, nor more civilized than his old friends of California; how he pacified his men by letting them pick the bones of a great Venetian which was going on shore upon Islay, (by which they got booty enough to repay them for the whole voyage), and offended them again by refusing to land and plunder two great Spanish wrecks on the Mull of Cantire (whose crews, by-the-bye, James tried to smuggle off secretly into Spain in ships of his own, wishing to play, as usual, both sides of the game at once; but the Spaniards were stopped at Yarmouth till the council's pleasure was known—which was, of course, to let the poor wretches go on their way, and be hanged elsewhere); how they passed a strange island, half black, half white, which the wild people called Raghery, but Cary christened it "the drowned magpie"; how the *Sta Catharina* was near lost on the Isle of Man, and then put into Castleton (where the Manxmen slew a whole boat's-crew with their arrows), and then put out again, when Amyas fought with her a whole day, and shot away her mainyard; how the Spaniard blundered down the coast of Wales, not knowing whither he went; how they were both nearly lost on Holyhead, and again on Bardsey Island; how they got on a lee shore in Cardigan Bay, before a heavy westerly gale, and the *Sta Catharina* ran aground on Sarn David, one of those strange subaqueous pebble-dykes which are said to be the remnants of the lost land of Gwalior, destroyed by the carelessness of Prince Seithenin, the drunkard, at whose name each loyal Welshman spits; how she got off again at the rising of the tide, and fought with Amyas a fourth time; how the wind changed, and she got round St David's Head;—these, and many more moving accidents of this eventful voyage, I must pass over without details, and go on to the end; for it is time that the end should come.

It was now the sixteenth day of the chase. They had seen, the evening before, St David's Head, and then the Welsh coast round Milford Haven, looming out black and sharp before the blaze of the inland thunderstorm; and it had lightened all round them during the fore part of the night, upon a light south-western breeze.

In vain they had strained their eyes through the darkness, to catch, by the fitful glare of the flashes, the tall masts of the Spaniard. Of one thing at least they were certain, that with the wind as it was, she could not have gone far to the westward; and to attempt to pass them again, and go northward, was more than she dare do. She was probably lying-to ahead of them, perhaps between them and the land; and when, a little after midnight, the wind chopped up to the west, and blew stiffly till daybreak, they felt sure that, unless she had attempted the desperate expedient of running past them, they had her safe in the mouth of the Bristol Channel. Slowly and wearily broke the dawn, on such a day as often follows heavy thunder, a sunless, drizzly day, roofed with low dingy cloud, barred, and netted, and festooned with black, a sign that the storm is only taking breath a while before it bursts again; while all the narrow horizon is dim and spongy with vapour drifting before a chilly breeze. As the day went on, the breeze died down, and the sea fell to a long glassy foam-flecked roll, while overhead brooded the inky sky, and round them the leaden mist shut out alike the shore and the chase.

Amyas paced the sloppy deck fretfully and fiercely. He knew that the Spaniard could not escape; but he cursed every moment which lingered between him and that one great revenge which blackened all his soul. The men sate sulkily about the deck, and whistled for a wind; the sails flapped idly against the masts; and the ship rolled in the long troughs of the sea, till her yard-arm almost dipped right and left.

"Take care of those guns. You will have something loose next," growled Amyas.

"We will take care of the guns, if the Lord will take care of the wind," said Yeo.

"We shall have plenty before night," said Cary, "and thunder too."

"So much the better," said Amyas. "It may roar till it splits the heavens, if it does but let me get my work done."

"He's not far off, I warrant," said Cary. "One lift of the cloud, and we should see him."

"To windward of us, as likely as not," said Amyas. "The devil fights for him, I believe. To have been on his heels sixteen days, and not sent this through him yet!" And he shook his sword impatiently.

So the morning wore away, without a sign of a living thing, not even a passing gull; and the black melancholy of the heaven reflected itself in the black melancholy of Amyas. Was he to lose his prey after all? The thought made him shudder with rage and disappointment. It was intolerable. Anything but that.

"No, God!" he cried, "let me but once feel this in his accursed heart, and then—strike me dead, if Thou wilt!"

"The Lord have mercy on us," cried John Brimblecombe. "What have you said?"

"What is that to you, sir? There, they are piping to dinner. Go down. I shall not come."

And Jack went down, and talked in a half-terrified whisper of Amyas's ominous words.

All thought that they portended some bad luck, except old Yeo.

"Well, Sir John," said he, "and why not? What better can the Lord do for a man, than take him home when he has done his work? Our captain is wilful and spiteful, and must needs kill his man himself; while for me, I don't care how the Don goes, provided he does go. I owe him no grudge, nor any man. May the Lord give him repentance, and forgive him all his sins; but if I could but see him once safe ashore, as he may be ere nightfall, on the Morestone, or the back of Lundy, I would say, 'Lord, now lettest Thou Thy servant depart in peace,' even if it were the lightning which was sent to fetch me."

"But, Master Yeo, a sudden death?"

"And why not a sudden death, Sir John? Even fools long for a short life and a merry one, and shall not the Lord's people pray for a short death and a merry one? Let it come as it will to old Yeo. Hark! there's the captain's voice."

"Here she is!" thundered Amyas from the deck; and in an instant all were scrambling up the hatchway as fast as the frantic rolling of the ship would let them.

Yes. There she was. The cloud had lifted suddenly, and to the south a ragged bore of blue sky let a long stream of sunshine down on her tall masts and stately hull, as she lay rolling some four or five miles to the eastward; but as for land, none was to be seen.

"There she is; and here we are," said Cary; "but where is here? and where is there? How is the tide, master?"

"Running up Channel by this time, sir."

"What matters the tide?" said Amyas, devouring the ship with terrible and cold blue eyes. "Can't we get at her?"

"Not unless some one jumps out and shoves behind," said Cary. "I shall down again and finish that mackerel, if this roll has not chucked it to the cockroaches under the table."

"Don't jest, Will! I can't stand it," said Amyas, in a voice which quivered so much that Cary looked at him. His whole frame was trembling like an aspen. Cary took his arm, and drew him aside.

"Dear old lad," said he as they leaned over the bulwarks, "what is this? You are not yourself, and have not been these four days."

"No. I am not Amyas Leigh. I am my brother's avenger. Do not reason with me, Will: when it is over, I shall be merry old Amyas again," and he passed his hand over his brow.

"Do you believe," said he, after a moment, "that men can be possessed by devils?"

"The Bible says so."

"If my cause were not a just one, I should fancy I had a devil in me. My throat and heart are as hot as the pit. Would to God it were done, for done it must be! Now go."

Cary went away with a shudder. As he passed down the hatchway he looked back. Amyas had got the hone out of his pocket, and was whetting away again at his sword-edge, as if there was some dreadful doom on him, to whet, and whet for ever.

The weary day wore on. The strip of blue sky was curtained over again, and all was dismal as before, though it grew sultrier every moment; and now and then a distant mutter shook the air to westward. Nothing could be done to lessen the distance between the ships, for the *Vengeance* had had all her boats carried away but one, and that was much too small to tow her; and while the men went down again to finish dinner, Amyas worked on at his sword, looking up every now and then suddenly at the Spaniard, as if to satisfy himself that it was not a vision which had vanished.

About two Yeo came up to him.

"He is ours safely now, sir. The tide has been running to the eastward for this two hours."

"Safe as a fox in a trap. Satan himself cannot take him from us."

"But God may," said Brimblecombe simply.

"Who spoke to you, sir? If I thought that He——There comes the thunder at last!"

And as he spoke, an angry growl from the westward heavens seemed to answer his wild words, and rolled and loudened nearer and nearer, till right over their heads it crashed against some cloud-cliff far above, and all was still.

Each man looked in the other's face: but Amyas was unmoved.

"The storm is coming," said he, "and the wind in it. It will be Eastward-ho now, for once, my merry men all!"

"Eastward-ho never brought us luck," said Jack in an undertone to Cary. But by this time all eyes were turned to the north-west, where a black line along the horizon began to define the boundary of sea and air, till now all dim in mist.

"There comes the breeze."

"And there the storm, too."

And with that strangely accelerating pace which some storms seem to possess, the thunder, which had been growling slow and seldom far away, now rang peal on peal along the cloudy floor above their heads.

"Here comes the breeze. Round with the yards, or we shall be taken aback."

The yards creaked round; the sea grew crisp around them; the hot air swept their cheeks, tightened every rope, filled every sail, bent her over. A cheer burst from the men as the helm went up, and they staggered away before the wind, right down upon the Spaniard, who lay still becalmed.

"There is more behind, Amyas," said Cary. "Shall we not shorten sail a little?"

"No. Hold on every stitch," said Amyas. "Give me the helm, man. Boatswain, pipe away to clear for fight."

It was done, and in ten minutes the men were all at quarters while the thunder rolled louder and louder overhead, and the breeze freshened fast.

"The dog has it now. There he goes!" said Cary.

"Right before the wind. He has no liking to face us."

"He is running into the jaws of destruction," said Yeo. "An hour more will send him either right up the Channel, or smack on shore somewhere."

"There! he has put his helm down. I wonder if he sees land?"

"He is like a March hare beat out of his country," said Cary, "and don't know whither to run next."

Cary was right. In ten minutes more the Spaniard fell off again, and went away dead down wind, while the *Vengeance* gained on him fast. After two hours more, the four miles had diminished to one, while the lightning flashed nearer and nearer as the storm came up; and from the vast mouth of a black cloud-arch poured so fierce a breeze that Amyas yielded unwillingly to hints which were growing into open murmurs, and bade shorten sail.

On they rushed with scarcely lessened speed, the black arch following fast, curtained by one flat grey sheet of pouring rain, before which the water was boiling in a long white line; while every moment, behind the watery veil, a keen blue spark leapt down into the sea, or darted zigzag through the rain.

"We shall have it now, and with a vengeance; this will try your tackle, Master," said Cary.

The functionary answered with a shrug, and turned up the collar of his rough frock, as the first drops flew stinging round his ears. Another minute, and the squall burst full upon them in rain, which cut like hail—hail which lashed the sea into froth, and wind which whirled off the heads of the surges, and swept the waters into one white seething waste. And above them, and behind them, and before them, the lightning leapt and ran, dazzling and blinding, while the deep roar of the thunder was changed to sharp ear-piercing cracks.

"Get the arms and ammunition under cover, and then below with you all," shouted Amyas from the helm.

"And heat the pokers in the galley fire," said Yeo, "to be ready if the rain puts our linstocks out. I hope you'll let me stay on deck, sir, in case——"

"I must have some one, and who better than you? Can you see the chase?"

No; she was wrapped in the grey whirlwind. She might be within half-a-mile of them for ought they could have seen of her.

And now Amyas and his old liegeman were alone. Neither spoke; each knew the other's thoughts, and knew that they were his own. The squall blew fiercer and fiercer, the rain poured heavier and heavier. Where was the Spaniard?

"If he has laid-to, we may overshoot him, sir!"

"If he has tried to lay-to, he will not have a sail left in the bolt-ropes, or perhaps a mast on deck. I know the stiff-neckedness of those Spanish tubs. Hurrah! there he is, right on our larboard bow!"

There she was indeed, two musket-shots off, staggering away with canvas split and flying.

"He has been trying to hull, sir, and caught a buffet," said Yeo, rubbing his hands. "What shall we do now?"

"Range alongside, if it blow live imps and witches, and try our luck once more. Pah! how this lightning dazzles!"

On they swept, gaining fast on the Spaniard.

"Call the men up, and to quarters; the rain will be over in ten minutes."

Yeo ran forward to the gangway; and sprang back again, with a face white and wild—

"Land right ahead! Port your helm, sir! For the love of God, port your helm!"

Amyas, with the strength of a bull, jammed the helm down, while Yeo shouted to the men below.

She swung round. The masts bent like whips; crack went the foresail like a cannon. What matter? Within two hundred yards of them was the Spaniard; in front of her, and above her, a huge dark bank rose through the dense hail, and mingled with the clouds; and at its foot, plainer every moment, pillars and spouts of leaping foam.

"What is it? Morte? Hartland?"

It might be anything for thirty miles.

"Lundy!" said Yeo. "The south end! I see the head of the Shutter in the breakers! Hard a-port yet, and get her close-hauled as you can, and the Lord may have mercy on us still! Look at the Spaniard!"

Yes, look at the Spaniard!

On their left hand, as they broached-to, the wall of granite sloped down from the clouds toward an isolated peak of rock, some two hundred feet in height. Then a hundred yards of roaring breaker upon a sunken shelf, across which the race of the tide poured like a cataract; then, amid a column of salt smoke, the Shutter, like a huge black fang, rose waiting for its prey; and between the shutter and the land, the great galleon loomed dimly through the storm.

He, too, had seen his danger, and tried to broach-to. But his clumsy mass refused to obey the helm; he struggled a moment, half hid in foam; fell away again, and rushed upon his doom.

"Lost! lost! lost!" cried Amyas madly, and throwing up his hands, let go the tiller. Yeo caught it just in time.

"Sir! sir! What are you at? We shall clear the rock yet."

"Yes!" shouted Amyas in his frenzy; "But he will not!"

Another minute. The galleon gave a sudden jar, and stopped. Then one long heave and bound, as if to free herself. And then her bows lighted clean upon the Shutter.

An awful silence fell on every English soul. They heard not the roaring of wind and surge; they saw not the blinding flashes of lightning; but they heard one long ear-piercing wail to every saint in heaven rise from from five hundred human throats; they saw the mighty ship heel over from the wind, and sweep headlong down the cataract of the race, plunging her yards into the foam, and showing her whole black side even to her keel, till she rolled clean over, and vanished for ever and ever.

"Shame!" cried Amyas, hurling his sword far into the sea, "to lose my right, my right! when it was in my very grasp! Unmerciful!"

A crack which rent the sky, and made the granite ring and quiver; a bright world of flame, and then a blank of utter darkness, against which stood out, glowing red-hot, every mast, and sail, and rock, and Salvation Yeo as he stood just in front of Amyas, the tiller in his hand. All red-hot, transfigured into fire; and behind, the black, black night.

THE MAN WITH THE BELT OF GOLD[1]

Robert Louis Stevenson

(1850–1894)

MORE than a week went by, in which the ill-luck that had hitherto pursued the *Covenant* upon this voyage grew yet more strongly marked. Some days she made a little way; others, she was driven actually back. At last we were beaten so far to the south that we tossed and tacked to and fro the whole of the ninth day, within sight of Cape Wrath and the wild, rocky coast on either hand of it. There followed on that a council of the officers, and some decision which I did not rightly understand, seeing only the result: that we had made a fair wind of a foul one and were running south.

---

[1]From *Kidnapped*. Reprinted by permission of Mr. Lloyd Osbourne.

The tenth afternoon, there was a falling swell and a thick, wet, white fog that hid one end of the brig from the other. All afternoon, when I went on deck, I saw men and officers listening hard over the bulwarks—"for breakers," they said; and though I did not so much as understand the word, I felt danger in the air, and was excited.

Maybe about ten at night, I was serving Mr Riach and the captain at their supper, when the ship struck something with a great sound, and we heard voices singing out. My two masters leaped to their feet.

"She's struck," said Mr Riach.

"No, sir," said the captain. "We've only run a boat down."

And they hurried out.

The captain was in the right of it. We had run down a boat in the fog, and she had parted in the midst and gone to the bottom with all her crew, but one. This man (as I heard afterwards) had been sitting in the stern as a passenger, while the rest were on the benches rowing. At the moment of the blow, the stern had been thrown into the air, and the man (having his hands free, and for all he was encumbered with a frieze overcoat that came below his knees) had leaped up and caught hold of the brig's bowsprit. It showed he had luck and much agility and unusual strength, that he should have thus saved himself from such a pass. And yet, when the captain brought him into the round-house, and I set eyes on him for the first time, he looked as cool as I did.

He was smallish in stature, but well set and as nimble as a goat; his face was of a good open expression, but sunburnt very dark, and heavily freckled and pitted with the small-pox; his eyes were unusually light and had a kind of dancing madness in them, that was both engaging and alarming; and when he took off his great-coat, he laid a pair of fine, silver-mounted pistols on the table, and I saw that he was belted with a great sword. His manners, besides, were elegant, and he pledged the captain handsomely. Altogether I thought of him, at the first sight, that here was a man I would rather call my friend than my enemy.

The captain, too, was taking his observations, but rather of the man's clothes than his person. And to be sure, as soon as he had taken off the great coat, he showed forth mighty fine for the round-house of a merchant brig: having a hat with feathers, a red waistcoat, breeches of black plush, and a blue coat with silver buttons and handsome silver lace: costly clothes, though somewhat spoiled with the fog and being slept in.

"I'm vexed, sir, about the boat," says the captain.

"There are some pretty men gone to the bottom," said the stranger, "that I would rather see on the dry land again than half a score of boats."

"Friends of yours?" said Hoseason.

"You have none such friends in your country," was the reply. "They would have died for me like dogs."

"Well, sir," said the captain, still watching him, "there are more men in the world than boats to put them in."

"And that's true too," cried the other, "and ye seem to be a gentle-man of great penetration."

"I have been in France, sir," says the captain, so that it was plain he meant more by the words than showed upon the face of them.

"Well, sir," says the other, "and so has many a pretty man, for the matter of that."

"No doubt, sir," says the captain; "and fine coats."

"Oho!" says the stranger, "is that how the wind sets?" And he laid his hand quickly on his pistols.

"Don't be hasty," said the captain. "Don't do a mischief, before ye see the need for it. Ye've a French soldier's coat upon your back and a Scotch tongue in your head, to be sure; but so has many an honest fellow in these days, and I dare say none the worse of it."

"So?" said the gentleman in the fine coat: "are ye of the honest party?" (meaning, Was he a Jacobite? for each side, in these sort of civil broils, takes the name of honesty for its own.)

"Why, sir," replied the captain, "I am a true-blue Protestant, and I thank God for it." (It was the first word of any religion I had ever heard from him, but I learnt afterwards he was a great church-goer while on shore.) "But, for all that," says he, "I can be sorry to see another man with his back to the wall."

"Can ye so, indeed?" asks the Jacobite. "Well, sir, to be quite plain with ye, I am one of those honest gentlemen that were in trouble about the years forty-five and six; and (to be still quite plain with ye) if I got into the hands of any of the red-coated gentry, it's like it would go hard with me. Now, sir, I was for France; and there was a French ship cruising here to pick me up; but she gave us the go-by in the fog—as I wish from the heart ye had done yoursel'! And the best that I can say is this; If ye can set me ashore where I was going, I have that upon me will reward you highly for your trouble."

"In France?" says the captain. "No, sir; that I cannot do. But where ye come from—we might talk of that."

And then, unhappily, he observed me standing in my corner, and packed me off to the galley to get supper for the gentleman. I lost no time I promise you; and when I came back into the round-house, I found the gentleman had taken a money-belt from about his waist, and poured out a guinea or two upon the table. The captain was looking at the guineas, and then at the belt, and then at the gentleman's face; and I thought he seemed excited.

"Half of it," he cried, "and I'm your man!"

The other swept back the guineas into the belt, and put it on again under his waistcoat. "I have told ye, sir," said he, "that not one doit of it belongs to me. It belongs to my chieftain"—and here he touched his hat—"and while I would be but a silly messenger to grudge some of it that the rest might come safe, I should show myself a hound indeed

if I bought my own carcase any too dear. Thirty guineas on the seaside, or sixty if ye set me on the Linnhe loch. Take it, if ye will; if not,
ye can do your worst."

"Ay," said Hoseason. "And if I give ye over to the soldiers?"

"Ye would make a fool's bargain," said the other. "My chief, let me
tell you, sir, is forfeited, like every honest man in Scotland. His estate is
in the hands of the man they call King George; and it is his officers that
collect the rents, or try to collect them. But for the honour of Scotland,
the poor tenant bodies take a thought upon their chief lying in exile;
and his money is a part of that very rent for which King George is looking. Now, sir, ye seem to me to be a man that understands things: bring
this money within the reach of Government, and how much of it 'll
come to you?"

"Little enough, to be sure," said Hoseason; and then, "If they knew,"
he added, dryly. "But I think, if I was to try, that I could hold my tongue about it."

"Ah, but I'll begowk[1] ye there," cried the gentleman. "Play me false,
and I'll play you cunning. If a hand's laid upon me, they shall ken what
money it is."

"Well," returned the captain, "what must be must. Sixty guineas,
and done. Here's my hand upon it."

"And here's mine," said the other.

And thereupon the captain went out (rather hurriedly, I thought),
and left me alone in the round-house with the stranger.

At that period (so soon after the forty-five) there were many exiled
gentlemen coming back at the peril of their lives, either to see their
friends or to collect a little money; and as for the Highland chiefs that
had been forfeited, it was a common matter of talk how their tenants
would stint themselves to send them money, and their clansmen outface
the soldiery to get it in, and run the gauntlet of our great navy to carry
it across. All this I had, of course, heard tell of; and now I had a man
under my eyes whose life was forfeit on all these counts and upon one
more; for he was not only a rebel and a smuggler of rents, but had taken
service with King Louis of France. And as if all this were not enough, he
had a belt full of golden guineas round his loins. Whatever my opinions,
I could not look on such a man without a lively interest.

"And so you're a Jacobite?" said I, as I set meat before him.

"Ay," said he, beginning to eat. "And you, by your long face, should
be a Whig."

"Betwixt and between," said I, not to annoy him; for indeed I was as
good a Whig as Mr Campbell could make me.

"And that's naething," said he. "But I'm saying, Mr Betwixt-and-
Between," he added, "this bottle of yours is dry; and it's hard if

---

[1]Befool.

I'm to pay sixty guineas and be grudged a dram upon the back of it."

"I'll go and ask for the key," said I, and stepped on deck.

The fog was as close as ever, but the swell almost down. They had laid the brig to, not knowing precisely where they were, and the wind (what little there was of it) not serving well for their true course. Some of the hands were still hearkening for breakers; but the captain and the two officers were in the waist with their heads together. It struck me, I don't know why, that they were after no good; and the first word I heard, as I drew softly near, more than confirmed me.

It was Mr Riach, crying out as if upon a sudden thought.

"Couldn't we wile him out of the round-house?"

"He's better where he is," returned Hoseason; "He hasn't room to use his sword."

"Well, that's true," said Riach; "but he's hard to come at."

"Hut!" said Hoseason. "We can get the man in talk, one upon each side, and pin him by the two arms; or if that'll not hold, sir, we can make a run by both the doors and get him under hand before he has the time to draw."

At this hearing, I was seized with both fear and anger at these treacherous, greedy, bloody men that I sailed with. My first mind was to run away; my second was bolder.

"Captain," said I, "the gentleman is seeking a dram, and the bottle's out. Will you give me the key?"

They all started and turned about.

"Why, here's our chance to get the firearms!" Riach cried; and then to me: "Hark ye, David," he said, "do ye ken where the pistols are?"

"Ay, ay," put in Hoseason. "David kens; David's a good lad. Ye see, David my man, yon wild Hielandman is a danger to the ship, besides being a rank foe to King George, God bless him!"

I had never been so be-Davided since I came on board; but I said yes, as if all I heard were quite natural.

"The trouble is," resumed the captain, "that all our firelocks great and little, are in the round-house under this man's nose; likewise the powder. Now, if I, or one of the officers, was to go in and take them, he would fall to thinking. But a lad like you, David, might snap up a horn and a pistol or two without remark. And if ye can do it cleverly, I'll bear it in mind when it'll be good for you to have friends; and that's when we come to Carolina."

Here Mr Riach whispered him a little.

"Very right, sir," said the captain; and then to myself: "And see here, David, yon man has a beltful of gold, and I give you my word that you shall have your fingers in it."

I told him I would do as he wished, though indeed I had scarce breath to speak with; and upon that he gave me the key of the spirit-locker, and I began to go slowly back to the round-house. What was I to do?

They were dogs and thieves; they had stolen me from my own country; they had killed poor Ransome; and was I to hold the candle to another murder? But then, upon the other hand, there was the fear of death very plain before me; for what could a boy and a man, if they were as brave as lions, against a whole ship's company.

I was still arguing it back and forth, and getting no great clearness, when I came into the round-house and saw the Jacobite eating his supper under the lamp; and at that my mind was made up all in a moment. I have no credit by it; it was by no choice of mine, but as if by compulsion, that I walked right up to the table and put my hand on his shoulder.

"Do ye want to be killed?" said I.

He sprang to his feet, and looked a question at me as clear as if he had spoken.

"Oh!" cried I, "they're all murderers here; it's a ship full of them! They've murdered a boy already. Now it's you."

"Ay, ay," said he; "but they haven't got me yet." And then looking at me curiously, "Will ye stand with me?"

"That will I!" said I. "I am no thief, nor yet murderer. I'll stand by you."

"Why, then," said he, "what's your name?"

"David Balfour," said I; and then thinking that a man with so fine a coat must like fine people, I added for the first time, "of Shaws."

It never occurred to him to doubt me, for a Highlander is used to see great gentlefolk in great poverty; but as he had no estate of his own, my words nettled a very childish vanity he had.

"My name is Stewart," he said, drawing himself up. "Alan Breck, they call me. A king's name is good enough for me, though I bear it plain and have the name of no farm-midden to clap to the hind-end of it."

And having administered this rebuke as though it were something of a chief importance, he turned to examine our defences.

The round-house was built very strong, to support the breaching of the seas. Of its five apertures, only the skylight and the two doors were large enough for the passage of a man. The doors, besides, could be drawn close; they were of stout oak, and ran in grooves, and were fitted with hooks to keep them either shut or open, as the need arose. The one that was already shut, I secured in this fashion; but when I was proceeding to slide to the other, Alan stopped me.

"David," said he—"for I cannae bring to mind the name of your landed estate, and so will make so bold as call you David—that door, being open, is the best part of my defences."

"It would be better shut," says I.

"Not so, David," says he. "Ye see, I have but one face; but so long as that door is open and my face to it, the best part of my enemies will be in front of me, where I would aye wish to find them."

Then he gave me from the rack a cutlass (of which there were a few besides the firearms), choosing it with great care, shaking his head and saying he had never in all his life seen poorer weapons; and next he set me down to the table with a powder-horn, a bag of bullets, and all the pistols, which he bade me charge.

"And that will be better work, let me tell you," said he, "for a gentle-man of decent birth, than scraping plates and raxing[1] drams to a wheen tarry sailors."

Thereupon he stood up in the midst with his face to the door, and drawing his great sword, made trial of the room he had to wield it in.

"I must stick to the point," he said, shaking his head; "And that's a pity, too. It doesn't set my genius, which is all for the upper guard. And now," said he, "do you keep on charging the pistols, and give heed to me."

I told him I would listen closely. My chest was tight, my mouth dry, the light dark to my eyes; the thought of the numbers that were soon to leap in upon us kept my heart in a flutter; and the sea, which I heard washing round the brig, and where I thought my dead body would be cast ere morning, ran in my mind strangely.

"First of all," said he, "how many are against us?"

I reckoned them up; and such was the hurry of my mind, I had to cast the numbers twice. "Fifteen," said I.

Alan whistled. "Well," said he, "that can't be cured. And now follow me. It is my part to keep this door, where I look for the main battle. In that, ye have no hand. And mind and dinna fire to this side unless they get me down; for I would rather have ten foes in front of me than one friend like you cracking pistols at my back."

I told him, indeed, I was no great shot.

"And that's very bravely said," he cried, in a great admiration of my candour. "There's many a pretty gentleman that wouldnae dare to say it."

"But then, sir," said I, "there is the door behind you, which they may perhap break in."

"Ay," said he, "and that is a part of your work. No sooner the pistols charged, than ye must climb up into yon bed where ye're handy at the window; and if they lift hand against the door, ye're to shoot. But that's not all. Let's make a bit of a soldier of ye, David. What else have ye to guard?"

"There's the skylight," said I. "But indeed, Mr Stewart, I would need to have eyes upon both sides to keep the two of them; for when my face is at the one, my back is to the other."

"And that's very true," said Alan. "But have ye no ears to your head?"

---

[1]Reaching.

"To be sure!" cried I. "I must hear the bursting of the glass!"

"Ye have some rudiments of sense," said Alan, grimly.

But now our time of truce was come to an end. Those on deck had waited for my coming till they grew impatient; and scarce had Alan spoken, when the captain showed face in the open door.

"Stand!" cried Alan, and pointed his sword at him.

The captain stood, indeed; but he neither winced nor drew back a foot.

"A naked sword?" says he. "This is a strange return for hospitality."

"Do ye see me?" said Alan. "I am come of kings; I bear a king's name. My badge is the oak. Do ye see my sword? It has slashed the heads off mair Whigamores than you have toes upon your feet. Call up your vermin to your back, sir, and fall on! The sooner the clash begins, the sooner ye'll taste this steel throughout your vitals."

The captain said nothing to Alan, but he looked over at me with an ugly look. "David," said he, "I'll mind this"; and the sound of his voice went through me with a jar.

Next moment he was gone.

"And now," said Alan, "let your hand keep your head, for the grip is coming."

Alan drew a dirk, which he held in his left hand in case they should run in under his sword. I, on my part, clambered up into the berth with an armful of pistols, and something of a heavy heart, and set open the window where I was to watch. It was a small part of the deck that I could overlook, but enough for our purpose. The sea had gone down, and the wind was steady and kept the sails quiet; so that, there was a great stillness in the ship, in which I made sure I heard the sound of muttering voices. A little after, and there came a clash of steel upon the deck, by which I knew they were dealing out the cutlasses and one had been let fall; and after that, silence again.

I do not know if I was what you call afraid; but my heart beat like a bird's, both quick and little; and there was a dimness came before my eyes which I continually rubbed away, and which continually returned. As for hope, I had none; but only a darkness of despair and a sort of anger against all the world that made me long to sell my life as dear as I was able. I tried to pray, I remember, but that same hurry of my mind, like a man running, would not suffer me to think upon the words; and my chief wish was to have the thing begin and be done with it.

It came all of a sudden when it did, with a rush of feet and a roar, and then a shout from Alan, and a sound of blows and some one crying out as if hurt. I looked back over my shoulder, and saw Mr Shuan in the doorway, crossing blades with Alan.

"That's him that killed the boy!" I cried.

"Look to your window!" said Alan, and as I turned back to my place, I saw him pass his sword through the mate's body.

It was none too soon for me to look to my own part; for my head was scarce back at the window, before five men carrying a spare yard for a battering-ram, ran past me and took post to drive the door in. I had never fired with a pistol in my life, and not often with a gun; far less against a fellow-creature. But it was now or never; and just as they swang the yard, I cried out, "Take that!" and shot into their midst.

I must have hit one of them, for he sang out and gave back a step, and the rest stopped as if a little disconcerted. Before they had time to recover, I sent another ball over their heads; and at my third shot (which went as wide as the second) the whole party threw down the yard and ran for it.

Then I looked round again into the deck-house. The whole place was full of the smoke of my own firing, just as my ears seemed to be burst with the noise of the shots. But there was Alan, standing as before; only now his sword was running blood to the hilt, and himself so swelled with triumph and fallen into so fine an attitude, that he looked to be invincible. Right before him on the floor was Mr Shuan, on his hands and knees; the blood was pouring from his mouth, and he was sinking slowly lower, with a terrible, white face; and just as I looked, some of those from behind caught hold of him by the heels and dragged him bodily out of the round-house. I believe he died as they were doing it.

"There's one of your Whigs for ye!" cried Alan; and then turning to me, he asked if I had done much execution.

I told him I had winged one, and thought it was the captain.

"And I've settled two," says he. "No, there's not enough blood let; they'll be back again. To your watch, David. This was but a dram before meat."

I settled back to my place, re-charging the three pistols I had fired, and keeping watch with both eye and ear.

Our enemies were disputing not far off upon the deck, and that so loudly that I could hear a word or two above the washing of the seas.

"It was Shuan bauchled[1] it," I heard one say.

And another answered him with a "Wheesht, man! He's paid the piper."

After that the voices fell again into the same muttering as before. Only now, one person spoke most of the time, as though laying down a plan, and first one and then another answered him briefly, like men taking orders. By this, I made sure they were coming on again, and told Alan.

"It's what we have to pray for," said he. "Unless we can give them a good distaste of us, and done with it, there'll be nae sleep for either you or me. But this time, mind, they'll be in earnest."

By this, my pistols were ready, and there was nothing to do but listen

---

[1]Bungled.

and wait. While the brush lasted, I had not the time to think if I was frighted; but now, when all was still again, my mind ran upon nothing else. The thought of the sharp swords and the cold steel was strong in me; and presently, when I began to hear stealthy steps and a brushing of men's clothes against the round-house wall, and knew they were taking their places in the dark, I could have found it in my mind to cry out aloud.

All this was upon Alan's side; and I had begun to think my share of the fight was at an end, when I heard some one drop softly on the roof above me.

Then there came a single call on the sea-pipe, and that was the signal. A knot of them made one rush of it, cutlass in hand, against the door; and at the same moment, the glass of the skylight was dashed in a thousand pieces, and a man leaped through and landed on the floor. Before he got his feet, I had clapped a pistol to his back, and might have shot him, too; only at the touch of him (and him alive) my whole flesh misgave me, and I could no more pull the trigger than I could have flown.

He had dropped his cutlass, as he jumped, and when he felt the pistol, whipped straight round and laid hold of me, roaring out an oath; and at that either my courage came again, or I grew so much afraid as came to the same thing; for I gave a shriek and shot him in the midst of the body. He gave the most horrible ugly groan and fell to the floor. The foot of a second fellow, whose legs were dangling through the skylight, struck me at the same time upon the head; and at that I snatched another pistol and shot this one through the thigh, so that he slipped through and tumbled in a lump on his companion's body. There was no talk of missing, any more than there was time to aim; I clapped the muzzle to the very place and fired.

I might have stood and stared at them for long, but I heard Alan shout as if for help, and that brought me to my senses.

He had kept the door so long; but one of the seamen, while he was engaged with others, had run in under his guard and caught him about the body. Alan was dirking him with his left hand, but the fellow clung like a leech. Another had broken in and had his cutlass raised. The door was thronged with their faces. I thought we were lost, and catching up my cutlass, fell on them in flank.

But I had not time to be of help. The wrestler dropped at last; and Alan, leaping back to get his distance, ran upon the others like a bull, roaring as he went. They broke before him like water, turning, and running, and falling one against another in their haste. The sword in his hand flashed like quicksilver into the huddle of our fleeing enemies; and at every flash there came the scream of a man hurt. I was still thinking we were lost, when lo! they were all gone, and Alan was driving them along the deck as a sheepdog chases sheep.

Yet he was no sooner out than he was back again, being as cautious as he was brave; and meanwhile the seamen continued running and crying out as if he was still behind them; and we heard them tumble one upon another into the forecastle, and clap-to the hatch upon the top.

The round-house was like a shambles; three were dead inside, another lay in his death agony across the threshold; and there were Alan and I victorious and unhurt.

He came up to me with open arms. "Come to my arms!" he cried, and embraced and kissed me hard upon both cheeks. "David," said he, "I love you like a brother. And oh, man," he cried in a kind of ecstasy, "am I no a bonny fighter?"

Thereupon he turned to the four enemies, passed his sword clean through each of them, and tumbled them out of doors one after the other. As he did so, he kept humming and singing and whistling to himself, like a man trying to recall an air; only what *he* was trying, was to make one. All the while, the flush was in his face, and his eyes were as bright as a five-year-old child's with a new toy. And presently he sat down upon the table, sword in hand; the air that he was making all the time began to run a little clearer, and then clearer still; and then out he burst with a great voice into a Gaelic song.

I have translated it here, not in verse (of which I have no skill) but at least in the king's English. He sang it often afterwards, and the thing became popular; so that I have heard it, and had it explained to me, many's the time.

> This is the song of the sword of Alan:
> The smith made it,
> The fire set it;
> Now it shines in the hand of Alan Breck.
>
> Their eyes were many and bright,
> Swift were they to behold,
> Many the hands they guided:
> The sword was alone.
>
> The dun deer troop over the hill,
> They are many, the hill is one;
> The dun deer vanish,
> The hill remains.
>
> Come to me from the hills of heather,
> Come from the isles of the sea.
> O far-beholding eagles,
> Here is your meat.

ABANDONING SHIP[1]

Joseph Conrad

(1857–1924)

THE skipper lingered disconsolately, and we left him to commune alone for a while with his first command. Then I went up again and brought him away at last. It was time. The ironwork on the poop was hot to the touch.

Then the painter of the long-boat was cut, and the three boats, tied together, drifted clear of the ship. It was just sixteen hours after the explosion when we abandoned her. Mahon had charge of the second boat, and I had the smallest—the 14-foot thing. The long-boat would have taken the lot of us; but the skipper said we must save as much property as we could—for the underwriters—and so I got my first command. I had two men with me, a bag of biscuits, a few tins of meat, and a breaker of water. I was ordered to keep close to the long-boat, that in case of bad weather we might be taken into her.

And do you know what I thought? I thought I would part company as soon as I could. I wanted to have my first command all to myself. I wasn't going to sail in a squadron if there were a chance for independent cruising. I would make land by myself. I would beat the other boats. Youth! All youth! The silly, charming, beautiful youth.

But we did not make a start at once. We must see the last of the ship. And so the boats drifted about that night, heaving and setting on the swell. The men dozed, waked, sighed, groaned. I looked at the burning ship.

Between the darkness of earth and heaven she was burning fiercely upon a disc of purple sea shot by the blood-red play of gleams; upon a disc of water glittering and sinister. A high, clear flame, an immense and lonely flame, ascended from the ocean, and from its summit the black smoke poured continuously at the sky. She burned furiously, mournful and imposing like a funeral pile kindled in the night, surrounded by the sea, watched over by the stars. A magnificent death had come like a grace, like a gift, like a reward to that old ship at the end of her laborious days. The surrender of her weary ghost to the keeping of stars and sea was stirring like the sight of a glorious triumph. The masts fell just before daybreak, and for a moment there was a burst and turmoil of sparks that seemed to fill with flying fire the night patient and watchful, the vast night lying silent upon the sea. At daylight she was only a charred shell, floating still under a cloud of smoke and bearing a glowing mass of coal within.

Then the oars were got out, and the boats forming in a line moved

[1]From *Youth*. Reprinted by permission of the Trustees.

round her remains as if in procession—the long-boat leading. As we pulled across her stern a slim dart of fire shot out viciously at us, and suddenly she went down, head first, in a great hiss of steam. The unconsumed stern was the last to sink; but the paint had gone, had cracked, had peeled off, and there were no letters, there was no word, no stubborn device that was like her soul, to flash at the rising sun her creed and her name.

We made our way north. A breeze sprang up, and about noon all the boats came together for the last time. I had no mast or sail in mine, but I made a mast out of a spare oar and hoisted a boat-awning for a sail, with a boat-hook for a yard. She was certainly over-masted, but I had the satisfaction of knowing that with the wind aft I could beat the other two. I had to wait for them. Then we all had a look at the captain's chart, and, after a sociable meal of hard bread and water, got our last instructions. These were simple: steer north, and keep together as much as possible. "Be careful with that jury-rig, Marlow," said the captain; and Mahon, as I sailed proudly past his boat, wrinkled his curved nose and hailed, "You will sail that ship of yours under water, if you don't look out, young fellow." He was a malicious old man—and may the deep sea where he sleeps now rock him gently, rock him tenderly to the end of time!

Before sunset a thick rain-squall passed over the two boats, which were far astern, and that was the last I saw of them for a time. Next day I sat steering my cockle-shell—my first command—with nothing but water and sky around me. I did sight in the afternoon the upper sails of a ship far away, but said nothing, and my men did not notice her. You see I was afraid she might be homeward bound, and I had no mind to turn back from the portals of the East. I was steering for Java—another blessed name—like Bankok, you know. I steered many days.

I need not tell you what it is to be knocking about in an open boat. I remember nights and days of calm when we pulled, we pulled, and the boat seemed to stand still, as if bewitched within the circle of the sea horizon. I remember the heat, the deluge of rain-squalls that kept us baling for dear life (but filled our water-cask), and I remember sixteen hours on end with a mouth dry as a cinder and a steering-oar over the stern to keep my first command head on to a breaking sea. I did not know how good a man I was till then. I remember the drawn faces, the dejected figures of my two men, and I remember my youth and the feeling that will never come back any more—the feeling that I could last for ever, outlast the sea, the earth, and all men; the deceitful feeling that lures us on to joys, to perils, to love, to vain effort—to death; the triumphant conviction of strength, the heat of life in the handful of dust, the glow in the heart that with every year grows dim, grows cold, grows small, and expires—and expires, too soon, too soon—before life itself.

And this is how I see the East. I have seen its secret places and have looked into its very soul; but now I see it always from a small boat, a high outline of mountains, blue and afar in the morning; like faint mist at noon; a jagged wall of purple at sunset. I have the feel of the oar in my hand, the vision of a scorching blue sea in my eyes. And I see a bay, a wide bay, smooth as glass and polished like ice, shimmering in the dark. A red light burns far off upon the gloom of the land, and the night is soft and warm. We drag at the oars with aching arms, and suddenly a puff of wind, a puff faint and tepid and laden with strange odours of blossoms, of aromatic wood, comes out of the still night—the first sigh of the East on my face. That I can never forget. It was impalpable and enslaving, like a charm, like a whispered promise of mysterious delight.

We had been pulling this finishing spell for eleven hours. Two pulled, and he whose turn it was to rest sat at the tiller. We had made out the red light in that bay and steered for it, guessing it must mark some small coasting port. We passed two vessels, outlandish and high-sterned, sleeping at anchor, and, approaching the light, now very dim, ran the boat's nose against the end of a jutting wharf. We were blind with fatigue. My men dropped the oars and fell off the thwarts as if dead. I made fast to a pile. A current rippled softly. The scented obscurity of the shore was grouped into vast masses, a density of colossal clumps of vegetation, probably—mute and fantastic shapes. And at their foot the semicircle of beach gleamed faintly, like an illusion. There was not a light, not a stir, not a sound. The mysterious East faced me, perfumed like a flower, silent like death, dark like a grave.

And I sat weary beyond expression, exulting like a conqueror, sleepless and entranced as if before a profound, a fateful enigma.

A splashing of oars, a measured dip reverberating on the level of water, intensified by the silence of the shore into loud claps, made me jump up. A boat, a European boat, was coming in. I invoked the name of the dead; I hailed: *Judea* ahoy. A thin shout answered.

It was the captain. I had beaten the flagship by three hours, and I was glad to hear the old man's voice again, tremulous and tired. "Is it you, Marlow?" "Mind the end of that jetty, sir," I cried.

He approached cautiously, and brought up with the deep-sea lead-line which we had saved—for the underwriters. I eased my painter and fell alongside. He sat, a broken figure at the stern, wet with dew, his hands clasped in his lap. His men were asleep already. "I had a terrible time of it," he murmured. "Mahon is behind—not very far." We conversed in whispers, in low whispers, as if afraid to wake up the land. Guns, thunder, earthquakes would not have awakened the men just then.

THE LOFTY-MINDED MARINER[1]

Morley Roberts

(1857-   )

THEY were very quiet in the bar of the Old Brig at Anchor and, seeing that the weather was far too threatening for fishing on the morrow, they were glad to make themselves comfortable when the night came down. It was fine to take a rest and get cleaned up from the fish-muck that the gulls were now dreaming of and the cats still quarrelling over on the wharf and beach just outside the warm inn's hospitable door. They were good men and comfortable and had a pleasant sense of the fireside when the glass went down and there was every sign of heavy weather to be seen in the early high dawn and wild-coloured oily sky. So at the onset of the squally night they said it was the kind of time to stay at home and, resting their hard hands on their warming knees by the fire, kept on repeating that for comfort. But the big old seaman in the fire corner made japes about it, for his notion was that every sea-dog should be at sea when he could get there, weather or none. It was no jolly thought to them, but all the same they reckoned him a pleasant man and kindly though queer in his notions and not so sane as some. Tall he was and somewhat thin, but mighty in the shoulders and big-jointed. He was broad-chested too and deep, and his hands were like the flukes of an anchor, and the skin of his face the colour of a tanned sail. His eyebrows were heavy, but his eyes were so like the eyes of an eagle that it seemed he looked through the world and even beyond it. That he was a wise man these folks felt sure, for he had seen the great world and his skull was big, and his thatch of hair, which projected over his brow, hid not the shape of it. They said amon egach other that he looked like a great wise bird, and he was, as they knew well, properly full of wondrous tales like all ancient pilgrims of the sea. And he had a mighty power of big words.

"Come now," said the stranger, "who'll drink with me? Those that won't are no friends of mine, for rich or poor I'm a free man with money and I have a very lofty mind."

So they all drank with him and wondered how it was he had a lofty mind.

"Aye, I'm a wonder of a man," said the stranger as he pondered. "I'm all for deep water; tall water's what I love, the big seas of the good round world. There's scarce a port betwixt heaven and hell I've not been into. Aye, and I've been into the port of heaven, too, or anchored in the roads of it with heaven just under my lee! If you'd like to hear

---

[1] From *Tales of Changing Seas*. Reprinted by permission of the author and of Eveleigh Nash & Grayson, Ltd.

I'll tell you about it when I have my drink upon my knee, here in my fist, after the manner of a good sailorman."

Some of the quiet crowd at the Brig almost shook in their shoes. This was strange talk of the harbour of heaven. What did the man mean? They knew not whence he had come, and when they asked him he swore strange long-winded, new-fangled foreign oaths, as long as a main-royal-backstay. And then he shook his head and owned he knew it was wrong to swear.

"But you see, mates, so far as swearing is concerned I've always been a wet ship, so to speak, and can't help it. 'Tis the ancient nature of me coming out and I'm full of ancient nature though I have a lofty mind. Where did I come from, young man? What does that matter? Say I walked ashore from a pirate ship, or maybe I was spanged off an angel's thumb nail and tumbled, tumbled, tumbled through all space till I brought up at the Brig at Anchor! Come, you fine young woman, get me some brandy."

And the wondering young woman got him brandy.

"This is a sweet quiet place, this fishing port of yours," said the stranger, " 'tis a good spot to lay up in for a full due. But why is it that some of you likely young men are not out at sea this night, fishing for the glory of God and the due profit of your families?"

"Oh, sir," said little John Jose, who was in the other corner by the fire, " 'tis going to be a wild night, and 'tis best here by long chalks."

The stranger shook his head.

"Aye, but you have mostly the look of those that'd stay in for a wild night that wasn't too wild. No doubt you have a fine handy port and a comfortable home under your lee when it blows a capful of wind. But the right thing is to be driven in, not to stay in, lads. But how can I blame you? No, little man, you've not had my trials nor the wisdom that came to me nor my native strength, which I've proved all the world over, even before I grew lofty in my thoughts."

"Why," said Bill Tregenna, who sat next to John Jose and stared at the seaman with awe-stricken eyes, "why, sir, you've the look of a man that could tell strange tales. That you've seen things is as plain as this pipe in my fist."

"That's true," said the kindly-eyed seaman, "I've seen the strange wonders of the deep. I could spin you a yarn as thick as your thigh and as long as a cable, a terrible yarn and as true as the Book."

"Aye, tell us one, do," said John Jose eagerly.

"Do, do!" said half the others, with their eyes fixed upon the talker.

" 'Twould be almost waste to tell you longshore fishermen tales of the deep sea," he said thoughtfully, with his hands upon his bony knees.

Yet he shook his head and seemed to ponder as though he were hunting in the lockers of his mind for some coil of a yarn fit for such babes of the comfortable land. And presently he spoke, half as if he was speaking to himself, though his eyes bored through John Jose, till John wondered whether he was being hurt or whether the stranger saw him at all.

"There's a tale I have in my mind that I've had coiled up there this long time. I was thinking of my old ship, the *Fair Maid of Perth*, the fine old barque I was bos'un in. That little man in front of me reminded me of her, for he spoke a while back of 'fair maids,' and when I asked what they might be he allowed they were fish, 'pilchards,' said he, 'why, man alive, pilchards are fair maids.' And it brought back the *Fair Maid* to me. Oh, she was a comfortable ship and sea-kindly, a noble and a wholesome ship, and very weatherly, with a clean entrance and a fine clear run, and she went through the water most sweetly. She'd a good skipper, a grand comfortable man, fat and broad, but knowledgeable and good to work with. And under him was a mate who was after my own heart and the dead spit of me for size and the power of his hands. We respected each other therefore and never had a hard word between us, for I was a good bo'sun and knew my work, and the *Fair Maid* was a wife to me and I'd have her as handsome as I could. And there was a second mate that I loved as if he were my brother. He was a bright boy and virtuous, a strange thing in a seaman who had blue eyes and a skin like a woman's, that the women wanted to kiss. And now we was out in the Eastern seas, wimble-wambling about this way and that way. I was a fine young man in those days and, for all my bigness, as quick up aloft as any boy. And here I am now on my hunkers, set on a bench in an inn called the Brig at Anchor, and all I own is under my hat, and I'm set about by strange men who know nothing of the big world. But listen and mark me, for if you've the sense and feelings of shotten herrings I'll make you little men shiver."

And shiver they did.

"The world's a strange place, but the East's a wonder," said the old seaman.

And he looked away beyond them. Some of them knew that he saw the wild shining beaches and the scented woods that dipped their roots in the ocean, and the glittering oily rivers, for of these things their fathers and grandfathers had spoken, since some of them had ploughed the great seas in their youth. And they knew his mind must be on many a sweet dark maid or on wild men and strange and marvellous beasts for whom man was a prey.

" 'Tis a wild taking place the East," he said at last, "one does strange things there, for being so far from the manners one was born with a man isn't kept up tight. I've done things I shouldn't; I know it, for now I'm a lofty-minded man with a certain greatness and fineness of the spirit and a mighty content in me at being what I am. And high and lofty things have happened to me. I've had rises and falls that I'll tell you, things you never dreamed of, for as I let on to you I'm lofty-minded and my nature's big and pleasant when not crossed. But let's get back to the

Fair Maid of Perth, as pleasant a ship as ever any man sailed in, with as kindly a crowd as I was ever shipmates with. And they're all dead. And here I sit on my hunkers with hot brandy and water in my claw. Now in those times we made many a circumbendibus among the islands of the East, by Ombay and Gillolo Strait, and Dampier Strait, for we knocked about in those wild parts for trade, and we saw the Java Sea and the Celebes and Banka Strait and Carinata and Gaspar: and Macassar we knew and the Arafura Sea and the Moluccas. And I disremember many of the places that we put in at and many of the passages, but all the inner and the outer routes we knew like the insides of our sea-chests, Palawan and Bali Strait and Sapie Strait and Pitt's Passage, and many others I disremember. A chart with our traverses plotted out would have looked like a Portugee pig-knot, or a ground-swell knot, or a skein of wool a kitten has played with in your missus's Sunday parlour. Then at last there came the big day that began the time at which I got to be a lofty man, a lofty-minded man, with a knowledge of high things and the great angels and the soundings about the high gates of Heaven. For the skipper and the mate grew uneasy, talking of signs of a typhoon or a cyclone, the great winds that sink lofty ships. For a little fall of the glass in such latitudes may mean much. Now, they said it tumbled downstairs, and there was a strange look about the sky as the mate owned, for without a cloud the sun covered herself, and there was a heavy vapour in the upper air. And before that the moon had been a bit greenish with a little blue in it. It made us look forty ways for Sunday and put the fear of God in our hearts. For the unnatural wrote out on the great scroll of the heavens makes strong men fearful in their proud hearts. And the skipper said to the mate, with a little trembling in his voice:

"'As we're so close, we'll lie up in the old place.'

"'Aye,' said the mate, 'aye, sir, 'tis a good sound thought; though it blew seventy cyclones outside we'd be as safe there as a fish in a pool.'

"So, getting a slant of wind, we put her about and sailed for an island to the south-east of us. The skipper made very free with the land, but all the same there was bold water there with the blueness of a tub of indigo. And the skipper and the mate knew the soundings as though they were pilots born: they knew 'em like the inside of their hats. The old *Fair Maid* seemed to get littler and littler there in the shadow of the land as she held her nose straight for it as though she'd butt her way through the forests that came down to the water's edge. The big mate conned her from the foretopsail yard, and the skipper was as easy in his mind while he smoked a long cigar at the break of the poop as if he'd been in his own High Street. And all of a sudden when I reckoned to see the *Fair Maid* picking flowers with her jib-boom the land opened on us most magical and, with a little steady air that kept us going, right into it we went. But, after a long narrow neck, the passage opened out and all was peace in a strange land-locked harbour as tight as any bottle, and

with a cork in it we'd have been there for ever but for the hand of God
and the strange workings of those fiery mountains in such wondrous
seas. It was very peaceful and there was no fear in my heart, nor did I
bode evil. 'Twas a round harbour, and there are many such, and the
mate said such places had been fiery mountains that had sunk down with
the tops of them still above the water. But there were high hills round
this, even though she had sunk down and had let water into the circle
of high hills where once was great fire. For all round us on every far island
there was fiery mountains, such as shake their sides and spit fire and
smoke and open out and loose melted rock upon the sea. And whether or
no they do harm they have always a pipe between their teeth and they
sit there smoking, smoking. All along Java and Sumatra that's the way
with the fiery mountains. They blink at you out of their loftiness and
sometimes die down and are seen no more. There's the like nearer home,
Volcano and Stromboli. I seen them blinking red just as I've seen greater
mountains in Eastern seas. And there we was, all quiet and peaceful
and hunky, so to speak. But what I want you men to know is that the
Fair Maid never went out the common way she went in to that round
harbour! You'd not guess the how or the why or the wherefore in a whole
month of Sundays; no, nor in a thousand years of long Sundays. 'Tis
a great thing to think on and 'twould be a mighty puzzle to any sailorman who'd had no lofty thoughts or great trials and had not been shaken
in the palm of the hand of the Lord! Ah, but here I am sitting comfortable on a wooden bench by a good fire with a glass of hot liquor in my
fist, and there's none, no, not one, of the fine men that was in the *Fair
Maid*, as I remember 'em breasting the rail and looking ashore, who's yet
alive. And yet they said:

"" 'Tis a fair wonder of a safe harbour we're in!'

"But all those sailormen are dead, and our mate too. He was a fine
man all over, and we respected each other for our strength, but never
tried it man against man. And you'll be wondering how it was they're
all dead men, and him so fine a man. And you'll be saying 'cannibals'
and 'strange wild beasts' and 'sea sarpents' maybe, for I see this kind
of talk in the eyes of you. But what do you know, mates? You're only a
lot of longshore fishermen and what should you savvy of the wonders of
the deep? You're good men at your trade and it's a fine thing to bring
home a great haul of fish. But, as for me, I'd as soon be a farmer and milk
Crumple and stick a pig fiercely. Aye, and you're herring hunters and a
lot of them make a hurrah day for you. Oh, but you're proud that day
when you come in loaded up with herrings! But I've seen for fish the
mighty whales, the spermaceti and the rorquals and the wonders of the
deep and the great squids and all the terrors of the deep. Yet none of
those took my fine mates or that wholesome and noble ship the *Fair
Maid of Perth*. That night the weather was wildly hot; you never felt
the likes of it. This very night I heard one of you say, ' 'Tis warm.'

And that little man over yonder wiped his wet face with a rag and allowed it was awful hot. 'Tis cold to what I've known and I might well shiver in it. Come, young woman, give me more hot brandy and I'll tell these old customers of your high yarn of the *Fair Maid*. 'Twas long ago it happened, yet, even now, old as I am, and I'm a mighty age, I'm strong. But when I was young I could have reached up and scoffed the moon and stars by main strength and the power of my teeth. Do you hear that, mates?"

"Oh, yes, we hear you," said little John Jose.

And the others said among themselves that the teller of tales was a strange man; they knew not what to make of him. But they settled themselves eagerly in their hard seats and held their peace that he might talk.

"Well, there we was," said the stranger, "and as I said the heat was horrid. And some of us would go aloft to the main-royal-yard night or day to look over the biggest gap to the winking and blinking old mountain, which was mighty hot and fiery. Sometimes such mountains wave to and fro and the houses set under them open and throw folks out and close up and fall in just like a pack of cards. And the sea rises up and comes ashore as it did at Sunda, when the big hill blew out like a cylinder head and there was a hole in the nature of the earth and the sea rushed roaring into it. And the water boiled living creatures unnumbered. Ah, but God's a great man-of-war when He goes out to fight; He can slay his millions in a minute. And there we lay at anchor with the glass going up and the glass going down and playing a dreadful hanky-panky, and the sky all a monstrous colour and the moon blue and hot smells in the air. And the second night says I to myself, 'I'll away aloft to the main-royal-yard and smoke my pipe and take a look at the winker and blinker that the men let on about so much.' So I went aloft, it being then two bells in the first watch, and looking out towards the south-east I saw nothing. There was no blinker there and I rubbed my eyes and looked again, but there was never any red sign nor high lighthouse of God Almighty showing fine across the sea. And I thought that dead queer, and down on deck I went and going to the mate said to him:

"'Why, sir, that's a pretty tale they tell! Liars they are. There's no winker and blinker to be seen up there, sir.'

"And with that he looked at me and said:

"'Why, bo'son, ain't it winking and blinking? That surprise me some, because I was up aloft myself last night and there was that same old fiery mountain with its flashtricks, queer, very odd and frightful.'

"That's what he said. And there was no wind in any quarter of the compass, and the air was as heavy to breathe as muck, for it was a clock-calm. There was something about the nature of things that was against the nature of man, for I felt as if a typhoon was breeding when there are wild signs in the sky and smoking clouds and darkness round

about the horizon and strange bellowings like far-off beasts in awful woods.
Aye, like the wild dogs of the Cape, for off the Cape the Cape dogs do
bark, and many sailormen who have shivered when they was warm in
their bunks can bear witness to the same. Then me and the mate heard
the natives on the shore cry out to their gods. And our men came out on
deck uneasy saying they couldn't sleep, and they paddled about on deck
in their own sweat, like cats that sweat through their feet. Some came
and asked me what I reckoned to think, and I told them they was curs,
for I feared neither man nor devil nor God as I thought them, but later
I knew the difference when I'd been tried high and had become a lofty-
minded man and big in my thoughts and more merciful. For now I reckon
there was a bigness in me all the time even when I was a man of sin, as
I am now, no doubt, though loftiness of mind makes a difference and a
sense of loftiness is of the nature of grace. There have been times when I
thought the Lord said to Himself and to His angels, 'Here's a sinner, yet
he that has the makings of a man in him shall have a cup of grace,'
But though I feared nothing, or said so, my heart inside me quavered
queerly; it was as if something unnatural was to happen and my inward
nature foresaw it. I had not less than another's nature, but more. And
now, in the very middle of the night, for I had just struck eight bells
myself, there was an awful roaring and it was as if a mighty hand came
up through the deep water and pounded the *Fair Maid* on her keel and
shook the guts out of her and us. After there came a heavy silence for a
while that almost struck a man like a blow in the face. Then all the crowd
ran out on deck again, some holding to each other and saying, 'What is
it?' Three even laid their hands on me, but I shook them off. And I
heard the sound of the roaring sea as it broke outside our island on all
the big beaches round about, and the sea came in through the harbour
entrance and rose us up feet like a great bore rushing into a river, no
allowance. Some of the men went down on their knees and others came
crying to me and the mate. And the 'old man' ran up on the poop looking
forty ways for Sunday, for the fear of God was in his heart. Yet all the
same he stood at the break of the poop and said in a quiet voice:

"'Tis all right, my men, this kind of thing happens frequent in the
Eastern seas.'

"But he shook in his shoes. And when the day came there was still a
big darkness and we all reckoned we'd been in that inner harbour long
enough, so we put the boats out and started to row the *Fair Maid* to the
entrance. But the boats went ashore in the first narrows where the water
had been good and deep, for in the night the sea bottom had risen up and
there was our *Fair Maid* with no way out to the great seas. Then our
skipper, a high religious man he was, though very sinful, stood at the
break of the poop and tore his hair. And he said:

"'Oh, but this is most unnatural. I never heard the like. What will we
be doing?'

And the mate lifted up his big eyebrows and worked them up and down again and scratted his cheek with his finger but said nothing. He'd a hard and shiny skin on him but no beard, only here and there a stray hair as coarse as a rope yarn. And he was the only man aboard that could stand up to me. So he shook his bull head again and so did the young second mate after him. And the 'old man' cried out quite sudden and savage:

"'Why, damn your eyes, you're a hopeful lot, you're a hopeful lot!'

"Then I heard the men in the boats sing out. The boat they went ashore in couldn't get off. We seed 'em rise up just as if they was on a bank and the tide ebbed beyond knowledge. But they cried out to us that even now the sea bottom was pushing itself up while the water bubbled and boiled about us and there was a great shake in the hills. And one of the hills, with a sound of thunder, fetched away from its ancient moorings and fell into the channel. And them fine men was all dead and covered up. And those that were still aboard cried out and some took to their knees. But I remember one just taking out his pipe and filling it very quiet and striking three matches and letting each go out. I remember his name, it stuck in my mind, for he threw his pipe overboard and looked surprised at himself. And that same while there was three others on their knees at the spare topmast, praying so hard it'd surprise the most religious among you. For sweat ran down them. And the water bubbled heavy with air in it, white water and foaming, and there were jets of steam that rose out of it like great white feathers. And the 'old man' tore his beard. So the mate laid hold of him and said:

"'Why, sir, what are you doing a-tearing of your beard?'

"But the *Fair Maid* belonged to the 'old man' and he loved her more than his mother. And, being religious, it seemed the sense of his sins got hold of him and so he tore his beard. Likewise the sense of my sins got hold of me, but I was proud and shook them off, being young and in the gayness of my strength. But the skipper was getting old and he prayed right there at the break of the poop:

"'Be merciful to me a sinner.'

"None of us knew what he meant though we knew well he was a hard case, although so religious. And I remembered my father who'd been a minister and prayed over me frequent, but got nothing for his prayers but my going to sea. He was a holy great preacher and very powerful, with words at his command, even more than I have though I am his sinful son. But my father was a scholar and had great books beyond number and he drove his words before him like a flock of sheep, and they did his bidding before the Lord and he slung them at sinners like the sling-stones of David. And now there came an awful sound; it was solid like millions of great guns going, the most immortal thunder that ever the angels of the air let off out of heaven or in any strange places of the earth, and the roar of it shook my in'ards and the props and pillars of my brain. The minds of some of the men tumbled in on them and they went mad. For there was a great and pitchy darkness upon us. And there we was as if we was down in a hollow a million miles below all light. Thereupon I called Lamps and bid him light up. But he was doddering on his bent knees alongside the spare topmast. I'd never reckoned to see Lamps on his knees, for he was a good-natured swine with a tongue as foul as Black Goree. So I lighted the lamps myself, for I couldn't see my way to disturb the likes of him at his prayers, for few they must be and his time was short. Aye, and now the sweat boiled out of us and the pitch in the seams of the deck boiled out and stuck to our bare feet. The sea bubbled and trembled and strong sea lights came into the moving water with a great shine. The sea was all a-boil with little shining shaking stars such as you see sometimes just on the crest of a wave in these Northern waters of a fine summer night. But, oh! the wonder of it there, and the shining, with all the little stars going in and out of it, all fire and gold, with great spots that had no darkness in them at all but were all tumbling water of fire and gold so that you could look for a million million miles past the very gates of hell and up to heaven again the other side of the earth. The great golden fire of the bubbling tumbling seas seemed to shine out on the dark woods and hills that clipped us so close. For the hills bent over us and there was no difference in darkness between the woods and the sky. Presently the water boiled and the fiery lights went out and we padded round in darkness with great gloomy lamps and held them up to each other's faces, saying in a whisper, 'Hullo, my lad, is it you?' And fine ashes began to fall out of the darkness and they was in our eyes and ears and thick on the sweat that ran down us and we looked like painted gods or savages out for war. And the mate said to me:

"'Dip a bucket of water, bo'son, from over the side.'

"And to my hand it was nigh boiling. The water was moving and we heard noises come out of it and sometimes it seemed it was the fiery nature of the deep coming up and then it was the strange things of the sea, those that live at the deep bottom of it. And by this time the *Fair Maid* began to roll and we heard the water break first on one beach and then on the other, for so you might take a dish and lop the water first one side and then over the other. I heard the second mate say to the mate:

"'Why, sir, we're in the hands of Providence.'

"And the mate who was a good man but given to blasphemy and as strong as a bollard and as bold as brass, though as kind as any woman, said:

"'I wish he'd hold us steady!'

"That's what the mate said, he wished he'd hold us steady. And there came a thump upon the keel of the *Fair Maid* as if the bottom rose on us. When I went for'ard to see how the cable grew, she that had been lying easy at a fairish scope was up and down as if she was hove short and down by the head, ready to break the hook out of the ground. And I hiked myself about and fetched the mate. He looked down at the cable and scratted his bull-head and swore a great oath the length of the mainbrace. And he said:

"'Slack away, bo'son, or the hawse pipes will be cut down to the water's edge if she holds and rolls.'

But all of a sudden she broke the mud-hook out of the ground and rose up half a fathom.

"'The Lord help us,' said I.

"'He helps those that help themselves,' said the mate as bold as brass, more bold than he would have done a bit later.

"But, though he allowed that the men should turn in, none would, so we kept watch together. And one said:

"'Let's sing.'

"But others said:

"'Oh, hush it, hush it!'

"For they didn't like to hear the sound of their own voices. And still the glass tumbled down. And the mate called to me and allowed it was so and said:

"'I've got a kinkle as to its meaning.'

"'What is its meaning, sir?' I asked.

"'Why,' said the mate, 'it's not the weather, but we're rising up!'

"And I didn't tumble, whereon and wherefore he called me seventeen unholy names when I said it was the bottom going down. I know now that he had the sow by the right ear, for the water was rising us in the round lake that we was in. And soon a little light came through, a grey scaring sort of glimmer, and we saw strange sea beasts that squirmed in the water as they boiled and some lay out big lengths dead. And the mate said to me when the grey light grew and the deeper darkness passed away:

"'By the glass we're thousands of feet up,' said he, grinning. 'We've risen up tremendous in the night, nigh to the tops of the mountains, bo'-son.'

"So I looked out around and now the mountains was little and the lake was bigger. And the men, hearing us, came aft too, some of them, and said:

"'Oh, sir! oh, sir!'

"That's what they said. Just 'Oh, sir!' And one young chap let on:

"'Oh, sir, it's awful, awful hot!'

"Then he catched hold of the mate, and as the mate turned, angry-like, the boy keeled over and went down on deck with a heavy wallop. We brought him to for a bit and laid him out flat, but he never left the spot we laid him on. And the 'old man' was walking to and fro on the poop in his pyjamas wiping his face with a bandana, wringing his hands and shaking his head. And still the mate kept on saying:

"'Bo'son, we're rising up!'

"He kept on saying it, no allowance. And of the heat three men died that day. They were all nice fine men and they struggled and looked up and clutched at their throats, and went down wallop and struggled a little while, not very long. And one of them said, 'Oh, Lord!' That's what he said, and gasped like a fish and flip-flapped a little and was gone. The rest of us was down around 'em holding our lamps for them to die by, for the darkness was on us once more. All the time there was a devil in the land, for all the shut-up earthquakes and the mighty fiery cisterns of the Lord was working in the underneath parts of the world. But at last the skipper, with his long white beard and his white face, made out to say:

"'Cheer up, men, we'll be all right, we'll be all right.'

"And by and by they passed the word for'ard for me. I went aft stripped to the waist as if I was a pirate at a gun in the old days, and the mate bid me to take one of the boats that was still over the side and go ashore and climb up the hill so that I could tell them whether the sea was down below or on a main level with us. I asked one of the men to come with me, and none of them would though I called them all the curs I could lay my tongue to, and I lambasted them and their mothers and their maids with a devil's tongue which I'd got then when I was mad. For in those days I was a wild man and an arguer and a rare jaw-me-down and few could tackle me. But at last the boy, little Tom that was in the mate's watch, wiped his hand across his mouth and said:

"'I'll come with you, bo'son.'

"And oh, it was mighty dark when I and the lad got into the boat and I sculled her through the thick ash on the water. It was a little lighter when I got ashore and struggled through the dry brush and deep ash, labouring in my breath. At last I came up to the gap in the hills and stood and looked down. And fine breathable air came to me just for a while and I filled my heavy lungs. As I looked out in the thick darkness, I could see no sign of water, but I had the feelings of being lifted high in a bad dream. And I set my lantern on a rock and climbed down a bit and came to a big rock with no way down past it. So I laid there and put my hands to my ears and heard the roat of our island shore, deep, very deep below me. Aye, there I heard the roat of the shore below me and our sole ship was up aloft carried in the hands of the Lord, and beneath me was the great roaring sea beating and lashing on rocks that hadn't seen the light since the holy foundations of the world. Having been witness to this I climbed back, stumbling through the ashes and these shaking trees and the darkness, to my own little light high up above me on the rock. I looked for death and the end of all things. And soon I called out:

"'Tommy, where are you?'

"And the little chap piped bravely:

"'Here I am, bo'son. This is the way, bo'son.'

"I remember his words. He was a good boy and had a mother in

Plymouth. And when we came aboard I went aft to the Captain and said:

"'You're right, sir, we're a terrible long ways up.'

"Thereupon I told them how I'd listened with my hands to my ears and had heard the wash of breakers below me. It was a strange hard trial of God for sailormen to be aloft in such high waters. And the mate scratted his bull-head and the second greaser laughed very queer. At that time the lungs of me, the strongest man in the ship, laboured heavy and my legs were heavy on me. And the Captain who was oldish and fat said one word or two: aye, what he said was, 'My God!' and he keeled over and gave a kick or two, and they was quiet kicks. He was a gentleman always. And that's the way he died. Having laid him straight I went for'ard to the men and told them, and one of them keeled over. And the rest kept on saying as they choked:

"'Oh, bo'son, this is bloody awful!'

"Soon there was but me and the mate and poor little Tom Duckett from Plymouth the only ones alive in the good old *Fair Maid*. Oh, but she was the ship I loved, and being bo'son and careful for her I had as much joy in seeing her shipshape as ever any man had about a great king's ship, for though she was small she was very fast and sea-kindly and a wholesome and noble ship. And there was only three of us alive and the weight on my chest I could scarce a-bear. But all the time little Tommy followed me around, and presently as I had hold of him he'd have keeled over but for me. And I called to the mate and picked the lad up in my arms, and the mate and I went up aloft with him, but when we came to the main-top Tommy died. I laid him down there with his hands crossed upon his breast and the mate and I went right up to the main-royal yard hoping there'd be something to breathe there. The mate was surely thinking of those he'd never see again and the tears ran down his face. And I said:

"'Don't, sir, don't!'

"That's what I said. And on my speaking, the *Fair Maid* in the boiling water did a strange heave and tumble and the water bubbled up in fountains like great mounds. The *Fair Maid* she nid-nodded in those strange waters so high up towards the sky of heaven. And the dryness was awful and the parrals creaked and every block cheeped a bit now and then, and her uneasy motion was uneasy for us, we being so weak and heavy in our breathing and overpowered in our minds by the great calamity and disaster of the high water. So we cut away the port and starboard gaskets of the royal and made ourselves fast up aloft there, and the *Fair Maid* went heaving and shaking with all the dead men down on her deck. Then a little more light came down to us and we saw the hills and the shore. And there was a great mound of bubbling water in the midst of our lake like a big rounded breast and about it there was thick ashes. Then the mate said we was got to the tops of the hills and soon the water would fall over them and the *Fair Maid* would sail down thousands of feet. The moorings of his mind had fetched away and it grieved me sore for he was a fine man and strong and knew his work. But madness always made me tremble, for I felt then in my inward mind that the moorings of a man's intellects are not the strength they might be. Yet I was still strong and kept a hard grip on my wambling mind, but the mate's mind was gone and he tore away his shirt and I saw the great frame of the man, and the arch of his chest like a bridge and the muscles laid in and out of him like woven sennit and his arms as mighty as mine. But weakness was in them and in his brain. I could see his heart was giving way and he died very hard. So I'd seen a big fish turn over sideways in the bubbling water and struggle a bit and then struggle no more. And there was our mate with a gasket round him and round the mast and him all sunk down, hanging in his lashings like wet canvas in the brails. And for a long time after he was dead, or so I reckoned, the muscles in his skin jumped like little fish. But maybe he wasn't as dead as those who strewed the deck below. And then the big darkness rolled off sudden in a breeze, as if they up aloft had slid the scuttle off the deck of the world. And being all alone and very sorrowful and aghast I own I looked for the great Captain or some great angel mate of his to shove his head out of the skies above me and sing out 'Below there!' And now there was all the stars, very bright and fine in their rows and ranks, hung up like jewels and like lamps, some near and some far. But the little stars were like seed pearls scattered. The moon herself hung sideways, like a horse-shoe for the world's luck to fall out of, but she hitched herself over a high-lifted spike of mighty mountain rock. And with the waters rising it seemed I could see through far gaps to the Eastern sea where there was a little glow like the climbing dawn. But sleep kept on coming over me like the march of the tides. And suddenly as I woke again it was the dawn, clear and cold. And the stars were gone out in the east and the moon that was off her peak was like a crescent that I've seen in Eastern pictures on the head and brow of the young dawn. But waters still came up from the great springs of the world. And I says to myself, says I:

"'When she's filled right up and cuts her way out we'll be launched through the dock gates of God's waterways ten thousand feet above the sea.'

"I have a strange notion that I sang hymns and made my prayers to the dawn, the great maid of the East who puts the stars out with her hands: she who had a young moon upon her brow and her golden feet upon the Eastern world. And the terrific heat was gone and I hugged myself and shivered as the sun made his way through a great gap and winked at me But I cursed him to his face. And now the *Fair Maid* took a notion and a motion with the draft of the water or the little wind out of the east to go away to the north-west and see the lowest gap in the hills. Soon I began to hear very great waters thundering, and staring eager I saw the waters fall out of the littlest low gap. And the old hooker jiggled and danced and turned round about and went faster as though she was laid hold of by the tide. For a long time now I'd cast off my lashings and, standing on the royal yard, I hugged the mast close and looked out on the world all by my lone. And down below, the dead men were dotted about just where they'd lopped down. But I looked out to the east and west and the high waters were green and blue with the blue of the early sky. And soon they were on a slope like the rapids of a river, and the water was streaky with running ash. And at that time the old *Fair Maid* went like an arrow up to the gap, and we came to the narrows and I heard the thunder of the tumbling waters and the hills bowed down with trees upon their crests that fell into the flood and were washed away like trash upon a rising river. And soon the *Fair Maid* was drawn on the streaming water, oh, very fast she went, and I waved my hands and cried out:

"'Hurrah! Hurrah!'

"So she stood out through the land and came to an awful pitch in the water and I saw the world beneath me and the open sea and the islands, the silent peaceful islands thousands of feet below. And in my mind, loosed from its moorings, 'twas as if I saw all the lands of the world and the big seas, Asia and Europe and Africa and the great Americas and the far shining oceans of the spread world. And here was death and none could save me and yet I feared nothing; for the fear of death had passed in the bitter night. It seemed unto me that I was already dead and that nought but my spirit stood upon the main-royal-yard, dancing, dancing! And at that very moment the sweet old *Fair Maid* went over the crest in a roar of waters which was like the voice of God. Even as I sang prayers of praise and pieces of great psalms that came out of my heart we pitched a thousand feet or ten thousand, and I was spanged out into space. 'Tis in my mind that I fell all among the suns and stars and I reached out to them. So I fell for years among the suns and moons and stars till a great darkness came to me. 'Twas as if I fell asleep and when I woke or seemed to wake I lay upon a big shining plain that was a great flat polished pink pearl or some fine flat jewel, and I rose up on it in a great calm and feared nothing, though it seemed to me that a mighty face looked at me, a face that was wonderful beyond the words of any man though he drove them before him with power as my old father did. And I stood up and spoke and said:

"'Where am I?'

"And I heard a voice answer:

"'Little man, you're on my thumb-nail.'

"And it was not strange to me nor did I wonder at the nature of him whose thumb-nail was a polished jewel or some great marble plain.

"'Your thumb-nail?' said I, as bold as brass and bravely. 'Then, who are you?'

"'Little man, I am an angel,' said the voice.

"'Are you a great angel?' I asked.

"But he answered:

"'No, little man, I am but one of the least of the angels, and I work upon the outskirts of the heavenly stars. And thus it was that I reached out and plucked you off a star and stood you here upon my nail.'

"It all seemed natural to me and I feared nothing. But I looked over the edge of his thumb-nail and I saw the earth and her comfortable moon and her sun that was very busy warming her. And there was a city on the earth that was very dear to me that shone like a jewel in the ear of a sweet maid. So I said:

"'Angel, put me back upon the earth.'

"For there was no comfort in the polish of him and I hadn't the faith in him I'd have in a good kind man. So:

"'Put me back upon the earth, angel,' said I, 'for it's warm there.'

"I hankered for my home. And what I thought was that I'd rather go to hell than stay aloft with him. That's what I thought in my mind. And whether I said so or not to the angel as I stood on his thumb-nail, it seemed to me that he knew it, for what he said was, in a kind of politeful way:

"'Ashes to ashes and dust to dust, little man.'

"Whereupon he lifted up his other mighty finger and thumb and spanged me out into great space. And as I fell I knew not whether I was bound for a port in hell or the dear comfortable earth. And as I fell so I fell asleep, or so it seemed, and maybe I slept for a million years. But I woke up lying on strange home-like warm sand and the feeling of the warm earth was at the back of me, and there was the heavy comfortable smells of the East about me and a fine brown woman sitting alongside of me crying. I felt weak as I looked up at her, but I knew I'd done great things and seen more than many, and my mind was still lofty though I was as naked as a needle upon the hot warm sand. I looked at my own big arms and saw the old familiar tattooing of them and the names of the girls that I'd loved and I knowed that I was I. Ah, there was comfort in the pattern of the tattooing! And I was all alone but for this kind weeping woman, for I was the last of the crowd of the old *Fair Maid*, and she at the bottom of the sea and all her fine men dead and deep in the sea. Then the brown woman rose me up and took me by the hand and led me like a little child through comfortable dark woods. 'Twas a long time after that I got the smell of the North in my mind and the thought of these sweet clouded skies and the Northern tumbling seas all so grey and taking. And I sickened of the East and her skies were a terror to me and so were the big open nights. I desired the plain old stars we have in our own country. So I swam through a sea of sharks to a ship that passed and they took me in. And it may be I'll see the East again and that good woman waiting on the beach, but it's great now to hear the old familiar winds roaring and to look out and see the same old moon that stood on the brow of the dawn and to see her flying through the scud like a tight ship in a gale, and to reach out one's hands to one's own countrymen, though they are strange little people I could break between my thumb and forefinger, or, like the great angel who was also a little angel, could take them up and put them on my thumb-nail and spang them to the Southern seas. 'Tis a fine thing to be home after years though all are dead one knew, all gone down like the old *Fair Maid*, for there are still the places they loved and the air they breathed when they lived and thought kindly of a man and hoped for their wanderer to come back once more, once more."

And the old man ceased his tale and pulled at his beard and smiled and nodded his head. For a space there was silence. The others nodded their heads solemnly and kept their eyes fixed on him. But at last little John Jose spoke.

"Oh, sir; oh, mates, 'tis a great story," said John Jose, "a most wonderful tale. The far world's a strange place for those that see the marvels of it. But as for me I am no more than an unconsidered man who goes a-fishing and the deep waters are beyond me."

"Aye, that's as may be," said the old man, "it isn't given to us all to see what I've seen or to live through it. Yet great and little have their places, for the world's great and little, so there's a place for you and a place for me. But it's a pleasant thing to be back in old England among such company and I'll ask you to take a drink with me. Give it a name. And you, ma'am, I'll ask kindly to get the drinks for the men and for me."

And one by one they said they would drink with him again.

"'Tis a very strange tale you've told us," they said, in a nodding chorus.

"Aye," said the stranger, "but it's a wonderful, wonderful world and who shall fathom it?"

IN THE ABYSS[1]

H. G. Wells

(1866–   )

THE lieutenant stood in front of the steel sphere and gnawed a piece of pine splinter. "What do you think of it, Steevens?" he asked.

"It's an idea," said Steevens, in the tone of one who keeps an open mind.

"I believe it will smash—flat," said the lieutenant.

[1]From *The Plattner Story and Other Stories*. Reprinted by permission of the author.

"He seems to have calculated it all out pretty well," said Steevens, still impartial.

"But think of the pressure," said the lieutenant. "At the surface of the water it's fourteen pounds to the inch, thirty feet down it's double that; sixty, treble; ninety, four times; nine hundred, forty times; five thousand, three hundred—that's a mile—it's two hundred and forty times fourteen pounds; that's—let's see—thirty hundredweight—a ton and a half, Steevens; *a ton and a half* to the square inch. And the ocean where's he's going is five miles deep. That's seven and a half——"

"Sounds a lot," said Steevens, "but it's jolly thick steel."

The lieutenant made no answer, but resumed his pine splinter. The object of their conversation was a huge ball of steel, having an exterior diameter of perhaps nine feet. It looked like the shot for some Titanic piece of artillery. It was elaborately nested in a monstrous scaffolding built into the framework of the vessel, and the gigantic spars that were presently to sling it overboard gave the stern of the ship an appearance that had raised the curiosity of every decent sailor who had sighted it, from the Pool of London to the Tropic of Capricorn. In two places, one above the other, the steel gave place to a couple of circular windows of enormously thick glass, and one of these, set in a steel frame of great solidity, was now partially unscrewed. Both the men had seen the interior of this globe for the first time that morning. It was elaborately padded with air cushions, with little studs sunk between bulging pillows to work the simple mechanism of the affair. Everything was elaborately padded, even the Myers apparatus which was to absorb carbonic acid and replace the oxygen inspired by its tenant, when he had crept in by the glass manhole, and had been screwed in. It was so elaborately padded that a man might have been fired from a gun in it with perfect safety. And it had need to be, for presently a man was to crawl in through that glass manhole, to be screwed up tightly, and to be flung overboard, and to sink down—down—down, for five miles, even as the lieutenant said. It had taken the strongest hold of his imagination; it made him a bore at mess; and he found Steevens, the new arrival aboard, a godsent to talk to about it, over and over again.

"It's my opinion," said the lieutenant, "that that glass will simply bend in and bulge and smash, under a pressure of that sort. Daubrée has made rocks run like water under big pressures—and, you mark my words——"

"If the glass did break in," said Steevens, "what then?"

"The water would shoot in like a jet of iron. Have you ever felt a straight jet of high pressure water? It would hit as hard as a bullet. It would simply smash him and flatten him. It would tear down his throat, and into his lungs; it would blow in his ears——"

"What a detailed imagination you have!" protested Steevens, who saw things vividly.

"It's a simple statement of the inevitable," said the lieutenant.

"And the globe?"

"Would just give out a few little bubbles, and it would settle down comfortably against the day of judgment, among the oozes and the bottom clay—with poor Elstead spread over his own smashed cushions like butter over bread."

He repeated this sentence as though he liked it very much. "Like butter over bread," he said.

"Having a look at the jigger?" said a voice, and Elstead stood behind them, spick and span in white, with a cigarette between his teeth, and his eyes smiling out of the shadow of his ample hat-brim. "What's that about bread and butter, Weybridge? Grumbling as usual about the insufficient pay of naval officers? It won't be more than a day now before I start. We are to get the slings ready to-day. This clean sky and gentle swell is just the kind of thing for swinging off a dozen tons of lead and iron, isn't it?"

"It won't affect you much," said Weybridge.

"No. Seventy or eighty feet down, and I shall be there in a dozen seconds, there's not a particle moving, though the wind shriek itself hoarse up above, and the water lifts halfway to the clouds. No. Down there"— He moved to the side of the ship and the other two followed him. All three leant forward on their elbows and stared down into the yellow-green water.

"*Peace*," said Elstead, finishing his thought aloud.

"Are you dead certain that clockwork will act?" asked Weybridge presently.

"It has worked thirty-five times," said Elstead. "It's bound to work."

"But if it doesn't."

"Why shouldn't it?"

"I wouldn't go down in that confounded thing," said Weybridge, "for twenty thousand pounds."

"Cheerful chap you are," said Elstead, and spat sociably at a bubble below.

"I don't understand yet how you mean to work the thing," said Steevens.

"In the first place, I'm screwed into the sphere," said Elstead, "and when I've turned the electric light off and on three times to show I'm cheerful, I'm swung out over the stern by that crane, with all those big lead sinkers slung below me. The top lead weight has a roller carrying a hundred fathoms of strong cord rolled up, and that's all that joins the sinkers to the sphere, except the slings that will be cut when the affair is dropped. We use cord rather than wire rope because it's easier to cut and more buoyant—necessary points, as you will see.

"Through each of these lead weights you notice there is a hole, and an iron rod will be run through that and will project six feet on the lower side.

If that rod is rammed up from below, it knocks up a lever and sets the clockwork in motion at the side of the cylinder on which the cord winds.

"Very well. The whole affair is lowered gently into the water, and the slings are cut. The sphere floats—with the air in it, it's lighter than water,—but the lead weights go down straight and the cord runs out. When the cord is all paid out, the sphere will go down too, pulled down by the cord."

"But why the cord?" asked Steevens. "Why not fasten the weights directly to the sphere?"

"Because of the smash down below. The whole affair will go rushing down, mile after mile, at a headlong pace at last. It would be knocked to pieces on the bottom if it wasn't for that cord. But the weights will hit the bottom, and directly they do, the buoyancy of the sphere will come into play. It will go on sinking slower and slower; come to a stop at last, and then begin to float upward again.

"That's where the clockwork comes in. Directly the weights smash against the sea bottom, the rod will be knocked through and will kick up the clockwork, and the cord will be rewound on the reel. I shall be lugged down to the sea bottom. There I shall stay for half an hour, with the electric light on, looking about me. Then the clockwork will release a spring knife, the cord will be cut, and up I shall rush again, like a soda-water bubble. The cord itself will help the flotation."

"And if you should chance to hit a ship?" said Weybridge.

"I should come up at such a pace, I should go clean through it," said Elstead, "like a cannon ball. You needn't worry about that."

"And suppose some nimble crustacean should wriggle into your clock-work——"

"It would be a pressing sort of invitation for me to stop," said Elstead, turning his back on the water and staring at the sphere.

They had swung Elstead overboard by eleven o'clock. The day was serenely bright and calm, with the horizon lost in haze. The electric glare in the little upper compartment beamed cheerfully three times. Then they let him down slowly to the surface of the water, and a sailor in the stern chains hung ready to cut the tackle that held the lead weights and the sphere together. The globe, which had looked so large on deck, looked the smallest thing conceivable under the stern of the ship. It rolled a little, and its two dark windows, which floated uppermost, seemed like eyes turned up in round wonderment at the people who crowded the rail. A voice wondered how Elstead liked the rolling. "Are you ready?" sang out the commander. "Ay, ay, sir!" "Then let her go!"

The rope of the tackle tightened against the blade and was cut, and an eddy rolled over the globe in a grotesquely helpless fashion. Some one waved a handkerchief, some one else tried an ineffectual cheer, a middy was counting slowly, "Eight, nine, ten!" Another roll, then with a jerk and a splash the thing righted itself.

It seemed to be stationary for a moment, to grow rapidly smaller, and then the water closed over it, and it became visible, enlarged by refraction and dimmer, below the surface. Before one could count three it had disappeared. There was a flicker of white light far down in the water, that diminished to a speck and vanished. Then there was nothing but a depth of water going down into blackness, through which a shark was swimming.

Then suddenly the screw of the cruiser began to rotate, the water was crickled, the shark disappeared in a wrinkled confusion, and a torrent of foam rushed across the crystalline clearness that had swallowed up Elstead. "What's the idea?" said one A. B. to another.

"We're going to lay off about a couple of miles, 'fear he should hit us when he comes up," said his mate.

The ship steamed slowly to her new position. Aboard her almost everyone who was unoccupied remained watching the breathing swell into which the sphere had sunk. For the next half-hour it is doubtful if a word was spoken that did not bear directly or indirectly on Elstead. The December sun was now high in the sky, and the heat very considerable.

"He'll be cold enough down there," said Weybridge. "They say that below a certain depth sea water's always just about freezing."

"Where'll he come up?" asked Steevens. "I've lost my bearings."

"That's the spot," said the commander, who prided himself on his omniscience. He extended a precise finger southeastward. "And this, I reckon, is pretty nearly the moment," he said. "He's been thirty-five minutes."

"How long does it take to reach the bottom of the ocean?" asked Steevens.

"For a depth of five miles, and reckoning—as we did—an acceleration of two feet per second, both ways, is just about three-quarters of a minute."

"Then he's overdue," said Weybridge.

"Pretty nearly," said the commander. "I suppose it takes a few minutes for that cord of his to wind in."

"I forgot that," said Weybridge, evidently relieved.

And then began the suspense. A minute slowly dragged itself out, and no sphere shot out of the water. Another followed, and nothing broke the low oily swell. The sailors explained to one another that little point about the winding-in of the cord. The rigging was dotted with expectant faces. "Come up, Elstead!" called one hairy-chested salt impatiently, and the others caught it up, and shouted as though they were waiting for the curtain of a theatre to rise.

The commander glanced irritably at them.

"Of course, if the acceleration is less than two," he said, "he'll be all the longer. We aren't absolutely certain that was the proper figure. I'm no slavish believer in calculations."

Steevens agreed concisely. No one on the quarter-deck spoke for a couple of minutes. Then Steevens' watchcase clicked.

When, twenty-one minutes after, the sun reached the zenith, they were still waiting for the globe to reappear, and not a man aboard had dared to whisper that hope was dead. It was Weybridge who first gave expression to that realization. He spoke while the sound of eight bells still hung in the air. "I always distrusted that window," he said quite suddenly to Steevens.

"Good God!" said Steevens; "you don't think——?"

"Well!" said Weybridge, and left the rest to his imagination.

"I'm no great believer in calculations myself," said the commander dubiously, "so that I'm not altogether hopeless yet." And at midnight the gunboat was steaming slowly in a spiral round the spot where the globe had sunk, and the white beam of the electric light fled and halted and swept discontentedly onward again over the waste of phosphorescent waters under the little stars.

"If his window hasn't burst and smashed him," said Weybridge, "then it's a cursed sight worse, for his clockwork has gone wrong, and he's alive now, five miles under our feet, down there in the cold and dark, anchored in that little bubble of his, where never a ray of light has shone or a human being lived, since the waters were gathered together. He's there without food, feeling hungry and thirsty and scared, wondering whether he'll starve or stifle. Which will it be? The Myers apparatus is running out, I suppose. How long do they last?"

"Good heavens!" he exclaimed; "what little things we are! What daring little devils! Down there, miles and miles of water—all water, and all this empty water about us and this sky. Gulfs!" He threw his hands out, and as he did so, a little white streak swept noiselessly up the sky, travelled more slowly, stopped, became a motionless dot, as though a new star had fallen up into the sky. Then it went sliding back again and lost itself amidst the reflections of the stars and the white haze of the sea's phosphorescence.

At the sight he stopped, arm extended and mouth open. He shut his mouth, opened it again, and waved his arms with an impatient gesture. Then he turned, shouted "El-stead ahoy!" to the first watch, and went at a run to Lindley and the search-light. "I saw him," he said. "Starboard there! His light's on, and he's just shot out of the water. Bring the light round. We ought to see him drifting, when he lifts on the swell."

But they never picked up the explorer until dawn. Then they almost ran him down. The crane was swung out and a boat's crew hooked the chain to the sphere. When they had shipped the sphere, they unscrewed the manhole and peered into the darkness of the interior (for the electric light chamber was intended to illuminate the water about the sphere, and was shut off entirely from its general cavity).

The air was very hot within the cavity, and the indiarubber at the lip of the manhole was soft. There was no answer to their eager questions and no sound of movement within. Elstead seemed to be lying motionless, crumpled up in the bottom of the globe. The ship's doctor crawled in and lifted him out to the men outside. For a moment or so they did not know whether Elstead was alive or dead. His face, in the yellow light of the ship's lamps, glistened with perspiration. They carried him down to his own cabin.

He was not dead, they found, but in a state of absolute nervous collapse, and besides cruelly bruised. For some days he had to lie perfectly still. It was a week before he could tell his experiences.

Almost his first words were that he was going down again. The sphere would have to be altered, he said, in order to allow him to throw off the cord if need be, and that was all. He had had the most marvellous experience. "You thought I should find nothing but ooze," he said. "You laughed at my explorations, and I've discovered a new world!" He told his story in disconnected fragments, and chiefly from the wrong end, so that it is impossible to re-tell it in his words. But what follows is the narrative of his experience.

It began atrociously, he said. Before the cord ran out, the thing kept rolling over. He felt like a frog in a football. He could see nothing but the crane and the sky overhead, with an occasional glimpse of the people on the ship's rail. He couldn't tell a bit which way the thing would roll next. Suddenly he would find his feet going up, and try to step, and over he went rolling, head over heels, and just anyhow, on the padding. Any other shape would have been more comfortable, but no other shape was to be relied upon under the huge pressure of the nethermost abyss.

Suddenly the swaying ceased; the globe righted, and when he had picked himself up, he saw the water all about him greeny-blue, with an attenuated light filtering down from above, and a shoal of little floating things went rushing up past him, as it seemed to him, towards the light. And even as he looked, it grew darker and darker, until the water above was as dark as the midnight sky, albeit of a greener shade, and the water below black. And little transparent things in the water developed a faint glint of luminosity, and shot past him in faint greenish streaks.

And the feeling of falling! It was just like the start of a lift, he said, only it kept on. One has to imagine what that means, that keeping on. It was then of all times that Elstead repented of his adventure. He saw the chances against him in an altogether new light. He thought of the big cuttle-fish people knew to exist in the middle waters, the kind of things they find half digested in whales at times, or floating dead and rotten and half eaten by fish. Suppose one caught hold and wouldn't let go. And had the clockwork really been sufficiently tested? But whether he wanted to go on or to go back mattered not the slightest now.

In fifty seconds everything was as black as night outside, except where the beam from his light struck through the waters, and picked out every

now and then some fish or scrap of sinking matter. They flashed by too
fast for him to see what they were. Once he thinks he passed a shark.
And then the sphere began to get hot by friction against the water. They
had under-estimated this, it seems.

The first thing he noticed was that he was perspiring, and then he
heard a hissing growing louder under his feet, and saw a lot of little bubbles—very little bubbles they were—rushing upward like a fan through
the water outside. Steam! He felt the window, and it was hot. He turned
on the minute glow-lamp that lit his own cavity, looked at the padded
watch by the studs, and saw he had been travelling now for two minutes. It came into his head that the window would crack through
the conflict of temperatures, for he knew the bottom water is very near
freezing.

Then suddenly the floor of the sphere seemed to press against his feet,
the rush of bubbles outside grew slower and slower, and the hissing diminished. The sphere rolled a little. The window had not cracked, nothing had given, and he knew that the dangers of sinking, at any rate, were
over.

In another minute or so he would be on the floor of the abyss. He
thought, he said, of Steevens and Weybridge and the rest of them five
miles overhead, higher to him than the very highest clouds that ever
floated over land are to us, steaming slowly and staring down and wondering what had happened to him.

He peered out of the window. There were no more bubbles now, and
the hissing had stopped. Outside there was a heavy blackness—as black
as black velvet—except where the electric light pierced the empty water
and showed the colour of it—a yellow-green. Then three things like
shapes of fire swam into sight, following each other through the water.
Whether they were little and near or big and far off he could not tell.

Each was outlined in a bluish light almost as bright as the lights of a
fishing smack, a light which seemed to be smoking greatly, and all along
the sides of them were specks of this, like the lighter portholes of a ship.
Their phosphorescence seemed to go out as they came within the radiance
of his lamp, and he saw then that they were little fish of some strange
sort, with huge heads, vast eyes, and dwindling bodies and tails. Their
eyes were turned towards him, and he judged they were following him
down. He supposed they were attracted by his glare.

Presently others of the same sort joined them. As he went on down, he
noticed that the water became of a pallid colour, and that little specks
twinkled in his ray like motes in a sunbeam. This was probably due to the
clouds of ooze and mud that the impact of his leaden sinkers had disturbed.

By the time he was drawn down to the lead weights he was in a dense
fog of white that his electric light failed altogether to pierce for more than
a few yards, and many minutes elapsed before the hanging sheets of

sediment subsided to any extent. Then, lit by his light and by the transient phosphorescence of a distant shoal of fishes, he was able to see under the huge blackness of the super-incumbent water an undulating expanse of greyish-white ooze, broken here and there by tangled thickets of a growth of sea lilies, waving hungry tentacles in the air.

Farther away were the graceful, translucent outlines of a group of gigantic sponges. About this floor there were scattered a number of bristling flattish tufts of rich purple and black, which he decided must be some sort of sea-urchin, and small, large-eyed or blind things having a curious resemblance, some to woodlice, and others to lobsters, crawled sluggishly across the track of the light and vanished into the obscurity again, leaving furrowed trails behind them.

Then suddenly the hovering swarm of little fishes veered about and came towards him as a flight of starlings might do. They passed over him like a phosphorescent snow, and then he saw behind them some larger creature advancing towards the sphere.

At first he could see it only dimly, a faintly moving figure remotely suggestive of a walking man, and then it came into the spray of light that the lamp shot out. As the glare struck it, it shut its eyes, dazzled. He stared in rigid astonishment.

It was a strange vertebrated animal. Its dark purple head was dimly suggestive of a chameleon, but it had such a high forehead and such a braincase as no reptile ever displayed before; the vertical pitch of its face gave it a most extraordinary resemblance to a human being.

Two large and protruding eyes projected from sockets in chameleon fashion, and it had a broad reptilian mouth with hoary lips beneath its little nostrils. In the position of the ears were two huge gill-covers, and out of these floated a branching tree of coralline filaments, almost like the tree-like gills that very young rays and sharks possess.

But the humanity of the face was not the most extraordinary thing about the creature. It was a biped; its almost globular body was poised on a tripod of two frog-like legs and a long thick tail, and its fore limbs, which grotesquely caricatured the human hand, much as a frog's do, carried a long shaft of bone, tipped with copper. The colour of the creature was variegated; its head, hands, and legs were purple; but its skin, which hung loosely upon it, even as clothes might do, was a phosphorescent grey. And it stood there blinded by the light.

At last this unknown creature of the abyss blinked its eyes open, and, shading them with its disengaged hand, opened its mouth and gave vent to a shouting noise, articulate almost as speech might be, that penetrated even the steel case and padded jacket of the sphere. How a shouting may be accomplished without lungs Elstead does not profess to explain. It then moved sideways out of the glare into the mystery of shadow that bordered it on either side, and Elstead felt rather than saw that it was coming towards him. Fancying the light had attracted it, he turned the switch that cut off the current. In another moment something soft dabbed upon the steel, and the globe swayed.

Then the shouting was repeated, and it seemed to him that a distant echo answered it. The dabbing recurred, and the globe swayed and ground against the spindle over which the wire was rolled. He stood in the blackness and peered out into the everlasting night of the abyss. And presently he saw, very faint and remote, other phosphorescent quasi-human forms hurrying towards him.

Hardly knowing what he did, he felt about in his swaying prison for the stud of the exterior electric light, and came by accident against his own small glow-lamp in its padded recess. The sphere twisted, and then threw him down; he heard shouts like shouts of surprise, and when he rose to his feet, he saw two pairs of stalked eyes peering into the lower window and reflecting his light.

In another moment hands were dabbing vigorously at his steel casing, and there was a sound, horrible enough in his position, of the metal protection of the clockwork being vigorously hammered. That, indeed, sent his heart into his mouth, for if these strange creatures succeeded in stopping that, his release would never occur. Scarcely had he thought as much when he felt the sphere sway violently, and the floor of it press hard against his feet. He turned off the small glow-lamp that lit the interior, and sent the ray of the large light in the separate compartment out into the water. The sea-floor and the man-like creatures had disappeared, and a couple of fish chasing each other dropped suddenly by the window.

He thought at once that these strange denizens of the deep sea had broken the rope, and that he had escaped. He drove up faster and faster, and then stopped with a jerk that sent him flying against the padded roof of his prison. For half a minute, perhaps, he was too astonished to think.

Then he felt that the sphere was spinning slowly, and rocking, and it seemed to him that it was also being drawn through the water. By crouching close to the window, he managed to make his weight effective and roll that part of the sphere downward, but he could see nothing save the pale ray of his light striking down ineffectively into the darkness. It occurred to him that he would see more if he turned the lamp off, and allowed his eyes to grow accustomed to the profound obscurity.

In this he was wise. After some minutes the velvety blackness became a translucent blackness, and then, far away, and as faint as the zodiacal light of an English summer evening, he saw shapes moving below. He judged these creatures had detached his cable, and were towing him along the sea bottom.

And then he saw something faint and remote across the undulations of the submarine plain, a broad horizon of pale luminosity that extended this way and that way as far as the range of his little window permitted him to see. To this he was being towed, as a balloon might be towed by men out of the open country into a town. He approached it very slowly, and very slowly the dim irradiation was gathered together into more definite shapes.

It was nearly five o'clock before he came over this luminous area, and by that time he could make out an arrangement suggestive of streets and houses grouped about a vast roofless erection that was grotesquely suggestive of a ruined abbey. It was spread out like a map below him. The houses were all roofless enclosures of walls, and their substance being, as he afterwards saw, of phosphorescent bones, gave the place an appearance as if it were built of drowned moonshine.

Among the inner caves of the place waving trees of crinoid stretched their tentacles, and tall, slender, glassy sponges shot like shining minarets and lilies of filmy light out of the general glow of the city. In the open spaces of the place he could see a stirring movement as of crowds of people, but he was too many fathoms above them to distinguish the individuals in those crowds.

Then slowly they pulled him down, and as they did so, the details of the place crept slowly upon his apprehension. He saw that the courses of the cloudy buildings were marked out with beaded lines of round objects, and then he perceived that at several points below him, in broad open spaces, were forms like the encrusted shapes of ships.

Slowly and surely he was drawn down, and the forms below him became brighter, clearer, more distinct. He was being pulled down, he perceived, towards the large building in the centre of the town, and he could catch a glimpse ever and again of the multitudinous forms that were lugging at his cord. He was astonished to see that the rigging of one of the ships, which formed such a prominent feature of the place, was crowded with a host of gesticulating figures regarding him, and then the walls of the great building rose about him silently, and hid the city from his eyes.

And such walls they were, of water-logged wood, and twisted wire-rope, and iron spars, and copper, and the bones and skulls of dead men. The skulls ran in zigzag lines and spirals and fantastic curves over the building; and in and out of their eye-sockets, and over the whole surface of the place, lurked and played a multitude of silvery little fishes.

Suddenly his ears were filled with a low shouting and a noise like the violent blowing of horns, and this gave place to a fantastic chant. Down the sphere sank, past the huge pointed windows, through which he saw vaguely a great number of these strange, ghostlike people regarding him, and at last he came to rest, as it seemed, on a kind of altar that stood in the centre of the place.

And now he was at such a level that he could see these strange people of the abyss plainly once more. To his astonishment, he perceived that they were prostrating themselves before him, all save one, dressed as it seemed in a robe of placoid scales, and crowned with a luminous diadem, who stood with his reptilian mouth opening and shutting, as though he led the chanting of the worshippers.

A curious impulse made Elstead turn on his small globe-lamp again, so that he became visible to these creatures of the abyss, albeit the glare made them disappear forthwith into night. At this sudden sight of him, the chanting gave place to a tumult of exultant shouts; and Elstead, being anxious to watch them, turned his light off again, and vanished from before their eyes. But for a time he was too blind to make out what they were doing, and when at last he could distinguish them, they were kneeling again. And thus they continued worshipping him, without rest or intermission, for a space of three hours.

Most circumstantial was Elstead's account of this astounding city and its people, these people of perpetual night, who have never seen sun or moon or stars, green vegetation, nor any living, air-breathing creatures who know nothing of fire, nor any light but the phosphorescent light of living things.

Startling as is his story, it is yet more startling to find that scientific men, of such eminence as Adams and Jenkins, find nothing incredible in it. They tell me they see no reason why intelligent, water-breathing, vertebrated creatures, inured to a low temperature and enormous pressure, and of such a heavy structure, that neither alive nor dead would they float, might not live upon the bottom of the deep sea, and quite unsuspected by us, descendants like ourselves of the great Theriomorpha of the New Red Sandstone age.

We should be known to them, however, as strange meteoric creatures, wont to fall catastrophically dead out of the mysterious blackness of their watery sky. And not only we ourselves, but our ships, our metals, our appliances, would come raining down out of the night. Sometimes sinking things would smite down and crush them, as if it were the judgment of some unseen power above, and sometimes would come things of the utmost rarity or utility, or shapes of inspiring suggestion. One can understand, perhaps, something of their behaviour at the descent of a living man, if one thinks what a barbaric people might do, to whom an enhaloed, shining creature came suddenly out of the sky.

At one time or another Elstead probably told the officers of the *Ptarmigan* every detail of his strange twelve hours in the abyss. That he also intended to write them down is certain, but he never did, and so unhappily we have to piece together the discrepant fragments of his story from the reminiscences of Commander Simmons, Weybridge, Steevens, Lindley and the others.

We see the thing darkly in fragmentary glimpses—the huge ghostly building, the bowing, chanting people, with their dark chameleon-like heads and faintly luminous clothing, and Elstead, with his light turned on again, vainly trying to convey to their minds that the cord by which the sphere was held was to be severed. Minute after minute slipped away, and Elstead, looking at his watch, was horrified to find that he had oxygen only for four hours more. But the chant in his honour kept on as remorselessly as if it was the marching song of his approaching death.

The manner of his release he does not understand, but to judge by the end of cord that hung from the sphere, it had been cut through by rubbing against the edge of the altar. Abruptly the sphere rolled over, and he swept up, out of their world, as an ethereal creature clothed in a vacuum would sweep through our own atmosphere back to its native ether again. He must have torn out of their sight as a hydrogen bubble hastens upward from our air. A strange ascension it must have seemed to them.

The sphere rushed up with even greater velocity than, when weighted with the lead sinkers, it had rushed down. It became exceedingly hot. It drove up with the windows uppermost, and he remembers the torrent of bubbles frothing against the glass. Every moment he expected this to fly. Then suddenly something like a huge wheel seemed to be released in his head, the padded compartment began spinning about him, and he fainted. His next recollection was of his cabin, and of the doctor's voice.

But that is the substance of the extraordinary story that Elstead related in fragments to the officers of the *Ptarmigan*. He promised to write it all down at a later date. His mind was chiefly occupied with the improvement of his apparatus, which was effected at Rio.

It remains only to tell that on February 2, 1896, he made his second descent into the ocean abyss, with the improvements his first experience suggested. What happened we shall probably never know. He never returned. The *Ptarmigan* beat about over the point of his submersion, seeking him in vain for thirteen days. Then she returned to Rio, and the news was telegraphed to his friends. So the matter remains for the present. But it is hardly probable that no further attempt will be made to verify his strange story of these hitherto unsuspected cities of the deep sea.

THE DERELICT[1]

H. M. Tomlinson

(1873–   )

IN A tramp steamer, which was overloaded, and in midwinter, I had crossed to America for the first time. What we experienced of the western ocean during that passage gave me so much respect for it that the prospect of the return journey, three thousand miles of those seas between me and home, was already the gloom of augury.

---

[1]From *Old Junk*. Reprinted by permission of Jonathan Cape, Ltd.

The shipping posters of New York, showing stately liners too lofty even to notice the Atlantic, were arguments good enough for steerage passengers, who do, I know, reckon a steamer's worth by the number of its funnels; but the pictures did nothing to lessen my regard for that dark outer world I knew. And having no experience of ships installed with racquet courts, Parisian *cafés*, swimming baths, and pergolas, I was naturally puzzled by the inconsequential behaviour of the first-class passengers at the hotel. They were leaving by the liner which was to take me, and, I gathered, were going to cross a bridge to England in the morning. Of course, this might have been merely the innocent profanity of the simple-minded.

Embarking at the quay next day, I could not see that our ship had either a beginning or an end. There was a blank wall which ran out of sight to the right and left. How far it went, and what it enclosed, were beyond me. Hundreds of us in a slow procession mounted stairs to the upper floor of a warehouse, and from thence a bridge led us to a door in the wall half-way in its height. No funnels could be seen. Looking straight up from the embarkation gangway, along what seemed the parapet of the wall was a row of far-off indistinguishable faces peering straight down at us. There was no evidence that this building we were entering, of which the high black wall was a part, was not an important and permanent feature of the city. It was in keeping with the magnitude of New York's skyscrapers, which this planet's occasionally irritable skin permits to stand there to afford man an apparent reason to be gratified with his own capacity and daring.

But with the knowledge that this wall must be afloat there came no sense of security when, going through that little opening in its altitude, I found myself in a spacious decorated interior which hinted nothing of a ship, for I was puzzled as to direction. My last ship could be surveyed in two glances; she looked, and was, a comprehensible ship, no more than a manageable handful for an able master. In that ship you could see at once where you were and what to do. But in this liner you could not see where you were, and would never know which way to take unless you had a good memory. No understanding came to me in that hall of a measured and shapely body, designed with a cunning informed by ages of sea-lore to move buoyantly and surely among the ranging seas, to balance delicately, a quick and sensitive being, to every precarious slope, to recover a lost poise easily and with the grace natural to a quick creature controlled by an alert mind.

There was no shape at all to this structure. I could see no line the run of which gave me warrant that it was comprised in the rondure of a ship. The lines were all of straight corridors, which, for all I knew, might have ended blindly on open space, as streets which traverse a city and are bare in vacancy beyond the dwellings. It was possible we were encompassed by walls, but only one wall was visible. There we idled, all strangers, and to remain strangers, in a large hall roofed by a dome of coloured glass. Quite properly, palms stood beneath. There were offices and doors everywhere. On a broad staircase a multitude of us wandered aimlessly up and down. Each side of the stairway were electric lifts, intermittent and brilliant apparitions. I began to understand why the saloon passengers thought nothing of the voyage. They were encountering nothing unfamiliar. They had but come to another hotel for a few days.

I attempted to find my cabin, but failed. A uniformed guide took care of me. But my cabin, curtained, upholstered, and warm, with mirrors and plated ware, sunk somewhere deeply among carpeted and silent streets down each of which the perspective of glow-lamps looked interminable, left me still questioning. The long walk had given me a fear that I was remote from important affairs which might be happening beyond. My address was 323. The street door—I was down a side turning, though—bore that number. A visitor could make no mistake, supposing he could find the street and my side turning. That was it. There was a very great deal in this place for everybody to remember, and most of us were strangers. No doubt, however, we were afloat, if the lifebelts in the rack meant anything. Yet the cabin, insulated from all noise, was not soothing, but disturbing. I had been used to a ship in which you could guess all that was happening even when in your bunk; a sensitive and communicative ship.

A steward appeared at my door, a stranger out of nowhere, and asked whether I had seen a bag not mine in the cabin. He might have been created merely to put that question, for I never saw him again on the voyage. This liner was a large province having irregular and shifting bounds, permitting incontinent entrance and disappearance. All this should have inspired me with an idea of our vastness and importance, but it did not. I felt I was one of a multitude included in a nebulous mass too vague to hold together unless we were constantly wary.

In the saloon there was the solid furniture of rare woods, the ornate decorations, and the light and shadows making vague its limits and giving it an appearance of immensity, to keep the mind from the thought of our real circumstances. At dinner we had valentine music, dreamy stuff to accord with the shaded lamps which displayed the tables in a lower rosy light. It helped to extend the mysterious and romantic shadows. The pale, disembodied masks of the waiters swam in the dusk above the tinted light. I had for a companion a vivacious American lady from the Middle West, and she looked round that prospect we had of an expensive café, and said, "Well, but I am disappointed. Why, I've been looking forward to seeing the ocean, you know. And it isn't here."

"Smooth passage," remarked a man on the other side. "No sea at all worth mentioning." Actually, I know there was a heavy beam sea running before a half-gale. I could guess the officer in charge somewhere on the exposed roof might have another mind about it; but it made no difference to us in our circle of rosy intimate light bound by those vague shadows which were alive with ready servitude.

"And I've been reading *Captains Courageous* with this voyage in view. Isn't this the month when the forties roar? I want to hear them roar, just once, you know, and as gently as any sucking dove." We all laughed. "We can't even tell we're in a ship."

She began to discuss Kipling's book. "There's some fine seas in that. Have you read it? But I'd like to know where that ocean is he pretends to have seen. I do believe the realists are no more reliable than the romanticists. Here we are a thousand miles out, and none of us have seen the sea yet. Tell me, does not a realist have to magnify his awful billows just to get them into his reader's view?"

I murmured something feeble and sociable. I saw then why sailors never talk directly of the sea. I, for instance, could not find my key at that moment—it was in another pocket somewhere—so I had no iron to touch. Talking largely of the sea is something like the knowing talk of young men about women; and what is a simple sailor man that he should open his mouth on mysteries?

Only on the liner's boat-deck, where you could watch her four funnels against the sky, could you see to what extent the liner was rolling. The arc seemed to be considerable then, but slowly described. But the roll made little difference to the promenaders below. Sometimes they walked a short distance on the edges of their boots, leaning over as they did so, and swerving from the straight, as though they had turned giddy. The shadows formed by the weak sunlight moved slowly out of ambush across the white deck, but often moved indecisively, as though uncertain of a need to go; and then slowly went into hiding again. The sea whirling and leaping past was far below our wall side. It was like peering dizzily over a precipice when watching those green and white cataracts.

The passengers, wrapped and comfortable on the lee deck, chatted as blithely as at a garden-party, while the band played medleys of national airs to suit our varied complexions. The stewards came round with loaded trays. A diminutive and wrinkled dame in costly furs frowned through her golden spectacles at her book, while her maid sat attentively by. An American actress was the centre of an eager group of grinning young men; she was unseen, but her voice was distinct. The two Vanderbilts took their brisk constitutional among us as though the liner had but two real passengers though many invisible nobodies.

The children, who had not ceased laughing and playing since we left New York, waited for the slope of the deck to reach its greatest, and then ran down towards the bulwarks precipitously. The children, happy and innocent, completed for us the feeling of comfortable indifference and security which we found when we saw there was more ship than ocean. The liner's deck canted slowly to leeward, went over more and more, beyond what it had done yet, and a pretty little girl with dark curls riotous from under her red tam-o'-shanter, ran down, and brought up against us violently with both hands, laughing heartily. We laughed too. Looking seawards, I saw receding the broad green hill, snow-capped, which had lifted us and let us down. The sea was getting up.

Near sunset, when the billows were mounting express along our run, sometimes to leap and snatch at our upper structure, and were rocking us with some ease, there was a commotion forward. Books and shawls went anywhere as the passengers ran. Something strange was to be seen upon the waters.

It looked like a big log out there ahead, over the starboard bow. It was not easy to make out. The light was failing. We overhauled it rapidly, and it began to shape as a ship's boat. "Oh, it's gone," exclaimed someone then. But the forlorn object lifted high again, and sank once more. Whenever it was glimpsed it was set in a patch of foam.

That flotsam, whatever it was, was of man. As we watched it intently, and before it was quite plain, we knew intuitively that hope was not there, that we were watching something past its doom. It drew abeam, and we saw what it was, a derelict sailing ship, mastless and awash. The alien wilderness was around us now, and we saw a sky that was overcast and driven, and seas that were uplifted, which had grown incredibly huge, swift, and perilous, and they had colder and more sombre hues.

The derelict was a schooner, a lifeless and soddened hulk, so heavy and uncontesting that its foundering seemed at hand. The waters poured back and forth at her waist, as though holding her body captive for the assaults of the active seas which came over her broken bulwarks, and plunged ruthlessly about.

There was something ironic in the indifference of her defenceless body to these unending attacks. It mocked this white and raging post-mortem brutality, and gave her a dignity that was cold and superior to all the eternal powers could now do. She pitched helplessly head first into a hollow, and a door flew open under the break of her poop; it surprised and shocked us, for the dead might have signed to us then. She went astern of us fast, and a great comber ran at her, as if it had but just spied her, and thought she was escaping. There was a high white flash; we heard that blow. She had gone. But she appeared again far away, forlorn on a summit in desolation, black against the sunset. The stump of her bowsprit, the accusatory finger of the dead, pointed at the sky.

I turned, and there beside me was the lady who had wanted to find the sea. She was gazing at the place where the wreck was last seen, her eyes fixed, her mouth a little open in awe and horror.

·A MEMORY[1]

John Masefield

(1874–   )

IN THESE first frosty days, now that there is mist at dusk into which the sun's red ball drops, one can gather to the fire as soon as the lamps are lit and take the old book from the shelf, the old tune from the fiddle, and the old memory from its cupboard in the brain. Memory is a thing of rags and patches, an odd heap of gear, a bag of orts. It is a record of follies, a jumble of sketch and etching, heaped anyhow, torn, broken, blurred. One can turn it over, and see now a deck scene, with a watch at the halliards, now a woman weeping, now a carthorse tearing down a road, scattering the crowd. That is the common, haphazard, perishing memory, which is what one has to show for the privilege and glory of being man. But among these shadows, these fugitive pictures, these ghosts, there are persistent memories. Besides those angry and wretched faces, and the flaring lights, and terrible suspenses of the common records, there are others. When those pale faces cease to haunt and the sobs of the women leave the heart unwrung for a little, then the grander memory comes flooding in, august, symbolic, like the rising of the full moon; like the coming of the tide out of the hollows of the sea. A scene, an event, some little thing, will take to itself a significant beauty. What did this mean, or this, or this? Was it that common thing, was it what we thought? It was a King passing, it was Life going by, it was life laid bare, the tick of the red heart, the face under the veil, the tune's meaning. We thought that it was this, or this: the woman's hand putting back her hair, the haze lifting from the sea. It was a revelation: it was a miracle; it was a sweeping back of Death to his place in chaos.

Now that these frosty days are on us, and the fires are lit, the memory wakens and quickens. Those recurrent images, having the strength of symbols, rise up within me, suggesting their concealed truth. That single memory, which has haunted me so long, persists. It comes to me day after day, charged with meaning, beautiful and solemn, hinting at secrets. The thing was so beautiful, it could not be a chance, a mere event, finite, a thing of a day. Like all beautiful things, it is a symbol of all beauty, a hand flinging back the window, the touch bringing the grass blade from the seed, the fire destroying Troy. All lovely things have that symbolic power, that key of release. One has but to fill the mind, and to meditate upon a lovely thing, to pass out of this world, where the best is but a shadow, to that other world, the world of beauty, "where the golden blossoms burn upon the trees for ever."

I was at sea in a sailing ship, walking up and down the lee side of the

---

[1] From *A Tarpaulin Muster*. Reprinted by permission of The Richards Press, Ltd.

poop, keeping the time, and striking the bell at each half hour. It was early in the morning watch, a little after four in the morning. We were in the tropics, not very far from the Doldrums, in the last of the Trades. We were sailing slowly, making perhaps some three or four knots an hour under all sail. The dawn was in the sky to leeward of us, full of wonderful colour, full of embers and fire, changing the heaven, smouldering and burning, breaking out into bloody patches, fading into faint gold, into grey, into a darkness like smoke. There was a haze on the sea, very white and light, moving and settling. Dew was dripping from the sails, from the ropes, from the eaves of the charthouse. The decks shone with dew. In the half-light of the dusk, the binnacle lamps burnt pale and strangely. There was a red patch forward, in the water and on the mist, where the sidelight burned. The men were moving to and fro on the deck below me, walking slowly in couples, one of them singing softly, others quietly talking. They had not settled down to sleep since the muster, because they were expecting the morning "coffee," then brewing in the galley. The galley funnel sent trails of sparks over to leeward, and now and then the cook passed to the ship's side to empty ashes into the sea. It was a scene common enough. The same pageant was played before me every other day, whenever I had the morning watch. There was the sunrise and the dewy decks, the sails dripping, and the men shuffling about along the deck. But on this particular day the common scenes and events were charged with meaning as though they were the initiation to a mystery, the music playing before a pageant. It may have been the mist, which made everything unreal and uncertain, especially in the twilight, with the strange glow coming through it from the dawn. I remember that a block made a soft melancholy piping noise in the mizen rigging as though a bird had awakened upon a branch, and the noise, though common enough, made everything beautiful, just as a little touch of colour will set off a sombre picture and give a value to each tint. Then the ball of the sun came out of the sea in a mass of blood and fire, spreading streamers of gold and rose along the edges of the clouds to the mid-heaven. As he climbed from the water, and the last stars paled, the haze lifted and died. Its last shadows moved away from the sea like grey deer going to new pasture, and as they went, the look-out gave a hail of a ship being to windward of us.

When I saw her first there was a smoke of mist about her as high as her foreyard. Her topsails and flying kites had a faint glow upon them where the dawn caught them. Then the mist rolled away from her, so that we could see her hull and the glimmer of the red sidelight as it was hoisted inboard. She was rolling slightly, tracing an arc against the heaven, and as I watched her the glow upon her deepened, till every sail she wore burned rosily like an opal turned to the sun, like a fiery jewel. She was radiant, she was of an immortal beauty, that swaying, delicate clipper. Coming as she came, out of the mist into the dawn, she was like a spirit, like an intellectual presence. Her hull glowed, her rails glowed; there was colour upon the boats and tackling. She was a lofty ship (with skysails and royal staysails), and it was wonderful to watch her, blushing in the sun, swaying and curveting. She was alive with a more than mortal life. One thought that she would speak in some strange language or break out into a music which would express the sea and that great flower in the sky. She came trembling down to us, rising up high and plunging; showing the red lead below her water-line; then diving down till the smother bubbled over her hawseholes. She bowed and curveted; the light caught the skylights on the poop; she gleamed and sparkled; she shook the sea from her as she rose. There was no man aboard of us but was filled with the beauty of that ship. I think they would have cheered her had she been a little nearer to us; but, as it was, we ran up our flags in answer to her, adding our position and comparing our chronometers, then dipping our ensigns and standing away. For some minutes I watched her, as I made up the flags before putting them back in their cupboard. The old mate limped up to me, and spat and swore. "That's one of the beautiful sights of the world," he said. "That, and a cornfield, and a woman with her child. It's beauty and strength. How would you like to have one of them skysails round your neck?" I gave him some answer, and continued to watch her, till the beautiful, precise hull, with all its lovely detail, had become blurred to leeward, where the sun was now marching in triumph, the helm of a golden warrior plumed in cirrus.

DAVY JONES'S GIFT[1]

John Masefield

(1874–   )

ONCE upon a time," said the sailor, "the Devil and Davy Jones came to Cardiff, to the place called Tiger Bay. They put up at Tony Adams's, not far from Pier Head, at the corner of Sunday Lane. And all the time they stayed there they used to be going to the rumshop, where they sat at a table, smoking their cigars, and dicing each other for different persons' souls. Now you must know that the Devil gets landsmen, and Davy Jones gets sailor-folk; and they get tired of having always the same, so then they dice each other for some of another sort.

"One time they were in a place in Mary Street, having some burnt brandy, and playing red and black for the people passing. And while they were looking out on the street and turning the cards, they saw all the people on the sidewalk breaking their necks to get into the gutter. And they saw all the shop-people running out and kowtowing, and all the carts pulling up, and all the police saluting. 'Here comes a big nob,'

---

[1]From A Tarpaulin Muster. Reprinted by permission of The Richards Press, Ltd.

said Davy Jones. 'Yes,' said the Devil; 'it's the Bishop that's stopping with the Mayor.' 'Red or black?' said Davy Jones, picking up a card. 'I don't play for bishops,' said the Devil. 'I respect the cloth,' he said. 'Come on, man,' said Davy Jones. 'I'd give an admiral to have a bishop. Come on, now: make your game. Red or black?' 'Well, I say red,' said the Devil. 'It's the ace of clubs,' said Davy Jones; 'I win; and it's the first bishop ever I had in my life.' The Devil was mighty angry at that—at losing a bishop. 'I'll not play any more,' he said; 'I'm off home. Some people gets too good cards for me. There was some queer shuffling when that pack was cut, that's my belief.'

"'Ah, stay and be friends, man,' said Davy Jones. 'Look at what's coming down the street. I'll give you that for nothing.'

"Now, coming down the street there was a reefer—one of those apprentice fellows. And he was brass-bound fit to play music. He stood about six feet, and there were bright brass buttons down his jacket, and on his collar, and on his sleeves. His cap had a big gold badge, with a house-flag in seven different colours in the middle of it, and a gold chain cable of a chinstay twisted round it. He was wearing his cap on three hairs, and he was walking on both the sidewalks and all the road. His trousers were cut like wind-sails round the ankles. He had a fathom of red silk tie rolling out over his chest. He'd a cigarette in a twisted clay holder a foot and a half long. He was chewing tobacco over his shoulders as he walked. He'd a bottle of rum-hot in one hand, a bag of jam tarts in the other, and his pockets were full of love-letters from every port between Rio and Callao, round by the East.

"'You mean to say you'll give me that?' said the Devil. 'I will,' said Davy Jones, 'and a beauty he is. I never see a finer.' 'He is, indeed, a beauty,' said the Devil. 'I take back what I said about the cards. I'm sorry I spoke crusty. What's the matter with some more burnt brandy?' 'Burnt brandy be it,' said Davy Jones. So then they rang the bell, and ordered a new jug and clean glasses.

"Now the Devil was so proud of what Davy Jones had given him, he couldn't keep away from him. He used to hang about the East Bute Docks, under the red-brick clock-tower, looking at the barque the young man worked aboard. Bill Harker his name was. He was in a West Coast barque. The *Coronel*, loading fuel for Hilo. So at last, when the *Coronel* was sailing, the Devil shipped himself aboard her, as one of the crowd in the fo'c'sle, and away they went down the Channel. At first he was very happy, for Bill Harker was in the same watch, and the two would yarn together. And though he was wise when he shipped, Bill Harker taught him a lot. There was a lot of things Bill Harker knew about. But when they were off the River Plate, they got caught in a pampero, and it blew very hard, and a big green sea began to run. The *Coronel* was a wet ship, and for three days you could stand upon her poop, and look forward and see nothing but a smother of foam from the break of the poop to the jib-

boom. The crew had to roost on the poop. The fo'c'sle was flooded out.
So while they were like this the flying jib worked loose. 'The jib will be
gone in half a tick,' said the mate. 'Out there, one of you, and make it
fast before it blows away.' But the boom was dipping under every minute, and the waist was four feet deep, and green water came aboard all
along her length. So none of the crowd would go forward. Then Bill
Harker shambled out, and away he went forward, with the green seas
smashing over him, and he lay out along the jib-boom, and made the sail
fast, and jolly nearly drowned he was. 'That's a brave lad, that Bill
Harker,' said the Devil. 'Ah, come off,' said the sailors. 'Them reefers,
they haven't got souls to be saved.' It was that that set the Devil thinking.

"By and by they came up with the Horn; and if it had blown off the
Plate, it now blew off the roof. Talk about wind and weather. They got
them both for sure aboard the *Coronel*. And it blew all the sails off her,
and she rolled all her masts out, and the seas made a breach of her bulwarks, and the ice knocked a hole in her bows. So watch and watch they
pumped the old *Coronel*, and the leak gained steadily, and there they
were hove to under a weather cloth, five and a half degrees to the south
of anything. And while they were like this, just about giving up hope,
the old man sent the watch below, and told them they could start prayers. So the Devil crept on to the top of the half-deck, to look through the
scuttle, to see what the reefers were doing, and what kind of prayers Bill
Harker was putting up. And he saw them all sitting round the table, under the lamp, with Bill Harker at the head. And each of them had a hand
of cards, and a length of knotted rope-yarn, and they were playing able-
whackets. Each man in turn put down a card, and swore a new blasphemy, and if his swear didn't come as he played the card, then all the
others hit him with their teasers. But they never once had a chance to
hit Bill Harker. 'I think they were right about his soul,' said the Devil.
And he sighed, like he was sad.

"Shortly after that the *Coronel* went down, and all hands drowned in
her, saving only Bill and the Devil. They came up out of the smothering
green seas, and saw the stars blinking in the sky, and heard the wind
howling like a pack of dogs. They managed to get aboard the *Coronel's*
hen-house, which had come adrift, and floated. The fowls were all
drowned inside, so they lived on drowned hens. As for drink, they had to
do without, for there was none. When they got thirsty they splashed
their faces with salt water; but they were so cold they didn't feel thirst
very bad. They drifted three days and three nights, till their skins were
all cracked and salt-caked. And all the Devil thought of was whether Bill
Harker had a soul. And Bill kept telling the Devil what a thundering big
feed they would have as soon as they fetched to port, and how good a
rum-hot would be, with a lump of sugar and a bit of lemon peel.

"And at last the old hen-house came bump on to Terra del Fuego, and there were some natives cooking rabbits. So the Devil and Bill made a raid of the whole jing bang, and ate till they were tired. Then they had a drink out of a brook, and a warm by the fire, and a pleasant sleep. 'Now,' said the Devil, 'I will see if he's got a soul. I'll see if he gives thanks.' So after an hour or two Bill took a turn up and down and came to the Devil. 'It's mighty dull on this forgotten continent,' he said. 'Have you got a ha'penny?' 'No,' said the Devil. 'What in joy d'ye want with a ha'penny?' 'I might have played you pitch and toss,' said Bill. 'It was better fun on the hen-coop than here.' 'I give you up,' said the Devil; 'you've no more soul than the inner part of an empty barrel. And with that the Devil vanished in a flame of sulphur.

"Bill stretched himself, and put another shrub on the fire. He picked up a few round shells, and began a game of knuckle-bones."

"T' WIND'ARD!"[1]

Captain David Bone

(1874–   )

FOR over a week of strong westerly gales we had kept the open sea, steering to the north as best the wind allowed. A lull had come—a break in the furious succession, though still the sea ran high—and the Old Man, in part satisfied that he had made his northing, put the helm up and squared away for the land. In this he was largely prompted by the coasting pilot (sick of a long unprofitable passage—on a 'lump-sum' basis), who confidently asked to be shown but one speck of Irish land, and, "I'll tell 'oo the road t' Dub-lin, Capt'in!"

Moderately clear at first, but thickening later, as we closed the land, it was not the weather for running in on a dangerous coast, ill-lighted and unmarked, but, had we waited for clear weather, we might have marked time to the westward until the roses came; the wind was fair, we were over-long on our voyage; sheet and brace and wind in squared sail thrummed a homeward song for us as we came in from the west.

At close of a day of keen sailing, the outposts of the Irish coast, bleak, barren, inhospitable, lay under our lee—a few bold rocks, around and above wreathed in sea-mist, and the never-dying Atlantic swell breaking heavily at base.

"Iss, indeed, Capt'in! The Stags! The Stags of Broad-haven I tell 'oo," said the pilot, scanning through his glasses with an easy assurance. "Indeed to goodness, it iss the best landfall I haf ever seen, Capt'in!"

Though pleased with his navigation, the Old Man kept his head. "Aye, aye," he said. "The Stags, eh? Well, we'll haul up t' th' wind anyway— t' make sure!" He gave the order, and went below to his charts.

[1] From *The Brassbounder*. Reprinted by permission of Gerald Duckworth & Co., Ltd.

Rolling heavily, broad to the sea and swell, we lay awhile. There was no sign of the weather clearing, no lift in the grey mist that hung dense over the rugged coast-line. On deck again, the Old Man stared long and earnestly at the rocky islets, seeking a further guidemark. In the waning daylight they were fast losing shape and colour. Only the breaking sea, white and sightly, marked them bold in the grey mist-laden breath of the Atlantic. "'Present themselves, consisting of four high rocky islets of from two thirty-three to three ought-six feet in height, an' steep-to'" he said, reading from a book of sailing directions. "Damme! I can only see three." To the pilot, "D'ye know the Stags well, Mister? Are ye sure of ye're ground?"

"*Wel, wel!* Indeed, Capt'in" (Mr. Williams laughed). "I know the Stags, yess! Ass well ass I know Car-narvon! The Stags of Broad-haven, I tell 'oo. When I wass master of the *Ann Pritchard*, of Beaumaris, it wass always to the West of Ireland we would be goin'. Summer and winter, three years, I tell 'oo, before I came to pilotin', an' there iss not many places between the Hull and Missen Head that I haf nor seen in daylight an' dark. It iss the Stags, indeed! East, south-east now, Capt'in, an' a fine run to Sligo Bar!"

Still unassured, the Old Man turned his glasses on the rocky group. "One—two—three—perhaps that was the fourth just open to the south'-ard"—they certainly tallied with the description in the book—"high, steep-to." A cast of the lead brought no decision. Forty-seven! He might be ten miles north and south by that and former soundings. It was rapidly growing dark, the wind freshening. If he did not set course by the rocks—Stags they seemed to be—he would lose all benefit of landfall—would spend another week or more to the west-ward waiting for a rare slant on this coast of mist and foul weather! Already eighteen days from Falmouth! The chance of running in was tempting! Hesitating, uncertain, he took a step or two up and down the poop, halting at turns to stare anxiously at the rocks, in the wind's eye, at the great Atlantic combers welling up and lifting the barque to leeward at every rise. On the skylight sat Mr Williams, smiling and clucking in his beard that "he did not know the Stags, indeed!"

"We haul off, Pilot," said stout Old Jock, coming at a decision. "If it had been daylight . . . perhaps . . . but I'm for takin' no risks. They may be th' Stags, belike they are, but I'm no' goin' oan in weather like this! We'll stand out t' th' norrard—'mainyards forward, Mister'—till daylight onyway!"

Sulkily we hauled the yards forward and trimmed sail, leaving the rocks to fade under curtain of advancing night, our high hopes of making port dismissed. The "navigators" among us were loud of their growling, as the ship lurched and wallowed in the trough of the sea, the decks waist-high with a wash of icy water—a change from the steadiness and comfort of a running ship.

Night fell black dark. The moon not risen to set a boundary to sea and sky; no play of high light on the waste of heaving water; naught but the long inky ridges, rolling out of the west, that, lifting giddily to crest, sent us reeling into the windless trough. On the poop the Old Man and Pilot tramped fore and aft, talking together of landfalls and coasting affairs. As they came and went, snatches of their talk were borne to us, the watch on deck—sheltering from the weather at the break. The Old Man's "Aye, ayes," and "Goad, man's," and the voluble Welshman's "Iss, indeed, Capt'in," and "I tell 'oo's." The Pilot was laying off a former course of action. "'. . . Mister Williams,' he said, 'I can see that 'oo knows th' coast,' he said, 'an' . . . I 'oodn't go in myself,' he said; 'but if 'oo are sure——'"

"*Brea-kers a-head!*"—a stunning period to his tale, came in a long shout, a scream almost, from the look-out!

Both sprang to the lee rigging, handing their eyes to shield the wind and spray. Faint as yet against the sombre monotone of sea and sky, a long line of breaking water leapt to their gaze, than vanished, as the staggering barque drove to the trough; again—again; there could be no doubt. Breakers! On a lee shore!!

"*Mawdredd an'l!* O Christ! The Stags, Capt'in. . . . My God! My God!" Wholly unmanned, muttering in Welsh and English, Mr Williams ran to the compass to take bearings.

Old Jock came out of the rigging. Then, in a steady voice, more ominous than a string of oaths, "Luff! Down helm m'lad, an' keep her close!" And to the Pilot, "Well? What d'ye make of it, Mister?"

"Stags, Capt'in! *Diwedd i!* That I should be mistake . . . The others . . . God knows! . . . If it iss the Stags, Capt'in . . . the passage t' th' suth'ard . . . I know it . . . we can run . . . if it iss the Stags, Capt'in!"

"An' if it's no' th' Stags! M' Goad! Hoo many Stags d'ye know, Mister? No! No! We'll keep th' sea, if she can weather thae rocks . . . and if she canna!" A mute gesture—then passionately, "T'hell wi' you an' yer b—y Stags: I back ma ship against a worthless pilot! All hands, there, Mister—mains'l an' to'galn's'l oan her! Up, ye hounds; up, if ye look fur dry berryin'!"

All hands! No need for a call! "Breakers ahead"—the words that sent us racing to the yards, to out knife and whip at the gaskets that held our saving power in leash. Quickly done, the great mainsail blew out, thrashing furiously till steadied by tack and sheet. Then topgal'n'sail, the spars buckling to overstrain; staysail, spanker—never was canvas crowded on a ship at such a pace; a mighty fear at our hearts that only frenzied action could allay.

Shuddering, she lay down to it, the lee rail entirely awash, the decks canted at a fearsome angle; then righted—a swift, vicious lurch, and her head sweeping wildly to windward till checked by the heaving helmsman. The wind that we had thought moderate when running before it now held at half a gale. To that she might have stood weatherly, but the great western swell—spawn of uncounted gales—was matched against her, rolling up to check the windward snatches and sending her reeling to leeward in a smother of foam and broken water.

A gallant fight! At the weather gangway stood Old Jock, legs apart and sturdy, talking to his ship.

"Stand, good spars," he would say, casting longing eyes aloft. Or, patting the taffrail with his great sailor hands, "Up tae it, ye bitch! Up!! Up!!!" as, raising her head, streaming in cascade from a sail-pressed plunge, she turned to meet the next great wall of water that set against her. "She'll stand it, Mister," to the Mate at his side. "She'll stand it, an' the head gear holds. If she starts that!"—he turned his palms out— "If she starts th' head gear, Mister!"

"They'll hold, Sir! . . . good gear," answered the Mate, hugging himself at thought of the new landyards, the stout Europe gammon lashings, he had rove off when the boom was rigged. Now was the time when Sanny Armstrong's spars would be put to the test. The relic of the ill-fated *Glenisla* now a shapely to'gallant mast, was bending like a whip! "Good iron," he shouted as the backstays twanged a high note of utmost stress.

Struggling across the heaving deck, the Pilot joined the group. Brokenly, shouting down the wind, "She'll never do it, Capt'in, I tell 'oo! . . . An' th' tide. . . . Try th' south passage . . . Stags, sure! . . . See them fair now! . . . Th' south passage, Capt'in . . . It iss some years, indeed, but . . . I know. *Diwedd an'l!* She'll never weather it, Capt'in!"

"Aye . . . and weather it . . . an' the gear holds! Goad, man! Are ye sailor enough t' know what'll happen if Ah start a brace, wi' this press o' sail oan her? T' wind'ard . . . she goes. Ne'er failed me yet"—a mute caress of the stout taffrail, a slap of his great hand. "Into it, ye bitch! T' wind'ard! T' wind'ard!"

Staggering, taking the shock and onset of the relentless seas, but ever turning the haughty face of her anew to seek the wind, she struggled on, nearing the cruel rocks and their curtain of hurtling breakers. Timely, the moon rose, herself invisible, but shedding a diffused light in the east, showing the high summits of the rocks, upreared above the blinding spindrift. A low moaning boom broke on our strained ears, turning to the hoarse roar of tortured waters as we drew on.

"How does 't bear noo, M'Kellar? Is she makin' oan't?" shouted the Old Man.

The second mate, at the binnacle, sighted across the wildly swinging compass card. "No' sure, Sir. . . . Th' caird swingin' . . . think there's hauf a p'int. . . . Hauf a p'int, onyway!"

"Half a pint!" A great comber upreared and struck a deep resounding blow—"That for yeer half a point"—as her head swung wildly off—off, till the stout spanker, the windward driver, straining at the stern sheets, drove her anew to a seaward course.

Nearer, but a mile off, the rocks plain in a shaft of breaking moonlight. "How now, M'Kellar?"

"Nae change, Sir! . . . 'bout east, nor'-east . . . deefecult . . . the caird swingin'. . . ."

The Old Man left his post and struggled to the binnacle. "East, nor'-east . . . east o' that, mebbe," he muttered. Then to "Dutchy" at the weather helm, "Full, m'lad! Keep 'er full an' nae mair! Goad, man! Steer as ye never steered . . . th' wind's yer mairk. . . . Goad! D'na shake her!

Grasping the binnacle to steady himself against the wild lurches of the staggering hull, the Old Man stared steadily aloft, unheeding the roar and crash of the breakers, now loud over all—eyes only for the straining canvas and standing spars above him.

"She's drawin' ahead, Sir," shouted M'Kellar, tense, excited. "East, b'nor' . . . an' fast!"

The Old Man raised a warning hand to the steersman. "Nae higher! Nae higher! Goad, man! Dinna let 'r gripe!"

Dread suspense! Would she clear? A narrow lane of open water lay clear of the bow—broadening as we sped on.

"Nae higher! Nae higher! Aff! Aff! Up hellum, up!" His voice a scream the Old Man turned to bear a frantic heave on the spokes.

Obedient to the helm and the Mate's ready hand at the driver sheets, she flew off, free of the wind and sea—tearing past the towering rocks, a cable's length to leeward. Shock upon shock, the great Atlantic sea broke and shattered and fell back from the scarred granite face of the outmost Stag; a seething maelstrom of tortured waters, roaring, crashing, shrilling into the deep, jagged fissures—a shriek of Furies bereft. And, high above the tumult of the waters and the loud, glad cries of us, the hoarse, choking voice of the man who had backed his ship.

"Done it, ye bitch!"—and now a trembling hand at his old grey head. "Done it! Weathered—by Goad!"

THE VOYAGE OF THE *JAMES CAIRD*[1]

Sir Ernest Shackleton

(1874–1922)

I DISCUSSED with Wild and Worsley the chances of reaching South Georgia before the winter locked the seas against us. Some effort had to be made to secure relief. Privation and exposure had left their mark on the party, and the health and mental condition of several men were

---

[1]From *South*. Reprinted by permission of William Heinemann, Ltd., and the Macmillan Co.

causing me serious anxiety. Then the food-supply was a vital consideration. We had left ten cases of provisions in the crevice of the rocks at our first camping-place on the island. An examination of our stores showed that we had full rations for the whole party for a period of five weeks. The rations could be spread over three months on a reduced allowance and probably would be supplemented by seals and sea-elephants to some extent. I did not dare to count with full confidence on supplies of meat and blubber, for the animals seemed to have deserted the beach and the winter was near. Our stocks included three seals and two and a half skins (with blubber attached). We were mainly dependent on the blubber for fuel, and, after making a preliminary survey of the situation, I decided that the party must be limited to one hot meal a day.

A boat journey in search of relief was necessary and must not be delayed. That conclusion was forced upon me. The nearest port where assistance could certainly be secured was Port Stanley, in the Falkland Islands, 540 miles away, but we could scarcely hope to beat up against the prevailing north-westerly wind in a frail and weakened boat with a small sail area. South Georgia was over 800 miles away, but lay in the area of the west winds, and I could count upon finding whalers at any of the whaling-stations on the east coast. A boat party might make the voyage and be back with relief within a month, provided that the sea was clear of ice and the boat survive the great seas. It was not difficult to decide that South Georgia must be the objective, and I proceeded to plan ways and means. The hazards of a boat journey across 800 miles of stormy sub-Antarctic ocean were obvious, but I calculated that at worst the venture would add nothing to the risks of the men left on the island. There would be fewer mouths to feed during the winter and the boat would not require to take more than one month's provisions for six men, for if we did not make South Georgia in that time we were sure to go under. A consideration that had weight with me was that there was no chance at all of any search being made for us on Elephant Island.

The case required to be argued in some detail, since all hands knew that the perils of the proposed journey were extreme. The risk was justified solely by our urgent need of assistance. The ocean south of Cape Horn in the middle of May is known to be the most tempestuous storm-swept area of water in the world. The weather then is unsettled, the skies are dull and overcast, and the gales are almost unceasing. We had to face these conditions in a small and weather-beaten boat, already strained by the work of the months that had passed. Worsley and Wild realized that the attempt must be made, and they both asked to be allowed to accompany me on the voyage. I told Wild at once that he would have to stay behind. I relied upon him to hold the party together while I was away, and to make the best of his way to Deception Island with the men in the spring in the event of our failure to bring help. Worsley I would take with me, for I had a very high opinion of his accuracy and quickness as a navigator, and especially in the snapping and working out of positions in difficult circumstances—an opinion that was only enhanced during the actual journey. Four other men would be required and I decided to call for volunteers, although, as a matter of fact, I pretty well knew which of the people I would select. Crean I proposed to leave on the isand as a right-hand man for Wild, but he begged so hard to be allowed to come in the boat that, after consultation with Wild, I promised to take him. I called the men together, explained my plan, and asked for volunteers. Many came forward at once. Some were not fit enough for the work that would have to be done, and others would not have been much use in the boat since they were not seasoned sailors, though the experiences of recent months entitled them to some consideration as seafaring men. I finally selected McNeish, McCarthy, and Vincent in addition to Worsley and Crean. The crew seemed a strong one, and as I looked at the men I felt confidence increasing.

The decision made, I walked through the blizzard with Worsley and Wild to examine the *James Caird*. The 20-ft. boat had never looked big; she appeared to have shrunk in some mysterious way when I viewed her in the light of our new undertaking. She was an ordinary ship's whaler, fairly strong, but showing signs of the strains she had endured since the crushing of the *Endurance*. Where she was holed in leaving the pack was, fortunately, about the water-line and easily patched. Standing beside her, we glanced at the fringe of the storm-swept, tumultuous sea that formed our path. Clearly, our voyage would be a big adventure. I called the carpenter and asked him if he could do anything to make the boat more seaworthy. He first inquired if he was to go with me, and seemed quite pleased when I said "Yes." He was over fifty years of age, and not altogether fit, but he had a good knowledge of sailing boats and was very quick. McCarthy said that he could contrive some sort of covering for the *James Caird* if he might use the lids of the cases and the four sledge-runners that we had lashed inside the boat for use in the event of a landing on Graham Land at Wilhelmina Bay. This bay, at one time the goal of our desire, had been left behind in the course of our drift, but we had retained the runners. The carpenter proposed to complete the covering with some of our canvas, and he set about making his plans at once.

Noon had passed and the gale was more severe than ever. We could not proceed with our preparations that day. The tents were suffering in the wind and the sea was rising. The gale was stronger than ever on the following morning (April 20). No work could be done. Blizzard and snow, snow and blizzard, sudden lulls and fierce returns. During the lulls we could see on the far horizon to the north-east bergs of all shapes and sizes driving along before the gale, and the sinister appearance of the swift-moving masses made us thankful indeed that instead of battling with the storm amid the ice, we were required only to face the drift from the glaciers and the inland heights. The gusts might throw us off our feet, but at least we fell on solid ground and not on rocking floes.

There was a lull in the bad weather on April 21, and the carpenter started to collect material for the decking of the *James Caird*. He fitted the mast of the *Stancomb Wills* fore and aft inside the *James Caird* as a hog-back, and thus strengthened the keel with the object of preventing our boat "hogging"—that is, buckling in heavy seas. He had not sufficient wood to provide a deck, but by using the sledge-runners and box-lids he made a framework extending from the forecastle aft to a well. It was a patched-up affair, but it provided a base for a canvas covering. He had a bolt of canvas frozen stiff, and this material had to be cut and then thawed out over the blubber-stove, foot by foot, in order that it might be sewn into the form of a cover. When it had been nailed and screwed into position it certainly gave an appearance of safety to the boat, though I had an uneasy feeling that it bore a strong likeness to stage scenery, which may look like a granite wall and is in fact nothing better than canvas and lath. As events proved, the covering served its purpose well. We certainly could not have lived through the voyage without it.

Another fierce gale was blowing on April 22, interfering with our preparations for the voyage. We were setting aside stores for the boat journey and choosing the essential equipment from the scanty stock at our disposal. Two ten-gallon casks had to be filled with water melted down from ice collected at the foot of the glacier. This was rather a slow business.

The weather was fine on April 23, and we hurried forward our preparations. It was on this day I decided finally that the crew for the *James Caird* should consist of Worsley, Crean, McNeish, McCarthy, Vincent and myself. A storm came on about noon, with driving snow and heavy squalls. Occasionally the air would clear for a few minutes, and we could see a line of pack-ice, five miles out, driving across from west to east. The sight increased my anxiety to get away quickly. Winter was advancing, and soon the pack might close completely round the island and stay our departure for days, or even weeks.

Worsley, Wild, and I climbed to the summit of the seaward rocks and examined the ice from a better vantage-point than the beach offered. The belt of pack outside appeared to be sufficiently broken for our purposes, and I decided that, unless the conditions forbade it, we would make a start in the *James Caird* on the following morning. Obviously the pack might close at any time. This decision made, I spent the rest of the day looking over the boat, gear, and stores, and discussing plans with Worsley and Wild.

Our last night on the solid ground of Elephant Island was cold and uncomfortable. We turned out at dawn and had breakfast. Then we launched the *Stancomb Wills* and loaded her with stores, gear, and ballast, which would be transferred to the *James Caird* when the heavier boat had been launched. The ballast consisted of bags made from blankets and filled with sand, making a total weight of about 1000 lb. In addition we had gathered a number of round boulders and about 250 lb. of ice, which would supplement our two casks of water.

The swell was slight when the *Stancomb Wills* was launched and the boat got under way without any difficulty; but half an hour later, when we were pulling down the *James Caird*, the swell increased suddenly. Apparently the movement of the ice outside had made an opening and allowed the sea to run in without being blanketed by the line of pack. The swell made things difficult. Many of us got wet to the waist while dragging the boat out—a serious matter in that climate. When the *James Caird* was afloat in the surf she nearly capsized among the rocks before we could get her clear, and Vincent and the carpenter, who were on the deck, were thrown into the water. This was really bad luck for the two men would have small chance of drying their clothes after we had got under way.

The *James Caird* was soon clear of the breakers. We used all the available ropes as a long painter to prevent her drifting away to the north-east, and then the *Stancomb Wills* came alongside, transferred her load, and went back to the shore for more.

By midday the *James Caird* was ready for the voyage. Vincent and the carpenter had secured some dry clothes by exchange with members of the shore party (I heard afterwards that it was a full fortnight before the soaked garments were finally dried), and the boat's crew was standing by waiting for the order to cast off. A moderate westerly breeze was blowing, I went ashore in the *Stancomb Wills* and had a last word with Wild, who was remaining in full command, with directions as to his course of action in the event of our failure to bring relief, but I practically left the whole situation and scope of action and decision to his own judgment, secure in the knowledge that he would act wisely. I told him that I trusted the party to him, and said good-bye to the men. Then we pushed off for the last time, and within a few minutes I was aboard the *James Caird*. The crew of the *Stancomb Wills* shook hands with us as the boats bumped together and offered us the last good wishes. Then, setting our jib, we cut the painter and moved away to the north-east. The men who were staying behind made a pathetic little group on the beach, with the grim heights of the island behind them and the sea seething at their feet, but they waved to us and gave three hearty cheers. There was hope in their hearts and they trusted us to bring the help that they needed.

I had all sails set, and the *James Caird* quickly dipped the beach and its line of dark figures. The westerly wind took us rapidly to the line of pack, and as we entered it I stood up with my arm around the mast, directing the steering, so as to avoid the great lumps of ice that were flung about in the heave of the sea. The pack thickened and we were forced to turn almost due east, running before the wind towards a gap I had seen in the morning from the high ground. I could not see the gap now, but we had come out on its bearing and I was prepared to find that it had been influenced by the easterly drift. At four o'clock in the afternoon we found the channel, much narrower than it had seemed in the morning but still navigable. Dropping sail we rowed through without touching the ice anywhere, and by 5.30 P. M. we were clear of the pack with open water before us. We passed one more piece of ice in the darkness an hour later, but the pack lay behind, and with a fair wind swelling the sails we steered our little craft through the night, our hopes centered on our distant goal. The swell was very heavy now, and when the time came for our first evening meal we found great difficulty in keeping the Primus lamp alight and preventing the hoosh splashing out of the pot. Three men were needed to attend to the cooking, one man holding the lamp and two men guarding the aluminium cooking-pot, which had to be lifted clear of the Primus whenever the movement of the boat threatened to cause a disaster. Then the lamp had to be protected from water, for sprays were coming over the bows and our flimsy decking was by no means water-tight. All these operations were conducted in the confined space under the decking, where the men lay or knelt and adjusted themselves as best they could to the angles of our cases and ballast. It was uncomfortable, but we found consolation in the reflection that without the decking we could not have used the cooker at all.

The tale of the next sixteen days is one of supreme strife amid heaving waters. The sub-Antarctic Ocean lived up to its evil winter reputation. I decided to run north for at least two days while the wind held and so get into warmer weather before turning to the east and laying a course for South Georgia. We took two-hourly spells at the tiller. The men who were not on watch crawled into the sodden sleeping-bags and tried to forget their troubles for a period; but there was no comfort in the boat. The bags and cases seemed to be alive in the unfailing knack of presenting their most uncomfortable angles to our rest-seeking bodies. A man might imagine for a moment that he had found a position of ease, but always discovered quickly that some unyielding point was impinging on muscle or bone. The first night aboard the boat was one of acute discomfort for us all, and we were heartily glad when the dawn came and we could set about the preparation of a hot breakfast.

By running north for the first two days I hoped to get warmer weather and also to avoid lines of pack that might be extending beyond the main body. We needed all the advantage that we could obtain from the higher latitude for sailing on the great circle, but we had to be cautious regarding possible ice streams. Cramped in our narrow quarters and continually wet by the spray, we suffered severely from cold throughout the journey. We fought the seas and the winds, and at the same time, had a daily struggle to keep ourselves alive. At times we were in dire peril. Generally we were upheld by the knowledge that we were making progress towards the land where we would be, but there were days and nights when we lay hove to, drifting across the storm-whitened seas and watching, with eyes interested rather than apprehensive, the uprearing masses of water, flung to and fro by Nature in the pride of her strength. Deep seemed the valleys when we lay between the reeling seas. High were the hills when we perched momentarily on the tops of giant combers. Nearly always there were gales. So small was our boat and so great were the seas that often our sail flapped idly in the calm between the crests of two waves. Then we would climb the next slope and catch the full fury of the gale where the wool-like whiteness of the breaking water surged around us.

The wind came up strong and worked into a gale from the north-west on the third day out. We stood away to the east. The increasing seas discovered the weakness of our decking. The continuous blows shifted the box-lids and sledge-runners so that the canvas sagged down and accumulated water. Then icy trickles, distinct from the driving sprays, poured fore and aft into the boat. The nails that the carpenter had extracted from cases at Elephant Island and used to fasten down the battens were too short to make firm the decking. We did what we could to secure it, but our means were very limited, and the water continued to enter the boat at a dozen points. Much bailing was necessary, and nothing that we could do prevented our gear from becoming sodden. The searching runnels from the canvas were really more unpleasant than the sudden definite douches of the sprays. Lying under the thwarts during watches below, we tried vainly to avoid them. There were no dry places in the boat, and at last we simply covered our heads with our Burberrys and endured the all-pervading water. The bailing was work for the watch. Real rest we had none. The perpetual motion of the boat made repose impossible; we were cold, sore, and anxious. We moved on hands and knees in the semi-darkness of the day under the decking. The darkness was complete by 6 P. M., and not until 7 A. M. of the following day could we see one another under the thwarts. We had a few scraps of candle, and they were preserved carefully in order that we might have light at meal-times. There was one fairly dry spot in the boat, under the solid original decking at the bows, and we managed to protect some of our biscuit from the saltwater; but I do not think any of us got the taste of salt out of our mouths during the voyage.

The difficulty of movement in the boat would have had its humorous side if it had not involved us in so many aches and pains. We had to crawl under the thwarts in order to move along the boat, and our knees suffered considerably. When a watch turned out it was necessary for me to direct each man by name when and where to move, since if all hands had crawled about at the same time the result would have been dire confusion and many bruises. Then there was the trim of the boat to be considered.

The order of the watch was four hours on and four hours off, three men to the watch. One man had the tiller-ropes, the second man attended to the sail, and the third bailed for all he was worth. Sometimes when the water in the boat had been reduced to reasonable proportions, our pump could be used. This pump, which Hurley had made from the Flinders bar case of our ship's standard compass, was quite effective, though its capacity was not large. The man who was attending to the sail could pump into the big outer cooker, which was lifted and emptied overboard when filled. We had a device by which the water could go direct from the pump into the sea through a hole in the gunwale, but this hole had to be blocked at an early stage of the voyage, since we found that it admitted water when the boat rolled.

While a new watch was shivering in the wind and spray, the men who had been relieved groped hurriedly among the soaked sleeping-bags and tried to steal a little of the warmth created by the last occupants; but it was not always possible for us to find even this comfort when we went off watch. The boulders that we had taken aboard for ballast had to be shifted continually in order to trim the boat and give access to the pump, which became choked with hairs from the moulting sleeping-bags and finneskoe. The four reindeer-skin sleeping-bags shed their hair freely owing to the continuous wetting, and soon became quite bald in appearance. The moving of the boulders was very weary and painful work. We came to know every one of the stones by sight and touch, and I have vivid memories of their angular peculiarities even to-day. They might have been of considerable interest as geological specimens to a scientific man under happier conditions. As ballast they were useful. As weights to be moved about in cramped quarters they were simply appalling. They spare no portion of our poor bodies.

Our meals were regular in spite of the gales. Breakfast, at 8 A. M., consisted of a pannikin of hot hoosh made from Bovril sledging ration, two biscuits, and some lumps of sugar. Lunch came at 1 P. M., and comprised Bovril sledging ration, eaten raw, and a pannikin of hot milk for each man. Tea, at 5 P. M., had the same menu. Then during the night we had a hot drink, generally of milk. The meals were the bright beacons in those cold and stormy days. The glow of warmth and comfort produced by the food and drink made optimists of us all.

A severe south-westerly gale on the fourth day out forced us to heave to. I would have liked to have run before the wind, but the sea was very high and the *James Caird* was in danger of broaching to and swamping. The delay was vexatious, since up to that time we had been making sixty or seventy miles a day; good going with our limited sail area. We hove to under double-reefed mainsail and our little jigger, and waited for the gale to blow itself out. During that afternoon we saw bits of wreckage, the remains probably of some unfortunate vessel that had failed to weather the strong gales south of Cape Horn. The weather conditions did not improve, and on the fifth day out the gale was so fierce that we were compelled to take in the double-reefed mainsail and hoist our small jib instead. We put out a sea-anchor to keep the *James Caird's* head up to the sea. This anchor consisted of a triangular canvas bag fastened to the end of the painter and allowed to stream out from the bows. The boat was high enough to catch the wind, and as she drifted to leeward the drag of the anchor kept her head to windward. Thus our boat took most of the seas more or less end on. Even then the crests of the waves often would curl right over us and we shipped a great deal of water, which necessitated unceasing baling and pumping. Looking out abeam, we would see a hollow like a tunnel formed as the crest of a big wave toppled over on to the swelling body of water. A thousand times it appeared as though the *James Caird* must be engulfed; but the boat lived. The south-westerly gale had its birthplace above the Antarctic Continent and its freezing breath lowered the temperature far towards zero. The sprays froze upon the boat, and gave bows, sides, and decking a heavy coat of mail. This accumulation of ice reduced the buoyancy of the boat, and to that extent was an added peril; but it possessed a notable advantage from one point of view. The water ceased to drop and trickle from the canvas, and the spray came in solely at the well in the after part of the boat. We could not allow the load of ice to grow beyond a certain point, and in turns we crawled about the decking forward, chipping and picking at it with the available tools.

When daylight came on the morning of the sixth day out, we saw and felt that the *James Caird* had lost her resiliency. She was not rising to the oncoming seas. The weight of the ice that had formed in her and upon her during the night was having its effect, and she was becoming more like a log than a boat. The situation called for immediate action. We first broke away the spare oars, which were encased in ice and frozen to the sides of the boat, and threw them overboard. We retained two oars for use when we got inshore. Two of the fur sleeping-bags went over the side; they were thoroughly wet, weighing probably 40 lb. each, and they had frozen stiff during the night. Three men constituted the watch below, and when a man went down it was better to turn into the wet bag just vacated by another man than to thaw out a frozen bag with the heat of his unfortunate body. We now had four bags, three in use, and one for emergency use in case a member of the party should break down permanently. The reduction of weight relieved the boat to some extent, and vigorous chipping and scraping did more. We had to be very careful not to put axe or knife through the frozen canvas of the decking as we crawled over it, but gradually we got rid of a lot of ice. The *James Caird* lifted to the endless waves as though she lived again.

About 11 A. M. the boat suddenly fell off into the trough of the sea. The painter had parted and the sea-anchor had gone. This was serious. The *James Caird* went away to leeward, and we had no chance at all of recovering the anchor and our valuable rope, which had been our only means of keeping the boat's head up to the seas without the risk of hoisting sail in a gale. Now we had to set the sail and trust to its holding. While the *James Caird* rolled heavily in the trough, we beat the frozen canvas until the bulk of the ice had cracked off it, and then hoisted it. The frozen gear worked protestingly, but after a struggle our little craft came up to the wind again, and we breathed more freely.

We held the boat up to the gale during that day, enduring as best we could discomforts that amounted to pain. The boat tossed interminably on the big waves under grey, threatening skies. Our thoughts did not embrace much more than the necessities of the hour. Every surge of the sea was an enemy to be watched and circumvented. We ate our scanty meals, treated our frost-bites, and hoped for the improved conditions that the morrow might bring. Night fell early, and in the lagging hours of darkness we were cheered by a change for the better in the weather. The wind dropped, the snow-squalls became less frequent, and the sea moderated. When the morning of the seventh day dawned, there was not much wind. We shook the reef out of the sail and laid our course once more for South Georgia. The sun came out bright and clear, and presently Worsley got a snap for longitude. We hoped that the sky would remain clear until noon, so that we could get the latitude. We had been six days out without an observation, and our dead reckoning naturally was uncertain. The boat must have presented a strange appearance that morning. All hands basked in the sun. We hung our sleeping-bags to the mast and spread our socks and other gear all over the deck. Some of the ice had melted off the *James Caird* in the early morning after the gale began to slacken, and dry patches were appearing in the decking. Porpoises came blowing round the boat, and Cape pigeons wheeled and swooped within a few feet of us. These little black-and-white birds have an air of friendliness that is not possessed by the great circling albatross. They had looked grey against the swaying sea during the storm as they darted about over our heads and uttered their plaintive cries. The albatrosses, of the black or sooty variety, had watched with hard, bright eyes, and seemed to have a quite impersonal interest in our struggle to keep afloat amid the battering seas. In addition to the Cape pigeons an occasional stormy petrel flashed overhead. Then there was a small bird, unknown to me, that appeared always to be in a fussy, bustling state, quite out of keeping with the surroundings. It irritated me. It had practically no tail, and it flitted about vaguely as though in search of the lost member. I used to find myself wishing it would find its tail and have done with the silly fluttering.

We revelled in the warmth of the sun that day. Life was not so bad, after all. We felt we were well on our way. Our gear was drying, and we could have a hot meal in comparative comfort. The swell was still heavy, but it was not breaking and the boat rode easily. At noon Worsley balanced himself on the gunwale and clung with one hand to the stay of the mainmast while he got a snap of the sun. The result was more than encouraging. We had done over 380 miles and were getting on for half-way to South Georgia. It looked as though we were going to get through.

The wind freshened to a good stiff breeze during the afternoon, and the *James Caird* made satisfactory progress. I had not realized until the sunlight came how small our boat really was. There was some influence in the light and warmth, some hint of happier days, that made us revive memories of other voyages, when we had stout decks beneath our feet, unlimited food at our command, and pleasant cabins for our ease. Now we clung to a battered little boat, "alone, alone, all, all alone, alone on a wide, wide, sea." So low in the water were we that each succeeding swell cut off our view of the sky-line. We were a tiny speck in the vast vista of the sea—the ocean that is open to all, and merciful to none, that threatens even when it seems to yield, and that is pitiless always to weakness. For a moment the consciousness of the forces arrayed against us would be almost overwhelming. Then hope and confidence would rise again as our boat rose to a wave and tossed aside the crest in a sparkling shower like the play of prismatic colours at the foot of a waterfall. My double-barrelled gun and some cartridges had been stowed aboard the boat as an emergency precaution against a shortage of food, but we were not disposed to destroy our little neighbours, the Cape pigeons, even for the sake of fresh meat. We might have shot an albatross, but the wandering king of the ocean aroused in us something of the feeling that inspired, too late, the Ancient Mariner. So the gun remained among the stores and sleeping-bags in the narrow quarters beneath our leaking deck, and the birds followed us unmolested.

The eighth, ninth, and tenth days of the voyage had few features worthy of special note. The wind blew hard during those days, and the strain of navigating the boat was unceasing, but always we made some advance towards our goal. No bergs showed on our horizon, and we knew that we were clear of the ice-fields. Each day brought its little round of troubles, but also compensation in the form of food and growing hope. We felt that we were going to succeed. The odds against us had been great, but we were winning through. We still suffered severely from the cold, for, though the temperature was rising, our vitality was declining owing to shortage of food, exposure, and the necessity of maintaining our cramped positions day and night. I found that it was now absolutely necessary to prepare hot milk for all hands during the night, in order to sustain life till dawn. This meant lighting the Primus lamp in the darkness and involved an increased drain on our small store of matches. It was the rule that one match must serve when the Primus was being lit. We had no lamp for the compass, and during the early days of the voyage we would strike a match when the steersman wanted to see the course at night; but later the necessity for strict economy impressed itself upon us, and the practice of striking matches at night was stopped. We had one water-tight tin of matches. I had stowed away in a pocket, in readiness for a sunny day, a lens from one of the telescopes, but this was of no use during the voyage. The sun seldom shone upon us. The glass of the compass got broken one night, and we contrived to mend it with adhesive tape from the medicine-chest. One of the memories that comes to me from those days is of Crean singing at the tiller. He always sang while he was steering, and nobody ever discovered what the song was. It was devoid of tune and as monotonous as the chanting of a Buddhist monk at his prayers; yet somehow it was cheerful. In moments of inspiration Crean would attempt "The Wearing of the Green."

On the tenth night Worsley could not straighten his body after his spell at the tiller. He was thoroughly cramped, and we had to drag him beneath the decking and massage him before he could unbend himself and get into a sleeping-bag. A hard north-westerly gale came up on the eleventh day (May 5) and shifted to the south-west in the late afternoon. The sky was overcast and occasional snow squalls added to the discomfort produced by a tremendous cross-sea—the worst, I thought, that we had experienced. At midnight I was at the tiller and suddenly noticed a line of clear sky between the south and south-west. I called to the other men that the sky was clearing, and then a moment later I realized that what I had seen was not a rift in the clouds but the white crest of an enormous wave. During twenty-six years' experience of the ocean in all its moods I had not encountered a wave so gigantic. It was a mighty upheaval of the ocean, a thing quite apart from the big white-capped seas that had been our tireless enemies for many days. I shouted, "For God's sake, hold on! It's got us!" Then came a moment of suspense that seemed drawn out into hours. White surged the foam of the breaking sea around us. We felt our boat lifted and flung forward like a cork in breaking surf. We were in a seething chaos of tortured water; but somehow the boat lived through it, half-full of water, sagging to the dead weight and shuddering under the blow. We bailed with the energy of men fighting for life, flinging the water over the sides with every receptacle that came to our hands, and after ten minutes of uncertainty we felt the boat renew her life beneath us. She floated again and ceased to lurch drunkenly as though dazed by the attack of the sea. Earnestly we hoped that never again would we encounter such a wave.

The conditions in the boat, uncomfortable before, had been made worse by the deluge of water. All our gear was thoroughly wet again. Our cooking-stove had been floating about in the bottom of the boat, and portions of our last hoosh seemed to have permeated everything. Not until 3 A. M., when we were all chilled almost to the limit of endurance, did we manage to get the stove alight and make ourselves hot drinks. The carpenter was suffering particularly, but he showed grit and spirit. Vincent had for the past week ceased to be an active member of the crew, and I could not easily account for his collapse. Physically he was one of the strongest men in the boat. He was a young man, he had served on North Sea trawlers, and he should have been able to bear hardships better than McCarthy, who, not so strong, was always happy.

The weather was better on the following day (May 6), and we got a glimpse of the sun. Worsley's observation showed that we were not more than a hundred miles from the north-west corner of South Georgia. Two more days with a favourable wind and we would sight the promised land. I hoped that there would be no delay, for our supply of water was running very low. The hot drink at night was essential, but I decided that the daily allowance of water must be cut down to half a pint per man. The lumps of ice we had taken aboard had gone long ago. We were dependent upon the water we had brought from Elephant Island, and our thirst was increased by the fact that we were now using the brackish water in the breaker that had been slightly stove in in the surf when the boat was being loaded. Some sea-water had entered at that time.

Thirst took possession of us. I dared not permit the allowance of water to be increased since an unfavourable wind might drive us away from the island and lengthen our voyage by many days. Lack of water is always the most severe privation that men can be condemned to endure, and we found, as during our earlier boat voyage, that the salt water in our clothing and the salt spray that lashed our faces made our thirst grow quickly to a burning pain. I had to be very firm in refusing to allow anyone to anticipate the morrow's allowance, which I was sometimes begged to do. We did the necessary work dully and hoped for the land. I had altered the course to the east so as to make sure of our striking the island, which would have been impossible to regain if we had run past the northern end. The course was laid on our scrap of chart for a point some thirty miles down the coast. That day and the following day passed for us in a sort of nightmare. Our mouths were dry and our tongues were swollen. The wind was still strong and the heavy sea forced us to navigate carefully, but any thought of our peril from the waves was buried beneath the consciousness of our raging thirst. The bright moments were those when we each received our one mug of hot milk during the long, bitter watches of the night. Things were bad for us in those days, but the end was coming. The morning of May 8 broke thick and stormy, with squalls from the north-west. We searched the waters ahead for a sign of land, and though we could see nothing more than had met our eyes for many days, we were cheered by a sense that the goal was near at hand. About ten o'clock that morning we passed a little bit of kelp, a glad signal of the proximity of land. An hour later we saw two shags sitting on a big mass of kelp, and knew then that we must be within ten or fifteen miles of the shore. These birds are as sure an indication of the proximity of land as a lighthouse is, for they never venture far to sea. We gazed ahead with increasing eagerness, and at 12.30 P. M., through a rift in the clouds, McCarthy caught a glimpse of the black cliffs of South Georgia, just fourteen days after our departure from Elephant Island. It was a glad moment. Thirst-ridden, chilled, and weak as we were, happiness irradiated us. The job was nearly done.

We stood in towards the shore to look for a landing-place, and presently we could see the green tussock-grass on the ledges above the surf-beaten rocks. Ahead of us and to the south, blind rollers showed the presence of uncharted reefs along the coast. Here and there the hungry rocks were close to the surface, and over them the great waves broke, swirling viciously and spouting thirty and forty feet into the air. The rocky coast appeared to descend sheer to the sea. Our need of water and rest was wellnigh desperate, but to have attempted a landing at that time would have been suicidal. Night was drawing near, and the weather indications were not favourable. There was nothing for it but to haul off till the following morning, so we stood away on the starboard tack until we had made what appeared to be a safe offing. Then we hove to in the high westerly swell. The hours passed slowly as we waited the dawn, which would herald, we fondly hoped, the last stage of our journey. Our thirst was a torment and we could scarcely touch our food; the cold seemed to strike right through our weakened bodies. At 5 A. M. the wind shifted to the north-west and quickly increased to one of the worst hurricanes any of us had ever experienced. A great cross-sea was running, and the wind simply shrieked as it tore the tops off the waves and converted the whole seascape into a haze of driving spray. Down into valleys, up to tossing heights, straining until her seams opened, swung our little boat, brave still but labouring heavily. We knew that the wind and set of the sea was driving us ashore, but we could do nothing. The dawn showed us a storm-torn ocean, and the morning passed without bringing us a sight of the land; but at 1 P. M., through a rift in the flying mists, we got a glimpse of the huge crags of the island and realized that our position had become desperate. We were on a dead lee shore, and we could gauge our approach to the unseen cliffs by the roar of the breakers against the sheer walls of rock. I ordered the double-reefed mainsail to be set in the hope that we might claw off, and this attempt increased the strain upon the boat. The *James Caird* was bumping heavily, and the water was pouring in everywhere. Our thirst was forgotten in the realization of our imminent danger, as we bailed unceasingly, and adjusted our weights from time to time; occasional glimpses showed that the shore was nearer. I knew that Annewkow Island lay to the south of us, but our small and badly marked chart showed uncertain reefs in the passage between the island and the mainland, and I dared not trust it, though as a last resort we could try to lie under the lee of the island. The afternoon wore away as we edged down the coast, with the thunder of the breakers in our ears. The approach of evening found us still some distance from Annewkow Island, and, dimly in the twilight, we could see a snow-capped mountain looming above us. The chance of surviving the night, with the driving gale and the implacable sea forcing us on to the lee shore, seemed small. I think most of us had a feeling that the end was very near. Just after 6 P. M., in the dark, as the boat was in the yeasty backwash from the seas flung from this iron-bound coast, then, just when things looked their worst, they changed for the best. I have marvelled often at the thin line that divides success from failure and the sudden turn that leads from apparently certain disaster to comparative safety. The wind suddenly shifted, and we were free once more to make an offing. Almost as soon as the gale eased, the pin that locked the mast to the thwart fell out. It must have been on the point of doing this throughout the hurricane, and if it had gone nothing could have saved us; the mast would have snapped like a carrot. Our backstays had carried away once before when iced up, and were not too strongly fastened now. We were thankful indeed for the mercy that had held that pin in its place throughout the hurricane.

We stood off shore again, tired almost to the point of apathy. Our water had long been finished. The last was about a pint of hairy liquid, which we strained through a bit of gauze from the medicine chest. The pangs of thirst attacked us with redoubled intensity, and I felt that we must make a landing on the following day at almost any hazard. The night wore on. We were very tired. We longed for day. When at last the dawn came on the morning of May 10 there was practically no wind, but a high cross-sea was running. We made slow progress towards the shore. About 8 A. M. the wind backed to the northwest and threatened another blow. We had sighted in the meantime a big indentation which I thought must be King Haakon Bay, and I decided that we must land there. We set the bows of the boat towards the bay and ran before the freshening gale. Soon we had angry reefs on either side. Great glaciers came down to the sea and offered no landing-place. The sea spouted on the reefs and thundered against the shore. About noon we sighted a line of jagged reef, like blackened teeth, that seemed to bar the entrance to the bay. Inside, comparatively smooth water stretched eight or nine miles to the head of the bay. A gap in the reef appeared, and we made for it. But the fates had another rebuff for us. The wind shifted and blew from the east right out of the bay. We could see the way through the reef, but we could not approach it directly. That afternoon we bore up, tacking five times in the strong wind. The last tack enabled us to get through, and at last we were in the wide mouth of the bay. Dusk was approaching. A small cove, with a boulder-strewn beach guarded by a reef, made a break in the cliffs on the south side of the bay, and we turned in that direction. I stood in the bows directing the steering as we ran through the kelp and made the passage of the reef. The entrance was so narrow that we had to take in the oars, and the swell was piling itself right over the reef into the cove; but in a minute or two we were inside, and in the gathering darkness the *James Caird* ran in on a swell and touched the beach. I sprang ashore with the short painter and held on when the boat went out with the backward surge. When the *James Caird* came in again, three of the men got ashore, and they held the painter while I climbed some rocks with another line. A slip on the wet rocks twenty feet up nearly closed my part of the story just at the moment when we were achieving safety. A jagged piece of rock held me and at the same time bruised me sorely. However, I made fast the line, and in a few minutes we were all safe on the beach with the boat floating in the surging water just off the shore. We heard a gurgling sound that was sweet music in our ears, and, peering around, found a stream of fresh water almost at our feet. A moment later we were down on our knees drinking the pure ice-cold water in long draughts that put new life into us.

HOW THE *CUTTY SARK* RACED THE *THERMOPYLÆ*[1]

Basil Lubbock

(1876–   )

A GREAT duel was arranged in 1872 between *Cutty Sark* and *Thermopylæ*. Both vessels left Shanghai on the same day and within an hour or two of each other. They were, however, some time in getting clear away owing to fresh gales and thick fogs in which it was impossible to proceed, and *Cutty Sark* did not drop her pilot until 21st June.

They were then held up by calms and fogs until 2 A. M. on the 23rd, when the N. E. monsoon began to blow strong and soon freshened to a gale, which split the *Cutty Sark's* fore top-gallant sail to pieces.

The monsoon held until the 26th when at 1 A. M., in lat. 20° 27′ N., long. 114° 43′ E., the two racers were in sight of each other, *Cutty Sark* being in the lead.

On the 28th June they were again together, this time with *Thermopylæ* 6 miles to windward of her opponent, the wind being fresh from the S. W. with heavy squalls, but did not meet again until approaching Gaspar Straits. The weather continued boisterous until the 1st July, up to which date *Cutty Sark* had only had one observation since leaving port.

On the Cochin China Coast the usual land and sea breezes were worked but crossing to the Natunas fresh gales and squalls and split sails were the experience of both clippers.

On 15th July in 108° 18′ E. on the equator, *Thermopylæ* sighted *Cutty Sark* about eight miles ahead, but gradually fell astern, and on the following morning *Cutty Sark* could only just be seen from the fore topsail

[1]From *The China Clippers*. Reprinted by permission of the author.

yard bearing S. E. At 10 A. M. on 17th July *Cutty Sark* led *Thermopylæ* through Stolzes Channel, but on the 18th some unfriendly waterspouts compelled the former to bear up out of her course and take in sail and this let *Thermopylæ* up. At 6 A. M. on the 19th both ships arrived off Anjer, *Thermopylæ* now having a lead of 1½ miles. Here *Cutty Sark* was hove to for a couple of hours whilst Captain Moodie went ashore with letters. At noon on the 20th, *Thermopylæ* was three miles W. by S. of *Cutty Sark*, both vessels being hung up by calms and baffling airs. And it was not until the 26th, with Keeling Cocos Island in sight to the nor'rard, that there was any strength in the S. E. trade; from this point, however, the wind came fresh from the E. S. E. and stunsail booms began to crack like carrots.

This was the sort of weather that *Cutty Sark* revelled in, and she went flying to the front with three consecutive runs of 340, 327 and 320 miles. She carried the trades until 7th August, when at 1 P. M. the wind suddenly took off as if cut by a knife, and remained calm and baffling until the 9th when it commenced to breeze up rapidly from the S. W.

The 11th August found *Cutty Sark* battling with a strong westerly gale, but with a good lead of *Thermopylæ*. From this date, however, the weather fought for the latter, and the following quotations from Captain Moodie's private log will show the bad luck which attended *Cutty Sark* in losing her rudder.

August 13. Lat. 34° 3′ S., long. 28° 7′ E. Distance 83 miles. Strong gale from N. E. At 5 A. M. the wind hauled to west. Rest of day blowing a very heavy gale. Fore and main lower topsails went to pieces.

August 14. Lat. 34° 6′ S., long. 28° 7′ E. Heavy gale from W. with severe squalls and tremendous sea.

August 15. Lat. 34° 26′ S. long. 28° 1′ E. At 6.30 A. M. a heavy sea struck the rudder and carried it away from the trunk downwards. Noon, wind more moderate, tried a spar over the stern but would not steer the ship. Thereupon began construction of a jury rudder, with a spare spar 70 feet long.

August 16. 34° 13′ S., 28° 24′ E. Light winds from south. P. M. strong breezes from E. N. E. Constructing jury rudder and sternpost as fast as possible.

August 17. 34° 43′ S. 28° 25′ E. Strong winds from east to E. S. E. Constructing jury rudder and sternpost.

August 18. 34° 58′ S., 28° 11′ E. Strong winds from E. N. E. Constructing jury rudder and sternpost.

August 19. 34° 51′ S., 27° 58′ E. Strong winds from N. E. Constructing jury rudder and sternpost.

August 19. 34° 51′ S. 27° 58′ E. Strong winds from N. E. Constructing jury rudder and sternpost.

August 20. 34° 38′ S., 27° 36′ E. Light wind from westward. Noon, strong westerly breeze and clear. About 2 P. M. shipped jury rudder and sternpost, a difficult job as there was a good deal of sea on. [It will be noticed that whilst *Cutty Sark* lay hove to, with her crew working night and day on the jury rudder, fine fair winds, which carried *Thermopylæ* round the Cape, were blowing, but no sooner was the rudder ready for shipping into place than the wind chopped round into the west and began to blow up for a further series of head gales.]

August 21. 34° 19′ S. 26° 58′ E. Distance 36 miles. Strong westerly gale.

August 23. 35° 49′ S., 20° 58′ E. Distance 194 miles. Stiff breeze from south to E. N. E. and sharp head sea. Midnight, wind hauled to N. W. Rounded Cape Agulhas. [On this day *Thermopylæ* was in 31° 43′ S., 13° E., 490 miles ahead.]

Cutty Sark next had a succession of heavy head gales, which did not let up until the 31st, and sorely tested the capabilities of the jury rudder. The awning stanchions which connected the steering chains to the back of the rudder were carried away, and several of the eye-bolts which held the rudder to the post were broken, but they managed to steer with two wire rope pennants shackled to an eye-bolt placed in the back of the rudder in case of accident to the chains.

The jury rudder, however, carried *Cutty Sark* to 7° 28′ N., 20° 37′ W., without further accident. The ship was found to steer very well with the wind right aft, but with strong beam winds and when going anything over 10 knots the rudder was not nearly so efficient, and it was often necessary to reduce sail to keep the ship down to about eight knots.

On 1st September in 30° 44′ S., 12° 24′ E., the succession of fierce northerly gales at last grew tired of buffeting the lame duck and the normal weather for running down to St Helena set in. The island was passed at 9 A. M. on 9th September, and on the 15th *Cutty Sark* crossed the line. Her best runs between 1st September and this date were 210, 211, 214, 226, 227, 221, and 207, pretty good work for a ship which was not allowed to do more than eight knots.

All this time, however, the jury rudder was gradually breaking its fastenings and on the 20th September the last of the eye-bolts holding the rudder to the post gave way and the whole contrivance had to be hoisted up for repairs. Captain Moodie was now so short of material that he had to shape flat pieces of iron so that they would work on the iron stanchions instead of the eye-bolts. The repairs were smartly done and on the following day the jury rudder was once more ready for lowering. On the first occasion a kedge anchor of 5½ cwt. had been used to sink it into place, but owing to the bad sea running this had been lost. On 21st September Moodie determined to fix the post and rudder in place without using any weight to sink it. When all was ready the sails were filled and the ship given a little headway, the rudder and post were then lowered and streamed right astern, the rudder was then hauled close to the trunk and the sails laid back. As the ship lost headway the weight of the chains partially sank the rudder, then as the ship slowly gathered sternway and the slack of the guys was hauled in, the heel of the rudder sank and allowed the head to be easily hauled up through the trunk. This operation is very easy to write about, but in its proper execution it required such seamanship as is hardly known nowadays.

Cutty Sark had fine strong N. E. trades to within a day of the Western Islands, but, unfortunately, had to be kept down to a speed of 200 miles a day, as beyond that her jury rudder could not control her.

On the last lap of the passage she unfortunately met with strong winds and gales from the nor'rard and eastward, and on 12th October, the day that *Thermopylæ* arrived in the Downs, she was battling against a fresh N. N. E., gale in 45° 37′ N., 13° 26′ W. This gale lasted until *Cutty Sark* also reached the Downs on 18th October, less than a week behind her rival, for which fine performance Captain Moodie received great praise in shipping circles. Indeed, though *Thermopylæ* arrived first, all the honours of the race belonged to *Cutty Sark*, for she was hove to for more than six days whilst the jury rudder was being made. And between the day on which she lost her rudder and that of her arrival, she wasted eleven days making 139 miles, added to which, when she had a chance to go ahead, her speed had to be reduced to eight knots or half of what she was capable of doing. It therefore seemed pretty certain that, but for her accident, *Cutty Sark* must have beaten *Thermopylæ* by several days.

THE GHOST SHIP[1]

Richard Middleton

(1882–1911)

FAIRFIELD is a little village lying near the Portsmouth Road about half-way between London and the sea. Strangers who find it by accident now and then, call it a pretty, old-fashioned place; we, who live in it and call it home, don't find anything very pretty about it, but we should be sorry to live anywhere else. Our minds have taken the shape of the inn and the church and the green, I suppose. At all events we never feel comfortable out of Fairfield.

Of course the Cockneys, with their vasty houses and their noise-ridden streets, can call us rustics if they choose, but for all that Fairfield is a better place to live in than London. Doctor says that when he goes to London his mind is bruised with the weight of the houses, and he was a Cockney born. He had to live there himself when he was a little chap, but he knows better now. You gentlemen may laugh—perhaps some of you come from London way—but it seems to me that a witness like that it worth a gallon of arguments.

Dull? Well, you might find it dull, but I assure you that I've listened

[1]From *The Ghost Ship and Other Tales*. Reprinted by permission of Ernest Benn, Ltd.

to all the London yarns you have spun to-night, and they're absolutely nothing to the things that happen at Fairfield. It's because of our way of thinking and minding our own business. If one of your Londoners were set down on the green of a Saturday night when the ghosts of the lads who died in the war keep tryst with the lasses who lie in the churchyard, he couldn't help being curious and interfering, and then the ghosts would go somewhere where it was quieter. But we just let them come and go and don't make any fuss, and in consequence Fairfield is the ghostiest place in all England. Why, I've seen a headless man sitting on the edge of the well in broad daylight, and the children playing about his feet as if he were their father. Take my word for it, spirits know when they are well off as much as human beings.

Still, I must admit that the thing I'm going to tell you about was queer even for our part of the world, where three packs of ghost-hounds hunt regularly during the season, and blacksmith's great-grandfather is busy all night shoeing the dead gentlemen's horses. Now that's a thing that wouldn't happen in London, because of their interfering ways, but blacksmith he lies up aloft and sleeps as quiet as a lamb. Once when he had a bad head he shouted down to them not to make so much noise, and in the morning he found an old guinea left on the anvil as an apology. He wears it on his watch-chain now. But I must get on with my story; if I start telling you about the queer happenings at Fairfield I'll never stop.

It all came of the great storm in the spring of '97, the year that we had two great storms. This was the first one, and I remember it very well, because I found in the morning that it had lifted the thatch of my pigsty into the widow's garden as clean as a boy's kite. When I looked over the hedge, widow—Tom Lamport's widow that was—was prodding for her nasturtiums with a daisy-grubber. After I had watched her for a little I went down to the Fox and Grapes to tell landlord what she had said to me. Landlord he laughed, being a married man and at ease with the sex. "Come to that," he said, "the tempest has blowed something into my field. A kind of a ship I think it would be."

I was surprised at that until he explained that it was only a ghost-ship and would do no hurt to the turnips. We argued that it had been blown up from the sea at Portsmouth, and then we talked of something else. There were two slates down at the parsonage and a big tree in Lumley's meadow. It was a rare storm.

I reckon the wind had blown our ghosts all over England. They were coming back for days afterwards with foundered horses and as footsore as possible, and they were so glad to get back to Fairfield that some of them walked up the street crying like little children. Squire said that his great-grandfather's great-grandfather hadn't looked so dead-beat since the battle of Naseby, and he's an educated man.

What with one thing and another, I should think it was a week before we got straight again, and then one afternoon I met the landlord on the green and he had a worried face. "I wish you'd come and have a look at that ship in my field," he said to me; "it seems to me it's leaning real hard on the turnips. I can't bear thinking what the missus will say when she sees it."

I walked down the lane with him, and sure enough there was a ship in the middle of his field, but such a ship as no man had seen on the water for three hundred years, let alone in the middle of a turnip-field. It was all painted black and covered with carvings, and there was a great bay window in the stern for all the world like the Squire's drawing-room. There was a crowd of little black cannon on deck and looking out of her port-holes, and she was anchored at each end to the hard ground. I have seen the wonders of the world on picture-postcards, but I have never seen anything to equal that.

"She seems very solid for a ghost-ship," I said, seeing the landlord was bothered.

"I should say it's a betwixt and between," he answered, puzzling it over, "but it's going to spoil a matter of fifty turnips, and missus she'll want it moved." We went up to her and touched the side, and it was as hard as a real ship. "Now there's folks in England would call that very curious," he said.

Now I don't know much about ships, but I should think that that ghost-ship weighed a solid two hundred tons, and it seemed to me that she had come to stay, so that I felt sorry for landlord, who was a married man. "All the horses in Fairfield won't move her out of my turnips," he said, frowning at her.

Just then we heard a noise on her deck, and we looked up and saw that a man had come out of her front cabin and was looking down at us very peaceably. He was dressed in a black uniform set out with rusty gold lace, and he had a great cutlass by his side in a brass sheath. "I'm Captain Bartolomew Roberts," he said, in a gentleman's voice, "put in for recruits. I seem to have brought her rather far up the harbour."

"Harbour!" cried landlord; "why, you're fifty miles from the sea."

Captain Roberts didn't turn a hair. "So much as that, is it?" he said coolly. "Well, it's of no consequence."

Landlord was a bit upset at this. "I don't want to be unneighbourly," he said, "but I wish you hadn't brought your ship into my field. You see, my wife sets great store on these turnips."

The captain took a pinch of snuff out of a fine gold box that he pulled out of his pocket, and dusted his fingers with a silk handkerchief in a very genteel fashion. "I'm only here for a few months," he said; "but if a testimony of my esteem would pacify your good lady I should be content," and with the words he loosed a great gold brooch from the neck of his coat and tossed it down to landlord.

Landlord blushed as red as a strawberry. "I'm not denying she's fond of jewellery," he said, "but it's too much for half a sackful of turnips." And indeed it was a handsome brooch.

The captain laughed. "Tut, man," he said, "it's a forced sale, and you deserve a good price. Say no more about it"; and nodding good-day to us, he turned on his heel and went into the cabin. Landlord walked back up the lane like a man with a weight off his mind. "That tempest has blowed me a bit of luck," he said; "the missus will be main pleased with that brooch. It's better than the blacksmith's guinea any day."

Ninety-seven was Jubilee year, the year of the second Jubilee, you remember, and we had great doings at Fairfield, so that we hadn't much time to bother about the ghost-ship, though anyhow it isn't our way to meddle in things that don't concern us. Landlord, he saw his tenant once or twice when he was hoeing his turnips and passed the time of day, and landlord's wife wore her new brooch to church every Sunday. But we didn't mix much with the ghosts at any time, all except an idiot lad there was in the village, and he didn't know the difference between a man and a ghost, poor innocent! On Jubilee Day, however, somebody told Captain Roberts why the church bells were ringing, and he hoisted a flag and fired off his guns like a royal Englishman. 'Tis true the guns were shotted, and one of the round shot knocked a hole in Farmer Johnstone's barn, but nobody thought much of that in such a season of rejoicing.

It wasn't till our celebrations were over that we noticed that anything was wrong in Fairfield. 'Twas shoemaker who told me first about it one morning at the Fox and Grapes. "You know my great great-uncle?" he said to me.

"You mean Joshua, the quiet lad," I answered, knowing him well.

"Quiet!" said shoemaker indignantly. "Quiet you call him, coming home at three o'clock every morning as drunk as a magistrate and waking up the whole house with his noise."

"Why, it can't be Joshua!" I said, for I knew him for one of the most respectable young ghosts in the village.

"Joshua it is," said shoemaker; "and one of these nights he'll find himself out in the street if he isn't careful."

This kind of talk shocked me, I can tell you, for I don't like to hear a man abusing his own family, and I could hardly believe that a steady youngster like Joshua had taken to drink. But just then in came butcher Aylwin in such a temper that he could hardly drink his beer. "The young puppy! the young puppy!" he kept on saying; and it was some time before shoemaker and I found out that he was talking about his ancestor that fell at Senlac.

"Drink?" said shoemaker hopefully, for we all like company in our misfortunes, and butcher nodded grimly.

"The young noodle," he said, emptying his tankard.

Well, after that I kept my ears open, and it was the same story all over the village. There was hardly a young man among all the ghosts of Fairfield who didn't roll home in the small hours of the morning the worse for liquor. I used to wake up in the night and hear them stumble past my house, singing outrageous songs. The worst of it was that we couldn't keep the scandal to ourselves, and the folk at Greenhill began to talk of "sodden Fairfield" and taught their children to sing a song about us:

Sodden Fairfield, sodden Fairfield, has no use for bread-and-butter, Rum for breakfast, rum for dinner, rum for tea, and rum for supper!

We are easy-going in our village, but we didn't like that.

Of course we soon found out where the young fellows went to get the drink, and landlord was terribly cut up that his tenant should have turned out so badly, but his wife wouldn't hear of parting with the brooch, so that he couldn't give the Captain notice to quit. But as time went on, things grew from bad to worse, and at all hours of the day you would see those young reprobates sleeping it off on the village green. Nearly every afternoon a ghost-waggon used to jolt down to the ship with a lading of rum, and though the older ghosts seemed inclined to give the Captain's hospitality the go-by, the youngsters were neither to hold nor to bind.

So one afternoon when I was taking my nap I heard a knock at the door, and there was parson looking very serious, like a man with a job before him that he didn't altogether relish. "I'm going down to talk to the Captain about all this drunkenness in the village, and I want you to come with me," he said straight out.

I can't say that I fancied the visit much myself, and I tried to hint to parson that as, after all, they were only a lot of ghosts, it didn't very much matter.

"Dead or alive, I'm responsible for their good conduct," he said, "and I'm going to do my duty and put a stop to this continued disorder. And you are coming with me, John Simmons." So I went, parson being a persuasive kind of man.

We went down to the ship, and as we approached her I could see the Captain tasting the air on deck. When he saw parson he took off his hat very politely, and I can tell you that I was relieved to find that he had a proper respect for the cloth. Parson acknowledged his salute and spoke out stoutly enough. "Sir, I should be glad to have a word with you."

"Come on board, sir, come on board," said the Captain, and I could tell by his voice that he knew why we were there. Parson and I climbed up an uneasy kind of ladder, and the Captain took us into the great cabin at the back of the ship, where the bay-window was. It was the most wonderful place you ever saw in your life, all full of gold and silver plate, swords with jewelled scabbards, carved oak chairs, and great chests that looked as though they were bursting with guineas. Even parson was surprised, and he did not shake his head very hard when the Captain took down some silver cups and poured us out a drink of rum. I tasted mine, and I don't mind saying that it changed my view of things entirely. There was nothing betwixt and between about that rum, and I felt that it was ridiculous to blame the lads for drinking too much of stuff like that. It seemed to fill my veins with honey and fire.

Parson put the case squarely to the Captain, but I didn't listen much to what he said; I was busy sipping my drink and looking through the window at the fishes swimming to and fro over landlord's turnips. Just then it seemed the most natural thing in the world that they should be there, though afterwards, of course, I could see that that proved it was a ghost-ship.

But even then I thought it was queer when I saw a drowned sailor float by in the thin air with his hair and beard all full of bubbles. It was the first time I had seen anything quite like that at Fairfield.

All the time I was regarding the wonders of the deep, parson was telling Captain Roberts how there was no peace or rest in the village owing to the curse of drunkenness, and what a bad example the youngsters were setting to the older ghosts. The Captain listened very attentively, and only put in a word now and then about boys being boys and young men sowing their wild oats. But when parson had finished his speech he filled up our silver cups and said to parson, with a flourish, "I should be sorry to cause trouble anywhere where I have been made welcome, and you will be glad to hear that I put to sea to-morrow night. And now you must drink me a prosperous voyage." So we all stood up and drank the toast with honour, and that noble rum was like hot oil in my veins.

After that Captain showed us some of the curiosities he had brought back from foreign parts, and we were greatly amazed, though afterwards I couldn't clearly remember what they were. And then I found myself walking across the turnips with parson, and I was telling him of the glories of the deep that I had seen through the window of the ship. He turned on me severely. "If I were you, John Simmons," he said, "I should go straight home to bed." He has a way of putting things that wouldn't occur to an ordinary man, has parson, and I did as he told me.

Well, next day it came on to blow, and it blew harder and harder, till about eight o'clock at night I heard a noise and looked out into the garden. I dare say you won't believe me, it seems a bit tall even to me, but the wind had lifted the thatch of my pigsty into the widow's garden a second time. I thought I wouldn't wait to hear what widow had to say about it, so I went across the green to the Fox and Grapes, and the wind was so strong that I danced along on tip-toe like a girl at the fair. When I got to the inn landlord had to help me shut the door; it seemed as though a dozen goats were pushing against it to come in out of the storm.

"It's a powerful tempest," he said, drawing the beer. "I hear there's a chimney down at Dickory End."

"It's a funny thing how these sailors know about the weather," I answered. "When Captain said he was going to-night, I was thinking it would take a capful of wind to carry the ship back to sea, but now here's more than a capful."

"Ah, yes," said landlord, "it's to-night he goes true enough, and, mind you, though he treated me handsome over the rent, I'm not sure it's a loss to the village. I don't hold with gentrice who fetch their drink from London instead of helping local traders to get their living."

"But you haven't got any rum like his," I said to draw him out.

His neck grew red above his collar, and I was afraid I'd gone too far; but after a while he got his breath with a grunt.

"John Simmons," he said, "if you've come down here this windy night to talk a lot of fool's talk, you've wasted a journey."

Well, of course, then I had to smooth him down with praising his rum and Heaven forgive me for swearing it was better than Captain's. For the like of that rum no living lips have tasted save mine and parson's. But somehow or other I brought landlord round, and presently we must have a glass of his best to prove its quality.

"Beat that if you can!" he cried, and we both raised our glasses to our mouths, only to stop half-way and look at each other in amaze. For the wind that had been howling outside like an outrageous dog had all of a sudden turned as melodious as the carol-boys of a Christmas Eve.

"Surely that's not my Martha," whispered landlord; Martha being his great-aunt that lived in the loft overhead.

We went to the door, and the wind burst it open so that the handle was driven clean into the plaster of the wall. But we didn't think about that at the time; for over our heads, sailing very comfortably through the windy stars, was the ship that had passed the summer in landlord's field. Her portholes and her bay-window were blazing with lights, and there was a noise of singing and fiddling on her decks. "He's gone," shouted landlord above the storm, "and he's taken half the village with him!" I could only nod in answer, not having lungs like bellows of leather.

In the morning we were able to measure the strength of the storm, and over and above my pigsty there was damage enough wrought in the village to keep us busy. True it is that the children had to break down no branches for the firing that autumn, since the wind had strewn the woods with more than they could carry away. Many of our ghosts were scattered abroad, but this time very few came back, all the young men having sailed with Captain; and not only ghosts, for a poor half-witted lad was missing, and we reckoned that he had stowed himself away or perhaps shipped as cabin-boy, not knowing any better.

What with the lamentations of the ghost-girls and the grumblings of families who had lost an ancestor, the village was upset for a while, and the funny thing was that it was the folk who had complained most of the carryings-on of the youngsters, who made most noise now that they were gone. I hadn't any sympathy with shoemaker or butcher, who ran about saying how much they missed their lads, but it made me grieve to hear the poor bereaved girls calling their lovers by name on the village green at nightfall. It didn't seem fair to me that they should have lost their men a second time, after giving up life in order to join them, as like as not. Still, not even a spirit can be sorry for ever, and after a few months we made up our mind that the folk who had sailed in the ship were never coming back, and we didn't talk about it any more.

And then one day, I dare say it would be a couple of years after, when the whole business was quite forgotten, who should come trapesing along the road from Portsmouth but the daft lad who had gone away with the ship, without waiting till he was dead to become a ghost. You never saw such a boy as that in all your life. He had a great rusty cutlass hanging to a string at his waist, and he was tattooed all over in fine colours, so that even his face looked like a girl's sampler. He had a handkerchief in his hand full of foreign shells and old-fashioned pieces of small money, very curious, and he walked up to the well outside his mother's house and drew himself a drink as if he had been nowhere in particular.

The worst of it was that he had come back as soft-headed as he went, and try as we might we couldn't get anything reasonable out of him. He talked a lot of gibberish about keel-hauling and walking the plank and crimson murders—things which a decent sailor should know nothing about, so that it seemed to me that for all his manners Captain had been more of a pirate than a gentleman mariner. But to draw sense out of that boy was as hard as picking cherries off a crab-tree. One silly tale he had that he kept on drifting back to, and to hear him you would have thought that it was the only thing that happened to him in his life. "We was at anchor," he would say, "off an island called the Basket of Flowers, and the sailors had caught a lot of parrots and we were teaching them to swear. Up and down the decks, up and down the decks, and the language they used was dreadful. Then we looked up and saw the masts of the Spanish ship outside the harbour. Outside the harbour they were, so we threw the parrots into the sea and sailed out to fight. And all the parrots were drownded in the sea and the language they used was dreadful." That's the sort of boy he was, nothing but silly talk of parrots when we asked him about the fighting. And we never had a chance of teaching him better, for two days after he ran away again, and hasn't been seen since.

That's my story, and I assure you that things like that are happening at Fairfield all the time. The ship has never come back, but somehow as people grow older they seem to think that one of these windy nights, she'll come sailing in over the hedges with all the lost ghosts on board. Well, when she comes, she'll be welcome. There's one ghost-lass that has never grown tired of waiting for her lad to return. Every night you'll see her out on the green, straining her poor eyes with looking for the mast-lights among the stars. A faithful lass you'd call her, and I'm thinking you'd be right.

Landlord's field wasn't a penny the worse for the visit, but they do say that since then the turnips that have been grown in it have tasted of rum.

THE SEALING OF ZEEBRUGGE[1]

Sir Archibald Hurd

(1869–   )

SITUATED on the Belgian coast, some twelve miles apart, and facing a little to the west of north, Zeebrugge was in reality but a sea-gate of the inland port of Bruges—the latter being the station to which the enemy destroyers and submarines were sent in parts from the German workshops; where they were assembled; and whence, by canal, they proceeded to sea by way of Zeebrugge and Ostend. Of these two exits, Zeebrugge, the northernmost, was considerably the nearer to Bruges and the more important—Zeebrugge being eight, while Ostend was eleven miles distant from their common base—and to receive an adequate impression of what was subsequently achieved there it is necessary to bear in mind its salient features.

Unlike Ostend, apart from its harbour, it possessed no civic importance, merely consisting of a few streets of houses clustering about its railway station, locks, wharves, and store-houses, its sandy roadstead being guarded from the sea by an immensely powerful crescentic Mole. It was into this roadstead, that the Bruges canal opened between heavy timbered breakwaters, having first passed through a sea-lock, some half a mile higher up. Between the two lighthouses, each about twenty feet above high-water level, that stood upon the ends of these breakwaters, the canal was 200 yards wide, narrowing to a width, in the lock itself, of less than seventy feet.

Leading from the canal entrance to the tip of the Mole, on which stood a third lighthouse, and so out to sea, was a curved channel, about three-quarters of a mile long, kept clear by continual dredging; and this was protected both by a string of armed barges and by a system of nets on its shoreward side. It was in its great sea-wall, however, some eighty yards broad and more than a mile long, that Zeebrugge's chief strength resided; and this had been utilized, since the German occupation, to

---

[1] From *Sons of the Admiralty*. Reprinted by permission of the author and of Constable & Co.

the utmost extent. Upon the seaward end of it, near the lighthouse, a battery of 6-inch guns had been mounted, other batteries and machine-guns being stationed at various points throughout its length. With a parapet along its outer side, some sixteen feet higher than the level of the rest of the Mole, it not only carried a railway-line but contained a sea-plane shed, and shelters for stores and *personnel*. It was connected with the shore by a light wood and steel viaduct—a pile-work structure, allowing for the passage of the through-current necessary to prevent silting.

Emplaced upon the shore, on either side of this, were further batteries of heavy guns; while, to the north of the canal entrance, and at a point almost opposite to the tip of the Mole, was the Goeben Fort, containing yet other guns covering both the Mole and the harbour. Under the lee of the parapet were dug-outs for the defenders, while, under the lee of the Mole itself, was a similar shelter for the enemy's submarines and destroyers. Nor did this exhaust the harbour's defences, since it was further protected not only by minefields, but by natural shoals, always difficult to navigate, and infinitely more so in the absence of beacons.

Even to a greater extent was this last a feature of Ostend, though here the whole problem was somewhat simpler, there being no Mole, and therefore no necessity—though equally no opportunity—for a subsidiary attack. Covered, of course, from the shore by guns of all calibres—and here it should be remembered that there were 225 of these between Nieuport and the Dutch frontier—the single object in this case was to gain the entrance, before the block ships should be discovered by the enemy, and sunk by his gunners where their presence would do no harm. Since for complete success, however, it was necessary to seal both places, and, if possible, to do so simultaneously, it will readily be seen that, in the words of Sir Eric Geddes—the successor, as First Lord of the Admiralty, to Mr Balfour and Sir Edward Carson—it was, "a particularly intricate operation which had to be worked strictly to time-table." It was also one that, for several months before, required the most arduous and secret toil.

Begun in 1917 while Sir John Jellicoe was still First Sea Lord, the plan ultimately adopted—there had been several previous ones, dropped for military reasons—was devised by Vice-Admiral Roger Keyes, then head of the Plans Division at the Admiralty. From the first it was realized, of course, by all concerned that the element of surprise would be the determining factor; and it was therefore decided that the attempt to block the harbours should take place at night. It was also clear that, under modern conditions of star-shells and searchlights, an extensive use would have to be made of the recent art of throwing out smoke-screens; and fortunately, in Commander Brock, Admiral Keyes had at his disposal just the man to supply this need. A Wing-Commander in the Royal Naval Air Service, in private life Commander Brock was a

partner in a well-known firm of firework makers; and his inventive ability had already been fruitful in more than one direction. A first-rate pilot
and excellent shot, Commander Brock was a typical English sportsman;
and his subsequent death during the operations, for whose success he
had been so largely responsible, was a loss of the gravest description
both to the Navy and the empire.

The next consideration was the choosing of the block-ships and for
these the following vessels were at last selected—the *Sirius* and *Brilliant*
to be sunk at Ostend, and the *Thetis, Iphigenia*, and *Intrepid* to seal the
canal entrance at Zeebrugge. These were all old cruisers, and they were
to be filled with cement, which when submerged would turn into concrete, fuses being so placed that they could be sunk by explosion as soon
as they had reached the desired position; and it was arranged that motor-
launches should accompany them in order to rescue their crews.

So far these general arrangements were applicable to both places; but,
as regarded Zeebrugge, it was decided to make a diversion in the shape
of a subsidiary attack on the Mole, in which men were to be landed and
to do as much damage as possible. Such an attack, it was thought, would
help to draw the enemy's attention from the main effort, which was to be
the sinking of the block-ships, and, apart from this, would have valuable
results both material and moral. For this secondary operation, three
other vessels were especially selected and fitted out—two Liverpool
ferry boats, the *Iris* and *Daffodil*, obtained by Captain Grant, not without some difficulty, owing to the natural reluctance of the Liverpool
authorities and the impossibility of divulging the object for which they
were wanted—and the old cruiser *Vindictive*. This latter vessel had been
designed as a "ram" ship more than twenty years before, displacing about
5,000 tons and capable of a speed of some twenty knots. She had no
armour-belt, but her bow was covered with plates, two inches thick and
extending fourteen feet aft, while her deck was also protected by hardened plates, covered with nickel steel, from a half to two inches thick.
Originally undergunned, she had subsequently been provided with ten
6-inch guns and eight 12-pounders.

This was the vessel chosen to convey the bulk of the landing party,
and, for many weeks, under the supervision of Commander E. O. B. S.
Osborne, the carpenters and engineers were hard at work upon her. An
additional high deck, carrying thirteen brows or gangways, was fitted
upon her port side; pom-poms and machine-guns were placed in her
fighting-top; and she was provided with three howitzers and some Stokes
mortars. A special flame—throwing cabin, fitted with speaking tubes,
was built beside the bridge, and another on the port quarter.

It was thus to be the task of the *Vindictive* and her consorts to lay
themselves alongside the Mole, land storming and demolition parties,
and protect these by a barrage as they advanced down the Mole; and,
in order to make this attack more effective, yet a third operation was

designed. This was to cut off the Mole from the mainland, thus isolating its defenders and preventing the arrival of reinforcements; and, in order to do so, it was decided to blow up the viaduct by means of an old submarine charged with high explosives. Meanwhile the whole attempt was to be supported from out at sea by a continuous bombardment from a squadron of monitors; sea-planes and aeroplanes, weather permitting, were to render further assistance; and flotillas of destroyers were to shepherd the whole force and to hold the flanks against possible attack.

This then was the plan of campaign, one of the most daring ever conceived, and all the more so in face of the difficulty of keeping it concealed from the enemy during the long period of preparation—a difficulty enhanced in that it was not only necessary to inform each man of his particular *rôle*, but of the particular objectives of each attack and the general outline of the whole scheme. That was unavoidable since it was more than likely that, during any one of the component actions, every officer might be killed or wounded and the men themselves become responsible. Nor was it possible, even approximately, to fix a date for the enterprise, since this could only be carried out under particular conditions of wind and weather. Thus the night must be dark and the sea calm; the arrival on the other side must be at high water; and there must above all things be a following wind, since, without this, the smoke screens would be useless. Twice, when all was ready, these conditions seemed to have come, and twice, after a start had been made, the expedition had to return; and it was not until April 22nd, 1918, that the final embarkation took place.

By this time Vice-Admiral Keyes had succeeded Vice-Admiral Bacon in command of the Dover Patrol; and he was therefore in personal charge of the great adventure that he had initiated and planned with such care. Every man under him was not only a volunteer fully aware of what he was about to face, but a picked man, selected and judged by as high a standard, perhaps, as the world could have provided. Flying his own flag on the destroyer *Warwick*, Admiral Keyes had entrusted the *Vindictive* to acting Captain A. F. B. Carpenter, the *Iris* and the *Daffodil* being in the hands respectively of Commander Valentine Gibbs and Lieutenant Harold Campbell. The marines, consisting of three companies of the Royal Marine Light Infantry and a hundred men of the Royal Marine Artillery, had been drawn from the Grand Fleet, the Chatham, Portsmouth, and Devonport Depots, and were commanded by Lieutenant-Colonel Bertram Elliot. The three block-ships that were to be sunk at Zeebrugge, the *Thetis*, *Intrepid*, and *Iphigenia*, were in charge of Commander Ralph S. Sneyd, Lieutenant Stuart Bonham-Carter, and Lieutenant E. W. Billyard Leake; while the old submarine *C3* that was to blow up the viaduct was commanded by Lieutenant R. D. Sandford. In control of the motor-launches, allotted to the attack on Zeebrugge, was Admiral Keyes' flag-captain, Captain R. Collins, those at Ostend being directed by Commander Hamilton Benn, M. P.—the operations at the latter place being in charge of Commodore Hubert Lynes. Also acting in support, was a large body of coastal motor-boats under Lieutenant A. E. P. Wellman, and a flotilla of destroyers under Captain Wilfred Tomkinson, the general surveying of the whole field of attack—including the fixing of targets and firing-points—being in the skilful hands of Commander H. P. Douglas and Lieutenant-Commander F. E. B. Haselfoot.

Included among the monitors were the *Erebus* and *Terror*, each mounting 15-inch guns, to operate at Zeebrugge; and the *Prince Eugene*, *General Craufurd*, and *Lord Clive*, carrying 12-inch guns, and the *Marshal Soult*, carrying 15-inch guns, to assist at Ostend. To the old *Vindictive* Admiral Keyes had presented a horseshoe that had been nailed for luck to her centre funnel; and, to the whole fleet, on its way across, he signalled the message, "St George for England." Few who received that message expected to return unscathed, and in the block-ships none; but it is safe to say that, in the words of Nelson, they would not have been elsewhere that night for thousands.

Such then were the forces that, on this still dark night, safely arrived at their first rendezvous and then parted on their perilous ways, some to Zeebrugge and some to Ostend. It was at a point about fifteen miles from the Belgian coast that the two parties separated; and, since it is impossible to follow them both at once, let us confine ourselves at first to the former. Theirs was the more complicated, though, as it afterwards proved, the more swiftly achieved task, the first to arrive on the scene of action, almost at the stroke of midnight, being the old cruiser *Vindictive* with her two stout little attendants. These she had been towing as far as the rendezvous; but, at this point, she had cast them off, and they were now following her, under their own steam, to assist in berthing her and to land their own parties. Ahead of them the small craft had been laying their smoke-screens, the north-east wind rolling these shorewards, while already the monitors could be heard at work bombarding the coast defences with their big guns. Accustomed as he was to such visitations, this had not aroused in the enemy any particular alarm; and it was not until the *Vindictive* and the two ferry-boats were within 400 yards of the Mole that the off-shore wind caused the smoke-screen to lift somewhat and left them exposed to the enemy. By this time the marines and bluejackets, ready to spring ashore, were mustered on the lower and main decks; while Colonel Elliot, Major Cordner, and Captain Chater, who were to lead the marines, and Captain Halahan, who was in charge of the bluejackets, were waiting on the high false deck.

It was a crucial moment, for there could be no mistaking now what was the *Vindictive's* intention. The enemy's star-shells, soaring into the sky, broke into a baleful and crimson light; while his searchlights, that had been wavering through the darkness, instantly sprang together and fastened upon the three vessels. This, as Captain Carpenter afterwards confessed, induced "an extraordinarily naked feeling," and then, from every gun that could be brought to bear, both from the Mole and the coast, there burst upon her such a fire as, given another few minutes, must inevitably have sunk her. Beneath it Colonel Elliot, Major Cordner, and Captain Halahan, all fell slain; while Captain Carpenter himself had the narrowest escape from destruction. His cap—he had left his best one at home—was two or three times over pierced by bullets, as was the case of his binoculars, slung by straps over his back; while, during the further course of the action, both his searchlight and smoke-goggles were smashed.

The surprise had so far succeeded, however, that, within less than five minutes, the *Vindictive's* bow was against the side of the Mole, and all but her upper works consequently protected from the severest of the enemy's fire. Safe—or comparatively so—as regarded her water-line, she was nevertheless still a point-blank target; her funnels were riddled over and over again, the one carrying the horse-shoe suffering least; the signal-room was smashed and the bridge blown to pieces, just as Commander Carpenter entered the flame-throwing cabin; and this in its turn, drawing the enemy's fire, was soon twisted and splintered in all directions. It was now raining; explosion followed explosion till the whole air quaked as if in torment; and meanwhile a new and unforeseen danger had just made itself apparent. Till the harbour was approached, the sea had been calm, but now a ground-swell was causing a "scend" against the Mole, adding tenfold not only to the difficulties of landing, but of maintaining the *Vindictive* at her berth. In this emergency, it was the little *Daffodil* that rose to and saved the situation. Her primary duty, although she carried a landing party, had been to push the *Vindictive* in until the latter had been secured; but, as matters were, she had to hold her against the Mole throughout the whole hour and a quarter of her stay there. Even so, the improvised gangways that had been thrust out from the false deck were now some four feet up in the air and now crashing down from the top of the parapet; and it was across these brows, splintering under their feet, and in the face of a fire that baffled description, that the marines and bluejackets had to scramble ashore with their Lewis guns, hand-grenades, and bayonets.

Under such conditions, once a man fell, there was but little hope of his regaining his feet; and it was only a lucky chance that saved one of the officers from being thus trodden to death. This was Lieutenant H. T. C. Walker, who, with an arm blown away, had stumbled and fallen on the upper deck, the eager storming parties, sweeping over him until he was happily discovered and dragged free. Let it be said at once that Lieutenant Walker bore no malice, and waved them good luck with his remaining arm. The command of the marines had now devolved upon Major Weller; and, of the 300 or so who followed him ashore, more than half were soon to be casualties. But the landing was made good; the awkward drop from the parapet was successfully negotiated thanks to the special scaling-ladders; the barrage was put down; and they were soon at hand-to-hand grips with such of the German defenders as stayed to face them. Many of these were in the dug-out under the parapets, but, seeing that to remain there was only to be bayoneted, they made a rush for some of their own destroyers that were hugging the lee of the Mole. But few reached these, however, thanks to the vigour of the marines and the fire of the machine-guns from the *Vindictive's* top, while one of the destroyers was damaged by hand-grenades and by shells lobbed over the Mole from the *Vindictive's* mortars.

Meanwhile the *Vindictive* was still the object of a fire that was rapidly dismantling all of her that was visible. A shell in her fighting-top killed every man at the guns there except Sergeant Finch of the Royal Marine Artillery, who was badly wounded, but who extricated himself from a pile of corpses, and worked his gun for a while single-handed. Another shell, bursting forward, put the whole of a howitzer crew out of action, and yet a third, finding the same place, destroyed the crew that followed.

Fierce as was the ordeal through which the *Vindictive* was passing, however, that of the *Iris* was even more so. Unprotected, as was her fellow the *Daffodil*, boring against the side of the larger *Vindictive*, the *Iris*, with her landing-party, was trying to make good her berth lower down the Mole, ahead of Captain Carpenter. Unfortunately the grapnels with which she had been provided proved to be ineffective owing to the "scend," and, with the little boat tossing up and down, and under the fiercest fire, two of the officers, Lieutenant-Commander Bradford and Lieutenant Hawkins, climbed ashore to try and make them fast. Both were killed before they succeeded, toppling into the water between the Mole and the ship, while, a little later, a couple of shells burst aboard with disastrous results. One of these, piercing the deck, exploded among a party of marines, waiting for the gangways to be thrust out, killing forty-nine and wounding seven; while another, wrecking the ward-room, killed four officers and twenty-six men. Her Captain, Commander Gibbs, had both his legs blown away, and died in a few hours, the *Iris* having been forced meanwhile to change her position, and take up another astern of the *Vindictive*.

Before this happened, however, every man aboard her, as aboard the *Vindictive, Daffodil*, and upon the Mole, had been thrilled to the bone by the gigantic explosion that had blown up the viaduct lower down. With a deafening roar and a gush of flame leaping up hundreds of yards into the night, Lieutenant Sandford had told them the good tidings of his success with the old submarine. Creeping towards the viaduct, with his little crew on deck, he had made straight for an aperture between the steel-covered piles, and to the blank amazement and apparent paralysis of the Germans crowded upon the viaduct, had rammed in the submarine up to her conning-tower before lighting the fuse that was to start the explosion.

Before himself doing this, he had put off a boat, his men needing no orders to tumble into her, followed by their commander, as soon as the fuse was fired, with the one idea of getting away as far as possible. As luck would have it, the boat's propeller fouled, and they had to rely for safely upon two oars only, pulling, as Lieutenant Sandford afterwards described it, as hard as men ever pulled before. Raked by machine-gun fire and with shells plunging all round them, most of them, including Lieutenant Sandford, were wounded; but they were finally borne to safety by an attendant picket-boat under his brother, Lieutenant-Commander F. Sandford.

That had taken place about fifteen minutes after the *Vindictive* and her consorts had reached their berths, and a few minutes before the block-ships, with *Thetis* leading, had rounded the light-house at the tip of the Mole. In order to assist these to find their bearings, an employee of Commander Brock, who had never before been to sea, had for some time been firing rockets from the after cabin of the *Vindictive;* and presently they came in sight, exposed as the *Vindictive* had been, by the partial blowing back of their smoke screen. Steaming straight ahead for their objectives, they were therefore opposed by the intensest fire; and the spirit in which they proceeded is well illustrated by what had just taken place on board the *Intrepid.* It had been previously arranged that, for the final stage of their journey, the crews of the block-ships should be reduced to a minimum; but, when the moment came to disembark the extra men, those on the *Intrepid,* so anxious were they to remain, actually hid themselves away. Many of them did in fact succeed in remaining, and sailed with their comrades into the canal.

The first to draw the enemy's fire, the *Thetis,* had the misfortune, having cleared the armed barges, to foul the nets—bursting through the gate and carrying this with her, but with her propellers gathering in the meshes and rendering her helpless. Heavily shelled, she was soon in a sinking condition, and Commander Sneyd was obliged to blow her charges, but not before he had given the line, with the most deliberate coolness, to the two following block-ships—Lieutenant Littleton, in a motor-launch, then rescuing the crew.

Following the *Thetis* came the *Intrepid,* with all her guns in full action, and Lieutenant Bonham-Carter pushed her right into the canal up to a point actually behind some of the German batteries. Here he ran her nose into the western bank, ordered his crew away, and blew her up, the engineer remaining down below in order to be able to report results. These being satisfactory, and every one having left, Lieutenant Bonham-Carter committed himself to a Carley float—a kind of lifebuoy that, on contact with the water, automatically ignited a calcium flare. Illumined by this, the *Intrepid's* commander found himself the target of a machine-gun on the bank, and, but for the smoke still pouring from the *Intrepid*, he would probably have been killed before the launch could rescue him.

Meanwhile the *Iphigenia*, close behind, had been equally successful under more difficult conditions. With the *Intrepid's* smoke blowing back upon her, she had found it exceedingly hard to keep her course, and had rammed a dredger with a barge moored to it, pushing the latter before her when she broke free. Lieutenant Billyard-Leake, however, was able to reach his objective—the eastern bank of the canal entrance—and here he sank her in good position, with her engines still working to keep her in place. Both vessels were thus left lying well across the canal, as aeroplane photographs afterwards confirmed; and thanks to the persistent courage of Lieutenant Percy Dean, the crews of both block-ships were safely removed.

With the accompanying motor-launch unhappily sunk as she was going in, Lieutenant Dean, under fire from all sides, often at a range of but a few feet, embarked in *Motor-Launch 282* no less than 101 officers and men. He then started for home, but, learning that there was an officer still in the water, at once returned and rescued him, three men being shot at his side as he handled his little vessel. Making a second start, just as he cleared the canal entrance, his steering-gear broke down; and he had to manœuvre by means of his engines, hugging the side of the Mole to keep out of range of the guns. Reaching the harbour mouth he then, by a stroke of luck, found himself alongside the destroyer *Warwick*, who was thus able to take on board and complete the rescue of the block-ships' crews.

It was now nearly one o'clock on the morning of the 23rd; the main objects of the attack had been secured; and Captain Carpenter, watching the course of events, decided that it was time to recall his landing-parties. It had been arranged to do so with the *Vindictive's* siren, but this, like so much of her gear, was no longer serviceable; and it was necessary to have recourse to the *Daffodil's* little hooter, so feebly opposed to the roar of the guns. Throughout the whole operation, humble as her part had been, the *Daffodil* had been performing yeoman's service, and, but for the fine seamanship of Lieutenant Harold Campbell, and the efforts of her engine-room staff, it would have been quite impossible to re-embark the marines and bluejackets from the Mole. In the normal way her boilers developed some 80-lbs steam-pressure per inch; but, for the work of holding the *Vindictive* against the side of the Mole, it was necessary throughout to maintain double this pressure. All picked men, under Artificer-Engineer Sutton, the stokers held to their task in the ablest fashion; and, in ignorance of what was happening all about them, and to the muffled accompaniment of bursting shells, they worked themselves out, stripped to their vests and trousers, to the last point of exhaustion.

Nor did their colleagues on board the *Vindictive* fall in any degree short of the same high standard, as becomes clear from the account afterwards given by one of her stokers, Alfred Dingle. "My pigeon," he said, "was in the boiler room of the *Vindictive*, which left with the other craft at two o'clock on Tuesday afternoon. We were in charge of Chief Artificer-Engineer Campbell, who was formerly a merchant-service engineer and must have been specially selected for the job. He is a splendid fellow. At the start he told us what we were in for, and that before we had finished we should have to feed the fires like mad. 'This ship was built at Chatham twenty years ago,' he said, 'and her speed is 19 knots, but if you don't get 21 knots out of her when it is wanted, well—it's up to you to do it anyway.' We cheered, and he told us, when we got the order, to get at it for all we were worth, and take no notice of anybody. We were all strong fellows, the whole thirteen of us. . . . The *Vindictive* was got to Zeebrugge; it was just before midnight when we got alongside the Mole. We had gas-masks on then, and were stoking furiously all the time, with the artificer-engineer backing us up, and joking and keeping us in the best of spirits. Nobody could have been down-hearted while he was there. There is no need to say it was awful; you know something from the accounts in the papers, although no written accounts could make you understand what it was really like. . . . Well, there we were, bump, bump, bump against the Mole for I don't know how long, and all the time shells shrieking and crashing, rockets going up, and a din that was too awful for words, added to which were the cries and shrieks of wounded officers and men. . . . Several times Captain Carpenter came below and told us how things were going on. That was splendid of him, I think. He was full of enthusiasm, and cheered us up wonderfully. He was the same with the seamen and men on deck. . . . I can't help admiring the marines. They were a splendid lot of chaps, most of them seasoned men, whilst the bluejackets (who were just as good) were generally quite young men. The marines were bursting to get at the fight and were chafing under the delay all the time. . . . While we were alongside I was stoking and took off my gas-mask, as it was so much in the way. It was a silly thing to do, but I couldn't get on with the work with it on. Suddenly I smelt gas. I don't know whether it came from an ordinary shell, but I know it was not from the smoke screen, and you ought to have seen me nip round for the helmet. I forgot where I put it for the moment, and there was I running round with my hand clapped on my mouth till I found it. In the boiler-room our exciting time was after the worst was over on shore. All of a sudden the telegraph rang down, 'Full speed ahead,' and then there was a commotion. The artificer-engineer shouted 'Now for it; don't forget what you have to do—21 knots, if she never does it again.' In a minute or two the engines were going full pelt. Somebody came down and said we were still hitched on to the Mole, but Campbell said he didn't care if we towed the Mole back with us; nothing was going to stop him. As a matter of fact, we pulled away great chunks of the masonry with the grappling irons, and brought some of it back with us. Eventually we got clear of the Mole, and there was terrific firing up above. Mr Campbell was urging us on all the time, and we were shoving in the coal like madmen. We were all singing. One of the chaps started with 'I want to go home,' and this eventually developed into a verse, and I don't think we stopped singing it for three and a half hours—pretty nearly all the time we were coming back. In the other parts of the ship there wasn't much singing, for all the killed and wounded men we could get hold of had been brought on board, and were being attended to by the doctors and sick bay men. I don't know if we did the 21 knots, but we got jolly near it, and everybody worked like a Trojan, and was quite exhausted when it was all over. When we were off Dover the Engineer-Commander came down into the boiler-room and asked Artificer-Engineer Campbell, 'What have you got to say about your men?' He replied 'I'm not going to say anything for them or anything against them; but if I was going to hell to-morrow night I would have the same men with me.'"

Not until the Mole had been cleared of every man that could possibly be removed did the *Vindictive* break away, turning in a half-circle and belching flames from every pore of her broken funnels. That was perhaps her worst moment, for now she was exposed to every angry and awakened battery; her lower decks were already a shambles; and many of her navigating staff were killed or helpless. But her luck held; the enemy's shells fell short; and soon she was comparatively safe in the undispersed smoke-trails, with the glorious consciousness that she had indeed earned the Admiral's "Well done, *Vindictive*."

THE FIVE WOUNDS ENCOUNTERS A GALE[1]

Vere Hutchinson

W E SAILED from Isola Sound just past midnight on Christmas Day. A warm night with a gold sky, so fiercely did the stars jostle with each other. We were one hundred and eighty-one all told; and, mad as each man was who set about that expedition, he was no madder than those he left behind.—They followed us out, some waist high in the water, others rowing helter-skelter in the boats. They sent toast upon toast bawling after us, breaking their bottles on the ship's side, drinking from the cracked mouths. They lit great torches so that even when we were quite out of the shoals we could yet see those tossing flares of light rushing hither and thither as comets race.

For my part one thing stood out above the riot of that night, a matter of mine own. Months past my father had taught me the way of the shal-

[1]From *Great Waters*. Reprinted by permission of the author and of Hutchinson & Co., Ltd.

lows; now I, for the first time, took the helm of the brig and followed in the wake of *The Five Wounds*. Doing so I knew then how completely I was my father's son. He had said nothing. Made no certain sign, but almost stealthily had passed his office on; had beckoned me in closer to his side. Here went the signal to each man, and no man could fail to see it. "When the time comes, here stands your leader. When the hour strikes, here is the hand ready to steer you on."

Three hours later I was back again in *The Five Wounds*, and later still at my watch. I loved such nights. I loved such quiet sea. I was the wakeful man, and I alone: the drowsy fellow on the look-out did not matter. I was the waking watching man then, and all about me lazy, sluggish forms slept and groaned and dreamed. But I had all the wonder of that great still sea, I had all the beauty of that spreading sky, I had all the magic of complete tranquillity. I might have been the only living soul amongst dead men. The only moving thing on a phantom ship—mine was this moment, and the wonder of the next few hours kept secret only to me. This night! I think the night bewitched me.

I fancied there seemed some stealthy movement in the very night itself. Some hidden mystery I could not comprehend. A sense of beauty, dim, remote, piled up with wonder; a sudden hungry dread lest it would pass before I understood. Something out there beyond that cloak of darkness. Some hidden loveliness too far for my reach, too wise for my vain looking? How mad is dreaming! Nothing beyond that space and quiet but Santa Verde. One week and I would sack a town; one week and I would lead a fight; one week, and where there had been peace and content there would be wreckage and disorder. And yet the spell still held me. And when it passed I was conscious of a curious ecstasy and uplift of spirit as if in one swift moment I had glimpsed the edge of some grave sweetness, as if the time would come when I might touch it with my hand and marvel at its beauty, at my understanding.

It was Jamie who disturbed my dream. His pale mooning face peered suddenly at my elbow, and his slow drawl broke in upon my thoughts.

"What think you, Mister Peter, of this coming business?"

I knew that tone. He was in his most detestably sober mood, when he would "Mister" me with every word and all the sexton side of him showed uppermost. I said curtly—for somehow I resented this break, yet I knew I could not shake him off—

"Why, God, man, what's wrong with it? Would you suck your thumbs for ever? What do I think—why nothing but it's been monstrous slow in coming."

He shook his head gloomily. "As Pascal says, it is but crazy to get infighting; I care not what I fight nor how, but 'tis no proper season to go out with bloody hands."

I said brutally, "You'd stay at home and sing hymns? Men are not wanted with faint stomachs!"

I saw him flush; I knew the drunken Jamie would have drawn at that sneer. Then I would never have spoken so. It was this sober, pious, morose mood which teased each sense of mine—or did to-night.

He answered slowly, "Lord, Lord, do I offend? My stomach is well enough, though empty maybe, and like to grow melancholy."

I said impatiently, "Plague take your trick of tongue which leads mine on! We go together when the time comes; let it be cheerily. The thing is settled, the season has no part in it."

He retorted with sudden heat, "Easy for him and his face buried in the scriptures!" He was staring at the light from the skylight of the cabin where I knew my father still read and prayed. "Easy for him, he does not need the drink; so easy he must check the bottles when we go sailing! But I—I am all shivering and cold without the warmth, and full of ghosts. He should remember, it's not Christian to keep me from my quiet."

I cried irritably, "Why, go hang for a crazy fool! are we not all the same? Would you have us reeling round the decks because of parched gullets?"

He retorted with undue savageness, "Different for you, different for you, young fool! For me—" he stopped and turned away; and I could hear him muttering in his old timid way, "for me it presses close, but there's the steward; I must remember, for I love him; ay so, I love him heartily."

I crossed to glance at the compass; and then walked aft to the rail and stared down at the running water. It was no use arguing with Jamie; I could only hope he might forget and go and seek his beloved steward. I knew well enough my father would not care. I think he hated Jamie as much as I when this fit held him, for I had seen him ply him with wine, yet keep it well from Pascal and me. He knew his men. We two drunk were little worse than dead; Jamie—Jamie was worth two sober men when well filled.

So I kept to the rail and felt for my pipe and tobacco. . . .

We were three days out when the weather took on a change. The wind died, so we moved hardly at all; but the whole sea was caught in a sudden swell, and the ship lurched and pitched until hardly a man could walk straight. That night there were no stars, and when the moon rose it showed dull and thick, and the heat of that night was such that the men lay huddled about the deck all naked, and Pascal for once discarded his wig and showed a steaming head and a clammy shirt. That night also the swell increased, until, when the sun came yellow as an orange, we were staggering against each other, and some were caught with most deadly sickness.

By noon it had grown very dark, by the early evening we moved in immense blackness. Hardly one went to their beds, but stayed out on deck not sleeping, but rather wakeful and stirred by much uneasiness.

Just before we struck eight bells my father gave the order to lower top-sails.

Said Pascal, when we were done:

"A timely order, but I would strip the poles; I'll swear a most provoking end to this vile sea—curse me if I speak not right."

I said, "They have done with the brig," and handed him my glass that he might see the better. We could just make her out by the light from her lantern and her round-house. Smaller than we, she was already shipping water, and we could see it foam across her deck and beat against her poop. Said Pascal with a shrug:

"Pox me, they'll die wet to-night! I will be damned where I stand, if you and I, my pretty dear, do not suck much salt e'er we see the sun again."

And almost at once my father cried suddenly, "Aft here, another to the wheel!" And a man came stumbling from the gloom and set his hands on the spokes beside that of the helmsman. At that instant there came the lightning.

It was as if a giant fist thrust from heaven, sword in hand, and cut and thrust, and drove and slashed, and ripped the blackness from top to bottom and ripped again a racing running ribbon of flame. So were we then caught in the trough of fire—a fire which seemed to light our ship from bow to stern, and make each one of us a living flame, staggering and trembling in bewildered fright. Swiftly—this assault of fire; and swiftly finished. And all those multitude of cracks which had rent the sky were instantly closed up, and we left silent and staring in wild expectancy of what was still to come from that pitch night.

I heard some voice cry, "Why, now we run in hell; this is a bloody end."

And then there broke the shrill pipe of the bos'n, and with it my father's voice: "All hands furl sail!" . . .

They came out with a rush and scrambling of feet, but I think they were dazed if not frightened by the tense atmosphere, for they showed no order and went clumsily for the shrouds. I know I leapt into the midst of them and struck at those in my reach and bawled:

"Up, you dogs, up, you lame cattle. Drive to it, drive to it! Are you turned all thumbs, you infernal idle ducks!"

Give them their due, they sprung to it well enough, and put good speed into their work, for it was none too pleasant clinging to the yards. At such a height we seemed pressed right up into the blackness, yet ducking this way and that with each plunge of the ship. It was just as we furled the mainsail that the rain came. Cold rain: thick, cutting, driving rain! High as I was, I could hear it crashing to the deck like the breaking of thousands of eggshells, like the splintering of broken glass. Dark as it had been before, this rushing rain completely cut away all sight. We groped and fumbled and caught at each other like blind men; it pricked and bruised our skin until I bent my stinging face. How I got down I know not, nor how any other of us managed. Once on deck I sprawled and slid every inch of my way back to Pascal, where now, with another man, he was fighting the wheel.

He put his mouth to my ear and blared, "Hold to it, Peter, hold to it! By God, she tears like an untrained colt. Harris is gone, whipped overboard like a handkerchief. 'Pon wig, there is no nicety in so much water."

I squeezed the water from my eyes and shouted, "Where's my father?"

"Below with Jamie. Extra lashings needed for the guns; one gone loose when you were a-top." He screamed suddenly: "Here comes the wind. Now use your wrists!"

It seemed to leap at us like a hound suddenly unleashed; it caught our ship and shook her as such a hound would when closing with his prey. It was all over and around us. Flogging, thrashing, beating, pitching us this way and that, pitching the ship until it seemed she must be dragged down and beneath the surging sea.

Nothing so drunk as *The Five Wounds*. Staggering, heaving, beating into the very depth of the sea, yet mounting to top it, caught by an immense pillar of water, yet crashing through with water streaming from her like a cataract.

Once, and we went down, down, down; and a figure came hurtling past me battered, screaming, and clutching, only to be sucked over the rail. And up, up, up—and the whole ship on top of us, and the breath of my body seemed knocked clean out. Then, with a rush and a stagger, she was steady, and with a rush and a stagger the wind caught her again and battered at her sides until she seemed to shriek like a live thing. And all this while the wheel tore and raged and kicked beneath our bleeding hands, until the other man screamed aloud with pain in his arms, and sank to our feet, when Pascal let out a kick and an oath and his body slid away in the wash and was beaten and tossed from side to side until it vanished out of sight.

And Pascal shrieked: "This is a pretty way to hell; praised be, though, I can dry my shirt."

I shouted back at him, "Here goes our expedition!"

But he only roared, "Nay, 'tis part of it: this is our merry holiday— yet but the start."

I said in his ear, "God grant a merrier finish." He leant to me, but what he cried I never heard. There came a sudden crash, a tearing rending sound, and with it, even above the storm, shriek after shriek of dreadful pain. The whole ship seemed to stagger and even stand still, then pitch so to her side that I could see the sea surging like a whirlpool beneath me, then as suddenly seemed to right herself yet lie aslant. I shrieked at Pascal:

"God's mercy, are we struck?"

He shouted back, "The foremast," and screamed louder, "Now burst your heart if need be—cling to her, my duck; if we break loose we'll lick the sand e'er the hour past!"

We stood there, blinded and beaten by the sea, cursing and sore from rain, battered and bruised by wind—cursing each other till our tongues ached as our bodies. Said I, as Pascal nearly pitched flat to the deck and the wheel dragged at my tortured arms:

"Are your legs water? Twist them about the yard. Fat fool, press in with your belly, hold to it, hold to it!"

And Pascal, "A babe I'd rather have! A two-year weakling than thy flesh of powder! Off with shoes—cling naked—ah, be damned!" and he slipped again cursing, and I storming at him the more.

"Dance with each swing; must there be a petticoat for ever to help your balance? Swing to it, swing, God damr. thee."

And Pascal, "She's over now! 'Pon wig, here goes our end! Now, now, this way, this way!—with me, loon, with me."

And I, with some triumph, "By God, she's not! Now pull, pull, I say. Lay to it; ho, ho! she's speaking!"

There seemed some pause in the gale, and I stared at Pascal, my lids stiff with salt, and he at me, the water running like a river down his face. And we both grinning and mouthing terrific oaths.

Said Pascal, "My duckling, I would kiss you, as cunning a hand as I have known! 'Pon wig, I may have ducats yet for that pretty jade in New York!"

I said joyously, "I thought you gone once. By God we'll make a day of it if we see shore."

There was a light at the edge of the sky which gave hope the weather was passing, and though the sea burst with as much fury, there showed a lull to the wind. Out of the gloom came suddenly my father, his coat torn and his cheek bloody, yet with a curious gleam in his eyes. He drew very near to us, his hand upon my shoulder. He cried in a huge trumpeting voice:

"Did I not tell you? There is no beauty like a ship—my ship, mark ye—baring her naked breast to the storm. She has a grace not known by any creature, when she goes riding out, when I can see her lift her face and laugh the sea away."

I heard a snort from Pascal: he screamed some answer which was lost in the wind; it did not matter; I had my own shouting to do. We were sodden to our very bones, there was no part of us which was not torn or bruised or was not numbed with weariness, yet my father could only babble of the ship.

I snarled in his face: "God's sake, what time have we to watch her beauty? Did we not hold her to it? I tell you, she kicks like a mule, and enough to break one as the rack!"

He did not seem to hear. He was caught by his own tremendous ecstasy, and even the continuous pitching did not seem to waken him.

He cried aloud, stretching both hands out to the maddened sea. "Ah, but you cannot rend her! She is a peerless thing. A spirit divine, which can break the sea as Christ once broke the tomb! I would not close my eyes to this, my darling; I would not deafen my ears to all these trumpets. Ride on! Ride on! Here walks my God this night!"

I wanted news; I shouted up at him, "We were near done, when the mast went—how with the rest?"

He stared at me as if I were some stranger, and cried with an oath: "What do I care? Men come and go; what is their value but to answer when the challenge comes? I tell you, boy, I have no part with men, save to use their fingers and thumbs! Six feed the salt, seven are work for the doctor. They showed a clumsiness, and paid their toll."

I cried in dismay: "Thirteen! Hell to it, we have a villainous trouble!"

He retorted, "What of it? What of it? We have the ship!"

I cried, exasperated, "What use the ship when we go inland? What of the brig?"

He shrugged his shoulders. "I know not, or any man. With the light——"

Said Pascal with sudden fury, " 'Pon wig, a pretty picnic, so we turn home with empty baskets!"

My father turned on him with sudden savageness. "Is your tail down, dog? Our road is straight."

I heard Pascal gasp, and he spat a great oath. "On now? By God, you mean it?"

Said my father, "By God, I do!" and stalked forward.

CANADA

THE FRUITS OF TOIL[1]

Norman Duncan

NOW the wilderness, savage and remote, yields to the strength of men. A generation strips it of tree and rock, a generation tames it and tills it, a generation passes into the evening shadows as into rest in a garden, and thereafter the children of that place possess it in peace and plenty, through succeeding generations, without end, and shall to the end of the world. But the sea is tameless: as it was in the beginning, it is now, and shall ever be—mighty, savage, dread, infinitely treacherous and hateful, yielding only that which is wrested from it, snarling, raging, snatching lives, spoiling souls of their graces. The tiller of the soil sows in peace, and in a yellow, hazy peace he reaps; he passes his hand over a field, and, lo, in good season he gathers a harvest, for the earth rejoices to serve him. The deep is not thus subdued; the toiler of the sea—the Newfoundlander of the upper shore—is born to conflict, ceaseless and deadly, and, in the dawn of all the days, he puts forth anew to wage it, as his father did, and his father's father, and as his children must, and his children's children, to the last of them; nor from day to day can he foresee the issue, nor from season to season foretell the worth of the spoil, which is what chance allows. Thus laboriously, precariously, he slips through life: he follows hope through the toilsome years; and past summers are a black regret and bitterness to him, but summers to come are all rosy with new promise.

Long ago, when young Luke Dart, the Boot Bay trader, was ambitious for Shore patronage, he said to Solomon Stride, of Ragged Harbour, a punt fisherman: "Solomon, b'y, an you be willin', I'll trust you with twine for a cod-trap. An you trade with me, b'y, I'll trade with you, come good times or bad." Solomon was young and lusty, a mighty youth in bone and seasoned muscle, lunged like a blast furnace, courageous and finely sanguine. Said he: "An you trust me with twine for a trap, skipper, I'll deal fair by you, come good times or bad. I'll pay for us, skipper, with the first fish I cotches." Said Luke Dart: "When I trust, b'y, I trust. You pays for un when you can." It was a compact, so, at the end of the season, Solomon builded a cottage under the Man-o'-War, Broad Cove way, and married a maid of the place. In five months of that winter he made the trap, every net of it, leader and all, with his own hands, that he might know that the work was good, to the last knot and splice. In the spring, he put up the stage and the flake, and made the skiff;

[1]From *The Way of the Sea*. Reprinted by permission of Fleming H. Revell Company.

which done, he waited for a sign of fish. When the tempered days came, he hung the net on the horse, where it could be seen from the threshold of the cottage. In the evenings he sat with Priscilla on the bench at the door, and dreamed great dreams, while the red sun went down in the sea, and the shadows crept out of the wilderness.

"Woman, dear," said this young Solomon Stride, with a slap of his great thigh, "'twill be a gran' season for fish this year."

"Sure, b'y," said Priscilla, tenderly; "'twill be a gran' season for fish."

"Ay," Solomon sighed, "'twill that—this year."

The gloaming shadows gathered over the harbour water, and hung, sullenly, between the great rocks, rising all roundabout.

"'Tis handy t' three hundred an' fifty dollars I owes Luke Dart for the twine," mused Solomon.

"'Tis a hape o' money t' owe," said Priscilla.

"Hut!" growled Solomon, deep in his chest. "'Tis like nothin'."

"'Tis not much," said Priscilla, smiling, "when you has a trap."

Dusk and a clammy mist chased the glory from the hills, the rocks turned black, and a wind, black and cold, swept out of the wilderness and ran to sea.

"Us'll pay un all up this year," said Solomon. "Oh," he added, loftily, "'twill be easy. 'Tis t' be a gran' season!"

"Sure!" said she, echoing his confidence.

Night filled the cloudy heavens overhead. It drove the flush of pink in upon the sun, and, following fast and overwhelmingly, thrust the flaring red and gold over the rim of the sea; and it was dark.

"Us'll pay un for a trap, dear," chuckled Solomon, "an' have enough left over t' buy a——"

"Oh," she cried, with an ecstatic gasp, "a sewin' machane."

"Iss," he roared. "Sure, girl!"

But, in the beginning of that season, when the first fish ran in for the caplin and the nets were set out, the ice was still hanging off shore, drifting vagrantly with the wind; and there came a gale in the night, springing from the north-east—a great, vicious wind, which gathered the ice in a pack and drove it swiftly in upon the land. Solomon Stride put off in a punt, in a sea tossing and white, to loose the trap from its moorings. Three times, while the pack swept nearer, crunching and horribly groaning, as though lashed to cruel speed by the gale, the wind beat him back through the tickle; and, upon the fourth essay, when his strength was breaking, the ice ran over the place where the trap was, and chased the punt into the harbour, frothing upon its flank. When, three days thereafter, a west wind carried the ice to sea, Solomon dragged the trap from the bottom. Great holes were bruised in the nets, head rope and span line were ground to pulp, the anchors were lost. Thirty-seven days and nights it took him to make the nets whole again, and in that time the great spring run of cod passed by. So, in the next Spring, Solomon was deeper in the debt of sympathetic Luke Dart—for the new twine and for the winter's food he had eaten; but, of an evening, when he sat on the bench with Priscilla, he looked through the gloaming shadows gathered over the harbour water and hanging between the great rocks, to the golden summer approaching, and dreamed gloriously of the fish he would catch in his trap.

"Priscilla, dear," said Solomon Stride, slapping his iron thigh, "they be a fine sign o' fish down the coast. 'Twill be a gran' season, I'm thinkin'."

"Sure, b'y," Priscilla agreed; " 'twill be a gran' cotch o' fish you'll have this year."

Dusk and the mist touched the hills, and, in the dreamful silence, their glory faded; the rocks turned black, and the wind from the wilderness ruffled the water beyond the flake.

"Us'll pay Luke Dart this year, I tells you," said Solomon, like a boastful boy. "Us'll pay un twice over."

" 'Twill be fine t' have the machane," said she, with shining eyes.

"An' the calico t' use un on," said he.

And so, while the night spread overhead, these two simple folk feasted upon all the sweets of life; and all that they desired they possessed, as fast as fancy could form wishes, just though as the bench were a bit of magic furniture, to bring dreams true—until the night, advancing, thrust the red and gold of the sunset clouds over the rim of the sea, and it was dark.

"Leave us goa in," said Priscilla.

"This year," said Solomon, rising, "I be goain' t' cotch three hundred quintals o' fish. Sure, I be—this year."

" 'Twill be fine," said she.

It chanced in that year that the fish failed utterly; hence, in the winter following, Ragged Harbour fell upon days of distress; and three old women and one old man starved to death—and five children, of whom one was the infant son of Solomon Stride. Neither in that season, nor in any one of the thirteen years coming after, did this man catch three hundred quintals of cod in his trap. In pure might of body—in plenitude and quality of strength—in the full, eager power of brawn—he was great as the men of any time, a towering glory to the whole race, here hidden; but he could not catch three hundred quintals of cod. In spirit—in patience, hope, courage, and the fine will for toil—he was great; but, good season or bad, he could not catch three hundred quintals of cod. He met night, cold, fog, wind, and the fury of waves, in their craft, in their swift assault, in their slow, crushing descent; but all the cod he could wrest from the sea, being given into the hands of Luke Dart, an honest man, yielded only sufficient provision for food and clothing for himself and Priscilla—only enough to keep their bodies warm and still the crying of their stomachs. Thus, while the nets of the trap rotted, and Solomon came near to middle age, the debt swung from seven hundred dollars to seven, and back to seventy-three, which it was on an evening in spring, when he sat with Priscilla on the sunken bench at the door, and dreamed great dreams, as he watched the shadows gather over the harbour water and sullenly hang between the great rocks, rising all roundabout.

"I wonder, b'y," said Priscilla, "if 'twill be a good season—this year."

"Oh, sure!" exclaimed Solomon. "Sure!"

"D'ye think it, b'y?" wistfully.

"Woman," said he, impressively, "us'll cotch a hape o' fish in the trap this year. They be millions o' fish t' the say," he went on excitedly; "millions o' fish t' the say. They be there, woman. 'Tis oan'y for us t' take un out. I be goain' t' wark hard this year."

"You be a great warker, Solomon," said she; "my, but you be!"

Priscilla smiled, and Solomon smiled; and it was as though all the labour and peril of the season were past, and the stage were full to the roof with salt cod. In the happiness of this dream they smiled again, and turned their eyes to the hills, from which the glory of purple and yellow was departing to make way for the misty dusk.

"Skipper Luke Dart says t' me," said Solomon, "that 'tis the luxuries that keeps folk poor."

Priscilla said nothing at all.

"They be nine dollars agin me in seven years for crame o' tartar," said Solomon. "Think o' that!"

"My," said she, "but 'tis a lot! But we be used to un now, Solomon, an' we can't get along with un."

"Sure," said he, "'tis good we're not poor like some folk."

Night drove the flush of pink in upon the sun and followed the red and gold of the horizon over the rim of the sea.

"'Tis growin' cold," said she.

"Leave us goa in," said he.

In thirty years after that time, Solomon Stride put to sea ten thousand times. Ten thousand times he passed through the tickle rocks to the free, heaving deep for salmon and cod, thereto compelled by the inland waste, which contributes nothing to the sustenance of the men of that coast. Hunger, lurking in the shadows of days to come, inexorably drove him into the chances of the conflict. Perforce he matched himself ten thousand times against the restless might of the sea, immeasurable and unrestrained, surviving the gamut of its moods because he was great in strength, fearlessness, and cunning. He weathered four hundred gales, from the grey gusts which came down between Quid Nunc and the Man-o'-War, leaping upon the fleet, to the summer tempests, swift and black, and the first blizzards of winter. He was wrecked off the Mull, off the Three Poor Sisters, on the Pancake Rock, and again off the Mull. Seven times he was swept to sea by the off-shore wind. Eighteen times he was frozen to the seat of his punt; and of these, eight times his feet were frozen, and thrice his festered right hand. All this he suffered, and more, of which I may set down six separate periods of starvation, in which thirty-eight men, women, and children died—all this, with all the toil, cold, despair, loneliness, hunger, peril, and disappointment therein contained. And so he came down to old age—with a bent back, shrunken arms, and filmy eyes—old Solomon Stride, now prey for the young sea. But, of an evening in spring, he sat with Priscilla on the sunken bench at the door, and talked hopefully of the fish he would catch from his punt.

"Priscilla, dear," said he, rubbing his hand over his weazened thigh, "I be thinkin' us punt fishermen 'll have a——"

Priscilla was not attending; she was looking into the shadows above the harbour water, dreaming deeply of a mystery of the Book, which had long puzzled her; so, in silence, Solomon, too, watched the shadows rise and sullenly hang between the great rocks.

"Solomon, b'y," she whispered, "I wonder what the seven thunders uttered."

"'Tis quare, that—what the seven thunders uttered," said Solomon. "My, woman, but 'tis!"

"'An' he set his right foot upon the sea,'" she repeated, staring over the greying water to the clouds which flamed gloriously at the edge of the world, "'an' his left foot on the earth——'"

"'An' cried with a loud voice,'" said he, whispering in awe, "'as when a lion roareth; an' when he had cried, *seven thunders uttered their voices.*'"

"'Seven thunders uttered their voices,'" said she; "'an' when the seven thunders had uttered their voices, I was about to write, an' I heard a voice from heaven sayin' unto me, Seal up those things which the seven thunders uttered, an' write them not.'"

The wind from the wilderness, cold and black covered the hills with mist; the dusk fell, and the glory faded from the heights.

"Oh, Solomon," she said, clasping her hands, "I wonder what the seven thunders uttered! Think you, b'y, 'twas the kind o' sins that can't be forgiven?"

"'Tis the seven mysteries."

"I wonder what they be," said she.

"Sh-h-h, dear," he said, patting her grey head; "thinkin' on they things'll capsize you an you don't look out."

The night had driven all the colour from the sky; it had descended upon the red and gold of the cloudy west, and covered them. It was cold and dark.

"'An' seven thunders uttered their voices,'" she said, dreamily.

"Sh-h-h, dear!" said he. "Leave us goa in."

Twenty-one years longer old Solomon Stride fished out of Ragged Harbour. He put to sea five thousand times more, weathered two hun-

dred more gales, survived five more famines—all in the toil for salmon
and cod. He was a punt fisherman again, was old Solomon; for the nets
of the trap had rotted, had been renewed six times, strand by strand, and
had rotted at last beyond repair. What with the weather he dared not
pit his failing strength against, the return of fish to Luke Dart fell off
from year to year; but, as Solomon said to Luke, "livin' expenses kep'
up wonderful," notwithstanding.

"I be so used t' luxuries," he said, running his hand through his long
grey hair, "that 'twould be hard t' come down t' common livin'. Sure,
'tis sugar I wants t' me tea—not black-strap. 'Tis what I l'arned," he
added, proudly, "when I were a trap fisherman."

"'Tis all right, Solomon," said Luke. "Many's the quintal o' fish you
traded with me."

"Sure," Solomon chuckled; "'twould take a year t' count un."

In course of time it came to the end of Solomon's last season—those
days of it when, as the folk of the coast say, the sea is hungry for lives—
and the man was eighty-one years old, and the debt to Luke Dart had
crept up to $230.80. The off-shore wind, rising suddenly, with a blizzard
in its train, caught him alone on the Grappling Hook grounds. He was
old, very old—old and feeble and dull: the cold numbed him; the snow
blinded him; the wind made sport of the strength of his arms. He was
carried out to sea, rowing doggedly, thinking all the time that he was
drawing near the harbour tickle; for it did not occur to him then that
the last of eight hundred gales could be too great for him. He was carried
out from the sea, where the strength of his youth had been spent, to the
Deep, which had been a mystery to him all his days. That night he passed
on a pan of ice, where he burned his boat, splinter by splinter, to keep
warm. At dawn he lay down to die. The snow ceased, the wind changed;
the ice was carried to Ragged Harbour. Eleazar Manuel spied the body
of Solomon from the lookout, and put out and brought him in—revived
him and took him home to Priscilla. Through the winter the old man
doddered about the harbour, dying of consumption. When the tempered
days came—the days of balmy sunshine and cold evening winds—he
came quickly to the pass of glittering visions, which, for such as die of
the lung trouble, come at the end of life.

In the spring, when the *Lucky Star*, three days out from Boot Bay,
put into Ragged Harbour to trade for the first catch, old Skipper Luke
Dart was aboard, making his last voyage to the shore; for he was very
old, and longed once more to see the rocks of all that coast before he
made ready to die. When he came ashore, Eleazar Manuel told him that
Solomon Stride lay dying at home; so the skipper went to the cottage
under Man-o'-War to say good-bye to his old customer and friend—
and there found him, propped up in bed, staring at the sea.

"Skipper Luke," Solomon quavered, in deep excitement, "be you
just come in, b'y?"

"Iss—but an hour gone."

"What be the big craft hangin' off shore? Eh—what be she, b'y?"

There had been no craft in sight when the *Lucky Star* beat in. "Were she a fore-an'-after, Solomon?" said Luke, evasively.

"Sure, noa, b'y," cried Solomon. "She were a square-rigged craft, with all sail set—a great, gran' craft—a quare craft, b'y—like she were made o' glass, canvas an' hull an' all; an' she had shinin' ropes, an' she were shinin' all over. Sure, they be a star t' the tip o' her bowsprit, b'y, an' a star t' the peak o' her mainmast—seven stars they be, in all. Oh, she were a gran' sight!"

"Hem-m!" said Luke, stroking his beard. "She've not come in yet."

"A gran' craft!" said Solomon.

"'Tis accordin'," said Luke, "t' whether you be sot on oak bottoms or glass ones."

"She were bound down north t' the Labrador," Solomon went on quickly, "an' when she made the Grapplin' Hook grounds she come about an' headed for the tickle, with her sails squared. Sure she ran right over the Pancake, b'y, like he weren't there at all, an'——How's the wind, b'y?"

"Dead off shore from the tickle."

Solomon stared at Luke. "She were comin' straight in agin the wind," he said, hoarsely. "Maybe, skipper," he went on, with a little laugh, "she do be the ship for souls. They be many things strong men knows nothin' about. What think you?"

"Ay—maybe; maybe she be."

"Maybe—maybe—she do be invisible t' mortal eyes. Maybe, skipper, you hasn't seed her; maybe 'tis that my eyes do be opened t' such sights. Maybe she've turned in—for me."

The men turned their faces to the window again, and gazed long and intently at the sea, which a storm cloud had turned black. Solomon dozed for a moment, and when he awoke, Luke Dart was still staring dreamily out to sea.

"Skipper Luke," said Solomon, with a smile as of one in an enviable situation, "'tis fine t' have nothin' agin you on the books when you come t' die."

"Sure, b'y," said Luke, hesitating not at all, though he knew to a cent what was on the books against Solomon's name, "'tis fine t' be free o' debt."

"Ah," said Solomon, the smile broadening gloriously, "'tis fine, I tells you! 'Twas the three hundred quintal I cotched last season that paid un all up. 'Twas a gran' cotch—last year. Ah," he sighed, "'twas a gran' cotch o' fish."

"Iss—you be free o' debt now, b'y."

"What be the balance t' my credit, skipper? Sure I forget."

"Hem-m," the skipper coughed, pausing to form a guess which might be within Solomon's dream; then he ventured: "Fifty dollars."

"Iss," said Solomon, "fifty an' more, skipper. Sure, you has forgot the the eighty cents."

"Fifty-eighty," said the skipper, positively. "'Tis that. I call un t' mind now. 'Tis fifty-eight—iss, sure. Did you get a receipt for un, Solomon?"

"I doan't mind me now."

"Um-m-m-well," said the skipper, "I'll send un t' the woman the night—an order on the *Lucky Star*."

"Fifty-eighty for the woman!" said Solomon. "'Twill kape her off the Gov'ment for three years, and she be savin'. 'Tis fine—that!"

When the skipper had gone, Priscilla crept in, and sat at the head of the bed, holding Solomon's hand; and they were silent for a long time, while the evening approached.

"I be goain' t' die the night, dear," said Solomon at last.

"Iss, b'y," she answered; "you be goain' t' die."

Solomon was feverish now; and, thereafter, when he talked his utterance was thick and fast.

"'Tis not hard," said Solomon. "Sh-h-h," he whispered, as though about to impart a secret. "The ship that's hangin' off shoare, waitin' for me soul, do be a fine craft—with shinin' canvas an' ropes. Sh-h. She do be t'other side o' Mad Mull now—waitin'."

Priscilla trembled, for Solomon had come to the time of visions—when the words of the dying are the words of prophets, and contain revelations. What of the utterings of the seven thunders?

"Sure the Lord he've blessed us, Priscilla," said Solomon, rational again. "Goodness an' mercy has followed us all the days o' our lives. Our cup runneth over."

"Praise the Lord," said Priscilla.

"Sure," Solomon went on, smiling like a little child, "we've had but eleven famines, an' we've had the means o' grace pretty reg'lar, which is what they hasn't t' Round 'Arbour. We've had one little baby for a little while. Iss—one de'are little baby, Priscilla; an' there's them that's had none o' their own at all. Sure we've had enough t'eat when they wasn't a famine—an' bakin powder, an' raisins, an' all they things, an' sugar, an' rale good tea. An' you had a merino dress, an' I had a suit o' rale tweed—come straight from England. We hasn't seed a railway train, dear, but we've seed a steamer, and we've heard tell o' the quare things they be t' St Johns. Ah, the Lard he've favoured us above our deserts. He've been good t' us, Priscilla. But, oh, you hasn't had the sewin' machane, an' you hasn't had the peach-stone t' plant in the garden. 'Tis my fault, dear—'tis not the Lard's. I should 'a' got you the peach-stone from St Johns, you did want un so much—oh, so much! 'Tis that I be sorry for, now, dear; but 'tis all over, an' I can't help it. It wouldn't 'a' growed anyway, I know it wouldn't; but you thought it would, an' I wisht I'd got un for you."

"'Tis nothin', Solomon," she sobbed. "Sure, I was joakin' all the time. 'Twouldn't 'a' growed."

"Ah," he cried, radiant, "was you joakin'?"

"Sure," she said.

"We've not been poor, Priscilla," said he, continuing. "An' they be many folk that's poor. I be past me labour now," he went on, talking with rising effort, for it was at the sinking of the sun, "an' 'tis time for me t' die. 'Tis time—for I be past me labour."

Priscilla held his hand a long time after that—a long, silent time, in which the soul of the man struggled to release itself, until it was held but by a thread.

"Solomon!"

The old man seemed not to hear.

"Solomon, b'y!"

"Iss?" faintly.

She leaned over him to whisper in his ear, "Does you see the gates o' heaven?" she said. "Oh, does you?"

"Sure, dear; heaven do be——"

Solomon had not strength enough to complete the sentence.

"B'y! B'y!"

He opened his eyes and turned them to her face. There was the gleam of a tender smile in them.

"The seven thunders," she said. "The utterin's of the seven thunders —what was they, b'y?"

"'An' the seven thunders uttered their voices,'" he mumbled, "'an'—'

She waited, rigid, listening, to hear the rest; but no words came to her ears.

"Does you hear me, b'y?" she said.

"'An' seven—thunders—uttered their voices,'" he gasped, "'an' the seven thunders—said—said——'"

The light failed; all the light and golden glory went out of the sky, for the first cloud of a tempest had curtained the sun.

"'An' said——" she prompted.

"'An' uttered—an' said—an' said——'"

"Oh, what?" she moaned.

Now, in that night, when the body of old Solomon Stride, a worn-out hulk, aged and wrecked in the toil of the deep, fell into the hands of Death, the sea, like a lusty youth, raged furiously in those parts. The ribs of many schooners, slimy and rotten, and the white bones of men in the off-shore depths, know of its strength in that hour—of its black, hard wrath, in gust and wave and breaker. Eternal in might and malignance is the sea! It groweth not old with the men who toil from its coasts. Generation upon the heels of generation, infinitely arising, go forth in hope against it, continuing for a space, and returning spent to the dust. They age and crumble and vanish, each in its turn, and the wretchedness of the first is the wretchedness of the last. Ay, the sea has measured the strength of the dust in old graves, and, in this day, contends with the sons of dust, whose sons will follow to the fight for an hundred generations and thereafter, until harvest may be gathered from rocks. As it is written, the life of a man is a shadow, swiftly passing, and the days of his strength are less; but the sea shall endure in the might of youth to the wreck of the world.

AUSTRALIA

FOURTEEN FATHOMS BY QUETTA ROCK[1]

Randolph Bedford
(1868–   )

THE palm-fronds threshed softly. Night to midnight the land breeze became too strong for anything but the frangipani scent; the palm-fronds threshed through the air saturated with moonlight; the red lamp on the jetty showed as a purple stain.

The last of the pilots of Torres Straits went to bed; the Grand Hotel of Thursday Island closed its bar; but the two barefoot men on the veranda talked on the topic that had lasted since dusk—the wreck of the *Pandora*—and one man, Pipon, tried to soothe the other, Moresby, who talked without ceasing of the wreck and twenty thousand pounds' worth of pearls.

"Can we get a launch, Jim?" he asked.

"I told you no," replied Pipon. "Bear up, old man; y' can have a lugger."

"A lugger and a dead calm? It would be worse than waiting here."

"Well, quiet a bit!"

"Quiet! How can I be—when I am in a fever to be there?"

He looked south as if trying to make out the coast of Australia, now the ghost of a shadow in the moon haze and sea blur."

"What could you do if you were, Martin?"

"I could stand by the wreck; I could——"

"You couldn't do any good. It's lucky Phil Regard is coming to-morrow. He's the British India diver. He'll do all there is to be done."

"My pearls, Tom! The big one and nine ounces of little ones. Oyley was bringing them up. What depths did the *Pandora* sink in?"

"Nobody knows, old man, or how she went. The skipper was a good man—exempt, too. Knew every key and every inch of reef—and there's millions of 'em."

"It was my rotten luck, Tom, to miss the *Pandora* by five minutes and then pick up the *Maranea* to catch her here, and find when I did get here that she'd sunk fifty or a hundred miles south. And there's my pearls —Oyley was taking charge of them—and then I missed the ship. Oh, gimme a raft and I'll start!"

"Not you! Come on, take a fool's advice and sleep. You'll leave it all to Phil Regard."

---

[1]Reprinted by permission of the author.

The grass trees rustled softly to the poinciana as the men went to bed; the breeze strengthened to a wind and replaced perfume with a taste of salt; from the veranda above a man began to whimper—a man that had seen death and terror and was now dreaming it all over again and shrieking out the story in his recurrent nightmare—the one survivor of the *Pandora*, who had been picked up by a pearling lugger.

"She's going! Two minutes—you can't get the boats out of the chocks. Why didn't they have boat practice? You can't! You can't! Don't scream, women—dear women, don't scream—it's better to drown than——Ah, my God, the sharks! the sharks!"

Druce, the pilot of Torres Straits, boarded that slow, comfortable, old-time high-pooped steamer of the tea-clipper type, the *Airlie*, at Goode Island, and brought her up in the early dawn to the wharf at Thursday. A big, brown-eyed man was the first to land; he was a man in a hurry—in a hurry for news, at least. He waited for neither bath nor breakfast, but aroused an irritated postmaster and begged so for telegrams that the postmaster gave him his mail long before the beginning of office hours. There were many newspapers, and he did not look at them; a dozen letters, all man-directed and official, and he put them in his pocket. A bitter disappointment settled on his face—the letter from the beloved was not there. He found new hope in the telegrams. Alas! They were as the letters; and his heart was heavy then. This diver, who knew no fear that he could not fight down, fought against his disappointment and could not conquer it.

"I telegraphed her from Darwin, and she hasn't wired a reply. She's thoughtless, not cruel, not cruel—my girl."

He took from his pocket-book a photograph; looked at it and put it back again.

"God bless her! I'll telegraph again, and in seven days we'll be together—for a month, anyhow. But—she might have made sure of not missing the post; a letter would make me a king to-day."

He returned to duty by taking a telegram from his pockets, and a fierce resentment held him for a moment as he read it:

"*Pandora* sunk; locate wreck; if not impossible, recover gold, ship's papers. B. P. provide tug and tender; made splendid terms."

So he would not see her in a week—happiness was to be postponed again. He thought of the long two months of salvage diving in the Flores Sea. Three months since he had seen her, and now there was to be another fortnight of hunger for her!

But hope came to his comfort. "Another year and I'll have made enough to retire on, with this new chance. Then no separation!

So he went to Burns Philip, and arranged for the departure of the little steamer, hired diving tenders and had his diving gear brought from the *Airlie's* hold. It was then that Moresby found him—Moresby of the drowned pearls; and the commission made Phil Regard almost gay.

"Oyley had 'em," said Moresby. "I gave them to him to mind because I was going on a spree in Brisbane."

"Was he straight, d'ye think?"

"I think so. He put 'em in a little steel box in his trunk—he had his own pearls in the box—and his wife had the key on a chain round her neck."

"What was the number of his cabin, and what was he like?"

"A dark, red-moustached chap—cabin number 41–43B, port side, near the music room."

"You know the ship?"

"I tell you I sailed on her from Sydney to Brisbane and lost my passage at Brisbane through going to the races. I gave the pearls to Oyley when I was going ashore. But you will get 'em again, mate?"

"I don't know. Nobody knows where she foundered. But if I do?"

"Five hundred pounds."

With the lack of ceremony characteristic of the latitude, every man in the bar joined in the conversation.

"Five hundred pounds!" said Druce, the pilot. "Five hundred pounds for dredgin' fifteen or twenty thousand pounds out o' the Pacific Ocean! It's worth that to find the old hulk that hit the rock somewhere, and did me out o' pilot fees."

"I thought it wouldn't be hard to find the wreck," said Moresby. "If——"

"Oh," replied Druce, "if your aunt had whiskers she'd be your uncle. Why, I know ten wrecks about here that no man knows the name of—ships that were never missed. You know, too, don't you, Dan'l?"

An old man, bent and wizened, replied quaveringly, "I've seen below me—when I've been down—old Spanish ships an' old Dutch ships an' old Portugees down below; me in twenty fathoms water an' them deep below, me man——"

"Twenty fathoms—too much," said the big diver. "I've got a girl at home and she wants me. Fifteen fathoms is all I care to go."

"Aa-ah!" said the old diver, nipping with his strong and crooked fingers the arm and leg muscles of Phil Regard, "I was as strong and straight as ye; but deep divin' and showin' off above the other min, an' takin' no notice o' the shootin' pains in me legs—callin' it rheumatics, an' all the time 'tis the paralyser warnin' ye. An' then twenty-three fathom I went, an' hauled up—I was a cripple."

He laughed as he spoke, but there was in his eye a tear of sorrow for his own dead strength; and, to cover his self-pity, he said, with a feeble attempt at gaiety:

"But 'tis only here I am a cripple! Put me down in fifteen or twenty fathom and give me the pressure on me skin again an' a four-knot tide, an' I'll fly along the floorin' of the sea like a sunbird."

"And you're offering five hundred pounds for the chance of that?" said Druce to Moresby. "Open your heart, Moresby."

"A thousand, then," said Moresby. "I want to be fair, and it's all to nothing."

"It isn't," said Phil Regard. "I've got to go below on another contract, and you think I've only got to open a cabin door and take a key from some poor dead woman and open a box. But that means two extra corners to go round, and the more corners the more chances of fouling. It's your pearls to my life. I want a certainty."

"Here y' are, then," said Moresby. "A hundred pounds for opening the cabin door and I'll take your word for it, and a thousand if you bring back the pearls."

"It's a deal," agreed Phil Regard.

The warning bell of the *Airlie* clanged, and Druce departed to his pilotage, Phil Regard, as yet only half resigned, saw the steamer that should have borne him south disappear down the channel, rounding the Residency, and so away to open sea, then he resolutely put regrets behind him and went to his tug and tender to prepare for his attempt to find a few thousand tons of foundered metal in an immensity of blue.

The survivor of the *Pandora* had become quiet enough to talk of the wreck.

"I was steerage steward," he said. "Mister, I can't think! Stay by me, mister—don't leave me alone."

"Hold on to my coat, if you like. I'll stand by."

"We never had a boat practice—rottin' in the chocks, the boats were. It was about eleven at night—moonlight, quiet; y' could hear the scrapin' of shovels in the stoke-hole on the flat sheets, and the noise came up the ventilators. An' not a ripple. An' there I'm smokin' by the rail, waitin' till I can sneak out on the boat deck to sleep—the glory hole being so hot. An' then it comes. It seemed to get her amidships—that was because she was drawing a lot more water aft. Only one man came out of the engine-room. The quiet people in the cabins had the best death. Sharks got all the deck lot. She ran a minute or two an' I saw the water risin' closer up—an' loosed a raft and went over. It was like hell, mister, the howls. Her decks blew up amidships. . . . An' then on the raft I see white fire cutting the water all over, criss-crossin' it. It was sharks. An' then a yell, an' more criss-crossin' of fire, an' another yell."

"I know! I know!" said Phil Regard, soothingly. "Don't think of it! Help me. Tell me where you think she went down."

"I can't help thinkin' of it. Oh—oh!"

"Steady! Steady! Take a pull at yourself. Where did she go down?"

"A girl of twenty or so—I heard her singing in the saloon the night before—a song about 'Mine, forever Mine,' an' her husband lookin' at her as if he was dyin' for her while she was singin'. He was swimmin' with her when the sharks took him; an' I beat the sea with me 'ands an' brought the raft close, an' I was bringin' her up to the raft—swish! comes the shark fire, an' she went, too."

The diver's eyes grew moist at that; he thought of his beloved safe at home, and the tragedy touched him nearly. But he said again:

"Where's the *Pandora?*"

"I drifted to an island, an' then I went mad, an' the lugger found me."

"To-day is Wednesday. When did the *Pandora* sink? Now, think— listen! We may pick up somebody yet. Tell me."

"She sank on Monday night."

"Where?"

"We made twelve knots to Cape Grenville; then we slowed to ten."

"What time at Cape Grenville?"

The survivor of the *Pandora* wrinkled his brows as if thought were a physical pain, and replied: "Twelve o'clock in the mornin'. Y' can't find her—she'd got no masts, on'y hydraulic winchpoles."

Phil Regard, with the dividers in his hand, said inquiringly:

"And she struck at eleven in the night?"

"It might have been later."

"We'll go on that. Where were you picked up?"

"The lugger came from Bushby Island."

Regard pricked off one hundred and ten miles on the chart.

"Somewhere east of Newcastle Bay," he said.

Before noon he had left Thursday Island, taking the direct track with his light-draught tugboat east between Tuesday and Horn Islands; and then, after easting Mount Adolphus Island and thridding the reefs to the south of it, steering south through the turquoise of shallow water and into the sapphire of deep sea, he ran south to Bushby Island and then east over reefs and then north again, and then west, and then zig-zag. And the next day he drove slowly over a blackness in the coral bed; a monstrous black thing surrounded by lazy sharks; the *Pandora*—al-most on an even keel and sunk in fourteen fathoms.

With a little reluctance, Regard made the preparations necessary for such as dive in dress and helmet, and shaved the moustache that had grown since he had dived in Flores Seas. The growing of the moustache had been an innocent vanity for the pleasure of his wife, who objected to his professionally beardless face, just as the new suit was for her bene-fit and not to be worn until the day of happy meeting, that he might shine all freshly in her eyes. Then, in the warm shadow of the white awning he stripped and donned the many woollen undergarments and the canvas dress, with its water-tight red-rubber bands at wrists and ankles.

The tender put on his feet the great brass-toed boots of twenty-eight pounds weight; and when he had climbed to the ladder and placed his feet upon the rungs, they screwed his twenty-eight pound copper helmet on the collar-ring and hung thirty-eight pounds of lead upon his breast and thirty-eight pounds of lead at his back. Lifeline, piping, corselet, helmet, brass boots and leaden weight complete, the men at the pump began to turn; the tender screwed the face-glass into the helmet and tapped upon it as a signal; the pumps lifted the pressure of the weights from the diver's chest. The air thudded irritatingly into the copper prison that was the helmet; the sense of confinement and the close smell of the natural breathing element of man unnaturally compressed, returned to Phil Regard. He thought of the wife in Sydney—the last thought of the divinity before bracing himself to work that had the chance of death in it always, though use had brought danger into contempt; then he opened the valve and dropped easily and gently into the caresses of the water.

The black corpse of the *Pandora* seemed to rise to him. He closed the valve and sank as through a cataract of feathers. Avoiding the deck, he dropped to the bottom for a survey of the hull. Moving lightly as a feather-weight, Regard studied the situation.

All about him stretched tangles of seaweed and coral with white walks between the spongy copses and the brakes. A yellow water-snake followed his every movement with curious imitation, and white fish circled around his helmet so that a green hand must have become dizzy. From a rift in the rock wavered the tentacles of a devil-fish, feeling its way to crime with every cup and sucker. . . .

The weight of ocean pressed the diver softly in his armour of the air; his body felt as if stroked by the silky hands of the caressing sea. And then from the great tunnel in the hull of the *Pandora* came floating the horrors of the deep.

Used as he was to these cruel cowards, in the light of the story of the bride who had died in the wreck, they held for him a new horror, and for a moment he was afraid. Their gorged habit, their slow, plethoric movements, their dull eyes, forgetting for a moment to be greedy, told the tale. Regard felt almost physically sick. All those eyes looked at him threateningly, contemptuously; the little fish that swam up to his face-glass and gazed at him did not seem to be frightened as quickly as usual by the movement of his hands.

The sharks came nearer, and Regard, lifting the rubber wristband, shot air at them in a succession of silver bullets, and the cowards became energetic and fled. A carpet-bag shark, the incarnation of filthy malevolence, hovered above him until Regard turned the escape-valve on his helmet and shot a madness of fear into the horrible thing.

He finished his survey of the hull with difficulty. For an hour Regard rested and fed; then he went to the ladder, and was loaded and imprisoned again, and sank to the deck of the *Pandora*.

His retinue of enemies left him at the entrance to the saloon; but the small fish, their brilliance seeming to light the half-gloom, swam into the depths and in and out at the portholes—"like schoolboys playing a game," thought Phil Regard. Even there some little things had begun already to benefit by the fall of greatness; little pearl shells as big as a thumb-nail had here spun their byssus to tie them to the saloon stairs, hiding their weakness in this unexpected asylum.

"All this death to make a safe hiding-place for a shell," thought Regard bitterly, as he walked on tiptoe through this silent world where all values of vision were distorted.

He talked to himself, and the words reverberated to him from the helmet: "I'll bring dynamite and a wire down and blow the specie-room open, rig a winch, and haul out the gold boxes. That'll be to-morrow. And while I'm here I'll do the horrible job—Moresby's pearls."

He went back to the saloon stairs. Above it a great grey shape hung watchfully, patiently, as if it had all eternity to wait in. Regard, with never a quickening of the pulse, fired the silver bullets from his wristband, and the grey shape backed and fled. Regard laughed and went on to find Moresby's pearls.

He opened a cabin door; two fish fled through the port-hole and the body of a woman came at him in the swirl of the water. The dead face struck his helmet. Regard cried out in horror, and backed away. But in a moment he caught his courage and closed the porthole; then he shut the cabin door again and went to the next. He could not distinguish the letter denoting the corridor nor the number either.

He opened an inner cabin and a drowned man came out and struck him. He opened another and there were in it a dead man and a dead woman trying with her floating skirts to hide a little child from the sea. Horror gripped the diver as with fingers of cold steel.

Yet his duty was to be done, and he did it. He found B corridor, and the first cabin had in it a dead girl with her hands clasped as if she still prayed. He closed the cabin reverently and came to another, in which an old man and an old woman had died in their bed-places; and then to an outer cabin opposite the one he had first entered. The light was better there; he saw that this was B41 at last.

The lock of B41 did not yield to the lifting of the handle, so Regard inserted the point of his small axe between the door and the beading and levered it open. Two bodies, those of a man and a woman—the man's as if he had died standing, the woman's in the lower berth floating up against the wires of the upper berth—moved queerly in the disturbed liquid, as if they were alive.

"Porthole closed," muttered Regard to himself, trying not to look at the dead for a moment. "He had the fan going—the lever's on the top speed."

He looked at the body of the man, and turned him around in the water.

"That'll be the man Moresby gave the pearls to. Oyley was the name, and he looks it. There's the trunk under the berth. And this poor soul has the key round her neck. I can't do it. But I promised. I'll do it to-morrow. No; better now—get it done with. Forgive—whoever you are, forgive me. Young, too, and pretty." With a shaking hand and covering his face, he touched the woman's neck, and there he felt the necklet and the key.

"It's horrible. I'll have to use both hands for the fastening."

As if he were physically afraid of it, he looked back at the sinister dead man floating near the porthole; then, swiftly and without looking, he unfastened the necklet and held it up—a necklet and a key. The movement floated the body from its position against the springs of the upper berth; it turned upright, floating by his head—through the little circle of the face-glass its dead eyes looked sorrowfully into his own.

And then—madness! Unbelief! Doubt! Unbelief again! And again madness, clamoured through his brain. The air seemed to be withdrawn; the helmet became a mountain of copper; the weights upon his back and breast were each a ton of lead. He looked at the necklet—yes, it was so! He had given it. He released it, and it sank to the ooze upon the sodden carpet. He looked at the bracelet of opal before the mirror, and recognized it, too; and then at the dead woman gazing at him mournfully with eyes that seemed to plead: "Forgive; I have been punished and repented so; forgive."

Still unbelieving, but stunned, he pushed the dead man through the door. Then he turned back and re-entered the cabin. There could be no doubt—no doubt!

He left her there and fastened the cabin door behind him. And then his heart broke.

He could not live! With his last conscious instinct he hacked with uncertain hand at the airpipe and missed it; then the weight of all the ocean settled on his heart and he wavered to the floor.

He had a conscientious tender. At that sudden jag upon the lifeline the tender hauled carefully, and by that luck which shames the best judgment, drew Philip Regard safely through the alleyway to the deck of the *Pandora*, and up to sunlight.

But they might as well have left him there, for the strong man who had dived never returned to the surface.

"Beats me!" said Druce, looking pityingly at the withered wreck that sat every day through all the daylight hours of every day, upon the veranda of Thursday Island Hospital. "Can't understand it. A fine, big, strong world-beater of a man paralysed in fourteen fathoms. It beats me!"

UNITED STATES

THE VOYAGE OF *THE MAYFLOWER*[1]

William Bradford

(1590–1657)

ALL things being now ready, and every business dispatched, the company was caled togeather. Then they ordered and distributed their company for either shipe, as they conceived for the best. And chose a Governour and 2 or 3 assistants for each shipe, to order the people by the way, and see to the dispossing of there provissions, and shuch like affaires. All which was not only with the liking of the maisters of the ships, but according to their desires. Which being done, they sett sayle from thence aboute the 5 of August.

Being thus put to sea they had not gone farr, but Mr Reinolds the master of the leser ship complained that he found his ship so leak as he durst not put further to sea till she was mended. So the master of the biger ship (caled Mr Joans) being consulted with, they both resolved to put into Dartmouth and have her ther searched and mended, which accordingly was done, to their great charg and losse of time and a faire wind. She was hear thorowly searcht from steme to sterne, some leaks were found and mended, and now it was conceived by the workmen and all, that she was sufficiente, and they might proceede withbut either fear or danger. So with good hopes from hence, they put to sea againe, conceiving they should goe comfortably on, not looking for any more lets of this kind; but it fell out otherwise, for after they were gone to sea againe above 100 leagues without the Lands End, houlding company togeather all this while, the master of the small ship complained his ship was so leake as he must beare up or sinke at sea, for they could scarce free her with much pumping. So they came to consultation againe, and resolved both ships to bear up backe againe and put into Plimmoth, which accordingly was done. But no spetiall leake could be founde, but it was judged to be the generall weaknes of the shipe, and that shee would not prove sufficiente for the voiage. Upon which it was resolved to dismise her and parte of the companie, and proceede with the other shipe. The which (though it was greeveous, and caused great discouragemente) was put in execution. So after they had tooke out shuch provission as the other ship could well stow, and concluded both what number and what persons to send bak, they made another sad parting, the one ship going backe to London, and the other was to proceede on her viage. Those that went

[1]From *History of the Plymouth*.

bak were for the most parte shuch as were willing so to doe, either out of
some discontente, or feare they conceived of the ill success of the vioage,
seeing so many croses befale, and the year time so farr spente; but others,
in regarde of their owne weaknes, and charge of many yonge children,
were thought least usefull, and most unfite to bear the brunte of this
hard adventure; unto which worke of God, and judgmente of their
brethern, they were contented to submite. And thus, like Gedions armie,
this small number was devided, as if the Lord by this worke of his providence thought these few to many for the great worke he had to doe.
But here by the way let me show, how afterward it was found that the
leaknes of this ship was partly by being overmasted, and too much pressed
with sayles; for after she was sould and put into her old trime, she made
many viages and performed her service very sufficiently, to the great
profite of her owners. But more espetially, by the cuning and deceite of
the master and his company, who were hired to stay a whole year in the
cuntrie, and now fancying dislike and fearing wante of victeles, they
ploted this strategem to free them selves; as afterwards was knowne, and
by some of them confessed. For they apprehended that the greater ship,
being of force, and in whom most of the provissions were stowed, she
would retayne enough for her selfe, what soever became of them or the
passengers; and indeed such speeches had been cast out by some of them;
and yet, besides other incouragements, the cheefe of them that came from
Leyden wente in this shipe to give the master contente. But so strong
was self love and his fears, as he forgott all duty and former kindnesses,
and delt thus falsly with them, though he pretended otherwise.

These troubles being blowne over, and now all being compacte togeather in one shipe, they put to sea againe with a prosperus winde, which
continued diverce days togeather, which was some incouragemente unto
them; yet according to the usuall maner many were afflicted with sea-
sicknes. And I may not omite hear a spetiall worke of Gods providence.
Ther was a proud and very profane yonge man, one of the sea-men, of
a lustie, able body, which made him the more hauty; he would allway
be contemning the poore people in their sicknes, and cursing them dayly
with greevous execrations, and did not let to tell them, that he hoped
to help to cast halfe of them over board before they came to their jurneys
end, and to make mery with what they had; and if he were by any gently
reproved, he would curse and swear most bitterly. But it pleased God
before they came halfe seas over, to smite this yong man with a greeveous
disease, of which he dyed in a desperate maner, and so was him selfe
the first that was throwne overbord. Thus his curses light on his owne
head; and it was an astonishmente to all his fellows, for they noted
it to be the just hand of God upon him.

After they had injoyed faire winds and weather for a season, they were
incountred many times with crosse winds, and mette with many feirce
stormes, with which the shipe was shroudly shaken, and her upper works

made very leakie; and one of the maine beames in the midd ships was bowed and craked, which put them in some fear that the shipe could not be able to performe the voiage. So some of the cheefe of the company, perceiveing the mariners to feare the suffisiencie of the shipe, as appeared by their mutterings, they entred into serious consulltation with the master and other officers of the ship, to consider in time of the danger; and rather to returne then to cast them selves into a desperate and inevitable perill. And truly ther was great distraction and differance of oppinion amongst the mariners them selves; faine would they doe what could be done for their wages sake, (being now halfe the seas over) and on the other hand they were loath to hazard their lives too desperately. But in examening of all oppinions, the master and others affirmed they knew the ship to be stronge and firme underwater; and for the buckling of the maine beame, ther was a great iron scrue the passengers brought out of Holland, which would raise the beame into his place; the which being done, the carpenter and master affirmed that with a post put under it, set firme in the lower deck, and otherways bounde, he would make it sufficiente. And as for the decks and uper workes they would calke them as well as they could, and though with the workeing of the ship they would not longe keepe stanch, yet ther would otherwise be no great danger, if they did not overpress her with sails.

So they commited them selves to the will of God, and resolved to proceede. In sundrie of these stormes the winds were so feirce, and the seas so high, as they could not beare a knote of saile, but were forced to hull, for diverce days togither. And in one of them, as they thus lay at hull, in a mighty storme, a lustie yonge man (called John Howland) coming upon some occasion above the grattings, was, with a seele[1] of the shipe throwne into the sea; but it pleased God that he caught hould of the top-saile halliards, which hunge over board, and rane out at length; yet he held his hould (though he was sundrie fadomes under water) till he was hald up by the same rope to the brime of the water, and then with a boathooke and other means got into the shipe againe, and his life saved; and though he was something ill with it, yet he lived many years after, and became a profitable member both in church and commone wealthe. In all this viage ther died but one of the passengers, which was William Butten, a youth, servant to Samuell Fuller, when they drew near the coast. But to omite other things, (that I may be breefe,) after longe beating at sea they fell with that land which is called Cape Cod; the which being made and certainly knowne to be it, they were not a little joyfull. After some deliberation had amongst them selves, and with the master of the ship, they tacked aboute and resolved to stande for the southward (the wind and weather being faire) to finde some place aboute Hudsons river for their habitation.

---

[1]Roll.

But after they had sailed that course aboute halfe the day, they fell amongst deangerous shoulds and roring breakers, and they were so farr intangled ther with as they conceived them selves in great danger; and the wind shrinking upon them withall, they resolved to bear up againe for the Cape, and thought them selves hapy to gett out of those dangers before night overtooke them, as by Gods good providence they did. And the next day they gott into the Cape-harbor wher they ridd in saftie. A word or too by the way of this cape; it was thus first named by Capten Gosnole and his company, Anno: 1602, and after by Capten Smith was caled Cape James; but it retains the former name amongst sea-men. Also that pointe which first shewed those dangerous shoulds unto them, they called Pointe Care, and Tuckers Terrour; but the French and Dutch to this day call it Malabarr, by reason of those perilous shoulds, and the losses they have suffered their.

Being thus arived in a good harbor and brought safe to land, they fell upon their knees and blessed the God of heaven, who had brought them over the vast and furious ocean, and delivered them from all the periles and miseries therof, againe to set their feete on the firme and stable earth, their proper elemente.

THE PHANTOM ISLAND

Washington Irving

(1783–1859)

THERE are more things in heaven and earth than are dreamed of in our philosophy," and among these may be placed that marvel and mystery of the seas, the Island of St Brandan. Those who have read the history of the Canaries—the Fortunate Islands of the ancients—may remember the wonders told of this enigmatical island. Occasionally it would be visible from their shores, stretching away in the clear bright west, to all appearance substantial like themselves, and still more beautiful. Expeditions would launch forth from the Canaries to explore this land of promise. For a time its sun-gilt peaks and long shadowy promontories would remain distinctly visible, but in proportion as the voyagers approached, peak and promontory would gradually fade away, until nothing would remain but blue sky above, and deep blue water below. Hence this mysterious isle was stigmatized by ancient cosmographers with the name of Aprositus or the Inaccessible. The failure of numerous expeditions sent in quest of it, both in ancient and modern days, have at length caused its very existence to be called in question, and it has been rashly pronounced a mere optical illusion, like the Fata Morgana of the Straits of Messina, or has been classed with those unsubstantial regions known to mariners as Cape Fly-away, and the coast of Cloud Land.

Let us not permit, however, the doubts of worldly-wise sceptics to rob us of all the glorious realms owned by happy credulity in days of yore. Be assured, O reader of easy faith!—thou for whom it is my delight to labour—be assured that such an island actually exists, and has from time to time been revealed to the gaze, and trodden by the feet of favoured mortals. Historians and philosophers may have their doubts, but its existence has been fully attested by that inspired race, the poets; who, being gifted with a kind of second-sight, are enabled to discern those mysteries of nature hidden from the eyes of ordinary men. To this gifted race it has ever been a kind of wonder-land. Here once bloomed, and perhaps still blooms, the famous garden of the Hesperides, with its golden fruit. Here, too, the sorceress Armida had her enchanted garden, in which she held the Christian paladin, Rinaldo, in delicious but inglorious thraldom, as set forth in the immortal lay of Tasso. It was in this island that Sycorax the witch held sway, when the good Prospero and his infant daughter Miranda, were wafted to its shores. Who does not know the tale as told in the magic page of Shakespere? The isle was then

> . . . full of noises,
> Sounds, and sweet airs, that give delight, and hurt not.

The island, in fact, at different times, has been under the sway of different powers—genii of earth, and air, and ocean, who have made it their shadowy abode. Hither have retired many classic but broken-down deities, shorn of almost all their attributes, but who once ruled the poetic world. Here Neptune and Amphitrite hold a diminished court—sovereigns in exile. Their ocean chariot, almost a wreck, lies bottom upward in some sea-beaten cavern; their pursy Tritons and haggard Nereids bask listlessly like seals about the rocks. Sometimes those deities assume, it is said, a shadow of their ancient pomp, and glide in state about a summer sea; and then, as some tall Indiaman lies becalmed with idly-flapping sail, her drowsy crew may hear the mellow note of the Triton's shell swelling upon the ear as the invisible pageant sweeps by.

On the shores of this wondrous isle the kraken heaves its unwieldy bulk, and wallows many a rood. Here the sea-serpent, that mighty but much-contested reptile, lies coiled up during the intervals of its revelations to the eyes of true believers. Here even the Flying Dutchman finds a port, and casts his anchor, and furls his shadowy sail, and takes a brief repose from his eternal cruisings.

In the deep bays and harbours of the island lies many a spell-bound ship, long since given up as lost by the ruined merchant. Here too its crew, long, long bewailed in vain, lie sleeping from age to age, in mossy grottoes, or wander about in pleasing oblivion of all things. Here, in caverns, are garnered up the priceless treasures lost in the ocean. Here sparkles in vain the diamond, and flames the carbuncle. Here are piled up rich bales of Oriental silks, boxes of pearls, and piles of golden ingots.

Such are some of the marvels related of this island, which may serve to throw light upon the following legend, of unquestionable truth, which I recommend to the implicit belief of the reader.

THE ADALANTADO OF THE SEVEN CITIES

A Legend of St Brandan

In the early part of the fifteenth century, when Prince Henry of Portugal, of worthy memory, was pushing the career of discovery along the western coast of Africa, and the world was resounding with reports of golden regions on the mainland, and new-found islands in the ocean, there arrived at Lisbon an old bewildered pilot of the seas, who had been driven by tempests, he knew not whither, and raved about an island far in the deep, upon which he had landed, and which he had found peopled with Christians, and adorned with noble cities.

The inhabitants, he said, having never before been visited by a ship, gathered round, and regarded him with surprise. They told him they were descendants of a band of Christians who fled from Spain when that country was conquered by the Moslems. They were curious about the state of their fatherland, and grieved to hear that the Moslems still held possession of the kingdom of Granada. They would have taken the old navigator to church, to convince him of their orthodoxy; but, either through lack of devotion, or lack of faith in their words, he declined their invitation, and preferred to return on board his ship. He was properly punished. A furious storm arose, drove him from his anchorage, hurried him out to sea, and he saw no more of the unknown island.

This strange story caused great marvel in Lisbon and elsewhere. Those versed in history, remembered to have read, in an ancient chronicle, that, at the time of the conquest of Spain, in the eighth century, when the blessed cross was cast down, and the crescent erected in its place, and when Christian churches were turned into Moslem mosques, seven bishops at the head of seven bands of pious exiles, had fled from the peninsula, and embarked in quest of some ocean island or distant land, where they might found seven Christian cities, and enjoy their faith unmolested.

The fate of these saints-errant had hitherto remained a mystery, and their story had faded from memory; the report of the old tempest-tossed pilot, however, revived this long-forgotten theme; and it was determined by the pious and enthusiastic, that the island thus accidentally discovered, was the identical place of refuge, whither the wandering bishops had been guided by a protecting Providence, and where they had folded their flocks.

This most excitable of worlds has always some darling object of chimerical enterprise; the "Island of the Seven Cities" now awakened as much interest and longing among zealous Christians, as has the renowned city of Timbuctoo among adventurous travellers, or the north-west passage among hardy navigators; and it was a frequent prayer of the devout, that these scattered and lost portions of the Christian family might be discovered, and reunited to the great body of Christendom.

No one, however, entered into the matter with half the zeal of Don Fernando de Ulmo, a young cavalier of high standing in the Portuguese court, and of most sanguine and romantic temperament. He had recently come to his estate, and had run the round of all kinds of pleasures and excitements, when this new theme of popular talk and wonder presented itself. The island of the Seven Cities became now the constant subject of his thoughts by day, and his dreams by night: it even rivalled his passion for a beautiful girl, one of the greatest belles of Lisbon, to whom he was betrothed. At length, his imagination became so inflamed on the subject, that he determined to fit out an expedition at his own expense, and set sail in quest of this sainted island. It could not be a cruise of any great extent; for, according to the calculations of the tempest-tossed pilot, it must be somewhere in the latitude of the Canaries; which at that time, when the New World was as yet undiscovered, formed the frontier of ocean enterprise. Don Fernando applied to the crown for countenance and protection. As he was a favourite at court, the usual patronage was readily extended to him; that is to say, he received a commission from the king, Dom Ioam II., constituting him Adalantado, or military governor, of any country he might discover, with the single proviso, that he should bear all the expenses of the discovery, and pay a tenth of the profits to the crown.

Don Fernando now set to work in the true spirit of a projector. He sold acre after acre of solid land, and invested the proceeds in ships, guns, ammunition, and sea-stores. Even his old family mansion in Lisbon was mortgaged without scruple, for he looked forward to a palace in one of the Seven Cities of which he was to be Adalantado. This was the age of nautical romance, when the thoughts of all speculative dreamers were turned to the ocean. The scheme of Don Fernando, therefore, drew adventurers of every kind. The merchant promised himself new marts of opulent traffic; the soldier hoped to sack and plunder some one or other of those Seven Cities—even the fat monk shook off the sleep and sloth of the cloister, to join in a crusade which promised such increase to the possessions of the Church.

One person alone regarded the whole project with sovereign contempt and growling hostility. This was Don Ramiro Alvarez, the father of the beautiful Serafina, to whom Don Fernando was betrothed. He was one of those perverse, matter-of-fact old men, who are prone to oppose everything speculative and romantic. He had no faith in the Island of the Seven Cities; regarded the projected cruise as a crackbrained freak; looked with angry eye and internal heartburning on the conduct of his intended son-in-law, chaffering away solid lands for lands in the moon; and scoffingly dubbed him Adalantado of Cloud Land. In fact, he had never really relished the intended match, to which his consent had been slowly extorted, by the tears and entreaties of his daughter. It is true he could have no reasonable objections to the youth, for Don Fernando was the very flower of Portuguese chivalry. No one could excel him at the tilting-match or the riding at the ring; none was more bold and dexterous in the bull-fight; none composed more gallant madrigals in praise of his lady's charms, or sang them with sweeter tones to the accompaniment of her guitar; nor could any one handle the castanets and dance the bolero with more captivating grace. All these admirable qualities and endowments, however, though they had been sufficient to win the heart of Serafina, were nothing in the eyes of her unreasonable father. O Cupid, god of Love! why will fathers always be so unreasonable?

The engagement to Serafina had threatened at first to throw an obstacle in the way of the expedition of Don Fernando, and for a time perplexed him in the extreme. He was passionately attached to the young lady; but he was also passionately bent on this romantic enterprise. How should he reconcile the two passionate inclinations? A simple and obvious arrangement at length presented itself: marry Serafina, enjoy a portion of the honeymoon at once, and defer the rest until his return from the discovery of the Seven Cities!

He hastened to make known this most excellent arrangement to Don Ramiro, when the long-smothered wrath of the old cavalier burst forth. He reproached him with being the dupe of wandering vagabonds and wild schemers, and with squandering all his real possessions in pursuit of empty bubbles. Don Fernando was too sanguine a projector, and too young a man, to listen tamely to such language. He acted with what is technically called "becoming spirit." A high quarrel ensued; Don Ramiro pronounced him a madman, and forbade all farther intercourse with his daughter, until he should give proof of returning sanity, by abandoning this madcap enterprise; while Don Fernando flung out of the house, more bent than ever on the expedition, from the idea of triumphing over the incredulity of the grey-beard when he should return successful. Don Ramiro's heart misgave him. Who knows, thought he, but this crackbrained visionary may persuade my daughter to elope with him, and share his throne in this unknown paradise of fools? If I could only keep her safe until his ships are fairly out at sea!

He repaired to her apartment, represented to her the sanguine, unsteady character of her lover and the chimerical value of his schemes, and urged the propriety of suspending all intercourse with him until he should recover from his present hallucination. She bowed her head as if in filial acquiescence, whereupon he folded her to his bosom with parental fondness, and kissed away a tear that was stealing over her cheek, but as he left the chamber quietly turned the key in the lock; for though he was a fond father, and had a high opinion of the submissive temper of his child, he had a still higher opinion of the conservative virtues of lock and key, and determined to trust to them until the caravels should sail. Whether the damsel had been in any wise shaken in her faith as to the schemes of her lover by her father's eloquence, tradition does not say; but certain it is, that, the moment she heard the key turn in the lock, she became a firm believer in the Island of the Seven Cities.

The door was locked; but her will was unconfined. A window of the chamber opened into one of those stone balconies, secured by iron bars, which project like huge cages from Portuguese and Spanish houses. Within this balcony the beautiful Serafina had her birds and flowers, and here she was accustomed to sit on moonlight nights as in a bower, and touch her guitar and sing like a wakeful nightingale. From this balcony an intercourse was now maintained between the lovers, against which the lock and key of Don Ramiro were of no avail. All day would Fernando be occupied hurrying the equipments of his ships, but evenings found him in sweet discourse beneath his lady's window.

At length the preparations were completed. Two gallant caravels lay at anchor in the Tagus ready to sail at sunrise. Late at night, by the pale light of a waning moon, the lover had his last interview. The beautiful Serafina was sad at heart and full of dark forebodings; her lover full of hope and confidence. "A few short months," said he, "and I shall return in triumph. Thy father will then blush at his incredulity, and hasten to welcome to his house the Adalantado of the Seven Cities."

The gentle lady shook her head. It was not on this point she felt distrust. She was a thorough believer in the Island of the Seven Cities, and so sure of the success of the enterprise that she might have been tempted to join it had not the balcony been high and the grating strong. Other considerations induced that dubious shaking of the head. She had heard of the inconstancy of the seas, and the inconstancy of those who roam them. Might not Fernando meet with other loves in foreign ports? Might not some peerless beauty in one or other of those Seven Cities efface the image of Serafina from his mind? Now let the truth be spoken—the beautiful Serafina had reason for her disquiet. If Don Fernando had any fault in the world, it was that of being rather inflammable and apt to take fire from every sparkling eye. He had been somewhat of a rover among the sex on shore—what might he be on sea?

She ventured to express her doubt, but he spurned at the very idea. "What! he false to Serafina! He bow at the shrine of another beauty? Never! never!" Repeatedly did he bend his knee, and smite his breast, and call upon the silver moon to witness his sincerity and truth.

He retorted the doubt, "Might not Serafina herself forget her plighted faith? Might not some wealthier rival present himself while he was tossing on the sea, and, backed by her father's wishes, win the treasure of her hand?"

The beautiful Serafina raised her white arms between the iron bars of the balcony, and, like her lover, invoked the moon to testify her vows. Alas! how little did Fernando know her heart. The more her father should oppose, the more would she be fixed in faith. Though years should intervene, Fernando on his return would find her true. Even should the salt sea swallow him up (and her eyes shed salt tears at the very thought), never would she be the wife of another!—Never, *never*, NEVER! She drew from her finger a ring gemmed with a ruby heart, and dropped it from the balcony, a parting pledge of constancy.

Thus the lovers parted, with many a tender word and plighted vow. But will they keep those vows? Perish the doubt! Have they not called the constant moon to witness?

With the morning dawn the caravels dropped down the Tagus, and put to sea. They steered for the Canaries, in those days the regions of nautical discovery and romance, and the outposts of the known world— for as yet Columbus had not steered his daring barks across the ocean. Scarce had they reached those latitudes, when they were separated by a violent tempest. For many days was the caravel of Don Fernando driven about at the mercy of the elements; all seamanship was baffled, destruction seemed inevitable, and the crew were in despair. All at once the storm subsided; the ocean sank into a calm; the clouds which had veiled the face of heaven were suddenly withdrawn, and the tempest-tossed mariners beheld a fair and mountainous island, emerging as if by enchantment from the murky gloom. They rubbed their eyes, and gazed for a time almost incredulously; yet there lay the island spread out in lovely landscapes, with the late stormy sea laving its shores with peaceful billows.

The pilot of the caravel consulted his maps and charts; no island like the one before him was laid down as existing in those parts. It is true, he had lost his reckoning in the late storm; but, according to his calculations, he could not be far from the Canaries, and this was not one of that group of islands. The caravel now lay perfectly becalmed off the mouth of a river, on the banks of which, about a league from the sea, was descried a noble city, with lofty walls and towers and a protecting castle.

After a time, a stately barge with sixteen oars was seen emerging from the river and approaching the caravel. It was quaintly carved and gilt; the oarsmen were clad in antique garb, their oars painted of a bright crimson; and they came slowly and solemnly, keeping time as they rowed to the cadence of an old Spanish ditty. Under a silken canopy in the stern sat a cavalier richly clad, and over his head was a banner bearing the sacred emblem of the cross.

When the barge reached the caravel, the cavalier stepped on board. He was tall and gaunt; with a long Spanish visage, moustaches that curled up to his eyes, and a forked beard. He wore gauntlets reaching to his elbows, a Toledo blade strutting out behind, with a basket-hilt, in which he carried his handkerchief. His air was lofty and precise, and bespoke indisputably the hidalgo. Thrusting out a long, spindle leg, he took off a huge sombrero, and swaying it until the feather swept the ground, accosted Don Fernando in the old Castilian language, and with the old Castilian courtesy welcomed him to the Island of the Seven Cities.

Don Fernando was overwhelmed with astonishment. Could this be true? Had he really been tempest-driven to the very land of which he was in quest?

It was even so. That very day the inhabitants were holding high festival in commemoration of the escape of their ancestors from the Moors. The arrival of the caravel at such a juncture was considered a good omen—the accomplishment of an ancient prophecy, through which the island was to be restored to the great community of Christendom. The cavalier before him was grand-chamberlain, sent by the alcayde to invite him to the festivities of the capital.

Don Fernando could scarce believe that this was not all a dream. He made known his name, and the object of his voyage. The grand-chamberlain declared that all was in perfect accordance with the ancient prophecy, and that the moment his credentials were presented, he would be acknowledged as the Adalantado of the Seven Cities. In the meantime, the day was waning; the barge was ready to convey him to the land, and would as assuredly bring him back.

Don Fernando's pilot, a veteran of the seas, drew him aside and expostulated against his venturing, on the mere word of a stranger, to land in a strange barge on an unknown shore. "Who knows, Señor, what land this is, or what people inhabit it?"

Don Fernando was not to be dissuaded. Had he not believed in this island when all the world doubted? Had he not sought it in defiance of storm and tempest, and was he now to shrink from its shores when they lay before him in calm weather? In a word, was not faith the very cornerstone of his enterprise?

Having arrayed himself, therefore, in gala dress befitting the occasion, he took his seat in the barge. The grand-chamberlain seated himself opposite. The rowers plied their oars, and renewed the mournful old ditty, and the gorgeous but unwieldy barge moved slowly through the water.

The night closed in before they entered the river, and swept along past rock and promontory, each guarded by its tower. At every post they were challenged by the sentinel.

"Who goes there?"

"The Adalantado of the Seven Cities."

"Welcome, Señor Adalantado. Pass on."

Entering the harbour they rowed close by an armed galley of ancient form. Soldiers with crossbows patrolled the deck.

"Who goes there?"

"The Adalantado of the Seven Cities."

"Welcome, Señor Adalantado. Pass on."

They landed at a broad flight of stone steps, leading up between two massive towers, and knocked at the water-gate. A sentinel, in ancient steel casque, looked from the barbican.

"Who is there?"

"The Adalantado of the Seven Cities."

"Welcome, Señor Adalantado."

The gate swung open, grating upon rusty hinges. They entered between two more rows of warriors in Gothic armour, with crossbows, maces, battle-axes, and faces old-fashioned as their armour. There were processions through the streets, in commemoration of the landing of the seven Bishops and their followers, and bonfires at which effigies of losel Moors expiated their invasion of Christendom by a kind of *auto-da-fé*. The groups round the fires, uncouth in their attire, looked like the fantastic figures that roam the streets in Carnival time. Even the dames who gazed down from Gothic balconies hung with antique tapestry, resembled effigies dressed up in Christmas mummeries. Everything, in short, bore the stamp of former ages, as if the world had suddenly rolled back for several centuries. Nor was this to be wondered at. Had not the Island of the Seven Cities been cut off from the rest of the world for several hundred years; and were not these the modes and customs of Gothic Spain before it was conquered by the Moors?

Arrived at the palace of the alcayde, the grand-chamberlain knocked at the portal. The porter looked through a wicket, and demanded who was there.

"The Adalantado of the Seven Cities."

The portal was thrown wide open. The grand-chamberlain led the way up a vast, heavily-moulded marble staircase, and into a hall of ceremony where was the alcayde with several of the principal dignitaries of the city, who had a marvellous resemblance, in form and feature, to the quaint figures in old illuminated manuscripts.

The grand-chamberlain stepped forward and announced the name and title of the stranger guest, and the extraordinary nature of his mission. The announcement appeared to create no extraordinary emotion or surprise, but to be received as the anticipated fulfilment of a prophecy.

The reception of Don Fernando, however, was profoundly gracious, though in the same style of stately courtesy which everywhere prevailed. He would have produced his credentials, but this was courteously declined. The evening was devoted to high festivity; the following day, when he should enter the port with his caravel, would be devoted to business, when the credentials would be received in due form, and he inducted into office as Adalantado of the Seven Cities.

Don Fernando was now conducted through one of those interminable suites of apartments, the pride of Spanish palaces, all furnished in a style of obsolete magnificence. In a vast saloon blazing with tapers, was assembled all the aristocracy and fashion of the city; stately dames and cavaliers, the very counterpart of the figures in the tapestry which decorated the walls. Fernando gazed in silent marvel. It was a reflex of the proud aristocracy of Spain in the time of Roderick the Goth.

The festivities of the evening were all in the style of solemn and anti-quated ceremonial. There was a dance, but it was as if the old tapestry were put in motion, and all the figures moving in stately measure about the floor. There was one exception, and one that told powerfully upon the susceptible Adalantado. The alcayde's daughter—such a ripe, melt-ing beauty! Her dress, it is true, like the dresses of her neighbours, might have been worn before the flood, but she had the black Andalusian eye, a glance of which, through its long dark lashes, is irresitible. Her voice, too, her manner, her undulating movements, all smacked of Andalusia, and showed how female charms may be transmitted from age to age, and clime to clime, without ever going out of fashion. Those who know the witchery of the sex, in that most amorous part of amorous old Spain, may judge of the fascination to which Don Fernando was exposed, as he joined in the dance with one of its most captivating descendants.

He sat beside her at the banquet—such an old-world feast! such obsolete dainties! At the head of the table the peacock, that bird of state and ceremony, was served up in full plumage on a golden dish. As Don Fernando cast his eyes down the glittering board, what a vista presented itself of odd heads and head-dresses—of formal bearded dignitaries and stately dames, with castellated locks and towering plumes! Is it to be wondered at that he should turn with delight from these antiquated figures to the alcayde's daughter, all smiles and dimples, and melting looks and melting accents? Besides—for I wish to give him every excuse in my power—he was in a particularly excitable mood from the novelty of the scene before him, from this realization of all his hopes and fancies, and from frequent draughts of the wine-cup presented to him at every moment by officious pages during the banquet.

In a word—there is no concealing the matter—before the evening was over, Don Fernando was making love outright to the alcayde's daughter. They had wandered together to a moonlit balcony of the palace, and he was charming her ear with one of those love-ditties with which, in a like balcony, he had serenaded the beautiful Serafina.

The damsel hung her head coyly. "Ah! Señor, these are flattering words; but you cavaliers who roam the seas are unsteady as its waves. To-morrow you will be throned in state, Adalantado of the Seven Cities; and will think no more of the alcayde's daughter."

Don Fernando, in the intoxication of the moment, called the moon to witness his sincerity. As he raised his hand in adjuration, the chaste moon cast a ray upon the ring that sparkled on his finger. It caught the damsel's eye. "Señor Adalantado," said she archly, "I have no faith in the moon, but give me that ring upon your finger in pledge of the truth of what you profess."

The gallant Adalantado was taken by surprise; there was no parrying this sudden appeal; before he had time to reflect, the ring of the beautiful Serafina glittered on the finger of the alcayde's daughter.

At this eventful moment the chamberlain approached with lofty demeanour, and announced that the barge was waiting to bear him back to the caravel. I forbear to relate the ceremonious partings with the alcayde and his dignitaries, and the tender farewell of the alcayde's daughter. He took his seat in the barge opposite the grand-chamberlain. The rowers plied their crimson oars in the same slow and stately manner to the cadence of the same mournful old ditty. His brain was in a whirl with all that he had seen, and his heart now and then gave him a twinge as he thought of his temporary infidelity to the beautiful Serafina. The barge sallied out into the sea, but no caravel was to be seen; doubtless she had been carried to a distance by the current of the river. The oarsmen rowed on; their monotonous chant had a lulling effect. A drowsy influence crept over Don Fernando. Objects swam before his eyes. The oarsmen assumed odd shapes as in a dream. The grand-chamberlain grew larger and larger, and taller and taller. He took off his huge sombrero, and held it over the head of Don Fernando, like an extinguisher over a candle. The latter cowered beneath it; he felt himself sinking in the socket.

"Good-night, Señor Adalantado of the Seven Cities!" said the grand-chamberlain.

The sombrero slowly descended—Don Fernando was extinguished!

How long he remained extinct no mortal man can tell. When he returned to consciousness, he found himself in a strange cabin, surrounded by strangers. He rubbed his eyes, and looked round him wildly. Where was he? On board a Portuguese ship, bound to Lisbon. How came he there? He had been taken senseless from a wreck drifting about the ocean.

Don Fernando was more and more confounded and perplexed. He recalled, one by one, everything that had happened to him in the Island of the Seven Cities, until he had been extinguished by the sombrero of the grand-chamberlain.

But what had happened to him since? What had become of his caravel? Was it the wreck of her on which he had been found floating?

The people about him could give no information on the subject. He entreated them to take him to the Island of the Seven Cities, which could not be far off. Told them all that had befallen him there. That he had but to land to be received as Adalantado; when he would reward them magnificently for their services.

They regarded his words as the ravings of delirium, and in their honest solicitude for the restoration of his reason, administered such rough remedies, that he was fain to drop the subject and observe a cautious taciturnity.

At length they arrived in the Tagus, and anchored before the famous city of Lisbon. Don Fernando sprang joyfully on shore, and hastened to his ancestral mansion. A strange porter opened the door, who knew nothing of him or of his family; no people of the name had inhabited the house for many a year.

He sought the mansion of Don Ramiro. He approached the balcony beneath which he had bidden farewell to Serafina. Did his eyes deceive him? No! There was Serafina herself among the flowers in the balcony. He raised his arms toward her with an exclamation of rapture. She cast upon him a look of indignation, and, hastily retiring, closed the casement with a slam that testified her displeasure.

Could she have heard of his flirtation with the alcayde's daughter? But that was mere transient gallantry. A moment's interview would dispel every doubt of his constancy.

He rang at the door; as it was opened by the porter he rushed up stairs; sought the well-known chamber, and threw himself at the feet of Serafina. She started back with affright, and took refuge in the arms of a youthful cavalier.

"What mean you, Señor," cried the latter, "by this intrusion?"

"What right have you to ask the question?" demanded Don Fernando fiercely.

"The right of an affianced suitor!"

Don Fernando started and turned pale. "O Serafina! Serafina!" cried he in a tone of agony, "is this thy plighted constancy?"

"Serafina? What mean you by Serafina, Señor? If this be the lady you intend, her name is Maria."

"May I not believe my senses? May I not believe my heart?" cried Don Fernando. "Is not this Serafina Alvarez, the original of yon portrait, which, less fickle than herself, still smiles on me from the wall?"

"Holy Virgin!" cried the young lady, casting her eyes upon the portrait. "He is talking of my great-grandmother!"

An explanation ensued, if that could be called an explanation, which plunged the unfortunate Fernando into tenfold perplexity. If he might believe his eyes, he saw before him his beloved Serafina; if he might believe his ears, it was merely her hereditary form and features, perpetuated in the person of her great-granddaughter.

His brain began to spin. He sought the office of the Minister of Marine, and made a report of his expedition, and of the Island of the Seven Cities, which he had so fortunately discovered. Nobody knew anything of such an expedition or such an island. He declared that he had undertaken the enterprise under a formal contract with the crown, and had received a regular commission, constituting him Adalantado. This must be a matter of record, and he insisted loudly that the books of the department should be consulted. The wordy strife at length attracted the attention of an old gray-headed clerk, who sat perched on a high stool, at a high desk, with iron-rimmed spectacles on the top of a thin, pinched nose, copying records into an enormous folio. He had wintered and summered in the department for a great part of a century, until he had almost grown to be a piece of the desk at which he sat; his memory was a mere index of official facts and documents, and his brain was little better than red tape and parchment. After peering down for a time from his lofty perch, and ascertaining the matter in controversy, he put his pen behind his ear, and descended. He remembered to have heard something from his predecessor about an expedition of the kind in question, but then it had sailed during the reign of Dom Ioam II., and he had been dead at least a hundred years. To put the matter beyond dispute, however, the archives of the Torre do Tombo, that sepulchre of old Portuguese documents, were diligently searched, and a record was found of a contract between the crown and one Fernando de Ulmo, for the discovery of the Island of the Seven Cities, and of a commission secured to him as Adalantado of the country he might discover.

"There!" cried Don Fernando triumphantly, "there you have proof before your own eyes of what I have said. I am the Fernando de Ulmo specified in that record. I have discovered the Island of the Seven Cities, and am entitled to be Adalantado, according to contract."

The story of Don Fernando had certainly, what is pronounced the best of historical foundation, documentary evidence; but when a man, in the bloom of youth, talked of events that had taken place above a century previously, as having happened to himself, it is no wonder that he was set down for a madman.

The old clerk looked at him from above and below his spectacles, shrugged his shoulders, stroked his chin, reascended his lofty stool, took the pen from behind his ears, and resumed his daily and eternal task, copying records into the fiftieth volume of a series of gigantic folios. The other clerks winked at each other shrewdly, and dispersed to their several places, and poor Don Fernando, thus left to himself, flung out of the office, almost driven wild by these repeated perplexities.

In the confusion of his mind, he instinctively repaired to the mansion of Alvarez, but it was barred against him. To break the delusion under which the youth apparently laboured, and to convince him that the Serafina about whom he raved was really dead, he was conducted to her tomb. There she lay, a stately matron, cut out in alabaster; and there lay her husband beside her—a portly cavalier in armour; and there knelt, on each side, the effigies of a numerous progeny, proving that she had been a fruitful vine. Even the very monument gave evidence of the lapse of time; the hands of her husband, folded as if in prayer, had lost their fingers, and the face of the once lovely Serafina was without a nose.

Don Fernando felt a transient glow of indignation at beholding this monumental proof of the inconstancy of his mistress; but who could expect a mistress to remain constant during a whole century of absence? And what right had he to rail about constancy, after what had passed between himself and the alcayde's daughter? The unfortunate cavalier performed one pious act of tender devotion; he had the alabaster nose of Serafina restored by a skilful statuary, and then tore himself from the tomb.

He could now no longer doubt the fact, that, somehow or other, he had skipped over a whole century, during the night he had spent at the Island of the Seven Cities; and he was now as complete a stranger in his native city as if he had never been there. A thousand times did he wish himself back to that wonderful island, with its antiquated banquet halls, where he had been so courteously received; and now that the once young and beautiful Serafina was nothing but a great-grandmother in marble, with generations of descendants, a thousand times would he recall the melting black eyes of the alcayde's daughter, who doubtless, like himself, was still flourishing in fresh juvenility, and breathe a sweet wish that he were seated by her side.

He would at once have set on foot another expedition, at his own expense, to cruise in search of the sainted island, but his means were exhausted. He endeavoured to rouse others to the enterprise, setting forth the certainty of profitable results, of which his own experience furnished such unquestionable proof. Alas! no one would give faith to his tale; but looked upon it as the feverish dream of a shipwrecked man. He persisted in his efforts; holding forth in all places and all companies, until he became an object of jest and jeer to the light-minded, who mistook his earnest enthusiasm for a proof of insanity; and the very children in the streets bantered him with the title of "The Adalantado of the Seven Cities."

Finding all efforts in vain, in his native city of Lisbon, he took shipping for the Canaries, as being nearer the latitude of his former cruise, and inhabited by people given to nautical adventure. Here he found ready listeners to his story; for the old pilots and mariners of those parts were notorious island-hunters, and devout believers in all the wonders of the seas. Indeed, one and all treated his adventure as a common occurrence, and turning to each other, with a sagacious nod of the head, observed, "He has been at the Island of St Brandan."

They then went on to inform him of that great marvel and enigma of the ocean; of its repeated appearance to the inhabitants of their islands; and of the many but ineffectual expeditions that had been made in search of it. They took him to a promontory of the island of Palma, whence the shadowy St Brandan had oftenest been descried, and they pointed out the very tract in the west where its mountains had been seen.

Don Fernando listened with rapt attention. He had no longer a doubt that this mysterious and fugacious island must be the same with that of the Seven Cities; and that some supernatural influence connected with it had operated upon himself, and made the events of a night occupy the space of a century.

He endeavoured, but in vain, to rouse the islanders to another attempt at discovery; they had given up the Phantom Island as indeed inaccessible. Fernando, however, was not to be discouraged. The idea wore itself deeper and deeper in his mind, until it became the engrossing subject of his thoughts and object of his being. Every morning he would repair to the promontory of Palma, and sit there throughout the livelong day, in hopes of seeing the fairy mountains of St Brandon peering above the horizon; every evening he returned to his home a disappointed man, but ready to resume his post on the following morning.

His assiduity was all in vain. He grew grey in his ineffectual attempt; and was at length found dead at his post. His grave is still shown in the island of Palma, and a cross is erected on the spot where he used to sit and look out upon the sea, in hopes of the reappearnce of the Phantom Island.

THE *RED ROVER* AND THE *ROYAL CAROLINE*[1]

J. Fenimore Cooper

(1789–1851)

THE night was misty rather than dark. A full and bright moon had arisen; but it pursued its path through the heavens, behind a body of dusky clouds, that was much too dense for the borrowed rays to penetrate. Here and there a straggling gleam appeared to find its way through a covering of vapour less dense than the rest, falling upon the water like the dim illumination of a distant taper. As the wind was fresh and easterly, the sea seemed to throw upward from its agitated surface more light than it received; long lines of glittering foam following each other, and lending a distinctness to the waters, that the heavens themselves wanted. The ship was bowed low on its side; and, as it entered each rolling swell, a wide crescent of foam was driven ahead, the element appearing to gambol along its path. But, though the time was propitious, the wind not absolutely adverse, and the heavens rather gloomy than threatening, an uncertain, (and to a landsman, it might seem an unnatural) light gave a character of the wildest loneliness to the view.

Gertrude shuddered on reaching the deck, while she murmured an expression of strange delight. But Wilder looked upon the scene as one fastens his gaze on a placid sky. To him the view possessed neither novelty, nor dread, nor charm. His look was always in the direction of the

---

[1]From *The Red Rover*.

wind, which, though far from a gale, frequently fell upon the sails in heavy and sullen puffs. After a long examination, the young mariner muttered his thoughts to himself, and commenced pacing the deck rapidly. Still he would make sudden and short pauses, riveting his gaze on the point of the compass whence the blasts came, as if he distrusted the weather, and would fain penetrate the gloom of might, in order to relieve some painful doubt. At length his step became arrested, in one of those quick turns that he made at each end of his narrow walk. Mrs Wyllys and Gertrude stood near at hand, and were enabled to read with distinctness the anxious character of his countenance, as his eye became suddenly fastened on a distant point of the ocean, though in a quarter exactly opposite to that in which his former looks had been directed.

"Do you see reason to distrust the weather?" asked the governess, when she thought his examination had endured long enough to become ominous of evil.

"One does not look to leeward for the signs of the weather, in a breeze like this."

"What is there, that you fasten your eye on so intently?"

Wilder raised his arm, and was about to speak, when the limb suddenly fell.

"It was delusion!" he muttered, turning and pacing the deck more rapidly than ever.

His companions watched the extraordinary and apparently unconscious movements of the young commander with amazement, and not without a little secret dismay. Their own looks wandered over the expanse of troubled water to leeward, but nowhere could they see more than the tossing element, capped with those ridges of garish foam which served only to make the chilly waste more dreary and imposing.

"We see nothing," said Gertrude, when Wilder again stopped to gaze, as before, on the seeming void.

"Look!" he answered, directing their eyes with his finger, "is there nothing there?"

"Nothing."

"You look into the sea. Here, just where the heavens and the waters meet; along that streak of misty light, into which the waves are tossing themselves like little hillocks. There; now 'tis smooth again, and my eyes did not deceive me. By heavens, it is a ship!"

"Sail, ho!" shouted a voice from a-top. The cry sounded, in the ears of our adventurer, like the croaking of a sinister spirit.

"Where away?" he sternly demanded.

"Here on our lee-quarter, sir," returned the seaman, at the top of his voice. "I make her out a ship close-hauled; but, for an hour past, she has looked more like a mist than a vessel."

"He is right," muttered Wilder; "and yet 'tis a strange thing that a ship should be just there."

He soon summoned the officer of the watch to his councils, and they consulted together apart, for many minutes.

"Is it not extraordinary that she should be just there?" demanded Wilder, after each, in turn, had made a closer examination of the faint object, by the aid of an excellent night-glass.

"She would certainly be better off here," returned the literal seaman, who had an eye only for the nautical situation of the stranger; "we should be none the worse for being a dozen leagues more to the eastward, ourselves. If the wind holds here at east-by-south-half-south, we shall have need of all that offing. I got jammed once between Hatteras and the Gulf——"

"Do you not perceive that she is where no vessel could or ought to be, unless she has run exactly the same course with ourselves?" interrupted Wilder. "Nothing, from any harbour south of New York, could have such northing, as the wind has held; while nothing from the colony of York would stand on this tack, if bound east; or would be there, if going southward."

The plain-going ideas of the honest mate were open to a reasoning which the reader may find a little obscure; for his mind contained a sort of chart of the ocean, to which he could at any time refer, with a proper discrimination between the various winds and all the different points of the compass. When properly directed, he was not slow to see the probable justice of his young commander's inferences; and then wonder, in its turn, began to take possession of his more obtuse faculties.

"It is downright unnatural, truly, that the fellow should be just there!" he replied, shaking his head, but meaning no more than that it was entirely out of the order of nautical propriety; "I see the reason of what you say, Captain Wilder; and I don't know how to explain it. It is a ship, to a moral certainty!"

"Of that there is no doubt. But a ship most strangely placed!"

"I doubled the Good Hope in the year '46," continued the other, and we saw a vessel lying, as it might be, here on our weather-bow—which is just opposite to this fellow, since he is on our lee-quarter—but there I saw a ship standing for an hour across our fore-foot, and yet, though we set the azimuth, not a degree did he budge, starboard or larboard, during all that time, which, as it was heavy weather, was, to say the least, something out of the common order."

"It was remarkable!" returned Wilder, with an air so vacant, and to prove that he rather communed with himself than attended to his companion.

"There are mariners who say that the Flying Dutchman cruises off that Cape, and that he often gets on the weather-side of a stranger, and bears down upon him like a ship about to lay him aboard. Many is the King's cruiser, as they say, that has turned her hands up from a sweet sleep, when the look-outs have seen a doubledecker come down in the night, with ports up, and batteries lighted; but then this can't be any such craft as the Dutchman, since she is, at the most, no more than a large sloop of war, if a cruiser at all."

"No," said Wilder, "this can never be the Dutchman."

"Yon vessel shows no lights; and, for that matter, she has such a misty look, that one might well question its being a ship at all. Then, again, the Dutchman is always seen to windward, and the strange sail we have here lies broad on our lee-quarter!"

"It is no Dutchman," said Wilder, drawing a long breath, like a man awaking from a trance. "Main-topmast cross-trees, there!"

The man stationed aloft answered the hail in the customary manner, the short conversation that succeeded being necessarily maintained in shouts rather than in speeches.

"How long have you seen the stranger?" was the first demand of Wilder.

"I have just come aloft, sir; but the man I relieved tells me more than an hour."

"And has the man you relieved come down? Or who is that I see sitting on the lee side of the mast-head?"

"'Tis Bob Brace, sir; who says he cannot sleep, and so he stays upon the yard to keep me company."

"Send the man down. I would speak with him."

While the wakeful seaman was descending the rigging, the two officers continued silent, finding sufficient occupation in musing on what had already passed.

"Why are you not in your hammock?" said Wilder, a little sternly, to the man who, in obedience to his order, had descended to the quarter-deck.

"I am not sleep-bound, your honour, and, to own the truth, sir, my mind has been a little misgiving about this passage, since the moment we lifted our anchor. There is something in the ship to leeward that comes athwart my fancy like a drag, and I confess, your honour, that I should make but little headway in a nap, though I should try the swing of a hammock."

"How long is it since you made out the ship to leeward?"

"I will not swear that a real living ship has been made out at all, sir. Something I did see, just before the bell struck seven, and there it is, just as clear, and just as dim, to be seen now, by them that have good eyes."

"And how did she bear when you first saw her?"

"Two or three points more upon the beam than now."

"Then we are passing her!" exclaimed Wilder, with a pleasure too evident to be concealed.

"No, your honour, no. You forget, sir, the ship has come closer to the wind since the middle watch was set."

"True," returned his young commander, in disappointment, "true, very true, too true. And her bearing has not changed since you first made her out?"

"Not by compass, sir. It is a quick boat, that, or it would never hold such way with the *Royal Caroline*, and that too upon a stiffened bow-line, which everybody knows is the real play of this ship."

"Go, get you to your hammock. In the morning we may have a better look at the fellow. Mr Earing, we will bring the ship upon the other tack, and get more easting while the land is so far from us. This course will be setting us upon Hatteras. Besides——"

"Yes, sir," the mate replied, observing his superior to hesitate, "as you were saying,—besides, no one can foretell the length of a gale, nor the real quarter from which it may come."

"Precisely. No one can answer for the weather. The men are scarcely in their hammocks; turn them up at once, sir, before their eyes are heavy, and we will get the ship's head the other way."

The mate instantly sounded the well-known cry which summoned the watch below to the assistance of their ship-mates on deck. Little delay occurred, and not a word was uttered, but the short, authoritative mandates which Wilder saw fit to deliver from his own lips. No longer pressed up against the wind, the ship, obedient to her helm, gracefully began to incline her head from the waves, and to bring the wind abeam. Then, instead of breasting and mounting the endless hillocks, like a being that toiled heavily along its path, she fell into the trough of the sea, from which she issued like a courser, who having conquered an ascent, shoots along the track with redoubled velocity. For an instant the wind appeared to lull, though the wide ridgets of foam which rolled along on each side of the vessel's bows, sufficiently proclaimed that she was skimming before it. In another moment, the tall spars began to incline again to the west, and the vessel came swooping up to the wind, until her plunges and shocks against the seas were renewed as violently as before. When every yard and sheet were properly trimmed to meet the new position of the vessel, Wilder turned to get a glimpse of the stranger. A minute was lost in ascertaining the precise spot where he ought to appear; for, in such a chaos of water, and with no guide but the judgment, the eye was apt to deceive itself, by referring to the nearer and more familiar objects by which the spectator was surrounded.

"The stranger has vanished!" said Earing, with a voice in which mental relief and distrust were oddly manifesting themselves.

"He should indeed be on this quarter, but I see him not!"

"Aye, aye, sir; this is the way that the midnight cruiser off the Hope is said to come and go. There are men who have seen that vessel shut in by a fog, in as fine a starlight night as was ever met in a southern latitude. But then this cannot be the Dutchman, since it is so many long leagues from the pitch of the Cape to the coast of North America."

"There he lies; and, by heaven, he has already gone about!"

The truth of what Wilder affirmed was sufficiently evident to the eye of a seaman. The same diminutive and misty tracery, as before, was to be seen on the light background of the horizon, looking not unlike the faintest shadows cast upon some brighter surface by the deception of the phantasmagoria. But to the mariners, who so well knew how to distinguish between the different lines of her masts, it was very evident that her course had been suddenly and dexterously changed, and that she was now steering no longer to the south and west, but, like themselves, holding her way towards the northeast, or broadly off towards the middle of the Atlantic. The fact appeared to make a sensible impression on them all; though probably, had their reasons been sifted, they would have been found to be entirely different.

"That fellow has truly tacked!" said Earing, after a long meditative pause, and with a voice in which awe was beginning to get the ascendency of doubt. "Long as I have followed the sea, have I never before seen a vessel tack against such a head-beating sea. He must have been all shaking in the wind, when we gave him the last look, or we should have lost sight of him."

"A lively and quick working vessel might do it," said Wilder; "especially if strong-handed."

"Aye, the hand of Beelzebub is always strong; and a light job would he make of even a more difficult manoeuvre!"

"Mr Earing," interrupted Wilder, "we will pack upon the Caroline, and try our sailing with this stranger. Get the main tack aboard, and set the top-gallant sail."

The slow-minded mate would have remonstrated against the order, had he dared; but there was that in the calm manner of his young commander, which admonished him of the hazard. He was not wrong, however, in considering the duty he was now to perform as one that was not entirely free from risk. The ship was already moving under quite as much canvas as he deemed it prudent to show at such an hour, and with so many threatening symptoms of heavier weather hanging about the horizon. The necessary orders were, however, repeated as promptly as they had been given. The seamen had already begun to consider the stranger, and to converse among themselves concerning his appearance and situation; and they obeyed with an alacrity that might perhaps have been traced to a secret but common wish to escape from his vicinity. The sails were successively and speedily set; and then each man folded his arms, and stood gazing steadily and intently at the shadowy object to leeward, in order to witness the effect of the change.

The Royal Caroline seemed, like her crew, sensible of the necessity of increasing her speed. As she felt the pressure of the broad sheets of canvas that had just been distended, the ship bowed lower, appearing to recline on the bed of water which rose under her lee nearly to the scuppers.

On the other side, the dark planks and polished copper lay bare for many feet, though often washed by the waves that came sweeping along her length, green and angrily, still capped, as usual, with crests of lucid foam. The shocks, as the vessel tilted against the billows, were becoming every moment more severe; and, from each encounter, a bright cloud of spray arose, which either fell glittering on the deck, or drove, in brilliant mist, across the rolling water, far to leeward.

Wilder long watched the ship with a clouded brow, but with the steady intelligence of a seaman. Once or twice, when she trembled, and appeared to stop in her violent encounter with a wave as suddenly as if she had struck a rock, his lips severed, and he was about to give the order to reduce the sail; but a glance at the misty-looking image in the western horizon caused him to change his purpose. Like a desperate adventurer, who had cast his fortunes on some hazardous experiment, he appeared to await the issue with a resolution as haughty as it was unconquerable.

"The top-gallant is bending like a whip," muttered the careful Earing, at his elbow.

"Let it go, we have spare spars enough to put in its place."

"I have always found the *Caroline* leaky, after she has been strained by driving her against the sea."

"We have our pumps."

"True, sir, but in my poor judgement, it is idle to think of outsailing a craft that the devil commands, if he does not altogether handle."

"One will never know that, Mr Earing, till he tries."

"We gave the Dutchman a chance of that sort; and, I must say, we not only had the most canvas spread, but much the best of the wind; and what good did it do? There he lay, under his three top-sails, driver, and jib; and we, with studding-sails alow and aloft, couldn't alter his bearing a foot."

"The Dutchman is never seen in a northern latitude."

"Well, I cannot say he is," returned Earing, in a sort of compelled resignation; "but he who has put that flyer off the Cape may have found the cruise so profitable, as to wish to send another ship into these seas."

Wilder made no reply. He had either humoured the superstitious apprehension of his mate enough, or his mind was too intent on its principal object to dwell longer on a foreign subject.

Notwithstanding the seas that met her advance, in such quick succession as greatly to retard her progress, the Bristol trader had soon toiled her way through a league of the troubled element. At every plunge she took, the bows divided a mass of water that appeared to be fast getting more vast and more violent, and more than once the struggling hull was nearly buried forward, in some wave which it had equal difficulty in mounting or penetrating.

The mariners narrowly watched the smallest movements of their vessel. Not a man left her deck for hours. The superstitious awe, which had taken such a deep hold of the untutored faculties of the chief mate, had not been slow in extending its influence to the meanest of her crew. Even the accident which had befallen her former commander, and the sudden and mysterious manner in which the young officer who now trod the quarter-deck; so singularly firm and calm under circumstances deemed so imposing, had their influence in heightening the wild impression. The impunity with which the *Caroline* bore such a press of canvas, under the circumstances in which she was placed, added to their kindling admiration; and, ere Wilder had determined in his own mind on the powers of his ship, in comparison with those of the vessel that so strangely hung on the horizon, he was himself becoming the subject of unnatural and revolting suspicions to his own crew.

After the ship had been wore, and during the time that Wilder, with a view to lose sight of his unwelcome neighbour, was endeavouring to urge her through the seas in the manner already described, the second mate remained in the waist of the vessel, surrounded by a few of the older and more experienced seamen, holding converse on the remarkable appearance of the phantom to leeward, and of the extraordinary manner in which their unknown officer saw fit to attest the enduring qualities of their own vessel.

"I have heard it said, by older seafaring men than any in this ship," he said, "that the devil has been known to send one of his mates aboard a lawful trader, to lead her astray among shoals and quicksands, in order that he might make a wreck, and get his share of the salvage among the souls of the people. What man can say who gets into the cabin, when an unknown name stands first in the shipping-list of a vessel?"

"The stranger is shut in by a cloud!" exclaimed one of the mariners, who still kept an eye riveted on the mysterious object to leeward.

"Aye, aye; it would occasion no surprise to me to see that craft steering into the moon! I have doubled the Horn, brothers, in a king's ship, and I have seen the bright cloud that never sets, and I have held a living corposant in my own hand. But these are things which any man may look on, who will go upon a yard in a gale, or ship aboard a South-seaman; still, I pronounce it uncommon for a vessel to see her shadow in the haze, as we have ours at this moment; there it comes again!—here-away, between the after-shroud and the backstay—or for a trader to carry sail in a fashion that would make every knee in a bomb-ketch work like a tooth brush fiddling across a passenger's mouth, after he has had a smart bout with the sea-sickness."

"And yet the lad holds the ship in hand," said the oldest of all the seamen, who kept his gaze fastened on the proceedings of Wilder: "he is driving her through it in a mad manner, I will allow; but yet, so far, he has not parted a yarn."

"Yarns!" repeated the mate, in a tone of contempt; "What signify yarns, when the whole cable is to snap, and in such a fashion as to leave no hope for the anchor, except in a buoy-rope? Hark ye, old Bill; the devil never finishes his jobs by halves. What is to happen will happen bodily; and no easing off. Mr Bale no doubt thought he was doing the clever thing for the owners, when he shipped this Mr Wilder; but then, perhaps he did not know that the vessel was sold to——It becomes a plain-going seaman to have a respect for all he sails under; so I will not, unnecessarily, name the person who, I believe, has got, whether he came by it in a fair purchase or not, no small right in this vessel."

"I have never seen a ship got out of irons more handsomely than he handled the *Caroline* this very morning."

Knighthead indulged in a low laugh.

"When a ship has a certain sort of captain, one is not to be surprised at anything," he answered, "For my own part, I shipped to go from Bristol to the Carolinas and Jamaica, touching at Newport out and home; and I will say, boldly, I have no wish to go anywhere else. As to backing the *Caroline* from her awkward berth alongside the slaver, why, it was well done; too well for so young a mariner. But what think you, brothers—?"

"In the waist there!" cried Wilder.

Had a warning voice arisen from the turbulent and rushing ocean itself, it would not have sounded more alarming in the startled ears of the conscious seamen, than this sudden hail. Their young commander found it necessary to repeat it, before even Knighthead, the proper and official spokesman could muster resolution to answer.

"Get the fore-top-gallant-sail on the ship, sir," continued Wilder, when the customary reply let him know that he had been heard.

The mate and his companions regarded each other for a moment, in dull admiration; and many a melancholy shake of the head was exchanged, before one of the party threw himself into the weather-rigging, proceeding aloft with a doubting mind, in order to loosen the sail in question.

There was certainly enough, in the desperate manner with which Wilder pressed the canvas on the vessel, to excite distrust, either of his intentions or judgement, in the opinions of men less influenced by superstition than those it was now his lot to command. It had long been apparent to Earing, and his more ignorant and consequently more obstinate brother officer, that their young superior had the same desire to escape from the spectral looking ship, which so strangely followed their movements, as they had themselves. They only differed in the mode; but this difference was so very material that the two mates consulted together apart, and then Earing, something stimulated by the hardy opinion of his coadjutor, approached his commander with the determination of delivering the results of their united judgements, with the directness which he thought the occasion now demanded. But there was that in the steady eye and calm mien of Wilder, that caused him to touch on the dangerous subject with discretion. He stood watching the effect of the sail recently spread, for several minutes, before he even presumed to open his mouth. But a terrible encounter between the vessel and a wave that lifted its angry crest apparently some dozen feet above the approaching bows, gave him courage to proceed.

"I do not see that we drop the stranger, though the ship is wallowing through the water so heavily," he commenced.

Wilder bent another of his frequent glances on the misty object in the horizon, and then turned his frowning eye towards the point whence the wind proceeded, as if he would invite its heaviest blasts; he, however, made no answer.

"We have ever found the crew discontented at the pumps sir," resumed the other, after a sufficient pause for the reply he in vain expected. "I need not tell an officer who knows his duty so well, that seamen rarely love their pumps."

"Whatever I may find it necessary to order, Mr Earing, this ship's company will find it necessary to execute."

There was a settled air of command in the manner with which this tardy answer was given, that did not fail of its effect. Earing recoiled a step submissively, affecting to be lost in consulting the driving masses of clouds; then, summoning his resolution, he attempted to renew the attack in a different quarter.

"Is it your deliberate opinion, Captain Wilder," he said, "that the *Royal Caroline* can, by any human means, be made to drop yonder vessel?"

"I fear not," returned the young man, drawing a breath so long, that all his secret concern seemed struggling in his breast for utterance.

"And, sir, with proper submission to your better education and authority in this ship, I *know* not. I have often seen these matches tried in my time; and well do I know that nothing is gained by straining a vessel with the hope of getting to windward of one of these flyers!"

"Take the glass, Earing, and tell me under what canvas the stranger is going, and what you think his distance may be," said Wilder, without appearing to advert at all to what the other had just observed.

The honest and really well-meaning mate deposited his hat on the quarter-deck, and did as desired. When his look had been long, grave, and deeply absorbed, he closed the glass with the palm of his broad hand, and replied in the manner of one whose opinion was sufficiently matured,—

"If yonder sail had been built and fitted like other craft," he said, "I should not be backward in pronouncing her a full-rigged ship, under the three single-reefed topsails, courses, spanker, and jib."

"And yet, Earing, with all this press of canvas, by the compass we have not left her a foot."

"Lord, sir," returned the mate, shaking his head like one who was well convinced of the folly of such efforts, "if you were to split every cloth in the main-course, you will never alter the bearings of that craft an inch, till the sun shall rise! Then, indeed, such as have eyes that are good enough might perhaps see her sailing about among the clouds; though it has never been my fortune, be it bad, or be it good, to fall in with one of these cruisers after the day has fairly dawned."

"And the distance?" said Wilder; "You have not yet spoken of her distance."

"That is much as people choose to measure. She may be here, nigh enough to toss a biscuit into our tops; or she may be there, where she seems to be, hull down in the horizon."

"But if where she seems to be?"

"Why, she seems to be a vessel of about six hundred tons, and, judging from appearances only, a man might be tempted to say she was a couple of leagues, more or less, under our lee."

"I put her the same! Six miles to windward is not a little advantage in a hard chase. By heavens, Earing, I'll drive the *Caroline* out of the water, but I'll leave him!"

"That might be done, if the ship had wings like a curlew, or a sea-gull; but as it is, I think we are more likely to drive her under."

"She bears her canvas well, so far. You know not what the boat can do when urged."

"I have seen her sailed in all weathers, Captain Wilder, but——"

His mouth was suddenly closed. A vast block wave reared itself between the ship and the eastern horizon, and came rolling onward, seeming to threaten to engulf all before it. Even Wilder watched the shock with breathless anxiety, conscious, for the moment, that he had exceeded the bounds of sound discretion in urging his ship so powerfully against such a mass of water. Luckily the sea broke a few fathoms from the bows of the *Caroline*, sending its surge in a flood of foam upon her decks. For half a minute the forward part of the vessel disappeared as if, unable to mount the swell, it were striving to go through it, and then she heavily emerged, gemmed with a million of the scintillating insects of the ocean. The ship stopped, trembling in every joint of her massive and powerful frame, like some affrighted courser; and, when she resumed her course, it was with a moderation that appeared to warn those who governed her movements of their indiscretion.

Earing faced his commander in silence, perfectly conscious that nothing he could utter contained an argument like this. The seamen no longer hesitated to mutter their disapprobation aloud, and many a prophetic opinion was ventured concerning the consequences of such reckless risks. To all this Wilder turned an insensible ear. Firm in his secret purpose, he would have braved a greater hazard to accomplish his object. . . .

"Mr Earing!" Wilder pointed to the dim object to leeward; and handing him the glass, desired that he would take another view. Each again looked, in turn, long and closely.

"He shows no more sail!" said the commander impatiently, when his own prolonged gaze was ended.

"Not a cloth, sir. But what matters it to such a craft, how much canvas is spread, or how the wind blows?"

"Earing, I think there is too much southing in this breeze; and there is more brewing in yonder streak of dusky clouds on our beam. Let the ship fall off a couple of points or more, and take the strain off the spars by a pull upon the weather-braces."

The mate heard the order with an astonishment he did not care to conceal. There needed no explanation to teach one of his experience that the effect would be to go over the same track they had just passed; and that it was, in substance, abandoning the objects of the voyage.

"I hope there is no offense for an elderly seaman, like myself, Captain Wilder, in venturing an opinion on the weather," he said. "When the pocket of the owner is interested, my judgement approves of going about, for I have no taste for land that the wind blows on, instead of off. But by easing the ship with a reef or two, she would always be jogging seaward; and all we gain would be clear gain, because it is so much off the Hatteras. Besides, who can say that to-morrow, or the next day we sha'n't have a pull out of America, here at northwest?"

"A couple of points fall off, and a pull upon your weather-braces!" said Wilder, in a way to show that he was in earnest.

The orders were given, and obeyed—though ill-suppressed and portentous sounds of discontent, at the undetermined and seemingly unreasonable, changes in their officer's mind, might have been heard issuing from the mouths of Knighthead and the other veterans of the crew.

To all these symptoms of disaffection Wilder remained uttely indifferent. If he heard them at all, he either disdained to yield them any notice, or, guided by a temporizing policy, he chose to appear unconscious of their import. In the mean time the vessel, like a bird whose wing had wearied with struggling against the tempest, and which inclines from the gale to choose an easier course, glided swiftly away, quartering the crests of the waves, or sinking gracefully in their troughs, as she yielded to the force of a wind that was now made to be favourable. The sea rolled on, in a direction no longer adverse to her course, and, by receding from the breeze, the quality of sail spread was no longer trying to her powers of endurance. Still, in the opinion of all her crew, she had quite enough canvas exposed to a night of so portentous aspect. But not so in the judgment of the stranger who was charged with the guidance of her destinies. In a voice that still admonished his inferiors of the danger of disobedience, he commanded several broad sheets of

studding-sails to be set in quick succession. Urged by these new im-
pulses, the ship went careering over the waves, leaving a train of foam in
in her track, that rivalled, in its volume and brightness, the tumbling
summit of the largest swell.

When sail after sail had been set, until even Wilder was obliged to
confess to himself that the *Royal Caroline*, staunch as she was, would
bear no more, our adventurer began to pace the deck again, and to cast
his eyes about him to watch the fruits of his new experiment. The change
in the course of the Bristol trader had made a corresponding change
in the apparent direction of the stranger, who yet floated in the
horizon like a diminutive and misty shadow. Still the unerring compass
told the watchful mariner that she continued to maintain the same relative position as when first seen. No effort, on the part of Wilder, could
alter her bearing an inch. Another hour soon passed away, during which,
as the log told him, his own ship had rolled through three leagues of
water, and still there lay the stranger in the west, as if he were merely
a lessened shadow of herself, cast by the *Caroline* upon the distant and
dusky clouds. An alteration in his course exposed a broader surface of his
canvas to the eyes of those who watched him, but in nothing else was
there a visible change. If his sail had been materially increased, the
distance and the obscurity prevented even the understanding Earing
from detecting it. Perhaps the excited mind of the worthy mate was too
much disposed to believe in the miraculous powers possessed by his unaccountable neighbour, to admit of the full exercise of his experienced
faculties on the occasion; but even Wilder, who vexed his sight, in often-
repeated examinations, was obliged to confess to himself, that the
stranger seemed to glide across the waste of waters, more like a body
floating in the air, than a ship resorting to the known expedients of
mariners.

While our adventurer was engaged in the gloomy musings that such
impressions were not ill adapted to excite, the heavens and the sea began
to exhibit new aspects. The bright streak which had so long hung along
the eastern horizon, as if the curtain of the firmament had been slightly
opened to admit a passage for the winds, was now suddenly closed; and
heavy masses of black clouds began to gather in that quarter, until
vast volumes of the vapour were piled upon the water, blending the two
elements in one. On the other hand, the gloomy canopy lifted in the west,
and a long belt of lurid light was shed athwart the view. In this flood of
bright and portentous mist the stranger still floated, though there were
moments when his faint and fanciful outlines seemed to be melting into
air.

Our watchful adventurer was not blind to these sinister omens. No
sooner did the peculiar atmosphere by which the mysterious image that
he had so often examined was suddenly surrounded, catch his eye, than

his voice was raised in the clear, powerful, and exciting notes of warn-ing.

"Stand by!" he called aloud, "to in all studding-sails! Down with them!" he added, scarcely giving his former words time to reach the ears of his subordinates. "Down with every rag of them, fore and aft the ship! Man the Top-gallant clew-lines, Mr Earing. Clew up, and clew down! In with everything, cheerily, men! In!"

This was a language to which the crew of the *Caroline* were no stran-gers, and it was doubly welcome, since the meanest seaman amongst them had long thought that his unknown commander had been heed-lessly trifling with the safety of the vessel, by the hardy manner in which he disregarded the wild symptoms of the weather. But they under-valued the keen-eyed vigilance of Wilder. He had certainly driven the Bristol trader through the water at a rate she had never been known to go before; but thus far, the facts themselves gave evidence in his favour, since no injury was the consequence of what they deemed temerity. At the quick sudden order just given, however, the whole ship was in an uproar. A dozen seamen called to each other, from different parts of the vessel, each striving to lift his voice above the roaring ocean; and there was every appearance of a general and inextricable confusion; but the same authority which had so unexpectedly aroused them into activity, produced order from their ill-directed though vigorous efforts.

Wilder had spoken, to awaken the drowsy and to excite the torpid. The instant he found each man on the alert, he resumed his orders with a calmness that gave a direction to the powers of all, and yet with an energy that he well knew was called for by the occasion. The enormous sheets of duck, which had looked like so many light clouds in the murky and threatening heavens, were soon seen fluttering wildly, as they de-scended from their high places, and, in a few minutes, the ship was re-duced to the action of her more secure and heavier canvas. Then followed a short and apprehensive pause. All eyes were turned towards the quarter where the ominous signs had been discovered.

The dim tracery of the stranger's form had been swallowed by the flood of misty light, which, by this time, rolled along the sea like drifting vapour, semi-pellucid, preternatural, and seemingly tangible. The ocean itself appeared admonished that a quick and violent change was nigh. The waves ceased to break in their former foaming and brilliant crests, and black masses of the water lifted their surly summits against the eastern horizon, no longer shedding their own peculiar and lu-cid atmosphere around them. The breeze, which had been so fresh, and which had even blown with a force that nearly amounted to a gale, was lulling and becoming uncertain, as if it might be awed by the more violent power that was gathering along the borders of the sea, in the direction of the neighbouring continent. Each moment the eastern puffs of air lost their strength, becoming more and more feeble, until, in an incredibly short period, the heavy sails were heard flapping against the masts. A frightful and ominous calm succeeded. At this instant, a gleam flashed from the fearful obscurity of the ocean, and a roar, like that of a sudden burst of thunder, bellowed along the waters. The seamen turned their startled looks on each other, standing aghast, as if a warning of what was to follow had come out of the heavens themselves. But their calm and more sagacious commander put a different construction on the signal. His lip curled, in high professional pride, and he muttered with scorn,—

"Does he imagine that we sleep? Aye, he has got it himself, and would open our eyes to what is coming! What does he conjecture we have been about, since the middle watch was set?"

Wilder made a swift turn or two on the quarter-deck, turning his quick glances from one quarter of the heavens to another; from the black and lulling water on which his vessel was rolling, to the sails; and from his silent and profoundly expectant crew, to the dim lines of spars that were waving above his head, like so many pencils tracing their curvilinear and wanton images over the murky volumes of the superincumbent clouds.

"Lay the after-yards square!" he said, in a voice which was heard by every man on deck, though his words were apparently spoken but little above his breath. The creaking of the blocks, as the spars came slowly and heavily round to the indicated position, contributed to the imposing character of the moment, sounding like notes of fearful preparation.

"Haul up the courses!" resumed Wilder, with the same eloquent calmness of manner. Then, taking another glance at the threatening horizon, he added slowly but with emphasis, "Furl them—furl them both. Away aloft, and hand your courses," he continued in a shout; "roll them up cheerily; in with them, boys, cheerily; in!"

In a moment twenty dark forms were leaping up the rigging. In another, the vast and powerful sheets of canvas were effectually rendered harmless, by securing them in tight rolls to their respective spars. The men descended as swiftly as they had mounted to the yards; and then succeeded another breathing pause. At this appalling moment, a candle would have sent its flame perpendicularly towards the heavens. The ship, missing the steadying power of the wind, rolled heavily in the troughs of the seas, which began to lessen at each instant, as if the startled element was recalling into the security of its own vast bosom that portion of its particles which had so lately been permitted to gambol madly over its surface. The water washed sullenly along the side of the ship, or, as she labouring rose from one of her frequent falls into the hollow of the waves, it shot back into the ocean from her decks in glittering cascades. Every hue of the heavens, every sound of the element, and each dusky and anxious countenance, helped to proclaim the intense interest of the moment. In this brief interval of expectation and inactivity, the mates again approached their commander.

"It is an awful night, Captain Wilder!" said Earing, presuming on his rank to be the first to speak.

"I have known far less notice given of a shift of wind," was the answer.

"We have had time to gather in our kites, 'tis true, sir; but there are signs and warnings that come with this change which the oldest seaman must dread!"

"Yes," continued Knighthead, in a voice that sounded hoarse and powerful, even amid the fearful accessories of that scene; "yes, it is no trifling commission that can call people that I shall not name out upon the water in such a night as this. It was in just such weather that I saw the *Vesuvius* ketch go to a place so deep, that her own mortar would not have been able to have sent a bomb into the open air, had hands and fire been there fit to let it off!"

"Aye; and it was in such a time that the Greenlandman was cast upon the Orkneys, in as flat a calm as ever lay on the sea."

"Gentlemen," said Wilder, with a peculiar and perhaps an ironical emphasis on the word, "what would ye have? There is not a breath of air stirring, and the ship is raked to her top-sails!"

It would have been difficult for either of the two malcontents to give a very satisfactory answer to this question. Both were secretly goaded by mysterious and superstitious apprehensions, that were powerfully aided by the more real and intelligible aspect of the night; but neither had so far forgotten his manhood, and his professional pride, as to lay bare the full extent of his own weakness, at a moment when he was liable to be called upon for the exhibition of qualities of a more positive and determined character. The feeling that was uppermost betrayed itself in the reply of Earing though in an indirect and covert manner.

"Yes, the vessel is snug enough now," he said, "though eyesight has shown us it is no easy matter to drive a freighted ship through the water as fast as one of those flying craft aboard which no man can say who stands at the helm, by what compass she steers, or what is her draught!"

"Aye," resumed Knighthead, "I call the *Caroline* fast for an honest trader. There are few square-rigged boats who do not wear the pennants of the king, that can eat her out of the wind on a bow-line, or bring her into their wake with studding-sails set. But this is a time and an hour to make a seaman think. Look at yon hazy light, here in with the land, that is coming so fast down upon us, and then tell me whether it comes from the coast of America, or whether it comes from out of the stranger who has been so long running under our lee, but who has got, or is fast getting, the wind of us at last, while none here can say how, or why. I have just this much, and no more, to say; give me for consort a craft whose captain I know, or give me none!"

"Such is your taste, Mr Knighthead," said Wilder, coldly, "mine may, by some accident, be different."

"Yes, yes," observed the more cautious and prudent Earing, "in time of war, and with letters of marque aboard, a man may honestly hope the sail he sees should have a stranger for her master; or other wise he would never fall in with an enemy. But though an Englishman born myself, I would rather give the ship in that mist a clear sea, seeing that I neither know her nation nor her cruise. Ah, Captain Wilder, this is an awful sight for the morning watch! Often and often have I seen the sun rise in the east, and no harm done; but little good can come of a day when the light first breaks in the west. Cheerfully would I give the owners the last month's pay, hard as it has been earned, did I but know under what flag the stranger sails."

"Frenchman, Don, or Devil, yonder he comes!" cried Wilder. Then, turning toward the attentive crew, he shouted, in a voice that was appalling by its vehemence and warning, "Let run the after-halyards! round with the fore-yard; round with it, men, with a will!"

These were cries that the startled crew but too well understood. Every nerve and muscle were exerted to execute the orders, to be in readiness for the tempest. No man spoke, but each expended the utmost of his power and skill in direct and manly efforts. Nor was there, in verity, a moment to lose, or a particle of human strength expended here, without a sufficient object.

The lurid and fearful-looking mist, which, for the last quarter of an hour, had been gathering in the northwest, was driving down upon them with the speed of a race-horse. The air had already lost the damp and peculiar feeling of an easterly breeze; and little eddies were beginning to flutter among the masts—precursors of the coming squall. Then, a rushing, roaring sound was heard moaning along the ocean, whose surface was first dimpled, next ruffled, and finally covered with a sheet of clear, white, and spotless foam. At the next moment, the power of the wind fell upon the inert and labouring Bristol trader.

While the gust was approaching, Wilder had seized the slight opportunity afforded by the changeful puffs of air to get the ship as much as possible before the wind; but the sluggish movement of the vessel met neither the wishes of his own impatience nor the exigencies of the moment. Her bows slowly and heavily fell off from the north, leaving her precisely in a situation to receive the first shock on her broadside. Happy it was, for all who had life at risk in that defenseless vessel, that she was not fated to receive the whole weight of the tempest at a blow. The sails fluttered and trembled on their massive yards, bellying and collapsing alternately for a minute, and then the rushing wind swept over them in a hurricane.

The *Caroline* received the blast like a stout and buoyant ship as she was, yielding to its impulse until her side lay nearly incumbent on the element; and then, as if the fearful fabric were conscious of its jeopardy, it seemed to lift its reclining masts again, struggling to work its way through the water.

"Keep the helm-a-weather! Jam it a-weather, for your life!" shouted Wilder, amid the roar of the gust.

The veteran seaman at the wheel obeyed the order with steadiness, but in vain did he keep his eyes on the margin of his head sail, to watch the manner in which the ship would obey its power. Twice more, in as many moments, the giddy masts fell towards the horizon, waving as often gracefully upward, and then they yielded to the mighty pressure of the wind, until the whole machine lay prostrate on the water.

"Be cool!" said Wilder, seizing the bewildered Earing by the arm, as the latter rushed madly up the steep of the deck; "bring hither an axe."

Quick as the thought which gave the order, the mate complied, jumping into the mizzen-channels of the ship, to execute with his own hands the mandate that he knew must follow.

"Shall I cut?" he demanded, with uplifted arms, and in a voice that atoned for his momentary confusion, by its steadiness and force.

"Hold! Does the ship mind her helm at all?"

"Not an inch, sir."

"Then cut!"

A single blow sufficed. Extended to the utmost powers of endurance, by the vast weight it upheld, the lanyard struck by Earing no sooner parted than each of its fellows snapped in succession, leaving the mast dependent on its wood for the support of all the ponderous and complicated hamper it upheld. The cracking of the spar came next; and the whole fell like a tree that had been snapped at its foundation.

"Does she fall off?" called Wilder, to the seamen at the wheel.

"She yielded a little, sir; but this new squall is bringing her up again."

"Shall I cut?" shouted Earing from the main-rigging, whither he had leaped, like a tiger who had bounded on his prey.

"Cut!"

A louder and more imposing crash succeeded this order, though not before several heavy blows had been struck into the massive mast itself. As before, the sea received the tumbling maze of spars, rigging, and sails; the vessel surging, at the same instant, from its recumbent position, and rolling far and heavily to windward.

"She rights! she rights!" exclaimed twenty voices which had been mute, in a suspense that involved life and death.

"Keep her dead away!" added the calm but authoritative voice of the young commander. "Stand by to furl the fore-top-sail—let it hang a moment to drag the ship clear of the wreck—cut, cut—cheerily men—hatchets and knives—cut *with* all, and cut *off* all!"

As the men now worked with the vigour of hope, the ropes that still confined the fallen spars to the vessel were quickly severed; and the *Caroline*, by this time dead before the gale, appeared barely to touch the foam that covered the sea. The wind came over the waste in gusts that rumbled like distant thunder, and with a power that seemed to threaten to lift the ship from its proper element. As a prudent and sagacious seaman had let fly the halyards of the solitary sail that remained, at the moment the squall approached, the loosened but lowered top-sail was now distended in a manner that threatened to drag after it the only mast which still stood. Wilder saw the necessity of getting rid of the sail, and he saw also the utter impossibility of securing it. Calling Earing to his side, he pointed out the danger, and gave the necessary order.

"The spar cannot stand such shocks much longer," he concluded; "should it go over the bows, some fatal blow might be given to the ship at the rate she is moving. A man or two must be sent aloft to cut the sail from the yards."

"The stick is bending like a willow whip," returned the mate, "and the lower mast itself is sprung. There would be great danger in trusting a hand in that top, while these wild squalls are breathing around us."

"You may be right," returned Wilder, with a sudden conviction of the truth of what the other had said. "Stay you then here; if anything befall me, try to get the vessel into port as far north as the Capes of Virginia, at least; on no account attempt Hatteras, in the present condition of——"

"What would you do, Captain Wilder?" interrupted the mate, laying his hand on the shoulder of his commander, who had already thrown his sea-cap on the deck, and was preparing to divest himself of some of his outer garments.

"I go aloft to ease the mast of that top-sail, without which we lose the spar, and possibly the ship."

"I see that plain enough, sir; but, shall it be said that another did the duty of Edward Earing? It is your business to carry the vessel into the Capes of Virginia, and mine to cut the top-sail adrift. If harm comes to me, why, put it in the log, with a word or two about the manner in which I played my part. That is the most proper epitaph for a sailor."

Wilder made no resistance. He resumed his watchful and reflecting attitude, with the simplicity of one who had been too long trained to the discharge of certain obligations himself, to manifest surprise that another should acknowledge their imperative character. In the mean time, Earing proceeded steadily to perform what he had just promised. Passing into the waist of the ship, he provided himself with a suitable hatchet, and then, without speaking a syllable he sprang into the fore-rigging, every strand and rope-yarn of which was tightened by the strain nearly to snapping. The understanding eyes of his observers comprehended his intention; and with precisely the same pride of station as had urged him to the dangerous undertaking, four or five of the oldest mariners jumped upon the ratlines, to mount into an air that apparently teemed with a hundred hurricanes.

"Lie down out of that fore-rigging," shouted Wilder, through a deck trumpet; "lie down; all, but the mate, lie down!" His words were borne past the inattentive ears of the excited and mortified followers of Earing, but for once they failed of their effect. Each man was too earnestly bent on his purpose to listen to the sounds of recall. In less than a minute, the whole were scattered along the yards, prepared to obey the signal of their officer. The mate cast a look about him; perceiving that the time was comparatively favourable, he struck a blow upon the large rope that confined one of the lower angles of the distended and bursting sail to the yard. The effect was much the same as would be produced by knocking away the key-stone of an ill-cemented arch. The canvas broke from its fastenings with a loud explosion, and, for an instant, it was seen sailing in the air ahead of the ship, as if it were sustained on wings. The vessel rose on a sluggish wave—the lingering remains of the former breeze—and settled heavily over the rolling surge, borne down alike by its own weight and the renewed violence of the gusts. At this critical instant, while the seamen aloft were still gazing in the direction in which the little cloud of canvas had disappeared, a lanyard of the lower rigging parted, with a crack that reached the ears of Wilder.

"Lie down!" he shouted wildly through his trumpet; "down by the backstays; down for your lives; every man of you, down!"

A solitary individual profited by the warning, gliding to the deck with the velocity of the wind. But rope parted after rope, and the fatal snapping of the wood followed. For a moment, the towering maze tottered, seeming to wave towards every quarter of the heavens; and then, yielding to the movements of the hull, the whole fell, with a heavy crash, into the sea. Cord, lanyard, and stay snapped like thread, as each received in succession the strain of the ship, leaving the naked and despoiled hull of the *Caroline* to drive before the tempest, as if nothing had occurred to impede its progress.

A mute and eloquent pause succeeded the disaster. It seemed as if the elements themselves were appeased by their work, and something like a momentary lull in the awful rushing of the winds might have been fancied. Wilder sprang to the side of the vessel, and distinctly beheld the victims, who still clung to their frail support. He even saw Earing waving his hands, in adieu, with a seaman's heart, like a man who not only felt how desperate was his situation, but who knew how to meet it with resignation. Then the wreck of spars, with all who clung to it, was swallowed up in the body of the frightful, preternatural-looking mist which extended on every side of them, from the ocean to the clouds.

"Stand by, to clear away a boat!" shouted Wilder, without pausing to think of the impossibility of one's swimming, or of effecting the least good, in so violent a tornado.

But the amazed and confounded seamen who remained needed no instruction in this matter. Not a man moved, nor was the smallest symptom of obedience given. The mariners looked wildly around them, each endeavouring to trace in the dusky countenance of some shipmate his opinion of the extent of the evil; but not a mouth opened among them all.

"It is too late—it is too late!" murmured Wilder; "human skill and human efforts could not save them!"

"Sail, ho!" Knighthead shouted in a voice that was teeming with superstitious awe.

"Let him come on," returned his young commander, bitterly; "the mischief is ready done to his hands!"

"Should this be a true ship, it is our duty to the owners and the passengers to speak her, if a man can make his voice heard in this tempest," the second mate continued, pointing, through the haze, at the dim object that was certainly at hand.

"Speak her!—passengers!" muttered Wilder, involuntarily repeating his words. "No; anything is better than speaking her. Do you see the vessel that is driving down upon us so fast?" he sternly demanded of the watchful seaman who still clung to the wheel of the *Caroline*.

"Aye, aye, sir."

"Give her a berth—sheer away hard to port—perhaps he may pass us in the gloom, now we are no higher than our decks. Give the ship a broad sheer, I say, sir."

The usual laconic answer was given; and, for a few moments the Bristol trader was seen diverging a little from the line in which the other approached; but a second glance assured Wilder that the attempt was useless. The strange ship (every man on board felt certain that it was the same that had so long been seen hanging in the north-western horizon) came on through the mist, with a swiftness that nearly equalled the velocity of the tempestuous winds themselves. Not a thread of canvas was seen on board her. Each line of spars, even to the tapering and delicate top-gallant masts, was in its place, preserving the beauty and symmetry of the whole fabric; but nowhere was there the smallest fragment of a sail opened to the gale. Under her bows rolled a volume of foam that was even discernible amid the universal agitation of the ocean; and, as she came within sound, the sullen roar of the water might have been likened to the noise of a cascade. At first, the spectators on the decks of the *Caroline* believed they were not seen, and some of the men called madly for lights, in order that the disasters of the night might not terminate in an encounter.

"Too many see us there already!" said Wilder.

"No, no," muttered Knighthead; "no fear but we are seen; and by such eyes, too, as never yet looked out of mortal head!"

The seamen paused. In another instant, the long-seen and mysterious ship was within a hundred feet of them. The very power of that wind, which was wont usually to raise the billows, now pressed the element, with the weight of mountains, into its bed. The sea was everywhere a sheet of froth, but the water did not rise above the level of the surface. The instant a wave lifted itself from the security of the vast depths, the fluid was borne away before the tornado in glittering spray. Along this frothy but comparatively motionless surface, then, the stranger came booming with the steadiness and grandeur with which a cloud is seen sailing in the hurricane. No sign of life was discovered about her. If men looked out from their secret places, upon the straitened and discomfited wreck of the Bristol trader, it was covertly, and as darkly as the tempest before which they drove. Wilder held his breath for the moment the stranger was nighest, in the very excess of suspense; but, as he saw no signal of recognition, no human form, nor any intention to arrest, if possible, the furious career of the other, a smile gleamed across his countenance, and his lips moved rapidly, as if he found pleasure in being abandoned to his distress. The stranger drove by, like a dark vision; and ere another minute, her foam was beginning to grow less distinct, in the body of spray to leeward.

"She is going out of sight in the mist!" exclaimed Wilder, when he drew his breath, after the fearful suspense of the few last moments.

"Aye, in the mist or clouds," responded Knighthead, who now kept obstinately at his elbow, watching, with the most jealous distrust, the smallest movement of his unknown commander.

"In the heavens, or in the sea, I care not, provided he be gone."

"Most seamen would rejoice to see a strange sail, from the hull of a vessel shaved to the deck like this."

"Men often court their destruction, from ignorance of their own interests. Let him drive on, say I, and pray I! He goes four feet to our one; and I ask no better favour than that this hurricane may blow until the sun shall rise."

Knighthead, started, and cast an oblique glance, which resembled denunciation, at his companion. To his superstitious mind, there was profanity in thus invoking the tempest, at a moment when the winds seemed already to be pouring out their utmost wrath.

"This is a heavy squall, I will allow," he said, "and such as many mariners pass whole lives without seeing; but he knows little of the sea who thinks there is not more wind where this comes from."

"Let it blow!" cried the other, striking his hands together a little wildly; "I pray for wind!"

All the doubts of Knighthead, as to the character of the young stranger were now removed. He walked forward among the silent and thoughtful crew, with the air of a man whose opinion was settled. Wilder, however, paid no attention to the movements of his subordinate, but continued pacing the deck for hours; now casting his eye at the heavens, and now sending frequent and anxious glances around the limited horizon, while the *Royal Caroline* still continued drifting before the wind, a shorn and naked wreck.

A DESCENT INTO THE MAELSTROM[1]

Edgar Allan Poe

(1809–1849)

WE HAD now reached the summit of the loftiest crag. For some minutes the old man seemed too much exhausted to speak.

"Not long ago," said he at length, "and I could have guided you on this route as well as the youngest of my sons; but, about three years past, there happened to me an event such as never before happened to mortal man—or at least such as no man ever survived to tell of—and the six hours of deadly terror which I then endured have broken me up body and soul. You suppose me a *very* old man—but I am not. It took less than a single day to change these hairs from a jetty black to white, to weaken my limbs, and to unstring my nerves, so that I tremble at the least exertion, and am frightened at a shadow. Do you know that I can scarcely look over this little cliff without getting giddy?"

The "little cliff" upon whose edge he had so carelessly thrown himself down to rest that the weightier portion of his body hung over it, while he was only kept from falling by the tenure of his elbow on its extreme and slippery edge—this "little cliff" arose, a sheer unobstructed precipice of black shining rock, some fifteen or sixteen hundred feet from the world of crags beneath us. Nothing would have tempted me within half a dozen yards of its brink. In truth so deeply was I excited by the perilous position of my companion, that I fell at full length upon the ground, clung to the shrubs around me, and dared not even glance upward at the sky—while I struggled in vain to divest myself of the idea that the very foundations of the mountain were in danger from the fury of the winds. It was long before I could reason myself into sufficient courage to sit up and look out into the distance.

"You must get over these fancies," said the guide, "for I have brought you here that you might have the best possible view of the scene of that event I mentioned—and to tell you the whole story with the spot just under your eye.

"We are now," he continued, in that particularizing manner which distinguished him—"we are now close upon the Norwegian coast—in the sixty-eighth degree of latitude—in the great province of Nordland—and in the dreary district of Lofoden. The mountain upon whose top we sit is Helseggen, the Cloudy. Now raise yourself up a little higher—hold

---

[1]From *Tales of Mystery and Imagination*.

on to the grass if you feel giddy—so—and look out, beyond the belt of vapour beneath us, into the sea."

I looked dizzily, and beheld a wide expanse of ocean, whose waters were so inky a hue as to bring at once to my mind the Nubian geographer's account of the *Mare Tenebrarum*. A panorama more deplorably desolate no human imagination can conceive. To the right and left, as far as the eye could reach, there lay outstretched, like ramparts of the world, lines of horridly black and beetling cliff, whose character of gloom was but the more forcibly illustrated by the surf which reared high up against it, its white and ghastly crest, howling and shrieking for ever. Just opposite the promontory upon whose apex we were placed, and at a distance of some five or six miles out at sea, there was visible a small, bleak-looking island; or, more properly, its position was discernible through the wilderness of surge in which it was enveloped. About two miles nearer the land, arose another of smaller size, hideously craggy and barren, and encompassed at various intervals by a cluster of dark rocks.

The appearance of the ocean, in the space between the more distant island and the shore, had something very unusual about it. Although, at the time, so strong a gale was blowing landward that a brigg in the remote offing lay to under a double-reefed trysail, and constantly plunged her whole hull out of sight, still there was here nothing like a regular swell, but only a short, quick, angry cross dashing of water in every direction—as well in the teeth of the wind as otherwise. Of foam there was little except in the immediate vicinity of the rocks.

"The island in the distance," resumed the old man, "is Moskoe. That a mile to the northward is Ambaaren. Yonder are Islesen, Hotholm, Keildhelm, Suarven, and Buckholm. Farther off—between Moskoe and Vurrgh—are Otterholm, Flimen, Sandflesen, and Stockholm. These are the true names of the places—but why it has been thought necessary to name them at all, is more than either you or I can understand. Do you hear anything? Do you see any change in the water?"

We had now been about ten minutes upon the top of Helseggen, to which we had ascended from the interior of Lofoden, so that we had caught no glimpse of the sea until it had burst upon us from the summit. As the old man spoke I became aware of a loud and gradually increasing sound, like the moaning of a vast herd of buffaloes upon an American prairie; and at the same moment I perceived that what seamen term the 'chopping' character of the ocean beneath us, was rapidly changing into a current which set to the eastward. Even while I gazed, this current acquired a monstrous velocity. Each moment added to its speed—to its headlong impetuosity. In five minutes the whole sea, as far as Vurrgh, was lashed into ungovernable fury; but it was between Moskoe and the coast that the main uproar held its sway. Here the vast bed of the waters, seamed and scarred into a thousand conflicting channels, burst suddenly into frenzied convulsion—heaving, boiling, hissing—gyrating in gigantic and innumerable vortices, and all whirling and plunging on to the eastward with a rapidity which water never elsewhere assumes, except in precipitous descents.

In a few minutes more, there came over the scene another radical alteration. The general surface grew somewhat more smooth, and the whirlpools, one by one, disappeared, while prodigious streaks of foam became apparent where none had been seen before. These streaks, at length, spreading out to a great distance, and entering into combination, took unto themselves the gyratory motion of the subsided vortices, and seemed to form the germ of another more vast. Suddenly—very suddenly—this assumed a distinct and definite existence, in a circle of more than a mile in diameter. The edge of the whirl was represented by a broad belt of gleaming spray; but no particle of this slipped into the mouth of the terrific funnel, whose interior, as far as the eye could fathom it, was a smooth, shining, and jet-black wall of water, inclined to the horizon at an angle of some forty-five degrees, speeding dizzily round and round with a swaying and sweltering motion, and sending forth to the winds an appalling voice, half shriek, half roar, such as not even the mighty cataract of Niagara ever lifts up in its agony to Heaven.

The mountain trembled to its very base, and the rock rocked. I threw myself upon my face, and clung to the scant herbage in an excess of nervous agitation.

"This," said I at length, to the old man—"this *can* be nothing else but the great whirlpool of the Maelstrom."

"So it is sometimes termed," said he. "We Norwegians call it the Moskoe-strom, from the island of Moskoe in the midway."

The ordinary account of this vortex had by no means prepared me for what I saw. That of Jonas Ramus, which is perhaps the most circumstantial of any, cannot impart the faintest conception either of the magnificence or of the horror of the scene—or of the wild bewildering sense of *the novel* which confounds the beholder. I am not sure from what point of view the writer in question surveyed it, nor at what time, but it could neither have been from the summit of Helseggen, nor during a storm. There are some passages of his description nevertheless, which may be quoted for their details, although their effect is exceedingly feeble in conveying an impression of the spectacle.

"Between Lofoden and Moskoe," he says, "the depth of the water is between thirty-six and forty fathoms; but on the other side, toward Ver (Vurrgh) this depth decreases so as not to afford a convenient passage for a vessel, without the risk of splitting on the rocks, which happens even in the calmest weather. When it is flood, the stream runs up the country between Lofoden and Moskoe with a boisterous rapidity; but the roar of its impetuous ebb to the sea is scarce equalled by the loudest and most dreadful cataracts; the noise being heard several leagues off, and the vortices or pits are of such an extent and depth, that if a ship comes within its attraction, it is inevitably absorbed and carried down to the bottom, and there beat to pieces against the rocks; and when the water relaxes, the fragments thereof are thrown up again. But these intervals of tranquillity are only at the turn of the ebb and flood, and in calm weather, and last but a quarter of an hour, its violence gradually returning. When the stream is most boisterous, and its fury heightened by a storm, it is dangerous to come within a Norway mile of it. Boats, yachts, and ships have been carried away by not guarding against it before they were carried within its reach. It likewise happens frequently, that whales come too near the stream, and are overpowered by its violence; and then it is impossible to describe their howlings and bellowings in their fruitless struggles to disengage themselves. A bear once, in attempting to swim from Lofoden to Moskoe, was caught by the stream and borne down, while he roared terribly, so as to be heard on shore. Large stocks of firs and pine-trees, after being absorbed by the current, rise again broken and torn to such a degree as if bristles grew upon them. This plainly shows the bottom to consist of craggy rocks, among which they are whirled to and fro. This stream is regulated by the flux and reflux of the sea—it being constantly high and low water every six hours. In the year 1645, early in the morning of Sexagesima Sunday, it raged with such a noise and impetuosity that the very stones of the houses on the coast fell to the ground."

In regard to the depth of the water, I could not see how this could have been ascertained at all in the immediate vicinity of the vortex. The "forty fathoms" must have reference only to portions of the channel close upon the shore of either Moskoe or Lofoden. The depth in the middle of the Moskoe-strom must be ummeasurably greater; and no better proof of this fact is necessary than can be obtained from even the sidelong glance into the abyss of the whirl which may be had from the highest crag of Helseggen. Looking down from this pinnacle upon the howling Phlegethon below, I could not help smiling at the simplicity with which the honest Jonas Ramus records, as a matter difficult of belief, the anecdotes of the whales and the bears for it appeared to me, in fact, a self-evident thing, that the largest ships of the line in existence, coming within the influence of that deadly attraction, could resist it as little as a feather the hurricane, and must disappear bodily at once.

The attempts to account for the phenomenon—some of which I remember, seemed to me sufficiently plausible in perusal—now wore a very different and unsatisfactory aspect. The idea generally received is that this, as well as three smaller vortices among the Ferroe Islands, "have no other cause than the collision of waves rising and falling, at flux and reflux, against a ridge of rocks and shelves, which confines the water so that it precipitates itself like a cataract; and thus the higher the flood rises, the deeper the fall must be, and the natural result of all is a whirlpool or vortex, the prodigious suction of which is sufficiently known by lesser experiments.—" These are the words of the *Encyclopœ-dia Britannica*. Kircher and others imagine that in the centre of the chan-nel of the Maelstrom is an abyss penetrating the globe, and issuing in some very remote part—the Gulf of Bothnia being somewhat decidedly named in one instance. This opinion, idle in itself, was the one to which, as I gazed, my imagination most readily assented; and, mentioning it to the guide, I was rather surprised to hear him say that, although it was the view almost universally entertained of the subject by the Nor-wegians, it nevertheless was not his own. As to the former notion, he confessed his inability to comprehend it; and here I agreed with him—for, however conclusive on paper, it becomes altogether unintelligible, and even absurd, amid the thunder of the abyss.

"You have had a good look at the whirl now," said the old man, "and if you will creep round this crag, so as to get in its lee, and deaden the roar of the water, I will tell you a story that will convince you I ought to know something of the Moskoe-strom.

I placed myself as desired, and he proceeded.

"Myself and my two brothers once owned a schooner-rigged smack of about seventy tons burthen, with which we were in the habit of fishing among the islands beyond Moskoe, nearly to Vurrgh. In all vio-lent eddies at sea there is good fishing at proper opportunities, if one has only the courage to attempt it; but among the whole of the Lofoden coastmen, we three were the only ones who made a regular business of going out to the islands, as I tell you. The usual grounds are a great way down to the southward. There fish can be got at all hours, without much risk, and therefore these places were preferred. The choice spots over here among the rocks, however, not only yield the finest variety, but in far greater abundance; so that we often got in a single day, what the more timid of the craft could not scrape together in a week. In fact, we made it a matter of desperate speculation—the risk of life standing instead of labour, and courage answering for capital.

"We kept the smack in a cove about five miles higher up the coast than this; and it was our practice, in fine weather, to take advantage of the fifteen minutes' slack to push across the main channel of the Moskoe-strom, far above the pool, and then drop down upon anchorage some-where near Otterholm, or Sandflesen, where the eddies are not so violent as elsewhere. Here we used to remain until nearly time for slack-water again, when we weighed and made for home. We never set out upon this expedition without a steady side wind for coming and going,—one that we felt sure would not fail us before our return—and we seldom made a miscalculation upon this point. Twice, during six years, we were forced to stay all night at anchor on account of a dead calm, which is a rare thing indeed just about here; and once we had to remain on the grounds nearly a week, starving to death, owing to a gale which blew up shortly after our arrival, and made the channel too boisterous to be thought of.

Upon this occasion we should have been driven out to sea in spite of everything, (for the whirlpools threw us round and round so violently, that, at length, we fouled our anchor and dragged it,) if it had not been that we drifted into one of the innumerable cross-currents—here to-day and gone to-morrow,—which drove us under the lee of Flimen, where, by good luck, we brought up.

"I could not tell you the twentieth part of the difficulties we encountered 'on the ground'—it is a bad spot to be in even in good weather —but we made shift always to run the gauntlet of the Moskoe-strom itself without accident, although at times my heart has been in my mouth when we happened to be a minute or so behind or before the slack. The wind sometimes was not as strong as we thought it at starting, and then we made rather less way than we could wish, while the current rendered the smack unmanageable. My eldest brother had a son eighteen years old, and I had two stout boys of my own. These would have been of great assistance at such times, in using the sweeps as well as afterward in fishing—but, somehow, although we ran the risk ourselves, we had not the heart to let the young ones get into danger—for, after all said and done, it *was* a horrible danger, and that is the truth.

"It is now within a few days of three years since what I am going to tell you occurred. It was on the 10th of July, 18—, a day which the people of this part of the world will never forget—for it was one in which blew the most terrible hurricane that ever came out of the heavens. And yet all the morning, and indeed until late in the afternoon, there was a gentle and steady breeze from the south-west, while the sun shone brightly, so that the oldest seaman among us could not have foreseen what was to follow.

"The three of us—my two brothers and myself—had crossed over to the islands about two o'clock P.M., and soon nearly loaded the smack with fine fish, which, we all remarked were more plenty that day than we had ever known them. It was just seven, *by my watch*, when we weighed and started for home, so as to make the worst of the Strom at slack water, which we knew would be at eight.

"We set out with a fresh wind on our starboard quarter, and for some time spanked along at a great rate, never dreaming of danger, for indeed we saw not the slightest reason to apprehend it. All at once we were taken aback by a breeze from over Helseggen. This was most unusual— something that had never happened to us before—and I began to feel a little uneasy, without exactly knowing why. We put the boat on the wind, but could make no headway at all for the eddies, and I was upon the point of proposing to return to the anchorage, when, looking astern, we saw the whole horizon covered with a singular copper-coloured cloud that rose with the most amazing velocity.

"In the meantime the breeze that had headed us off fell away and we were dead becalmed, drifting about in every direction. This state of things, however, did not last long enough to give us time to think about it. In less than a minute the storm was upon us—in less than two the sky was entirely overcast—and what with this and the driving spray, it become suddenly so dark that we could not see each other in the smack.

"Such a hurricane as then blew it is folly to attempt describing. The oldest seaman in Norway never experienced anything like it. We had to let our sails go by the run before it cleverly took us; but, at the first puff, both our masts went by the board as if they had been sawed off—the mainmast taking with it my youngest brother who had lashed himself to it for safety.

"Our boat was the lightest feather of a thing that ever sat upon water. It had a complete flush deck, with only a small hatch near the bow, and this hatch it had always been our custom to batten down when about to cross the Strom, by way of precaution against the chopping seas. But for this circumstance we should have foundered at once—for we lay entirely buried for some moments. How my eldest brother escaped destruction I cannot say, for I never had an opportunity of ascertaining. For my part, as soon as I had let the foresail run, I threw myself flat on deck, with my feet against the narrow gunwale of the bow, and with my hands grasping a ring-bolt near the foot of the foremast. It was mere instinct that prompted me to do this—which was undoubtedly the best thing I could have done—for I was much too flurried to think.

"For some moments we were completely deluged, as I say, and all this time I held my breath, and clung to the bolt. When I could stand it no longer, I raised myself upon my knees, still keeping hold with my hands and thus got my head clear. Presently our little boat gave herself a shake just as a dog does in coming out of the water, and thus rid herself, in some measure, of the seas. I was now trying to get the better of the stupor that had come over me, and to collect my senses so as to see what was to be done, when I felt somebody grasp my arm. It was my eldest brother, and my heart leaped for joy, for I had made sure that he was overboard—but the next moment all this joy was turned to horror—for he put his mouth close to my ear, and screamed out the word '*Moskoe-strom!*'

"No one will ever know what my feelings were at that moment. I shook from head to foot as if I had had the most violent fit of ague. I knew what he meant by that one word well enough—I knew what he wished to make me understand. With the wind that now drove us on, we were bound for the whirl of the Strom, and nothing could save us.

"You perceive that in crossing the Strom *channel*, we always went a long way up above the whirl, even in the calmest weather, and then had to wait and watch carefully for the slack—but now we were driving right upon the pool itself, and in such a hurricane as this! 'To be sure,' I thought, 'we shall get there just about the slack—there is some little hope in that'—but in the next moment I cursed myself for being so great

a fool as to dream of hope at all. I knew very well that we were doomed,
had we been ten times a ninety-gun ship.

"By this time the first fury of the tempest had spent itself, or perhaps
we did not feel it so much, as we scudded before it, but at all events the
seas, which at first had been kept down by the wind, and lay flat and
frothing, now got up into absolute mountains. A singular change, too,
had come over the heavens. Around in every direction it was still as
black as pitch, but nearly overhead there burst out, all at once, a
circular rift of clear sky—as clear as I ever saw—and of a deep bright
blue—and through it there blazed forth the full moon with a lustre
that I never before knew her to wear. She lit up everything about
us with the greatest distinctness—but, oh God, what a scene it was to
light up!

"I now made one or two attempts to speak to my brother—but in some
manner which I could not understand, the din had so increased that I
could not make him hear a single word, although I screamed at the top
of my voice in his ear. Presently he shook his head, looking as pale as
death, and held up one of his fingers, as if to say '*listen!*'

"At first I could not make out what he meant—but soon a hideous
thought flashed upon me. I dragged my watch from its fob. It was not
going. I glanced at its face in the moonlight and then burst into tears as I
flung it far away into the ocean. *It had run down at seven o'clock! We were
behind the time of the slack and the whirl of the Strom was in full fury!*

"When a boat is well built, properly trimmed, and not deep laden, the
waves in a strong gale, when she is going large, seem always to slip from
beneath her—which appears strange to a landsman, and this is what is
called '*riding*,' in sea phrase.

"Well, so far we had ridden the waves very cleverly; but presently a
gigantic sea happened to take us right under the counter, and bore us
with it as it rose—up—up—as if into the sky. I would not have believed
that any wave could rise so high. And then down we came with a sweep,
a slide, and a plunge that made me feel sick and dizzy, as if I was falling
from some lofty mountain-top in a dream. But while we were up I had
thrown a quick glance around—and that one glance was all-sufficient.
I saw our exact position in an instant. The Moskoe-strom whirlpool was
about a quarter of a mile dead ahead—but no more like the every-day
Moskoe-strom than the whirl, as you now see it, is like a mill race. If I
had not known where we were, and what we had to expect, I should not
have recognized the place at all. As it was, I involuntarily closed my
eyes in horror. The lids clenched themselves together as if in a spasm.

"It could not have been more than two minutes afterwards until we
suddenly felt the waves subside, and were enveloped in foam. The boat
made a sharp half-turn to larboard, and then shot off in its new direction
like a thunderbolt. At the same moment the roaring noise of the water
was completely drowned in a kind of shrill shriek—such a sound as you

might imagine given out by the water-pipes of many thousand steam-vessels letting off their steam all together. We were now in the belt of surf that always surrounds the whirl; and I thought, of course, that another moment would plunge us into the abyss, down which we could only see indistinctly on account of the amazing velocity with which we were borne along. The boat did not seem to sink into the water at all, but to skim like an air-bubble upon the surface of the surge. Her starboard side was next the whirl, and on the larboard arose the world of ocean we had left. It stood like a huge writhing wall between us and the horizon.

"It may appear strange, but now, when we were in the very jaws of the gulf, I felt more composed than when we were only approaching it. Having made up my mind to hope no more, I got rid of a great deal of that terror which unmanned me at first. I supposed it was despair that strung my nerves.

"It may look like boasting—but what I tell you is the truth—I began to reflect how magnificent a thing it was to die in such a manner, and how foolish it was in me to think of so paltry a consideration as my own individual life, in view of so wonderful a manifestation of God's power. I do believe that I blushed with shame when this idea crossed my mind. After a little while I became possessed with the keenest curiosity about the whirl itself. I positively felt a *wish* to explore its depths, even at the sacrifice I was going to make; and my principal grief was that I should never be able to tell my old companions on shore about the mysteries I should see. These, no doubt, were singular fancies to occupy a man's mind in such extremity—and I have often thought since, that the revolutions of the boat around the pool might have rendered me a little light-headed.

"There was another circumstance which tended to restore my self-possession; and this was the cessation of the wind, which could not reach us in our present position—for, as you saw for yourself, the belt of the surf is considerably lower than the general bed of the ocean, and this latter now towered above us, a high, black, mountainous ridge. If you have never been at sea in a heavy gale, you can form no idea of the confusion of mind occasioned by the wind and spray together. They blind, deafen, and strangle you, and take away all power of action or reflection. But we were now, in a great measure, rid of these annoyances—just as death-condemned felons in prison are allowed petty indulgences, forbidden them while their doom is yet uncertain.

"How often we made the circuit of the belt it is impossible to say. We careered round and round for perhaps an hour, flying rather than floating, getting gradually more and more into the middle of the surge, and then nearer and nearer to its horrible inner edge. All this time I had never let go of the ring-bolt. My brother was at the stern, holding on to a small empty water-cask which had been securely lashed under the coop of the counter, and was the only thing on deck that had not been swept

overboard when the gale first took us. As we approached the brink of the
pit he let go his hold upon this, and made for the ring, from which, in the
agony of his terror, he endeavoured to force my hands, as it was not
large enough to afford us both a secure grasp. I never felt deeper grief
than when I saw him attempt this act—although I knew he was a madman when he did it—a raving maniac through sheer fright. I did not
care, however, to contest the point with him. I knew it could make no
difference whether either of us held on at all; so I let him have the bolt,
and went astern to the cask. This there was no great difficulty in doing;
for the smack flew round steadily enough, and upon an even keel—only
swaying to and fro with the immense sweeps and swelters of the whirl.
Scarcely had I secured myself in my new position, when we gave a wild
lurch to starboard, and rushed headlong into the abyss. I muttered a
hurried prayer to God and thought all was over.

"As I felt the sickening sweep of the descent, I had instinctively
tightened my hold upon the barrel, and closed my eyes. For some
seconds I dared not open them—while I expected instant destruction,
and wondered that I was not already in my death-struggles with the
water. But moment after moment elapsed. I still lived. The sense of
falling had ceased; and the motion of the vessel seemed much as it had
been before, while in the belt of foam, with the exception that she now
lay more along. I took courage and looked once again upon the scene.

"Never shall I forget the sensation of awe, horror, and admiration
with which I gazed about me. The boat appeared to be hanging, as if by
magic, midway down, upon the interior surface of a funnel vast in
circumference, prodigious in depth, and whose perfectly smooth sides
might have been mistaken for ebony, but for the bewildering rapidity
with which they spun round, and for the gleaming and ghastly radiance
they shot forth, as the rays of the full moon, from that circular rift amid
the clouds which I have already described, streamed in a flood of golden
glory along the black walls, and far away down into the inmost recesses
of the abyss.

"At first I was too much confused to observe anything accurately.
The general burst of terrific grandeur was all that I beheld. When I
recovered myself a little, however, my gaze fell instinctively downward.
In this direction I was able to obtain an unobstructed view, from the
manner in which the smack hung on the inclined surface of the pool. She
was quite upon an even keel—that is to say, her deck lay in a plane
parallel with that of the water—but this latter sloped at an angle of
more than forty-five degrees, so that we seemed to be lying upon our
beam-ends. I could not help observing, nevertheless, that I had scarcely
more difficulty in maintaining my hold and footing in this situation,
than if we had been upon a dead level; and this I suppose was owing to
the speed at which we revolved.

"The rays of the moon seemed to search to the very bottom of the profound gulf; but still I could make out nothing distinctly on account of a thick mist in which everything there was enveloped, and over which there hung a magnificent rainbow, like that narrow and tottering bridge which Mussulmans say is the only pathway between Time and Eternity. This mist, or spray, was no doubt occasioned by the clashing of the great walls of the funnel, as they all met together at the bottom—but the yell that went up to the Heavens from out of that mist I dare not attempt to describe.

"Our first slide into the abyss itself, from the belt of foam above, had carried us a great distance down the slope; but our further descent was by no means proportionate. Round and round we swept—not with any uniform movement—but in dizzying swings and jerks, that sent us sometimes only a few hundred yards—sometimes nearly the complete circuit of the whirl. Our progress downward, at each revolution, was slow, but very perceptible!

"Looking about me upon the wide waste of liquid ebony on which we were thus borne, I perceived that our boat was not the only object in the embrace of the whirl. Both above and below us were visible fragments of vessels, large masses of building-timber and trunks of trees, with many smaller articles, such as pieces of house furniture, broken boxes, barrels and staves. I have already described the unnatural curiosity which had taken the place of my original terrors. It appeared to grow upon me as I drew nearer and nearer to my dreadful doom. I now began to watch, with a strange interest, the numerous things that floated in our company. I *must* have been delirious, for I even sought *amusement* in speculating upon the relative velocities of their several descents toward the foam below. 'This fir-tree,' I found myself at one time saying, 'will certainly be the next thing that takes the awful plunge and disappears,'—and then I was disappointed to find that the wreck of a Dutch merchant ship overtook it and went down before. At length, after making several guesses of this nature, and being deceived in all—this fact—the fact of my invariable miscalculation, set me upon a train of reflection that made my limbs again tremble, and my heart beat heavily once more.

"It was not a new terror that thus affected me, but the dawn of a more exciting *hope*. This hope arose partly from memory, and partly from present observation. I called to mind the great variety of buoyant matter that strewed the coast of Lofoden, having been absorbed and then thrown forth by the Moskoe-strom. By far the greater number of the articles were shattered in the most extraordinary way—so chafed and roughened as to have the appearance of being stuck full of splinters —but then I distinctly recollected that there were *some* of them which were not disfigured at all. Now I could not account for this difference except by supposing that the roughened fragments were the only ones

which had been *completely absorbed*—that the others had entered into
the whirl at so late a period of the tide, or, from some reason, had
descended so slowly after entering, that they did not reach the bottom
before the turn of the flood came, or of the ebb, as the case might be. I
conceived it possible, in either instance, that they might thus be whirled
up again to the level of the ocean, without undergoing the fate of those
which had been drawn in more early or absorbed more rapidly. I made,
also, three important observations. The first was, that as a general rule,
the larger the bodies were, the more rapid their descent—the second,
that, between two masses of equal extent, the one spherical, and the
other *of any other shape* the superiority in speed of descent was with the
sphere—the third, that, between two masses of equal size, the one cylindrical, and the other of any other shape, the cylinder was absorbed more
slowly. Since my escape, I have had several conversations on this subject with an old schoolmaster in the district; and it was from him that I
learned the use of the words 'cylinder' and 'sphere.' He explained to me—
although I have forgotten the explanation—how what I observed was,
in fact, the natural consequence of the forms of the floating fragments—
and showed me how it happened that a cylinder, swimming in a vortex,
offered more resistance to its suction, and was drawn in with greater
difficulty than an equally bulky body, of any form whatever.

"There was one startling circumstance which went a great way in
enforcing these observations, and rendering me anxious to turn them to
account, and this was that, at every revolution we passed something like
a barrel, or else the yard or the mast of a vessel, while many of these
things, which had been on our level when I first opened my eyes upon the
wonders of the whirlpool, were now high up above us, and seemed to
have moved but little from their original station.

"I no longer hesitated what to do. I resolved to lash myself securely to
the water-cask upon which I now held, to cut it loose from the counter,
and to throw myself with it into the water. I attracted my brother's attention by signs, pointed to the floating barrels that came near us, and
did everything in my power to make him understand what I was about
to do. I thought at length that he comprehended my design—but,
whether this was the case or not, he shook his head despairingly, and
refused to move from his station by the ring-bolt. It was impossible to
reach him; the emergency admitted of no delay; and so, with a bitter
struggle, I resigned him to his fate, fastened myself upon the cask by
means of the lashings which secured it to the counter, and precipitated
myself with it into the sea, without another moment's hesitation.

"The result was precisely what I had hoped it might be. As it is myself who now tell you this tale—as you see that I *did* escape—and as you
are already in possession of the mode in which this escape was effected,
and must therefore anticipate all that I have farther to say—I will bring
my story quickly to conclusion. It might have been an hour, or there-

about, after my quitting the smack, when, having descended to a vast distance beneath me, it made three or four wild gyrations in rapid succession, and, bearing my beloved brother with it, plunged headlong, at once and forever, into the chaos of foam below. The barrel to which I was attached sunk very little farther than half the distance between the bottom of the gulf and the spot at which I leaped overboard, before a great change took place in the character of the whirlpool. The slope of the sides of the vast funnel became momently less and less steep. The gyrations of the whirl grew, gradually, less and less violent. By degrees, the froth and the rainbow disappeared, and the bottom of the gulf seemed slowly to uprise. The sky was clear, the winds had gone down and the full moon was setting radiantly in the west, when I found myself on the surface of the ocean, in full view of the shores of Lofoden, and above the spot where the pool of the Moskoe-strom *had been.* It was the hour of the slack—but the sea still heaved in mountainous waves from the effects of the hurricane. I was borne violently into the channel of the Strom, and in a few minutes, was hurried down the coast into the 'grounds' of the fishermen. A boat picked me up—exhausted from fatigue—and (now that the danger was removed) speechless from the memory of its horror. Those who drew me on board were my old mates and daily companions—but they knew me no more than they would have known a traveller from the spirit-land. My hair which had been raven black the day before, was white as you see it now. They say too that the whole expression of my countenance had changed. I told them my story— they did not believe it. I now tell it to *you*—and I can scarcely expect you to put more faith in it than did the merry fishermen of Lofoden."

THE *CHESAPEAKE* AND THE *SHANNON*[1]

John Bach McMaster

(1852–   )

CAPTAIN PHILIP BOWES VERE BROKE, of his Majesty's frigate *Shannon,* was all that an officer ought to be, and had brought his crew to a state of proficiency in the use of the broadsword, pike, musket, and great guns which was most unusual in the British navy. To his lot it fell in the spring of 1813 to guard the coast east of Cape Cod with the *Shannon* and the *Tenedos,* and blockade the four American frigates *Congress, President, Chesapeake,* and *Constitution,* then in the harbour of Boston. But blockading was too tame a duty, and more than once he endeavoured to persuade some one of them to come out and fight. For a time he was not successful, and Commodore Rodgers,

[1]From *A History of the People of the United States.* Reprinted by permission of D. Appleton & Co.

declining the challenge, ran out on the night of April thirteenth with the *President* and *Congress*. Greatly disappointed, Broke thereupon sent away the *Tenedos*, and formally challenged Lawrence to meet him in the *Chesapeake*.

James Lawrence was a native of New Jersey, where he was born in 1781. At the age of seventeen, in the midst of the excitement produced by the X. Y. Z. despatches, he entered the navy then being formed, and saw service in the West Indies during the *quasi* French War, in the Mediterranean during the Tripolitan War, and by 1810 had reached the grade of commander. With this rank he had sailed in the *Vixen*, the *Wasp*, the *Argus*, and the *Hornet*, in which he fought that ever-memorable duel with Peacock. For this signal victory he was promptly rewarded with command of the *Chesapeake*, whose old captain was too ill to go to sea. From the day when she struck to the *Leopard* the *Chesapeake* had been looked on by both officers and men as a most unlucky ship, a superstition which no event in her career ever tended to dispel. On her return to port, April 9th, after an unsuccessful cruise, her old crew left her, to seek for better fortune in some more lucky ship, and such new men as could be secured had been enlisted to fill their places. Some were British, a few were Portuguese; others had never yet seen service on an armed ship. All were unknown to each other and to their officers, and, having never been to sea together, they were without discipline or training. Indeed, it was not till the anchor was about to be weighed that the last draft came aboard, and these still had their hammocks and bags stowed in the boats that brought them when the *Chesapeake* surrendered.

The *Shannon*, on the other hand, was commanded by an officer as courageous, as skilful, and as energetic as Lawrence, and manned by a well-disciplined and well-practised crew. Every day in the forenoon the men were exercised at training the guns, and in the afternoon in the use of the broadsword, the musket, and the pike. Twice each week the crew fired at targets with great guns and musketry, and on such occasions the man who hit the bull's-eye received a pound of tobacco. At times Broke would order a cask thrown overboard and then suddenly command some particular gun to be manned to sink it, a practice more than once witnessed by the American officers at the Charlestown Navy Yard. Save in discipline and number of men (for the *Chesapeake* had forty-nine more than the *Shannon*), the two frigates were not ill matched, as in length, in breadth of beam, in guns, and weight of metal they were almost exactly equal.

Considering the *Chesapeake* to be a fair match for the *Shannon* Broke had been most anxious to meet her. Accordingly, on June 1st, seeing the *Chesapeake* riding at anchor below Fort Independence as if waiting to put to sea, Broke ran into the harbour and raised his flag. Lawrence immediately fired a gun and displayed his colours, mustered his crew, told them he intended to fight, and when the tide turned went down the harbour under a press of sail.

News of the coming duel spread fast and wide, and long before Lawrence was under way thousands of people were hurrying toward every point likely to afford a view. The bay was covered with boats. Hundreds stood on Blue Hill and on the heights of Malden. Hundreds more went down to Nahant, Cohasset, and Scituate. Lynn, Salem, and Marblehead were full of strangers eager to see the fight. All were disappointed, for the *Chesapeake*, having rounded the Boston Light, bore off to the eastward, and with the *Shannon* was soon lost to sight. The guns were heard, but almost three weeks passed before it was finally known how the fight ended. The pilot who left the *Chesapeake* at five in the afternoon reported to Commodore Bainbridge that the firing began at six; that in twelve minutes both ships were laying alongside each other as if for boarding; that at this moment a dreadful explosion occurred on the *Chesapeake*, and that when the smoke had blown away the British flag was seen flying over the American. His story was strictly true. But, though confirmed by a Cape Ann fishing boat and by some gentlemen who claimed to have been within two miles of the frigates in a packet, the people could not believe it. Even when a boat belonging to the *Chesapeake* was picked up at sea, and when word came from Bangor that the *Tenedos* had brought-to an American coaster and told the captain that the *Chesapeake* was a prize and Lawrence buried at Halifax, the public refused to give up hope. All over the country the greatest anxiety prevailed. Everywhere the post-offices were thronged; everywhere travellers by stage were beset for information. In many places the citizens day after day would ride out for miles on the highway to meet the mail in hopes of getting news. Some earnestly urged that a flag of truce be sent to Halifax to find out what really had happened. At last, June 18th, Halifax newspapers with a long account of the funeral honours paid to Lawrence and Ludlow reached Boston, and all doubt was removed.

It then appeared that after passing the lighthouse at one o'clock the *Chesapeake* followed her enemy till five, when the *Shannon* luffed and waited for her to come up. The wind blowing fresh from the west, Lawrence might easily have chosen his position. But he threw away this advantage, came down on the *Shannon's* quarter, luffed, and ranged up some fifty yards from her starboard side. At ten minutes before six the firing began, and for seven minutes the frigates ran on side by side. Then, some shot from the *Shannon* having crippled the sails of the *Chesapeake*, she came up into the wind and was taken aback, and drifted slowly stern foremost toward the enemy. Every gun on the *Shannon's* broadside swept her from stem to stern. Man after man was shot down at the wheel. A hand grenade blew up the arms chest, and the stern of the *Chesapeake*, drifting helplessly, struck the *Shannon* amidships. A fluke of the *Shannon's* anchor caught in a port of the *Chesapeake*. A boatswain rushed forward to lash the ships, and Broke, calling up his boarders, stepped on the muzzle of one of the *Chesapeake's* guns and leaped over the bulwark to her quarter-deck. Just at this moment Captain Lawrence fell, mortally wounded, and was carried below, crying out, "Don't give up the ship!" "Keep the guns going!" "Fight her till she sinks!" Obedient to his orders, a few men on the quarter-deck made a desperate resistance. In all, some fifty men followed Broke, and, as they came forward, not a live man was on the quarter-deck and not an officer on the spar-deck. Lawrence and Ludlow, his first lieutenant, had been mortally wounded and carried to the cock-pit. The second lieutenant was stationed below. The third lieutenant fled; whereupon the foreigners and raw sailors, seeing the British on the spar-deck, deserted their quarters, and a Portuguese boatswain, having removed the gratings of the berth-deck, the men rushed headlong down the after-ladders. Then was it that Lawrence, hearing the men come down, cried out repeatedly, "Don't give up the ship! Blow her up!" But he was helpless. Broke was in possession of the spar-deck. Still the English captain might have been beaten, for at this moment the two frigates parted, leaving fifty Englishmen on the *Chesapeake's* deck. Seeing this, a few Americans of spirit made a desperate attack, in the course of which Broke almost lost his life. But resistance was useless. The guns ceased firing, the flag came down, and without any formal surrender the *Chesapeake* passed into British hands for the second time, and was taken into Halifax a prize. There Lawrence and Ludlow, having died of their wounds on the way in, were buried with military honors on the 6th of June. Their bodies were not, however, destined to rest long in foreign soil. Deeply as their countrymen felt the humiliation of the defeat, they did not forget the patriotism, the devotion, the inspiring death of Lawrence. They put on mourning. They made of the injunction "Don't give up the ship!" a war cry which has never since been forgotten, and ten of them, all masters of vessels, under the lead of George Crowninshield, Jr. having obtained a flag of truce, brought back the bodies of Lawrence and Ludlow a few weeks later to Salem, whence they were carried by land to New York city and laid with all the honours of war in the yard of Trinity Church.

From Halifax news of the capture was carried to England by a brig which reached Plymouth on July 7th, and the next night the glad tidings were announced in Parliament, and received with boundless joy. So important was the victory in English eyes that the Tower guns were fired, and in time Captain Broke was made a baronet and a knight commander of the Bath, and received from London a sword and the freedom of the city. Concerning the fate of the frigate, whose history is bound up with so much that is shameful and so much that is heroic in our annals, it is worth while to recall that she was taken to England, and in 1820 was condemned and sold. Neither our Government nor our people had patriotism enough to buy her, and her shot-marked, blood-stained timbers were bought by a miller of Wickham, Hants, and were used to build a flour-mill, which is still standing.

HOMEWARD BOUND[1]

Richard Henry Dana, Jr.

(1815–1882)

THE *California* had finished discharging her cargo, and was to get under way at the same time with us. Having washed down decks and got breakfast, the two vessels lay side by side, in complete readiness for sea, our ensigns hanging from the peaks, and our tall spars reflected from the glassy surface of the river, which, since sunrise, had been unbroken by a ripple. At length a few whiffs came across the water, and by eleven o'clock the regular northwest wind set steadily in. There was no need of calling all hands, for we had all been hanging about the forecastle the whole forenoon, and were ready for a start upon the first sign of a breeze. Often we turned our eyes aft upon the captain, who was walking the deck, with every now and then a look to windward. He made a sign to the mate, who came forward, took his station deliberately between the knight-heads, cast a glance aloft, and called out, "All hands, lay aloft and loose the sails!" We were half in the rigging before the order came, and never since we left Boston were the gaskets off the yards, and the rigging over-hauled, in shorter time. "All ready forward, sir!"— "All ready the main!"—"Cross-jack yards all ready, sir!"—"Lay down, all hands but one on each yard!" The yard-arm and bunt gaskets were cast off; and each sail hung by the jigger, with one man standing by the tie to let it go. At the same moment that we sprang aloft, a dozen hands sprang into the rigging of the *California*, and in an instant were all over her yards; and her sails, too, were ready to be dropped at the word. In the mean time our bow gun had been loaded and run out, and its discharge was to be the signal for dropping the sails. A cloud of smoke came out of our bows; the echoes of the gun rattled our farewell among the hills of California, and the two ships were covered, from head to foot, with their white canvas. For a few minutes all was uproar and apparent confusion; men jumping about like monkeys in the rigging; ropes and blocks flying, orders given and answered amid the confused noises of men singing out at the ropes. The topsails came to the mast-heads with "Cheerily men!" and, in a few minutes, every sail was set, for the wind was light. The head sails were backed, the windlass came round "slip-slap" to the cry of the sailors;—"Hove short, sir," said the mate;— "Up with him!"—"Aye, aye, sir." A few hearty and long heaves, and

[1]From *Two Years Before the Mast.*

the anchor showed its head. "Hook cat!" The fall was stretched along the decks; all hands laid hold;—"Hurrah, for the last time," said the mate; and the anchor came to the cat-head to the tune of "Time for us to go," with a rollicking chorus. Everything was done quick, as though it *was* for the last time. The head yards were filled away, and our ship began to move through the water on her homeward-bound course.

The *California* had got under way at the same moment, and we sailed down the narrow bay abreast, and were just off the mouth, and, gradually drawing ahead of her, were on the point of giving her three parting cheers, when suddenly we found ourselves stopped short, and the *California* ranging fast ahead of us. A bar stretches across the mouth of the harbour, with water enough to float common vessels, but, being low in the water, and having kept well to leeward, as we were bound to the southward, we had stuck fast, while the *California*, being light, had floated over.

We kept all sail on, in the hope of forcing over, but, failing in this, we hove aback, and lay waiting for the tide, which was on the flood, to take us back into the channel. This was something of a damper to us, and the captain looked not a little mortified and vexed. "This is the same place where the *Rosa* got ashore, sir," observed our red-headed second mate, most *mal à propos*. A malediction on the *Rosa* and him too, was all the answer he got, and he slunk off to leeward. In a few minutes the force of the wind and the rising of the tide backed us into the stream, and we were on our way to our old anchoring-place, the tide setting swiftly up, and the ship barely manageable in the light breeze. We came-to in our old berth opposite the hide-house, whose inmates were not a little surprised to see us return. We felt as though we were tied to California; and some of the crew swore that they never should get clear of the *bloody* coast.

In about half an hour, which was near high water, the order was given to man the windlass, and again the anchor was catted; but there was no song, and not a word was said about the last time. The *California* had come back on finding that we had returned, and was hove-to, waiting for us, off the point. This time we passed the bar safely, and were soon up with the *California*, who filled away, and kept us company. She seemed desirous of a trial of speed, and our captain accepted the challenge, although we were loaded down to the bolts of our chain-plates, as deep as a sand-barge, and bound so taut with our cargo that we were no more fit for a race than a man in fetters; while our antagonist was in her best trim. Being clear of the point, the breeze became stiff, and the royal-masts bent under our sails, but we would not take them in until we saw three boys spring aloft into the rigging of the *California*, when they were all furled at once, but with orders to our boys to stay aloft at the top-gallant mast-heads and loose them again at the word. It was my duty to furl the fore royal; and, while standing by to loose it again, I had a fine view of the scene. From where I stood, the two vessels seemed nothing but spars and sails, while their narrow decks, far below, slanting over by the force of the wind aloft, appeared hardly capable of supporting the great fabrics raised upon them. The *California* was to windward of us, and had every advantage; yet, while the breeze was stiff, we held our own. As soon as it began to slacken, she ranged a little ahead, and the order was given to loose the royals. In an instant the gaskets were off and the bunt dropped. "Sheet home the fore royal!—Weather sheet's home!"—"Lee sheet's home!"—"Hoist away, sir!" is bawled from aloft. "Overhaul your clew-lines!" shouts the mate. "Aye, aye, sir! all clear!" —"Taut leech! belay! Well the lee brace; haul taut to windward,"— and the royals are set. These brought us up again; but, the wind continuing light, the *California* set hers, and it was soon evident that she was walking away from us. Our captain then hailed, and said that he should keep off to his course; adding, "She isn't the *Alert* now. If I had her in your trim she would have been out of sight by this time." This was good-naturedly answered from the *California*, and she braced sharp up, and stood close upon the wind up the coast; while we squared away our yards, and stood before the wind to the south-southwest. The *California's* crew manned her weather-rigging, waved their hats in the air, and gave us three hearty cheers, which we answered as heartily, and the customary single cheer came back to us from over the water. She stood on her way, doomed to eighteen months' or two years' hard service upon that hated coast, while we were making our way to our home, to which every hour and every mile was bringing us nearer.

As soon as we parted company with the *California*, all hands were sent aloft to set the studding-sails. Booms were rigged out, tacks and halyards rove, sail after sail packed upon her, until every available inch of canvas was spread, that we might not lose a breath of the fair wind. We could now see how much she was cramped and deadened by her cargo; for with a good breeze on her quarter, and every stitch of canvas spread, we could not get more than six knots out of her. She had no more life in her than if she were water-logged. The log was hove several times; but she was doing her best. We had hardly patience with her, but the older sailors said, "Stand by! you'll see her work herself loose in a week or two, and then she'll walk up to Cape Horn like a race-horse."

When all sail had been set, and the decks cleared up, the *California* was a speck in the horizon, and the coast lay like a low cloud along the northeast. At sunset they were both out of sight, and we were once more upon the ocean, where sky and water meet.

STORM IN THE PACIFIC[1]

Richard Henry Dana, Jr.

(1815–1882)

EVERYTHING being now ready, and the passengers aboard, we ran up the ensign and board pennant (for there was no man-of-war, and we were the largest vessel on the coast), and the other vessels ran up their ensigns. Having hove short, cast off the gaskets, and made the bunt of each sail fast by the jigger, with a man on each yard, at the word the whole canvas of the ship was loosed, and with the greatest rapidity possible everything was sheeted home and hoisted up, the anchor tripped and cat-headed, and the ship under headway. The royal yards were all crossed at once, and royals and sky-sails set, and, as we had the wind free, the booms were run out, and all were aloft, active as cats, laying out on the yards and booms, reeving the studding-sail gear; and sail after sail the captain piled upon her, until she was covered with canvas, her sails looking like a great white cloud, resting upon a black speck. Before we doubled the point, we were going at a dashing rate, and leaving the shipping far astern. We had a fine breeze to take us through the Canal, as they call this bay of forty miles long by ten wide. The breeze died away at night, and we were becalmed all day on Sunday, about half-way between Santa Barbara and Point Conception. Sunday night we had a light, fair wind, which set us up again; and having a fine sea-breeze on the first part of Monday we had the prospect of passing, without any trouble, Point Conception—the Cape Horn of California, where, the sailors say, it begins to blow the first of January, and blows until the last of December. Toward the latter part of the afternoon, however, the regular northwest wind, as usual, set in, which brought in our studding-sails, and gave us the chance of beating round the Point, which we were now just abreast of, and which stretched off into the Pacific, high, rocky, and barren, forming the central point of the coast for hundreds of miles north and south. A cap-full of wind will be a bag-full here, and before night our royals were furled, and the ship was labouring hard under her topgallant-sails. At eight bells our watch went below, leaving her with as much sail as she could stagger under, the water flying over the forecastle at every plunge. It was evidently blowing harder, but then there was not a cloud in the sky, and the sun had gone down bright.

We had been below but a short time, before we had the usual premonitions of a coming gale—seas washing over the whole forward part of the vessel, and her bows beating against them with a force and sound like the driving of piles. The watch, too, seemed very busy trampling about decks, and singing out at the ropes. A sailor can tell, by the sound,

[1]From *Two Years Before the Mast.*

what sail is coming in; and, in a short time, we heard the top-gallant-sails come in, one after another, and then the flying jib. This seemed to ease her a good deal, and we were fast going off to the land of Nod, when —bang, bang, bang—on the scuttle, and "All hands, reef topsails, ahoy!" started us out of our berths; and, it not being very cold weather, we had nothing extra to put on, and were soon on deck. I shall never forget the fineness of the sight. It was a clear, and rather a chilly night; the stars were twinkling with an intense brightness, and as far as the eye could reach there was not a cloud to be seen. The horizon met the sea in a defined line. A painter could not have painted so clear a sky. There was not a speck upon it. Yet it was blowing great guns from the northwest. When you can see a cloud to windward, you feel that there is a place for the wind to come from; but here it seemed to come from nowhere. No person could have told from the heavens, by their eyesight alone, that it was not a still summer's night. One reef after another we took in the topsails, and before we could get them hoisted up we heard a sound like a short, quick rattling of thunder, and the jib was blown to atoms out of the bolt-rope. We got the topsails set, and the fragments of the jib stowed away, and the fore topmast staysail set in its place, when the great mainsail gaped open, and the sail ripped from head to foot. "Lay up on that main yard and furl the sail, before it blows to tatters!" shouted the captain; and in a moment we were up, gathering the remains of it upon the yard. We got it wrapped round the yard, and passed gaskets over it as snugly as possible, and were just on deck again, when with another loud rent, which was heard throughout the ship, the fore topsail, which had been double-reefed, split in two athwartships, just below the reef-band, from earing to earing. Here again it was—down yard, haul out reef-tackles, and lay out upon the yard for reefing. By hauling the reef-tackles chock-a-block we took the strain from the other earings, and passing the close-reef earing, and knotting the points carefully, we succeeded in setting the sail, close reefed.

We had but just got the rigging coiled up, and were waiting to hear "Go below the watch!" when the main royal worked loose from the gaskets, and blew directly out to leeward, flapping, and shaking the mast like a wand. Here was a job for somebody. The royal must come in or be cut adrift, or the mast would be snapped short off. All the light hands in the starboard watch were sent up one after another, but they could do nothing with it. At length, John, the tall Frenchman, the head of the starboard watch (and a better sailor never stepped upon a deck), sprang aloft, and, by the help of his long arms and legs, succeeded, after a hard struggle—the sail blowing over the yard-arm to leeward, and the skysail adrift directly over his head—in smothering it and frapping it with long pieces of sinnet. He came very near being blown or shaken from the yard several times, but he was a true sailor, every finger a fish-hook. Having made the sail snug, he prepared to send the yard down, which was a long and difficult job, for, frequently, he was obliged to stop, and hold on with all his might for several minutes, the ship pitching so as to make it impossible to do anything else at that height. The yard at length came down safe, and, after it, the fore and mizzen royal yards were sent down. All hands were then sent aloft, and for an hour or two we were hard at work, making the booms well fast, unreeving the studding-sail and royal and skysail gear, getting rolling-ropes on the yard, setting up the weather breast-backstays, and making other preparations for a storm. It was a fine night for a gale; just cool and bracing enough for quick work, without being cold, and as bright as day. It was sport to have a gale in such weather as this. Yet it blew like a hurricane. The wind seemed to come with a spite, an edge to it, which threatened to scrape us off the yards. The force of the wind was greater than I had ever felt it before; but darkness, cold, and wet are the worst parts of a storm, to a sailor.

Having got on deck again, we looked round to see what time of night it was, and whose watch. In a few minutes the man at the wheel struck four bells, and we found that the other watch was out, and our own half out. Accordingly, the starboard watch went below, and left the ship to us for a couple of hours, yet with orders to stand by for a call.

Hardly had they got below, before away went the fore topmast stay-sail, blown to ribands. This was a small sail, which we could manage in the watch, so that we were not obliged to call up the other watch. We laid out upon the bowsprit, where we were under water half the time, and took in the fragments of the sail, and, as she must have some head sail on her, prepared to bend another staysail. We got the new one out into the nettings; seized on the tack, sheets, and halyards, and the hanks; manned the halyards, cut adrift the frapping-lines, and hoisted away; but before it was half-way up the stay it was blown all to pieces. When we belayed the halyards, there was nothing left but the bolt-rope. Now large eyes began to show themselves in the foresail, and, knowing that it must soon go, the mate ordered us upon the yard to furl it. Being unwilling to call up the watch who had been on deck all night, he roused out the carpenter, sailmaker, cook, and steward, and with their help we manned the fore yard, and, after nearly half an hour's struggle, mastered the sail, and got it well furled round the yard. The force of the wind had never been greater than at this moment. In going up the rigging, it seemed absolutely to pin us down to the shrouds; and, on the yard, there was no such thing as a face to windward. Yet here was no driving sleet, and darkness, and wet, and cold, as off Cape Horn; and instead of stiff oil-cloth suits, southwester caps, and thick boots, we had on hats, round jackets, duck trousers, light shoes, and everything light and easy. These things make a great difference to a sailor. When we got on deck, the man at the wheel struck eight bells (four o'clock in the morning), and "All Star-bowlines, ahoy!" brought the other watch up, but there was no going below for us. The gale was now at its height, "blowing like scissors and thumb-screws"; the captain was on deck; the ship, which was light, rolling and pitching as though she would shake the long sticks out of her, and the sails were gaping open and splitting in every direction. The mizzen topsail, which was a comparatively new sail, and close reefed, split from head to foot, in the bunt; the fore topsail went, in one rent, from clew to earing, and was blowing to tatters; one of the chain bowstays parted; the spritsail yard sprung in the slings; the martingale had slued away off to leeward; and owing to the long dry weather, the lee rigging hung in large bights at every lurch. One of the main top-gallant shrouds had parted; and, to crown all, the galley had got adrift, and gone over to leeward, and the anchor on the lee bow had worked loose, and was thumping the side. Here was work enough for all hands for half a day. Our gang laid out on the mizzen topsail yard, and after more than half an hour's hard work, furled the sail, though it bellied out over our heads, and again, by a slat of the wind, blew in under the yard with a fearful jerk, and almost threw us off from the foot-ropes.

Double gaskets were passed round the yards, rolling tackles and other gear bowsed taut, and everything made as secure as it could be. Coming down, we found the rest of the crew just laying down the fore rigging, having furled the tattered topsail, or, rather, swathed it round the yard, which looked like a broken limb, bandaged. There was no sail now on the ship, but the spanker and the close-reefed main topsail, which still held good. But this was too much after sail, and order was given to furl the spanker. The brails were hauled up, and all the light hands in the starboard watch sent out on the gaff to pass the gaskets; but they could do nothing with it. The second mate swore at them for a parcel of "sogers," and sent up a couple of the best men; but they could do no better, and the gaff was lowered down. All hands were now employed in setting up the lee rigging, fishing the spritsail yard, lashing the galley, and getting tackles upon the martingale, to bowse it to windward. Being in the larboard watch, my duty was forward, to assist in setting up the martingale. Three of us were out on the martingale guys and back-ropes for more than an half an hour, carrying out, hooking and unhooking the tackles, several times buried in the seas, until the mate ordered us in, from fear of our being washed off. The anchors were then to be taken up on the rail, which kept all hands on the forecastle for an hour, though every now and then the seas broke over it, washing the rigging off to leeward, filling the lee scuppers breast-high, and washing chock aft to the taffrail.

Having got everything secure again, we were promising ourselves some breakfast, for it was now nearly nine o'clock in the forenoon, when the main topsail showed evident signs of giving way. Some sail must be kept on the ship, and the captain ordered the fore and main spencer gaffs to be lowered down, and the two spencers (which were storm sails, bran-new, small, and made of the strongest canvas) to be got up and bent; leaving the topsail to blow away, with a blessing on it, if it would only last until we could get the spencers. These we bent on very carefully, with strong robands and seizings, and, making tackles fast to the clews, bowsed them down to the water-ways. By this time the main topsail was among the things that have been, and we went aloft to stow away the remnant of the last sail of all those which were on the ship twenty-four hours before. The spencers were now the only whole sails on the ship, and, being strong and small, and near the deck, presenting but little surface to the wind above the rail, promised to hold out well. Hove-to under these, and eased by having no sail above the tops, the ship rose and fell, and drifted off to leeward like a line-of-battle ship.

It was now eleven o'clock, and the watch was sent below to get break-fast, and at eight bells (noon), as everything was snug, although the gale had not in the least abated, the watch was set, and the other watch and idlers sent below. For three days and three nights the gale continued with unabated fury, and with singular regularity. There were no lulls, and very little variation in its fierceness. Our ship, being light, rolled so as almost to send the fore-yard-arm under water, and drifted off bodily to leeward. All this time there was not a cloud to be seen in the sky, day or night; no, not so large as a man's hand. Every morning the sun rose cloudless from the sea, and set again at night in the sea, in a flood of light. The stars, too, came out of the blue one after another, night after night, un-obscured, and twinkled as clear as on a still, frosty night at home, until the day came upon them. All this time the sea was rolling in immense surges, white with foam, as far as the eye could reach, on every side, for we were now leagues and leagues from shore.

The between-decks being empty, several of us slept there in ham-mocks, which are the best things in the world to sleep in during a storm; it not being true of them, as it is of another kind of bed, "when the wind blows the cradle will rock;" for it is the ship that rocks, while they hang vertically from the beams. During these seventy-two hours we had noth-ing to do but to turn in and out, four hours on deck, and four below, eat, sleep, and keep watch. The watches were only varied by taking the helm in turn, and now and then by one of the sails, which were furled, blowing out of the gaskets, and getting adrift, which sent us up on the yards, and by getting tackles on different parts of the rigging, which were slack. Once the wheel-rope parted, which might have been fatal to us, had not the chief mate sprung instantly with a relieving tackle to windward, and kept the tiller up, till a new rope could be rove. On the morning of the twentieth, at daybreak, the gale had evidently done its worst, and had somewhat abated; so much so that all hands were called to bend new sails, although it was still blowing as hard as two common gales. One at a time, and with great difficulty and labour, the old sails were unbent and sent down by the buntlines, and three new topsails, made for the homeward passage round Cape Horn, which had never been bent, were got up from the sail-room, and, under the care of the sailmaker, were fitted for bending, and sent up by the halyards into the tops, and, with stops and frapping-lines, were bent to the yards, close-reefed, sheeted home, and hoisted. These were bent one at a time, and with the greatest care and difficulty. Two spare courses were then got up and bent in the same manner and furled, and a storm-jib, with the bonnet off, bent and furled to the boom. It was twelve o'clock before we got through, and five hours of more exhausting labour I never experienced; and no one of that ship's crew, I will venture to say, will ever desire again to unbend and bend five large sails in the teeth of a tremendous northwester. Towards night a few clouds appeared in the horizon, and, as the gale moderated, the usual appearance of driving clouds relieved the face of the sky. The fifth day after the commencement of the storm, we shook a reef out of each topsail, and set the reefed foresail jib, and spanker, but it was not until after eight days of reefed topsails that we had a whole sail on the ship, and then it was quite soon enough, for the captain was anxious to make up for leeway, the gale having blown us half the distance to the Sandwich Islands.

Inch by inch, as fast as the gale would permit, we made sail on the ship, for the wind still continued ahead, and we had many days' sailing to get back to the longitude we were in when the storm took us. For eight days more we beat to windward under a stiff top-gallant breeze, when the wind shifted and became variable. A light southeaster, to which we could carry a reefed topmast studding sail, did wonders for our dead reckoning.

Friday, December 4th. After a passage of twenty days, we arrived at the mouth of the Bay of San Francisco.

MOBY DICK[1]

Herman Melville

(1819–1891)

I

Sing Out for the Whale

ONE morning shortly after breakfast, Ahab, as was his wont, ascended the cabin gangway to the deck. There most sea-captains usually walk at that hour, as country gentlemen, after the same meal, take a few turns in the garden.

Soon his steady, ivory stride was heard, as to and fro he paced his old rounds, upon planks so familiar to his tread, that they were all over

---

[1]From *Moby Dick, or the White Whale.*

dented, like geological stones, with the peculiar mark of his walk. Did you fixedly gaze, too, upon that ribbed and dented brow; there also, you would see still stranger footprints—the footprints of his one unsleeping, ever pacing thought.

But on the occasion in question, these dents looked deeper, even as his nervous step that morning left a deeper mark. And, so full of his thought was Ahab, that at every uniform turn that he made, now at the mainmast and now at the binnacle, you could almost see that thought turn in him as he turned, and pace in him as he paced; so completely possessing him, indeed, that it all but seemed the inward mould of every outer movement.

"D'ye mark him, Flask?" whispered Stubb; "the chick that's in him pecks the shell. 'Twill soon be out."

The hours wore on;—Ahab now shut up within his cabin; anon, pacing the deck, with the same intense bigotry of purpose in his aspect.

It drew near the close of day. Suddenly he came to a halt by the bulwarks, and inserting his bone leg into the auger-hole there, and with one hand grasping a shroud, he ordered Starbuck to send everybody aft.

"Sir!" said the mate, astonished at an order seldom or never given on shipboard except in some extraordinary case.

"Send everybody aft," repeated Ahab. "Mastheads, there! come down!"

When the entire ship's company were assembled, and with curious and not wholly unapprehensive faces, were eyeing him, for he looked not unlike the weather horizon when a storm is coming up, Ahab, after rapidly glancing over the bulwarks, and then darting his eyes among the crew, started from his standpoint; and as though not a soul were nigh him resumed his heavy turns upon the deck. With bent head and half-slouched hat he continued to pace, unmindful of the wondering whispering among the men; till Stubb cautiously whispered to Flask, that Ahab must have summoned them there for the purpose of witnessing a pedestrian feat. But this did not last long. Vehemently pausing he cried:—

"What do ye do when ye see a whale, men?"

"Sing out for him!" was the impulsive rejoinder from a score of clubbed voices.

"Good!" cried Ahab, with a wild approval in his tones; observing the hearty animation into which his unexpected question had so magnetically thrown them.

"And what do ye next, men?"

"Lower away, and after him!"

"And what tune is it ye pull to, men?"

"A dead whale or a stove boat!"

More and more strangely and fiercely glad and approving grew the countenance of the old man at every shout; while the mariners began to gaze curiously at each other, as if marvelling how it was that they themselves became so excited at such seemingly purposeless questions.

But, they were all eagerness again, as Ahab, now half revolving in his pivot-hole, with one hand reaching high up a shroud, and tightly, almost convulsively grasping it, addressed them thus—

"All ye mastheaders have before now heard me give orders about a white whale. Look ye! d'ye see this Spanish ounce of gold?"—holding up a broad bright coin to the sun— "it is a sixteen dollar piece, men. D'ye see it? Mr Starbuck, hand me yon top-maul."

While the mate was getting the hammer, Ahab, without speaking, was slowly rubbing the gold piece against the skirts of his jacket, as if to heighten its lustre, and without using any words was meanwhile lowly humming to himself, producing a sound so strangely muffled and inarticulate that it seemed the mechanical humming of the wheels of his vitality in him.

Receiving the top-maul from Starbuck, he advanced towards the mainmast with the hammer uplifted in one hand, exhibiting the gold with the other, and with a high raised voice exclaiming: "Whosoever of ye raises me a white-headed whale with a wrinkled brow and a crooked jaw; whosoever of ye raises me that white-headed whale, with three holes punctured in his starboard fluke—look ye, whosoever of ye raises me that same white whale, he shall have this gold ounce, my boys!"

"Huzza! huzza!" cried the seamen, as with swinging tarpaulins they hailed the act of nailing the gold to the mast.

"It's a white whale, I say," resumed Ahab, as he threw down the top-maul; "a white whale. Skin your eyes for him men; look sharp for white water; if ye see but a bubble, sing out."

All this while Tashtego, Daggoo, and Queequeg had looked on with even more intense interest and surprise than the rest, and at the mention of the wrinkled brow and crooked jaw, they had started as if each was separately touched by some specific recollection.

"Captain Ahab," said Tashtego, "that white whale must be the same that some call Moby Dick."

"Moby Dick?" shouted Ahab. "Do ye know the white whale then, Tash?"

"Does he fan-tail a little curious, sir, before he goes down?" said the Gay-Header deliberately.

"And he has a curious spout too," said Daggoo, "very bushy, even for a parmacetty, and mighty quick, Captain Ahab?"

"And he have one, two, tree—oh! good many iron in him hide, too, Captain," cried Queequeg disjointedly. "All twisketee be-twisk, like him—him——" faltering hard for a word, and screwing his hand round and round as though uncorking a bottle—"like him—him——"

"Corkscrew!" cried Ahab; "ay, Queequeg, the harpoons lie all twisted and wrenched in him; ay, Daggoo, his spout is a big one, like a whole

shock of wheat, and white as a pile of our Nantucket wool after the great
annual sheep-shearing; aye, Tashtego, and he fan-tails like a split jib
in a squall. Death and devils! Men, it is Moby Dick ye have seen—Moby
Dick—Moby Dick!"

"Captain Ahab," said Starbuck, who with Stubb and Flask, had thus
far been eyeing his superior with increasing surprise, but at last seemed
struck with a thought which somewhat explained all the wonder. "Captain Ahab, I have heard of Moby Dick—but it was not Moby Dick that
took off thy leg?"

"Who told thee that?" cried Ahab; then pausing. "Aye, Starbuck;
aye, my hearties all round; it was Moby Dick that dismasted me; Moby
Dick that brought me to this dead stump I stand on now. Aye, Aye,"
he shouted with a terrific, loud, animal sob, like that of a heart-stricken
moose; "aye, aye! it was that accursed white whale that razed me; made
a poor pegging lubber of me for ever and a day!" Then tossing both
arms, with measureless imprecations, he shouted out: "Aye, Aye! and
I'll chase him round Good Hope, and round the Horn, and round the
Norway Maelstrom, and round perdition's flames before I give him up.
And this is what ye have shipped for, men! to chase that white whale on
both sides of land, and over all sides of earth, till he spouts black blood
and rolls fin out. What say ye, men, will ye splice hands on it, now?
I think ye do look brave."

"Aye, aye!" shouted the harpooners and seamen, running closer to the
excited old man: "a sharp eye for the White Whale: a sharp lance for
Moby Dick!"

"God bless ye," he seemed to half sob and half shout, "God bless
ye, men. Steward! go draw the great measure of grog. Death to Moby
Dick! God hunt us all, if we do not hunt Moby Dick to his death!"

II

The White Whale

I, Ishmael, was one of that crew; my shouts had gone up with the rest;
my oath had been welded with theirs; and stronger I shouted, and more
did I hammer and clinch my oath, because of the dread in my soul. A
wild, mystical sympathetical feeling was in me; Ahab's quenchless feud
seemed mine. With greedy ear I learned the history of that murderous
monster against whom I and all the others had taken our oaths of violence and revenge.

For some time past, though at intervals only, the unaccompanied,
secluded White Whale had haunted those uncivilized seas mostly frequented by the Sperm Whale fishermen. But not all of them knew of his
existence; only a few of them, comparatively, had knowingly seen him;
while the number who as yet had actually and knowingly given battle to
him, was small indeed. For, owing to the large number of whale cruisers;

the disorderly way they were sprinkled over the entire watery circumference, many of them adventurously pushing their quest along solitary latitudes, so as seldom or never for a whole twelvemonth or more on a stretch, to encounter a single news-telling sail of any sort; the inordinate length of each separate voyage; the irregularity of the times of sailing from home; all these, with other circumstances, direct and indirect, long obstructed, the spread through the whole world-wide whaling-fleet of the special individualizing tidings concerning Moby Dick. It was hardly to be doubted, that several vessels reported to have encountered, at such or such a time, or on such or such a meridian, a sperm whale of uncommon magnitude and malignity, which whale, after doing great mischief to his assailants, had completely escaped them; to some minds it was not an unfair presumption, I say, that the whale in question must have been no other than Moby Dick. Yet as of late the sperm whale fishery had been marked by various and not unfrequent instances of great ferocity, cunning, and malice in the monster attacked; therefore it was, that those who by accident ignorantly gave battle to Moby Dick; such hunters, perhaps, for the most part, were content to ascribe the peculiar terror he bred, more, as it were, to the perils of the Sperm Whale fishery at large, than to the individual cause. In that way, mostly, the disastrous encounter between Ahab and the whale had hitherto been popularly regarded.

As for those who, previously hearing of the White Whale, by chance caught sight of him; in the beginning of the thing they had every one of them, almost, as boldly and fearlessly lowered for him, as for any other whale of that species. But at length, such calamities did ensue in these assaults—not restricted to sprained wrists and ankles, broken limbs, or devouring amputations—but fatal to the last degree of fatality; those repeated disastrous repulses, all accumulating and piling their terrors upon Moby Dick; those things had gone far to shake the fortitude of many brave hunters, to whom the story of the White Whale had eventually come.

Nor did wild rumours of all sorts fail to exaggerate, and still the more horrify the true histories of these deadly encounters. For not only do fabulous rumours naturally grow out of the very body of all surprising terrible events—as the smitten tree gives birth to its fungi; but, in maritime life, far more than in that of *terra firma*, wild rumours abound, wherever there is any adequate reality for them to cling to. And as the sea surpasses the land in this matter, so the whale fishery surpasses every other sort of maritime life, in the wonderfulness and fearfulness of the rumours which sometimes circulate there.

No wonder, then, that ever gathering volume from the mere transit over the widest watery spaces, the outblown rumours of the White Whale did in the end incorporate with themselves all manner of morbid hints, the half-formed fœtal suggestions of supernatural agencies, which eventually invested Moby Dick with new terrors unborrowed from any-thing that visibly appears. So that in many cases such a panic did he finally strike, that few who by those rumours, at least, had heard of the White Whale, few of those hunters were willing to encounter the perils of his jaw.

One of the wild suggestions referred to, as at last coming to be linked with the White Whale in the minds of the superstitiously inclined, was the unearthly conceit that Moby Dick was ubiquitous; that he had ac-tually been encountered in opposite latitudes at one and the same instant of time.

Nor, credulous as such minds must have been, was this conceit alto-gether without some faint show of superstitious probability. For as the secrets of the currents in the seas have never yet been divulged even to the most erudite research, so the hidden ways of the Sperm Whale when beneath the surface remain, in great part, unaccountable to his pursuers; and from time to time have originated the most curious and contra-dictory speculations regarding them, especially concerning the mystic modes whereby, after sounding to a great depth, he transports himself with such vast swiftness to the most widely distant points.

It is a thing well known to both American and English whaleships, and as well a thing placed upon authoritative record years ago by Scoresby, that some whales have been captured far north in the Pacific, in whose bodies have been found the barbs of harpoons darted in the Greenland seas. Nor is it to be gainsaid, that in some of these instances it has been declared that the interval of time between the two assaults could not have exceeded very many days. Hence, by inference, it has been believed by some whalemen, that the Nor'-West Passage, so long a problem to man, was never a problem to the whale. So that here, in the real living experience of living men, the prodigies related in old times of the inland Strello mountain in Portugal (near whose top there was said to be a lake in which the wrecks of ships floated up to the surface); and that still more wonderful story of the Arethusa fountain near Syracuse (whose waters were believed to have come from the Holy Land by an underground passage); these fabulous narrations are almost fully equalled by the realities of the whaleman.

Forced into familiarity, then, with such prodigies as these, and know-ing that after repeated, intrepid assaults, the White Whale had escaped alive; it cannot be much matter of surprise that some whalemen should go still further in their superstitions; declaring Moby Dick not only ubiquitous, but immortal. (For immortality is but ubiquity in time); and though groves of spears should be planted in his flanks, he would still swim away unharmed; or if indeed he should ever be made to spout thick blood, such a sight would be but a ghastly deception; for again in unensanguined billows hundred of leagues away, his unsullied jet would once more be seen.

But even stripped of these supernatural surmisings, there was enough in the earthly make and incontestable character of the monster to strike the imagination with unwonted power. For, it was not so much his uncommon bulk that so much distinguished him from other sperm whales, but, as was elsewhere thrown out—a peculiar show-white wrinkled forehead, and a high, pyramidal white hump. These were his prominent features; the tokens whereby, even in the limitless, uncharted seas, he revealed his identity, at a long distance, to those who knew him.

The rest of his body was so streaked, and spotted, and marbled with the same shrouded hue, that, in the end, he had gained his distinctive appellation of the White Whale; a name indeed, literally justified by his vivid aspect, when seen gliding a high noon through a dark blue sea, leaving a milky-way wake of creamy foam, all spangled with golden gleamings. Nor was it his unwonted magnitude, nor his remarkable hue, nor yet his deformed lower jaw, that so much invested the whale with natural terror, as that unexampled, intelligent malignity which, according to specific accounts, he had over and over again evinced in his assaults. More than all, his treacherous retreats struck more of dismay than perhaps else. For, when swimming before his exulting pursuers, with every apparent symptom of alarm, he had several times been known to turn round suddenly, and, bearing down upon them, either stave their boats to splinters, or drive them back in consternation to their ship.

Already several fatalities had attended his chase. But though similar disasters, however little bruited ashore, were by no means unusual in the fishery; yet, in most instances, such seemed the White Whale's infernal forethought of ferocity, that every dismembering or death that he caused, was not wholly regarded as having been inflicted by an unintelligent agent.

Judge, then, to what pitches of inflamed, distracted fury the minds of his more desperate hunters were impelled, when amid the chips of chewed boats, and the sinking limbs of torn comrades, they swam out of the white curds of the whale's direful wrath into the serene, exasperating sunlight, that smiled on, as if at a birth or a bridal.

His three boats stove around him, and oars and men both, whirling in the eddies; one captain, seizing the line-knife from his broken prow, had dashed at the whale, as an Arkansas duellist at his foe, blindly seeking with a six-inch blade, to reach the fathom-deep life of the whale. That captain was Ahab. And then it was, that suddenly sweeping his sickle-shaped lower jaw beneath him, Moby Dick had reaped away Ahab's leg, as a mower a blade of grass in the field. No turbaned Turk, no hired Venetian or Malay, could have smote him with more seeming malice. Small reason was there to doubt, then, that ever since that almost fatal encounter, Ahab had cherished a wild vindictiveness against the whale, all the more fell, for that in his frantic morbidness he at last came to identify with him, not only all his bodily woes, but all his intellectual and spiritual exasperations. The White Whale swam before him as the monomaniac incarnation of all those malicious agencies which some deep men feel eating in them, till they are left living on with half a heart and half a lung. That intangible malignity which has been found from the beginning; which the ancient Ophites of the east reverenced in their statue devil;—Ahab did not fall down and worship it like them; but deliriously transferring its idea to the abhorred white whale, he pitted himself, all mutilated, against it. All that most maddens and torments; all that stirs up the lees of things; all truth with malice in it; all that cracks the sinews and cakes the brain; the subtle demonisms of life and thought; all evil, to crazy Ahab, were visibly personified, and made practically assailable in Moby Dick. He piled upon the whale's white hump the sum of all the general rage and hate felt by his whole race from Adam down.

III

Moby Dick's Last Fight

That night, in the mid-watch, when the old man—as his wont at intervals—stepped forth from the scuttle in which he leaned, and went to his pivot-hole, he suddenly thrust out his face fiercely, snuffing up the sea air as a sagacious ship's dog will, in drawing nigh to some barbarous isle. He declared that a whale must be near. Soon that peculiar odour, sometimes to a great distance given forth by the living Sperm Whale, was palpable to all the watch; nor was any mariner surprised when, after inspecting the compass, and then the dog-vane, and then ascertaining the precise bearing of the odour as nearly as possible, Ahab rapidly ordered the ship's course to be slightly altered, and the sail to be shortened.

The acute policy dictating these movements was sufficiently vindicated at daybreak by the sight of a long sleek on the sea directly and lengthwise ahead, smooth as oil, and resembling in the pleated watery wrinkles bordering it, the polished metallic-like marks of some swift tide-rip, at the mouth of a deep, rapid stream.

"Man the mastheads! Call all hands!"

Thundering with the butts of three clubbed handspikes on the forecastle deck, Daggoo roused the sleepers with such judgement claps that they seemed to exhale from the scuttle, so instantaneously did they appear with their clothes in their hands.

"What d'ye see?" cried Ahab, flattening his face to the sky.

"Nothing, nothing, sir!" was the sound hailing down in reply.

"T'gallant-sails! stunsails alow and aloft, and on both sides!"

All sail being set, he now cast loose the life-line, reserved for swaying him to the mainroyal masthead; and in a few moments they were hoisting him thither, when, while but two-thirds of the way aloft, and while peering ahead through the horizontal vacancy between the maintopsail and top-gallant-sail, he raised a gull-like cry in the air, "There she blows! —there she blows! A hump like a snow-hill! It is Moby Dick!"

Fired by the cry which seemed simultaneously taken up by the three look-outs, the men on deck rushed to the rigging to behold the famous whale they had so long been pursuing. Ahab had now gained his final perch, some feet above the other look-outs, Tashtego standing just beneath him on the cap of the top-gallant-mast, so that the Indian's head was almost on a level with Ahab's heel. From this height the whale was now seen some mile or so ahead, at every roll of the sea revealing his high sparkling hump, and regularly jetting his silent spout into the air. To the credulous mariners it seemed the same silent spout they had so long ago beheld in the moonlit Atlantic and Indian Oceans.

"And did none of ye see it before?" cried Ahab, hailing the perched men all around him.

"I saw him almost the same instant, sir, that Captain Ahab did, and I cried out," said Tashtego.

"Not the same instant; not the same—no, the doubloon is mine, Fate reserved the doubloon for me. *I* only; none of ye could have raised the White Whale first. There she blows! there she blows! There she blows! There again!—there again!" he cried, in long-drawn, lingering, methodic tones, attuned to the gradual prolongings of the whale's visible jets. "He's going to sound! In stunsails! Down top-gallant-sails! Stand by three boats. Mr Starbuck, remember, stay on board, and keep the ship. Helm there! Luff, luff a point! So; steady, man, steady! There go flukes. No, no; only black water! All ready the boats there? Stand by, stand by! Lower me, Mr Starbuck; lower, lower,—quick, quicker!" and he slid through the air to the deck.

"He is heading straight to leeward, sir," cried Stubb; "right away from us; cannot have seen the ship yet."

"Be dumb, man! Stand by the braces! Hard down the helm!—brace up! Shiver her!—shiver her! So; well that! Boats, boats!"

Soon all the boats but Starbuck's were dropped; the boat-sails set; all the paddles plying; with rippling swiftness, shooting to leeward; and Ahab heading the onset. A pale, death-glimmer lit up Fedallah's sunken eyes; a hideous motion gnawed his mouth.

Like noiseless nautilus shells, their light prows sped through the sea; but only slowly they neared the foe. As they neared him, the ocean grew still more smooth; seemed drawing a carpet over its waves; seemed a noon-meadow, so serenely it spread. At length the breathless hunter came so nigh his seemingly unsuspecting prey, that his entire dazzling hump was distinctly visible, sliding along the sea as if an isolated thing, and continually set in a revolving ring of finest, fleecy, greenish foam. He saw the vast involved wrinkles of the slightly projecting head beyond. Before it, far out on the soft Turkish-rugged waters, went the glistening white shadows from his broad, milky forehead, a musical rippling play-

fully accompanying the shade; and behind, the blue waters interchange-
ably flowed over into the moving valley of his steady wake; and on either
hand bright bubbles arose and danced by his side. But these were broken
again by the light toes of hundreds of gay fowl softly feathering the sea,
alternate with their fitful flight; and like to some flagstaff rising from
the painted hull of an argosy, the tall but shattered pole of a recent lance
projected from the white whale's back; and at intervals one of the cloud
of soft-toed fowls hovering, and to and fro skimming like a canopy over
the fish, silently perched and rocked on this pole, the long tail feathers
streaming like pennons.

A gentle joyousness—a mighty mildness of repose in swiftness, invested the gliding whale. Not the white bull Jupiter swimming away
with ravished Europa clinging to his graceful horns; his lovely, leering
eyes sideways intent upon the maid; with smooth bewitching fleetness,
rippling straight for the nuptial bower in Crete; not Jove did surpass the
glorified White Whale as he so divinely swam.

On each soft side—coincident with the parted swell, that but once leaving him, then flowed so wide away—on each bright side, the whale shed
off enticings. No wonder there had been some among the hunters who
namelessly transported and allured by all this serenity had ventured to
assail it; but had fatally found that quietude but the vesture of tornadoes.
Yet, calm, enticing calm, oh, whale! thou glidest on, to all who for the
first time eye thee, no matter how many in that same way thou may'st
have bejuggled and destroyed before.

And thus, through the serene tranquillities of the tropical sea, among
waves whose hand-clappings were suspended by exceeding rapture,
Moby Dick moved on, still withholding from sight the full terrors of his
submerged trunk, entirely hiding the wretched hideousness of his jaw.
But soon the fore part of him slowly rose from the water; for an instant
his whole marbleised body formed a high arch, like Virginia's Natural
Bridge, and warningly waving his bannered flukes in the air. The grand
god revealed himself, sounded, and went out of sight. Hoveringly halting,
and dipping on the wing, the white sea-fowls longingly lingered over the
agitated pool that he left.

With oars apeak, and paddles down, the sheets of their sails adrift,
the three boats now stilly floated, awaiting Moby Dick's appearance.

"An hour," said Ahab, standing rooted in his boat's stern, and he
gazed beyond the whale's place, towards the dim blue spaces and wide
wooing vacancies to leeward. It was only an instant, for again his eyes
seemed whirling round in his head as he swept the watery circle. The
breeze now freshened; the sea began to swell.

"The birds!—the birds!" cried Tashtego.

In long Indian file, as when herons take wing, the white birds were
now all flying towards Ahab's boat; and when within a few yards began
fluttering over the water there, wheeling round and round, with joyous,

expectant cries. Their vision was keener than man's; Ahab could discover no sign in the sea. But suddenly as he peered down and into its depths, he profoundly saw a white living spot no bigger than a white weasel, with a wonderful celerity uprising, and magnifying as it rose, till it turned, and then there were plainly revealed two long crooked rows of white, glistening teeth, floating up from the undiscoverable bottom. It was Moby Dick's open mouth and scrolled jaw; his vast, shadowed bulk still half blending with the blue of the sea. The glittering mouth yawned beneath the boat like an open-doored marble tomb; and giving one sidelong sweep with his steering oar, Ahab whirled the craft aside from this tremendous apparition. Then, calling upon Fedallah to change places with him, went forward to the bows, and seizing Perth's harpoon, commanded his crew to grasp their oars and stand by to stern.

Now, by reason of this timely spinning round the boat upon its axis, its bow, by anticipation, was made to face the whale's head while yet under water. But as if perceiving this stratagem, Moby Dick, with that malicious intelligence ascribed to him, sidelingly transplanted himself, as it were, in an instant, shooting his plaited head lengthwise beneath the boat.

Through and through; through every plank and each rib, it thrilled for an instant, the whale obliquely lying on his back, in the manner of a biting shark, slowly and feelingly taking its bows full within his mouth, so that the long, narrow, scrolled lower-jaw curled high up into the open air, and one of the teeth caught in a rowlock. The bluish pearl-white of the inside of the jaw was within six inches of Ahab's head, and reached higher than that. In this altitude the White Whale now shook the slight cedar as a mildly cruel cat her mouse. With unastonished eyes Fedallah gazed, and crossed his arms; but the tiger-yellow crew were tumbling over each other's heads to gain the uttermost stern.

And now, while both elastic gunwales were springing in and out, as the whale dallied with the doomed craft in this devilish way; and from his body being submerged beneath the boat, he could not be darted at from the bows, for the bows were almost inside of him, as it were; and while the other boats involuntarily paused, as before a quick crisis impossible to withstand, then it was that monomaniac Ahab, furious with this tantalizing vicinity of his foe, which placed him all alive and helpless in the very jaws he hated; frenzied with all this, he seized the long bone with his naked hands, and wildly strove to wrench it from its grip. As he now thus vainly strove, the jaw slipped from him; the frail gunwales bent in, collapsed and snapped, as both jaws, like an enormous shears, sliding further aft, bit the craft completely in twain, and locked themselves fast again in the sea, midway between the two floating wrecks. These floated aside, the broken ends drooping, the crew at the stern-wreck clinging to the gunwales, and striving to hold fast to the oars to lash them across.

At that preluding moment, ere the boat was yet snapped, Ahab, the first to perceive the whale's intent, by the crafty upraising of his head, a movement that loosed his hold for the time; at that moment his hand had made one final effort to push the boat out of the bite. But only slipping further into the whale's mouth, and tilting over sideways as it slipped, the boat had shaken off his hold on the jaw; spilled him out of it, as he leaned to the push; and so he fell flat-faced upon the sea.

Ripplingly withdrawing from his prey, Moby Dick now lay at a little distance, vertically thrusting his oblong white head up and down in the billows; and at the same time slowly revolving his whole splendid body; so that when his vast wrinkled forehead rose—some twenty or more feet out of the water—the now rising swells, with all their confluent waves, dazzling broke against it; vindictively tossing their shivered spray still higher into the air. So, in a gale, the but half baffled Channel billows only recoil from the base of the Eddystone, triumphantly to over-lap its summit with their scud.

But soon resuming his horizontal attitude, Moby Dick swam swiftly round and round the wrecked crew; sideways churning the water in his vengeful wake, as if lashing himself up to still another and more deadly assault. The sight of the splintered boat seemed to madden him, as the blood of grapes and mulberries cast before Antiochus's elephants in the book of Maccabees. Meanwhile Ahab half smothered in the foam of the whale's insolent tail, and too much of a cripple to swim,—though he could still keep afloat, even in the heart of such a whirlpool as that; helpless Ahab's head was seen, like a tossed bubble which the least chance shock might burst. From the boat's fragmentary stern, Fedallah incuriously and mildly eyed him; the clinging crew, at the other drifting end, could not succour him; more than enough was it for them to look to themselves. For so revolvingly appalling was the White Whale's aspect, and so planetarily swift the ever-contracting circles he made, that he seemed horizontally swooping upon them. And though the other boats, unharmed, still hovered hard by, still they dared not pull into the eddy to strike, lest that should be the signal for the instant destruction of the jeopardized castaways, Ahab and all; nor in that case could they themselves hope to escape. With straining eyes, then, they remained on the outer edge of the direful zone, whose centre had now become the old man's head.

Meantime, from the beginning all this had been descried from the ship's mastheads; and squaring her yards, she had borne down upon the scene; and was now so nigh, that Ahab in the water hailed her;—"Sail on the"—but that moment a breaking sea dashed on him from Moby Dick, and whelmed him for the time. But struggling out of it again, and chancing to rise on a towering crest, he shouted,—"Sail on the whale!—Drive him off!"

The *Pequod's* prows were pointed; and breaking up the charmed circle, she effectually parted the White Whale from his victim. As he sullenly swam off, the boats flew to the rescue.

Dragged into Stubb's boat with bloodshot blinded eyes, the white brine caking in his wrinkles; the long tension of Ahab's bodily strength did crack, and helplessly he yielded to his body's doom: for a time, lying all crushed in the bottom of Stubb's boat, like one trodden under foot of herds of elephants. Far inland, nameless wails came from him, as desolate sounds from our ravines.

But the intensity of his physical prostration did but so much the more abbreviate it. In an instant's compass, great hearts sometimes condense to one deep pang, the sum-total of those shallow pains kindly diffused through feebler men's whole lives. And so, such hearts, though summary in each one suffering; still, if the gods decree it, in their lifetime aggregate a whole age of woe, wholly made up of instantaneous intensities; for even in their pointless centres those noble natures contain the entire circumferences of inferior souls.

"The harpoon," said Ahab, half-way rising, and draggingly leaning on one bended arm—"is it safe?"

"Aye, sir, for it was not darted; this is it," said Stubb, showing it.

"Say it before me;—any missing men?"

"One, two, three, four, five;—there were five oars, sir, and here are five men."

"That's good.—Help me, man; I wish to stand. So, so, I see him: there! there! going to leeward still; what a leaping spout!—Hands off from me! The eternal sap runs in Ahab's bones again! Set the sail; out oars; the helm!"

It is often the case that when a boat is stove, its crew, being picked up by another boat, help to work that second boat; and the chase is thus continued with what is called double-banked oars. It was thus now. But the added power of the boat did not equal the added power of the whale, for he seemed to have treble-banked his every fin; swimming with a velocity which plainly showed, that if now, under these circumstances, pushed on, the chase would prove an indefinitely prolonged, if not a hopeless one; nor could any crew endure for so long a period, such an unintermitted, intense straining at the oar; a thing barely tolerable only in some one brief vicissitude. The ship itself, then, as it sometimes happens, offered the most promising intermediate means of overtaking the chase. Accordingly, the boats now made for her, and were soon swayed up to their cranes—the two parts of the wrecked boat having been previously secured by her—and then hoisting everything to her side, and stacking the canvas high up, and sideways outstretching it with stunsails, like the double-jointed wings of an albatross; the *Pequod* bore down in the leeward wake of Moby Dick. At the well-known, methodical intervals, the whale's glittering spout was regularly announced from the manned mastheads; and when he would be reported as just gone down, Ahab

would take the time, and then pacing the deck, binnacle-watch in hand,
so soon as the last sound of the allotted hour expired, his voice was heard
—"Whose is the doubloon now? D'ye see him?" and if the reply was
"No, sir!" straightway he commanded them to lift him to his perch. In
this way the day wore on; Ahab, now aloft and motionless; anon, unrest-
ingly pacing the planks.

As he was thus walking, uttering no sound, except to hail the men aloft,
or to bid them hoist a sail still higher, or to spread one to a still greater
breadth—thus to and fro pacing, beneath his slouched hat, at every turn
he passed his own wrecked boat, which had been dropped upon the quarter-deck, and lay there reversed, broken bow to shattered stern. At last
he paused before it; and as in an already over-clouded sky fresh troops
of clouds will sometimes sail across, so over the old man's face there now
stole some such added gloom as this.

Stubb saw him pause; and perhaps intending, not vainly, though, to
evince his own unabated fortitude, and thus keep up a valiant place in
his Captain's mind, he advanced, and eyeing the wreck exclaimed—
"The thistle the ass refused; it pricked his mouth too keenly, sir; ha!
ha!"

"What soulless thing is this that laughs before a wreck? Man, man!
did I not know thee brave as fearless fire (and as mechanical) I could
swear thou wert a poltroon. Groan nor laugh should be heard before a
wreck."

"Aye, sir," said Starbuck, drawing near, "'tis a solemn sight; an
omen, and an ill one."

"Omen? omen?—the dictionary! If the gods think to speak outright
to man, they will honourably speak outright; not shake their heads,
and give an old wife's darkling hint.—Begone! Ye two are the opposite
poles of one thing; Starbuck is Stubb reversed, and Stubb is Starbuck; and
ye two are all mankind; and Ahab stands alone among the millions of the
peopled earth, nor gods nor men his neighbours! Cold, cold—I shiver!—
How now? Aloft there? D'ye see him? Sing out for every spout, though
he spout ten times a second!"

The day was nearly done; only the hem of his golden robe was rustling.
Soon, it was almost dark, but the look-out men still remained unset.

"Can't see the spout now, sir;—too dark"—cried a voice from the air.

"How heading when last seen?"

"As before, sir—straight to leeward."

"Good! he will travel slower now 'tis night. Down royals and top-
gallant stunsails, Mr Starbuck. We must not run over him before morning; he's making a passage now, and may heave-to a while. Helm there!
keep her full before the wind!— Aloft! come down!—Mr Stubb, send a
fresh hand to the foremast head, and see it manned till morning."—
Then advancing towards the doubloon in the mainmast—"Men, this
gold is mine, for I earned it; but I shall let it abide here till the White

Whale is dead; and then, whosoever of ye first raises him, upon the day he shall be killed, this gold is that man's; and if on that day I shall again raise him, then, ten times its sum shall be divided among all of ye! Away now!—the deck is thine, Sir."

And so saying, he placed himself half-way within the scuttle, and slouching his hat, stood there till dawn, except when at intervals rousing himself to see how the night wore on.

At daybreak the three mastheads were punctually manned afresh.

"D'ye see him?" cried Ahab after allowing a little space for the light to spread.

"See nothing, sir."

"Turn up all hands and make sail! he travels faster than I thought for;—the top-gallant sails!—aye, they should have been kept on her all night. But no matter—'tis but resting for the rush."

The ship tore on, leaving such a furrow in the sea as when a cannon-ball, missent, becomes a ploughshare and turns up the level field.

"By salt and hemp!" cried Stubb, "but this swift motion of the deck creeps up one's legs and tingles at the heart. This ship and I are two grave fellows! Ha! ha! Some one take me up, and launch me, spine-wise, on the sea, for by live-oaks! my spine's a keel. Ha, ha! we go the gait that leaves no dust behind!"

"There she blows—she blows!—she blows!—right ahead!" was now the masthead cry.

"Aye, aye!" cried Stubb, "I knew it—ye can't escape—blow on and split your spout, O Whale! the mad fiend himself is after ye! Blow your trump—blister your lungs! Ahab will dam off your blood, as a miller shuts his water-gate upon the stream."

And Stubb did but speak out for well-nigh all that crew. The frenzies of the chase had by this time worked them bubblingly up, like old wine worked anew. Whatever pale fears and forebodings some of them might have felt before; these were not only now kept out of sight through the growing awe of Ahab, but they were broken up, and on all sides routed, as timid prairie hares that scatter before the bounding bison. The hand of Fate had snatched all their souls; and by the stirring perils of the previous day; the rack of the past night's suspense; the fixed unfearing, blind, reckless way in which their wild craft went plunging towards its flying mark; by all these things, their hearts were bowled along. The wind that made great bellies of their sails, and rushed the vessel on by arms invisible as irresistible; this seemed the symbol of that unseen agency which so enslaved them to the race.

They were one man, not thirty. For as the one ship that held them all, though it was put together of all contrasting things—oak, and maple, and pine wood; iron, and pitch, and hemp—yet all these ran into each other in the one concrete hull, which shot on its way, both balanced and directed by the long central keel; even so, all the individualities of the crew. This man's valour, that man's fear; guilt and guiltiness, all varieties were welded into oneness, and were all directed to that fatal goal which Ahab their one lord and keel did point to.

The rigging lived. The mastheads, like the tops of tall palms, were outspreadingly tufted with arms and legs. Clinging to a spar with one hand, some reached forth the other with impatient wavings; others, shading their eyes from the vivid sunlight, sat far out on the rocking yards; all the spars in full bearing of mortals, ready and ripe for their fate. Ah! how they still strove through that infinite blueness to seek out the thing that might destroy them!

"Why sing ye not out for him, if ye see him?" cried Ahab, when, after the lapse of some minutes since the first cry, no more had been heard. "Sway me up, men; ye have been deceived; not Moby Dick casts one odd jet that way, and then disappears."

It was even so; in their headlong eagerness, the men had mistaken some other thing for the whale-spout, as the event itself soon proved; for hardly had Ahab reached his perch; hardly was the rope belayed to its pin on deck, when he struck the key-note to an orchestra, that made the air vibrate as with the combined discharges of rifles. The triumphant halloo of thirty buckskin lungs was heard, as—much nearer to the ship than the place of the imaginary jet, less than a mile ahead—Moby Dick bodily burst into view. For not by any calm and indolent spoutings; not by the peaceable gush of that mystic fountain in his head, did the White Whale now reveal his vicinity; but by the far more wondrous phenomenon of breaching. Rising with his utmost velocity from the furthest depths, the Sperm Whale thus booms his entire bulk into the pure element of air, and piling up a mountain of dazzling foam, shows his place to the distance of seven miles and more. In those moments, the torn, enraged waves he shakes off seem his mane; in some cases this breaching is his act of defiance.

"There she breaches! there she breaches!" was the cry, as in his immeasurable bravadoes the White Whale tossed himself salmon-like to Heaven. So suddenly seen in the blue plain of the sea, and relieved against the still bluer margin of the sky, the spray that he raised, for the moment, intolerably glittered and glared like a glacier; and stood there gradually fading away from its first sparkling intensity to the dim and fading mistiness of an advancing shower in a vale.

"Aye, breach your last to the sun, Moby Dick!" cried Ahab, "thy hour and thy harpoon are at hand! Down! down all of ye, but one man at the fore. The boats!—stand by!"

Unmindful of the tedious rope-ladders of the shrouds, the men, like shooting stars, slid to the deck, by the isolated backstays and halyards; while Ahab, less dartingly but still rapidly, was dropped from his perch.

"Lower away," he cried, so soon as he had reached his boat—a spare one, rigged the afternoon previous. "Mr Starbuck, the ship is thine—keep away from the boats, but keep near them. Lower all!"

As if to strike a quick terror into them, by this time being the first assailant himself, Moby Dick had turned, and was now coming for the three crews. Ahab's boat was central; and cheering his men, he told them he would take the whale head-and-head,—that is, pull straight up to his forehead,—a not uncommon thing; for when within a certain limit, such a course excludes the coming onset from the whale's sidelong vision. But ere that close limit was gained, and while yet all three boats were plain as the ship's three masts to his eye; the White Whale, churning himself into furious speed, almost in an instant as it were, rushing among the boats with open jaws, and lashing tail, offered appalling battle on every side; and heedless of the irons darted at him from every boat, seemed only intent on annihilating each separate plank of which those boats were made. But skilfully manœuvred, incessantly wheeling like trained chargers in the field; the boats for a while eluded him; though, at times, but by a plank's breadth; while all the time, Ahab's unearthly slogan tore every other cry but his to shreds.

But at last in his untraceable evolutions, the White Whale so crossed and recrossed, and in a thousand ways entangled the slack of the three lines now fast to him, that they foreshortened, and, of themselves, warped the devoted boats towards the planted irons in him; though now for a moment the whale drew aside a little, as if to rally for a more tremendous charge. Seizing that opportunity, Ahab first paid out more line; and then was rapidly hauling and jerking in upon it again—hoping that way to disencumber it of some snarls—when lo!—a sight more savage than the embattled teeth of sharks!

Caught and twisted—corkscrewed in the mazes of the line—loose harpoons and lances, with all their bristling barbs and points, came flashing and dripping up to the chocks in the bows of Ahab's boat. Only one thing could be done. Seizing the boat-knife, he critically reached within—through—and then, without—the rays of steel; dragged in the line beyond, passed it, inboard, to the bowsman, and then, twice sundering the rope near the chocks—dropped the intercepted fagot of steel into the sea; and was all fast again. That instant, the White Whale made a sudden rush among the remaining tangles of the other lines; by so doing, irresistibly dragged the more involved boats of Stubb and Flask towards his flukes; dashed them together like two rolling husks on a surf-beaten beach, and then, diving down into the sea, disappeared in a coiling maelstrom, in which, for a space, the odorous cedar chips of the wrecks danced round and round, like the grated nutmeg in a swiftly stirred bowl of punch.

While the two crews were yet circling in the waters, reaching out after the revolving line-tubs, oars, and other floating furniture, while aslope little Flask bobbed up and down like an empty vial, twitching his legs

upwards to escape the dreaded jaws of sharks; and Stubb was lustily
singing out for some one to ladle him up; and while the old man's line—
now parting—admitted of his pulling into the creamy pool to rescue
whom he could;—in that wild simultaneousness of a thousand concreted
perils,—Ahab's yet unstricken boat seemed drawn up towards Heaven
by invisible wires,—as, arrow-like, shooting perpendicularly from the
sea, the White Whale dashed his broad forehead against its bottom, and
sent it, turning over and over, into the air; till it fell again—gunwale
downwards—and Ahab and his men struggled out from under it, like
seals from a seaside cave.

The first uprising momentum of the whale—modifying its direction
as he struck the surface—involuntarily launched him along it, to a little
distance from the centre of the destruction he had made; and with his
back to it, he now lay for a moment slowly feeling with his flukes from
side to side; and whenever a stray oar, bit of plank, the least chip or
crumb of the boats touched his skin, his tail swiftly drew back, and came
sideways, smiting the sea. But soon, as if satisfied that his work for
that time was done, he pushed his plaited forehead through the ocean,
and trailing after him the intertangled lines, continued his leeward way
at a traveller's methodic pace.

As before, the attentive ship having descried the whole fight, again
came bearing down to the rescue, and dropping a boat, picked up the
floating mariners, tubs, oars, and whatever else could be caught at, and
safely landed them upon her decks. Some sprained shoulders, wrists,
and ankles; livid contusions; wrenched harpoons and lances; inextricable
intricacies of rope; shattered oars and planks; all these were there; but
no fatal or even serious ill seemed to have befallen anyone. As with
Fedallah the day before, so Ahab was now found grimly clinging to his
boat's broken half, which offered a comparatively easy float; nor did
it exhaust him as the previous day's mishap.

But when he was helped to the deck, all eyes were fastened upon him;
as instead of standing by himself he still half-hung upon the shoulder of
Starbuck, who had thus far been the foremost to assist him. His ivory
leg had been snapped off, leaving but one short sharp splinter.

"Aye, aye, Starbuck, 'tis sweet to lean sometimes, be the leaner who
he will; and would old Ahab had leaned oftener than he has."

"The ferrule has not stood, sir," said the carpenter, now coming up;
"I put good work into that leg."

"But no bones broken, sir, I hope," said Stubb with true concern.

"Aye! and all splintered to pieces, Stubb! d'ye see it? But even with a
broken bone, old Ahab is untouched; and I account no living bone of
mine one jot more me than this dead one that's lost. Nor white whale, nor
man, nor fiend, can so much as graze old Ahab in his own proper and inaccessible being. Can any lead touch yonder floor, any mast scrape yonder roof? Aloft there! which way?"

"Dead to leeward, sir."

"Up helm, then; pile on the sail again, shipkeepers; down the rest of the spare boats and rig them—Mr Starbuck, away, and muster the boat's crews."

"Let me first help thee towards the bulwarks, sir."

"Oh, oh, oh! how this splinter gores me now! Accursed fate! that the unconquerable captain in the soul should have such a craven mate!"

"Sir?"

"My body, man, not thee. Give me something for a cane—there, that shivered lance will do. Muster the men. Surely I have not seen him yet. By heaven, it cannot be!—missing?—quick! call them all."

The old man's hinted thought was true. Upon mustering the company, the Parsee was not there.

"The Parsee!" cried Stubb, "he must have been caught in——"

"The black vomit wrench thee! Run all of ye above, alow, cabin, forecastle—find him—not gone—not gone!"

But quickly they returned to him with the tidings that the Parsee was nowhere to be found.

"Aye, sir," said Stubb—"caught among the tangles of your line. I thought I saw him dragged under."

"*My* line? *My* line? Gone? Gone? What means that little word? What death-knell rings in it, that old Ahab shakes as if he were the belfry. The harpoon, too! Toss over the litter there, d'ye see it?—the forged iron, men, the white whale's—no, no, no, blistered fool! this hand did dart it! 'Tis in the fish! Aloft there! Keep him nailed. Quick! all hands to the rigging of the boats—collect the oars—harpooners! the irons, the irons! Hoist the royals higher—a pull on all the sheets! Helm there! steady, steady, for your life! I'll ten times girdle the unmeasured globe; yea and dive straight through it, but I'll slay him yet!"

"Great God! but for one single instant show thyself," cried Starbuck. "Never, never wilt thou capture him, old man. In Jesus' name, no more of this, that's worse than devil's madness. Two days chased; twice stove to splinters; thy very leg once more snatched from under thee; thy evil shadow gone—all good angels mobbing thee with warnings; what more wouldst thou have? Shall we keep chasing this murderous fish till he swamps the last man? Shall we be dragged by him to the bottom of the sea? Shall we be towed by him to the infernal world? Oh, oh! Impiety and blasphemy to hunt him more!"

"Starbuck, of late I've felt strangely moved to thee; ever since that hour we both saw—thou know'st what, in one another's eyes. But in this matter of the whale, be the front of thy face to me as the palm of this hand—a lipless, unfeatured blank. Ahab is for ever Ahab, man. This whole act's immutably decreed. 'Twas rehearsed by thee and me a billion years before this ocean rolled. Fool! I am the Fates' lieutenant; I act under orders. Look thou, underling! that thou obeyest mine. Stand round me, men. Ye see an old man cut down to the stump; leaning on a shivered lance; propped up on a lonely foot. 'Tis Ahab—his body's part; but Ahab's soul's a centipede, that moves upon a hundred legs. I feel strained, half stranded, as ropes that tow dismasted frigates in a gale; and I may look so. But ere I break, ye'll hear me crack; and till ye hear *that*, know that Ahab's hawser tows his purpose yet. Believe ye, men, in the things called omens? Then laugh aloud, and cry encore! For ere they drown, drowning things will twice rise to the surface; then rise again, to sink for evermore. So with Moby Dick—two days he's floated—to-morrow will be the third. Aye, men, he'll rise once more—but only to spout his last."

The morning of the third day dawned fair and fresh, and once more the solitary night-man at the fore-masthead was relieved by crowds of the daylight look-outs, who dotted every mast and almost every spar.

"D'ye see him?" cried Ahab. "Aloft there. What d'ye see?"

"Nothing, sir."

"Nothing! The doubloon goes a-begging! See the sun! Aye, aye, it must be so. I've over-sailed him. How, got the start? Aye, he's chasing *me*, now; not I, *him*—that's bad. I might have known it, too. Fool! the lines—the harpoons he's towing. Aye, aye, I have run him by last night. About! About! Come down, all of ye, but the regular look-outs! Man the braces!"

Steering as she had done, the wind had been somewhat on the *Pequod's* quarter, so that now being pointed in the reverse direction, the braced ship sailed hard upon the breeze as she rechurned the cream in her own white wake.

"Against the wind he now steers for the open jaw," murmured Starbuck to himself, as he coiled the new-hauled main-brace upon the rail. "God keep us, but already my bones feel damp within me, and from the inside wet my flesh. I misdoubt me that I disobeyed my God in obeying him!"

"Stand by to sway me up!" cried Ahab, advancing to the hempen basket. "We should meet him soon."

"Aye, aye, sir," and straightway Starbuck did Ahab's bidding, and once more Ahab swung on high.

A whole hour now passed; gold-beaten out to ages. Time itself now held long breaths with keen suspense. But at last, some three points off the weather-bow, Ahab descried the spout again, and instantly from the three mastheads three shrieks went up as if the tongues of fire had voiced it.

"Forehead to forehead I meet thee, this third time, Moby Dick! On deck there! Brace sharper up; crowd her into the wind's eye. He's too far off to lower yet, Mr Starbuck. The sails shake! Stand over that helmsman with a topmaul! So, so he travels fast, and I must down."

He gave the word, and still gazing round him, was steadily lowered through the cloven blue air to the deck.

In due time the boats were lowered; but as standing in his shallop's stern, Ahab just hovered upon the point of the descent, he waved to the mate, who held one of the tackle-ropes on deck, and bade him pause.

"Starbuck!"

"Sir?"

"For the third time my soul's ship starts upon this voyage, Starbuck."

"Aye, sir, thou wilt have it so."

"Some ships sail from their ports, and ever afterwards are missing, Starbuck! Some men die at ebb tide; some at low water; some at the full of the flood; and I feel now like a billow that's all one crested comb, Starbuck. Lower away! Stand by the crew!"

In an instant the boat was pulling round close under the stern.

"The sharks! the sharks!" cried a voice from the low cabin-window there. "O master, my master, come back!"

But Ahab heard nothing; for his own voice was high-lifted then; and the boat leaped on.

Yet the voice spake true; for scarce had he pushed from the ship, when numbers of sharks, seemingly rising from out the dark waters beneath the hull, maliciously snapped at the blades of the oars, every time they dipped in the water; and in this way accompanied the boat with their bites. It is a thing not uncommonly happening to the whale-boats in those swarming seas; the sharks at times apparently following them in the same prescient way that vultures hover over the banners of marching regiments in the east. But these were the first sharks that had been observed by the *Pequod* since the White Whale had been first descried; and whether it was that Ahab's crew were all such tiger-yellow barbarians, and therefore their flesh more musky to the senses of sharks —a matter sometimes well known to affect them—however it was, they seemed to follow that one boat without molesting the others.

"Heart of wrought steel," murmured Starbuck, gazing over the side, and following with his eyes the receding boat, "canst thou yet ring boldly to that sight? lowering thy keel among ravening sharks, and followed by them, open-mouthed, to the chase; and this the critical third day? For when three days flow together in one continuous intense pursuit, be sure the first in the morning, the second the noon, and the third the evening and the end of that thing—be that end what it may."

The boats had not gone very far, when by a signal from the mastheads —a downward pointed arm, Ahab knew that the whale had sounded; but intending to be near him at the next rising, he held on his way a little sideways from the vessel; the becharmed crew maintaining the profoundest silence, as the head-beat waves hammered and hammered against the opposing bow.

Suddenly the waters around them slowly swelled in broad circles, then quickly upheaved, as if sideways sliding from a submerged berg of ice, swiftly rising to the surface. A low rumbling sound was heard; a subterraneous hum; and then all held their breaths; as bedraggled with trailing ropes, and harpoons, and lances, a vast form shot lengthwise, but obliquely from the sea. Shrouded in a thin drooping veil of mist, it hovered for a moment in the rainbowed air; and then fell swamping back into the deep. Crushed thirty feet upwards, the waters flashed for an instant like heaps of fountains, then brokenly sank in a shower of flakes, leaving the circling surface creamed like new milk round the marble trunk of the whale.

"Give way!" cried Ahab to the oarsmen and the boats darted forward to the attack; but maddened by yesterday's fresh irons that corroded in him, Moby Dick seemed combinedly possessed by all the angels that fell from heaven. The wide tiers of welded tendons overspreading his broad white forehead, beneath the transparent skin, looked knitted together; as head on, he came churning his tail among the boats; and once more flailed them apart; spilling out the irons and lances from the two mates' boats, and dashing in one side of the upper part of their bows, but leaving Ahab's almost without a scar.

While Daggoo and Queequeg were stopping the strained planks; and as the whale swimming out from them, turned, and showed one entire flank as he shot by them again; at that moment a quick cry went up. Lashed round and round to the fish's back; pinioned in the turns upon turns in which, during the past night, the whale had reeled the involutions of the lines around him, the half-torn body of the Parsee was seen; his sable raiment frayed to shreds; his distended eyes turned full upon old Ahab.

The harpoon dropped from his hand.

"Befooled, befooled!"—drawing in a long lean breath—"Aye, Parsee! I see thee again. Aye, and thou goest before; and this, *this* then is the hearse that thou didst promise. But I hold thee to the last letter of thy word. Where is the second hearse? Away, mates, to the ship! Those boats are useless now; repair them if ye can in time, and return to me; if not, Ahab is enough to die. Down, men! the first thing that but offers to jump from this boat I stand in, that thing I harpoon. Ye are not other men, but my arms and legs; and so obey me. Where's the whale? gone down again?"

But he looked too nigh the boat; for as if bent upon escaping with the corpse he bore, and as if the particular place of the last encounter had been but a stage in his leeward voyage, Moby Dick was now again steadily swimming forward; and had almost passed the ship, which thus far had been sailing in the contrary direction to him, though for the present her headway had been stopped. He seemed swimming with his utmost velocity, and now only intent upon pursuing his own straight path in the sea.

"Oh! Ahab," cried Starbuck, "not too late is it, even now, the third day, to desist. See! Moby Dick seeks thee not. It is thou, thou, that madly seekest him!"

Setting sail to the rising wind, the lonely boat was swiftly impelled to leeward by both oars and canvas. And at last when Ahab was sliding by the vessel, so near as plainly to distinguish Starbuck's face as he leaned over the rail, he hailed him to turn the vessel about, and follow him, not too swiftly, at a judicious interval. Glancing upwards, he saw Tashtego, Queequeg, and Daggoo, eagerly mounting to the three mastheads; while the oarsmen were rocking in the two staved boats which had just been hoisted to the side, and were busily at work in repairing them. One after the other, through the port-holes, as he sped, he also caught flying glimpses of Stubb and Flask, busying themselves on deck among bundles of new irons and lances. As he saw all this; as he heard the hammers in the broken boats; far other hammers seemed driving a nail into his heart. But he rallied. And now marking that the vane of flag was gone from the main masthead, he shouted to Tashtego, who had just gained that perch, to descend again for another flag, and a hammer and nails, and so nail it to the mast.

Whether fagged by the three days' running chase, and the resistance to his swimming in the knotted hamper he bore; or whether it was some latent deceitfulness and malice in him; whichever was true, the White Whale's way now began to abate, as it seemed, from the boat so rapidly nearing him once more; though indeed the whale's last start had not been so long a one as before. And still as Ahab glided over the waves the unpitying sharks accompanied him; and so pertinaciously stuck to the boat; and so continually bit at the plying oars, that the blades became jagged and crunched, and left small splinters in the sea, at almost every dip.

"Heed them not! those teeth but give new rowlocks to your oars. Pull on! 'tis the better rest, the shark's jaw than the yielding water."

"But at every bite, sir, the thin blades grow smaller and smaller!"

"They will last long enough! Pull on! But who can tell"—he muttered —"whether these sharks swim to feast on a whale or on Ahab? But pull on! Aye, all alive now—we near him. The helm! take the helm; let me pass,"—and so saying, two of the oarsmen helped him forward to the bows of the still flying boat.

At length as the craft was cast to one side, and ran ranging along with the White Whale's flank, he seemed strangely oblivious of its advance —as the whale sometimes will—and Ahab was fairly within the smoky mountain mist, which, thrown off from the whale's spout, curled round his great Monadnock hump. He was even thus close to him; when, with body arched back, and both arms lengthwise high-lifted to the poise, he darted his fierce iron, and his far fiercer curse into the hated whale. As both steel and curse sank to the socket, as if sucked into a morass,

Moby Dick sideways writhed; spasmodically rolled his nigh flank against the bow, and, without staving a hole in it, so suddenly canted the boat over, that had it not been for the elevated part of the gunwale to which he then clung, Ahab would have once more been tossed into the sea. As it was, three of the oarsmen—who foreknew not the precise instant of the dart, and were therefore unprepared for its effects—these were flung out; but so fell, that, in an instant two of them clutched the gunwale again, and rising to its level on a combing wave, hurled themselves bodily inboard again; the third man helplessly drooping astern, but still afloat and swimming.

Almost simultaneously, with a mighty volition of ungraduated instantaneous swiftness, the White Whale darted through the weltering sea. But when Ahab cried out to the steersman to take new turns with the line, and hold it so; and commanded the crew to turn round on their seats, and tow the boat up to the mark; the moment the treacherous line felt that double strain and tug, it snapped in the empty air!

"What breaks in me? Some sinew cracks!—'tis whole again; oars! oars! Burst in upon him!"

Hearing the tremendous rush of the sea-crashing boat, the whale wheeled round to present his blank forehead at bay; but in that evolution, catching sight of the nearing black hull of the ship; seemingly seeing in it the source of all his persecutions; bethinking it—it may be—a larger and nobler foe; of a sudden he bore down upon its advancing prow, smiting his jaws amid fiery showers of foam.

Ahab staggered; his hand smote his forehead. "I grow blind; hands! stretch out before me that I may yet grope my way. Is't night?"

"The whale! The ship!" cried the clinging oarsmen.

"Oars! oars! Slope downwards to thy depths, O sea, that ere it be for ever too late, Ahab may slide this last, last time upon his mark! I see: the ship! the ship! Dash on, my men! Will ye not save my ship?"

But as the oarsmen violently forced their boat through the sledge-hammering seas, the before whale-smitten bow-ends of two planks burst through, and in an instant almost, the temporarily disabled boat lay nearly level with the waves; its half-wading, splashing crew, trying hard to stop the gap and bale out the pouring water.

Meantime, for that one holding instant, Tashtego's mast-head hammer remained suspended in his hand; and the red flag, half-wrapping him as with a plaid, then streamed itself straight out from him, as his own forward-flowing heart; while Starbuck and Stubb, standing upon the bowsprit beneath caught sight of the down-coming monster just as soon as he.

"The whale! the whale! Up helm, up helm! Oh, all ye sweet powers of air, now hug me close! Let not Starbuck die, if die he must, in a woman's fainting fit. Up helm, I say—ye fools, the jaw! the jaw! Is this the end of all my bursting prayers? all my life-long fidelities? Oh, Ahab, Ahab, lo, thy work. Steady! helmsman, steady! Nay, nay! Up helm again! He turns to meet us! Oh, his unappeasable brow drives on towards one, whose duty tells him he cannot depart. My God, stand by me now!"

"Stand not by me, but stand under me, whoever you are that will now help Stubb; for Stubb, too, sticks here. I grin at thee, thou grinning whale! Whoever helped Stubb, or kept Stubb awake, but Stubb's own unwinking eye? And now poor Stubb goes to bed upon a mattress that is all too soft; would it were stuffed with brushwood. I grin at thee, thou grinning whale! Look ye, moon and stars! I call ye assassins of as good a fellow as ever spouted up his ghost. For all that, I would yet ring glasses with ye, would ye but hand the cup! Oh, oh, oh, oh! thou grinning whale, but there'll be plenty of gulping soon! Why fly ye not, O Ahab? For me, off shoes and jacket to it; let Stubb die in his drawers! A most mouldy and over-salted death, though;—cherries! cherries! cherries! Oh, Flask, for one red cherry ere we die!"

"Cherries? I only wish that we were where they grow. Oh, Stubb, I hope my poor mother's drawn my part-pay ere this; if not, few coppers will come to her now, for the voyage is up."

From the ship's bows, nearly all the seamen now hung inactive; hammers, bits of plank, lances, and harpoons, mechanically retained in their hands, just as they had darted from their various employments; all their enchanted eyes intent upon the whale, which from side to side strangely vibrating his predestinating head, sent a broad band of over-spreading semi-circular foam before him as he rushed. Retribution, swift vengeance, eternal malice were in his whole aspect, and spite of all that mortal man could do, the solid white buttress of his forehead smote the ship's starboard bow, till men and timbers reeled. Some fell flat upon their faces. Like dislodged trucks, the heads of the harpooners aloft shook on their hull-like necks. Through the breach, they heard the waters pour, as mountain torrents down a flume.

"The ship! The hearse!—the second hearse!" cried Ahab from the boat; "its wood could only be American!"

Diving beneath the settling ship, the Whale ran quivering along its keel; but turning under water, swiftly shot to the surface again, far off the other bow, but within a few yards of Ahab's boat, where, for a time, he lay quiescent.

"I turn my body from the sun. What ho, Tashtego! let me hear thy hammer. Oh! ye three unsurrendered spires of mine; thou uncracked keel; and only god-bullied hull; thou firm deck, and haughty helm, and Pole-pointed prow—death-glorious ship! must ye then perish, and without me? Am I cut off from the last fond pride of meanest shipwrecked captains? Oh, lonely death on lonely life! Oh, now I feel my topmost greatness lies in my topmost grief. Ho, ho! from all your furthest bounds, pour ye now in, ye bold billows of my whole foregone life, and top this one piled comber of my death! Towards thee I roll, thou all-destroying but unconquering whale; to the last I grapple with thee; from hell's heart I stab at thee; for hate's sake I spit my last breath at thee. Sink all coffins and all hearses to one common pool! and since neither can be mine let me then tow to pieces, while still chasing thee, though tied to thee, thou damned whale! *Thus*, I give up the spear."

The harpoon was darted; the stricken whale flew forward; with igniting velocity the line ran through the groove; ran foul. Ahab stooped to clear it; he did clear it; but the flying turn caught him round the neck, and voicelessly as Turkish mutes bow-string their victims, he was shot out of the boat, ere the crew knew he was gone. Next instant, the heavy eye-splice in the rope's final end flew out of the stark-empty tub, knocked down an oarsman, and smiting the sea, disappeared in its depth.

For an instant, the tranced boat's crew stood still; then turned.

"The ship! Great God, where is the ship?"

Soon they through dim, bewildering mediums saw her sidelong fading phantom, as in the gaseous Fata Morgana; only the uppermost masts out of water; while fixed by infatuation or fidelity, or fate, to their once lofty perches, the pagan harpooners still maintained their sinking look-outs on the sea. And now, concentric circles seized the lone boat itself, and all its crew, and each floating oar, and every lance-pole and spinning, animate and inanimate, all round and round in one vortex, carried the smallest chip of the *Pequod* out of sight.

But as the last whelmings intermixingly poured themselves over the sunken head of the Indian at the mainmast, leaving a few inches of the erect spar yet visible, together with long streaming yards of the flag, which calmly undulated, with ironical coincidings, over the destroying billows they almost touched;—at that instant, a red arm and a hammer hovered backwardly uplifted in the open air, in the act of nailing the flag faster and yet faster to the subsiding spar. A sky-hawk that tauntingly had followed the main-truck downwards from its natural home among the stars, pecking at the flag, and incommoding Tashtego there; this bird now chanced to intercept its broad fluttering wing between the hammer and the wood; and simultaneously feeling that ethereal thrill, the submerged savage beneath, in his death-grasp, kept his hammer frozen there; and so the bird of heaven, with unearthly shrieks, and his imperial beak thrust upwards, and his whole captive form folded in the flag of Ahab, went down with his ship, which, like Satan, would not sink to hell till she had dragged a living part of heaven along with her, and helmeted herself with it.

Now small fowls flew screaming over the yet yawning gulf; a sullen white surf beat against its steep sides; then all collapsed, and the great shroud of the sea rolled on as it rolled five thousand years ago.

HOW QUINTUS ARRIUS DEFEATED THE PIRATES[1]

Lew Wallace

(1827–1905)

EVERY soul aboard, even the ship, awoke. Officers went to their quarters. The marines took arms, and were led out, looking in all respects like legionaries. Sheaves of arrows and armfuls of javelins were carried on deck. By the central stairs the oil-tanks and fire-balls were set ready for use. Additional lanterns were lighted. Buckets were filled with water. The rowers in relief assembled under guard in front of the chief. As Providence would have it, Ben-Hur was one of the latter. Overhead he heard the muffled noises of the final preparations—of the sailors furling sail, spreading the nettings, unslinging the machines, and hanging the armour of bull-hide over the sides. Presently quiet settled about the galley again; quiet full of vague dread and expectation, which, interpreted, means *ready*.

At a signal passed down from the deck and communicated to the hortator by a petty officer stationed on the stairs, all at once the oars stopped.

What did it mean?

Of the hundred and twenty slaves chained to the benches, not one but asked himself the question. They were without incentive. Patriotism, love of honour, sense of duty, brought them no inspiration. They felt the thrill common to men rushed helpless and blind into danger. It may be supposed the dullest of them, poising his oar, thought of all that might happen, yet could promise himself nothing; for victory would but rivet his chains the firmer, while the chances of the ship were his; sinking or on fire, he was doomed to her fate.

Of the situation without they might not ask. And who were the enemy? And what if they were friends, brethren, countrymen?

There was little time, however, for such thought with them.

A sound like the rowing of galleys astern attracted Ben-Hur and the *Astræa* rocked as if in the midst of countering waves. The idea of a fleet at hand broke upon him—a fleet in manœuvre—forming probably for attack. His blood started with the fancy.

Another signal came down from the deck. The oars dipped, and the galley started imperceptibly. No sound from without, none from within, yet each man in the cabin instinctively poised himself for a shock; the very ship seemed to catch the sense, and hold its breath, and go crouched tiger-like.

In such a situation time is inappreciable so that Ben-Hur could form no judgement of distance gone. At last there was a sound of trumpets on deck, full, clear, long-blown. The chief beat the sounding-board until it

[1] From *Ben Hur*.

rang; the rowers reached forward full-length, and, deepening the dip of their oars, pulled suddenly with all their united force. The galley, quivering in every timber, answered with a leap. Other trumpets joined in the clamour—all from the rear, none forward—from the latter quarter only a rising sound of voices in tumult heard briefly.

There was a mighty blow; the rowers in front of the chief's platform reeled, some of them fell; the ship bounded back, recovered, and rushed on more irresistibly than before. Shrill and high arose the shrieks of men in terror; over the blare of trumpets, and the grind and crash of the collision; they arose, then under his feet, under the keel, pounding, rumbling, breaking to pieces, drowning, Ben-Hur felt something overridden. The men about him looked at each other afraid. A shout of triumph from the deck—the beak of the Roman had won! But who were they whom the sea had drunk? Of what tongue, from what land were they?

No pause, no stay! Forward rushed the *Astræa;* and, as it went, some sailors ran down, and plunging the cotton balls into the oil-tanks, tossed them dripping to comrades at the head of the stairs: fire was to be added to other horrors of the combat.

Directly the galley heeled over so far that the oarsmen on the uppermost side with difficulty kept their benches. Again the hearty Roman cheer, and with it despairing shrieks. An enemy vessel, caught by the grappling-hooks of the great crane swinging from the prow, was being lifted into the air that it might be dropped and sunk.

The shouting increased on the right hand and on the left; before, behind, swelled an indescribable clamour. Occasionally there was a crash, followed by sudden peals of fright, telling of other ships ridden down, and their crews drowned in the vortexes.

Nor was the fight all on one side. Now and then a Roman in armour was borne down the hatchway, and laid bleeding, sometimes dying, on the floor.

Sometimes, also, puffs of smoke, blended with steam, and foul with the scent of roasting human flesh, poured into the cabin, turning the dimming light into yellow murk. Gasping for breath the while, Ben-Hur knew they were passing through the cloud of a ship on fire, and burning up with the rowers chained to the benches.

The *Astræa* all this time was in motion. Suddenly she stopped. The oars forward were dashed from the hands of the rowers, and the rowers from their benches. On deck, then, a furious trampling, and on the sides the grinding of ships afoul of each other. For the first time the beating of the gavel was lost in the uproar. Men sank on the floor in fear, or looked about seeking a hiding-place. In the midst of the panic a body plunged or was pitched headlong down the hatchway, falling near Ben-Hur. He beheld the half-naked carcass, a mass of hair blackening the face, and under it a shield of bull-hide and wicker-work—a barbarian from the white-skinned nations of the North whom death had robbed of plunder and revenge. How came he there? An iron hand had snatched him from the opposing deck—no, the *Astræa* had been boarded! The Romans were fighting on their own deck?

A chill smote the young Jew: Arrius was hard pressed—he might be defending his own life. If he should be slain! God of Abraham forfend! The hopes and dreams so lately come, were they only hopes and dreams? Mother and sister—house—home—Holy Land—was he not to see them after all? The tumult thundered above him; he looked around; in the cabin all was confusion—the rowers on the benches paralysed; men running blindly hither and thither; only the chief on his seat imperturbable, vainly beating the sounding-board, and waiting the orders of the tribune —in the red murk illustrating the matchless discipline which had won the world.

The example had a good effect upon Ben-Hur. He controlled himself enough to think. Honour and duty bound the Roman to the platform; but what had he to do with such motives then? The bench was a thing to run from; while, if he were to die a slave, who would be the better of the sacrifice? With him living was duty, if not honour. His life belonged to his people. They arose before him never more real; he saw them, their arms outstretched; he heard them imploring him. And he would go to them. He started—stopped. Alas! a Roman judgement held him in doom. While it endured escape would be profitless. In the wide, wide earth there was no place in which he would be safe from the imperial demand; upon the land none, nor upon the sea. That which he required was freedom according to the forms of law, so only could he abide in Judea and execute the filial purpose to which he would devote himself; in other land he would not live. Dear God! How he had waited and watched and prayed for such a release! And how it had been delayed! But at last he had seen it in the promise of the tribune. What else the great man's meaning? And if the benefactor so belated should now be slain! The dead come not back to redeem the pledges of the living. It should not be —Arrius should not die. At least, better perish with him than survive a galley-slave.

Once more Ben-Hur looked around. Upon the roof of the cabin the battle yet beat; against the sides the hostile vessels yet crushed and ground. On the benches, the slaves struggled to tear loose from their chains, and, finding their efforts vain, howled like madmen; the guards had gone upstairs; discipline was out, panic in. No, the chief kept his chair, unchanged, calm as ever—except for the gavel, weaponless. Vainly with his clangour he filled the lulls in the din. Ben-Hur gave him a last look, then broke away—not in flight, but to seek the tribune.

A very short space lay between him and the ladder of the hatchway aft. He took it with a leap, and was half-way up the steps—up far enough to catch a glimpse of the sky blood-red with fire, of the ships alongside, of the sea covered with ships and wrecks of the fight closed in about the pilot's quarter, the assailants many, the defenders few—when suddenly his foothold was knocked away, and he pitched backward. The floor, when he reached it, seemed to be lifting itself and breaking in pieces; then, in a twinkling, the whole after-part of the hull broke asunder, and, as if it had all the time been lying in wait, the sea, hissing and foaming, leaped in, and all became darkness and surging water to Ben-Hur.

The influx of the flood tossed him like a log forward into the cabin, where he would have drowned but for the refluence of the sinking motion. As it was, fathoms under the surface, the hollow mass vomited him forth, and he rose along with the loose debris. In the act of rising, he clutched something, and held to it. With a great gasp he filled his lungs afresh, and, tossing the water from his hair and eyes, climbed higher upon the plank he held, and looked about him.

Smoke lay upon the sea like a semi-transparent fog, through which here and there shone cores of intense brilliance. A quick intelligence told him that they were ships on fire. The battle was yet on; nor could he say who was victor. Within the radius of his vision, now and then ships passed, shooting shadows athwart lights. Out of the dun clouds farther on he caught the crash of other ships colliding.

The danger, however, was closer at hand. When the *Astrœa* went down, her deck, it will be recollected, held her own crew, and the crews of the two galleys which had attacked her, at the same time, all of whom were engulfed. Many of them came to the surface together, and on the same plank or support of whatever kind continued the combat, begun possibly in the vortex fathoms down. Writhing and twisting in deadly embrace, sometimes striking with sword or javelin they kept the sea around them in agitation, at one place inky-black, at another aflame with fiery reflections. With their struggles he had nothing to do; they were all his enemies: not one of them but would kill him for the plank upon which he floated. He made haste to get away.

About that time he heard oars in quickest movement, and beheld a galley coming down upon him. The tall prow seemed doubly tall, and the red light playing upon its gilt and carving gave it an appearance of snaky life. Under its foot the water churned to flying foam.

He struck out, pushing the plank, which was very broad and unmanageable. Seconds were precious—half a second might save or lose him.

In the crisis of the effort, up from the sea, within arm's reach, a helmet shot like a gleam of gold. Next came two hands with fingers extended—large hands were they, and strong—their hold once fixed, might not be loosed. Ben-Hur swerved from them appalled. Up rose the helmet and the head it encased—then two arms, which began to beat the water wildly—the head turned back, and gave the face to the light. The mouth gaping wide; the eyes open, but sightless, and the bloodless pallor of a drowning man—never anything more ghastly! Yet he gave a cry of joy at the sight, and as the face was going under again, he caught the sufferer by the chain which passed from the helmet beneath the chin, and drew him to the plank.

The man was Arrius, the tribune.

For a while the water foamed and eddied violently about Ben-Hur, taxing all his strength to hold to the support and at the same time keep the Roman's head above the surface. The galley had passed, leaving the two barely outside the stroke of its oars. Right through the floating men, over heads helmeted as well as heads bare, she drove, in her wake nothing but the sea sparkling with fire. A muffled crash, succeeded by a great outcry, made the rescuer look again from his charge. A certain savage pleasure touched his heart—the *Astræa* was avenged.

After that the battle moved on. Resistance turned to flight. But who were the victors? Ben-Hur was sensible how much his freedom and the life of the tribune depended upon that event. He pushed the plank under the latter until it floated him, after which all his care was to keep him there. The dawn came slowly. He watched its growing hopefully, yet, sometimes afraid. Would it bring the Romans or the pirates? If the pirates, his charge was lost.

At last morning broke in full, the air without a breath. Off to the left he saw the land, too far to think of attempting to make it. Here and there men were adrift like himself. In spots the sea was blackened by charred and sometimes smoking fragments. A galley up a long way was lying to with a torn sail hanging from the tilted yard, and the oars all idle. Still farther away, he could discern moving specks, which he thought might be ships in flight or pursuit, or they might be white birds a-wing.

An hour passed thus. His anxiety increased. If relief come not speedily, Arrius would die. Sometimes he seemed already dead, he lay so still. He took the helmet off, and then, with greater difficulty, the cuirass; the heart he found fluttering. He took hope at the sign, and held on. There was nothing to do but wait, and, after the manner of his people, pray.

The throes of recovery from drowning are more painful than the drowning. These Arrius passed through, and at length, to Ben-Hur's delight, reached the point of speech.

Gradually from incoherent questions as to where he was, and by whom and how he had been saved, he reverted to the battle. The doubt of the victory stimulated his faculties to full return, a result aided not a little by a long rest—such as could be had on their frail support. After a while he became talkative.

"Our rescue, I see, depends upon the result of the fight. I see also what thou hast done for me. To speak fairly, thou hast saved my life at the risk of thy own. I make the acknowledgement broadly; and, whatever cometh, thou hast my thanks. More than that, if fortune doth but serve me kindly, and we get well out of this peril, I will do thee such favour as becometh a Roman who hath power and opportunity to prove his gratitude. Yet—yet it is to be seen if, with thy good intent, thou hast really done me a kindness; or, rather, speaking to thy goodwill"—He hesitated —"I would exact of thee a promise to do me, in a certain event, the greatest favour one man can do another—and of that let me have thy pledge now."

"If the thing be not forbidden I will do it," Ben-Hur replied.

Arrius rested again.

"Art thou, indeed, a son of Hur, the Jew?" he next asked.

"It is as I have said."

"I knew thy father——"

Judah drew himself nearer, for the tribune's voice was weak—he drew nearer, and listened eagerly—at last he thought to hear of home.

"I knew him, and loved him," Arrius continued.

There was another pause, during which something diverted the speaker's thought.

"It cannot be," he proceeded, "that thou, a son of his, hast not heard of Cato and Brutus. They were very great men, and never as great as in death. In their dying, they left this law—A Roman may not survive his good fortune—Art thou listening?"

"I hear."

"It is a custom of gentlemen in Rome to wear a ring. There is one on my hand. Take it now."

He held his hand to Judah, who did as he asked.

"Now put it on thine own hand."

Ben-Hur did so.

"The trinket hath its uses," said Arrius next. "I have property and money. I am accounted rich even in Rome. I have no family. Show the ring to my freedman, who hath control in my absence; you will find him in a villa near Misenum. Tell him how it came to thee, and ask anything, or all he may have; he will not refuse the demand. If I live, I will do better by thee. I will make thee free, and restore thee to thy home and people; or thou mayst give thyself to the pursuit that pleaseth thee most. Dost thou hear?"

"I could not choose but hear."

"Then pledge me. By the gods——"

"Nay, good tribune, I am a Jew."

"By thy God, then, or in the form most sacred to those of thy faith, pledge me to do what I tell thee now, and as I tell thee; I am waiting, let me have thy promise."

"Noble Arrius, I am warned by thy manner to expect something of gravest concern. Tell me thy wish first."

"Wilt thou promise then?"

"That were to give the pledge, and—Blessed be the God of my fathers! yonder cometh a ship!"

"In what direction?"

"From the north."

"Canst thou tell her nationality by outward signs?"

"No. My service hath been at the oars."

"Hath she a flag?"

"I cannot see one."

Arrius remained quiet some time, apparently in deep reflection.

"Does the ship hold this way yet?" he at length asked.

"Still this way."

"Look for the flag now."

"She hath none."

"Nor any other sign?"

"She hath a sail set, and is of three banks, and cometh swiftly—that is all I can say of her."

"A Roman in triumph would have out many flags. She must be an enemy. Hear now," said Arrius, becoming grave again, "hear, while yet I may speak. If the galley be a pirate, thy life is safe; they may not give thee freedom; they may put thee to the oar again; but they will not kill thee. On the other hand, I——"

The tribune faltered.

"Perpol!" he continued resolutely. "I am too old to submit to dishonour. In Rome, let them tell how Quintus Arrius, as became a Roman tribune, went down with his ship in the midst of the foe. This is what I would have thee do. If the galley prove a pirate, push me from the plank and drown me. Dost thou hear? Swear thou wilt do it."

"I will not swear," said Ben-Hur firmly; "neither will I do the deed. The Law, which is to me most binding, O tribune, would make me answerable for thy life. Take back the ring"—he took the seal from his finger—"take it back, and all thy promises of favour in the event of delivery from this peril. The judgement which sent me to the oar for life made me a slave, yet I am not a slave; no more am I thy freedman. I am a son of Israel, and this moment, at least, my own master. Take back the ring."

Arrius remained passive.

"Thou wilt not?" Judah continued. "Not in anger, then, nor in any despite, but to free myself from a grateful obligation, I will give thy gift to the sea. See, O tribune!"

He tossed the ring away. Arrius heard the splash where it struck and sank, though he did not look.

"Thou hast done a foolish thing," he said; "foolish for one placed as thou art. I am not dependent upon thee for death. Life is a thread I can break without thy help; and if I do, what will become of thee? Men determined on death prefer it at the hand of others—for the reason that the soul which Plato giveth us is rebellious at the thought of self-destruction; that is all. If the ship be a pirate, I will escape from the world. My mind is fixed. I am a Roman. Success and honour are all in all. Yet I would have served thee; thou wouldst not. The ring was the only witness of my will available in this situation. We are both lost. I will die regretting the victory and glory wrested from me; thou wilt live to die a little later, mourning the pious duties undone because of this folly. I pity thee."

Ben-Hur saw the consequences of his act more distinctly than before, yet he did not falter.

"In the three years of my servitude, O tribune, thou wert the first to look upon me kindly. No, no! there was another." The voice dropped, the eyes became humid, and he saw plainly as if it were then before him the face of the boy who helped him to a drink by the old well at Nazareth. "At least," he proceeded, "thou wert the first to ask me who I was; and if, when I reached out and caught thee, blind and sinking the last time, I too had thought of the many ways in which thou couldst be useful to me in my wretchedness, still the act was not all selfish; this I pray you to believe. Moreover, seeing as God giveth me to know, the ends I dream of are to be wrought by fair means alone. As a thing of conscience, I would rather die with thee than be thy slayer. My mind is firmly set as thine; though thou wert to offer me all Rome, O tribune, and it belonged to thee to make the gift good, I would not kill thee. Thy Cato and Brutus were as little children compared to the Hebrew whose law a Jew must obey."

"But my request. Hast——"

"Thy command would be of more weight, and that would not move me. I have said."

Both became silent, waiting.

Ben-Hur looked often at the coming ship. Arrius rested with closed eyes, indifferent.

"Art thou sure she is an enemy?" Ben Hur asked.

"I think so," was the reply.

"She stops and puts a boat over the side."

"Dost thou see her flag?"

"Is there no other sign by which she may be known, if Roman?"

"If Roman, she hath a helmet over the mast's top."

"Then be of cheer. I see the helmet."

Still Arrius was not assured.

"The men in the small boat are taking in the people afloat. Pirates are not humane."

"They may need rowers," Arrius replied, recurring possibly to times when he had made rescues for the purpose.

Ben-Hur was very watchful of the actions of the strangers. "The ship moves off," he said presently.

"Whither?"

"Over on our right there is a galley which I take to be deserted. The new-comer heads towards it. Now she is alongside. Now she is sending men aboard."

Then Arrius opened his eyes, and threw off his calm.

"Thank thou thy God," he said to Ben-Hur, after a look at the galleys, "thank thou thy God, as I do my many gods. A pirate would sink, not save, yon ship. By the act and the helmet on the mast I know a Roman. The victory is mine. Fortune hath not deserted me. We are saved. Wave thy hand—call to them—bring them quickly. I shall be duumvir, and thou! I knew thy father, and loved him. He was a prince indeed. He taught me a Jew was not a barbarian. I will take thee with me. I will make thee my son. Give thy God thanks, and call the sailors. Haste! The pursuit must be kept. Not a robber shall escape. Hasten them."

Judah raised himself upon the plank, and waved his hand, and called with all his might; at last he drew the attention of the sailors in the small boat, and they were speedily taken up.

Arrius was received on the galley with all the honours due a hero so the favourite of Fortune. Upon a couch on the deck he heard the particulars of the conclusion of the fight. When the survivors afloat upon the water were all saved and the prize secured, he spread his flag of commandant anew, and hurried northward to rejoin the fleet and perfect the victory. In due time the fifty vessels coming down the channel closed in upon the fugitive pirates, and crushed them utterly; not one escaped. To swell the tribune's glory, twenty galleys of the enemy were captured.

Upon his return from the cruise, Arrius had a warm welcome on the mole at Misenum. The young man attending him very early attracted the attention of his friends there; and to their questions as to who he was the tribune proceeded in the most affectionate manner to tell the story of his rescue and introduced the stranger, omitting carefully all that pertained to the latter's previous history. At the end of the narrative he called Ben-Hur to him, and said, with a hand resting affectionately upon his shoulder.

"Good friends, this is my son and heir, who, as he is to take my property—if it be the will of the gods that I leave any—shall be known to you by my name. I pray you all to love him as you love me."

Speedily, as opportunity permitted, the adoption was formally perfected. And in such manner the brave Roman kept his faith with Ben-Hur, giving him happy introduction into the imperial world. The month succeeding Arrius' return, the armilustrium was celebrated with the utmost magnificence in the theatre of Scaurus. One side of the structure was taken up with military trophies; among which by far the most conspicuous and most admired were twenty prows, complemented by their corresponding aplustra, cut bodily from as many galleys—and over them, so as to be legible to the eighty thousand spectators in the seats, was this inscription:

TAKEN FROM THE PIRATES IN THE GULF OF EURIFUS
BY
QUINTUS ARRIUS
DUUMVIR

THE SKIPPER AND EL CAPITAN[1]

Frank R. Stockton

(1834–1902)

EARLY one summer morning there sailed into the harbour of Yakonsk, a seaport on the far north-western edge of the Pacific Ocean, the three-masted schooner *Molly Crenshaw*, of Gloucester, Mass.

The skipper of this vessel, Ezra Budrack by name, of domestic proclivities, had with him his family, consisting of his wife and daughter. The *Molly Crenshaw* was the Budrack home. In this good craft, which Ezra owned, they had sailed to many ports, sometimes on one errand and sometimes on another. They were now entering the harbour of Yakonsk, hoping to do a little trading. They had visited the town before, and the Commandant of the Russian garrison stationed there was glad to see them.

That night, before the moon had set, there steamed into the harbour a Spanish merchant vessel, the *Reina de la Plata*, of about seven hundred tons. She dropped anchor near the entrance to the roadstead, and early the next morning one of her boats started for the shore. In the stern sat Matias Romino, captain of the steamer. As the ship's boat neared the *Molly Crenshaw*, a clear, strong voice rang out from the schooner's deck:

"Hello, el Capitan! I am glad to see you. I made up my mind that was your vessel the moment my eyes fell upon her, before sunrise."

The captain in the stern of the little boat gave a start. He was a handsome, well-made man, to whom much of his youth remained. His hair was black and his eyes were bright.

"Hello!" he cried, and ordered his crew to make for the schooner.

In a few minutes the two men were shaking hands on the deck of the *Molly Crenshaw*. They were well acquainted, having frequently met at

[1]From *Afield and Afloat*. Copyright, 1900, by Charles Scribner's Sons. Reprinted by permission of the publishers.

ports where they had been trading, and they liked each other. El Capitan, as Ezra always called him, spoke English with an accent, now scarcely noticed by the Budrack family, and almost the first thing he did was to ask after the skipper's wife and daughter, and to hope that they were very well.

"They are all right," said Ezra, "and they'll be on deck in no time, when I tell them you're here."

Drusilla Budrack was a pretty girl and a good one. She had dark eyes, which she owed to her mother, and an embrowned complexion, which had been given her by the sea air. She was very glad to see el Capitan, although she did not say as much about it as her parents did. As for the Spaniard, he was delighted. For more than two years he had been in love with Drusilla. He had been in port with her for weeks at a time, and he had never met a Spanish woman who suited him so well. He longed to follow the example of the good Ezra Budrack, and sail the seas with a wife on board his ship. All these things were known to the Budracks, but nothing definite had been done in the matter.

As the Budracks and el Capitan were talking pleasantly together, relating their experiences since they had last met, they perceived a little gunboat approaching from the town.

"The Commandant treats you better than he treated me," said the skipper to the Spaniard; "I had to go in to see him and report my arrival, but he is coming to meet you."

"Perhaps he will do some fault-finding with me," replied el Capitan, with a smile, "because I did not go direct to pay my respects instead of stopping here."

In a few minutes the gunboat lay to near by, a small boat put out from her, and the Russian Commandant boarded the *Molly Crenshaw*. He was a stout man, with a countenance which was mostly hair, but he had a pleasant smile. He shook hands with el Capitan and the skipper, and bowed to the ladies.

"It astonishes me," said he to the two captains, "to see you consort in such a friendly way. Do you not know that your nations are at war?"

The three Budracks and el Capitan started in simultaneous amazement.

"What!" exclaimed the skipper. "I don't understand you! You said nothing of this to me yesterday."

"No," said the Russian; "I supposed, of course, you knew all about it, and when I was going to refer to the subject I was interrupted."

"I never heard of it!" cried Ezra. "It was not known at the port where I last stopped."

"No!" el Capitan cried, "I have had no news like this! War! I cannot believe it."

Then the Commandant drew from his pocket a dispatch he had received from his government, and read it. It was a fair account of the war between the United States and Spain.

The two women began to cry. The skipper walked to and fro across the deck in great agitation.

"It is amazing!" he exclaimed. "They must have been fighting for a long time. And I knew nothing about it!"

El Capitan stood up, tall, erect, and almost pale. His eyes were fixed upon Drusilla.

"My country at war with the Americans!" he groaned.

"Yes," said the Commandant; "and she has been getting the worst of it, too."

This further information did not affect el Capitan. The fact that his people were fighting Drusilla's people was all the bad news his soul could recognize at that moment.

"You are enemies," said the Russian, "and your ships and their officers and crews should be kept apart. It is my duty to keep you apart!"

"We are not enemies!" cried el Capitan. "No war can make us enemies."

Mrs Budrack looked at him with tearful gratitude. By nature she was afraid of all Spaniards, but she had learned to make an exception of el Capitan, and if he continued their friend what could there be to fear? Drusilla's eyes were downcast; she trembled with emotion, and if they had been alone she would have thanked her lover with a shake of the hand.

The skipper was not a sentimental person, and he was not in love with any Spanish woman; he had patriotic principles, and they came to the front.

"You are right, Mr Commandant," said he; "if the United States is at war with Spain, and if the two countries are now fighting as hard as they can, of course el Capitan is my enemy and I am his. There is no other way of looking at it. It is hard lines for me, for I've liked him ever since I first knew him, and my wife and daughter will be very much cut up, I know, but there's no getting around it. He is my enemy and I am his."

"But what of all that?" cried el Capitan. "A country does not mean every single person in it. In every nation there is always some one who is different from the rest. I cannot be an enemy to my friends."

"But you will have to be, el Capitan," said the skipper. "You are a good man, and I have a high respect for you, but your country has made you my enemy. You have nothing to say about it, and you can't help it."

"That is right," said the Commandant. "The rulers of your nations have made you enemies. You must submit. If one of you commanded a man-of-war it would be his duty to capture the other one as a prize. If both ships were war vessels, it would be your duty to fight. Your governments have arranged all that."

At the mention of fighting Mrs Budrack went below. She could hear no more. Drusilla, however, remained, silent, pale, with eager eyes.

The skipper knitted his brows and reflected. "Look here, Mr Commandant," he said; "my vessel is liable to be taken as a prize by the Spanish, is she?"

"By a Spanish war vessel, yes," was the answer.

"But if there are no war vessels in the case," said Ezra, "it seems to me that enemies should fight. If my vessel is liable to be taken as a prize, so is that Spanish vessel. How is that, according to your constitution?"

"My country has no constitution," said the Commandant; "her rulers decide according to circumstances."

"Do you sometimes have to decide according to circumstances?" asked the skipper.

"When I cannot communicate with my government I sometimes have to do so," answered the Russian.

"Well, then," said Ezra, "how do you decide now?"

"I must think," said the Commandant.

During this conversation el Capitan was silent, but looked very black. To be at war with Drusilla's country—it was a horrible fate.

"I have thought this," said the Commandant, presently: "I will have nothing to do with either of you, except to preserve strict neutrality. This is the order of my government. You are enemies, and at any moment you may begin to fight. I have nothing to do with that, but in this harbour you cannot fight. The laws of neutrality will not permit it."

The countenance of el Capitan began to brighten. Suddenly it beamed. "I will fight," he cried. "I am ready to do battle for the honour of my country. Since there is no war vessel here to uphold her honour, the *Reina de la Plata* will do it. I will sail outside the harbour together with the *Molly Crenshaw*, and I will fight her."

El Capitan was a good man, but a wily Spaniard; his vessel was larger than the schooner, he carried more men. If he could capture the *Molly Crenshaw* he would capture Drusilla. Then let the war go on; what mattered it to him! He would have her, and everything else could be settled afterward.

"No," said the Commandant, "you cannot sail out of this harbour with this vessel. You are enemies, and the laws of neutrality demand that one of you must remain here for twenty-four hours after the other has departed."

Drusilla wept, and went below to join her mother. If in this time of war the *Molly Crenshaw* should sail away in one direction and the *Reina de la Plata* in another, when would she ever see el Capitan again?

The Spaniard approached the skipper and extended his hand. "I will go outside," he said, "and wait there twenty-four hours until you come. Then I will fight you."

"Very good," said Ezra, giving his hand a hearty shake; "you may count on me."

"I do not think you have a right to fight," said the Commandant to

Ezra, when el Capitan had departed for his steamer. "You are both merchant-men."

"But we are each liable to be taken as a prize," said Ezra, "and I think that makes it square."

The Commandant shook his head. "Even if my country had a constitution," he said, "I do not know that it could settle that point. But I shall take no responsibility; all I can do is to preserve strict neutrality."

The next morning the good schooner *Molly Crenshaw*, with a fine breeze, sailed out of the harbour of Yakonsk, and she had scarcely reached the open sea before she saw, a few miles away, the smoking funnel of the *Reina de la Plata*. The Spanish vessel immediately changed her course and made directly for the *Molly Crenshaw*.

El Capitan was in high spirits. He had had twenty-four hours in which to reflect upon the state of affairs, and to construct a plan of battle, and he was entirely satisfied with the scheme he had worked out. As has been said before, he was so much stronger than his new enemy that he thought there would be very little trouble in capturing her, even if her skipper and her crew should make some show of resistance. His steamer rode much higher out of the water than did the schooner, and if he should lie alongside of the latter, which he could easily do, she, depending entirely upon the wind, while he possessed all the advantages afforded by steam, his men could easily slip down on her deck and quell any disorder which might be occasioned by his action.

Then, as soon as the schooner's company had surrendered and good-fellowship and order had been restored, he would take Skipper Budrack and his family on board his own steamer, where they would have the very best accommodations. He would put a prize crew on the *Molly Crenshaw*, and the two ships would sail away to a Spanish port. On this voyage, which naturally would be somewhat long, he would settle matters with Drusilla and her parents. He had no doubt that he could do so. He believed he knew a good deal concerning the young lady's state of mind, and her parents would not be in the position to resist his entreaties which they would have occupied had they been sailing in their own vessel, and able, whenever they chose, to put thousands of miles between him and the object of his hopes—of his life.

When he finally arrived at a Spanish port, and if the prize he had captured should be formally adjudicated to him, he would then make the *Molly Crenshaw* a wedding present to Drusilla. He would take command of the schooner, and his parents-in-law should sail with Drusilla and himself, if they so chose, or, if they liked it better, they should spend their declining years in any pleasant spot they might select, receiving regularly a portion of the profits of the voyages which he and Drusilla would make to various ports of the world. His face beaming with happy anticipations, he leaned over the rail as the steamer rapidly approached the schooner, which was now lying to.

Before the two vessels were within hailing distance, Skipper Ezra Budrack displayed a large flag of truce.

"You needn't do that!" roared el Capitan, through his speaking-trumpet. "I am not going to fight you without notice. I make for you only that I may plan the battle with you."

Now the two vessels lay, gently rolling, side by side, as near as safety would permit.

"Before we begin," shouted Ezra to el Capitan, "I want you to look at this pistol," and with this he held up a large revolver; "this is the only shooting-iron on board this vessel, and, as I don't want any accidents or unnecessary bloodshed, I am going to throw it into the sea. Look now! Down she goes!" And with that the skipper hurled the pistol into the water below him with such force that it must have made a hole in the bottom of the sea. "Now, then, el Capitan," cried he, "what are you going to do about fire-arms?"

The Spanish captain disappeared, but in a few moments he returned, bearing a large carbine. "This is the only gun we've got," said he, "and down she goes!" With these words he pitched it into the sea.

"That's all right," said the skipper; "and now, whenever you're ready to come on, we're ready to meet you. Of course, as you're a steamer, you'll have to do the coming on."

"I'll do that," said el Capitan; "but before we begin, I, too, have something to say. I shall subdue your men and capture your ship with as little violence as possible, but still there will be a scuffle, and there may be blows and a good deal of general disorder. That is to be expected, and I do not think either of us can prevent it. Therefore, I beg of you, my dear skipper, that you will keep your wife and daughter safely shut up in your cabin. I shall tell my men not to go aft if they can help it, and on no account to go below, and as I shall be on board I shall see that my orders are obeyed. Of course I shall allow no injury to come to the two ladies or yourself, but I do not wish that they shall even be frightened. I hope, if it can be so managed, that the whole affair may be transacted so quietly and promptly that it will seem to them like an ordinary nautical manœuvre."

"His English is wonderfully improved," thought Skipper Budrack; "when first I knew him he could not express himself like that." Then, with a gradually expanding grin, he called out to el Capitan; "I am much obliged to you for your kind consideration for my family, but you must not suppose that I would take my wife and daughter on board my vessel when I was going out for a fight. I left Mrs Budrack and Drusilla in the town. They are staying with the Commandant's family, who gave them a very kind invitation."

Now el Capitan stamped his feet and swore many Spanish oaths. Every plan he had made had been swept away as if it had been struck by a typhoon. If he could not capture Drusilla, what would a victory be worth to him? He was mad with rage and disappointment. All the time he had been talking his eyes had been scanning the cabin windows in the hope of seeing a fair face or a waving handkerchief. It was a vile trick the skipper had played on him. He had had such kind thoughts; he had planned to be so magnanimous; he would have taken the schooner so gently that the most tender heart would not have been made to flutter. But now everything was different. He would not say another word to that deceiving skipper. But suddenly an idea came into his fiery brain. "I will run down his schooner," he exclaimed. "I will utterly destroy it. I will sink it to the bottom. But I will be merciful; I will save his life; I will save all their lives if I can. But his vessel will be gone. Then I will take him on board my steamer, and I will keep him here. His wife and daughter must come to him; they cannot be left in Yakonsk, and there is no other ship in which they can get away. On the voyage I will plead my cause; I will make everything all right. I shall have time enough to do that before we reach port. Things will be not so good as they would be otherwise; I shall have no schooner to present to my wife on her wedding day, and I may not be able to do much for Skipper Budrack and his wife, but I will do what I can; they will be my parents-in-law."

He gave orders that the *Reina de la Plata* should be again put about and headed for the schooner under full steam. He put men in the bow with life-preservers, and two boats, with their crews, were made ready to be dropped from the davits the moment the two vessels should strike.

On board the *Molly Crenshaw* there was great stir of preparation. The skipper knew that if there was to be a fight at all the steamer must make the attack, and there could be no doubt that her best method of doing so would be to ram her antagonist. Therefore, he had spent the greater part of the preceding day in preparing for that contingency. His men were now placed in suitable positions on the deck, some armed with marline-spikes, some with capstan-bars, and a few with axes.

As the Spanish steamer came rapidly on, some of the men in her bow perceived something on the schooner which they had not noticed before. She appeared to have four masts, although one of them was much shorter than the others. They spoke of the matters to each other, but did not understand it.

Among the preparations the skipper had made for the approaching fight was this apparent fourth mast, which stood about midships, and consisted of a very large and strong spare spar. Its small end had been sharpened and shod with iron, while the other rested in a heavy socket, in which it could be moved at pleasure by means of blocks and tackle.

On came the Spanish steamer, heading directly for the *Molly Crenshaw*, and aiming to strike her about midships. On she came until the bright eyes of el Capitan could be seen shining over the rail. On she came, with the men in the bow ready to throw over their life-preservers, and the men in the boats ready to drop to the water and pull for any unfortunate

American sailors who might rise to the surface after their vessel had sunk. On she came until she was within a few hundred feet of the schooner. Then, suddenly, down dropped the big spar into an almost horizontal position; it was pulled a little forward in obedience to a quick command from the skipper, and pointed directly at the steamer's starboard bow.

El Capitan saw his danger and shouted to the steersman—but it was too late; the *Reina de la Plata* could not change her course, but went straight on. As the schooner was so much lower than the steamer, the iron-shod spar struck the latter about half-way between her water-line and her rail. It crashed through her sides and ran for nearly half its length into the vessel.

The force of the concussion was so great that both vessels went dashing through the water for a considerable distance, and if the spar had not held her in position the schooner would have been capsized, even if she had received no other damage. As they moved together they naturally swung toward each other, so that when the motion had nearly ceased they were lying side by side, the spar having accommodated itself to this change in position by ripping a large hole in the wooden side of the steamer.

Now there was a great yell on board the *Reina de la Plata*, and many heads appeared above her rail.

"Stand by to repel boarders!" shouted the skipper. But before any of his men could gather around him a dozen or more Spaniards were on his deck; they jumped, they slid down ropes, they dropped like cats. Capstan bars and marline-spikes were raised high in the air, but not one of them was brought down upon the heads of the enemy, for the skipper and his men were astonished to see that the Spaniards were unarmed. As soon as they reached the deck of the schooner they took off their caps and, bowing very low, approached the skipper. More Spaniards dropped down from the larger vessel, and some of them, who could speak English, explained why they came.

They were glad to be made prisoners; they did not wish to fight the Americans; all they asked was good and sufficient food and the payment of their wages, which were now a long time in arrears. These things were not to be obtained on the Spanish ship, and they were delighted to have an opportunity to surrender.

When his men had left him, el Capitan, disheartened and with downcast visage, slowly let himself down from the side of his vessel. He was dressed with unusual care, for he had expected to act on this occasion the part of a conquering hero in the presence of his mistress, and had arrayed himself accordingly. In his earlier days he had been an accomplished horseman as well as a seaman, and as a cavalier garb was more picturesque than that of an officer of a merchant vessel, he wore a broad hat with a feather, a bright-coloured sash, and high boots, to which were attached a pair of jingling spurs. He was, perhaps, the only man who had ever fought a marine battle in spurs.

El Capitan stalked toward the skipper. "I am your prisoner," he said. "I am disgraced. I have lost everything. I have no ship; I have nothing. Now I cannot ask you for your daughter."

"You are right, there," said the skipper, with a grin; "this isn't the time nor the place for that sort of thing. But what am I to do with all these fellows of yours? I don't want them on board my schooner."

"Send them back to my ship," said el Capitan, in a sombre voice. "Send me back to join them, if you please. Cut that spar in two with axes, push away from my poor, wounded craft, and set your sails. The force of the concussion has sent everything on board my ship to starboard, and as soon as you loose yourself from her she will list, she will take in water through that great hole, she will go to the bottom—down to the bottom with me and my men, and that will be the end of us. We will trouble you no more."

"No, sir," said the skipper; "that's not my way of doing business. I have made a prize of your steamer, and I am going to keep her. The hole in her bow can be repaired, and then I shall have a good vessel. I am going to make fast to her bow and stern, and that spar will keep her on an even keel until we get into port and ground or dock her."

"Have your own way," gloomily replied el Capitan; "take her into port, exhibit me as a captive at the tail of your chariot. Nothing matters to me. The best thing I can do is to jump overboard."

"No, sir!" cried the skipper; "you are my prisoner. You belong to me. You have no right to jump overboard. If you should do that you would not be honest. After surrender it is cowardly to resign or run away."

The Spaniard put his hand upon his heart. "I have nothing left but my honour," he said; "you may trust that."

"Now, el Capitan," said the skipper, "you can see for yourself that although your ship is my prize I cannot take her into port. She must take me. My sails are no good for that purpose. Tell your engineers and firemen to go on board and get ready to steam into the harbour. You, with your engine, will tow me along, and I, with my spar, will keep you from capsizing. We will make our vessels fast fore and aft, and then we'll get under headway as soon as possible."

Side by side, like a pair of nautical Siamese twins, the schooner and the steamer slowly approached the harbour of Yakonsk, but before they were in sight of the town they were met by the little gunboat, with the Commandant on board. They lay to and the Russian boarded the schooner. When the situation was explained to him, he was very much interested.

"I am amazed," said he to the skipper. "I did not suppose you could do this. And now what is your next step?"

"I want to take my prize into your port," said Ezra, "and have her re-paired. Then I'll put a prize crew on board of her, and take her away with me."

"No, sir," said the Commandant; "the laws of neutrality forbid that!"

"But what am I to do?" exclaimed the skipper. "If I separate from her she will list to starboard and go down, and if a gale comes up while we are fastened together in this fashion we shall both be wrecked."

"I am very sorry," said the Commandant, "but all I have to do is to observe the laws of neutrality. It is a bad way to capture a vessel, but I cannot help it. The laws of neutrality must be observed. Only one of the vessels can enter the harbour of Yakonsk."

El Capitan looked down over the side of his vessel, but said nothing. His heart was heavy, and he took but little interest in what might happen next.

The skipper was angry, and vehement in his expressions. He had always disliked war, and had accepted it only when it had been thrust upon him; but at this moment he hated neutrality worse than war, and was willing to accept none of it.

The Commandant stood in deep thought, and brushed his counte-nance with his hand. "There is one thing you can do," he said, presently. "Your two vessels can proceed together as near the mouth of the har-bour as the laws of neutrality will allow. Then you can set the steamer's crew to work to shift everything movable to the port side, and when you have cut away your spar I think she will be able to steam up to the town, as the sea is tolerably smooth. Then I can set all the ship-carpenters in Yakonsk to work on her. There are a good many of them, you know, for building small vessels is the main industry of our place. And you, Mr Skipper, can cruise out here until she is repaired, after which she will leave and you can come in and join your wife and daughter."

"And how long will it take to make the repairs?" impatiently asked the skipper.

"I will put the carpenters on her as close together as they can work, inside and out, and, from what I can judge of the damage, I think they can have her ready to sail in a week."

The skipper grumbled savagely, and wished he had not captured the Spaniard, but he made up his mind that he would have to be satisfied with things as they were, and he determined, if he must cruise for a week, to sail for Petrimetkoff, and try to do a little business there. This would occupy just about a week.

The two vessels moved on toward the harbour's mouth, the great spar was cut in twain, the *Reina de la Plata* steamed slowly toward the town, and the *Molly Crenshaw* set sail for Petrimetkoff.

It was nine days and twelve hours later when Ezra Budrack's three-masted schooner arrived at the port of Yakonsk. The skipper was very late; he had been detained by unfavourable winds and the exigencies of trade; but, dark as was the night, he entered the harbour, dropped anchor, and waited for daylight. Then he went ashore, and knocked at the door of the Commandant before any of the family was up. It was not long before that high official opened the door himself, still wearing his nightcap.

"I may be a little early," said the skipper, "but you must excuse me. You know a man who has not seen his wife and daughter for nearly ten days, and at a time when everything is in such an upset condition, is naturally anxious. Can I go to Mrs Budrack?"

"Your wife and daughter!" cried the Commandant. "They are not here! They sailed away in the Spanish vessel yesterday afternoon. They were so anxious about you, when you did not return at the time you fixed, that they determined to go to Petrimetkoff and join you. If you had left there they were sure they would meet you on the way."

"Did my wife and daughter hatch up that plan?" shouted the skipper. "I don't believe a word of it! It was that wretched el Capitan! It is a scheme worthy of a crafty Spaniard! He wanted to have them on board with him! That is all he cared about! He persuaded them to go; I am as sure of it as if I had been here and heard every word that was said! But I can wait no longer. I must put on every stitch of sail I can carry and go after them. When they find I am not at Petrimetkoff I don't know where he will take them."

"No, sir!" said the Commandant; "you cannot leave this port until twenty-four hours after they sailed. The laws of neutrality demand that you remain in the harbour until five o'clock this afternoon, and as that's the case you might as well come in and take breakfast with us."

The skipper expostulated violently, but it was of no use, and he went into the house and took breakfast.

At about noon, the Commandant and the skipper were standing on the pier of the town, when they saw in the offing the smoke of a steamer. In a few minutes they descried the *Reina de la Plata* coming in under full steam. The Commandant gave a great shout.

"The unprincipled Spaniard!" he cried. "He knows he has no right to enter this harbour until he is sure your vessel is not here. I must go and stop him. He must go back and lie outside until the laws of neutrality permit you to go out to him."

What the skipper then said concerning the laws of neutrality need not be recorded here, but the air quivered with the intensity of his ejaculations. "Make him go back!" he cried. "Do you suppose I am going to let that Spaniard steam away again with my wife and daughter? I shall row out to her, and you can do what you please with your gunboat." Then he shouted for his men, but only one of them was in his boat, which lay at the pier. The others were up in the town.

The Commandant ran to his gunboat, but steam was not up in that little vessel. He gave his orders and hurried back to the pier to prevent the skipper from holding communication with the Spanish vessel.

"What do you mean?" shouted the angry Ezra, when he saw three soldiers arrive on the pier. "That's my vessel—my property. She's no Spaniard now. And she has my wife and daughter on board."

"It is my duty," said the Commandant, "and I can't help it."

"Duty!" exclaimed the skipper. "If you are so particular about duty, why did you allow her to lie here for a week to be repaired? Do you call that neutrality?"

"I don't call that anything," said the Commandant. "I know of no decree issued by my government which would prevent my giving work to the ship-carpenters of this town. As soon as steam is up on my gunboat I shall go out and make that Spaniard turn back. Confound him!" he continued, "he is coming too far, and he is about to drop anchor."

"Yes!" exclaimed the skipper, "and they are making ready to lower a boat. Perhaps my wife and daughter will come ashore!"

"They shall not do it!" roared the Commandant. "There shall be no communication. O that my gunboat were under steam! I would sink that little boat. It is making directly for the pier."

"You'd better not try that," cried the skipper. "That would be a worse breach of neutrality than anything that has been mentioned yet. But mind you, Mr Commandant, that steamer does not leave this port until I get my wife and daughter. If I can't hinder it any other way I'll sink my schooner across the mouth of the harbour."

The Commandant paid very little attention to these words. The boat from the *Reina de la Plata* was approaching rapidly. El Capitan sat in the stern, and as he came nearer it was seen that his face was beaming.

"Keep off!" shouted the Commandant. "Don't try to land here, or——"

El Capitan may have been deaf with excitement, but, whether this was the case or not, he was standing on the pier in less than a minute after the Commandant had shouted to him.

"This is intolerable," said the Russian, advancing. "The laws of neutrality forbid communication——"

"Down with the laws of neutrality!" shouted el Capitan. "I trample them under my feet! I have nothing to do with them!"

The countenance of the Commandant bristled with rage. "Nothing to do with the laws of neutrality?" he yelled. "I will show you——"

"Ha!" cried el Capitan. "You cannot show me anything. To be neutral there must be enemies; to enforce neutrality there must be war. There is no war, therefore there is no neutrality. Peace has been proclaimed between the Spaniards and the Americans. I have the news. I got this Russian newspaper from a steamer I spoke, bound for Petrimetkoff, and I immediately put back here at full speed, Mr Budrack, because I wanted the Commandant to know everything in case you should arrive without my sighting you, which you did."

During this speech the skipper stood amazed. The war ended! Peace! What complications did this news bring with it! He wanted to row out to his wife and daughter, but he must wait and find out how matters stood. The Commandant had been reading an account of the peace protocol, and he now translated it into English for the skipper.

"Well?" said the Commandant, looking at el Capitan.

"It is well," said the Spaniard, "very well. There is no war; I am no longer a prisoner. There is no war, and my ship is no longer a prize."

"Stop there!" shouted the skipper. "I don't agree to that."

"But you must agree," said el Capitan. "Your prize has not been adjudicated to you, and I am sure no court would give it to you now."

"He is right," said the Commandant. "I am afraid he is right. But tell me this," said he, addressing the skipper: "if that ship is not your prize, who is going to pay the ship-carpenters for her repairs?"

It was el Capitan who made answer. "I do not know," he said, shaking his head; "but one thing is certain: I ordered no repairs."

"And I would not have had them made if you had ordered them," said the Commandant. "I do not believe you have any money. I set those carpenters to work because you ordered it, Mr Budrack."

"But if it is not my prize," said the skipper, "what had I to do with it, then, and what have I to do with it now?"

"Gentlemen," said el Capitan, "do not let us dispute about who shall pay those wretched carpenters. Do not let us give them a thought when there are so many joyful things to talk about. It is right that you should know, sir," he said, turning to the skipper, "because you are her father. And you, sir," to the Commandant, "because you are the chief official of the place, and there may be constitutional laws which would compel you to make some kind of a legal entry."

"We have no constitution, as I told you," said the Commandant; "but we have laws which compel the payment of mechanics."

"What are you talking about?" cried Ezra to el Capitan.

"It is this," answered the Spaniard. "When I took your wife and daughter on board the *Reina de la Plata* I considered their wishes as commands. I was a prisoner; I belonged to the husband of the one and the father of the other. The steamer was his property—I remembered my position. I said no word to them of what was in my heart. But this morning when I heard that I was free, that I stood on the deck of a vessel of which I was commander, then all was changed. I had a right to say what I pleased, and I told your daughter that I loved her. I will not speak of the details, but she accepted me, and my soul immediately floated as bravely as that proud flag of Spain you see upon my vessel."

"And her mother?" inquired the skipper. "What did she do?"

"She shed tears," replied el Capitan, "but I am sure they were tears of joy. She said she did not believe you would allow your daughter, sir, to wed an enemy, but she was sure you would not object to an alliance with the subject of a friendly power."

The skipper made no further remark, but got into his boat and was rowed to the steamer.

El Capitan, being a man of discretion, did not go to the vessel until half an hour later. The skipper met him at the rail.

"I have settled the whole matter," said Ezra. "I expected you to marry my daughter because my wife had made up her mind that it should be so. If your ship had been my prize I had intended to sell the *Molly Crenshaw*, and we would all have sailed on the *Reina*, because, in these days, a steamer is better for trading than any three-masted schooner, no matter how good she may be. Things are changed, but I shall still carry out my plan. I shall sell my schooner, and buy the steamer, if your owners will act reasonably about it. And then, of course, I will pay for the repairs, and I suppose I must settle the back wages of the sailors, if I expect to keep them."

That evening the three Budracks and el Capitan dined with the Commandant and his family. They spent a pleasant evening, and when they had returned to their schooner the skipper and his wife sat up for awhile in their little cabin, to talk over matters and things.

"This has all turned out very well for Drusilla and el Capitan," said Mrs Budrack, "but if we sell the *Molly Crenshaw* we shall lose a very pleasant home."

"Yes," said Ezra. "I don't suppose that Spanish steamer can be made to take her place as far as our comfort goes."

"And it may end," she continued, "in our buying a house on shore, somewhere, and living there. I don't believe el Capitan will be wanting us to be sailing about with him all the time."

"No," said Ezra, "and I don't believe we would like it, either."

"The Commandant was in a very good humour to-night," remarked Mrs Budrack. "He seemed to think it a fine thing for the town that his ship-carpenters had such a good job."

"Oh, yes," said Ezra, "I don't wonder he was pleased; but if I had known I should have to pay for that hole I made in that Spanish vessel, I would not have punched it."

"And listen to those sailors," said Mrs Budrack, "over there on the steamer. They are all singing. I expect it's the thought that they are going to get their back-wages that makes them so happy."

"Yes," said Ezra, somewhat dolefully, "and from what el Capitan told me this evening, some of their wages must be a long time in arrears. It will be a pretty heavy drain on me, but as that's going to be my ship, and as el Capitan is going to be my son-in-law, I suppose I've got to pay them, and make things square for him and Drusilla."

Mrs Budrack reflected for a moment. "Now, Ezra," said she, "let me tell you something. The next time you get mixed up in a war I'd advise you to get on the side that's beaten, or else on the side that's bound to preserve the laws of neutrality. It doesn't pay to conquer."

HIGH–WATER MARK[1]

Francis Bret Harte

(1839–1902)

WHEN the tide was out on the Dedlow Marsh its extended dreariness was patent. Its spongy, low-lying surface, sluggish, inky pools, and tortuous sloughs, twisting their slimy way, eel-like, toward the open bay, were all hard facts. So were the few green tussocks, with their scant blades, their amphibious flavour, and unpleasant dampness. And if you choose to indulge your fancy,—although the flat monotony of the Dedlow Marsh was not inspiring,—the wavy line of scattered drift gave an unpleasant consciousness of the spent waters, and made the dead certainty of the returning tide a gloomy reflection, which no present sunshine could dissipate. The greener meadow-land seemed oppressed with this idea, and made no positive attempt at vegetation until the work of reclamation should be complete. In the bitter fruit of the low cranberry-bushes one might fancy he detected a naturally sweet disposition curdled and soured by an injudicious course of too much regular cold water.

The vocal expression of the Dedlow Marsh was also melancholy and depressing. The sepulchral boom of the bittern, the shriek of the curlew, the scream of passing brent, the wrangling of quarrelsome teal, the sharp, querulous protest of the startled crane, and syllabled complaint of the "killdeer" plover, were beyond the power of written expression. Nor was the aspect of these mournful fowls at all cheerful and inspiring. Certainly not the blue heron standing mid-leg deep in the water, obviously catching cold in a reckless disregard of wet feet and consequences; nor the mournful curlew, the dejected plover, or the low-spirited snipe, who saw fit to join him in his suicidal contemplation; nor the impassive kingfisher—an ornithological Marius—reviewing the desolate expanse; nor the black raven that went to and fro over the face of the marsh continually, but evidently couldn't make up his mind whether the waters had subsided, and felt low-spirited in the reflection that, after all this trouble, he wouldn't be able to give a definite answer. On the contrary, it was evident at a glance that the dreary expanse of Dedlow Marsh told unpleasantly on the birds, and that the season of migration was looked forward to with a feeling of relief and satisfaction by the full-grown, and of extravagant anticipation by the callow, brood. But if Dedlow Marsh was cheerless at the slack of the low tide, you

[1]From *The Luck of Roaring Camp and Other Stories.*

should have seen it when the tide was strong and full; when the damp air blew chilly over the cold, glittering expanse, and came to the faces of those who looked seaward like another tide; when a steel-like glint marked the low hollows and the sinuous line of slough; when the great shell-incrusted trunks of fallen trees arose again, and went forth on their dreary, purposeless wanderings, drifting hither and thither, but getting no farther toward any goal at the falling tide or the day's decline than the cursed Hebrew in the legend; when the glossy ducks swung silently, making neither ripple nor furrow on the shimmering surface; when the fog came in with the tide and shut out the blue above, even as the green below had been obliterated; when boatmen, lost in that fog, paddling about in a hopeless way, started at what seemed the brushing of mermen's fingers on the boat's keel, or shrank from the tufts of grass spreading around like the floating hair of a corpse, and knew by these signs that they were lost upon Dedlow Marsh, and must make a night of it, and a gloomy one at that,—then you might know something of Dedlow Marsh at high water.

Let me recall a story connected with this latter view which never failed to recur to my mind in my long gunning excursions upon Dedlow Marsh. Although the event was briefly recorded in the county paper, I had the story, in all its eloquent detail, from the lips of the principal actor. I cannot hope to catch the varying emphasis and peculiar colouring of feminine delineation, for my narrator was a woman; but I'll try to give at least its substance.

She lived midway of the great slough of Dedlow Marsh and a good-sized river, which debouched four miles beyond into an estuary formed by the Pacific Ocean, on the long sandy peninsula which constituted the south-western boundary of a noble bay. The house in which she lived was a small frame cabin raised from the marsh a few feet by stout piles, and was three miles distant from the settlements upon the river. Her husband was a logger,—a profitable business in a county where the principal occupation was the manufacture of lumber.

It was the season of early spring, when her husband left on the ebb of a high tide, with a raft of logs for the usual transportation to the lower end of the bay. As she stood by the door of the little cabin when the voyagers departed she noticed a cold look in the south-eastern sky, and she remembered hearing her husband say to his companions that they must endeavour to complete their voyage before the coming of the south-westerly gale which he saw brewing. And that night it began to storm and blow harder than she had ever before experienced, and some great trees fell in the forest by the river, and the house rocked like her baby's cradle.

But, however the storm might roar about the little cabin, she knew that one she trusted had driven bolt and bar with his own strong hand, and that had he feared for her he would not have left her. This, and her domestic duties, and the care of her little sickly baby, helped to keep her mind from dwelling on the weather, except, of course, to hope that he was safely harboured with the logs at Utopia in the dreary distance. But she noticed that day, when she went out to feed the chickens and look after the cow, that the tide was up to the little fence of their garden-patch, and the roar of the surf on the south beach, though miles away, she could hear distinctly. And she began to think that she would like to have some one to talk with about matters, and she believed that if it had not been so far and so stormy, and the trail so impassable, she would have taken the baby and have gone over to Ryckman's, her nearest neighbour. But then, you see, he might have returned in the storm, all wet, with no one to see to him; and it was a long exposure for baby, who was croupy and ailing.

But that night, she never could tell why, she didn't feel like sleeping or even lying down. The storm had somewhat abated, but she still "sat and sat," and even tried to read. I don't know whether it was a Bible or some profane magazine that this poor woman read, but most probably the latter, for the words all ran together and made such sad nonsense that she was forced at last to put the book down and turn to that dearer volume which lay before her in the cradle, with its white initial leaf yet unsoiled, and ry to look forward to its mysterious future. And, rocking the cradle, she thought of everything and everybody, but still was wide awake as ever.

It was nearly twelve o'clock when she at last laid down in her clothes. How long she slept she could not remember, but she awoke with a dreadful choking in her throat, and found herself standing, trembling all over, in the middle of the room, with her baby clasped to her breast, and she was "saying something." The baby cried and sobbed, and she walked up and down trying to hush it, when she heard a scratching at the door. She opened it fearfully, and was glad to see it was only old Pete, their dog, who crawled, dripping with water, into the room. She would like to have looked out, not in the faint hope of her husband's coming, but to see how things looked; but the wind shook the door so savagely that she could hardly hold it. Then she sat down a little while, and then she lay down again a little while. Lying close by the wall of the little cabin, she thought she heard once or twice something scrape slowly against the clapboards, like the scraping of branches. Then there was a little gurgling sound, "like the baby made when it was swallowing"; then something went "click-click" and "cluck-cluck," so that she sat up in bed. When she did so she was attracted by something else that seemed creeping from the back door towards the centre of the room. It wasn't much wider than her little finger, but soon it swelled to the width of her hand, and began spreading all over the floor. It was water.

She ran to the front door and threw it wide open, and saw nothing but water. She ran to the back door and threw it open, and saw nothing but water. She ran to the side window, and, throwing that open, she saw nothing but water. Then she remembered hearing her husband once say that there was no danger in the tide, for that fell regularly, and people could calculate on it, and that he would rather live near the bay than the river, whose banks might overflow at any time. But was it the tide? So she ran again to the back door, and threw out a stick of wood. It drifted away towards the bay. She scooped up some of the water and put it eagerly to her lips. It was fresh and sweet. It was the river, and not the tide!

It was then—oh, God be praised for His goodness! she did neither faint nor fall; it was then—blessed be the Saviour, for it was His merciful hand that touched and strengthened her in this awful moment—that fear dropped from her like a garment, and her trembling ceased. It was then and thereafter that she never lost her self-command, through all the trials of that gloomy night.

She drew the bedstead towards the middle of the room, and placed a table upon it, and on that she put the cradle. The water on the floor was already over her ankles, and the house once or twice moved so perceptibly, and seemed to be racked so, that the closet doors all flew open. Then she heard the same rasping and thumping against the wall, and looking out, saw that a large up-rooted tree, which had lain near the road at the upper end of the pasture, had floated down to the house. Luckily its long roots dragged in the soil and kept it from moving as rapidly as the current, for had it struck the house in its full career, even the strong nails and bolts in the piles could not have withstood the shock. The hound had leaped upon its knotty surface, and crouched near the roots shivering and whining. A ray of hope flashed across her mind. She drew a heavy blanket from the bed, and, wrapping it about the babe, waded in the deepening waters to the door. As the tree swung again, broadside on, making the little cabin creak and tremble, she leaped on to its trunk. By God's mercy she succeeded in obtaining a footing on its slippery surface, and, twining an arm about its roots, she held in the other her moaning child. Then something cracked near the front porch, and the whole front of the house she had just quitted fell forward,—just as cattle fall on their knees before they lie down,—and at the same moment the great redwood-tree swung round and drifted away with its living cargo into the black night.

For all the excitement and danger, for all her soothing of her crying babe, for all the whistling of the wind, for all the uncertainty of her situation, she still turned to look at the deserted and water-swept cabin. She remembered even then, and she wonders how foolish she was to think of it at that time, that she wished she had put on another dress and the baby's best clothes; and she kept praying that the house would be spared so that he, when he returned, would have something to come to, and it wouldn't be quite so desolate, and—how could he ever know what had become of her and baby? And at the thought she grew sick and faint. But she had something else to do besides worrying, for whenever the long roots of her ark struck an obstacle, the whole trunk made half a revolution, and twice dipped her in the black water. The hound, who kept distracting her by running up and down the tree and howling, at last fell off at one of these collisions. He swam for some time beside her, and she tried to get the poor beast upon the tree, but he "acted silly" and wild, and at last she lost sight of him for ever. Then she and her baby were left alone. The light which had burned for a few minutes in the deserted cabin was quenched suddenly. She could not then tell whether she was drifting. The outline of the white dunes on the peninsula showed dimly ahead, and she judged the tree was moving in a line with the river. It must be about slack water, and she had probably reached the eddy formed by the confluence of the tide and the overflowing waters of the river. Unless the tide fell soon, there was present danger of her drifting to its channel, and being carried out to sea or crushed in the floating drift. That peril averted, if she were carried out on the ebb toward the bay, she might hope to strike one of the wooded promontories of the peninsula, and rest till daylight. Sometimes she thought she heard voices and shouts from the river, and the bellowing of cattle and bleating of sheep. Then again it was only the ringing in her ears and throbbing of her heart. She found at about this time that she was so chilled and stiffened in her cramped position that she could scarcely move, and the baby cried so when she put it to her breast that she noticed the milk refused to flow; and she was so frightened at that, that she put her head under her shawl, and for the first time cried bitterly.

When she raised her head again, the boom of the surf was behind her, and she knew that her ark had again swung round. She dipped up the water to cool her parched throat, and found that it was salt as her tears. There was a relief, though, for by this sign she knew that she was drifting with the tide. It was then the wind went down, and the great and awful silence oppressed her. There was scarcely a ripple against the furrowed sides of the great trunk on which she rested, and around her all was black gloom and quiet. She spoke to the baby just to hear herself speak, and to know that she had not lost her voice. She thought then,—it was queer, but she could not help thinking it,—how awful must have been the night when the great ship swung over the Asiatic peak, and the sounds of creation were blotted out from the world. She thought, too, of mariners clinging to spars, and of poor women who were lashed to rafts, and beaten to death by the cruel sea. She tried to thank God that she was thus spared, and lifted her eyes from the baby, who had fallen into a fretful sleep. Suddenly, away to the southward, a great light lifted itself out of the gloom, and flashed and flickered, and flickered and flashed again. Her heart fluttered quickly against the baby's cold cheek. It was the lighthouse at the entrance of the bay. As she was yet wondering, the tree suddenly rolled a little, dragged a little, and then seemed to lie quiet and still. She put out her hand and the current gurgled against it. The tree was aground, and, by the position of the light and the noise of the surf, aground upon the Dedlow Marsh.

Had it not been for her baby, who was ailing and croupy, had it not been for the sudden drying up of that sensitive fountain, she would have felt safe and relieved. Perhaps it was this which tended to make all her impressions mournful and gloomy. As the tide rapidly fell, a great flock of black brent fluttered by her, screaming and crying. Then the plover flew up and piped mournfully, as they wheeled around the trunk, and at last fearlessly lit upon it like a grey cloud. Then the heron flew over and around her, shrieking and protesting, and at last dropped its gaunt legs only a few yards from her. But, strangest of all, a pretty white bird, larger than a dove,—like a pelican, but not a pelican—circled around and around her. At last it lit upon a rootlet of the tree, quite over her shoulder. She put out her hand and stroked its beautiful white neck, and it never appeared to move. It stayed there so long that she thought she would lift up the baby to see it, and try to attract her attention. But when she did so, the child was so chilled and cold, and had such a blue look under the little lashes which it didn't raise at all, that she screamed aloud and the bird flew away, and she fainted.

Well, that was the worst of it, and perhaps it was not so much, after all, to any but herself. For when she recovered her senses it was bright sunlight, and dead low water. There was a confused noise of guttural voices about her, and an old squaw, singing an Indian "hushaby," and rocking herself from side to side before a fire built on the Marsh, before which she, the recovered wife and mother, lay weak and weary. Her first thought was for her baby, and she was about to speak, when a young squaw, who must have been a mother herself, fathomed her thought and brought her the "mowitch," pale but living, in such a queer little willow cradle all bound up, just like the squaw's own young one, that she laughed and cried together, and the young squaw and the old squaw showed their big white teeth and glinted their black eyes and said, "Plenty get well, skeena mowitch," "wagee man come plenty soon," and she could have kissed their brown faces in her joy. And then she found that they had been gathering berries on the marsh in their queer, comical baskets, and saw the skirt of her gown fluttering on the tree from afar, and the old squaw couldn't resist the temptation of procuring a new garment, and came down and discovered the "wagee" woman and child. And of course she gave the garment to the old squaw, as you may imagine, and when *he* came at last and rushed up to her, looking about ten years older in his anxiety, she felt so faint again that they had to carry her to the canoe. For, you see, he knew nothing about the flood until he met the Indians at Utopia, and knew by the signs that the poor woman was his wife. And at the next high-tide he towed the tree away back home, although it wasn't worth the trouble, and built another house, using the old tree for the foundation and props, and called it after her, "Mary's Ark!" But you may guess the next house was built above High-water Mark. And that's all.

Not much, perhaps, considering the malevolent capacity of the Dedlow Marsh. But you must tramp over it at low water, or paddle over it at high tide, or get lost upon it once or twice in the fog, as I have, to understand properly Mary's adventure, or to appreciate duly the blessing of living beyond High-water Mark.

THE DEVIL AT SEA[1]

Henry van Dyke

(1852–   )

THIS is a true tale of Holland in war-time. But it is not a military story. It is a story of the sea—

> The opaline, the plentiful and strong—

likewise the perilous.

I

In the quaint Dutch village of Oudwyk, on the shore of the North Sea, lived the widow Anny Minderop with her sons. In her girlhood she had been a school-teacher, and had married Karl Minderop, the handsome skipper of a fishing smack. Her husband was lost in a storm on the Dogger Bank; but he left her two boys, a little brick cottage, and a small sum of money invested in Dutch East India bonds. The income from these she doubled by turning her cottage into a modest tea-and-coffee house for the service of travellers by "fiets" or automobile, who "biked" or motored from The Hague, or Leyden, or Haarlem, to see the picturesque village with its ancient, high-shouldered church and its *koepeltje*, commanding a wide view over the ragged dunes and the long smooth beach.

The tea-house, with its gaily painted door and window-shutters, was set in a tiny, exuberant garden on the edge of the sand-hills, looking out across the tulip-flooded flatlands towards Haarlem, whose huge church of St Bavo dominated the level landscape like a mountain.

The drinkables provided by Mevrouw Minderop for her transient guests were cheering, and she had secret recipes for honey-cake and jam roly-poly of an incredible excellence. The fame of her neatness, her

---

[1]From *The Golden Key*. Reprinted by permission of Charles Scribner's Sons.

amiability, and her superior cookery spread abroad quietly among the *intelligentsia* in such matters. There was no publicity, no advertising except a little placard over the garden-gate, with WELTEVREDEN in gilt letters on a bright blue ground. But there was a steady trickle of patrons, and business was good enough to keep the house going.

I fell into the afternoon habit of riding out from my office in The Hague when work was slack, to have a cup of tea, a roly-poly, and perhaps a tiny glass of anisette with my pipe. These creature comforts were mildly spiced by talks with the plump widow in my stumbling Dutch, or her careful creaking English.

She always reminded me of the epitaph—in an Irish church I think— which recorded of a certain lady that "she was bland, passionate, and deeply religious, and worked beautifully in crewels." Anny Minderop was a Calvinist of the straitest sect, but distinctly of the Martha-type. She did not allow her faith in the absolute foreordination of all events to interfere with her anxious care in the baking of honey-cake and the brewing of tea and coffee.

The passionate element of her nature was centred on her two boys, who were rapidly growing to be equal to one man. He was a two-sided man. Karel, the older, was a brown-haired fleshy youth, with slow movements and a deep-rooted love of gardening. He had already found a good place with a tulip-grower in Oudwyk-Binnen. Klaas was a tow-headed, blue-eyed lad about thirteen years old, sturdy in figure, rather stolid in manner, but full of adventure. He dreamed of more exciting things than the growing of bulbs. He had the blood of old Tasman and Heemskerck in his veins. The sea had cast her spell upon him. He was determined to be a sailor, a fisherman, an explorer, a captain; and ultimately, of course, in his dreams he saw himself an admiral, or at least a rear-admiral—a *schout-bij-nacht*, as the Dutch picturesquely call it.

"Little Mother," he would say, "didn't Holland win her glory from the sea?"

"Yes, sonny," she would answer, "but it cost her dear. Many brave Dutch bones sleep under the waters."

"What difference? It's as good sleeping under the waters as in the wormy dust of the graveyard. A man must die some time."

"But you're not a man yet. You're only a boy. It is foolish to risk losing your life before you've got it."

"I've got it already, mother. Look how big and strong I am for my age. None of the boys can throw me; and Skipper Houthof says I can tie all the sailor's knots. You don't want me to waste all that sticking bulbs in the ground and waiting for 'em to grow."

"Gardening is a good business, sonny; it was the first that God gave to man. It is safe and quiet. It is just reaping the fruit of His bounty."

"Yes, but the Bible says that they that go down to the sea in ships behold His wonders in the deep. I'd rather see one wonder than raise a million tulips. Och, mammy dear, let me be a sailor."

"But how are you going to do it? Nobody wants a boy."

"Mother dear, I'll tell you. Skipper Houthof is going to sail in his new lugger *Zeehond*, June fifth, for the herring-fishing. He's got a great crew—those big Diepen brothers, very strong men, elders in the kirk, and the two brothers Wynkoop, and little Piet Vos, and old Steenis, and Beekman, Groen, and Bruin who always go together, and Brouwer— those are all good Christians, you know, always go to the meeting and sing hymns. The skipper is taking young Arie Bok—you know that nice boy in our school—just my age—as cabin boy—says he'll take me too. Won't you please let me go?"

"That would make just thirteen on the ship," said the widow, who had been counting her crochet-stitches.

"Yes, but what difference? You always told me not to have these by-beliefs."

"That is right. Yet old customs sometimes have good reasons. You must let me weigh it over in my mind, Klaas; to-morrow I will tell you."

The boy went out of the room, and the widow Minderop turned to me as I sat smoking and thinking.

"It is hard to decide," she said. "Skipper Houthof is a good man, though he's young for his place. Those big Diepen brothers are fine seamen, none better; they're God-fearing men, too, though they shout too loud in meeting, and sometimes they drink too much old *Jenever* and make trouble in the village. But it isn't the captain and the crew I'm afraid of. It's the sea—the hungry sea that took my lad's father."

"Well," I answered, "it surely is hard to decide for others; not easy even to decide for ourselves. Perhaps it is just as well that in the long run a Wiser Person decides what will happen to us. Your Klaas is a good boy, and this seems to be a good crew. When a lad is in love with the sea, you may hold him back for a while, but the only possible way to cure him is to let him try it—and even that doesn't always work. Perhaps it ought not to. It is in God's hand—the sea also is His."

"I believe it," she answered, "but it is a strain on my faith, when I remember——"

II

The fifth of June came around in due season. The sturdy *Zeehond*, spick and span with her new rigging, fresh paint, brown sails, nets neatly stowed under tarpaulin, rowboats on deck, lay with the rest of the herring fleet in the small stone-walled haven, easily the queen of the fleet. Flags and streamers fluttered in the light breeze; the stone walls were lined with people, chattering, singing, and shouting huzzah. As the little ships began to stir some one struck up a hymn. The loudest singers were the big Diepen brothers, tall, heavily built, masterful men. Their light grey eyes shone under heavy brows in their tanned faces, like lustrous shells in a tangle of brown seaweed. They shouted the familiar tune an octave below the key.

Some of the crowd were weeping. There is something like a wedding in the sailing of a ship; it draws tears from the sentimental.

But Anny Minderop was not crying. She wanted her eyes clear to see the last of her boy Klaas. She wanted her silk handkerchief dry to wave to him as he leaned over the *hakkebord*, looking back.

Nothing could have been more fair and promising than the departure of the herring fleet that year. It is true that the green-grey expanse of water which is called in Germany the German Ocean, and elsewhere the North Sea, is always harsh and treacherous, often covered with danger-hiding fog, and sometimes swept by insane tempests. It is true also that in the gruesome war-time the perils of the deep were increased by German submarines and floating mines. For these the cautious Captain Houthof kept a sharp look-out. But the big Diepen brothers, and under their influence the rest of the crew, recked little of these uncharted dangers. Their mind was on the fishing and the profits to follow. A typical Dutchman faces a risk calmly if there is a chance of good gain behind it.

The reports from the fishing banks were all encouraging. The fish were already there, and coming in abundantly. They could be seen on the surface, milling around in vast circles, as if baby whirlwinds were lightly passing over the water. It was going to be a great catch for the *Zeehond*, predicted the Diepens. God was on their side, this time. He was going to make them rich if they obeyed Him.

"Even you," said the giant Simon, clapping the boy Klaas on the shoulder with a hand like a baked ham, "even you, my young one, shall carry home a pocketful of gulden to your mother, if you are good and say your prayers every day."

The boy stood as stiff as he could under the heavy caress and thanked the big man, who seemed to be really fond of him.

So far as I was able to learn afterwards, the voyage went splendidly for about three weeks. Weather fair; fishing fine; eighty tons of herring; everybody working hard and cheerful. Klaas and Arie wore their fingers sore hauling and mending the nets. The salt stung them fiercely. But it was great fun. They ate like pigs and slept like logs. Simon Diepen never would let them go to sleep without saying their prayers. The tone of the lugger was a compound of fervent piety, tense work, and high good humour. Even if the other men had wanted to slacken on the piety, the Diepens would not allow it. By their bigness, their strength, and their masterful ways they bossed the ship, including the young captain. Little Piet Vos followed them like a dog. He looked on them as Apostles. The rest of the crew stood in awe, and if they sinned at all, were careful to do it out of sight and hearing of the devout giants.

With the fourth week of the voyage came a strange alteration in the luck. Weather grew cold, rough, foggy, dangerous. Fish became scarce and hard to catch. Worst of all, the gin, of which a liberal supply had been provided for daily use, gave out entirely. The Diepens, who were heavy drinkers but always steady on their legs, felt the lack more than they knew. They grew nervous, moody, quick-tempered, overbearing. They brooded over the Bible, and said there was something wrong with the *Zeehond;* God's judgment followed her for sin.

One evening in a billowing fog the lugger ran close to a mass of wreckage from some lost ship. Entangled in it were two wooden cases. The Diepens pulled them aboard, and took them down below to open them. No one dared dispute their right. They found the cases full of bottles, one of which they uncorked. It was a strange liquor, but it looked, and smelled, and tasted like dark gin. It made them feel at home. The second bottle added to this effect. The third and fourth bottles they took up to the skipper.

"Look, captain," they said very solemnly, "here is a proof that we are not yet castaways. God has warned us. Now if we repent and put away our sins, He will spare us. But we must pray hard and do His will."

Then they went below and opened another bottle. But before it was finished they fell asleep, with the Bible open between them at the Book of Revelation.

In the morning grey they came on deck and Piet Vos followed them. The skipper was taking a turn at the wheel. All three of the men seemed steady on their legs, but their eyes were wild. Simon lifted up his face and began to talk with God. The skipper said he could not hear the words, but he heard the trombone voice in which God answered. Then Simon came up close, and said:

"I am Christ. God has just told me that I must clean the Devil out of this ship. He is here, in the things, in the men, especially in that damned old helmsman, Steenis. You can see the Devil looking out of his eyes."

"But what will you do?" asked the skipper. "Have a care! We must answer for everything."

"I have no care," said Simon, "but to do what God tells me. You must follow. Men will judge us, but our conscience will be clean. My brother Jan and Piet Vos heard God speak to me. The ship must be cleaned. Do not interfere, or the Devil will get you too."

Simon went on his heel and went below. From that moment on the lugger a fatal insanity reigned and a superstitious cowardice trembled before it.

Just what happened on the doomed vessel will never be fully known. A week later a Norwegian steamship picked up the *Zeehond,* drifting helpless on the water. Three men were missing; mast and rigging, gear and boats, all gone; deck and forecastle smeared with blood; she was a gruesome floating ruin. The Norwegian towed her into Hull.

'The big Diepens, Piet Vos, and two others were sent to Holland in a fast steamer. The skipper and four others were brought on a slower boat, not yet in.

The general outline of the tragedy had been printed promptly in the newspapers. But I wanted to know the particulars. What happened to the two boys? Was my blue-eyed friend Klaas safe? How had he been affected by his first adventure at sea?

III

The summer day brightened and gloomed in the sky as I wheeled along the beach toward Oudwyk and the cottage Weltevreden.

"Well contented" the name means. It is much used for houses great and small in Holland, and represents one aspect of the Dutch character. Would Mevrouw Minderop be so well contented now, after this tragedy? Or would her calm be broken, as the July afternoon threatened to break under the heavy thunder-clouds looming in the west?

After I had passed the populous bathing-station of Scheveningen the coast stretched before me in long monotony. On the right rose the dunes; steep banks and hillocks, yellowish grey on their face, crested above with rusty shrubs and tufts of wire-grass, like the wisps of hair on an old man's head. Under my wheel crunched the ashen sand of the desolate beach; bare of life, empty even of beautiful shells; tossed and tormented by the fitful wind in the dry places; corroded and wrinkled in the damp places by the waves, which advanced menacing and roaring, spread out, and then withdrew whispering, as if they conspired some day to conquer and overwhelm, this low-lying, rich, obstinate land of dikes and dunes. On the left the North Sea brooded; pallid, *verdâtre*, like the rust on copper; a curious, envious, discontented sea, darkened by black cloud shadows, lit suddenly and strangely by vivid streaks of light like signals of danger, fading on the horizon into the grey mist and leaden clouds.

What wonder that the Hollanders, facing ever this menace and mystery of seeping tides and swelling billows that threaten to rob them of their hard-won land, have developed the stubborn courage, the dour pertinacity that mark their race? What wonder that on the other side, having thus far won the victory of resistance to wild waters and foreign tyrants, they are at times extravagantly merry, full of loud laughter and song, the best fighters and feasters in the world? Look at the brave gaiety of Franz Hals' *Arquebusiers* or Van der Helst's *Banquet of the Target Company*.

When I pushed my bicycle up one of the sandy tracks that lead inland, I found myself in another, and to my eyes pleasanter, world. The sea was hidden, for the most part, by the crest of the dunes. The hills and hollows lay around me in green confusion. Mosses and trailing vines covered the ground. Clumps of pine-trees, clusters of oaks, thickets of birch and alder, were scattered here and there. Larks warbled from the sky; wrens and finches sang in the copse; rabbits scuttled into the thick bushes. It was a little wilderness, but no desert.

Presently the outlying houses of Oudwyk appeared, and at last the red gable and blue gate of Weltevreden, sitting quiet in its gay little garden. Roses and lilies, geraniums and fuchsias portioned the light into many colours by the secret alchemy of flowers. The reseda sweetened the air with its clean scent. The place was a monument of the skill and care with which man makes the best of Nature's gifts.

Within, the widow Minderop sat at her crochet-work in the tea-room. The uncertain weather had hindered other guests. She rose from her chair, dropping her work, and came to meet me with unusual eagerness.

"Yes, mynheer," she cried as if there were only one subject worthy of speech, "my Klaas is safe. God has delivered him from the sea and from those wicked men. I have a telegram from him. He is coming home to-day. Och, how I hanker to see him, to know really how he is."

A moment later the door opened and the boy came in; tanned, weather-beaten, a bit the worse for wear, but stark and sound as ever. Only his face was older, as if he had lived through years. He embraced his mother with boyish affection, saluted me with grave friendliness, and then sat down at the table to partake of coffee with unlimited honey-cakes and rolls.

At our request he began to unfold the story of his weird adventure. Reluctantly at first, and with some interruptions, (which I leave out,) he told what had happened on the lugger, and how it had struck him.

"In the beginning," he said, "it was splendid. The weather was good. The *Zeehond* is a great ship. She rides over the waves like a water-fowl. None of them could smash her. The fishing was lucky. Everybody was in a good humour. Och, mother, the sea is just wonderful, I just love it.

"I don't know how long it was before the change came. The fishing petered out; the gin—you know how much those big Diepens drink—was all gone. They got cross and grumpy and angry at nothing. They sang and prayed more than ever; but it sounded to me as if they were not praying *to* God so much as *at* some one that they hated on the ship.

"Mother, that's an awful thing—to hear men pray *at* people instead of *to* God! It scared me. What if God should overhear them?

"Then, after four or five days, those Diepens fished up two boxes out of the sea, and took them below. They were full of strange liquor, and Simon and Jan began to drink again, more than ever. But the drink did not make them cheerful and friendly. It made them black and sour and full of wickedness.

"Something happened on deck in the morning, before I was up. Simon told how God had spoken to him, and said that 'he was Christ our Saviour, and that there were devils in the ship, and that Simon must clean them out, by hook or by crook, no matter what it cost, no matter who got hurt. That was what our Saviour did on earth.'

"But, mother, when Christ was here many people who had devils came to Him and He *never* hurt one of them. He was kind to them. He delivered them. He made them well. That is why I was sure that it could not be the spirit of Jesus who entered into Simon. It was the big Devil himself who came in with pride and anger and strong drink.

"But Jan believed what Simon said because he was like him. And Piet Vos believed because he was Simon's little hound. And the skipper thought he had heard God's voice speaking to Simon; but he was really just plain scared because the Diepens were so big and strong and fierce. The rest of the crew were scared too, except three men. These were the ones that Simon said had devils because he hated them.

"The first was old Steenis the helmsman. He wouldn't give in to the Diepens at all. He said they were just crazy. So Jan and Simon fell on him at the wheel; cracked his head open with a belaying pin so that the blood and brains spilled on the deck; and threw him into the sea.

"Och, mother, it was frightful. Arie Bok and I were scared sick. But inside I was not afraid. I remembered what you told me about God taking care of us if we try to do right, and I thought that a real Hollander ought never to *show* that he's afraid anyhow.

"Why didn't we do something to stop the butchery? But what could we do? If we had stood up against those big, beastly men, they would have laughed, and snapped us in two like a pipe-stem. All we could do was to cry, and beg them to stop, and say our prayers, and keep as far as we could from the bloody work.

"The next two that were killed were Beekman and Brouwer. They were quiet men, kind of dull and stupid. But Simon said they had devils —dumb devils, he called them. So he made them dance on the deck for about an hour to shake the devils out.

"But Simon and Jan and little Piet said the dancing was bad—Devil-dancing, they called it; no good at all. So they drove poor old Beekman and Brouwer down below, and bashed their heads in with iron bars, and cut their breasts open with knives to let the devils loose. Then they dragged the bodies on deck, all bloody, and threw them into the sea. While they were doing this all of them sang a hymn.

"Mother, it made me so sick, I thought I was going to die.

"The next day they set to work on the ship. They said it was poisoned by the devils and must be cleansed all over. So they cut down the mast and the rigging and threw them overboard. The rowboats, the nets, the empty barrels that stood on deck, everything was chucked into the water. Even the woodwork was hacked and broken. It made my heart bleed to see the lovely *Zeehond* abused and spoiled that way. She was so good and strong. What harm had she done?

"Then we drifted around three or four days—I don't know how long

—like a log in the sea. We had no food except salt herrings and a few crusts of bread. But at every meal those black Diepens prayed and sang hymns and drank gin. It was filthy.

"Then a ship from Norway picked us up, and I got home somehow, I don't know just how. Och, mother, mother, I've been through hell."

The lad lost control of himself; fell on his knees beside his mother and put his head on her lap, shaken by the dry sobs of a boy ashamed to cry. She stroked his yellow hair gently and dropped a kiss on it.

"Cry, darling," she murmured, "cry! It will do you good. You've come *through*. God has delivered you. And now you know what the sea can do to men, you'll give it up."

The boy lifted his head. His blue eyes sparkled through tears. His lips were firm again.

"Mother dear," he cried, "it was *not* the sea. It was the beastly *men*. The sea is *clean*. The sea was *kind* to us. It was vanity and hatred and drink that made the trouble. Rum and religion don't mix well. They let the big Devil into proud men. I'm going to sea again, some day. But I'll stay with you, dearest, till I grow up."

HOW THE GARDENER'S SON[1] FOUGHT THE *SERAPIS*[2]

Winston Churchill

(1871–   )

WHEN I came on deck the next morning our yards were a-drip with a clammy fog, and under it the sea was roughed by a south-west breeze. We were standing to the northward before it. I remember reflecting as I paused in the gangway that the day was Thursday, September the 23rd, and that we were near two months out of Groix with this tub of an Indiaman. In all that time we had not so much as got a whiff of an English frigate, though we had almost put a belt around the British Isles. Then straining my eyes through the mist, I made out two white blurs of sails on our starboard beam. Honest Jack Pearce, one of the few good seamen we had aboard, was rubbing down one of the nines beside me.

"Why, Jack," said I, "what have we there? Another prize?" For that question had become a joke on board the *Bon homme Richard* since the prisoners had reached an hundred and fifty, and half our crew was gone to man the ships.

"Bless your 'art, no, sir," said he. "'Tis that damned Frenchy

---

[1] John Paul Jones.

[2] From *Richard Carvel*. Reprinted by permission of Macmillan & Co., Ltd., and of the Macmillan Company.

Landais in th' *Alliance*. She turns up with the *Pallas* at six bells o' the middle watch."

"So he's back, is he?"

"Ay, he's back," he returned, with a grunt that was half a growl; "arter three weeks breakin' o' liberty. I tell 'ee what, sir, them Frenchies is treecherous devils, an' not to be trusted the len'th of a lead line. An' they beant seamen eno' to keep a full an' by with all their *takteek*. Ez fer that Landais, I hearn him whinin' at the commodore in the round house when we was off Clear, an' sayin' as how he would tell Sartin on us when he gets back to Paree. An' jabberin' to th' other Frenchmen as was there that this here butter-cask was er King's ship, an' that the commodore weren't no commodore nohow. They say as how Cap'n Jones be bound up in a hard knot by some articles of agreement, an' daresn't punish him. Be that so, Mr Carvel?"

I said that it was.

"Shiver my bulkheads!" cried Jack, "I gave my oath to that same, sir. For I knowed the commodore was the lad t' string 'em to the yard-arm an' he had the say on it. Oh, the devil take the Frenchies," said Jack, rolling his quid to show his pleasure of the topic, "they sits on their bottoms in Brest and L'Oriong an' talks *takteek* wi' their han's and mouths, and daresn't as much as show the noses o' their three-deckers in th' Bay o' Biscay, while Cap'n Jones pokes his bowsprit into every port in England, with a hulk the rats have left. I've had my bellyful o' Frenchies, Mr Carvel, save it to be to fight 'em. An' I tell 'ee 'twould give me the greatest joy in life t' leave loose *Scolding Sairy* at that there Landais. Th' gal ain't had a match on her this here cruise, an' t' my mind she couldn't be christened better, sir."

I left him patting the gun with a tender affection.

The scene on board was quiet and peaceful enough that morning. A knot of midshipmen on the forecastle were discussing Landais's conduct, and cursing the concordat which prevented our commodore from bringing him up short. Mr Stacey, the sailing-master, had the deck, and the coasting pilot was conning; now and anon the boatswain's whistle piped for Garrett or Quito or Fogg to lay aft to the mast, where the first lieutenant stood talking to Colonel de Chamillard, of the French marines. The scavengers were sweeping down, and part of the after guard was bending a new bolt-rope on a storm staysail.

Then the fore-topmast crosstrees reports a sail on the weather quarter, the *Richard* is brought around on the wind, and away we go after a brigantine, "flying like a scow laden with English bricks," as Midshipman Coram jokingly remarks. A chase is not such a novelty with us that we crane our necks to windward.

At noon, when I relieved Mr Stacey of the deck, the sun had eaten up the fog, and the shores of England stood out boldly. Spurn Head was looming up across our bows, while that of Flamborough jutted into the sea behind us. I had the starboard watch piped to dinner, and reported twelve o'clock to the commodore. And had just got permission to "make it," according to a time-honoured custom at sea, when another "Sail, ho!" came down from aloft.

"Where away?" called back Mr Linthwaite, who was midshipman of the forecastle.

"Starboard quarter, rounding Flamborough Head, sir. Looks like a full-rigged ship, sir."

I sent the messenger into the great cabin to report. He was barely out of sight before a second cry came from the masthead: "Another sail rounding Flamborough, sir!"

The officers on deck hurried to the taffrail. I had my glass, but not a dot was visible above the sea-line. The messenger was scarcely back again when there came a third hail: "Two more rounding the head, sir! Four in all, sir!"

Here was excitement indeed. Without waiting for instructions, I gave the command:

"Up royal yards! Royal yardmen in the tops!"

We were already swaying out of the chains, when Lieutenant Dale appeared and asked the coasting pilot what fleet it was. He answered that it was the Baltic fleet, under convoy of the *Countess of Scarborough*, twenty guns, and the *Serapis*, forty-four.

"Forty-four," repeated Mr Dale, smiling; "that means fifty, as English frigates are rated. We shall have our hands full this day, my lads," said he. "You have done well to get the royals on her, Mr Carvel."

While he was yet speaking, three more sail were reported from aloft. Then there was a hush on deck, and the commodore himself appeared. As he reached the poop we saluted him and informed him of what had happened.

"The Baltic fleet," said he, promptly. "Call away the pilot-boat with Mr Lunt to follow the brigantine, sir, and ease off before the wind. Signal 'General Chase' to the squadron, Mr Mayrant."

The men had jumped to the weather braces before I gave the command, and all the while more sail were counting from the crosstrees, until their number had reached forty-one. The news spread over the ship; the starboard watch trooped up with their dinners half eaten. Then a faint booming of guns drifted down upon our ears.

"They've got sight of us, sir," shouted the look-out. "They be firing guns to windward, an' letting fly their topgallant sheets."

At that the commodore hurried forward, the men falling back to the bulwarks respectfully, and he mounted the fore-rigging as agile as any topman, followed by his aide with a glass. From the masthead he sung out to me to set our stu'nsails, and he remained aloft till near seven bells of the watch. At that hour the merchantmen had all scuttled to safety behind the head, and from the deck a great yellow King's frigate could be plainly seen standing south to meet us, followed by her smaller consort. Presently she hove to, and through our glasses we discerned a small boat making for her side, and then a man clambering up her sea-ladder.

"That be the bailiff of Scarborough, sir," said the coasting pilot, "come to tell her cap'n 'tis Paul Jones he has to fight."

At that moment the commodore lay down from aloft, and our hearts beat high as he walked swiftly aft to the quarter-deck, where he paused for a word with Mr Dale. Meanwhile Mr Mayrant hove out the signal for the squadron to form line of battle.

"Recall the pilot-boat, Mr Carvel," said the commodore, quietly. "Then you may beat to quarters, and I will take the ship, sir."

"Ay, ay, sir." I raised my trumpet. "*All hands clear ship for action!*"

It makes me sigh now to think of the cheer which burst from that tatterdemalion crew. Who were they to fight the bone and sinew of the King's navy in a rotten ship of an age gone by? And who was he, that stood so straight upon the quarter-deck, to instil this scum with love and worship and fervour to blind them to such odds? But the bo'suns piped and sang out the command in fog-horn voices, the drums beat the long roll and the fifes whistled, and the decks became suddenly alive. Breech-ings were loosed and gun-tackles unlashed, rammer and sponge laid out, and pike and pistol and cutlass placed where they would be handy when the time came to rush the enemy's decks. The powder-monkeys tumbled over each other in their hurry to provide cartridges, and grape and can-ister and double-headed shot were hoisted up from below. The trimmers rigged the splinter nettings, got out spare spars and blocks and ropes against those that were sure to be shot away, and rolled up casks of water to put out the fires. Tubs were filled with sand, for blood is slippery upon the boards. The French marines, their scarlet and white very natty in contrast to most of our ragged wharf-rats at the guns, were mustered on poop and forecastle, and some were sent aloft to the tops to assist the tars there to sweep the British decks with hand-grenade and musket. And, lastly, the surgeon and his mates went below to cock-pit and steerage, to make ready for the grimmest work of all.

My own duties took me to the dark lower deck, a vile place indeed, and reeking with the smell of tar and stale victuals. There I had charge of the battery of old eighteens, while Mr Dale commanded the twelves on the middle deck. We loaded our guns with two shots apiece, though I had my doubts about their standing such a charge, and then the men stripped until they stood naked to the waist, waiting for the fight to begin. For we could see nothing of what was going forward. I was pacing up and down, for it was a task to quiet the nerves in that dingy place with the gunports closed, when about three bells of the dog, Mr Mease, the purser, appeared on the ladder.

"Lunt has not come back with the pilot-boat, Carvel," said he.

"I have volunteered for a battery, and am assigned to this. You are to report to the commodore."

I thanked him, and climbed quickly to the quarter-deck. The *Bon homme Richard* was lumbering like a leaden ship before the wind, swaying ponderously, her topsails flapping and her heavy blocks whacking against the yards. And there was the commodore, erect, and with fire in his eye, giving sharp commands to the men at the wheel. I knew at once that no trifle had disturbed him. He wore a brand-new uniform; a blue coat with red lapels and yellow buttons, and slashed cuffs and stand-up collar, a red waistcoat with tawny lace, blue breeches, white silk stockings, and a cocked hat and a sword. Into his belt were stuck two brace of pistols.

It took some effort to realize, as I waited silently for his attention, that this was the man of whose innermost life I had had so intimate a view. Who had taken me to the humble cottage under Criffel, who had poured into my ear his ambitions and his wrongs when we had sat together in the dingy room of the Castle Yard sponging-house. Then some of those ludicrous scenes on the road to London came up to me, for which the sky-blue frock was responsible. And yet this commodore was not greatly removed from him I had first beheld on the brigantine *John*. His confidence in his future had not so much as wavered since that day. That future was now not so far distant as the horizon, and he was ready to meet it.

"You will take charge of the battery of nines on this deck, Mr Carvel," said he, at length.

"Very good, sir," I replied, and was making my way down the poop ladder, when I heard him calling me, in a low voice, by the old name: "Richard!"

I turned and followed him aft to the taffrail, where we were clear of the French soldiers. The sun was hanging red over the Yorkshire Wolds, the Head of Flamborough was in the blue shadow, and the clouds were like rose leaves in the sky. The enemy had tacked and was standing west, with ensign and jack and pennant flying, the level light washing his sails to the whiteness of paper. 'Twas then I first remarked that the *Alliance* had left her place in line and was sailing swiftly ahead toward the *Serapis*. The commodore seemed to read my exclamation.

"Landais means to ruin me yet, by hook or crook," said he.

"But he can't intend to close with them," I replied. "He has not the courage."

"God knows what he intends," said the commodore, bitterly. "It is no good, at all events."

My heart bled for him. Some minutes passed that he did not speak, making shift to raise his glass now and again, and I knew that he was gripped by a strong emotion. 'Twas so he ever behaved when the stress was greatest. Presently he lays down the glass on the signal-chest, fumbles in his coat, and brings out the little gold brooch I had not set eyes on since Dolly and he and I had stood together on the *Betsy's* deck.

"When you see her, Richard, tell her that I have kept it as sacred as her memory," he said thickly. "She will recall what I spoke of you when she gave it me. You have been leal and true to me indeed, and many a black hour have you tided me over since this war began. Do you know how she may be directed to?" he concluded, with abruptness.

I glanced at him, surprised at the question. He was staring at the English shore.

"Mr Ripley, of Lincoln's Inn, used to be Mr Manners's lawyer," I answered.

He took out a little note-book and wrote that down carefully. "And now," he continued, "God keep you, my friend. We must win, for we fight with a rope around our necks."

"But you, Captain Paul," I said, "is—is there no one?"

His face took on the look of melancholy it had worn so often of late, despite his triumphs. That look was the stamp of fate.

"Richard," replied he, with an ineffable sadness, "I am naught but a wanderer upon the face of the earth. I have no ties, no kindred,—no real friends, save you and Dale, and some of these honest fellows whom I lead to slaughter. My ambition is seamed with a flaw. And all my life I must be striving, striving, until I am laid in the grave. I know that now, and it is you yourself who have taught me. For I have violently broken forth from those bounds which God in His wisdom did set."

I pressed his hand, and with bowed head went back to my station, profoundly struck by the truth of what he had spoken. Though he fought under the flag of freedom, the curse of the expatriated was upon his head.

Shortly afterward he appeared at the poop rail, straight and alert, his eye piercing each man as it fell on him. He was the commodore once more.

The twilight deepened, until you scarce could see your hands. There was no sound save the cracking of the cabins and the tumbling of the blocks, and from time to time a muttered command. An age went by before the trimmers were sent to the lee braces, and the *Richard* rounded lazily to. And a great frigate loomed out of the night beside us, half a pistol-shot away.

"What ship is that?" came the hail, intense out of the silence.

"I don't hear you," replied our commodore, for he had not yet got his distance.

Again came the hail: "What ship is that?"

John Paul Jones leaned forward over the rail.

"Pass the word below to the first lieutenant to begin the action, sir."

Hardly were the words out of my mouth before the deck gave a mighty leap, a hot wind that seemed half of flame blew across my face, and the roar started the pain throbbing in my ears. At the same instant the screech of shot sounded overhead, we heard the sharp crack-crack of wood rending and splitting,—as with a great broadaxe,—and a medley of blocks and ropes rattled to the deck with the thud of the falling bodies. Then, instead of stillness, moans and shrieks from above and below, oaths and prayers in English and French and Portuguese, and in the heathen gibberish of the East. As the men were sponging and ramming home in the first fury of hatred, the carpenter jumped out under the battle-lanthorn at the main hatch, crying in a wild voice that the old eighteens had burst, killing half their crews and blowing up the gundeck above them. At this many of our men broke and ran for the hatches.

"*Back, back to your quarters! The first man to desert will be shot down!*"

It was the same strange voice that had quelled the mutiny on the *John*, that had awed the men of Kirkcudbright. The tackles were seized and the guns run out once more, and fired, and served again in an agony of haste. In the darkness shot shrieked hither and thither about us like demons, striking everywhere, sometimes sending casks of salt water over the nettings. Incessantly the quartermaster walked to and fro scattering sand over the black pools that kept running, running together as the minutes were tolled out, and the red flashes from the guns revealed faces in a hideous contortion. One little fellow, with whom I had had many a lively word at mess, had his arm taken off at the shoulder as he went skipping past me with the charge under his coat, and I have but to listen now to hear the patter of the blood on the boards as they carried him away to the cockpit below. Out of the main hatch, from that charnel house, rose one continuous cry. It was an odd trick of the mind or soul that put a hymn on my lips in that dreadful hour of carnage and human misery, when men were calling the name of their Maker in vain. But as I ran from crew to crew, I sang over and over again a long-forgotten Christmas carol, and with it came a fleeting memory of my mother on the stairs at Carvel Hall, and of the negroes gathered on the lawn without.

Suddenly, glancing up at the dim cloud of sails above, I saw that we were aback and making sternway. We might have tossed a biscuit aboard the big *Serapis* as she glided ahead of us. The broadsides thundered, and great ragged scantlings brake from our bulwarks and flew as high as the mizzen-top; and the shrieks and groans redoubled. Involuntarily my eyes sought the poop, and I gave a sigh of relief at the sight of the commanding figure in the midst of the whirling smoke. We shotted our guns with double-headed, manned our lee braces, and gathered headway.

"*Stand by to board!*"

The boatswains' whistles trilled through the ship, pikes were seized, and pistol and cutlass buckled on. But even as we waited with set teeth, our bows ground into the enemy's weather quarter-gallery. For the *Richard's* rigging was much cut away, and she was crank at best. So we backed and filled once more, passing the Englishman close aboard, himself being aback at the time. Several of his shot crushed through the bulwarks in front of me, shattering a nine-pounder and killing half of its crew. And it is only a miracle that I stand alive to be able to tell the tale. Then I caught a glimpse of the quartermaster whirling the spokes of our wheel, and over went our helm to lay us athwart the forefoot of the *Serapis*, where we might rake and rush her decks. Our old Indiaman answered but doggedly; and the huge bowsprit of the *Serapis*, towering over our heads, snapped off our spanker gaff and fouled our mizzen rigging.

"A hawser, Mr Stacey, a hawser!" I heard the commodore shout, and saw the sailing-master slide down the ladder and grope among the dead and wounded and mass of broken spars and tackles, and finally pick up a smeared rope's end, which I helped him drag to the poop. There we found the commodore himself taking skilful turns around the mizzen with severed stays and shrouds dangling from the bowsprit, the French marines looking on.

"Don't swear, Mr Stacey," said he, severely; "in another minute we may all be in eternity."

I rushed back to my guns, for the wind was rapidly swinging the stern of the *Serapis* to our own bow, now bringing her starboard batteries into play. Barely had we time to light our matches and send our broadside into her at three fathoms before the huge vessels came crunching together, the disordered riggings locking, and both pointed northward to a leeward tide in a death embrace. The chance had not been given him to shift his crews or to fling open his starboard gun-ports.

Then ensued a moment's breathless hush, even the cries of those in agony lulling. The pall of smoke rolled a little, and a silver moonlight filtered through, revealing the weltering bodies twisted upon the boards. A stern call came from beyond the bulwarks.

"Have you struck, sir?"

The answer sounded clear, and bred hero-worship in our souls.

"*Sir, I have not yet begun to fight.*"

Our men raised a hoarse yell, drowned all at once by the popping of musketry in the tops and the bursting of grenades here and there about the decks. A mighty muffled blast sent the *Bon homme Richard* rolling to larboard, and the smoke eddied from our hatches and lifted out of the space between the ships. The Englishman had blown off his gun-ports. And next some one shouted that our battery of twelves was fighting them muzzle to muzzle below, our rammers leaning into the *Serapis* to send their shot home. No chance then for the thoughts which had tortured us in moments of suspense. That was a fearful hour, when a shot had scarce to leap a cannon's length to find its commission; when the belches of the English guns burned the hair of our faces; when Death was sovereign, merciful, or cruel at his pleasure. The red flashes disclosed many an act of coolness and of heroism. I saw a French lad whip off his coat when a gunner called for a wad, and another, who had been a scavenger, snatch the rammer from Pearce's hands when he staggered with a grape-shot through his chest. Poor Jack Pearce! He did not live to see the work *Scolding Sairy* was to do that night. I had but dragged him beyond reach of the recoil when he was gone.

Then a cry came floating down from aloft. Thrice did I hear it, like one waking out of a sleep, ere I grasped its import. "The *Alliance!* The *Alliance!*" But hardly had the name resounded with joy throughout the ship, when a hail of grape and canister tore through our sails from aft forward. "She rakes us! She rakes us!" And the French soldiers tumbled headlong down from the poop with a wail of "*Les Anglais l'ont prise!*" "Her Englishmen have taken her, and turned her guns against us!" Our captain was left standing alone beside the staff where the stars and stripes waved black in the moonlight.

"The *Alliance* is hauling off, sir!" called the midshipman of the mizzen-top. "She is making for the *Pallas* and the *Countess of Scarborough.*"

"Very good, sir," was all the commodore said.

To us hearkening for his answer his voice betrayed no sign of dismay. Seven times, I say, was that battle lost, and seven times regained again. What was it kept the crews at their quarters and the officers at their posts through that hell of flame and shot, when a madman could scarce have hoped for victory? What but the knowledge that somewhere in the swirl above us was still that unswerving and indomitable man who swept all obstacles from before him, and into whose mind the thought of defeat could not enter. His spirit held us to our task, for flesh and blood might not have endured alone.

We had now but one of our starboard nine-pounders on its carriage, and word came from below that our battery of twelves was all but knocked to scrap iron, and their ports blown into one yawning gap. Indeed, we did not have to be told that sides and stanchions had been carried away, for the deck trembled and teetered under us as we dragged *Scolding Sairy* from her stand in the larboard waist, clearing a lane for her between the bodies. Our feet slipped and slipped as we hove, and burning bits of sails and splinters dropping from aloft fell unheeded on our heads and shoulders. With the energy of desperation I was bending to the pull, when the Malay in front of me sank dead across the tackle. But, ere I could touch him, he was tenderly lifted aside, and a familiar figure seized the rope where the dead man's hands had warmed it. Truly, the commodore was everywhere that night.

"Down to the surgeon with you, Richard!" he cried. "I will look to the battery."

Dazed, I put my hand to my hair to find it warm and wringing wet. When I had been hit, I knew not. But I shook my head, for the very notion of that cockpit turned my stomach. The blood was streaming from a gash in his own temple, to which he gave no heed, and stood encouraging that panting line until at last the gun was got across and hooked to the ring-bolts of its companions that lay shattered there. "Serve her with double-headed, my lads," he shouted, "and every shot into the Englishman's mainmast!"

"Ay, ay, sir," came the answer from every man of that little remnant.

The *Serapis*, too, was now beginning to blaze aloft, and choking wood-smoke eddied out of the *Richard's* hold and mingled with the powder fumes. Then the enemy's fire abreast us seemed to lull, and Mr Stacey mounted the bulwarks, and cried out: "You have cleared their decks, my hearties!" Aloft, a man was seen to clamber from our main-yard into the very top of the Englishman, where he threw a hand-grenade, as I thought, down her main hatch. An instant after an explosion came like a clap of thunder in our faces, and a great quadrant of light flashed as high as the *Serapis's* trucks, and through a breach in her bulwarks I saw men running with only the collars of their shirts upon their naked bodies.

'Twas at this critical moment, when that fearful battle once more was won, another storm of grape brought the spars about our heads, and that name which we dreaded most of all was spread again. As we halted in consternation, a dozen round shot ripped through our un-engaged side, and a babel of voices hailed the treacherous Landais with oaths and imprecations. We made out the *Alliance* with a full head of canvas, black and sharp, between us and the moon. Smoke hung above her rail. Getting over against the signal fires blazing on Flamborough Head, she wore ship and stood across our bows, the midshipman on the forecastle singing out to her, by the commodore's orders, to lay the enemy by the board. There was no response.

"Do you hear us?" yelled Mr Linthwaite.

"Ay, ay," came the reply; and with it the smoke broke from her and the grape and canister swept our forecastle. Then the *Alliance* sailed away, leaving brave Mr Caswell among the many Landais had murdered.

The ominous clank of the chain pumps beat a sort of prelude to what happened next. The gunner burst out of the hatch with blood running down his face, shouting that the *Richard* was sinking, and yelling for quarter as he made for the ensign-staff on the poop, for the flag was shot away. Him the commodore felled with a pistol-butt. At the gunner's heels were the hundred and fifty prisoners we had taken, released by the master at arms. They swarmed out of the bowels of the ship like a horde of Tartars, unkempt and wild and desperate with fear, until I thought that the added weight on the scarce-supported deck would land us all in the bilges. Words fail me when I come to describe the frightful panic of these creatures, frenzied by the instinct of self-preservation. They surged hither and thither as angry seas driven into a pocket of a storm-swept coast. They trampled rough-shod over the moaning heaps of wounded and dying, and crowded the crews at the guns, who were power-less before their numbers. Some fought like maniacs, and others flung themselves into the sea.

Those of us who had clung to hope lost it then. Standing with my back to the mast, beating them off with a pike, visions of an English prison-ship, of an English gallows, came before me. I counted the seconds until the enemy's seamen would be pouring through our ragged ports. The seventh and last time, and we were beaten, for we had not men enough left on our two decks to force them down again. Yes,—I shame to confess it,—the heart went clean out of me, and with that the pain pulsed and leaped in my head like a devil unbound. At a turn of the hand I should have sunk to the boards, had not a voice risen strong and clear above that turmoil, compelling every man to halt trembling in his steps.

"*Cast off, cast off! The Serapis is sinking. To the pumps, ye fools, if you would save your lives!*"

That unerring genius of the gardener's son had struck the only chord! They were like sheep before us as we beat them back into the reeking hatches, and soon the pumps were heard bumping with a renewed and a desperate vigour. Then, all at once, the towering mainmast of the enemy cracked and tottered and swung this way and that on its loosened shrouds. The first intense silence of the battle followed, in the midst of which came a cry from our top:

"Their captain is hauling down, sir!"

The sound which broke from our men could scarce be called a cheer. That which they felt as they sank exhausted on the blood of their comrades may not have been elation. My own feeling was of unmixed wonder as I gazed at a calm profile above me, sharp-cut against the moon.

I was moved as out of a reverie by the sight of Dale swinging across to the *Serapis* by the main brace pennant. Calling on some of my boarders, I scaled our bulwarks and leaped fairly into the middle of the gangway of the *Serapis*.

Such is nearly all of my remembrance of that momentous occasion. I had caught the one glimpse of our first lieutenant in converse with their captain and another officer, when a naked seaman came charging at me. He had raised a pike above his shoulder ere I knew what he was about, and my senses left me.

THE *MERRIMAC* AND THE *MONITOR*[1]

Mary Johnston

WE WERE encamped on the Warwick River—infantry, and a cavalry company, and a battalion from New Orleans. Around us were green flats, black mud, winding creeks, waterfowl, earthworks, and what guns they could give us. At the mouth of the river across the

[1]From *The Long Roll*. Copyright, 1911, by Mary Johnston. Reprinted by permission of the author and of Thornton Butterworth, Ltd.

channel we had sunk twenty canal boats, to the end that Burnside should not get by. Beside the canal boats and the guns and the water-fowl there was a deal of fever-malarial—of exposure, of wet, of mouldy bread, of homesickness and general desolation. Some courage existed, too, and singing at times. We had been down there a long time among the marshes—all winter, in fact. About two weeks ago——"

"Oh, Edward, were you very homesick?"

"Devilish. For the certain production of a very curious feeling, give me picket duty on a wet marsh underneath the stars! Poetic places—marshes—with a strong suggestion about them of The Last Man . . . Where was I? Down to our camp one morning about two weeks ago came El Capitan Colorado—General Magruder, you know—gold lace, stars, and black plume! With him came Lieutenant Wood, C.S.N. We were paraded——"

"Edward, try as I may, I cannot get over the strangeness of your being in the ranks!"

Edward laughed. "There's many a better man than I in them, Aunt Lucy! They make the best of crows'-nests from which to spy on life, and that is what I always wanted to do—to spy on life!—The men were paraded, and Lieutenant Wood made us a speech. 'The old *Merrimac*, you know, men, that was burnt last year when the Yankees left Norfolk?—well, we've raised her, and cut her down to her berth deck, and made her what we call an ironclad. An ironclad is a new man-of-war that's going to take the place of the old. The *Merrimac* is not a frigate any longer; she's the ironclad *Virginia*, and we rather think she's going to make her name remembered. She's over there at the Gosport Navy Yard, and she's almost ready. She's covered over with iron plates, and she's got an iron beak, or ram, and she carries ten guns. On the whole, she's the ugliest beauty that you ever saw! She's almost ready to send to Davy Jones' locker a Yankee ship or two. Commodore Buchanan commands her, and you know who he is! She's got her full quota of officers, and, the speaker excepted, they're as fine a set as you'll find on the high seas! But man-of-war's men are scarcer, my friends, than hen's teeth! It's what comes of having no maritime population. Every man Jack that isn't on our few little ships is in the army—and the *Virginia* wants a crew of three hundred of the bravest of the brave! Now, I am talking to Virginians and Louisianians. Many of you are from New Orleans, and that means that some of you may very well have been seamen—seamen at an emergency, anyhow! Anyhow, when it comes to an emergency Virginians and Louisianians are there to meet it—on sea or on land! Just now there is an emergency—the *Virginia's* got to have a crew. General Magruder, for all he's got only a small force with which to hold a long line—General Magruder, like the patriot that he is, has said that I may ask this morning for volunteers. Men! any seaman among you has the chance to gather laurels from the strangest deck of the strangest ship that ever you saw! No fear for the laurels! They're fresh and green even under our belching smoke-stack. The *Merrimac* is up like the phoenix; the last state of her is greater than the first, and her name is going down in history! Louisianians and Virginians, who volunteers?'

"About two hundred volunteered——"

"Edward, what did you know about seamanship?"

"Precious little. Chiefly, Unity, what you have read to me from novels. But the laurels sounded enticing, and I was curious about the ship. Well, Wood chose about eighty—all who had been seamen or gunners and a baker's dozen of ignoramuses beside. I came in with that portion of the elect. And off we went, in boats, across the James to the southern shore and to the Gosport Navy Yard. That was a week before the battle."

"What does it look like, Edward—the *Merrimac?*"

"It looks, Judith, like Hamlet's cloud. Sometimes there is an appearance of a barn with everything but the roof submerged—or of Noah's Ark, three-fourths under water! Sometimes, when the flag is flying, she has the air of a piece of earthworks, mysteriously floated off into the river. Ordinarily, though, she is rather like a turtle, with a chimney sticking up from her shell. The shell is made of pitch-pine and oak, and it is covered with two-inch-thick plates of Tredegar iron. The beak is of cast iron, standing four feet out from the bow; that, with the rest of the old berth deck, is just awash. Both ends of the shell are rounded for pivot guns. Over the gun deck is an iron grating on which you can walk at need. There is the pilot-house covered with iron, and there is the smoke-stack. Below are the engines and boilers, condemned after the *Merrimac's* last cruise, and, since then, lying in the ooze at the bottom of the river. They are very wheezy, trembling, poor old men of the sea! It was hard work to get the coal for them to eat; it was brought at last from away out in Montgomery County, from the Price coalfields. The guns are two 7-inch rifles, two 6-inch rifles and six 9-inch smooth-bores; ten in all.—Yes, call her a turtle, plated with iron; she looks as much like that as like anything else.

"When we eighty men from the Warwick first saw her, she was swarming with workmen. They continued to cover her over and to make impossible any drill or exercise upon her. Hammer, hammer upon belated plates from the Tredegar! Tinker, tinker with the poor old engines! Make shift here and make shift there; work through the day and work through the night, for there was a rumour abroad that the *Ericsson*, that we knew was building, was coming down the coast! There was no chance to drill, to become acquainted with the turtle and her temperament. Her species had never gone to war before, and when you looked at her there was room for doubt as to how she would behave! Officers and men were strange to one another—and the gunners could not try the guns for the swarming workmen. There wasn't so much of the Montgomery coal that it could be wasted on experiments in firing up—and indeed it seemed wise not to experiment at all with the ancient engines! So we stood about the navy yard, and looked down the Elizabeth and across the flats to Hampton Roads, where we could see the *Cumberland,* the *Congress*, and the *Minnesota*, Federal ships lying off Newport News— and the workmen riveted the last plates—and smoke began to come out of the smoke-stack—and suddenly Commodore Buchanan, with his lieutenants behind him, appeared between us and the *Merrimac*—or the *Virginia*. Most of us still call her the *Merrimac*. It was the morning of the 8th. The sun shone brightly and the water was very blue—blue and still. There were sea-gulls, I remember, flying overhead, screaming as they flew—and the marshes were growing emerald——"

"Yes, yes! What did Commodore Buchanan want?"

"Don't be impatient, Molly! You women don't in the least look like Griseldas! Aunt Lucy has the air of her pioneer great-grandmother who has heard an Indian calling! And as for Judith—Judith!"

"Yes, Edward."

"Come back to Greenwood. You looked a listening Jeanne d'Arc. What did you hear?"

"I heard the engines working, and the sea-fowl screaming and the wind in the rigging of the *Cumberland*. Go on, Edward."

"We soldiers turned seamen came to attention. 'Get on board, men,'— said Commodore Buchanan. 'We are going out in the Roads and introduce a new era.' So off the workmen came and on we went—the flag officers and the lieutenants and the midshipmen and the surgeons and the volunteer aides and the men. The engineers were already below and the gunners were looking at the guns. The smoke rolled up very black, the ropes were cast off, a bugle blew, out streamed the stars and bars, all the workmen on the dock swung their hats, and down the Elizabeth moved the *Merrimac*. She moved slowly enough with her poor old engines, and she steered badly, and she drew twenty-two feet, and she was ugly, ugly, ugly—poor thing!

"Now we were opposite Craney Island, at the mouth of the Elizabeth. There's a battery there, you know, part of General Colston's line, and there are forts upon the main along the James. All these were now crowded with men, hurrahing, waving their caps. . . . As we passed Craney they were singing 'Dixie.' So we came out into the James to Hampton Roads.

"Now all the southern shore from Willoughby's Spit to Ragged Island is as grey as a dove, and all the northern shore from Old Point Comfort to Newport News is blue where the enemy has settled. In between are the shining Roads. Between the Rip Raps and Old Point swung at anchor the *Roanoke*, the *Saint Lawrence*, a number of gunboats, store ships, and transports, and also a French man-of-war. Far and near over the Roads were many small craft. The *Minnesota*, a large ship, lay half-way between

Old Point and Newport News. At the latter place there is a large Federal garrison, and almost in the shadow of its batteries rode at anchor the frigate *Congress* and the sloop *Cumberland*. The first had fifty guns, the second thirty. The *Virginia* or the *Merrimac*, or the turtle, creeping out from the Elizabeth, crept slowly and puffing black smoke into the South Channel. The pilot, in his iron-clad pilot-house no bigger than a hickory nut, put her head to the northwest. The turtle began to swim toward Newport News.

"Until now not a few of us within her shell, and almost all of the soldiers on the forts along the shore, had thought her upon a trial trip only—down the Elizabeth, past Craney Island, turn at Sewell's Point, and back to the dock of the Gosport Navy Yard! When she did not turn, the cheering on the shore stopped; you felt the breathlessness. When she passed the Point and took to the South Channel, when her head turned up-stream, when she came abreast of the Middle Ground, when they saw that the turtle was going to fight, from along the shore to Craney and from Sewell's Point there arose a yell. Every man in grey yelled. They swung hat or cap; they shouted themselves hoarse. All the flags streamed suddenly out, trumpets blared, the sky lifted, and we drank the sunshine in like wine. That is, some of us did. To others it came cold like hemlock against the lip. Fear is a horrible sensation. I was dreadfully afraid——"

"Edward!"

"Dreadfully. But you see I didn't tell anyone I was afraid, and that makes all the difference! Besides, it wore off ... It was a spring day and high tide, and the Federal works at Newport News and the *Congress* and the *Cumberland* and the more distant *Minnesota* all looked asleep in the calm, sweet weather. Washing day it was on the *Congress*, and clothes were drying in the rigging. That aspect as of painted ships, painted breastworks, a painted seapiece, lasted until the turtle reached mid-channel. Then the other side woke up. Upon the shore appeared a blue swarm—men running to and fro. Bugles signalled. A commotion, too, arose upon the *Congress* and the *Cumberland*. Her head toward the latter ship, the turtle puffed forth black smoke and wallowed across the channel. An uglier poor thing you never saw, nor a bolder! Squat to the water, belching black smoke, her engines wheezing and repining, unwieldy of management, her bottom scraping every hummock of sand in all the shoaly roads—ah, she was ugly and courageous! Our two small gunboats, the *Raleigh* and the *Beaufort*, coming from Norfolk, now overtook us,— we went on together. I was forward with the crew of the 7–inch pivot gun. I could see through the port, above the muzzle. Officers and men, we were all cooped under the turtle's shell; in order by the open ports, and the guns all ready. . . . We came to within a mile of the *Cumberland*, tall and graceful with her masts and spars and all the blue sky above. She looked a swan, and we, the ugly duckling. . . . Our ram, you know, was under water—seventy feet of the old berth deck, ending in a four-foot beak of cast iron . . . We came nearer. At three-quarters of a mile, we opened with the bow gun. The *Cumberland* answered, and the *Congress*, and their gunboats and shore batteries. Then began a frightful uproar that shook the marshes and sent the sea-birds screaming. Smoke arose, and flashing fire, and an excitement—an excitement—an excitement. Then it was, ladies, that I forgot to be afraid. The turtle swam on, toward the *Cumberland*, swimming as fast as Montgomery coal and the engines that had lain at the bottom of the sea could make her go. There was a frightful noise within her shell, a humming, a shaking. The *Congress*, the gunboats, and the shore batteries kept firing broadsides. There was an enormous thundering noise, and the air was grown a sulphurous cloud. Their shot came battering like hail, and like hail it rebounded from the ironclad. We passed the *Congress*,—very close to her tall side. She gave us a withering fire. We returned it, and steered on for the *Cumberland*. A word ran from end to end of the turtle's shell, 'We are going to ram her—stand by, men!'

"Within easy range we fired the pivot gun. I was of her crew; half naked we were, powder blackened and streaming with sweat. The shell she sent burst above the *Cumberland's* stern pivot, killing or wounding most of her crew that served it . . . We went on . . . Through the port I could now see the *Cumberland* plainly, her starboard side just ahead of us, men in the shrouds and running to and fro on her deck. When we were all but on her her starboard blazed. That broadside tore up the carriage of our pivot gun, cut another off at the trunnions, and the muzzle from a third, riddled the smoke-stack and steam-pipe, carried away an anchor, and killed or wounded nineteen men . . . The *Virginia* answered with three guns; a cloud of smoke came between the ironclad and the armed sloop; it lifted—and we were on her. We struck her under the fore rigging with a dull and grinding sound. The iron beak with which we were armed was wrested off.

"The *Virginia* shivered, hung a moment, then backed clear of the *Cumberland*, in whose side there was now a ragged and a gaping hole. The pilot in the iron-clad pilot-house turned her head up-stream. The water was shoal; she had to run up the James some way before she could turn and come back to attack the *Congress*. Her keel was in the mud; she was creeping now like a land turtle, and all the iron shore was firing at her . . . She turned at last in freer water and came down the Roads. Through the port we could see the *Cumberland* that we had rammed. She had listed to port and was sinking. The water had reached her main deck; all her men were now on her spar deck, where they yet served the pivot guns. She fought to the last. A man of ours, stepping for one moment through a port to the outside of the turtle's shell, was cut in two. As the water rose and rose the sound of her guns was like a lessening thunder. One by one they stopped . . . To the last she flew her colours. The *Cumberland* went down.

"By now there had joined us the small, small James River Squadron that had been anchored far up the river. The *Patrick Henry* had twelve guns, the *Jamestown* had two, and the *Teaser* one. Down they scurried like three valiant marsh hens to aid the turtle. With the *Beaufort* and the *Raleigh* there were five valiant pigmies, and they fired at the shore batteries, and the shore batteries answered like an angry Jove with solid shot, with shell, with grape, and with canister! A shot wrecked the boiler of the *Patrick Henry*, scalding to death the men who were near . . . The turtle sunk a transport steamer lying alongside the wharf at Newport News, and then she rounded the Point and bore down upon the *Congress*.

"The frigate had showed discretion, which is the better part of valour. Noting how deeply we drew, she had slipped her cables and run aground in the shallows, where she was safe from the ram of the *Merrimac*. We could get no nearer than two hundred feet. There we took up position, and there we began to rake her, the *Beaufort*, the *Raleigh*, and the *Jamestown* giving us what aid they might. She had fifty guns, and there were the heavy shore batteries, and below her the *Minnesota*. This ship, also aground in the Middle Channel, now came into action with a roar. A hundred guns were trained upon the *Merrimac*. The iron hail beat down every point, not iron-clad, that showed above our shell. The muzzles of two guns were shot away, the stanchions, the boat davits, the flagstaff. Again and again the flagstaff fell, and again and again we replaced it. At last we tied the colours to the smoke-stack. Beside the nineteen poor fellows that the *Cumberland's* guns had mowed down, we now had other killed and wounded. Commodore Buchanan was badly hurt, and the flag lieutenant, Minor. The hundred guns thundered against the *Merrimac* and the *Merrimac* thundered against the *Congress*. The tall frigate and her fifty guns wished herself an ironclad; the swan would have blithely changed with the ugly duckling. We brought down her mainmast, we disabled her guns, we strewed her decks with blood and anguish (war is a wild beast, nothing more, and I'll hail the day when it lies slain). We smashed in her sides and we set her afire. She hauled down her colours and ran up a white flag. The *Merrimac* ceased firing and signalled to the *Beaufort*. The *Beaufort* ran alongside, and the frigate's ranking officer gave up his colours and his sword. The *Beaufort* and the *Congress's* own boats removed the crew and the wounded . . . The shore batteries, the *Minnesota*, the picket boat *Zouave*, kept up a heavy firing all the while upon the *Merrimac*, upon the *Raleigh* and the *Jamestown*, and also upon the *Beaufort*. We waited until the crew was clear of the *Congress*, and then we gave her a round of hot shot that presently set her afire from stem to stern. This done, we turned to other work.

"The *Minnesota* lay aground in the North Channel. To her aid hurrying up from Old Point came the *Roanoke* and the *Saint Lawrence*. Our own batteries at Sewell's Point opened upon these two ships as they passed, and they answered with broadsides. We fed our engines, and under a billow of black smoke ran down to the *Minnesota*. Like the *Congress*, she lay upon a sand bar, beyond fear of ramming. We could only manœuvre for deep water, near enough to her to be deadly. It was now late afternoon. I could see through the port of the bow pivot the slant sunlight upon the water, and how the blue of the sky was paling. The *Minnesota* lay just ahead; very tall she looked, another of the *Congress* breed; the old warships singing their death song. As we came on we fired the bow gun, then, lying nearer her, began with broadsides. But we could not get near enough; she was lifted high upon the sand, the tide was going out, and we drew twenty-three feet. We did her great harm, but we were not disabling her. An hour passed, and the sun drew on to setting. The *Roanoke* turned and went back under the guns of Old Point, but the *Saint Lawrence* remained to thunder at the turtle's iron shell. The *Merrimac* was most unhandy, and on the ebb tide there would be shoals enough between us and a berth for the night. . . . The *Minnesota* could not get away, at dawn she would be yet aground, and we would then take her for our prize. 'Stay till dusk, and the blessed old iron box will ground herself where Noah's flood won't float her!' The pilot ruled, and in the gold and purple sunset we drew off. As we passed, the *Minnesota* blazed with all her guns; we answered her, and answered too, the *Saint Lawrence*. The evening star was shining when we anchored off Sewell's Point. The wounded were taken ashore, for we had no place for wounded men under the turtle's shell. Commodore Buchanan leaving us, Lieutenant Catesby Ap Rice Jones took command.

"I do not remember what we had for supper. We had not eaten since early morning, so we must have had something. But we were too tired to think or to reason or to remember. We dropped beside our guns and slept, but not for long. Three hours, perhaps, we slept, and then a whisper seemed to run through the *Merrimac*. It was as though the ironclad herself had spoken, 'Come! Watch the *Congress* die!' Most of us arose from beside the guns and mounted to the iron grating above, to the top of the turtle's shell. It was a night as soft as silk; the water smooth, in long, faint, olive swells; a half-moon in the sky. There were lights across at Old Point, lights on the battery at the Rip Raps, lights in the frightened shipping, huddled under the guns of Fortress Monroe, lights along either shore. There were lanterns in the rigging of the *Minnesota* where she lay upon the sand bar, and lanterns on the *Saint Lawrence* and the *Roanoke*. As we looked a small moving light, as low as possible to the water, appeared between the *Saint Lawrence* and the *Minnesota*. A man said, 'What's that? Must be a rowboat.' Another man answered, 'It's going too fast for a rowboat—funny! right on the water like that!' 'A launch, I reckon,' said a third, 'with plenty of rowers. Now it's behind the *Minnesota*.' 'Shut up, you talkers,' said a midshipman, 'I want to look at the *Congress!*'

"Four miles away, off Newport News, lay the burning *Congress*. In the still, clear night, she seemed almost at hand. All her masts, her spars, and her rigging showed black in the heart of a great ring of firelight. Her hull, lifted high by the sandbank which held her, had round red eyes. Her ports were windows lit from within. She made a vision of beauty and of horror. One by one, as they were reached by the flame, her guns exploded—a loud and awful sound in the night above the Roads. We stood and watched that sea picture, and we watched in silence. We are seeing giant things, and ere this war is ended we shall see more. At two o'clock in the morning the fire reached her powder magazine. She blew up. A column like the Israelite's Pillar shot to the zenith; there came an earthquake sound, sullen and deep; when all cleared there was only her hull upborne by the sand and still burning. It burned until the dawn, when it smouldered and went out."

The narrator arose, walked the length of the parlour, and came back to the four women. "Haven't you had enough for to-night? Unity looks sleepy, and Judith's knitting has lain this half-hour on the floor. Judith!"

Molly spoke. "Judith says that if there is fighting around Richmond she is going there to the hospitals, to be a nurse. The doctors here say that she does better than anyone——"

"Go on, Edward," said Judith. "What happened at dawn?"

"We got the turtle in order, and those ancient mariners, our engines, began to work, wheezing and slow. We ran up a new flagstaff, and every man stood to the guns, and the *Merrimac* moved from Sewell's Point, her head turned to the *Minnesota*, away across, grounded on a sand bank in the North Channel. The sky was as pink as the inside of a shell, and a thin white mist hung over the marshes and the shore and the great stretch of Hampton Roads. It was so thin that the masts of the ships huddled below Fortress Monroe rose clear of it into the flush of the coming sun. All their pennants were flying—the French man-of-war, and the Northern ships. At that hour the sea-gulls are abroad, searching for their food. They went past the ports, screaming and moving their silver wings.

"The *Minnesota* grew in size. Every man of us looked eagerly—from the pilot-house, from bow ports, and as we drew parallel with her from the ports of the side. We fired the bow gun as we came on, and the shot told. There was some cheering; the morning air was so fine, and the prize so sure! The turtle was in spirits—poor old turtle with her battered shell and her flag put back as fast as it was torn away! Her engines, this morning, were mortal slow and weak; they wheezed and whined, and she drew so deep that, in that shoaly water, she went aground twice between Sewell's Point and the stretch she had now reached of smooth pink water, with the sea-gulls dipping between her and the *Minnesota*. Despite the engines she was happy, and the gunners were all ready at the starboard ports——"

Leaning over, he took the poker and stirred the fire.

> "The best laid plans of mice and men
> Do aften gang agley——"

Miss Lucy's needles clicked. "Yes, the papers told us. The *Ericsson*." "There came," said Edward, "there came from behind the *Minnesota* a cheese-box on a shingle. It had lain there hidden by her bulk since midnight. It was its single light that we had watched and thought no more of! A cheese-box on a shingle, and now it darted into the open as though a boy's arm had sent it! It was little beside the *Minnesota*. It was little even beside the turtle. There was a silence when we saw it, a silence of astonishment. It had come so quietly upon the scene—a *deus ex machina* indeed, dropped from the clouds between us and our prey. In a moment we knew it for the *Ericsson*—the looked-for ironclad we knew to be a-building. The *Monitor*, they call it. . . . The shingle was just awash; the cheese-box turned out to be a revolving turret, mail clad and carrying two large, modern guns—11-inch. The whole thing was armoured, had the best of engines, and drew only twelve feet. . . . Well, the *Merrimac* had a startled breath, to be sure—there is no denying the drama of the *Monitor's* appearance—and then she righted and began firing. She gave to the cheese-box, or to the armoured turret, one after the other, three broadsides. The turret blazed and answered, and the balls rebounded from each armoured champion." He laughed. "By heaven! it was like our old favourites, Ivanhoe and De Bois-Guilbert— the ugliest squat gnomes of an Ivanhoe and of a Brian De Bois-Guilbert that ever came out of a nightmare! We thundered in the lists, and then we passed each other, turned, and again encountered. Sometimes we were a long way apart, and sometimes there was not ten feet of water between those sunken decks from which arose the iron shell of the *Merrimac*, and the iron turret of the *Monitor*. She fired every seven minutes; we as rapidly as we could load. Now it was the bow gun, now the after pivot, now a full broadside. Once or twice we thought her done for, but always her turret revolved, and her 11-inch guns opened again. In her lighter draught she had a great advantage; she could turn and wind where we could not. The *Minnesota* took a hand, and an iron battery from the shore. We were striving to ram the *Ericsson*, but we could not get close to her; our iron beak, too, was sticking in the side of the sunken *Cumberland* —we could only ram with a blunt prow. The *Minnesota*, as we passed, gave us all her broadside guns—a tremendous fusillade at point-blank range, which would have sunk any ship of the swan breed. The turtle shook off shot and shell, grape and canister, and answered with her bow gun. The shell which it threw entered the side of the frigate, and, burst-

ing amidship, exploded a store of powder and set the ship on fire. Leaving
disaster aboard the *Minnesota*, we turned and sunk the tugboat *Dragon*.
Then came manœuvre and manœuvre to gain position where we could
ram the *Monitor*. . . .

"We got it at last. The engines made an effort like the leap of the
spirit before expiring. 'Go ahead! Full speed!' We went; we bore down
upon the *Monitor*, now in deeper water. But at the moment that we saw
victory she turned. Our bow, lacking the iron beak, gave but a glancing
stroke. It was heavy as it was; the *Monitor* shook like a man with the
ague, but she did not share the fate of the *Cumberland*. There was no
ragged hole in her side; her armour was good, and held. She backed,
gathered herself together, then rushed forward, striving to ram us in her
turn. But our armour, too, was good, and held. Then she came upon the
Merrimac's quarter, laid her bow against the shell, and fired her 11-inch
guns twice in succession. We were so close, each to the other, that it was
as though two duellists were standing upon the same cloak. Frightful
enough was the concussion of those guns.

"That charge drove in the *Merrimac's* iron side three inches or more.
The shots struck above the ports of the after guns, and every man at
those guns was knocked down by the impact and bled at the nose and
ears. The *Monitor* dropped astern, and again we turned and tried to ram
her. But her far lighter draught put her where we could not go; our bow,
too, was now twisted and splintered. Our powder was getting low. We
did not spare it, we could not; we sent shot and shell continuously against
the *Monitor*, and she answered in kind. *Monitor* and *Merrimac*, we went
now this way, now that, the *Ericsson* much the lighter and quickest, the
Merrimac fettered by her poor old engines, and her great length, and her
twenty-three feet draught. It was two o'clock in the afternoon. . . . The
duellists stepped from off the cloak, tried operations at a distance, hung
for a moment in the wind of indecision, then put down the match from
the gunner's hands. The *Monitor* darted from us, her head toward the
shoal water known as the Middle Ground. She reached it and rested
triumphant, out of all danger from our ram, and yet where she could still
protect the *Minnesota*. . . . A curious silence fell upon the Roads; sullen
like the hush before a thunderstorm, and yet not like that, for we had had
the thunderstorm. It was the stillness, perhaps, of exhaustion. It was late
afternoon, the fighting had been heavy. The air was filled with smoke;
in the water were floating spars and wreckage of the ships we had destroyed. The weather was sultry and still. The dogged booming of a gun
from a shore battery sounded lonely and remote as a bell buoy. The tide
was falling; there were sand bars enough between us and Sewell's Point.
We waited an hour. The *Monitor* was rightly content with the Middle
Ground, and would not come back for all our charming. We fired at
intervals, upon her, and upon the *Minnesota*, but at last our powder grew
so low that we ceased. The tide continued to fall, and the pilot had much

to say. . . . The red sun sank in the west; the engineers fed the ancient mariners with Montgomery coal; black smoke gushed forth, and pilots felt their way into the South Channel, and slowly, slowly back toward Sewell's Point. The day closed in a murky evening with a taste of smoke in the air. In the night-time the *Monitor* went down the Roads to Fortress Monroe, and in the morning we took the *Merrimac* into dry dock at Norfolk. Her armour was dented all over, though not pierced. Her bow was bent and twisted, the iron beak lost in the side of the *Cumberland*. Her boats were gone, and her smoke-stack as full of holes as any colander, and the engines at the last gasp. Several of the guns were injured, and coal and powder and ammunition all lacked. We put her there—the dear and ugly warship, the first of the ironclads—we put her there in dry dock, and there she's apt to stay for some weeks to come. Lieutenant Wood was sent to Richmond with the report for the president and the secretary of the navy. He carried, too, the flag of the *Congress*, and I was one of the men detailed for its charge. . . . And now I have told you of the *Merrimac* and the *Monitor*."

BOUND FOR RIO GRANDE[1]

A. E. Dingle

(1874–   )

I

THE old man's broken teeth gleamed through tight, thin lips whenever his rheumy eyes glimpsed the lofty spars of the clipper in the bay. She was the only deepwaterman in port.

"Blood boat!" he chattered. "A blood boat. But you don't git no more o' my blood, not by a damn sight!"

Hastily turning away, the old man shambled along the wharf, at the end of which stood an office. Opposite the office, bright and cheery against the grey and dirt of the waterside, a tiny store kept its door open, revealing an interior to set the pulses of an ancient mariner leaping. Never a yellow oilskin, nor a bit of rope; nor one block or shackle offended the eye grown weary through half a century of salty servitude.

Glossy plugs of black tobacco; clay pipes of virgin whiteness and lissome shape; woolly comforters and stout shore-going winter socks; old, tasty cheese and soft, white bread; fat sausage and luscious, boneless ham; all these things, mere fancies of the dreaming sailor-man at sea, were clear to the view of old Pegwell through the open door of the little store as he paced up and down before the office, waiting for the man to whom he was to make application for the job of watchman of the wharf.

There was a sharp hint of frost in the air; a sharper threat of wind.

[1]Reprinted by permission of the author.

There was just enough of brine and breeze, just a trace. It smelt of salt water and of boats, with never an obtrusive reminder of hardcase deep-water ships.

Ah! There was a snug harbour indeed for a battered old seadog. If a chap could expect to come at last into such a fair haven as that little store now he wouldn't mind a few decades of bitter travail at sea.

"Hell's delight! Fat chance I got o' savin' money now!" he growled.

He sought for a match, found none. It was just his luck. But he had a few pennies. He would buy matches in that store. He waited until the stream of lunch customers thinned out, and entered.

"Box o' lucifers," he demanded, slapping down the coin. His eyes wandered around the homey little place. There were things he had not noticed before from outside. Red candy; bright painted toys; rubber balls. Children came there evidently. What sort of children would come to that neighbourhood for toys?

"Your matches, sir," said a rippling, laughing voice; and old Pegwell turned around sharply and discovered why children might well come to that store. Men, too. A twenty-year-old girl was offering him matches. Her big brown eyes danced mischievously. She was as trim as a brand-new China clipper.

"Thank 'e, ma'am," said Pegwell, as he grabbed the matches and shuffled out, dazzled and confused by the vision. He was still dazzled, his box of matches unopened, when he stumbled against the man he had waited to see.

"Heard you wanted a watchman, sir," said old Pegwell respectfully. He proffered a bundle of ship's discharges as evidence of character. The man glanced through them, glanced keenly at the old man, and nodded.

"Night work," he said. "Six to six. If you suit, in a month I'll give you a day shift, turn and turn about. Nothing much to do here, but you'll have to watch out for strangers. Lot of crooks on the water nowadays. Rum, dope, all sorts. Start to-night."

Old Pegwell had landed his first shore job. For the first time since starting out to earn his own living he could afford to gaze curiously at a sailorman, going large, staggering along to the next blind pig.

"Sailors is a lot o' lummoxes," he decided.

"Like kids."

> "If yuh save up yer money, an' don't git on th' rocks,
> Yuh'll have plenty o' tobacker in yer old tobacker box,"

he sang quaveringly.

He pulled up sharply, ceasing his song, and drifted over toward the little store again. He would have to find some place to live, to sleep at least. That girl looked different from others he had known. Perhaps she would tell him where to seek. He walked in, more confidently than before. He had a shore job now.

"Plug o' tobacker, miss," he asked for. The girl appeared from behind a provision case, putting on a smile as she emerged. A man thrust back deeper into the shadow. Pegwell saw nothing of the forced smile or the man. His eyes were roving, taking in the wealth of the stock. When he turned to take his tobacco the girl's smile was sunny enough. He felt encouraged.

"Beg y' pardon, miss, I just got a job on th' wharf, and thought likely you could direc' me where to git a bed, cheap. I ain't a pertickler chap. Just es long 's there ain't too many bugs, or——"

"You got a job on the wharf?" interrupted a man's voice. A youth, who might have been good-looking if he could have changed his eyes, came from behind the provision case and scowled surlily. "What job?"

"Watchman," said Pegwell importantly. "Night watchman. Know any place I kin get a doss?"

"How did you get to hear about this job? I'm livin' here right along, lookin' for a job, and a stranger comes along and lands it over my head. You're a sailor, ain't you?"

"No; watchman," retorted old Pegwell. "Was a sailorman. Had good discharges. I'm a watchman now. D'you know of a place I kin sleep, miss?"

The youth dragged the girl aside, and they muttered together, ignoring Pegwell. Presently the girl spoke sharply, angrily.

"It's best for you to go away, Larry. It's a good thing you never heard of the wharf job. Too many old friends hanging around there! You've signed on in the *Stella*. Now you go. You know what the judge said. Go to work, like a decent fellow, and you won't be watched like a——"

"Go to work? Hell! I'm willing to go to work, Mary, but what d'you want to shove me off into a damned old square rigger for? Ain't there work to be got——"

"It's best that you go away for a while," insisted the girl. "You were lucky to escape jail when that gang of smugglers got caught. I'm not sure now that the judge was satisfied about you. If you stay around here they're sure to watch you——"

"Beg pardon, miss, but if you know of a place——" interrupted Pegwell impatiently. Larry swung around and grinned crookedly.

"All right, sister," he told her. "I'll do it to please you." He took Pegwell's arm. "I'll find you a bed, old timer. What time d'you go to work?"

"Six. Want to get a sleepin' place afore that."

"Meet me here at five-thirty. I'll have a bunk for you by then."

Pegwell started off for a walk, but streets were a barren wilderness to him. He gravitated toward the harbour. He found himself somehow in front of the little store. It was a long time from five-thirty. Methodically he noted the contents of the window, grew amazed at the number and variety.

"Larry hasn't come back yet," the girl called out from the store. "Won't you wait inside?"

Pegwell looked sheepish. Sailors of the deep waters were always easily abashed in the presence of a decent woman. Pegwell scarcely dared to look up from the floor as he entered. But the girl began to chatter to him, and he felt at ease when she handed him a match for his cold pipe. In ten minutes he was spinning her fearsome yarns. In half an hour they were friends. She confided little scraps of her own affairs.

"Larry's a good fellow," she said, a bit sadly. "Too good. He's easy to lead. There has been a lot of smuggling along the front lately, and he ought to have kept away. But he always seems to have money, never goes to work, and when a big capture was made he was under suspicion. The judge told him he had better go to work, then folks would be apt to believe that he was innocent. Of course he is innocent! My brother Larry couldn't be a crook, Mr. Pegwell. But he has been under suspicion, and I made him join that big sailing ship, the *Stella*, for a voyage. When he comes back everything will be forgotten, and he can——Oh, here's Jack! Excuse me, Mr. Pegwell."

A tall, brown-faced man of thirty limped in. Pegwell was no keen-eyed Solon concerning women of Mary Bland's sort; but when he saw her pretty face light up and her big brown eyes flash at the appearance of this good-looking fellow who limped on a shortened leg, he knew he was intruding. Puffing furiously at his pipe, he stumped out upon the front.

At five-thirty Larry found Pegwell sitting on the cap log of the wharf.

"Come on, old timer. I got a fine bunk for you," said Larry. Pegwell followed him.

"I heared you be goin' in th' *Stella*," remarked Pegwell.

"I ain't proud of it," retorted Larry.

"I just come home in her. A hell ship, she is! Can sail, though. You ain't old an' stiff. Do yer work an' don't give th' mates no slack, an' you'll be all kiff, me son."

Larry glanced curiously at the queer old man who thought fit to preach duty to him.

They turned down by a disused and evil-smelling fish dock, out of sight of a growing district.

"Have to cross the creek in a boat," grinned Larry. "Save time, see. You have to be on the job, now, but other times you can walk around. Here y' are."

At the foot of a perpendicular ladder of boards nailed on a slimy pile a boat lay. Three husky boatmen grinned up knowingly at Larry. A blue canvas sea bag lay in the bottom of the boat, doubled up, like a dead man.

"Take good care of my old friend," Larry ordered. He gently drew Pegwell to the ladder. "Hurry up, old timer. Soon's they see you snug they have to come back for me."

Pegwell stepped on the ladder.

"Ho!" he said. "That's your sea bag, hey? Well, me son, do yer work an' give the mates no slack, an'——"

Something heavy fell upon his grey old head. He tumbled into the boat. As he pitched forward Pegwell heard the laugh of his friend Larry, and he realized the treatment awaiting him.

The tall clipper put to sea. On her forecastlehead men tramped drearily around the capstan. Hard-bitted officers cursed them; an exasperated tugboat skipper bawled; the anchor clung tenaciously to the mud.

> "An' awa-ay, Rio! Awa-ay, Rio!
> Sing fare yew well, my bonny young gal,
> We are boun' fer Rio Grande!"

A quavery, broken old pipe raised that chantey. The mate left the knighthead, plunging in among the desolate crew, thumping, thumping, cursing venomously.

"You sojers!" he yelped. "You double-left-legged sojers! Here's old Noah come to life again, and you let him show you your work! Heave, blind you! Heave! Sing out, old Noah! Why, damn my eyes, if it ain't old Pegwell come with us again!"

The mate stood off a pace, staring at Pegwell. Sailormen rarely made two voyages in the *Stella*.

"I didn't join, sir," protested Pegwell, ceasing his song. All the men stopped. Pegwell had tried to persuade the captain he was not one of his crew as soon as he recovered his wits. The result had been painful. "I got to be on the job at six, sir. I'll lose my new job. I wuz shanghaied——"

A fist thumped him hard between the shoulders, driving him back to his capstan bar with coughing lungs.

"Sing out! Start something! Heave, damn you!" retorted the mate, and fell upon the miserable gang tooth and nail. The tug hooted owlishly.

> A jolly good ship, an' a jolly good crew:
> Awa-ay, Rio!
> A jolly good mate, an' a good skipper, too,
> An' we're boun' for Rio Grande!

Pegwell tramped around the capstan. A donkey yoked to the bar of a mill. A sailor bound by a lifetime of hard usage to a habit of obedience.

Pegwell's bunk had bugs. All the bunks had bugs. Pegwell's bunk was beneath a sweat leak where a bit of dry rot had crumbled a corner of a deck beam. But Larry's sea bag, a blue canvas bag made by a sailorman, revealed itself full of amazing comforts. The old fellow had never owned such a bag. There were blankets. Woollen, not woolly. Warm underwear, stockings, shirts. Good oilskins, leakproof boots. There was a real steel razor; a real steel sheath-knife. A great bundle of soap and matches; white enamelware dish and pannikin; and a dainty thing that puzzled Pegwell until he opened it. It was a folder of blue cloth, tied about with a silken cord. On the flat side was worked in silk, beautifully, "Larry; from Mary."

Inside, cunning pockets were full of needles, thread, buttons, scissors. And tucked into the innermost fold was a note, in a slender hand bearing signs of stress, bidding Larry act the man, wishing him luck, praying for his safe return. The feel of it gave old Pegwell a warm thrill.

"Hey, me son, I want that bunk!" he announced grimly, shaking the shoulder of a sleeping ordinary seaman whose bunk was leakless. "C'm on. Out of it! Able seamen comes fust, me lad."

Pegwell carefully placed his needle case in a dry place, then hauled the youth out onto the filthy floor, cotton blanket and all. Even youth must yield to experience when youth is seasick, and experience runs along lines of deep water pully-haul.

Pegwell now had the cleanest, driest bunk in the forecastle. He stole lemons from the steward, which he hid cunningly. From time to time he cut one in slices, fastened it to ship's side or bunk board, thereby driving puzzled bugs to other, less exclusive quarters. He stole nails from Chips; made shelves for his little comforts, pegs for his fine new clothes. He stole a bit of white line from the bosun and made a pair of flat sennit bands by which his spare blankets swung from the bunk above.

By the time the clipper crossed the line Pegwell only dimly remembered Larry's treachery. He only mistily recalled the job he had got but had never worked at. It was easy for the old man to slip back into the habits of a lifetime; even though the ship was a hard place. The great outstanding point was that for the first time in his dreary life old Pegwell sailed deep water possessed of everything necessary for comfort, and some luxuries to boot. And this he owed to Mary Bland.

Old Pegwell usually fell asleep with a flash-back of memory to a snug little store on a dingy waterside, overladen with a stock of wonders, presided over by a laughing girl whose big, brown, friendly eyes sometimes held just a trace of trouble. Then he would think darkly of Larry, only to sink into sound slumber in the warmth of Larry's woollies under Larry's blankets.

II

Pegwell's bunk was no longer dry. No man's bunk was. The forecastle was a reeling, freezing, weeping dungeon peopled with miserable devils to whom hell would have been heaven. For thirty days the clipper had been battered by a northwesterly gale off Cape Horn.

When a man came from the wheel after a two hours' trick he was blue, and tottery, and grinning, and more than a little insane.

Pegwell stood his wheel warm and dry. He felt the bitterness of the weather and the ship's stress, but for once his old bones were not racked with extreme cold. The ship steered badly. They sent the young ordinary seamen to hold the lee spokes.

"You just put yer weight to it when I shoves the helm up or down, me son," said Pegwell. The lad's teeth chattered; his lanky body, undernourished, 'twixt boy and man, shook like a royal mast under a thrashing sail.

"Y—yessir!" he chattered, fearfully.

Pegwell glanced sharply at the lad once or twice. Since their first encounter over the change of bunks, the lad had not been remarkable for politeness toward the old man. But there was no hint of impudence in that "Yessir!" The boy looked blue.

Grumbling, taking a hand from the wheel when he could, gripping a spoke desperately to check it, the old man peeled off his heavy monkey jacket.

"Slip into this yer jacket, me son!" he roared, and put his shoulder to the spokes, bringing the ship to her course before the mate arrived. The lad thawed. When the watch was up, he was glowing. Old Pegwell was warm, but wet through with driving snow. He watched his chance to shuffle along the main deck between seas. The lad, less cautious, started first.

When they were in the deep waist, the new helmsman let the ship go off and a mile long hissing sea reared up and fell aboard the length of her. Pegwell grabbed a lifeline. When the decks cleared themselves through the ports, he clawed his way choking and blinded to the forecastle, soaked to the skin, his broken teeth chattering with the icy chill.

"Where's th' young feller?" he chattered.

"I see him bashed up against th' galley," growled the man nearest. "He'll git here. Can't lose them kind."

He didn't "git here." The young ordinary seaman never rounded the Horn. He went overboard to death wearing old Pegwell's monkey jacket.

Making northing and westing with dry decks, though the wind was bitterly cold, men with all the sailorman's improvidence discarded tattered oilskins and soggy socks. And with all the fiendish fraility of Cape Horn weather, the fair wind blew itself out, a rolling calm followed, and then another, fiercer northwesterly gale shrieked down and drove the ship back into the murderous gray seas to the southward.

Pegwell clambered stiffly out of the rigging after re-tying the points of the reefed main topsail. The maindeck was a seething chaos of rope-snarled water. In the roaring torrent men were being hurled along the deck. Only a frantically waving arm or leg indicated that a man was not dead. Then a greater sea thundered aboard. It smashed the boat gallows. The boats hung over the side, precariously held by the ropes.

A spare topmast was torn loose from chain lashings and chocks: a massive stick of Oregon pine, roughly squared, it hurtled aft on the torrent, broke a sailor's half drowned body cruelly, and crashed end on against the poop bulkhead.

Pegwell and the watch fought with the spar. The seas endued the timber with devilish spite. Twice all hands were torn from their hold, rolled about the flooded decks in the icy water, battered near to death by the murderous stick.

In a lull they secured the spar. The boats were gone. They picked up tangled gear, and took two mangled men from the meshes.

The wind struck afresh. It staggered the ship. And while she staggered and hung poised another chuckling sea climbed over the six foot bulwarks and filled her decks.

"Bill's hurted bad, now, sir," screamed Pegwell, shivering in the grip of cold and numb agony. Bill was the bosun. He hung twisted and pallid between the two men who lifted him. They bore him forward. Chips stood across the sill of the smashed door of the tiny cabin they shared.

"This ain't no place for a hurted man!" Chips grumbled. "Tell th' Old Man he ought t' be took care of aft."

They told the skipper.

"No room aft," the skipper howled at them. "Put him in the forecastle if it's any drier."

They bore the man below. Instinctively they laid him in old Pegwell's bunk, for it was driest. All were wet. Pegwell's at least boasted woollen coverings.

Pegwell himself covered the silent form with a blanket. He needed no hint to cover the pallid face too. He made no protest when a sailor gently pulled another blanket from under the bosun.

"Jack's cruel cold, mate," said the sailor. He wrapped Jack, another storm victim, in the blanket with roughened hands that trembled.

Overhead the seas thundered on deck. The *Stella* fought her stubborn way against the gale under three lower topsails, reefed upper main topsail, and treble reefed foresail with a ribbon of fore topmast staysail.

The gale died out. A fair wind came. The ship sped north again, scarred but sound, clothed in new canvas, triumphant. They buried Bill and Jack in Pegwell's bedding.

By this time Pegwell had little left of his grand outfit. As the rags of his mates gave out, he grumblingly gave of his store. Grumbled and gave. That was Pegwell. But he never let go of that little blue cloth needle case inscribed, "Larry; from Mary." Slyly he had picked at the stitches until the word "Larry" was becoming indistinguishable. When a few more threads fell out he could show his treasure to incredulous sailormen, and they would never know that the obliterated name was not his own.

The crew scuttled from the *Stella* like rats when she docked. Only Pegwell hung on. Alone of the outward bound crew before the mast, he stubbornly resisted all the efforts of the mates to get him out. They could ship a new crew homeward at half the wages paid outward. None of the deserters waited for their wages. Their forfeited pay was so much profit to the ship. But Pegwell refused to be driven out. Cheerless and bare his bunk might be. It was. There was always the little blue folded housewife to remind him that he had a shore job once over against a snug little store. And the ambition that had flamed then still burned.

As for quitting the ship, Pegwell had wages due. Not a lot, but wages still. If he completed the voyage, drawing no advance whatever, buying nothing from the slop chest, he would have coming to him a nice little nest egg which might hatch into a home at last. That nest egg loomed big to the captain.

"Set him to chipping cable," said the skipper. "Work him up!"

The mates worked him up, cruelly, but they could not work him out.

Homeward bound round the Horn. Pegwell showed his little blue housewife to the new hands. They were a hard lot. They made ribald fun about it. They stole his poor bedding, and dared him to identify it. He endured. They stole his sea boots. Pegwell endured that, too. But somebody stole his little blue housewife, worked in silk, "——; from Mary," and there was a fight.

It was a young weasel of a wastrel who tried to prevent Pegwell from taking back his treasure. A weasel bred in the muck of the water front; cunning and full of devious fighting tricks. But the old seaman fought on sure feet on a reeling deck; fought with righteous fury swelling his breast; fought without feeling the brutal knee or the gouging thumb. And he beat his man, recovered his treasure, and earned much freedom from molestation.

In the bleak, soul-searching gales off Cape Stiff, Pegwell suffered intensely. He shivered and froze in silence.

The old sailor had always his little blue cloth treasure. He whispered his troubles to it as he shivered in his wet bed—it was the one comfort nobody could take from him. He might shake with cold and wet all through a watch below, but there was ever before him the vision of that snug little store, the pretty, laughing girl whose big brown eyes yet held a trace of trouble. Somehow he grew to fasten the responsibility for that trouble on Larry. And, once established, his own grievance against the man smouldered fiercer.

When the tall clipper furled her sails in her home port again, Pegwell's bitterness against Larry Bland had intensified to such a degree as to surprise the old chap himself. Bitterness formed no part of his real nature. But it was winter again; the snow fell; the streets, from the ship, looked dreary and inhospitable. And old Pegwell had nothing but rags to cover his aching bones.

The rest of the fo'mast hands had drawn something on account of wages and gone ashore to spend that and mortgage the balance due. But not old Pegwell. He would carry ashore every dollar coming to him from the voyage he ought never to have made. He would buy a suit of clothes and stout shoes that would last, put the rest of his money in safe hands, then look for Larry.

"It'll be him and me fer it!" he muttered.

III

The ship paid off. Soulless wretches who had whined and cringed under the punishment of the sea rolled up bold and blusterous, full of hot courage at twenty-five cents a hot shot, cursing captain and mates and ship as they took their pitiful pay.

In an hour Pegwell entered the little store, and in ten seconds more a Cape Horn Voyage in a cardcase packet was a vanished horror. The big brown eyes of Mary Bland glistened with welcome, even though at first they had been cloudy with uncertainty.

"I am so glad to see you again, Pegwell," she cried. "It was so good of you to change places with Larry. I hope you had a good voyage. Won't you come inside?"

Pegwell grinned sourly as he followed her into the smug little room behind the shop. He had meant to say something about that change of jobs. Instead, with a warmth seeping through his bones clear to his heart, mellowing it again, he forgot Larry and smoked himself into rosy visions under the musical spell of her voice.

In an hour they were as intimate as before the *Stella* went out. Mary had told him, shyly, that Jack wanted a speedy wedding; she had barely hinted that brother Larry was a stumbling block, immediately suppressing the hint. She had offered to work Pegwell's name into the little blue housewife where the word "Larry" had been picked out; and when she took it from him her eyes were suspiciously moist. Pegwell noticed it, though the girl tried hard to hide her feelings.

Then Jack came in and old Pegwell went out. The gladness in Mary's eyes, the pride in those of the stalwart cripple, gave the old mariner a thrill. It made him boil, too. There was a couple just aching for each other, hindered by a waster of a brother not worth a crocodile's tear.

"Hullo, old Pegwell," smiled Jack as he passed. He stuck out a strong brown hand in a hearty grip. "Mighty glad to see you again. Ought to stay this time. Going to buy Mary's shop, she tells me. Hurry up, old fellow. She's keeping me waiting all on your account."

Jack laughed, and went to Mary's side, leaving Pegwell wondering. He waited out in the cold street until Jack came out, then joined him in his walk and put the question bluntly:

"What's Larry up to?"

Jack was serious. His smile fled at the blunt demand. Anger was in his eyes, but he dismissed it. Pegwell, shrewder perhaps than he was given credit for being, noticed these little things. He put two and two together handily enough, and found the amount was four—no more or less.

"I wish Larry would either get bumped off or caught with the goods, Pegwell," Jack said. "He's breaking Mary's heart. She won't believe any wrong about him, yet she knows he's bound hellbent for ruin. If he was dead she would be better off. The rat has taken all her little savings and is about eating up her profits now. She won't marry, though God knows Larry's way of living don't influence me a bit where she's concerned. If Larry got sent up for a long stretch it would be better for Mary, though she would mourn him as if he was dead. I wish she would get rid of the store, quit this neighbourhood, and let me make her happy. But she won't, as long as that rat is loose."

"Didn't 'e go to work on the dock?" asked Pegwell, raging. "'E bunged me off in th' *Stella* and took my job, didn't he?"

"He held the job for one week and quit," Jack replied. "He said he'd made a killing at the races. Two watchmen since have either fallen off the dock at night or been thrown off." Jack was silent for a moment.

"Pegwell," said Jack at length, "I'm glad you're home. You can do a lot for Mary. I ought not to mention this to a soul; but I believe you are her friend."

"Friend?" rasped Pegwell. "Mister, you're bloody foolish! That little gal kin use me fer a door mat an' I'll show you what sort of a friend I am fust time I set eyes on that Larry!"

"Not so loud," Jack whispered. They passed a policeman, who nodded to Jack. "Pegwell, they're out to get Larry now! I have done all I can. I can't shield him any longer. He's out of town for a while, but when he comes back he's going to be jumped on, and he'll get ten years."

"Wot d'you think I can do?" demanded Pegwell. "Can I save him when you can't? Want me to go up for him, same as I made a Cape voyage in a hell ship for him?" The old man was furious.

"You can only be a friend and comfort to Mary," said Jack quietly. Pegwell's wrinkled face was screwed up grotesquely with the intensity of his thought.

"Seems to me," he said, "if you was to sort of hurry her into a weddin', maybe you could do a bit o' comfortin' yourself. If I had money enough to offer to buy her shop off her I c'd take care o' the Larry rat."

"Oh, you have money enough," retorted Jack quietly. "Mary said long ago you could pay out of the profits. You only need about a hundred to pay down. I guess you have that much."

Pegwell was apparently not listening; yet in fact he was. He seemed to be looking sheer through the cold, grey drizzle into the future, and if his worn, lined old face was any guide, what he saw in the dim perspective of imagination held more light than shadow.

"What's th' wust this yer Larry's done?" he suddenly asked. "Killed anybody?"

"Oh, no," replied Jack swiftly. "Nothing like that."

"Been wreckin' some young gal——"

"No more than he has wrecked Mary's youth," Jack interrupted. "He's just a plain crook. Dope smuggling; peddling, too. The worst he's done is to sell dope to school kids. Bad enough I'd say."

"Not quite es bad es murder, I s'pose," Pegwell growled, "though be damned ef I know why it ain't. Anyhow, Jack, me lad, you take the advice of a old lummox, marry Mary whether she wants to or not, and I'll promise to take care o' Larry. I'll see he don't git sent up. You tell her. I be going round to-night again and see how fur you're right about that hunderd down and hunderd when you ketch me shop purchase proppisition. S'long, Jack. Set them weddin' bells to ringin'."

Late that night Mary Bland bade Pegwell good night at the door of the little shop. She was rosy and smiling. Her brown eyes were wide and bright. Pegwell had never seen her so completely alive and gladsome. She shook his hand twice, and just for a tiny instant a speck of cloud flickered in her eyes.

"If you believe you can help Larry, I know you can," she said. "I know he will be safe in your care, old Pegwell."

"He'll git a man's chance, you kin make sartin," stated Pegwell. "Good night, Missy, an' Gawd keep you smilin'. I'll be around to meet Jack in the mornin' and settle about the shop. Forgit yer troubles. Th' cops don't want Larry. If they did they couldn't git him."

At the end of the week Old Pegwell took undivided charge of the little shop, while Jack and Mary went about on some mysterious business connected with a license. Old Pegwell stood in the door watching them, and his old pipe emitted clouds of smoke in sympathy with the depth of his breathing. He felt queerly tight about the heart.

"Gawd bless 'em, goddammit!" he barked chokily.

A man came to buy tobacco. The two men stared at each other.

"Damn my eyes if 't ain't old Pegwell!" roared the mate of the *Stella*. "Come to moorings at last, hey, you old fox?"

"Aye, mister, you won't bullydam old Pegwell no more. When d'ye sail?"

The mate laughed, picking up his change.

"Next Saturday. I'll put yer name on yer old bunk. Or p'raps you'd like to sail bosun, hey?"

Pegwell laughed comfortably. He spread his feet wide as he stood again in the doorway, gazing after the rolling figure of the mate. At last, at last he was man enough to tell a first mate to go scratch his ear. He turned to go inside, for the air was cold in spite of the sun, and the shop must be kept warm, when a scurrying figure doubled the corner, burst in after him, and slammed the door.

Larry Bland stood there before him, panting, wild-eyed.

"Where's Mary?" he rasped.

"Gone out, me son," said Pegwell grimly. "Just calm down. I own this here shop now. What kin I do for you?"

Larry glanced around the place furtively. He had a hunted look. Pegwell remembered Jack's words. A dark shape appeared against the glass of the door outside and Larry made for the inside room. Pegwell hastened him in as the door opened and a policeman entered.

"Larry Bland just came in here. Where is he?" he demanded.

"Orf'cer, Larry Bland shanghaied me a v'yage round Cape Stiff," grinned Pegwell. "D'you 'magine he'd come where I be?"

"I saw him open the door."

"Aye, an' he dam' soon shut it again!"

The policeman stepped to the door of the inner room and peered inside. Old Pegwell heaved a tremendous sigh of relief when he quickly turned and bolted from the shop. Larry had taken care of his own concealment. He crawled in through a rear window when Pegwell called his name.

"Where's Mary gone?" he asked hoarsely. Larry looked scared. "I got to get to her."

"You can't get to her," returned Pegwell. "If it's the coppers you're scared of, lay low and keep your head. I won't let no cops git you, 'less you cuts up rough. You git upstairs to yer own room, while I thinks out what to do."

"You ain't gettin' even are you?" snarled Larry suspiciously.

"In my own way, yes, me son. My way don't mean lettin' no cops git Mary Bland's brother. You duck into cover."

When Mary and Jack returned she ran up to old Pegwell and kissed him warmly. She blushed at his gaze and shyly showed him a brand-new wedding ring. Jack laughed.

"I took your advice, Pegwell," he said. "No time like the present. So now you're sole proprietor here. We'll come back to-morrow to get Mary's few belongings. Just now I want her to myself. So long. Come, Mary!"

They left quickly, leaving old Pegwell hot with unspoken felicitations. Larry crept down. He had heard Mary's voice.

"Get outa sight!" snapped Pegwell. "Damnit! The street's full o' coppers!"

Larry ducked. He was frankly terrified.

When Mary appeared in the morning to pack her things Larry was securely out of sight. Old Pegwell had been busy all night. He had made a stout, roomy chest, iron cleated and hinged. He had made Larry help him, keeping him in mind of the police. Now Larry crouched in the big chest in the cellar, while Mary sang happily and packed her small trifles in the bright little rooms above.

"I do hope you will enjoy every hour here, Pegwell," Mary said when ready to leave. "Jack rather rushed me off my feet; but I'm glad, because he said you promised to see that Larry comes to no harm."

"Missy," replied Pegwell gravely, "I won't let Larry get into no trouble with the police. I'm goin' to try to make a man outa him. So good luck to you, and God bless you. May all yer troubles be little 'uns, and if so be you wants a rattle, why——"

The old fellow glanced around the little shop, seeking for the bundle of rattles that hung somewhere; but he felt a warm, moist kiss on his cheek, the door opened, and she was gone.

On Thursday the police visited the shop again. Larry was known to be in the district.

"He wuz here, but I ain't seen him to-day," said Pegwell. The old chap was in a sweating fret. Larry was getting impatient. He had demanded to see his sister and threatened to take his chance on the street. Pegwell had to lock the chest on him.

"He's likely to come back then," decided the officer in charge. "One o' you camp here," he told one of his men.

"I don't think he'll bother me much," Pegwell volunteered. "He done me dirt and knows I'll git even."

Pegwell was outwardly cool; inwardly, when that policeman took up his station in the inner room, he was all a-quiver. The noon stream of customers came in and kept him busy; but he dreaded the quiet of the afternoon. Another policeman came to take a turn of duty over night, and slept in a chair in the back room. Pegwell, upstairs, remained awake all night, listening lest the officer go exploring, dreading every moment to hear some betraying sound from the cramped Larry in the cellar.

All day Friday he had no chance to give Larry either food or water. All he could do was to pass hurriedly by and murmur through the lid of the chest a few harsh words of reassurance that relief was at hand. In the evening he closed the shop, left the policeman in sole charge, and went out for an hour. When he came back again he began to make up several small parcels of tobacco.

"Got a bit o' trade from the *Stella*," he told the policeman. "Nothin' like slops and tobacker for profits, mister. Ever think o' startin' a shop?"

"Shop, hell!" growled the policeman. "I deal in men, old salt."

"Men is queer, that's true," said Pegwell.

At eleven o'clock a cart rattled up to the door, loaded up with sea chests and bags, with two husky toughs beside the driver and a heap of brutish bodies snoring in the back.

"Come for th' slops an' tobacker," they said.

"Here's th' tobacker," said Pegwell. "Slop chest is in th' basement. Pretty heavy. I'll give y' a hand."

"We can handle it," returned the huskies, and one of them winked at Pegwell.

Pegwell chatted to the policeman as he handed out the tobacco parcels. He talked loudly, calling the policeman "officer" as the chest was carried past. That was for Larry's benefit. Otherwise Larry might wonder what was being done to him and make some unfortunate noise.

"All right?" asked Pegwell.

"O. K.," the leader said, and paid over the money he had been counting out to Pegwell. Pegwell carefully set it aside, to buy a wedding present for somebody he knew; then he joined the policeman for a good-night smoke, chatting quite brilliantly, surprising himself.

Before daylight the next morning, old Pegwell was busy with broom and scraper on his sidewalk, for snow had fallen in the night. The water of the harbour was grey and cruel. Old Pegwell glanced out, shivered, and plied his broom. He was glad he had not to be out there, perhaps stamping around a capstan. It felt good to know that. It made him sing.

> And awa-ay, Rio! Awa-ay, Rio!
> Then fare you well, my bonny young gal,
> For we're bound for Rio Grande!

From down the bay came the hoot of a tug. And, clear and sharp, metallically shattering the morning heaviness, came also the clack, clack, clack of capstan pawls, the "fare you well" of an outward bounder.

ROUNDING CAPE HORN[1]

Felix Riesenberg

(1879–   )

ON A clear Monday morning, the 7th of February, 1898, to be exact, the captain, after working up his A.M. sight, came on deck and announced a good observation. It was the first time the sun had been visible in some days, and by working a Sumner, he found we were on a line cutting close past Cape St John, on Staten Land, having sailed the ship down between the Falkland Islands and Cape Virgins by dead reckoning. We were coiling down the gear after the morning washdown, and I was busy at the monkey rail, when he came on deck with his results, and imparted the above information to the mate in my hearing.

"Better send a hand to the main skys'l yard, Mr Zerk," said the captain, in conclusion.

I was handy, and at a nod from the mate sprang up the Jacob's ladder and on to the ratlines, going up like a monkey, out over the futtock shrouds, up the topmast rigging, narrowing to the topmast crosstrees,

---

[1] From *Under Sail*. Reprinted by permission of Harcourt Brace & Company, Inc., and of Jonathan Cape, Ltd.

in through the horns of the crosstrees, and on farther up the t'gallant and royal rigging, on the slight rope ladders abaft the mast. Coming to the skysail mast, hardly larger round than the stick of a fair catboat, I shinned up with the help of the halyards, and swung myself astride of the yard, my arm about the aerie pinnacle of the main truck. From my vantage point, the sea was truly an inspiring sight; clear as crystal, the limpid air stretched free to the distant horizon without a mist or cloud to mar the panorama of vast blue ocean. I felt as though I had suddenly been elevated to a heaven far above the strife and trouble of the decks below.

For the moment I forgot the object of my climb, in the contemplation of the sparkling scene stretching as far as eye could reach. I glanced down to the narrow deck far beneath, white in the sun, the black top of the bulwarks outlining the plan of the ship against the deep blue waters; my eye followed the easy curves of the square canvas on the main, the great breadth of the yards extending to port and starboard, and I wondered that so small a ship could support such an avalanche of sail as bowled along under my feet. Aft, a foamy wake stretched for a mile or two, for we were sailing at a fairish speed with the wind from the north, a point on the port quarter.

I saw the men flaking down the fore tops'l halyards, clear for running, on the top of the forward house, and I saw the mate watching me from the weather fore pinrail, his head thrown back as he gazed aloft; something told me to get busy, and I looked far ahead to the south.

A faint blue streak on the horizon held my eyes. Accustomed to the sight of land from out at sea, through my voyages in the schoolship; still I hesitated to name it land. We were sixty-two days out, and land looked strange. Again I brought my sight to bear upon the distant sky-line ahead; there was no mistaking the dim outline of land rising from the sea at a point immediately to the south of us and reaching westward.

"*Land ho!*" I hailed the deck.

"Where away?" came the voice of Captain Nichols.

"A point on the lee bow, sir!"

"All right! lay down!" shouted the mate, evidently not intending that I should further enjoy my lofty perch on the skysail yard.

We raised the land rapidly, the breeze increasing slightly as the day advanced. At noon Staten Land was visible from the deck, and by eight bells in the afternoon watch we were sailing past the bold shores, some ten miles distant, and drawing the land well abeam. Running south for a good offing, and taking in our light sails with the coming of darkness, we hauled our wind to the starboard quarter at the end of the last dog watch and headed bravely for old "Cape Stiff."

Captain Nichols might have ventured through the Strait of Le Maire, with the weather we were having, though at the best it is taking chances to keep the land too close aboard when in the troubled latitudes of Terra

Del Fuego. Countless ships, with the fine *Duchesse de Berry* among the last of them, have ground their ribs against the pitiless rocks that gird those coasts. However, we were enjoying the rarest of Cape Horn weather —sunshine, fair wind, and a moderate sea.

For the first time in many weary days, we livened things up with a chantey as we swigged away on the braces and tautened every stitch of canvas with well stretched sheets and halyards.

Jimmy Marshall had just started "Whiskey for my Johnnie," and the captain came forward on the break of the poop and joined in the chorus in a funny, squeaky voice—but none of us dared laugh at him. He was so delighted with the progress we were making, and the chance that we might slip by the "corner" in record time, that nothing was too good for us. The mate came down from his high-horse, and with Mr. Stoddard and Chips, who had just finished their supper and were stepping out on deck, to join them, the full after guard took up the refrain— and the words rose in a great volume of deep sea song.

> "Oh, whiskey—my Johnnie;
> Yes, whiskey made me sell my coat,
> Whiskey, my Johnnie.
> Oh, whiskey's what keeps me afloat,
> Oh, whiskey for my Johnnie."

When we pumped her out that night at the main pump, for the ship was almost on an even keel, we noted the skipper had begun to stump the quarter deck in a very excited way, constantly ducking up and down the companion, and scanning the horizon with an anxious eye. Cape pigeons were circling close to the ship with an endless chatter, and far above us swung a huge, dun-coloured fulmar gull, its white belly clean against the grey sky.

"There is something doing with the glass," remarked Frenchy, eyeing the skipper. "We'll have some weather to look out for before long," and all of us watched the gull with fascinated eyes. Jimmy and Brenden agreed with Frenchy that we were in for heavy weather.

But in spite of these dire predictions, and in spite of a "red dawn," the day broke and continued fair, and we were again regaled with a glimpse of land, jagged sombre peaks, jutting into the sky to the north like the cruel teeth of a ragged saw, grey-blue above the far horizon.

I was aft flaking down the mizzen tops'l halyards on the morning following the landfall, when Captain Nichols stumped past me from the break of the poop to the companion. He had been up all night, and the continuation of fine weather evidently pleased and surprised him. He had a pair of binoculars in his hand, and, in passing, he stopped and offered the glasses to me, pointing to the southernmost promontory, a cold blue knob rising from the sea.

"That's Cape Horn over there, Felix. Take a good look at it. You may never see it again, if you were born lucky."

Almost staggered by this sudden good fortune, I brought the captain's glasses in focus on the dreaded cape, my whole being thrilled with the pleasure of looking through those excellent binoculars at that distant point of rock, the outpost of the New World, jutting far into the southern ocean. I doubt if the gallant old Dutchman, Schouten, who first "doubled" it, experienced half the exhilaration that I did on first beholding that storied headland. At four bells in the morning watch I went to the wheel, and while the watch swabbed down the decks after the morning washdown, I was privileged to look at the Cape out of the corner of my eye, between times keeping the "lubber's line" of the compass bowl on sou'west by sou', for the skipper had shaped a course a point or so further off shore, as the currents had evidently set us in toward the land during the night and he wished to keep his safe offing.

The wind in the meantime had veered round to west-nor'-west, blowing directly off the land and with increasing force. The light sails were taken in again, and by eight bells we were under t'gans'ls, upper and lower tops'ls, reefed fores'l, reefed mains'l, spanker, jib, and topmast stays'ls.

As I left the wheel and went forward, I determined to attempt a pencil sketch of Cape Horn, the weather being too dull for a photograph, even if the land were not too distant. The result, after some trials, and the loss of my breakfast, which was nothing, resulted in a fair representation of what we saw of the Cape, and I turned into my bunk with a feeling of satisfaction. After all, it was worth a good deal to have actually set eyes upon the Horn.

When we turned out at one bell, for dinner, we found the wind had veered farther to the west, we were sailing by the wind with the starboard tacks aboard, the cold spray from a rising sea, breaking over the fo'c'sle head, and spattering against the fo'c'sle door.

Jimmy sat up and rubbed his eyes as the watch was called, and swore gently under his breath. Brenden went out on deck to take a look at the weather. "Hell, we got it now. I have seen this before. D'you feel the ice?" he asked.

Indeed we all felt the drop in the temperature, and the short snappy jerk of the ship, as she met the new direction of the sea, was anything but pleasant.

Coffee was served out to us that noon instead of lime juice, and the warmth was welcome; it helped wash down the last cooked meal that Chow was able to prepare for ten days.

Mustering on deck at eight bells, we found we were driving south under a leaden sky. Cape Horn, still dimly visible, was soon shut off, vanishing in a cloud cap over the land astern. We were sailing due south, the wind having headed us, and at four bells, the wind rapidly increasing in violence, the starboard watch turned out to help in shortening down.

We at once took in the t'gans'ls, mains'l, and jib, and these were followed in quick succession by other canvas, until at eight bells we had the *Fuller* stripped to her lower tops'ls, close reefed main upper tops'l, and storm stays'ls. The sea rose to mammoth proportions, fetching as it did from the very edge of the Antarctic ice barrier.

The canvas aloft soon became stiff with ice, and all gear on the ship was coated with frozen rain, as we were swept by a succession of rain and hail storms. At nightfall we were hove to, on the starboard tack under goose-winged main lower tops'l, reefed main trys'l, and storm stays'l. The oil tank forward was dripping its contents on the sea, and two oil bags were slung from the fore and main weather channels.

The storm, for the wind had now increased to fully sixty miles an hour, held steady from the west until midnight. Then it suddenly went to nor'west, and in the squalls, when the wind rose to hurricane force, the *Fuller* lay over on her beam ends. A vicious cross sea added its danger to the situation. All hands were then on deck, remaining aft near the mizzen rigging. The fo'c'sle, galley, and forward cabin were awash. Four men braced themselves at the spokes of the wheel, under the eye of the second mate, and relieving tackles were hooked to ease the "kick" of the tiller. Preventer braces and rolling tackles, got up earlier in the day, were hove taut to steady the heavy spars aloft. All loose gear was streaming to leeward, washing in the sea, through the open scuppers and freeing ports. A fierce boiling of white phosphorescent wave caps lit the sea as it broke over the ship, intensifying the black pandemonium overhead. The sleet-laden spume shot over the prostrate vessel in a continuous roar, drowning all attempts at shouting of orders.

It was during the wild but fascinating hours of this night, that I realized the high quality of seamanship that had prepared us for an ordeal such as we are going through. The consummate skill with which the great wooden craft was being handled, came home to me with a force that could not be denied. How easily a bungling lubber might have omitted some precaution, or carried sail improperly, or have done, or not done, the thousand things that would have spelled disaster!

The captain and mate stood at the lee of the mizzen mast, each with a turn of the tops'l sheets about him, and hitched over the monkey rail. The rest of us, crouching at the lee of the cabin trunk, knee deep in the water when she went over in the heavier squalls, held our places wondering what turn things would take next. Looking through one of the after cabin ports, on my way to the wheel, I saw Chow and Komoto, the cabin boy, packing a box by the light of the small lamp swinging in its gimbals. They were evidently getting ready to leave—where to—themselves and their gods alone knew.

All things have an end, and the Stygian blackness of the night gave way to grey streaks of dawn that broke upon us, revealing a scene of utmost desolation. A note of order was given to the wild confusion of the gale-wracked fabric, when Chips, his lanky figure skimming along the life line, and his sounding rod sheltered under his long oil coat, ventured to the main fife rail to sound the well. As for the crew, we were soaked with salt water and frozen to the marrow. The main lower tops'l had blown from the bolt ropes during the night; we never missed it until morning. Twenty feet of the lee bulwark—the port side—was gone, and a flapping rag of canvas at the main hatch told us that the tarpaulin was torn. Looking forward through the whistle of wind and spume that cut across the sharply tilted rigging, the scene was one of terrific strife, as though some demon ruler of the sea had massed his forces, and was making a desperate drive for the destruction of the wooden handiwork of man upon which he dared to venture over those forbidden wastes.

No matter how miserable one may be, action of some kind always comes as a relief. Our hard lot on the *Fuller* was positively made more bearable by the added hardships of the storm, and when the night was past we were glad to force our chilled limbs and hungry bellies to some sort of effort. Anything was better than to hang to the mizzen rigging and slowly freeze to death. The torn hatch tarpaulin was a serious matter. The merchant service holds no higher duty, where passengers are not carried, than the duty towards cargo. This is often forgotten by men who lack the true traditions of the sea. But our officers were well alive to the importance, not only of bringing our ship around the Horn, but of bringing her cargo through in good condition.

The mate, followed by Axel, Brenden, Frenchy, and Mike, a husky, well-set-up sailor of the starboard watch, went into the waist and worked their way along the deck at great peril. After much trouble they managed to wedge down the flapping canvas, which was under a constant deluge of blue water, whole seas coming aboard in quick succession.

By noon the weather abated somewhat, and we got the ship under fore and mizzen lower tops'ls, and close reefed main upper tops'l. Before nightfall we had sent down what remained of the main lower tops'l, and bent a new sail. That afternoon we experienced an adventure fraught with much excitement to us of the port watch. The jib having worked loose from the gaskets, by constant dipping into the sea, as the ragged crests of blue water buried the bowsprit and jibboom, six of us were ordered out to secure the sail by passing a three-inch manila line around the sail and boom.

Brenden, Scouse, Frenchy, and I were on the weather side, and Joe and Martin went out on the boom to leeward. The job was almost finished, two seas had already drenched us, and we were chilled with the dip in the cold water, when the ship rose to a heavy roller, her bow lifted high into the eye of the wind, and then plunged down into the deep trough between two seas. The momentum was so great that she failed to rise quickly enough, and her jibboom stabbed right into the heart of the onrushing wall of cold blue water, regardless of the half dozen luckless wretches clinging to the furled canvas with all their might. The great sea went on over us, thundering down on the fo'c'sle head, and rushing aft along the deck in a noisy white cataract of foam. When she shook free we were left clinging to the jibboom like drowned rats, that is, all of us but Joe.

Aft on the poop, the mate heard our cries, and, springing to the lee rail, he yanked a bight of line from a pin and hove it overboard, catching Joe just in time as he rose close along side. When she heeled to leeward, ready hands hauled the half-drowned Joe on board. Captain Nichols had come up on the first cry, and taking Joe into the cabin, he poured out a liberal hooker of whiskey from the medicine chest. The funny part of the whole thing was that Joe was more thankful for the drink than for his escape from certain death, for we never could have lowered a boat in that sea.

We got a watch below that night, and the cook managed to heat some coffee, but cold salt beef and hard tack were all that the kids contained when we went below for supper. Wrapped in our damp clothes we managed to peg in a few hours of necessary sleep. Life, for a week afterward, was not worth living, unless one held some latent strain of the old berserker flowing through his veins. It was a fight, and the elements charged us and flanked us in midnight fury, increasingly cold as we edged farther to the south in our attempt to round the meridian of Cape Horn.

In latitude 56° 29' S. and longitude 68° 42' W. From Greenwich, about sixty sea miles S.W. by W. from Cape Horn, lies the island of Diego Ramirez, a weather-worn rock jutting from the black waters of the sub-Antarctic. Ten days after fetching away from the Cape, we beat south and sighted this grim sentinel, the outpost of the tempest and the gale— ten days of such seagoing as seldom falls to the men who nowadays go down to the sea in steamers.

Under conditions of the kind we experienced, every man was put to the test, and his worth as a member of the crew clearly established. Fortunately for us, and for the races representive in our small company —of which we boasted quite a few—no strain of yellow fear developed during the days and nights when the work aloft called for the performance of duty dangerous in the extreme. Not one of us but had been shipmates with men lost overboard, or maimed for life in accidents to sail or spars. Never was there a moment's hesitation to lay aloft, or out on a swaying buckling yard in the black cover of night, to grapple with canvas hard and unruly. No work was too trying, and no hours of labour too long. We thought nothing of the eternal injustice of a fate that sent us out to sea to fight for our very lives on a ship far too big for so small a crew to handle safely, if indeed any crew of mere men could ever *safely* handle so large a ship.

Never was there a suspicion of holding back, and through it all, the discipline of the disgruntled warmer latitudes was dropped and orders were quickly obeyed as a matter of course; yes, as a matter of self-preservation. The disgusting profanity of warmer climes was laid in the discard for a while, and we were men doing men's work.

Wet and hunger were the rule; to be chilled with the cold was normal, and our salvation was the constant struggle with the working of the ship. Accidents occurred, and old Jimmy lay in his bunk with his right arm in a bandage from a dislocation due to a fall on the slippery deck. This was roughly set by the captain with the help of the mate and the carpenter. The galley fire had hardly been lighted an hour at a time, as the seas flooded everything forward. Cold salt junk—from the harness casks to the kids—comprised the mainstay of our ration, not to mention the daily whack of mouldy, weevily hard tack. Had it not been for an occasional steaming hot can of slops, called tea and coffee, we should have surely perished.

Our oilskins were in shreds, boots leaked, and every stitch of clothing in the ship was damp, except when dried by the heat of our bodies. Had I been told of this before starting out—well, I suppose I would not have believed it—and, when I say that during it all we had a fairly good time, and managed to crack jokes and act like a lot of irresponsible asses, it goes to prove that man was born to be kicked; be he on a sailing ship around the Horn, on the hard edge of the Arctic littoral, or in the bloody trenches; fate is always there to step in and deliver the necessary bumping.

THE YELLOW CAT[1]

Wilbur Daniel Steele

(1886–   )

AT LEAST once in my life I have had the good fortune to board a deserted vessel at sea. I say "good fortune" because it has left me the memory of a singular impression. I have felt a ghost of the same thing two or three times since then, when peeping through the doorway of an abandoned house.

Now that vessel was not dead. She was a good vessel, a sound vessel, even a handsome vessel, in her blunt-bowed, coastwise way. She sailed under four lowers across as blue and glittering a sea as I have ever known, and there was not a point in her sailing that one could lay a finger upon as wrong. And yet, passing that schooner at two miles, one knew, somehow, that no hand was on her wheel. Sometimes I can imagine a vessel, stricken like that, moving over the empty spaces of the sea, carrying it off quite well were it not for that indefinable suggestion of a stagger; and I can think of all those ocean gods, in whom no landsman will ever

---

[1] Reprinted by permission of the author and of the proprietors of *Harper's Magazine*.

believe, looking at one another and tapping their foreheads with just the shadow of a smile.

I wonder if they all scream—these ships that have lost their souls? Mine screamed. We heard her voice, like nothing I have ever heard before, when we rowed under her counter to read her name—the *Marionette* it was, of Halifax. I remember how it made me shiver, there in the full blaze of the sun, to hear her going on so, railing and screaming in that stark fashion. And I remember, too, how our footsteps, pattering through the vacant internals in search of that haggard utterance, made me think of the footsteps of hurrying warders roused in the night.

And we found a parrot in a cage; that was all. It wanted water. We gave it water and went away to look things over, keeping pretty close together, all of us. In the quarters the tables were set for four. Two men had begun to eat, by the evidence of the plates. Nowhere in the vessel was there any sign of disorder, except one sea-chest broken out, evidently in haste. Her papers were gone and the stern davits were empty. That is how the case stood that day, and that is how it has stood to this. I saw this same *Marionette* a week later, tied up to a Hoboken dock, where she awaited news from her owners; but even there, in the midst of all the water-front bustle, I could not get rid of the feeling that she was still very far away—in a sort of shippish other-world.

The thing happens now and then. Sometimes half a dozen years will go by without a solitary wanderer of this sort crossing the ocean paths, and then in a single season perhaps several of them will turn up: vacant waifs, impassive and mysterious—a quarter-column of tidings tucked away on the second page of the evening paper.

That is where I read the story about the *Abbie Rose*. I recollect how painfully awkward and out-of-place it looked there, cramped between ruled black edges and smelling of landsman's ink—this thing that had to do essentially with air and vast coloured spaces. I forget the exact words of the heading—something like "Abandoned Craft Picked Up At Sea" but I still have the clipping itself, couched in the formal patter of the marine-news writer.

The first hint of another mystery of the sea came in to-day when the schooner *Abbie Rose* dropped anchor in the upper river, manned only by a crew of one. It appears that the out-bound freighter *Mercury* sighted the *Abbie Rose* off Block Island on Thursday last, acting in a suspicious manner. A boat-party sent aboard found the schooner in perfect order and condition, sailing under four lower sails, the topsails being pursed up to the mastheads but not stowed. With the exception of a yellow cat the vessel was found to be utterly deserted, though her small boat still hung in the davits. No evidences of disorder were visible in any part of the craft. The dishes were washed up, the stove in the galley was still slightly warm to the touch, everything in its proper place with the exception of the vessel's papers, which were not to be found.

All indications being for fair weather, Captain Rohmer of the *Mercury* detailed two of his company to bring the find back to this port, a distance of one hundred and fifteen miles. The only man available with a knowledge of the fore-and-aft rig was Stewart McCord, the second engineer. A seaman by the name of Björnsen was sent with him. McCord arrived this noon, after a very heavy voyage of five days, reporting that Björnsen had fallen overboard while shaking out the foretopsail. McCord himself showed evidences of the hardships he has passed through, being almost a nervous wreck.

Stewart McCord! Yes, Stewart McCord would have a knowledge of the fore-and-aft rig, or of almost anything else connected with the affairs of the sea. It happened that I used to know this fellow. I had even been quite chummy with him in the old days—that is, to the extent of drinking too many beers with him in certain hot-country ports. I remembered him as a stolid and deliberate sort of a person, with an amazing hodge-podge of learning, a stamp collection, and a theory about the effects of tropical sunshine on the Caucasian race, to which I have listened half of more than one night, stretched out naked on a freighter's deck. He had not impressed me as a fellow who would be bothered by his nerves.

And there was another thing about the story which struck me as rather queer. Perhaps it is a relic of my seafaring days, but I have always been a conscientious reader of the weather reports; and I could remember no weather in the past week sufficient to shake a man out of a top, especially a man by the name of Björnsen—a thorough-going seafaring name.

I was destined to hear more of this in the evening, from the ancient boatman who rowed me out on the upper river. He had been to sea in his day. He knew enough to wonder about this thing, even to indulge in a little superstitious awe about it.

"No sir-ee. Something *happened* to them four chaps. And another thing——"

I fancied I heard a sea-bird whining in the darkness overhead. A shape moved out of the gloom ahead, passed to the left, lofty and silent, and merged once more with the gloom behind—a barge at anchor, with the sea-grass clinging around her waterline.

"Funny about that other chap," the old fellow speculated. "Björnsen —I b'lieve he called 'im. Now that story sounds to me kind of——" He feathered his oars with a suspicious jerk and peered at me. "This McCord a friend of yourn?" he inquired.

"In a way," I said.

"Hm-m—well——" He turned on his thwart to squint ahead. "There she is," he announced, with something of relief, I thought.

It was hard at that time of night to make anything but a black blotch out of the *Abbie Rose*. Of course I could see that she was pot-bellied, like the rest of the coastwise sisterhood. And that McCord had not stowed his topsails. I could make them out, pursed at the mastheads and hanging down as far as the crosstrees, like huge over-ripe pears. Then I recollected that he had found them so—probably had not touched them since; a queer way to leave tops, it seemed to me. I could see also the glowing tip of a cigar floating restlessly along the farthest rail. I called: "McCord! Oh, McCord!"

The spark came swimming across the deck. "Hello! Hello, there— ah——" There was a note of querulous uneasiness there that somehow jarred with my remembrance of this man.

"Ridgeway," I explained.

He echoed the name uncertainly, still with that suggestion of peevishness, hanging over the rail and peering down at us. "Oh! By gracious!" he exclaimed, abruptly. "I'm glad to see you, Ridgeway. I had a boatman coming out before this, but I guess—well, I guess he'll be along. By gracious! I'm glad——"

"I'll not keep you," I told the gnome, putting the money in his palm and reaching for the rail. McCord lent me a hand on my wrist. Then when I stood squarely on the deck beside him he appeared to forget my presence, leaned forward heavily on the rail, and squinted after my waning boatman.

"Ahoy—boat!" he called out, sharply, shielding his lips with his hands. His violence seemed to bring him out of the blank, for he fell immediately to puffing strongly at his cigar and explaining in rather a shamefaced way that he was beginning to think his own boatman had "passed him up."

"Come in and have a nip," he urged with an abrupt heartiness, clapping me on the shoulder.

"So you've——" I did not say what I had intended. I was thinking that in the old days McCord had made rather a fetish of touching nothing stronger than beer. Neither had he been of the shoulder-clapping sort. "So you've got something aboard?" I shifted.

"Dead men's liquor," he chuckled. It gave me a queer feeling in the pit of my stomach to hear him. I began to wish I had not come, but there was nothing for it now but to follow him into the after-house. The cabin itself might have been nine feet square, with three bunks occupying the port side. To the right opened the master's stateroom, and a door in the forward bulkhead led to the galley.

I took in these features at a casual glance. Then, hardly knowing why I did it, I began to examine them with greater care.

"Have you a match?" I asked. My voice sounded very small, as though something unheard of had happened to all the air.

"Smoke?" he asked. "I'll get you a cigar."

"No." I took the proffered match, scratched it on the side of the galley door, and passed out. There seemed to be a thousand pans there, throwing my match back at me from every wall of the box-like compartment. Even McCord's eyes, in the doorway, were large and round and shining. He probably thought me crazy. Perhaps I was, a little. I ran the match along close to the ceiling and came upon a rusty hook a little aport of the centre.

"There," I said. "Was there anything hanging from this—er—say a parrot—or something, McCord?" The match burned my fingers and went out.

"What do you mean?" McCord demanded from the doorway. I got myself back into the comfortable yellow glow of the cabin before I answered, and then it was a question.

"Do you happen to know anything about this craft's personal history?"

"No. What are you talking about! Why?"

"Well, I do," I offered. "For one thing she's changed her name. And it happens this isn't the first time she's——Well, damn it all, fourteen years ago I helped pick up this whatever-she-is off the Virginia Capes— in the same sort of condition. There you are!" I was yapping like a nerve-strung puppy.

McCord leaned forward with his hands on the table, bringing his face beneath the fan of the hanging-lamp. For the first time I could mark how shockingly it had changed. It was almost colourless. The jaw had somehow lost its old-time security and the eyes seemed to be loose in their sockets. I had expected him to start at my announcement; he only blinked at the light.

"I am not surprised," he remarked at length. "After what I've seen and heard——" He lifted his fist and brought it down with a sudden crash on the table. "Man—let's have a nip!"

He was off before I could say a word, fumbling out of sight in the narrow state-room. Presently he reappeared, holding a glass in either hand and a dark bottle hugged between his elbows. Putting the glasses down, he held up the bottle between his eyes and the lamp, and its shadow, falling across his face, green and luminous at the core, gave him a ghastly look—like a mutilation or an unspeakable birth-mark. He shook the bottle gently and chuckled his "Dead men's liquor" again. Then he poured two half-glasses of the clear gin, swallowed his portion, and sat down.

"A parrot," he mused, a little of the liquor's colour creeping into his cheeks. "No, this time it was a cat, Ridgeway. A yellow cat. She was——"

"*Was?*" I caught him up. "What's happened—what's become of her?"

"Vanished. Evaporated. I haven't seen her since night before last, when I caught her trying to lower the boat——"

"*Stop it!*" It was I who banged the table now, without any of the reserve of decency. "McCord, you're drunk—*drunk*, I tell you. A *cat*! Let a *cat* throw you off your head like this! She's probably hiding out below this minute, on affairs of her own."

"Hiding?" He regarded me for a moment with the queer superiority of the damned. "I guess you don't realize how many times I've been over this hulk, from decks to keelson, with a mallet and a foot-rule."

"Or fallen overboard," I shifted, with less assurance. "Like this fellow Björnsen. By the way, McCord——" I stopped there on account of the look in his eyes.

He reached out, poured himself a shot, swallowed it, and got up to shuffle about the confined quarters. I watched their restless circuit—my friend and his jumping shadow. He stopped and bent forward to examine a Sunday-supplement chromo tacked on the wall, and the two heads drew together, as though there were something to whisper. Of a sudden I seemed to hear the old gnome croaking, "Now that story sounds to me kind of——"

McCord straightened up and turned to face me.

"What do you know about Björnsen?" he demanded.

"Well—only what they had you saying in the papers," I told him.

"Pshaw!" He snapped his fingers, tossing the affair aside. "I found her log," he announced in quite another voice.

"You did, eh? I judged, from what I read in the paper, that there wasn't a sign."

"No, no; I happened on this the other night, under the mattress in there." He jerked his head towards the state-room. "Wait!" I heard him knocking things over in the dark and mumbling at them. After a moment he came out and threw on the table a long, cloth-covered ledger, of the common commercial sort. It lay open at about the middle, showing close script running indiscriminately across the column ruling.

"When I said 'log'," he went on, "I guess I was going it a little strong. At least, I wouldn't want that sort of log found around *my* vessel. Let's call it a personal record. Here's his picture, somewhere——" He shook the book by its back and a common kodak blue-print fluttered to the table. It was the likeness of a solid man with a paunch, a huge square beard, small squinting eyes, and a bald head. "What do you make of him—a writing chap?"

"From the nose down, yes," I estimated. "From the nose up, he will 'tend to his own business if you will 'tend to yours, strictly."

McCord slapped his thigh. "By gracious! that's the fellow! He hates the Chinaman. He knows as well as anything he ought not to put down in black and white how intolerably he hates the Chinaman, and yet he must sneak off to his cubby-hole and suck his pencil, and—and how is it Stevenson has it?—the 'agony of composition,' you remember. Can you imagine the fellow, Ridgeway, bundling down here with the fever on him——"

"About the Chinaman," I broke in. "I think you said something about a Chinaman?"

"Yes. The cook, he must have been. I gather he wasn't the master's pick, by the reading-matter here. Probably clapped on to him by the owners—shifted from one of their others at the last moment; a queer trick. Listen." He picked up the book and, running over the pages with a selective thumb, read:

"*August second*. First part, moderate southwesterly breeze—

and so forth—er—but here he comes to it:

"Anything can happen to a man at sea, even a funeral. In special to a Chinyman, who is of no account to social welfare, being a barbarian as I look at it.

'Something of a philosopher, you see. And did you get the reserve in that 'even a funeral'? An artist, I tell you. But wait; let me catch him a bit wilder. Here:

"I'll get that mustard-coloured—(This is back a couple of days.) Never can hear the—coming, in them carpet slippers. Turned round and found him standing right to my back this morning. Could have stuck a knife into me easy. 'Look here!' says I, and fetched him a tap on the ear that will make him walk louder next time, I warrant. He could have stuck a knife into me easy.

"A clear case of moral funk, I should say. Can you imagine the fellow, Ridgeway——"

"Yes; oh yes." I was ready with a phrase of my own. "A man handicapped with an imagination. You see he can't quite understand this 'barbarian,' who has him beaten by about thirty centuries of civilization —and his imagination has to have something to chew on, something to hit—a 'tap on the ear,' you know."

"By gracious! that's the ticket!" McCord pounded his knee. "And now we've got another chap going to pieces—Peters, he calls him. Refuses to eat dinner on August the third, claiming he caught the Chink making passes over the chowder-pot with his thumb. Can you believe it, Ridgeway—in this very cabin here?" Then he went on with a suggestion of haste, as though he had somehow made a slip. "Well, at any rate, the disease seems to be catching. Next day it's Bach, the second seaman, who begins to feel the gaff. Listen:

"Back he comes to me to-night, complaining he's being watched. He claims the—has got the evil eye. Says he can see you through a two-inch bulkhead, and the like. The Chink's laying in his bunk, turned the other way. 'Why don't you go aboard of him,' says I. The Dutcher says nothing, but goes over to his own bunk and feels under the straw. When he comes back he's looking queer. 'By God!' says he, 'the devil has swiped my gun!' ... Now if that's true there is going to be hell to pay in this vessel very quick. I figure I'm still master of this vessel."

"The evil eye," I grunted. "Consciences gone wrong there some-where."

"Not altogether, Ridgeway. I can see that yellow man peeking. Now just figure yourself, say, eight thousand miles from home, out on the water alone with a crowd of heathen fanatics crazy from fright, looking around for guns and so on. Don't you believe you'd keep an eye around the corners, kind of—eh? I'll bet a hat he was taking it all in, lying there in his bunk, 'turned the other way.' Eh? I pity the poor cuss——Well, there's only one more entry after that. He's good and mad. Here:

"Now, by God! this is the end. My gun's gone too; right out from under lock and key, by God! I been talking with Bach this morning. Not to let on, I had him in to clean my lamp. There's more ways than one, he says, and so do I."

McCord closed the book and dropped it on the table. "Finis," he said. "The rest is blank paper."

"Well!" I will confess I felt much better than I had for some time past. "There's *one* 'mystery of the sea' gone to pot, at any rate. And now, if you don't mind, I think I'll have another of your nips, McCord."

He pushed my glass across the table and got up, and behind his back his shadow rose to scour the corners of the room, like an incorruptible sentinel. I forgot to take up my gin, watching him. After an uneasy minute or so he came back to the table and pressed the tip of a forefinger on the book.

"Ridgeway," he said, "you don't seem to understand. This particular 'mystery of the sea' hasn't been scratched yet—not even *scratched*, Ridgeway." He sat down and leaned forward, fixing me with a didactic finger. "What happened?"

"Well, I have an idea the 'barbarian' got them, when it came to the pinch."

"And let the—remains over the side?"

"I should say."

"And they came back and got the 'barbarian' and let *him* over the side, eh? There were none left, you remember."

"Oh, good Lord, I don't know!" I flared with a childish resentment at this catechizing of his. But his finger remained there, challenging.

"I do," he announced. "The Chinaman put them over the side, as we have said. And then, after that, he died—of wounds about the head."

"So?" I had still sarcasm.

"You will remember," he went on, "that the skipper did not happen to mention a cat, a *yellow* cat, in his confessions."

"McCord," I begged him, "please drop it. Why in thunder *should* he mention a cat?"

"True. Why *should* he mention a cat? I think one of the reasons why he should *not* mention a cat is because there did not happen to be a cat aboard at that time."

"Oh, all right!" I reached out and pulled the bottle to my side of the table. Then I took out my watch. "If you don't mind," I suggested, "I think we'd better be going ashore. I've got to get to my office rather early in the morning. What do you say?"

He said nothing for the moment, but his finger had dropped. He leaned back and stared straight into the core of the light above, his eyes squinting.

"He would have been from the south of China, probably." He seemed to be talking to himself. "There's a considerable sprinkling of the belief down there, I've heard. It's an uncanny business—this transmigration of souls——"

Personally, I had had enough of it. McCord's fingers came groping across the table for the bottle. I picked it up hastily and let it go through the open companionway, where it died with a faint gurgle, out somewhere on the river.

"Now," I said to him, shaking the vagrant wrist, "either you come ashore with me or you go in there and get under the blankets. You're drunk, McCord—*drunk*. Do you hear me?"

"Ridgeway," he pronounced, bringing his eyes down to me and speaking very slowly. "You're a fool, if you can't see better than that. I'm not drunk. I'm sick. I haven't slept for three nights—and now I can't. And you say—you——" He went to pieces very suddenly, jumped up, pounded the legs of his chair on the decking, and shouted at me: "And you say that, you—you landlubber, you office coddler! You're so comfortably sure that everything in the world is cut and dried. Come back to the water again and learn how to wonder—and stop talking like a damn fool. Do know where—— Is there anything in your municipal budget to tell me where Björnsen went? Listen!" He sat down, waving me to do the same, and went on with a sort of desperate repression.

"It happened on the first night after we took this hellion. I'd stood the wheel most of the afternoon—off and on, that is, because she sails herself uncommonly well. Just put her on a reach, you know, and she carries it off pretty well——"

"I know," I nodded.

"Well, we mugged up about seven o'clock. There was a good deal of canned stuff in the galley, and Björnsen wasn't a bad hand with a kettle —a thorough-going Square-head he was—tall and lean and yellow-haired, with little fat, round cheeks and a white moustache. Not a bad chap at all. He took the wheel to stand till midnight, and I turned in, but I didn't drop off for quite a spell. I could hear his boots wandering around over my head, padding off forward, coming back again. I heard him whistling now and then—an outlandish air. Occasionally I could see the shadow of his head waving in a block of moonlight that lay on the decking right down there in front of the state-room door. It came from the companion; the cabin was dark because we were going easy on the oil. They hadn't left a great deal, for some reason or other."

McCord leaned back and described with his finger where the illumination had cut the decking.

"There! I could see it from my bunk, as I lay, you understand. I must have almost dropped off once when I heard him fiddling around out here in the cabin, and then he said something in a whisper, just to find out if I was still awake, I suppose. I asked him what the matter was. He came and poked his head in the door.

"'The breeze is going out,' says he. 'I was wondering if we couldn't get a little more sail on her.' Only I can't give you his fierce Square-head tang. 'How about the tops?' he suggested.

"I was so sleepy I didn't care, and I told him so. 'All right,' he says, 'but I thought I might shake out one of them tops.' Then I heard him blow at something outside. 'Scat, you—!' Then: 'This cat's going to set me crazy, Mr McCord,' he says, 'following me around everywhere.' He gave a kick, and I saw something yellow floating across the moonlight. It never made a sound—just floated. You wouldn't have known it ever lit anywhere, just like——"

McCord stopped and drummed a few beats on the table with his fist, as though to bring himself back to the straight narrative.

"I went to sleep," he began again. "I dreamed about a lot of things. I woke up sweating. You know how glad you are to wake up after a dream like that and find none of it is so? Well, I turned over and settled to go off again, and then I got a little more awake and thought to myself it must be pretty near time for me to go on deck. I scratched a match and looked at my watch. 'That fellow must be either a good chap or asleep,' I said to myself. And I rolled out quick and went above-decks. He wasn't at the wheel. I called him: 'Björnsen! Björnsen!' No answer."

McCord was really telling a story now. He paused for a long moment, one hand shielding an ear and his eyeballs turned far up.

"That was the first time I really went over the hulk," he ran on. "I got out a lantern and started at the forward end of the hold, and I worked aft, and there was nothing there. Not a sign, or a stain, or a scrap of clothing, or anything. You may believe that I began to feel funny inside. I went over the decks and the rails and the house itself—inch by inch. Not a trace. I went out aft again. The cat sat on the wheel-box, washing her face. I hadn't noticed the scar on her head before, running down between her ears—rather a new scar—three or four days old, I should say. It looked ghastly and blue-white in the flat moonlight. I ran over and grabbed her up to heave her over the side—you understand how upset I was. Now you know a cat will squirm around and grab something when you hold it like that, generally speaking. This one didn't. She just drooped and began to purr and looked up at me out of her moonlit eyes under that scar. I dropped her on the deck and backed off. You remember Björnsen had *kicked* her—and I didn't want anything like that happening to——"

The narrator turned upon me with a sudden heat, leaned over and shook his finger before my face.

"There you go!" he cried. "You with your stout stone buildings and your policemen and your neighbourhood church—you're so damn sure. But I'd just like to see you out there, alone, with the moon setting, and all the lights gone tall and queer, and a shipmate——" He lifted his hand overhead, the finger-tips pressed together and then suddenly separated as though he had released an impalpable something into the air.

"Go on," I told him.

"I felt more like you do, when it got light again, and warm and sun-shiny. I said 'Bah!' to the whole business. I even fed the cat, and I slept awhile on the roof of the house—I was so sure. We lay dead most of the day, without a streak of air. But that night—! Well, that night I hadn't got over being sure yet. It takes quite a jolt, you know, to shake loose several dozen generations. A fair, steady breeze had come along, the glass was high, she was staying herself like a doll, and so I figured I could get a little rest, lying below in the bunk, even if I didn't sleep.

"I tried not to sleep, in case something should come up—a squall or the like. But I think I must have dropped off once or twice. I remember I heard something fiddling around in the galley, and I hollered 'Scat!' and everything was quiet again. I rolled over and lay on my left side, staring at that square of moonlight outside my door for a long time. You'll think it was a dream—what I saw there."

"Go on," I said.

"Call this table-top the spot of light, roughly," he said. He placed a finger-tip at about the middle of the forward edge and drew it slowly towards the centre. "Here, what would correspond with the upper side of the companionway, there came down very gradually the shadow of a tail. I watched it streaking out there across the deck, wiggling the slightest bit now and then. When it had come down about half-way across the light, the solid part of the animal—its shadow, you understand—began to appear, quite big and round. But how could she hang there, done up in a ball, from the hatch?"

He shifted his finger back to the edge of the table and puddled it around to signify the shadowed body.

"I fished my gun out from behind my back. You see, I was feeling funny again. Then I started to slide one foot over the edge of the bunk, always with my eyes on that shadow. Now I swear I didn't make the sound of a pin dropping, but I had no more than moved a muscle when that shadowed thing twisted itself around in a flash—and there on the

floor before me was the profile of a man's head, upside down, listening—
a man's head with a tail of hair."

McCord got up hastily and stepped over in front of the stateroom
door, where he bent down and scratched a match.

"See," he said, holding the tiny flame above a splintered scar on the
boards. "You wouldn't think a man would be fool enough to shoot at a
shadow?"

He came back and sat down.

"It seemed to me all hell had shaken loose. You've no idea, Ridgeway,
the rumpus a gun raises in a box like this. I found out afterwards the slug
ricochetted into the galley, bringing down a couple of pans—and that
helped. Oh yes, I got out of here quick enough. I stood there, half out
of the companion, with my hands on the hatch and the gun between
them, and my shadow running off across the top of the house shivering
before my eyes like a dry leaf. There wasn't a whisper of sound in the
world—just the pale water floating past and the sails towering up like a
pair of twittering ghosts. And everything that crazy colour——

"Well, in a minute I saw it, just abreast of the mainmast, crouched
down in the shadow of the weather rail, sneaking off forward very slowly.
This time I took a good long sight before I let go. Did you ever happen to
see black-powder smoke in the moonlight? It puffed out perfectly round,
like a big pale balloon, this did, and for a second something was bounding
through it—without a sound, you understand—something a shade solider
than the smoke and big as a cow, it looked to me. It passed from the
weather side to the lee and ducked behind the sweep of the mainsail like
that——" McCord snapped his thumb and forefinger under the light.

"Go on," I said. "What did you do then?"

McCord regarded me for an instant from beneath his lids, uncertain.
His fist hung above the table. "You're——" He hesitated, his lips working
vacantly. A forefinger came out of the fist and gesticulated before my
face. "If you're laughing, why, damn me, I'll——"

"Go on," I repeated. "What did you do then?"

"I followed the thing." He was still watching me sullenly. "I got up
and went forward along the roof of the house, so as to have an eye on
either rail. You understand, this business had to be done with. I kept
straight along. Every shadow I wasn't absolutely sure of I *made* sure of—
point-blank. And I rounded the thing up at the very stem—sitting on
the butt of the bowsprit, Ridgeway, washing her yellow face under the
moon. I didn't make any bones about it this time. I put the bad end of
that gun against the scar on her head and squeezed the trigger. It snicked
on an empty shell. I tell you a fact; I was almost deafened by the report
that didn't come.

"She followed me aft. I couldn't get away from her. I went and sat on
the wheel-box and she came and sat on the edge of the house, facing me.

And there we stayed for upwards of an hour, without moving. Finally she went over and stuck her paw in the water-pan I'd set out for her; then she raised her head and looked at me and yawled. At sundown there'd been two quarts of water in that pan. You wouldn't think a cat could get away with two quarts of water in——"

He broke off again and considered me with a sort of weary defiance.

"What's the use?" He spread ou this hands in a gesture of hopelessness. "I knew you wouldn't believe it when I started. You *couldn't*. It would be a kind of blasphemy against the sacred institution of pavements. You're too damn smug, Ridgeway. I can't shake you. You haven't sat two days and two nights, keeping your eyes open by sheer teeth-gritting, until they got used to it and wouldn't shut any more. When I tell you I found that yellow thing snooping around the davits, and three bights of the boat-fall loosened out, plain on deck—you grin behind your collar. When I tell you she padded off forward and evaporated—flickered back to hell and hasn't been seen since, then—why, you explain to yourself that I'm drunk. I tell you——" He jerked his head back abruptly and turned to face the companionway, his lips still apart. He listened so for a moment, then he shook himself out of it and went on:

"I tell you, Ridgeway, I've been over this hulk with a foot-rule. There's not a cubic inch I haven't accounted for, not a plank I——"

This time he got up and moved a step toward the companion, where he stood with his head bent forward and slightly to the side. After what might have been twenty seconds of this he whispered, "Do you hear?"

Far and far away down the reach a ferry-boat lifted its infinitesimal wail, and then the silence of the night river came down once more, profound and inscrutable. A corner of the wick above my head sputtered a little—that was all.

"Hear what?" I whispered back. He lifted a cautious finger toward the opening.

"Somebody. Listen."

The man's faculties must have been keyed up to the pitch of his nerves, for to me the night remained as voiceless as a subterranean cavern. I became intensely irritated with him; within my mind I cried out against this infatuated pantomime of his. And then, of a sudden, there *was* a sound—the dying rumour of a ripple, somewhere in the outside darkness, as though an object had been let into the water with extreme care.

"You heard?"

I nodded. The ticking of the watch in my vest pocket came to my ears, shucking off the leisurely seconds, while McCord's finger-nails gnawed at the palms of his hands. The man was really sick. He wheeled on me and cried out, "My God! Ridgeway—why don't we go out?"

I, for one, refused to be a fool. I passed him and climbed out of the opening; he followed far enough to lean his elbows on the hatch, his feet and legs still within the secure glow of the cabin.

"You see, there's nothing." My wave of assurance was possibly a little over-done.

"Over there," he muttered, jerking his head towards the shore lights. "Something swimming."

I moved to the corner of the house and listened.

"River thieves," I argued. "The place is full of——"

"*Ridgeway. Look behind you!*"

Perhaps it *is* the pavements—but no matter; I am not ordinarily a jumping sort. And yet there was something in the quality of that voice beyond my shoulder that brought the sweat stinging through the pores of my scalp even while I was in the act of turning.

A cat sat there on the hatch, expressionless and immobile in the gloom. I did not say anything. I turned and went below. McCord was there already, standing on the farther side of the table. After a moment or so the cat followed and sat on her haunches at the foot of the ladder and stared at us without winking.

"I think she wants something to eat," I said to McCord.

He lit a lantern and went out into the galley. Returning with a chunk of salt beef, he threw it into the farther corner. The cat went over and began to tear at it, her muscles playing with convulsive shadow-lines under the sagging yellow hide.

And now it was she who listened, to something beyond the reach of even McCord's faculties, her neck stiff and her ears flattened. I looked at McCord and found him brooding at the animal with a sort of listless malevolence. "*Quick!* She has kittens somewhere about." I shook his elbow sharply. "When she starts, now——"

"You don't seem to understand," he mumbled. "It wouldn't be any use."

She had turned now and was making for the ladder with the soundless agility of her race. I grasped McCord's wrist and dragged him after me, the lantern banging against his knees. When we came up the cat was already amidships, a scarcely discernible shadow at the margin of our lantern's ring. She stopped and looked back at us with her luminous eyes, appeared to hesitate, uneasy at our pursuit of her, shifted here and there with quick, soft bounds, and stopped to fawn with her back arched at the foot of the mast. Then she was off with an amazing suddenness into the shadows forward.

"Lively now!" I yelled at McCord. He came pounding along behind me, still protesting that it was of no use. Abreast of the foremast I took the lantern from him to hold above my head.

"You see," he complained, peering here and there over the illuminated deck. "I tell you, Ridgeway, this thing——" But my eyes were in another quarter, and I slapped him on the shoulder.

"An engineer—an engineer to the core," I cried at him. "Look aloft, man."

Our quarry was almost to the cross-trees, clambering up the shrouds with a smartness no sailor has ever come to, her yellow body cut by the moving shadows of the ratlines, a queer sight against the mat of the night. McCord closed his mouth and opened it again for two words: "By gracious!" The following instant he had the lantern and was after her. I watched him go up above my head—a ponderous, swaying climber into the sky—come to the cross-trees, and squat there with his knees clamped around the mast. The clear star of the lantern shot this way and that for a moment, then it disappeared, and in its place there sprang out a bag of yellow light, like a fire-balloon at anchor in the heavens. I could see the shadow of his head and hands moving monstrously over the inner surface of the sail, and muffled exclamations without meaning came down to me. After a moment he drew out his head and called: "All right—they're here. Heads! there below!"

I ducked at his warning, and something spanked on the planking a yard from my feet. I stepped over to the vague blur on the deck and picked up a slipper—a slipper covered with some woven straw stuff and soled with a matted felt, perhaps a half-inch thick. Another struck somewhere abaft the mast, and then McCord reappeared above and began to stagger down the shrouds. Under his left arm he hugged a curious assortment of litter, a sheaf of papers, a brace of revolvers, a grey kimono, and a soiled apron.

"Well," he said when he had come to deck, "I feel like a man who has gone to hell and come back again. You know I'd come to the place where I really believed that about the cat. When you think of it——By gracious! we haven't come so far from the jungle, after all."

We went aft and below and sat down at the table as we had been. McCord broke a prolonged silence.

"I'm sort of glad he got away—poor cuss! He's probably climbing up a wharf this minute, shivering and scared to death. Over toward the gas-tanks, by the way he was swimming. By gracious! now that the world's turned over straight again, I feel I could sleep a solid week. Poor cuss! can you imagine him, Ridgeway——"

"Yes," I broke in. "I think I can. He must have lost his nerve when he made out your smoke and shinnied up there to stow away, taking the ship's papers with him. He would have attached some profound importance to them—remember, the 'barbarian,' eight thousand miles from home. Probably couldn't read a word. I suppose the cat followed him— the traditional source of food. He must have wanted water badly."

"I should say! He wouldn't have taken the chances he did."

"Well," I announced, "at any rate, I can say it now—there's another 'mystery of the sea' gone to pot."

McCord lifted his heavy lids.

"No," he mumbled. "The mystery is that a man who has been to sea all his life could sail around for three days with a man bundled up in his

top and not know it. When I think of him peeking down at me—and
playing off that damn cat—probably without realizing it—scared to
death—by gracious! Ridgeway, there was a pair of funks aboard this
craft, eh? Wow—yow—I could sleep——"

"I should think you could."

McCord did not answer.

"By the way," I speculated. "I guess you were right about Björnsen,
McCord—that is, his fooling with the foretop. He must have been caught
all of a bunch, eh?"

Again McCord failed to answer. I looked up, mildly surprised, and
found his head hanging back over his chair and his mouth opened wide.
He was asleep.

WAY FOR A SAILOR![1]

Bill Adams

THERE was once a ship. Her name was the *Golden Age*. She flew,
leaving them all astern of her. She beat into the wind. She ran down
it. She glittered along it, throwing salt sprays to, and far above, the stiff
bellied leeches of her great white upper topsails. With the wind before the
beam she flung her tall topgallants wet—wet and shining with the white
salt of the sea nigh two hundred feet beneath them. She seemed to laugh
as she ran; seeming to sing, to ripple, as she flew, scattering sea beauties
about her, gleaming as stars gleam when frosts are white along far inland
meadows. *She was a ship.*

She carried a captain, a mate, a second mate, a boatswain, a carpenter,
a steward, and a cook, and, in her forrard forecastle, a company of hard-
driven, face-furrowed sailormen from the bright wide water ports. She
carried also, in the little half-deck abaft her main-mast, a sea apprentice,
a lad with pink cheeks, the down upon his face.

She left Port Costa wharf before the dawn upon a bitter February
morning; chill mists hanging above the river, bluffs, and bay; a chill wind
blowing seaward; thin rain falling, dripping from mast and spar and backstay.

"Stand by to take in the tow-boat's line," said the mate.

"Stand by to take in the tow-boat's line, it is, sir," said the hands.

"Stand by with the cork fenders, lest the wharf shall scar her sides,"
said the mate.

"Stand by with the cork fenders, it is, sir," said the hands.

From ashore, from behind a warped gateway, a woman waved a shawl,
wondering why these men should leave *her* for the sea, and, seeing her,

[1]From *Fenceless Meadows*. Reprinted by permission of the author and of Hutchinson &
Co., Ltd.

sailors upon the *Golden Age* smiled, breaking old furrows on their faces wide, their eyes a-glint.

"Stand by to drop the hook," said the mate. "We'll wait awhile in the bay before we take her over the bar."

"Already, sir," said Chips, the carpenter.

"Let go," said the mate.

The anchor rattled down.

She lay as a swan awakening, waiting for the tide to take her to sea; the hands from twenty water ports sitting in her forecastle, drinking coffee.

"They say she can sail," said one.

"They say she's a flyer," said another.

"We make fly," said a black man, from Suva.

"Ha, ha, ha," laughed an old grey-bearded fellow, his nose in a tin pannikin.

"Where's she bound?" asked one.

"Queenstown for orders," answered another.

"The mate tol' me Liverpool direc'," said another.

"That's good! we'll dance when we get there," said another.

"We ain't there yet," said the old fellow with a grey beard.

"I 'aven't no oilskins. The crimp robbed me," said one.

"Nor 'aven't I no sea boots. The crimp robbed me too," said another.

"I've a couple o' poun's o' black baccy," said another.

"We make fly," said the Suva man.

"*Yes!* We'll make her fly!" said another.

"She'll fly, anyway. She couldn't help it," said another.

"It's cold," said the pink-cheeked apprentice, sitting alone in the half-deck, sipping his coffee.

"Stand by to heave in," shouted the mate, adding to himself, "tide's at the flood."

"Stand by to heave in, it is, sir," cried the hands, leaving pannikins strewn about an old wood table, hook-pots hooked to the table edge, rags in dark bunks.

A sailor was singing, twenty men bent over the windlass bars, a song of the sea echoing over the swirled tide; his voice, the voices of twenty, mingled with the "clank, clank, clank" of the windlass pawls, "clank, clank, clank."

> "Oh, Santa Ana won the day,
>   away, Santa Ana,
>   Santa Ana won the day,
>   all along the plains of Mexico.
>
> Oh, Santa Ana fought for fame,
>   away, Santa Ana,
>   Santa Ana fought for fame,
>   all along the plains of Mexico."

"Walk her down, sons—*walk her down!*" cried the mate, looking over the fo'c'sle rail at the gurgle-black tide below her.

"Walk 'er down, the mate says. Come on, sons," cried the chantey-man.

> "Oh, Santa Ana gained his name,
> away, Santa Ana,
> Santa Ana gained his name,
> all along the plains of Mexico."

"Walk her down, walk her down," cried the mate.
"We make fly," said the black man from Suva.
"She'll fly anyway—she couldn't 'elp it," murmured another.

> "All along the plains of Mexico."

"Let her have it. The wind's off-shore," cried the mate.
"Let 'er 'ave it, the mate says," shouted a sailor. "Wispy, give us 'Rovin'."
"I'm wid you," said old Wispy Cavendish, "'ere you are."

> "One night I crept from my abode,
> Mark well what I do say—
> One night I crept from my abode
> To meet this maiden down the road,
> We'll go no more a-roving with you fair maid!
> A-roving, a-roving,
> Oh, roving's been my ruin!
> We'll go no more a-roving with you fair maid!"

"Admiral, gi' us a chantey," cried one.
"Aye, that's it! Gi' us a chantey, admiral," cried another.
"Sing, admiral, sing!" said Wispy Cavendish.
"Walk her up, sons," cried the mate, "the wind's off-shore."
The sea-apprentice, pink-cheeked, the down upon his face, looking out to sea, bright-eyed, mist in his hair, sang—

> "Call all hands to man the capstan,
> See the cables are all clear:
> For to-day we'll weigh the anchor,
> And for distant shores we'll steer.
> Rolling home, rolling home,
> Rolling home across the sea."

They gathered it up, shouting it, roaring it, men of the water ports, taking the *Golden Age* across the bar.

> "Rolling home, rolling home,
> Rolling home across the sea."

"Loose the main topsail," shouted the mate. "Run that anchor to the hawse pipe, now—run her up!"

They ran, stamping round and round the windlass.

"Look alive aloft there! shake that tops'l loose," shouted the mate.

"Sheet home main tops'l," bellowed a sailor from aloft.

"Get up there. Loose that upper tops'l," shouted the mate.

The skipper, on his bridge, blew his whistle.

"Get sail on her, sir. Loose all! Crowd her to it," he called to his mate.

"Th' ol' man says to crowd 'er to it," said one.

They stood, waiting at the halyards, the morning breaking full across the sea; drizzle falling, dripping from mast and spar and back-stay.

"It's colder'n 'ell," said one.

"I got a couple o' poun's o' black baccy. 'Ere y'are," said another.

"'Ow many knots kin she make?" asked one.

"All clear main upper tops'l," shouted the man from Suva, from the yard above them.

"Hoist away," shouted the mate.

"Hoist away," shouted twenty sailors; taking the wet rope in their hands.

"We make fly," said the Suva man, sliding down the rigging to the deck, seizing the halyards.

"Someone gi' us *Boney!*" cried one.

"Aye! gi' us *Boney!*" cried another.

"Come on," said Wispy Cavendish, "'ere you are."

> "Oh, Boney was a warrior,
> to me way, hay, yoh!
> Oh, Boney was a warrior,
> an' a long time ago.
> An' Boneyparte met Wellington,
> to me way, hay, yoh!
> An' Boneyparte met Wellington,
> an' a long time ago."

"I 'ope 'ee drives 'er," said one.

"She'll fly anyway. She couldn't 'elp it," said another.

"Hoist that main topgallant," shouted the mate.

"Main topgallant, the mate says," cried one.

"Hop along there, hop along," cried another.

"Give us a bit of them halyards," cried another.

"Me too! Gimme a bit o' that there rope," cried another.

"Sing!" cried one.

"Aye, that's it! Sing!" cried another.

"Wispy, giv' us a chantey," cried another.

"'Ere you are, sons," said Wispy Cavendish.

"Oh, I say ol' man your horse will die,
 and I say so, and I hope so,
Oh, I say ol' man your horse will die,
 you po-o-o-ore old man!
Oh, if he dies I will jump upon his grave,
 and I say so, and I hope so,
Oh, if he dies I will jump upon his grave,
 you po-o-o-ore old man!"

"Belay those halyards! what y' tryin' to do? Carry 'em away?" cried the mate.

"'Ee says to belay them halyards, ha, ha, ha," laughed an old fellow with a grey beard.

"We make fly," said the Suva man.

"Look out, sons—she's goin' to ship it green. Duck y'r 'eads!" cried one.

"Let 'er rip!" cried another.

"Don't she lift to 'em nice?" said one.

"She's a *sea boat*," said another.

"'Ere she comes again—watch out!" cried another.

"Hoist that mizzen topgallant—never mind a drop of water," cried the mate.

"Ha, ha, ha," laughed twenty men, "the mate says to never mind a drop o' water."

"All clear mizzen 'gallant," bellowed a man from aloft, "*hoist away!*"

"Giv' us a bit o' them 'alyards. Me feet is cold. I ain't got no sea boots," said Wispy.

"I got two poun' o' black baccy," said another.

"Hoist away there," shouted the mate.

"Come on, sing!" cried a sailor.

"'Ere you are, lads," said Wispy Cavendish.

"W'en I was young an' in my prime,
 oh, roll the cotton down!
W'en I was young an' in my prime,
 oh, roll the cotton down!
On the 'Golden Age' I served my time,
 oh, roll the cotton down!
On the 'Golden Age' I served my time,
 oh, roll the cotton down!"

"'Ark at Wispy—'ee's makin' of it as 'ee goes," said one.

"Belay those halyards! What y' tryin' to do with her?" cried the mate.

"We wants to make her fly," said one.

"She'll fly anyway. She couldn't help it," said the mate.

"Walk those royals to the mast heads! Walk 'em up! Let's get her out and going," cried the mate, the shore line fading as the day broke wide.

"W'ere's that there admiral?" cried a sailor.

"Aye! where's th' admiral?" cried another. "Admiral, sing for us, son."

"Sing, admiral," cried another.

"Let 'er 'ave it, admiral, my little hearty," said old Wispy Cavendish.

"We make fly," murmured the Suva man, looking at the pink-cheeked sea apprentice, with the down upon his face.

> "John Brown's wife drinks whisky in her tea,
> John Brown's wife drinks whisky in her tea,
> John Brown's wife drinks whisky in her tea,
>   As we go rolling home.
> Glory, glory, hallelujah!
> Glory, glory, hallelujah!
> Glory, glory, hallelujah!
>   As we go rolling home!"

sang the sea apprentice, twenty sailors lifting it, stamping forty feet along her dancing teak wood decks.

"Belay them halyards! What y' tryin' to do with her?" yelled the mate.

"Ha, ha, ha," laughed a sailor, "th' admiral's tryin' to make 'er fly."

"She'll fly anyway. She's got to—*she can't help it*," said the skipper, on his bridge, overhearing them.

"Get all sail set on her. Set those staysails," shouted the skipper from his bridge, adding to himself. "Crowd her along. She wants to go."

The *Golden Age* buried her bow to the smother, lifting her bright foot high to the sea ridges, laughing along with a drench of sea upon her long white decks.

"Admiral, it's eight bells. It's your wheel, my little hearty," said Wispy Cavendish.

"I'll make her fly," murmured the apprentice.

"South," said the man at the wheel, turning the wheel over to him; adding, "South—to the Horn, son."

"South it is," said the apprentice, staring into the compass, giving her half a spoke of weather helm, the wind coming up from east by south.

"She's going to fly," said he.

"What's the course?" asked Wispy Cavendish, thirty days later, taking the wheel over from the Suva man, the clipper running down her easting for old Cape Stiff.

"Sou' east by east," said the Suva man, "make fly."

The wind cried out of the westerly, the sea racing along her slender quarters, broken ridges angry all about her.

"It's blowing, sir," said the mate, looking at the sky sail on the mizzen.

"Let it blow," said the skipper.

"She'll fly anyway," muttered an old sailor, on the quarterdeck beneath them.

At dusk the second mate, taking the bridge, stared along the swamped decks, deep in green water from forecastle to poop, the ports lashed wide open, the sky dark.

"It's blowing, sir," said he, looking at the sky sail on the mizzen.

"Let it blow," said the mate.

The skipper looked out of the chart house; watching the canvas on the bending topgallantmasts.

"Take nothing off her, sir," said he.

"Very good, sir," said the second mate, adding, as the skipper went below,

"If he can drive her, so can I! She's going to fly."

Night fell; the sky black above the *Golden Age*, flying, with everything set, down the easting to old Cape Stiff, the wash of an invisible sea noisy about her.

In the fo'c'sle the watch below sat at their supper.

"Pass that there skilly pot. Is it hot?" said one.

"It's cold. It got cold coming forrard from the galley," said another.

"Ain't there no hot skilly? Me feet is cold—I ain't got no sea boots," said Wispy Cavendish.

"I'm nigh froze; soaked to the bone," said another.

"Give us a bit o' hard tack out o' the bread barge; let's have something to bit on," said another.

"'As anybody got a dollop o' margarine left?" asked another.

"There ain't nuthin' left, and there won't be no more o' nuthin' served out till Monday night, what well you knows. What good's growlin'?" said one.

"Who's growlin'? I ain't growled. What ye talkin' about?" asked the other.

"These 'ere Mac Tosh ships is a 'ard lot," said one.

"They was, you mean. She's the last on 'em," said another.

"It's the owner's fault. 'Tain't the skipper," said another.

"It's comin' cold," said another.

"'Arris," said Wispy Cavendish. "Get out that concertina and give us a bit o' music."

"Aye! Go fetch that little admiral too. Get 'im to sing for us—'ee's a little brass bound singin' admiral, 'ee is," said another.

"That's what he is. Them apprentices is queer little ducks, isn't they?" said another.

In the half-deck sat the apprentice, eating a piece of hard tack, drinking cold coffee, without sugar or milk.

"She's taking water—hark at that!" he muttered.

The door banged upon from without, a man entered, peering from under a wet yellow sou'wester at the apprentice.

"Admiral, we wants you to come an' sing fer us."

The apprentice rose, grinning.

"Cold as hell, isn't it?" said he, putting soul and body lashings on his wrists and ankles and holding his wrists out to the sailor.

"Lash them for me. My fingers are frozen. My coffee's cold," said he.

They banged the door behind them, battling along the swamped deck.

"D'ye reckon the old man's going to carry those skysails all night?" asked the sailor. "She'll lose her sticks, won't she?"

"Let her lose 'em. We've got a carpenter and we've got extra sticks," said the admiral.

"There's three full suits of extra sail in the sail locker, ain't there?" shouted the sailor, waist deep in the sea.

"Three full suits—let her fly," shouted the apprentice.

"Hello, admiral! 'ow's she comin'? Come on an' sing for us," said a sailor.

They made him welcome, peering up at him through rings of tobacco smoke from eyes half shut; the sea roaring without; the ship a-tremble throughout her length; the night black.

The skipper, coming to the chart house, looked at the barometer and standing beside the wheel watched the compass; the helmsman fighting the clipper, holding her true.

"Call all hands on deck. Shorten sail," said the skipper to the mate. "She'll lose a stick. We'll have to ease her."

"All hands on deck!" bellowed the mate.

"All hands on deck!" bellowed the watch.

"All hands, sons," roared a man through a fo'c'sle port, stopping the song.

They piled out, on to the black, night-ridden decks, seas washing over the railings, sheets of water on the crying air.

"Clue the skysails up!" shouted the mate.

"Clue up the royals!" shouted the second mate.

"Down royal and topgallant skysails!" bellowed the mate.

"Down jib topsail and jigger topmast skysail!" roared the bosun.

Men ran from rope to rope, their voices mingled with the wind wail, the crash of canvas in the night above as the flap of great bird wings.

"Aloft an' furl them—step lively!" shouted the mate.

"Lay aloft—get 'em furled!" shouted the second.

"Aloft—aloft—come on, sons!" bellowed the bosun.

Silent they swarmed aloft, sprays striking them in the lower rigging, hurrying to rocking spars high in the night.

"The wind's freshening," said the skipper on the bridge.

"She's a free-foot ship," said the mate.

"She'd fly if you tied her down," said the second, "she couldn't help it."

Aloft in the darkness the watches gathered up the skysails, the royals and the fore and afters, rolling them tight, neater than window blinds in rich ladies' houses, snugging them down.

"Stow 'em snug!" cried the bosun.

"'Ello, me little admiral! is that you? Stow 'em snug. They'll blow out o' the gaskets if you don't," said a sailor on the mizzen.

"Can't see nuthin'. Black as crows, ain't it?" said one, passing a gasket.

"Black as Tess O'Leary's hair," said another.

"Black as the old devil what shovels hell's coals," said another.

"She fly?" said the Suva man, aloft on the fore.

"She's a rip-snorter," said old Wispy Cavendish at the end of the flying boom, snugging down the jib tops'l.

They came from aloft, leaping from the rigging to water swept decks, feeling their accustomed way with sure feet, and, eight bells striking, mustered upon the quarterdeck for the relieving of the wheel and lookout.

"All aft, sir!" cried Wispy Cavendish, knee-deep in the sea, growling as old dogs growl when gipsies go prowling.

"Relieve the wheel and look-out. Keep handy the watch," said the mate.

They went forrard, to the fo'c'sle, making short dashes, escaping the sprays under the shelter of the weather railing.

"Wind's freshenin'," said one.

"Let 'er freshen," said another.

"There's a Horn gale comin'," said another.

"She's bound east. She'll fly to it," said another.

"Chips," said Wispy Cavendish at the carpenter's door, "'ave you a bit o' burlap? I ain't got no sea boots. The crimp robbed me."

"'Ere you are. Roll 'em tight an' keep out the cold, Limbertoes," said Chips.

"Thankee. I'll do the like for you another day," said Wispy, going forrard to the fo'c'sle, to make his Prince Alberts—winding the burlap tight about his old legs and bare feet, to keep out the Horn cold—his next turn at the wheel.

"Look at Wispy! 'Ee's all dressed up in Prince Alberts," said one, "the crimp robbed 'im."

The clipper raced beneath her topgallant sails, dipping deep as the wind arose and the sea ran higher.

The watch below rolled into their bunks, on to "donkey-breakfast" straw mattresses, to dream of lights by many water fronts; of songs in strange places; of children who stared at them from doorsteps.

The watch on deck, smoking time-blackened pipes, sat in the fo'c'sle; hearing the wind's uproar, the sea's song without.

"It's coming cold, sir," said the mate to the skipper, on the bridge.

"There's ice about," said the skipper.

The mate said nothing.

"I'd hate to take a topgallant off," said the skipper. "She wants to fly."

The mate said nothing.

"I'd like to drive her," said the skipper, going below and staying a moment in the chart house door.

"If he can drive her," said the mate, "*so can I.*"

She flew, wind-staggered, down the night—*with ice about.*

Four bells went.

"Wo't's the course?" asked Wispy Cavendish, taking the wheel over.

"Sou' eas' by eas'," said the helmsman.

"Sou' eas' by eas', it is," said Wispy.

"'Ow's your feet? Ain't they colder'n hell wi'out sea boots?" asked the helmsman.

"I'm all dressed up in Prince Alberts," said Wispy.

"Sou' eas' by eas', sir," said the helmsman, reporting to the mate upon the bridge.

"South east by east," said the mate, adding. "Tell the watch to keep handy."

"Keep handy the watch," said the helmsman, entering the murky fo'c'sle.

"We're all 'andy," said one.

"An' colder'n hell," said another.

"What y' growlin' about?" said another.

"Who's growlin'?" growled the other.

"Was you ever in a Fernie ship?" asked one.

"I was in th' ol' *Silberhorn*," answered another.

"*Gawd!* was you?" cried another.

"Th' ol' *Silberhorn*," repeated another reminiscently, "one o' De Wolfe's."

"Gone, ain't she?" asked one.

"Wi' all 'ands," said the other.

"She could fly," said another.

"Ol' Wispy's all dressed up in Prince Alberts," said another.

"Ha, ha, ha!" laughed an old grey-bearded man, "ha, ha, ha!"

"Ha, ha, ha!" laughed all of them, staring at one another through the smoke.

"*All hands on deck—shorten sail!*" bellowed the mate, his head at the fo'c'sle door, "call the watch."

"Rouse her out there! rise and shine, you sleepers!" yelled a man at the door of the starboard fo'c'sle, waking the second mate's watch.

"Who's that a-singin' on them ropes?" muttered a man of the second mate's watch, wriggling into cold oilskins.

"That's th' admiral," said one.

"Let 'im sing. I likes to 'ear 'im," said another.

"Step lively, sons! get her shortened down—there's ice about," shouted the second mate.

"Ice about," mumbled one, biting a chew of black baccy.

"Ice—bergs—*hell!*" said another, reminiscently.

"Sing, admiral, sing," shouted another, stepping to the deck.

"It's six bells. Sing, admiral! It'll soon be eight bells an' we won't 'ave to go below again till four o' the mornin'," cried another.

"We've 'ad two whole hours' sleep—that's enough for any sailor," cried another.

"Aye—enough for any dog," cried another.

"Haw, haw, haw!" laughed some one, in the darkness.

"Sing, admiral, sing," cried some one in the darkness.

"Hi-leeee-yo-ho-ho-hi-leeee-yo-ho-ho, haul awa-ay-ay-ay-oh," sang the singing apprentice, waist deep in the sea.

"Hi-leeee-yo-ho-ho—hi-leeee-yo-ho-ho, haul awa-aya-ay-oh."

"Aloft an' make 'em fast," shouted the mate, "hop along!"

Save for the wash of the sea, and the wind wail, the night was silent.

"How's she heading?" asked the skipper, of Wispy, at the wheel.

"Sou' eas' by eas', sir."

"Bring her to east south east," said the skipper.

"Eas' sou' eas' it is, sir."

"There's ice about," said the skipper to himself. "I must keep her up a bit."

"Haul in the weather braces, sir, as soon as those 'gallants are furled," said the skipper to the mate upon the bridge.

"Aye, aye, sir," said the mate, descending to the deck.

"Starboard cross-jack brace," shouted the mate.

"Starboard cross-jack brace," shouted twenty sailors, in the hidden deeps of night.

"I want to drive her. I hate to take those 'gallants off," said the skipper to himself, looking at the Horn chart, out-stretched upon the chart house table.

"Here's a hell of a squall," cried a sailor.

"Stand by all hands," bellowed the mate.

"Take that cross-jack off her," shouted the skipper.

"Hi-leeee-yo-ho-ho, -hi-leeee-yo-ho-ho," sang the apprentice.

They went aloft to furl the cross-jack, and descending, furled the main-sail—the great storm main-sail; a hundred and two feet across the head, forty-seven and a half feet deep in the leech—storm canvas, soaked with sea water, and frozen stiff.

Their voices echoed in the limitless night, singing a chantey on the main yard.

"And that's the way we'll pay Paddy Doyle for his *boots*," they sang, roaring it, screaming it, bellowing it; their bare hands cold and raw.

"I ain't got no boots. I wish I did 'ave," said Wispy at the wheel.

"*She's got a crew*," said the skipper, to the mate upon the bridge.

The mate said nothing.

"Reef the fore-sail," said the skipper, "the wind's freshening."

They reefed the fore-sail, the clipper driving through the black smother; trembling throughout her length.

"Six topsails, and a reefed fore-sail. I *hate* to take another rag off her. I want her to fly," said the skipper, looking at the Horn chart.

"Cold, ain't it?" said the second to the mate, upon the bridge.

"Ice about. Feel it?" said the mate.

"Aye—colder'n Satan's lost ice box," said the second, beating his arms.

Eight bells went, clanging faintly along the deck, the hands mustering aft in the dark, shouting to one another; somebody singing—

"Now all young sailors take my tip!"

"All aft, sir!" shouted a sailor, from the mizzen shrouds.

"I'll go see what the skipper says," said the mate. "The wind's blowing up."

"A Horn gale coming," said the second, banging his bare hands upon his sides.

The mate looked in through the chart house door, a squall striking her, lifting her high, rushing her forward with a sudden jerk.

The skipper looked up.

"Freshening?"

The mate nodded.

The skipper stepped to the bridge.

"All aft, sir," shouted a sailor, waiting to go below.

"Me feet is cold," said Wispy, at the wheel. "I 'opes we get below. Mebbe me bunk'll be warm."

"Take that fore-sail off her," said the skipper.

"Haul the fore-sail up," shouted the mate.

"*Gawd!*" said a sailor, on the quarterdeck.

"Haw, haw, haw!" laughed another.

"Who wouldn't sell a farm an' go to sea?" said another.

"Haul her up, sons, haul her up!" shouted the bosun.

"Hi-leee-yo-ho-ho, -hi-leeee-yo-ho-ho."

"'Ark to th' admiral, ain't 'ee the little singer?" said the bosun, easing away the fore sheet.

"Come on, sons—aloft and make her fast," shouted the second.

"Come on, sons—sailors to windward! farmers to leeward!" shouted the bosun.

"That's the way we'll pay Paddy Doyle for his *boots*," sang twenty sailors on the jumping fore yard, in the middle of the night.

"It's going to blow," said the skipper to himself.

"It's going to blow," said the mate to himself.

"It's going to blow the headlights off of hell's front door," said a sailor in the fore rigging.

"We make fly," yelled the black man from Suva, standing on the fore yard, staring into nothingness, spray striking on him.

"She'd fly anyway. She couldn't help it," said the apprentice to himself.

"Hi-leeee-ho-yo-ho, hi-leeee-yo-ho-ho," he sang, all about nothing, on his way down from aloft.

"Haw, haw, haw," laughed an old grey-bearded man.

"I wonder will we go below *now*," said one.

"I'll bet we take that fore upper tops'l off her," said another.

They did.

They *reefed* three upper tops'ls, one after the other; and coming once again to deck, to go below, they went aloft; and, one after the other, they *furled* three upper tops'ls.

Snorting through the hidden smother of the black Horn she flew, unseen bergs about her, ice freezing upon shroud and backstay, snow, in driven flurries, circling her high mast heads.

At five o'clock, two bells, they went below; the second mate's watch to roll, as they were, into their bunks; the mate's watch, on deck now throughout the night, to sip their coffee.

"It's going to blow," said one.

"She's boun' for Liverpool direc'—I wish she was there," said another.

"Liverpool direct. We'll dance w'en we gets there," said another.

"We ain't there yet," said the old grey-bearded man.

"We make fly," said the Suva man.

"You'd oughter been a blasted albatross, you wants to be flyin' so," said another.

"A crow black albatross! Wouldn't that look queer now?" asked one.

"I seen a Cape pigeon wi' a w'ite 'ead once," said another.

"I seen a w'ite Mother Carey's chicken once, off Flattery," said another.

"Mother Carey's chickens—that's wot *we* be," said another.

"Gi' us a pipe full o' baccy," said another.

"Aye! let's 'ave a bit o' cheer," said another.

"W'oo's w'eel is it?" asked another. "W'ere's ol' Wispy Cavendish? It ain't '*is* w'eel *now*. It was '*is last* w'eel."

"My Gawd!" shouted another, springing up, throwing his pipe into a bunk, "it's *my* wheel. I forgot. I *was so damn cold*."

"Ol' Wispy's been at the wheel since—*Gawd!—since four bells o' the first watch*. That's—that's——" said one.

"We make fly," said the Suva man, grinning.

"*Fly? Hell!* Wispy's bin a-makin' 'er fly since four bells o' the first watch. That's—that's——" said another.

"That's seven hours an' over," said another. "Good Gawd!"

"'Ee's a blasted albatross—that's what Wispy is," said one.

"'Ee is all dressed up in Prince Alberts," said another.

A man arose from his sea chest, his pipe in one hand, his other hand outstretched toward them, his eyes starry beneath his yellow sou'wester brim.

"*Wispy Cavendish is a sailor*," said he.

"*That's what Wispy is*," said another.

The door opened, slowly, a man entering, stumbling over the high sill; his face drawn, his teeth tight set, his lips apart, his eyes half-closed, his body swaying a little.

They stared at him.

He closed the door behind him.

"Some one gi' us a pipe full o' baccy," said he, "me feet is cold."

Day broke cold above the racing clipper; tossed sea about her, green water mountains rolling up astern, her length lost, her height lost; her strength, her swiftness, blown fragments on the storm; the sky low-hung above her slender skysail-masts, threatening and black, tormented and tormenting; the horizon close hurled upon her, in tortured swells white crested and ominous.

"A berg to starboard, a berg to port. She has passed bergs in the night—many of them," said the skipper, on the bridge.

"We're abeam of the Diego Ramirez," said he, looking at the chart upon the chart house table; a squall striking her; hail, crashing upon masts, and spars, and hatches, beating the sea to thunderous gloom.

Upon either beam bergs rolled and rumbled, broken ice astream of them, crashing at their feet.

"The wind's going to come out of the easterly. It'll meet the current and the bergs. It'll be awful," said the skipper, looking out of the chart house door, shaking his head.

"If I head her northerly I must cross their path. If I stay astream of them it will prolong the peril," thought the skipper, watching lashed waters break high upon the towered bergs; listening to the thunder of the crashing fragments at their ponderous feet.

The skipper blew his whistle, calling the mate to the chart house.

"I'm going to head her northerly. One fast day's sailing will take her out of the ice region. The wind is beginning to haul south, and will come easterly, I think. Check in the starboard braces, sir."

"Starboard cross-jack brace," shouted the mate, the watch crowding from the fo'c'sle to the drenched decks.

Steadily the wind shifted from sou'westerly to south, and, through south to easterly; the gale driving against the opposing current, the sea becoming each hour more savage, more madly tormented.

Eight bells was struck; all hands, gathered about the slopped fore-deck, gazing at a berg close down on the lee bow; the mate's watch starting to go below, to rest at length, after a full night's duty.

"Clue up the fore lower topsail," said the skipper. "It's going to blow."

"Fore lower tops'l up," shouted the mate.

Again all hands stood at the frozen gear, buntlines and leechlines in their cold fingers.

"Watch yourselves," roared the mate, clinging to a life-line as the sea swept her. "Watch your chance—now!"

Leaping through the water smother of the fore deck he battled to the topsail sheets, to ease them away; the second and the bosun with him.

"Hi-leee-yo-ho-ho, haul awa-a-a-ay-ay-oh, hi-leee-oh," sang the singing apprentice, fore-hand at the weather clue line.

"Aloft and make her fast," bellowed the mate, the second and the bosun, all together; the bosun fighting into the shrouds to lead the way.

Above, the storm tops'l crashed and bellied at the buntlines; below, the quivering clipper staggered blindly, strained to the limit of her brave endurance; her main and mizzen tops'ls tighter than the heads of war drums; the sea shouting around her, threatening disaster, savagely wrathful.

"Aloft!" roared the mate, his voice lost in the tumultuous morning.

"Aloft!" roared the second, his face to the gale, his voice beaten back, his clenched jaws scowling to the weather.

"Aloft—get that sail stowed!" roared the mate, staring up at the sky-pointing skysailmast, trembling above the battered tops'l.

"We make fly," said the Suva man, his head beaten upon by great hailstones, his bare hands no blacker than the weather.

"*Look!*" yelled a sailor, his hand outstretched, his finger pointing where, ahead of the bosun, ragged burlap about his feet, Wispy Cavendish fought up the reeling ratlines towards the tops'l yard.

"A sailor—by Gosh!" shouted one, swarming to the shrouds, wind baffled.

"*Way for a sailor!*" shouted a young voice amidst grown warriors, the apprentice springing to the shrouds, aloft, higher and higher, defying wind and sea and hail, following where an old man led; passing the bosun.

"An' that's the way we'll pay Paddy Doyle for his *boots*," sang Wispy Cavendish, in the beating bunt of the topsail, his knuckles broken to bleeding, his arms waving, his burlapped feet upon the frozen foot ropes.

"And that's the way we'll pay Paddy Doyle for his boots," sang the

row of sailors on the fore lower topsail yard, their voices drowned, the
voice of each man sensed by the man beside him; snow driving over the
sea; the ship invisible from aloft; hatches, fiferails, houses, lost in driven
foam; only her four high masts rising from the fury, coated with ice,
lying over at a dreadful slope; the helmsman, vague in the turmoil about
him, as a haunted creature of the sea.

"A day, and she'll be safely through the ice," said the skipper, staring
at the Horn chart upon the table, his finger following the line of the
Antarctic ice drift.

The topsail furled, the mate's watch went below, rolling into their
bunks "all standing"—oilskins and sea boots, soul and body lashings,
upon their tired forms.

The second mate's watch, huddled beneath the fo'c'sle head, awaited
what should be.

The morning watch passed, Wispy and his fellows slumbering, motionless as stones, rolling as the ship rolled, unaware that they rolled.

Throughout the hours from half-past eight, when they came down from
the fore topsail yard, until they were again awakened at a quarter to
twelve, they rested tired limbs; the clipper speeding beneath black skies,
under two topsails, the sea whipped to fury, the weather bitter.

"A few hours and she'll be out of the ice," said the skipper.

"Nor' eas'," said the man at the wheel, turning it over to the apprentice, at the change of the watch.

"Nor' eas'," said the apprentice, "let her rip!"

"Liverpool direc'," said the other, grinning back at him.

"Nor' eas', sir," said he, reporting to the mate upon the bridge.

"Nor' east," said the mate, "all right."

"Skipper's holding her to the norrard, ain't he?" said the second to
the mate.

"Aye. He's getting her out of the ice," said the mate, "seen many
bergs in the morning?"

"A few," said the second, going below.

The mate's watch, huddled under the fo'c'sle head, awaited what
should be.

The watch passed, the trembling clipper driving.

The dog-watch coming, the hands gathered in the port fo'c'sle; the
mate's watch in oilskins; the others in oilskin trousers only, their upper
bodies freed, for a time, from that heavy clothing.

"Harris, where's that concertina?" asked one.

"Aye! get that concertina out an' give us some music," said another.

"We're bound for Liverpool direct," said another.

"Aye—an' we'll dance w'en we get there," said another.

"We ain't there yet," said an old grey-bearded man.

"Play that concertina, 'Arris," said another.

Harris played the concertina, its happy wheezes crying high above the weather's cry without; making music to roll and laugh above the sound of the sea, above the lash of the spray.

They sat smoking, twenty of them, seated at the little table, leaning against the bulk-heads, sitting dangle-legged in bunks; beating their feet, nodding their heads, to a concertina's merry tune.

Wispy, seated upon his old sea chest, rewrapped the Prince Alberts on his feet and legs.

"Wispy, y'er all dressed up, ain't ye, old son?" said one, between tunes.

"Make that concertina play. I likes to 'ear it," said Wispy, looking up.

"Aye—make that concertina play," said another.

"How's this then?" said Harris, smiling happily, his hands going out and in; his fingers pressing and releasing on the stops.

> "Oh, who's that a-knocking at my door?
>   says the fair young ladee,
> Oh, who's that a-knocking at my door?
>   says the fair young ladee,
> Oh, this is me, and no one else,
>   says Abel Brown, the sailor,
> Oh, this is me, and no one else,
>   says Abel Brown, the sailor."

They stamped their feet, heads nodding, eyes shining, pipes puffing white smoke, one of them lifting the song—all of them coming in on the chorus, drowning the roar of the Horn sea, the drive of the spray, the wind thunder.

"Make that concertina play. I likes to 'ear it," said Wispy.

"I likes to 'ear it, too. It's Liverpool direc'," said another.

"Liverpool direct," said another reminiscently.

"We'll dance w'en we get there, ol' son," said another.

"That's what we will," said another.

"We ain't there yet," said the old man with a grey beard.

Eight bells was struck upon the iron bell forward of the fo'c'sle; all hands crowding out to the night and the cold darkness.

"Wind's fallin', ain't it?" cried one.

"Aye! let it fall—let's get some sail on her. It's Liverpool direc'," laughed another. *"Look out there!"*

"Look out there!" cried another, feeling her tremble to the onrush of a boarding sea.

The sea roaring around them, they grasped life-lines, hand-rails, shrouds and backstays, in the darkness.

The mate's whistle sounded, shrilling, half heard, faint, along the uproarious deck.

"I'll bet he's going to make sail," cried one.

"She's out of the ice by now, sir," said the skipper on the bridge, "we've seen none since six bells of the afternoon watch. Set that fore lower, and main upper, topsail. I want to drive her."

"Loose fore lower tops'l—loose main upper tops'l," shouted the mate.

Men raced to the rigging, shouting one to another, unseen; their voices swept away.

Faintly, indistinguishable, a voice called from aloft, upon the fore.

"Sheet home—the man says 'sheet home,'" they shouted.

"It's that there black albatross—'ee wants 'er to fly," said one.

"He ought'er been a bird," said another.

"She'd fly, anyway. She couldn't 'elp it," said another.

"Sing there, admiral! Where's th' admiral?" cried another.

"He's aloft on the main—sing some one," cried another.

They set sail, crowding it upon the willing ship, giving her wing after wing; every one shouting, every one glad—for she was bound for Liverpool direct, and they would dance when they got there. They strung out in a long water-washed row upon the tops'l halyards, singing chantey after chantey, sending canvas, with the ice frozen stiff upon it, to the reeling mastheads—

> "Oh, Johnny's gone, what shall I do?
>   Shiloh, Shiloh Brown.
> Oh, Johnny's gone, what shall I do?
>   Johnny's gone to Rio.
> Where Johnny goes, I must go too,
>   Shiloh, Shiloh Brown.
> Where Johnny goes, I must go too,
>   Johnny's gone to Rio."

Their voices rang, above the wail of the Horn wind, the tumbled thunder of the boarding seas.

> "Said he, 'my son you'll rue the day,
>   to me way hay yoh yah!'
> Said he, 'my son you'll rue the day,
>   and a long time ago.
> When off to sea you go away
>   to me way hay yoh yah,
> When off to see you go away,
>   and a long time ago.'
> And often since have I thought of his word,
>   to me way hay yoh yah.
> And often since have I thought of his word,
>   and a long time ago."

The clipper leaped, gathering her free feet to great plunges, as a beautiful colt to the whip.

"Sheet home the fore-sail," cried the mate.

"Sheet home the fore-sail," bellowed twenty sailors.

"Loose the main-sail," shouted the skipper, from the bridge.

"I'll drive her," said he to himself.

"Gawd!" cried the bosun, to the second, "ain't she a flyer?"

"She knows she's going to Liverpool direct," laughed the second.

"We make fly," said the man from Suva.

"Bird—a blasted bird," yelled another.

"I'm goin' to dance at Mother Mitchell's when I gets to Liverpool," said one.

"You ain't there yet," said another. "Put y'r weight on them 'al-yards."

"Ha, ha, ha," laughed the old grey-bearded man.

"We'll see the moon when the clouds break. She'll be rising soon," said the bosun, to the second.

"Sing, admiral, sing—sing us a chantey," shouted one.

"Aye, sing, admiral—sing!" shouted another.

"Sing—sing, little admiral! Let the boys 'ear a *sailor* singing," said old Wispy Cavendish, beside the admiral, at the mizzen topgallant halyards.

> "Ranzo was no sailor,
>   Ranzo, boys, Ranzo.
> But the son of a New York tailor,
>   Ranzo, boys, Ranzo.
> And he shipped on board a whaler,
>   Ranzo, boys, Ranzo,
> And he shipped on board a whaler,
>   Poor old Reuben Ranzo."

"Belay!" yelled the mate, "what y' tryin' to do? Carry 'em away?"

"The mate says '*Belay*,'" yelled twenty sailors, on the mizzen top-gallant halyards.

"Hoist the fore," shouted the mate.

> "Old Storm-along is dead and gone,
>   to me wa-ay, Storm-along,
> Old Storm-along is dead and gone,
>   way, aye, aye, old Storm-along."

"*Belay—belay!* What in hell y' tryin' to do with her?" shouted the mate.

"Ha, ha, ha," laughed twenty sailors. "The mate says, 'what y' tryin' to do wi' her?'"

"Liverpool direc', sir," shouted one.

"We're goin' to dance at Mother Mitchell's," shouted another.

"Loose the royals—*walk 'em up*—lively does it," shouted the mate.

"She's got a crew," said the skipper to himself, upon the bridge.

"Sing, admiral, sing," cried a sailor.

"Walk her up, sons," shouted the apprentice, "*this way*—

> "John Brown's knapsack's number ninety-three,
> John Brown's knapsack's number ninety-three,
> John Brown's knapsack's number ninety-three,
> as we go rolling home.
>
> And it's glory, glory, hallelujah,
> And it's glory, glory, hallelujah,
> And it's glory, glory, hallelujah,
> as we go rolling home."

Twenty sailors lifted it, stamping forty feet along her dancing teak wood decks.

"Belay—belay all!" yelled the mate.

"Belay all—come up behind!" yelled the sailor at the pin.

"Liverpool direct!" yelled another.

"Mother Mitchell an' her gals," cried another.

"She's driving," said the skipper on the bridge.

"We make fly," said the Suva man.

"She'd fly anyway—she couldn't help it," said another.

"Check in the weather braces," shouted the skipper, from the bridge.

"Weather braces!" shouted the mate. "Starboard watch to the main, port watch to the cross-jack."

"Haul away, sons! Round 'em in. She wants to fly," shouted the second.

"Sing—some one sing, so's we can pull together," shouted one.

"Sing! for Liverpool direct, and a dance ashore," shouted another.

At the main braces Wispy Cavendish was singing, at the cross-jack the singing apprentice, keeping time together; all hands hauling to the long song of it, water to their knees.

"Hi-leeee-yo-ho! haul—away-ay-oh! Hi-leee-yo-ho! Hi-lee-OH!"

The clouds broke, above a ragged horizon; torn edges, frayed, and tumbled o'er the sea; masses of disaster heaped upon the sky rim; a cold moon shining through, silvering the water—gleaming a molten pathway down the stormy night.

"*My God!*" cried the skipper, on his bridge.

"*My God!*" cried the mate, at the lee main braces.

At the wheel the man from Suva stood, his great eyes bulged, his white teeth shining through far parted lips.

"Sing, admiral, sing," cried Wispy Cavendish, and turning *saw beyond the racing clipper's bow.*

"Sing, admiral, sing!" he yelled, "*sing wi' me, son!*"

"Hi-leeee-yo-ho-ho, hi-leee-yo-ho-ho, haul-awa-ay-ay-ay-OH!"

The *Golden Age*, her wide wings flying to the wild Horn wind, the grim sea fury lashed about her, a dim moon drear upon disastrous waters, swept upon her way.

"Hi-leeee-oh, hi-lee——"

Head on, high lifted, leaping all a-quiver, trembling throughout her lovely length, bound for bright dance floors of home, she struck upon the dismal parapet of an awaiting berg; the loose cakes grinding, roaring, tinkling, falling about her dying beauty; the storm clouds driving down across the moon's dimmed face, shading the sea—

Way-for-a-*Sailor!*

FRANCE

HOW PANTAGRUEL MET WITH A GREAT STORM AT SEA AND OF WHAT COUNTENANCES PANURGE AND FRIAR JOHN KEPT THEREIN[1]

François Rabelais

(1495–1553)

THE next Day we espied nine Sail that came spooming before the Wind; they were full of Dominicans, Jesuits, Capuchins, Hermits, Austins, Bernardins, Celestins, Theatins, Egnatins, Amadeans, Cordeliers, Carmelites, Minims, and the Devil and all of other holy Monks and Fryars, who were going to the Council of Chesil, to sift and garble some Articles of Faith against the new Hereticks. Panurge was overjoy'd to see them, being most certain of good Luck for that Day and a long Train of others. So, having courteously saluted the goodly Fathers, and recommended the Salvation of his precious Soul to their Devout Prayers and private Ejaculations, he caus'd seventy eight dozen of Westphalia Hams, Unites of Pots of Caviar, Tens of Bolonia Sawsages, Hundreds of Botargoes, and Thousands of fine Angels, for the Souls of the Dead, to be thrown on board their Ships.

Pantagruel seem'd metagroboliz'd, dozing, out of sorts, and as melancholick as a Cat; Friar John, who soon perceiv'd it, was enquiring of him whence should come this unusual Sadness? when the Master, whose Watch it was, observing the fluttering of the Ancient above the Poop, and seeing that it began to overcast, judg'd that we should have Wind; therefore he bid the Boatswain call Hands upon Deck, Officers, Sailors, Foremast Men, Swabbers and Cabin-boys, and even the Passengers; made 'em first settle their Top-sails, take in their Spreet-sail; then he cry'd:

"In with your Top-sails. Lower the Fore-sail. Tallow under the Parrels. Brace up close all them Sails. Strike your Top-masts to the Cap. Make all sure with your Sheeps-feet. Lash your guns fast."

All this was nimbly done. Immediately it blow'd a Storm; the Sea began to roar, and swell Mountain high: the Rut of the Sea was great, the Waves breaking upon our Ships Quarter, the North-West Wind bluster'd and overblow'd: boisterous Gusts; dreadful Clashings and deadly Scuds of Wind whistled through our Yards, and made our Shrouds rattle again. The Thunder grumbled so horridly that you would have thought Heaven

---

[1]From *Pantagruel's Voyage to the Oracle of the Bottle*. From the translation by Peter Motteux (1694).

had been tumbling about our Ears; at the same time it Lighten'd,
Rain'd, Hail'd; the Sky lost its transparent hue, grew dusky, thick, and
gloomy, so that we had no other Light than that of the Flashes of
Lightning and rending of the Clouds. The Hurrucans, Flaws, and sudden
Whirlwinds began to make a Flame about us by the Lightnings, Fiery
Vapours, and other Aerial Ejaculations. Oh! how our Looks were full of
Amazement and Trouble, while the sawcy Winds did rudely lift up
above us the Mountainous Waves of the Main. Believe me, it seem'd to
us a lively Image of the Chaos, where Fire, Air, Sea, Land, and all the
Elements were in a refractory Confusion.

Poor Panurge, having, with the full Contents of the inside of his
Doublet, plentifully fed the Fish, greedy enough of such odious Fare, sat
on the Deck all in a heap, most sadly cast down, moping and half dead;
invok'd and call'd to his Assistance all the blessed he and she Saints he
could muster up, swore and vow'd to confess in Time and Place convenient, and then bawl'd out frightfully:

"Steward, Maistre d'Hostel, see hoe, my Friend, my Father, my
Uncle, pr'ythee let's have a Piece of Powder'd Beef or Pork. We shall
drink but too much anon, for ought I see; eat little and drink the more
shall hereafter be my Motto, I fear. Would to our dear Lord, and to our
blessed, worthy and sacred Lady, I were now, I say, this very Minute
of an Hour, well on shore on *Terra firma*, hale and easie. O Twice and
thrice happy those that plant Cabbages! O Destinies, why did you not
spin me for a Cabbage Planter? O how few are they to whom Jupiter
hath been so favourable as to predestinate them to plant Cabbage!
They have always one Foot on the Ground, and the other not far from it.
Dispute who will of Felicity, and *summum bonum;* for my part, whosoever plants Cabbages, is now by my Decree proclaim'd most happy; for
as good a reason as the Philosopher Pyrho, being in the same Danger,
and seeing a Hog near the Shore eating some scatter'd Oats, declar'd it
happy in two respects, first, because it had plenty of Oats, and besides
that was on Shore. Hah, for a Divine and Princely Habitation, commend
me to the Cows Floor.

Murther! This Wave will sweep us away, blessed Saviour! O, my
Friends! a little Vinegar. I sweat again with meer Agony. Alas, the
Misen-Sail's split, the Gallery's wash'd away, the Masts are sprung, the
Main-Top-Mast Head dives into the Sea; the Keel is up to the Sun; our
Shrouds are almost all broke, and blown away. Alas! Alas! Where is our
Main Course? *Ael is verlooren by Godt.* Our Top-Mast is run adrift. Alas!
Who shall have this Wreck? Friends, lend me here behind you one of
these Wales. Your Lanthorn is fallen, my Lads. Alas! don't let go the
Main-tack nor the Bowlin. I hear the Block crack, is it broke? For the
Lord's sake, let us save the Hull, and let all the Rigging be damn'd.
Be be be bous, bous, bous. Look to the Needle of your Compass, I
beseech you, good Sir Astrophel, and tell us, if you can, whence comes

this storm. My Heart's sunk down below my Midriff. By my troth I am in a sad fright. Bou, bou, bou, bous, bous, I am lost for ever. Bou, bou, bou, bou, Otto to to to to ti. Bou, bou, bou, ou, ou, ou, bou, bou, bous. I sink, I'm drowned, I'm gone, good People, I'm drowned."

Pantagruel, having first implor'd the help of the Great and Almighty Deliverer, and pray'd publickly with fervent Devotion, by the Pilot's Advice held tightly the Mast of the Ship. Friar John had stript himself to his Waistcoat, to help the Seamen. Epistemon, Ponocrates, and the rest did as much. Panurge alone sat upon Deck, weeping and howling. Friar John espy'd him, going on the Quarter-Deck, and said to him:

"Odzoons, Panurge the Calf, Panurge the Whiner, Panurge the Brayer, would it not become thee much better to lend us here a helping Hand than to lie lowing like a Cow."

"Be, be, be, bous, bous, bous," return'd Panurge. "Friar John, my Friend, my good Father, I am drowning. The Water is got into my Shoes by the Collar. Alas! Alas! Now am I like your Tumblers, my Feet stand higher than my Head."

"Come hither, and be damn'd, thou pitiful Devil, and help us," (said Friar John) who fell a-swearing and cursing like a Tinker. "In the name of thirty Legions of black Devils, come, Will you come?"

"Don't let us swear at this time," said Panurge, "Holy Father, my Friend, don't swear, I beseech you. To-morrow as much as you please. Holos, holos, alas, our Ship leaks. Good People, I drown, I die. *Consummatum est*. I am sped."

"By the Virtue," (said Friar John) "of the Blood, if I hear thee again howling, I'll maul thee worse than any Sea-Wolf. Ods fish, why don't we take him up by the Lugs, and throw him overboard to the bottom of the Sea? Here, Sailor, how honest Fellow! Thus, thus, my Friend, hold fast above. In truth here is a sad Lightning and Thundering. I think that all the Devils are got loose. Here, Mate, my Lad, hold fast till I have made a double Knot. O brave Boy! Would to Heaven thou wert Abbot of Talemouze, and that he that is, were Guardian of Croullay. Hold Brother Ponocrates, you will hurt yourself, Man. Epistemon, pr'y thee stand off out of the Hatchway. Methinks I saw the Thunder fall there but just now. Con the Ship, so ho!"

"Be, be, be, bous, bous, bous," cry'd Panurge. "I am lost. I see neither Heaven nor Earth. Would I were at this present Hour in the Close at Sevillé, or at Innocent's the Pastry-Cook, over against the painted Wine-Vault at Chinon, though I were to strip to my Doublet, and bake the petty Pasties myself. Hark'ee, my Friends, since we cannot get safe into Port, let us come to an Anchor into some Road, no matter whither. Drop all your Anchors, let us be out of Danger, I beseech you. Here honest Tar, get you into the Chains and heave the Lead, an't please you. Let us know how many Fathom Water we are in. Sound, Friend, in the Lord Harry's Name!"

"Helm a lee, hoh," cry'd the Pilot. "Helm a lee. A Hand or two at the Helm. About Ships with her. Helm a lee. Helm a lee. Stand off from the Leech of the Sail. Hoh, Belay, here make fast below. Hoh, Helm a lee. Lash sure the Helm a lee, and let her drive."

"The Lord and the Blessed Virgin be with us," said Panurge. "Holas, alas. I drown, be be be bous, be bous bous. *In manus.* Good Heaven, send me some Dolphin to carry me safe on shore, like a pretty little Arion. I shall make shift to sound the Harp if it be not unstrung."

"Shore, shore!" cry'd Pantagruel. "Land to, my Friends. I see Land. Pluck up a good Spirit, Boys, 'tis within a kenning, so we are not far from a Port. I see the Sky clearing up to the Northwards. Look to the South-east."

"Courage, my Hearts," said the Pilot, "now she'll bear the hullock of a Sail. The sea is much smoother. Some Hands aloft, to the Main Top. Put the Helm a weather. Steady, steady. Haul your aftermisen Bowlins. Haul, haul, haul. Thus, thus, and no nearer. Mind your Steerage. Bring your main Tack aboard. Clear your Sheets. Clear your Bowlins. Port, port, helm a lee."

"Loff, loff," cry'd the Quartermaster, that con'd the Ship. "Keep her full. Loff the Helm."

"Loff it is," answer'd the Steersman.

"Keep her thus. Get the Bonnets fix'd. Steady, steady."

"That's well said," said Friar John, "Good. Loff, loff. Helm a weather. That's well said and thought on. Methinks the Storm is almost over. It was high time, faith. However, the Lord be thanked. Our Devils begin to scamper. Out with all your Sails. Hoist your Sails. Hoist. That's spoke like a Man. Hoist. Hoist."

"Cheer up, my merry Mates all," cry'd out Epistemon. "I see already Castor on the right. Ho, ho. I see Land too. Let her bear it with the Harbour. I see a good many People on the Beach. I see a Light on an Obeliscolychny."

"Shorten your Sails," said the Pilot. "Fetch the Sounding Line. We must double that point of Land and mind the Sands."

"We are clear of them," said the Sailors.

Soon after "Away she goes," quoth the Pilot, "and so doth the rest of our Fleet. Help came in good season."

"By St John," said Panurge, "this is spoke somewhat like. Oh the sweet Word! There's the Soul of Musick in it. What cheer ho? fore and aft? Oh ho! All is well. The Storm is over. I beseech ye, be so kind as to let me be the first that is set on shore. Shall I help you still? Here, let me see, I'll coyle this Rope. I have plenty of Courage, and of Fear as little as may be. Give it me yonder, honest Tar. No, no, I have not a bit of Fear. Indeed that same Decumane Wave that took us fore and aft somewhat alter'd my Pulse. Down with your Sails, well said. How now, Friar John, you do nothing? Is it time for us to drink now? Shall I come and

help you again? Pork and Pease choke me, if I do not heartily repent, tho'
too late, not having followed the doctrine of the good Philosopher, who
tells us, That to walk by the Sea, and to navigate by the Shore, are very
safe and pleasant Things; just as 'tis to go on foot when we hold our
Horse by the Bridle. Hah, hah, hah, by G— all goes well. —Hark you
me, dear Soul, a word with you—but pray be not angry. How thick do
you judge the Planks of our Ship to be?"

"Some two good Inches and upwards," return'd the Pilot. "Don't
fear."

"Odskilderkins," said Panurge, "it seems then we are within two
Fingers breadth of Damnation. Is this one of the nine Comforts of
Matrimony? Ah, dear Soul, you do well to measure the Danger by the
Yard of Fear. For my part I have none on't. My Name is William
Dreadnought. As for Heart, I have more than enough on't. I mean none
of your Sheeps Heart; but of Wolfs Heart, the Courage of a Bravoe.
By the Pavilion of Mars, I fear nothing but Danger."

HOW CAPTAIN JEAN RIBAULT CAME TO FLORIDA AND OF WHAT BEFELL THE MEN HE LEFT THERE[1]

René de Laudonnière

MY LORD ADMIRALL OF CHASTILLON, a noble man more
desirous of the publique then of his private benefite, understanding the pleasure of the King his prince, which was to discover new and
strange Countreys, caused vessels fit for this purpose to be made ready
with all diligence, and men to bee levied meete for such an enterprise:
Among whom hee chose Captaine John Ribault, a man in trueth expert
in sea causes: which having received his charge, set himselfe to Sea the
yeere 1562. the eighteenth of Februarie, accompanied onely with two
of the kings shippes, but so well furnished with Gentlemen, (of whose
number I my selfe was one) and with olde Souldiers, that he had meanes
to atchieve some notable thing and worthy of eternall memorie. Having
therefore sayled two moneths, never holding the usuall course of the
Spaniards, hee arrived in Florida landing neere a Cape or Promontorie,
which is no high lande, because the coast is all flatte, but onely rising by
reason of the high woods, which at his arrivall he called Cape François
in honour of our France. This Cape is distant from the Equator about
thirtie degrees.

Coasting from this place towards the North, he discovered a very
faire and great River, which gave him occasion to cast anker that hee

---

[1]From *The Principal Navigations, Voyages, and Discoveries of the English Nation.* Done
into English by Richard Hakluyt (c. 1553–1616).

might search the same the next day very early in the morning: which being done by the breake of day, accompanied with Captaine Fiquinville and divers other souldiers of his shippe, he was no sooner arrived on the brinke of the shoare, but straight hee perceived many Indians men and women, which came of purpose to that place to receive the Frenchmen with all gentlenesse and amitie, as they well declared by the Oration which their king made, and the presents of Chamois skinnes wherewith he honoured our Captaine, which the day following caused a pillar of hard stone to be planted within the sayde River, and not farre from the mouth of the same upon a little sandie knappe, in which pillar the Armes of France were carved and engraved. This being done hee embarked himselfe againe, to the ende alwayes to discover the coast toward the North which was his chiefe desire. After he had sayled a certaine time he crossed over to the other side of the river, and then in the presence of certaine Indians, which of purpose did attend him, hee commaunded his men to make their prayers, to give thankes to GOD, for that of his grace hee had conducted the French nation unto these strange places without any danger at all.

The prayers being ended, the Indians which were very attentive to hearken unto them, thinking in my judgement, that wee worshipped the Sunne, because wee always had our eyes lifted up toward heaven, rose all up and came to salute the Captaine John Ribault, promising to shew him their King, which rose not up as they did, but remained still sitting upon greene leaves of Bayes and Palmetrees: toward whom the Captaine went and sate downe by him, and heard him make a long discourse, but with no great pleasure, because hee could not understand his language, and much lesse his meaning. The King gave our Captaine at his departure a plume or fanne of Hernshawes feathers died in red, and a basket made of Palmeboughes after the Indian fashion, and wrought very artificially, and a great skinne painted and drawen throughout with the pictures of divers wilde beasts so lively drawen and portrayed, that nothing lacked but life. . . .

Soone after we returned to our shippes, wee weighed our ankers and hoysed our sailes to discover the coast farther forward, along the which wee discovered another faire River, which the Captaine himselfe was minded to search out, and having searched it out with the king and inhabitants thereof, hee named it Seine, because it is very like unto the River of Seine in France. From this River wee retired toward our shippes, where being arrived, we trimmed our sailes to saile further toward the North, and to descry the singularities of the coast. But wee had not sayled any great way before wee discovered another very faire River, which caused us to cast anker over against it, and to trimme out two Boates to goe to search it out. Wee found there an Ile and a king no lesse affable then the rest, afterwarde we named this River Somme. From thence wee sayled about six leagues, after wee discovered another

River, which after wee had viewed was named by us by the name of Loyre. And consequently we there discovered five others: whereof the first was named Cherente, the second Garonne, the third Gironde, the fourth Belle, the fift Grande: which being very well discovered with such things as were in them, by this time in lesse then the space of threescore leagues wee had found out many singularities along nine Rivers.

Neverthelesse not fully satisfied wee sayled yet further towarde the North, following the course that might bring us to the River of Jordan one of the fairest Rivers of the North, and holding our wonted course, great fogges and tempests came upon us, which constrained us to leave the coast to beare toward the maine Sea, which was the cause that we lost the sight of our Pinnesses a whole day and a night untill the next day in the morning, what time the weather waxing faire and the Sea calme, wee discovered a River which wee called Belle a veoir. After wee had sayled three or foure leagues, wee began to espie our Pinnesses which came straight toward us, and at their arrivall they reported to the Captaine, that while the foule weather and fogges endured, they harboured themselves in a mightie River which in bignesse and beautie exceeded the former: wherewithall the Captaine was exceeding joyfull, for his chiefe desire was to finde out an Haven to harbour his shippes, and there to refresh our selves for a while. Thus making thitherward wee arrived athwart the sayde River, (which because of the fairnesse and largenesse thereof wee named Port Royall) wee strooke our sailes and cast anker at ten fathom of water: for the depth is such, namely when the Sea beginneth to flowe, that the greatest shippes of France, yea, the Arguzes of Venice may enter in there. Having cast anker, the Captaine with his Souldiers went on shoare, and hee himselfe went first on land: where we found the place as pleasant as was possible, for it was all covered over with mightie high Oakes and infinite store of Cedars, and with Lentiskes growing underneath them, smelling so sweetly, that the very fragrant odor only made the place to seeme exceeding pleasant. As we passed thorow these woods we saw nothing but Turkeycocks flying in the Forrests, Partridges gray and red, little different from ours, but chiefly in bignesse. Wee heard also within the woods the voyces of Stagges, of Beares, of Lusernes, of Leopards, and divers other sortes of Beastes unknowen unto us. . . .

A little while after, John Ribault accompanied with a good number of souldiers imbarked himselfe, desirous to sayle further up into the arme that runneth toward the West, and to search the commodities of the place. Having sayled twelve leagues at the least, we perceived a troope of Indians, which assoone as ever they espied the Pinnesses, were so afrayd that they fled into the woods leaving behind them a young Lucerne which they were a turning upon a spit: for which cause the place was called Cape Lucerne: proceeding foorth on our way, we found another arme of the River, which ranne toward the East, up which the

Captaine determined to sayle and to leave the great current. A little while after they began to espie divers other Indians both men and women halfe hidden within the woods: who knowing not that wee were such as desired their friendship, were dismayed at the first, but soone after were emboldened, for the Captaine caused great store of marchandise to bee showed them openly whereby they knew that we meant nothing but well unto them: and then they made a signe that we should come on lande, which wee would not refuse. At our comming on shoare divers of them came to salute our Generall according to their barbarous fashion. Some of them gave him skins of Chamois, others little baskets made of Palme leaves, some presented him with Pearles, but no great number. Afterwards they went about to make an arbour to defend us in that place from the parching heate of the Sunne. . . .

Notwithstanding wee returned to our shippes, wnere after wee had bene but one night, the Captaine in the morning commanded to put into the Pinnesse a pillar of hard stone fashioned like a columne, wherein the Armes of the king of France were graven, to plant the same in the fairest place that he could finde. This done, wee imbarked our selves, and sayled three leagues towards the West: where we discovered a little river, up which we sayled so long, that in the ende we found it returned into the great current, and in his returne to make a little Iland separated from the firme land, where wee went on shore: and by commandement of the Captaine, because it was exceeding faire and pleasant, there wee planted the Pillar upon a hillock open round about to the view, and invironed with a lake halfe a fathom deepe of very good and sweete water. In which Iland wee saw two Stagges of exceeding bignesse, in respect of those which we had seene before, which we might easily have killed with our harguebuzes, if the Captaine had not forbidden us, mooved with the singular fairenesse and bignesse of them. But before our departure we named the little river which environed this Ile, the River of Liborne.

A few dayes afterward John Ribault determined to returne once againe toward the Indians which inhabited that arme of the River which runneth toward the West, and to carrie with him good store of souldiers. For his meaning was to take two Indians of this place to bring them into France, as the Queene had commanded him. With this deliberation againe wee tooke our former course so farre foorth, that at the last wee came to the selfe same place where at the first we found the Indians, from thence we tooke two Indians by the permission of the king, which thinking that they were more favoured then the rest, thought themselves very happy to stay with us. But after they had staied a while in our ships, they began to be sory, and resolved with themselves to steale away by night, and to get a litle boat which we had, and by the help of the tyde to saile home toward their dwellings, and by this meanes to save themselves. Which thing they failed not to doe. The Captaine cared not greatly for their departure, considering they had not bene used otherwise then well: and that therefore they woulde not estrange themselves from the Frenchmen.

Captaine Ribault therefore knowing the singular fairenes of this river, desired by all meanes to encourage some of his men to dwell there, well foreseeing that this thing might be of great importance for the King's service, and the reliefe of the Common wealth of France. Therefore proceeding on with his intent, he commanded the ankers to bee weighed and to set things in order to returne unto the opening of the river, to the ende that if the winde came faire he might passe out to accomplish the rest of his meaning. When therefore we were come to the mouth of the river, he made them cast anker, whereupon we stayed without discovering any thing all the rest of the day. The next day he commanded that all the men of his ship should come up upon the decke, saying that he had somewhat to say unto them. They all came up, and immediately the Captaine began to speake unto them in this manner.

I thinke there is none of you that is ignorant of how great consequence this our enterprise is, and also how acceptable it is unto our yong King. Therefore my friendes (as one desiring your honour and benefite) I would not faile to advertise you all of the exceeding good happe which should fall to them, which, as men of valure and worthy courage, would make tryall in this our first discoverie of the benefits and commodities of this new land. . . . I pray you therefore all to advise your selves thereof, and to declare your mindes freely unto mee, protesting that I will so well imprint your names in the kings eares, and the other princes, that your renowne shall hereafter shine unquenchable through our Realme of France.

He had scarcely ended his Oration, but the greatest part of our souldiers replyed: that a greater pleasure could never betide them, perceiving well the acceptable service which by this meanes they shoulde doe unto their Prince: besides that this thing should be for the increase of their honours: therefore they besought the Captaine, before he departed out of the place, to begin to build them a Fort, which they hoped afterward to finish, and to leave them munition necessarie for their defence. Whereupon John Ribault being as glad as might be to see his men so well willing, determined the next day to search the most fit and convenient place to be inhabited. Wherefore he embarked himselfe very earely in the morning and commanded them to followe him that were desirous to inhabite there, to the intent that they might like the beter of the place. Having sayled up the great river on the North side, he discovered a small river, which entred into the Islande, which hee would not faile to search out. Which done, and finding the same deep inough to harbour therein Gallies and Galliots in good number, proceeding further, he found a very open place, joyning upon the brinke thereof, where he went on land, and seeing the place fit to build a Fortresse in, and commodious for them that were willing to plant there, he resolved incontinent to cause the bignes of the fortification to be measured out. And considering that there stayed but sixe and twentie there, he caused the Fort to be made in length but six-teene fathome, and thirteene in breadth, with flankes according to the proportion thereof. The measure being taken by me and Captaine Salles, we sent unto the shippes for men, and to bring shovels, pickaxes and other instruments necessarie to make the fortification. We travailed so diligently, that in a short space the Fort was made in some sort de-fenciable. In which meane time John Ribault caused victuals and warre-like munition to be brought for the defence of the place. After he had furnished them with all such things as they had neede of, he determined to take his leave of them. But before his departure he used this speech unto Captaine Albert, which he left in this place.

Captaine Albert, I have to request you in the presence of all these men, that you would quit your selfe so wisely in your charge, and gov-erne so modestly your small companie which I leave you, which with so good cheere remaineth under your obedience, that I never have occa-sion but to commend you, and to recount unto the king (as I am de-sirous) the faithfull service which before us all you undertake to doe him in his new France: And you companions, (quoth he to the Souldiers) I beseech you also to esteeme of Captaine Albert as if hee were my selfe that stayed here with you, yeelding him that obedience which a true souldier oweth unto his Generall and Captaine, living as brethen one with another, without all dissention: and in so doing God wil assist you and blesse your enterprises.

Having ended his exhortation, we tooke our leaves of each of them, and sayled toward our shippes, calling the Forte by the name of Charles-fort, and the River by the name Chenonceau. The next day wee de-termined to depart from this place being as well contented as was possi-ble that we had so happily ended our busines. . . .

Our men after our departure never rested, but night and day did fortifie themselves, being in good hope that after their fort was finished, they would begin to discover farther up within the river. It happened one day, as certaine of them were in cutting of rootes in the groves, that they espied on the sudden an Indian that hunted the Deere, which finding himselfe so neere upon them, was much dismayed, but our men began to draw neere unto him and to use him so courteously, that he became as-sured and followed them to Charles-fort, where every man sought to doe him pleasure. Captaine Albert was very joyfull of his coming, which after he had given him a shirt and some other trifles, he asked him of his dwelling: the Indian answered him that it was farther up within the river, and that he was vassal of king Audusta: he also shewed him with his hand the limits of his habitation. After much other talke the Indian desired leave to depart, because it drew toward night, which Captaine Albert granted him very willingly.

Certaine dayes after the Captaine determined to saile toward Audusta, where being arrived, by reason of the honest entertaynment which he had given to the Indian, he was so courteously received, that the king talked with him of nothing else but of the desire which he had to become his friend: giving him besides to understand that he being his friend and allie, he should have the amitie of foure other kings, which in might and authorite were able to do much for his sake: Besides all this, in his necessitie they might be able to succour him with victuals. One of these kings was called Mayon, another Hoya, the third Touppo, and the fourth Stalame. He told him moreover, that they would be very glad, when they should understand the newes of his comming, and therefore he prayed him to vouchsafe to visit them. The Captaine willingly consented unto him, for the desire that he had to purchase friends in that place. Therefore they departed the next morning very earely, and first arrived at the house of king Touppa, and afterward went into the other kings houses, except the house of king Stalame. He received of each of them all the amiable courtesies that might be: they shewed themselves to be as affectioned friends unto him as was possible, and offered unto him a thousand small presents. After that he had remained by the space of certaine daies with these strange kings, he determined to take his leave: and being come backe to the house of Audusta, he commanded al his men to goe aboord their Pinnesse: for he was minded to goe towardes the countrey of king Stalame, which dwelt toward the North the distance of 15 great leagues from Charles-fort. Therefore as they sailed up the river they entred into a great current, which they followed so farre till they came at the last to the house of Stalame: which brought him into his lodging, where he sought to make them the best cheere he could devise. He presented immediately unto Captaine Albert his bow and arrowes, which is a signe and confirmation of alliance betweene them. He presented him with Chamoys skinnes. The Captaine seeing the best part of the day was now past, tooke his leave of king Stalame to return to Charles-fort, where hee arrived the day following. By this time the friendship was growne so great betweene our men and king Audusta, that in a manner all things were common betweene him and them: in such sort that this good Indian king did nothing of importance, but he called our men thereunto. For when the time drew neere of the celebrating their feasts of Toya, which are ceremonies most strange to recite, he sent Ambassadours to our men to request them on his behalfe to be there present. Whereunto they agreed most willingly. . . .

When the feast was finished our men returned unto Charles-fort: where having remained but a while their victualles beganne to waxe short, which forced them to have recourse unto their neighbours, and to pray them to succour them in their necessitie: which gave them part of all the victualles which they had, and kept no more unto themselves then would serve to sow their fieldes. They gave them also counsell to goe toward the countreys of King Covexis a man of might and renowne in this province, which maketh his aboad toward the South abounding at all seasons and replenished with such quantitie of mill, corne, and beanes that by his onely succour they might be able to live a very long time. But before they should come into his territories, they were to repayre unto a king called Ovade the brother of Covexis, which in mill, beanes, and corne was no less wealthy, and withall is very liberall, and which would be very joyfull if he might but once see them. Our men perceiving the good relation which the Indians made them of those two kings resolved to go thither; for they felt already the necessity which oppressed them. Therefore they made request unto king Maccou, that it would please him to give them one of his subjects to guide them the right way thither: whereupon he condescended very willingly, knowing that without his favour they should have much ado to bring their interprize to passe. Wherefore after they had given order for all things necessary for the voyage, they put themselves to Sea, and sayled so farre that in the end they came into the countrey of Ovade, which they found to be in the river Belle. Being there arrived . . . . they advertised the king by one of the guides which they brought with them, how that (having heard of his great liberalitie) they had put to the Sea to come to beseech him to succour them with victuals in their great want and necessitie: and that in so doing, he should binde them all hereafter to remaine his faithfull friends and loyall defenders against all his enemies. This good Indian assoone ready to doe them pleasure, as they were to demand it, commanded his subjects that they should fill our Pinnesse with mil and beanes. Afterward he caused them to bring him six pieces of his Tapistry made like litle coverlets, and gave them to our men with so liberal a minde, as they easily perceived the desire which he had to become their friend. In recompence of all these gifts our men gave him two cutting hookes and certaine other trifles, wherewith he held himselfe greatly satisfied. This being done, our men tooke their leave of the king, which for their farewell, sayd nothing els but that they should returne if they wanted victuals, and that they might assure themselves of him, that they should never want any thing that was in his power. Wherefore they imbarked themselves, and sayled towards Charles-fort, which from this place might be some five and twenty leagues distant.

But as soon as our men thought themselves at their ease, and free from the dangers whereunto they had exposed themselves night and day in gathering together of victuals here and there: Lo, even as they were asleepe, the fire caught in their lodgings with such furie, being increased by the winde, that the roome that was built for them before our mens departure, was consumed in an instant, without being able to save any thing, saving a little of their victualles. Whereupon our men being farre from all succours, found themselves in such extremitie, that without the ayd of Almighty God, they had bene quite and cleane out of all hope. For the next day betimes in the morning the King Audusta and

King Maccou came thither, accompanied with a very good companie of Indians, which knowing the misfortune, were very sorry for it. And then they uttered unto their subjects the speedy diligence which they were to use in building another house, shewing unto them that the Frenchmen were their loving freinds, and in lesse then 12 houres, they had begun and finished a house which was very neere as great as the former. Which being ended, they returned home fully contented with a few cutting hookes, and hatchets, which they received of our men. . . .

Behold therefore how our men behaved themselves very well hitherto, although they had endured many great mishaps. But misfortune or rather the just judgement of God would have it, that those which could not be overcome by fire nor water, should be undone by their owne selves. This is the common fashion of men, which cannot continue in one state, and had rather to overthrow themselves, then not to attempt some new thing dayly. We have infinite examples in the ancient histories, especially of the Romanes, unto which number this litle handfull of men, being farre from their countrey and absent from their countreymen, have also added this present example. They entred therefore into partialities and dissentions, which began about a souldier named Guernache, which was a drummer of the French bands: which, as it was told me, was very cruelly hanged by his owne captaine, and for a smal fault: which captaine also using to threaten the rest of his souldiers which staied behind under his obedience, and peradventure (as it is to be presumed) were not so obedient to him as they should have bene, was the cause that they fell into a mutinie, because that many times he put his threatnings in execution: whereupon they so chased him, that at the last they put him to death. And the principall occasion that moved them thereunto was, because he degraded another souldier named La Chere (which he had banished) and because he had not performed his promise: for hee had promised to send him victuals, from 8 dayes to 8 dayes, which thing he did not, but said on the contrary, that he would be glad to heare of his death. He said moreover, that he would chastise others also, and used so evil sounding speeches, that honestie forbiddeth me to repeat them. The souldiers seeing his madnes to increase from day to day, and fearing to fall into the dangers of the other, resolved to kil him. Having executed their purpose, they went to seeke the souldier that was banished, which was in a small Island distant from Charles-fort about 3 leagues, where they found him almost half dead for hunger. When they were come home againe, they assembled themselves together to choose one to be governour over them whose name was Nicolas Barre a man worthy of commendation, and one which knew so well to quite himselfe of his charge, that all rancour and dissention ceased among them, and they lived peaceably one with another.

During this time, they began to build a smal Pinnesse, with hope to returne into France, if no succours came unto them, as they expected from day to day. And though there were no man among them that had any skill, notwithstanding necessitie, which is the maistresse of all sciences, taught them the way to build it. And after it was finished, they thought of nothing else saving how to furnish it with all things necessarie to undertake the voyage. But they wanted those things that of all other were most needfull, as cordage and sayles, without which the enterprise coulde not come to effect. Having no meanes to recover these things, they were in worse case then at the first, and almost ready to fallin to despayre. But that good God, which never forsaketh the afflicted, did succour them in their necessitie.

As they were in these perplexities king Audusta and Maccou came to them, accompanied with two hundred Indians at the least, whom our Frenchmen went forth to meete withall, and shewed the king in what neede of cordage they stood: who promised them to returne within two daye, and to bring so much as should suffice to furnish the Pinnesse with tackling. Our men being pleased with these good newes and promises, bestowed upon them certaine cutting hookes and shirtes. After their departure our men sought all meanes to recover rosen in the woodes, wherein they cut the Pine trees round about, out of which they drew sufficient reasonable quantitie to bray the vessell. Also they gathered a kind of mosse which groweth on the trees of this countrey, to serve to calke the same withall. There now wanted nothing but sayles, which they made of their owne shirtes and of their sheetes. Within few dayes after the Indian kings returned to Charles fort with so good store of cordage, that there was found sufficient for tackling of the small Pinnesse. Our men as glad as might be, used great liberalitie towards them, and at their leaving of the countrey, left them all the marchandise that remained, leaving them thereby so fully satisfied, that they departed from them with all the contentation of the worlde. They went forward therefore to finish the Brigandine, and used so speedie diligence, that within a short time afterward they made it ready furnished with all things. In the meane season the winde came so fit for their purpose that it seemed to invite them to put to the Sea: which they did without delay, after they had set all their things in order. But before they departed they embarked their artillerie, their forge and other munitions of warre which Captaine Ribault had left them, and then as much mill as they could gather together. But being drunken with the too excessive joy, which they had conceived for their returning into France, or rather deprived of all foresight and consideration, without regarding the inconstancie of the winds, which change in a moment, they put themselves to sea, and with so slender victuals, that the end of their interprise became unlucky and unfortunate.

For after they had sayled the third part of their way, they were surprized with calmes which did so much hinder them, that in three weeks they sailed not above five and twentie leagues. During this time their

victuals consumed and became so short, that every man was constrained
to eate not past twelve graines of mill by the day, which may be in value
as much as twelve peason. Yea, and this felicitie lasted not long: for their
victuals failed them altogether at once: and they had nothing for their
more assured refuge but their shooes and leather jerkins which they did
eat. Touching their beverage, some of them dranke the sea water: and
they remained in such desperate necessitie a very long space, during the
which part of them died for hunger. Beside this extreme famine, which
did so grievously oppresse them, they fell every minute of an houre out
of all hope ever to see France againe, insomuch that they were constrained
to cast the water continually out, that on al sides entred into their Barke.
And every day they fared worse and worse: for after they had eaten up
their shooes and their leather jerkins, there arose so boystrous a winde
and so contrary to their course, that in the turning of a hande, the waves
filled their vessel halfe full of water and brused it upon the one side.
Being now more out of hope then ever to escape out of this extreme peril,
they cared not for casting out of the water which now was almost ready
to drowne them. And as men resolved to die, every one fell downe backe-
warde, and gave themselves over altogether unto the will of the waves.
When as one of them a little having taken heart unto him declared unto
them how litle way they had to sayle, assuring them, that if the winde
held, they should see land within three dayes. This man did so encourage
them, that after they had throwne the water out of the Pinnesse they
remained three dayes without eating or drinking, except it were of the sea
water. When the time of his promise was expired, they were more troubled then they were before, seeing they could not discry any land. Wherefore in this extreme despaire certaine among them made this motion that
it was better that one man should dye, then that so many men should
perish: they agreed therefore that one should die to sustaine the others.
Which thing was executed in the person of La Chere, of whom we have
spoken heretofore, whose flesh was devided equally among his fellowes:
a thing so pitifull to recite, that my pen is loth to write it.

After so long time and tedious travels, God of his goodnesse using his
accustomed favour, changed their sorow into joy, and shewed unto them
the sight of land. Whereof they were so exceeding glad, that the pleasure
caused them to remaine a long time as men without sence: whereby they
let the Pinnesse flote this and that way without holding any right way or
course. But a small English barke boarded the vessell, in the which there
was a Frenchman which had bene in the first voyage into Florida, who
easily knew them, and spake unto them, and afterward gave them meat
and drinke. Incontinently they recovered their naturall courages, and
declared unto him at large all their navigation. The Englishmen consulted a long while what were best to be done, and in fine they resolved
to put on land those that were most feeble, and to cary the rest unto the
Queene of England, which purposed at that time to send into Florida

Thus you see in briefe that which happened to them which Captaine John Ribault had left in Florida.

TELEMACHUS IN THE ISLAND OF CYPRUS[1]

François de la Mothe-Fénelon

(1651–1715)

I

AS SOON as Phœbus had spread the first Rays of his Glory upon the Earth, Mentor, hearing the Voice of the Goddess, who call'd to her Nymphs in the Wood, awaken'd Telemachus.

It is time, said he, to him, to shake off Sleep. Come, let us return to Calypso; but beware of her bewitching Tongue; never open your Heart to her, dread the insinuating Poison of her Praises. Yesterday she exalted you above your wise Father, above the invincible Achilles, the renowned Theseus, or even Hercules himself, who has obtain'd Immortality by his glorious Actions. Could you not perceive the Excess of these Commendations! Or did you believe what she said? Know, that she believes it not herself; she only commends you because she thinks you weak and vain enough to be deceiv'd with Praises far exceeding the Merit of your Actions.

After this Discourse, they went to the Place where the Goddess expected them. She smil'd when she saw them approaching, and, under an Appearance of Joy, conceal'd the Fears and Suspicions that disturb'd her Heart; for she foresaw that Telemachus, under the Conduct of Mentor, would escape her Hands, as Ulysses had done.

Go on, said she, my dear Telemachus, and satisfy my Curiosity. I thought all the Night, I saw you departing from Phenicia, and going to seek a new Destiny in the Island of Cyprus. Tell me then the Success of this Voyage, and let us not lose one Moment!

They immediately sat down in a shady Grove, upon the green Turf, enamell'd with Violets.

Calypso could not refrain from looking incessantly upon Telemachus with Tenderness and Passion; nor see, without Indignation, that Mentor observ'd even the least Motion of her Eyes. In the mean time, all the Nymphs in silence stoop'd forward to listen, forming a half Circle, that they might both hear and see with more Advantage. The Eyes of the whole Assembly were immovably fix'd upon the young Man. Telemachus, looking down, and gracefully blushing, thus resum'd the Thread of his Discourse.

Scarce had the softest Breath of a favourable Wind fill'd our Sails, when the Coast of Phenicia entirely vanish'd from our Eyes: And be-

[1]From *Telemachus*. Done into English by Mr Littlebury and Mr Boyer (1766).

cause I was with the Cyprians, whose Manners I knew not, I resolv'd to be silent, and to observe every Thing that pass'd, keeping myself within the strictest Rules of Discretion, that I might acquire their Esteem. But during my Silence, a soft and powerful Slumber seiz'd upon me; my Senses were bound and suspended; I found a sweet Serenity and home felt Joy overflow my Heart. On a sudden, methought, I saw Venus cleaving the Clouds in her flying Chariot, drawn by a pair of Doves. She had the same shining Beauty, the same lively Youth, and those blooming Graces that appear'd in her when she sprung from the Foam of the Ocean, and dazzl'd the Eyes of Jupiter himself. She descended all at once with extream Rapidity just by me, laid her Hand upon my Shoulder, call'd me by my Name, and, smiling, pronounc'd these Words: Young Greek, thou art going into my peculiar Empire; thou shalt soon arrive in that fortunate Island, where Pleasures, Sports, and wanton Joys attend my Steps: There thou shalt burn Perfumes upon my Altars: There I will plunge thee into a River of Delights: Open thy Heart to the most charming Hopes, and beware of resisting the most powerful of all Goddesses, who resolves to make thee happy.

At the same time, I saw young Cupid gently moving his little Wings, and hovering about his Mother. He had the tenderest Graces in his Face, and the Pleasantness of an Infant; yet there was something so piercing in his Eyes, as to make me afraid. He smil'd when he look'd upon me; but his Smiles were malicious, scornful, and cruel. He took the sharpest of his Arrows from his golden Quiver; he drew his Bow, and was going to pierce my Heart, when Minerva suddenly appear'd, and covered me with her impentrable Shield . . . The Arrow, too weak to pierce the Shield, fell down upon the Ground Cupid, in a Rage, sigh'd bitterly, and was asham'd to see himself defeated. Be gone, cried Minerva, rash Boy, be gone; thou canst conquer none but the Base, who prefer dishonourable Pleasures before Wisdom, Virtue, and Glory. At these Words, Cupid, incensed, flew away; and as Venus re-ascended towards Olympus, I saw her Chariot and two Doves, a long time rolling in a Cloud of Gold and Azure; at length she disappear'd. When I turn'd my Eyes toward the Earth, I could no where see Minerva.

Methought I was transported into a delicious Garden, such as Men paint the Elysian Fields. There I found Mentor, who said to me, Fly from this cruel Country, this pestilent Island, where the Inhabitants breathe nothing but Pleasure. The boldest Virtue ought to tremble here, and cannot be safe, but by Flight. As soon as I saw him, I endeavoured to throw my Arms about his Neck, and to embrace him; but I found my Feet unable to move, my Knees sunk under me; and my Hands, attempting to lay hold on Mentor, follow'd an empty Shadow that still mock'd my Grasp. As I was making this Effort, I awak'd, and perceiv'd, that this mysterious Dream was no less than a divine Admonition. I found in myself a firm Resolution against the Allurements of Pleasure, a watchful

Jealousy of my own Conduct, and a just Abhorrence of the dissolute Manners that reign'd in Cyprus. But that which wounded me to the Heart was, that I thought Mentor was dead, that he had pass'd the Stygian Lake, and was become an Inhabitant of those happy Mansions, where the Souls of the Just reside.

This Thought made me shed a Flood of Tears. The Cyprians ask'd me why I wept? These Tears, said I, are but too suitable to the Condition of an unhappy Stranger, who wanders, despairing of ever seeing his Country more. In the mean time, all the Cyprians that were in the Ship, abandon'd themselves to the most extravagant Pleasures; the Rowers, who hated to take Pains, fell asleep upon their Oars. The Pilot put a Garland of Flowers on his Head, quitted the Rudder, and held a vast Flaggon of Wine in his Hands, which he had almost emptied. He, and all the rest of the Crew, inflamed with the Fury of Bacchus, sung such Verses in Honour of Venus and Cupid, as ought to strike Horror into all that love Virtue.

Whilst they thus forgot the Dangers of the Sea, a sudden Tempest arose; the Sky and the Sea were agitated; the Winds, unchained, roar'd furiously in every Sail; the black Waves beat vehemently against the Sides of the Ship, which groan'd under the Weight of their Strokes. One while, we mounted upon the Back of the swelling Billows; another while the Sea seem'd to slip from under the Vessel, and to precipitate us into the dark Abyss. We saw the Rocks close by us, and the angry Waves dashing against them with a dreadful Noise. Then I found, by Experience, the Truth of what I had often heard from Mentor, that Men of dissolute Lives, and abandon'd to Pleasures, always want Courage in the Time of Danger. All our Cyprians sunk into Despair, and wept like Women. I heard nothing but piteous Exclamations; bitter Lamentations for the Loss of the Delights of Life; vain and insignificant Promises of large Sacrifices to the Gods, if they should arrive safe in the Harbour. No one had sufficient Presence of Mind, either to give necessary Orders, or to work the Ship. In this Condition, I thought myself obliged to save my own Life, and the Lives of those that were with me. I took the Rudder into my Hand, because the Pilot, disorder'd with Wine like a raving Bacchanal, was utterly incapable of knowing the Danger the Ship was in. I chear'd the astonish'd Mariners; I made them take down the Sails; they ply'd their Oars vigorously; we steer'd by the Rocks and Quicksands, and saw all the Horrors of Death staring us in the Face.

This Adventure seem'd like a Dream to all those who ow'd the Preservation of their Lives to my Care: They look'd upon me with Astonishment. We landed at Cyprus in that Month of the Spring which is consecrated to Venus. . . .

As soon as I arriv'd in the Island, I perceiv'd an unusual Mildness in the Air, rendering the Body slothful and unactive, but infusing a jovial and wanton Humour . . . I saw great Numbers of Maids and Women,

vainly and fantastically dress'd, singing the Praises of Venus, and going
to devote themselves to the Service of her Temple . . . A certain Air of
Wantoness, an artful Way of adjusting their Looks, their vain Dress,
their languishing Gait, their Eyes that seem'd to be in quest of the Eyes
of Men, their mutual Jealousy who should raise the greatest Passions;
in a word, all that I saw in these Women appear'd vile and contemptible
to me. . . .

I was conducted to a Temple of the Goddess, who has several in this
Island; for she is particularly ador'd at Cythera, Idalia, and Paphos;
it was to that of Cythera I was brought. The Temple is all built with
Marble; it is a perfect Peristyllium; the Pillars are so lofty, and so large,
that they give a majestic Air to the whole Fabric . . . Great Numbers of
People are always at the Gate, attending to make their Offerings. No
Victim is ever slain within the Precinct of the sacred Ground. The Fat
of Bulls and Heifers is not burnt here, as in other Places. No Blood is
ever shed here. The Victims to be offer'd, are only presented before the
Altar; and no Beast may be offer'd, unless it be young, white, without
Blemish or Defect. They are adorn'd with purple Fillets embroider'd
with Gold; their Horns are gilded, and garnish'd with Nosegays of the
most fragrant Flowers; and when they have been presented at the Altar,
they are led to a private Place without the Wall, and kill'd for the Banquet of the Priests that belong to the Goddess.

Here also are offer'd all sorts of perfum'd Liquors, and Wines, more
delicious than Nectar . . . The most exquisite Perfumes of the East are
burnt Night and Day upon the Altars, and form a curling Cloud as they
mount up to the Sky. All the Pillars are adorn'd with Festoons of
wreathed Flowers; all the Vessels for the Service of the Altar are of pure
Gold; a sacred Grove of Myrtle encompasses the Building; none but Boys
and Girls of singular Beauty may present the Victims to the Priests, or
kindle the Fire upon the Altars. But Dissoluteness and Impudence
dishonour this magnificent Temple.

At first I was struck with Horror at what I saw, but it insensibly began
to grow familiar to me. I was no longer afraid of Vice; all Companies
inspir'd me with I know not what Inclination to Intemperance. They
laughed at my Innocence; and my Reservedness and Modesty became
the Sport of this impudent People. They forgot nothing that might en-
snare me, excite my Passion, and awaken in me an Appetite to Pleasure.
I found myself losing Strength every Day . . . So my Eyes began to grow
dim, my Heart fainted, I could no longer recal either my Reason, or the
Remembrance of my Father's Virtues. The Dream that show'd me the
wise Mentor in the Elysian Fields, utterly discourag'd me. A soft and
secret Languishing seiz'd upon me; I already began to love the flattering
Poison that had crept into my Veins, and penetrated through the Marrow of my Bones. Yet, for all this, sometimes I would sigh deeply; I shed
bitter Tears; I roar'd like a Lion in his Fury. O! unhappy State of Youth!

said I. O Gods! that divert youselves so cruelly with the Fate of Men! Why do you cause them to pass through that Age, which is a Time of Folly, or rather a burning Fever? O! Why am not I cover'd with grey Hairs, bowed down and sinking into the Grave, like my Grandfather Laertes? Death would be more welcome to me, than the shameless Weakness I now feel.

Scarce had I uttered these Words when my Grief began to abate, and my Heart, intoxicated with a foolish Passion, shook off almost all Shame. After this, I found myself plung'd into an Abyss of Remorse. Whilst I was under these Disorders, I ran straying up and down the sacred Wood, like a Hind that has been wounded by the Huntsman; she crosses vast Forests to assuage her Pain, but the fatal Arrow sticks fast in her Side, and follows her wheresoever she flies. Wherever she goes, she carries the murderous Shaft. Thus I endeavour'd to run away from myself, but nothing could allay the Affliction of my Heart.

In that very Moment, I perceived, at some Distance from me, in the thick Shade of the Wood, the Figure of the wise Mentor: but his Face appear'd to me so pale, so sad, and so severe, that I felt no Joy at the Sight of him.

Is it you, then, O my dear Friend? My only Hope, is it you? Is it you yourself? Or, is it a deceitful Image come to abuse my Eyes? Is it you, O Mentor? Or, is it your Ghost, still sensible of my Misfortunes? Speak, Mentor, do you yet live? Or is it only the Shadow of my Friend? With these Words I ran to him, so transported, that I was quite out of Breath. He stood still unmov'd, and made not one Step towards me. O Gods! you know with what Joy I felt him in my Arms. No, 'tis not an empty Shadow, I hold him fast; I embrace him; my dear Mentor! Thus I cry'd out; I shed a Flood of Tears upon his Face; I hung about his Neck, and was not able to speak. He look'd sadly upon me, with Eyes full of tender Compassion.

At last I said to him. Alas! where have you been? To what Dangers have you exposed me, by your Absence? And what shall I now do without you?

But he, without answering my Questions, with a terrible Voice, cry'd out.

Fly, fly, without Delay: This Soil produces nothing but Poison: The Air you breathe is infected with the Plague: The Men are contagious, and converse with each other only to spread the fatal Venom: Base and infamous Voluptuousness, the worst of all those Evils that issued out of Pandora's Box, enervates their Souls, and suffers no Virtue in this place. Fly, stay not a Moment; look not once behind you; and, as you run, shake off the very Remembrance of this execrable Island.

He spoke, and immediately I felt as it were a thick Cloud dispersing from about my Eyes, and perceiv'd a more pure and beautiful Light. A sweet Serenity, accompanied with an invincible Resolution, reviv'd in my Heart . . . I began to shed Tears of Joy, and found that nothing was more sweet than to weep . . .

Here, Mentor said, I must leave you: I must depart this Moment: I am not allow'd to stay any longer.

Where, said I, are you going? Into what uninhabitable Desart will I not follow you? Don't think you can escape from me; for I will rather die at your Feet than not attend you.

In speaking these Words, I grasped him close, with all my Strength.

It is in vain, said he, for you to hope to detain me. The cruel Metophis sold me to certain Æthiopians, or Arabs. These Men, going to Damascus, in Syria, on the Account of Trade, resolv'd to sell me, supposing they should get a great Sum of Money for me of one Hazael, who wanted a Greek Slave to inform him of the Customs of Greece, and instruct him in our Arts and Sciences. Indeed Hazael purchased me at a great Price. What he has learn'd from me concerning our Manners, has given him a Curiosity to go into the Island of Crete, to study the wise Laws of Minos. During our Voyage, the Weather has forc'd us to put in at Cyprus; and in expectation of a favourable Wind, he is come to make his Offerings in the Temple: see, that is he, who is now coming out of it: The Winds call us; our Sails are hoisted: Adieu, my dear Telemachus; remember the Labours of Ulysses, and the Tears of Penelope: Remember that the Gods are just. O ye Gods! the Protectors of Innocence! in what a Country am I constrain'd to leave Telemachus!

No, no, said I, my dear Mentor, it shall not be in your Power to leave me here; I'll rather die, than see you depart without me. Is this Syrian Master inexorable? Was he suckled by a Tygress? I'll go to Hazael, perhaps he may compassionate my Youth and my Tears. I will throw myself at his Feet, I will embrace his Knees, I will not let him go till he has given me leave to follow you. My dear Mentor, I will be a Slave with you; I will give myself to him.

In this very Moment, Hazael call'd Mentor: I prostrated myself before him; he was surpriz'd to see an unknown Person in this Posture.

What is it you desire of me, said he?

Life, reply'd I; for I cannot live, unless you suffer me to follow Mentor, who belongs to you. I am the Son of the great Ulysses, the most wise of all those Grecian Kings that destroy'd the stately City of Troy, renown'd throughout all Asia. I have sought my Father in all the Seas, accompanied by this Man, who has been to me another Father. Fortune, to complete my Miseries, deprived me of him; she has made him your Slave; permit me to be so too. If it be true, that you are a Lover of Justice, and that you are going to Crete, to learn the Laws of the good King Minos, harden not your Heart against my Sighs and Tears. You see the Son of a King reduc'd to desire Servitude as his only Refuge. O Gods! see my Calamity! O Hazael! remember Minos, whose Wisdom you admire, and who will judge us both in the Kingdom of Pluto.

Hazael, looking upon me with Mildness and Humanity, stretch'd forth his Hand and rais'd me up.

I am not ignorant, said he, of the Wisdom and Virtue of Ulysses. Swift-wing'd fame has not been wanting to spread his Name over all the Nations of the East. Follow me, O Son of Ulysses, I will be your Father, till you find him again who gave you Life. Though I were not mov'd with the Glory of your Father, his Misfortunes, and your own; yet the Friendship I have for Mentor would engage me to take care of you. It is true I bought him as a Slave, but I keep him as a faithful Friend; in him I have found Wisdom; I owe all the Love I have for Virtue to his Instruction. From this Moment he is free, and you shall be so too; all I ask of either of you is your Heart.

In an instant, I pass'd from the bitterest Grief, to the most lively Joy that Mortals can feel; I saw myself deliver'd from the worst of Dangers; I was drawing near to my Country; I had found one to assist me in my Return; I had the Comfort of being with a Man, who lov'd me already for the sake of Virtue alone. In a word, I found every thing in finding Mentor again; whom I resolv'd to lose no more.

Hazael advances to the Shore; we follow; we embark with him; our Oars cut the gentle Waves; a soft Zephyr wantons in our Sails; it animates the whole Ship, and gives it an easy Motion; the Island of Cyprus soon disappears. Hazael, impatient to know my Sentiments, ask'd me what I thought of the Manners of that Island? I told him ingenuously to what Dangers my Youth had been expos'd, and the Conflict I had suffer'd within me. He was tenderly mov'd with my Abhorrence of Vice, and said these Words:

O Venus! I acknowledge your Power and that of your Son; I have burnt Incense upon your Altars; but give me leave to detest the infamous Effeminacy of the Inhabitants of your Island, and the brutal Impudence with which they celebrate your Festivals.

After this, he discours'd with Mentor of that first Being, which form'd the Heavens and the Earth; of that pure, infinite, and unchangeable Light, which communicates itself to all, without being divided; of that supreme and universal Truth, which enlightens the spiritual World, as the Sun enlightens the corporeal. He who has never seen this pure Light, added he, is as blind as one born without Sight; he passes his Life in a dismal Night, like that of those Regions, where the Sun never shines for many Months of the Year; he thinks himself wise, and is a Fool; he fancies he sees all, and sees nothing; he dies, without ever having seen anything; at the most he perceives only false and obscure Glimmerings, empty Shadows, Phantoms that have no Reality. . . .

Whilst Hazael and Mentor were conversing together, we saw great Numbers of Dolphins, cover'd with Scales that seemed to be of Gold and Azure. They play'd in the Sea, and lash'd the Floods into a Foam. After them came the Tritons, sounding their wreathed Trumpets, made of

Shells: They surrounded the Chariot of Amphytrite drawn by Sea-horses, whiter than Snow, and which, cutting the briny Flood, left vast Furrows in the Sea far behind them. Their eyes darted Fire, and Smoke issued from their Nostrils. The Chariot of the Goddess was a Shell of a wonderful Figure; it was more white than the finest Ivory, and the Wheels were all of Gold. This Chariot seem'd to fly upon the Surface of the gentle Waters. A Shoal of Sea-Nymphs, crown'd with Garlands, came swimming after the Chariot: Their lovely Hair hung loose upon their Shoulders, and wanton'd with the Winds. In one Hand the Goddess held a Golden Sceptre, to command the Waves; with the other, she held upon her Knee the little God Palæmon, her Son, who hung upon her Breast. Her Face was so serene and so sweetly majestic, that the black Tempest, and all the seditious Winds fled from before her. The Tritons guided the Horses, and held the Golden Reins. A large Sail of the richest Purple hung floating in the Air, above the Chariot; a Multitude of little Zephyrs hover'd about it, and labour'd to fill it with their Breath. In the Midst of the Air, Æolus appear'd, diligent, restless, and vehement; his stern and wrinkled Face, his menacing Voice, his thick over-hanging Eye-brows, his Eyes full of a dim and austere Fire, repell'd the Clouds, and kept the fierce and boisterous Winds in Silence. The vast Whales, and all the Monsters of the Sea, came in haste out of their profound Grottos to gaze upon the Goddess, and with their Nostrils made the briny Waters ebb and flow.

After we had admir'd this wonderful Sight, we began to discover the Mountains of Crete, tho' yet we could hardly distinguish them from the Clouds of Heaven, and the Billows of the Sea. We soon saw the Summit of Mount Ida, rising above all the other Mountains of the Island, as an ancient Stag carries his branching Head above the young Fauns that follow him in the Forest.

II

In the mean time, the Wind which filled our spreading Sails, seemed to promise a pleasant Voyage. Already Mount Ida began to decrease in our Sight, and look'd like a little Hill; the Cretan Shore disappear'd, and the Coast of Peloponnesus seemed to advance into the Sea to meet us. But on a sudden, a low'ring Storm over-cast the Sky, and stirr'd up all the Billows of the Sea; the Day was turn'd into Night, and ghastly Death hovered over us. O Neptune, it is you, who with your proud Trident, roused up the Rage of your watry Empire! Venus, to be re-venged upon us for despising her even in her Temple of Cythera, went to that God, and spoke to him, full of Grief, and with her beauteous Eyes dissolved in Tears; at least, it is what Mentor, who is acquainted with Celestial Things, has assured me.

O Neptune, said she, will you suffer those impious Wretches to mock my Power with Impunity? The Gods themselves acknowledge it; yet these rash Mortals have dared to condemn all the Customs of my Island; they pretend to a Wisdom, Proof against all Passions, and look upon Love as Folly and Madness. Have you forgot that I was born in your Dominion? Why do you delay any longer to bury in your deep Abysses, those two Wretches whom I abhor!

She had scarce done speaking when Neptune made his boisterous Waves rise up to the very Skies, and Venus smil'd believing our Wreck inevitable. Our Pilot, being now beside himself, cry'd out, That he could no longer oppose the Violence of the Winds, which fiercely drove us upon some Rocks; a Gust of Wind broke our Main Mast; and a Moment after, we heard the Bottom of our Ship split against the craggy Points of the Rock. The Water enters at several Places; the Ship sinks; all the Crew rend the Sky with lamentable Cries. I embraced Mentor, and said to him, Death is come; we must receive it with Courage; the Gods have deliver'd us from so many Dangers only to destroy us this Day: Let us die, O Mentor! let us die! it is a Comfort to me that I die with you; it were in vain to contend for our Lives against the Storm.

To this Mentor answer'd: True Courage finds always some Resource or other; it is not enough to expect Death calmly and unconcerned, we should also, without being afraid of it, use all our Endeavours to keep it off. Let you and I take one of the Rower's Seats. Whilst that Multitude of fearful and troubled Men regret the Loss of their Lives, without using Means to preserve them; let us not lose one Moment to save ourselves.

Thereupon he took a Hatchet, and cut off the broken Mast, which hanging into the Sea, made the Ship lean on one Side. The Mast being thus severed from its Stump, he shoved it out of the Ship, and leaped upon it amidst the furious Waves. Then, calling me by my Name, he encouraged me to follow him. As a great Tree, which all the confederate Winds attack in vain, and which remains unmoved, and fixed to its deep Roots, so that the Storm can only shake its Leaves: Thus Mentor, not only resolute and courageous, but also calm and undisturbed, seemed to command the Winds and Sea. I followed him; for, who could not have followed, being encouraged by Mentor? And now we steer ourselves upon the floating Mast. It prov'd a great help to us, for we sat a-stride upon it; whereas had we been forced to swim all the while, our Strength had soon been spent. But the Storm did often turn and over-set this huge Piece of Timber; so that, being plunged into the Sea, we swallowed large Draughts of the briny Flood, which ran afterwards out of our Mouths, Ears and Nostrils; and we were forc'd to contend with the Waves, to get uppermost again. Sometimes also we were over-whelm'd by a Billow as big as a Mountain, and then we kept fast to the Mast, for fear that violent Shock should make us lose hold of what was now our only Hope.

Whilst we were in that dreadful Condition, Mentor, as calm and unconcern'd as he is now upon this green Turf, said to me,

Do you think, O Telemachus! that your Life is at the Mercy of the Winds and the Waves? Do you believe, that they can destroy you, unless the Gods have order'd it? No, no; the Gods over-rule and decree all Things; and therefore it is the Gods, and not the Sea, you ought to fear. Were you in the deep Bottom of the Sea, great Jove's Hand were able to deliver you out of it; and were you on the Top of Olympus, having the Stars under your Feet, he could plunge you in the deep Abyss, or hurl you down into the Flames of black Tartarus.

I listened to, and admired his Speech, which gave me a little Comfort; but my Mind was not calm enough to answer him. We pass'd a whole Night without seeing one another, trembling, and half dead with Cold, not knowing whither the Storm would drive us. At length the Winds began to relent, and the roaring Sea was like one who having been a long Time in a great Passion, has almost Spent his Spirits, and feels only the Remains of a ruffled Motion which draws towards a Calm: Thus the Sea grown weary, as it were, of its own Fury, growled in hollow Murmurs, and its Waves became little higher than the Ridges of Land betwixt two Furrows in a ploughed Field.

In the mean time, bright Aurora, with her dewy Wings, came to open the Gates of the Sky, to introduce the radiant Sun, and seemed to promise a fair Day. All the East was streaked with fiery Beams; and the Stars, which had so long been hid, began to twinkle again, but withdrew as soon as Phœbus appeared on the lightened Horizon. We descry'd Land afar off, and the Wind wafted us towards it. Hereupon, I felt Hopes reviving in my Heart, but we saw none of our Companions. It is probable their Courage failed them, and the Tempest sunk them together with the Ship. Being come pretty near the Shore, the Sea drove us against the sharp Rocks, which were like to have beat us to pieces; but we endeavoured to oppose to them the End of our Mast, which Mentor used to as much Advantage, as a wise Steersman does the best Rudder. Thus we escap'd those dreadful Rocks, and found, at last, a clear and easy Coast, where we swam without any Hindrance, and landed, at last, on the sandy Shore. There you saw us, O great Goddess! You who reign over this Island; there you vouchsafed to receive and comfort us.

SHIPWRECK OF A MODEST YOUNG LADY[1]

Bernardin de Saint-Pierre

(1737–1814)

AT ABOUT seven in the morning we heard the sound of drums in the woods; it announced the approach of the governor, Monsieur de la Bourdonnais, who soon after arrived on horseback, at the head of a

[1]From *Paul and Virginia*.

detachment of soldiers armed with muskets, and a crowd of islanders and negroes. He drew up his soldiers upon the beach, and ordered them to make a general discharge. This was no sooner done, than we perceived a glimmering light upon the water, which was instantly followed by the report of a cannon. We judged that the ship was at no great distance, and all ran towards that part whence the light and sound proceeded. We now discerned through the fog the hull and yards of a large vessel. We were so near to her that, notwithstanding the tumult of the waves, we could distinctly hear the whistle of the boatswain and the shouts of the sailors, who cried out three times, *VIVE LE ROI!* this being the cry of the French in extreme danger, as well as in exuberant joy;—as though they wished to call their prince to their aid, or to testify to him that they are prepared to lay down their lives in his service.

As soon as the *Saint-Géran* perceived that we were near enough to render her assistance, she continued to fire guns regularly at intervals of three minutes. Monsieur de la Bourdonnais caused great fires to be lighted at certain distances upon the strand, and sent to all the inhabitants of the neighbourhood in search of provisions, planks, cables, and empty barrels. A number of people soon arrived, accompanied by their negroes loaded with provisions and cordage, which they had brought from the plantations of Golden Dust, from the district of La Flaque, and from the river of the Rampart. One of the most aged of these planters, approaching the governor, said to him:

"We have heard all night hollow noises in the mountains; in the woods, the leaves of the trees are shaken, although there is no wind; the sea-birds seek refuge upon the land; it is certain that all these signs announce a hurricane."

"Well, my friends," answered the governor, "we are prepared for it, and no doubt the vessel is also."

Everything, indeed, presaged the near approach of the hurricane. The centre of the clouds in the zenith was of a dismal black, while their skirts were tinged with a copper-coloured hue. The air resounded with the cries of tropic-birds, petrels, frigate-birds, and innumerable other sea-fowl which, notwithstanding the obscurity of the atmosphere, were seen coming from every point of the horizon to seek for shelter in the island.

Towards nine in the morning we heard in the direction of the ocean the most terrific noise, like the sound of thunder mingled with that of torrents rushing down the steeps of lofty mountains. A general cry was heard of "There is the hurricane!" and the next moment a frightful gust of wind dispelled the fog which covered the Isle of Amber and its channel. The *Saint-Géran* then presented herself to our view, her deck crowded with people, her yards and topmasts lowered, and her flag half-mast high, moored by four cables at her bow and one at her stern. She had anchored between the Isle of Amber and the mainland, inside the chain of reefs

which encircles the island, and which she had passed through in a place
where no vessel had ever passed before. She presented her head to the
waves that rolled in from the open sea, and as each billow rushed into the
narrow strait where she lay, her bow lifted to such a degree as to show
her keel; and at the same moment her stern, plunging into the water,
disappeared altogether from our sight, as if it were swallowed up by the
surges. In this position, driven by the winds and waves towards the shore,
it was equally impossible for her to return by the passage through which
she had made her way; or, by cutting her cables, to strand herself upon
the beach, from which she was separated by sandbanks and reefs of
rocks. Every billow which broke upon the coast advanced roaring to the
bottom of the bay, throwing up heaps of shingle to the distance of fifty
feet upon the land; then, rushing back, laid bare its sandy bed, from
which it rolled immense stones, with a hoarse and dismal noise. The sea,
swelled by the violence of the wind, rose higher every moment; and the
whole channel between this island and the Isle of Amber was soon one
vast sheet of white foam, full of yawning pits of black and deep billows.
Heaps of this foam, more than six feet high, were piled up at the bottom
of the bay; and the winds which swept its surface carried masses of it
over the steep sea-bank, scattering it upon the land to the distance of
half a league. These innumerable white flakes, driven horizontally even
to the very foot of the mountains, looked like snow issuing from the
bosom of the ocean. The appearance of the horizon portended a lasting
tempest; the sky and the water seemed blended together. Thick masses
of cloud, of a frightful form, swept across the zenith with the swiftness
of birds, while others appeared motionless as rocks. Not a single spot of
blue sky could be discerned in the whole firmament; and a pale yellow
gleam only lightened up all the objects of the earth, the sea, and the
skies.

From the violent rolling of the ship, what we all dreaded happened at
last. The cables which held her bow were torn away; she then swung to a
single hawser, and was instantly dashed upon the rocks, at the distance
of half a cable's length from the shore. A general cry of horror issued from
the spectators. Paul rushed forward to throw himself into the sea, when,
seizing him by the arm,

"My son," I exclaimed, "would you perish?"

"Let me go to save her," he cried, "or let me die!"

Seeing that despair had deprived him of reason, Domingo and I, in
order to preserve him, fastened a long cord round his waist, and held it
fast by the end. Paul then precipitated himself towards the *Saint-Géran*,
now swimming, and now walking upon the rocks. Sometimes he had hopes
of reaching the vessel, which the sea, by the reflux of its waves, had left
almost dry, so that you could have walked round it on foot; but suddenly the billows, returning with fresh fury, shrouded it beneath mountains of water, which then lifted it upright upon its keel. The breakers

at the same moment threw the unfortunate Paul far upon the beach, his legs bathed in blood, his bosom wounded, and himself half dead. The moment he had recovered the use of his senses, he arose, and returned with new ardour towards the vessel, the parts of which now yawned asunder from the violent strokes of the billows. The crew then, despairing of their safety, threw themselves in crowds into the sea upon yards, planks, hencoops, tables, and barrels.

At this moment we beheld an object which wrung our hearts with grief and pity: a young lady appeared in the stern-gallery of the *Saint-Géran*, stretching out her arms towards him who was making so many efforts to join her. It was Virginia. She had discovered her lover by his intrepidity. The sight of this amiable girl, exposed to such horrible danger, filled us with unutterable despair. As for Virginia, with a firm and dignified mien, she waved her hand, as if bidding us an eternal farewell. All the sailors had flung themselves into the sea, except one, who still remained upon the deck, and who was naked, and strong as Hercules. This man approached Virginia with respect, and kneeling at her feet, attempted to force her to throw off her clothes; but she repulsed him with modesty, and turned away her head. Then were heard redoubled cries from the spectators,

"Save her! Save her! Do not leave her!"

But at that moment a mountain billow, of enormous magnitude, engulfed itself between the Isle of Amber and the coast, and menaced the shattered vessel, towards which it rolled bellowing, with its black sides and foaming head. At this terrible sight the sailor flung himself into the sea, and Virginia, seeing death inevitable, crossed her hands upon her breast, and, raising upwards her serene and beauteous eyes, seemed an angel prepared to take her flight to heaven.

Oh, day of horror! Alas! everything was swallowed up by the relentless billows. The surge threw some of the spectators, whom an impulse of humanity had prompted to advance towards Virginia, far upon the beach, and also the sailor who had endeavoured to save her life. This man, who had escaped from almost certain death, kneeling upon the sand, exclaimed:

"Oh my God! Thou hast saved my life, but I would have given it willingly for that excellent young lady, who persevered in not undressing herself as I had done."

HOW MALICIOUS GILLIATT FOUGHT THE TEMPEST[1]

Victor Hugo

(1802–1885)

IN THE middle of the night he awoke suddenly and with a jerk like the recoil of a spring.

He opened his eyes.

The Douvres, rising high over his head, were lighted up as by the white glow of burning embers. Over all the dark escarpment of the rock there was a light like the reflection of a fire.

The aspect of the sea was extraordinary.

The water seemed a-fire. As far as the eye could reach, among the reefs and beyond them, the sea ran with flame. The flame was not red; it had nothing in common with the grand living fires of volcanic craters or of great furnaces. There was no sparkling, no glare, no purple edges, no noise. Long trails of a pale tint simulated upon the water the folds of a winding sheet. A trembling glow was spread over the waves. It was the spectre of a great fire rather than the fire itself. It was in some degree like the glow of unearthly flames lighting the inside of a sepculchre. A burning darkness.

The night itself, dim, vast and wide-diffused, was the fuel of that cold flame. It was a strange illumination issuing out of blindness. The shadows even formed part of that phantom-fire.

The sailors of the Channel are familiar with those indescribable phosphorescences, full of warning for the navigator. By this light surrounding objects lose their reality. A spectral glimmer renders them, as it were, transparent. Rocks become no more than outlines. Cables of anchors look like iron bars heated to a white heat. The nets of the fishermen beneath the water seem webs of fire. The half of the oar above the waves is dark as ebony, the rest in the sea like silver. Every boat leaves a furrow behind it like a comet's tail. The fish are tongues of fire, or fragments of the forked lightning, moving in the depths.

The reflection of this brightness had passed over the closed eyelids of Gilliatt in the sloop. It was this that had awakened him.

The ebb tide had run out, and the waters were beginning to rise again. The funnel, which had become disengaged during his sleep, was about to enter again into the yawning hollow above it.

It was rising slowly.

A rise of another foot would have entangled it in the wreck again. A rise of one foot is equivalent to half-an-hour's tide. If he intended, there-

---

[1]From *The Toilers of the Sea*. From the translation by W. Moy Thomas.

fore, to take advantage of that temporary deliverance once more within his reach, he had just half-an-hour before him.

He leaped to his feet.

Gilliatt knew the sea in all its phases. Notwithstanding all her tricks, and often as he had suffered from her terrors, he had long been her companion. That mysterious entity which we call the ocean had nothing in its secret thoughts which he could not divine. Observation, meditation, and solitude had given him a quick perception of coming changes, of wind, or cloud, or wave.

Gilliatt hastened to the top ropes and payed out some cable; then being no longer held fast by the anchors, he seized the boat-hook of the sloop, and pushed her towards the entrance to the gorge some fathoms from the *Durande*, and quite near to the breakwater. Here, as the Guernsey sailors say, it had *du rang*. In less than ten minutes the sloop was withdrawn from beneath the carcase of the wreck. There was no further danger of the funnel being caught in a trap. The tide might rise now.

And yet Gilliatt's manner was not that of one about to take his departure.

He stood considering the light upon the sea once more; but his thoughts were not of starting. He was thinking of how to fix the sloop again, and how to fix it more firmly than ever, though near to the exit from the defile.

Up to this time he had only used the two anchors of the sloop, and had not yet employed the little anchor of the *Durande*, which he had found among the breakers. He now let go this third anchor, taking care to fasten the cable to a rope, one end of which was slung through the anchor ring, while the other was attached to the windlass of the sloop. In this manner he made a kind of triangular, triple anchorage, much stronger than the moorings with two anchors. All this indicated keen anxiety, and a redoubling of precautions. The sloop being fixed in its new position, he went in quest of the strongest chain which he had in his store-cavern, and attaching it to the nails driven into the two Douvres, he fortified from within with this chain the rampart of planks and beams, already protected from without by the cross chain.

Suddenly he paused to listen.

A feeble, indistinct sound seemed to reach his ear from somewhere in the far distance.

He listened a second time. The distant noise recommenced. Gilliatt shook his head like one who recognizes at last something familiar to him.

A few minutes later he was at the other extremity of the alley between the rocks, at the entrance facing the east, which had remained open until then, and by heavy blows of his hammer was driving large nails into the sides of the gullet near "The Man" rock, as he had done at the gullet of the Douvres.

The nails being driven, Gilliatt dragged beams and cords and then chains to the spot; and without taking his eyes off his work, or permitting his mind to be diverted for a moment, he began to construct across the gorge of "The Man," with beams fixed horizontally, and made fast by cables, one of those open barriers which science has now adopted under the name of breakwaters.

Meanwhile the sun had risen, and was shining brightly. The sky was clear, the sea calm.

Gilliatt pressed on with his work. He, too, was calm; but there was anxiety in his haste. He passed with long strides from rock to rock, and returned dragging wildly sometimes a rider, sometimes a binding stake. The work was executed so fast that it was rather a rapid growth than a construction.

The first cross pieces of the breakwater being fixed, Gilliatt mounted upon them and listened once more.

The murmurs had become significant.

He continued his construction. He supported it with the two catheads of the *Durande*, bound to the frame of beams by cords passing through the three pulley-sheaves. The construction was little more than a colossal hurdle, having beams for rods and chains in the place of wattles.

He climbed again upon the barrier and listened.

The noises from the horizon had ceased; all was still.

The sea was smooth and quiet; the deep blue of the sky responded to the deep green tint of the ocean. Not a cloud on high; not a line of foam below. It was impossible to imagine a lovelier day.

On the verge of the horizon a flight of birds of passage formed a long dark line against the sky. They were flying fast as if alarmed.

Gilliatt set to work again to raise the breakwater. He raised it as high as he could; as high, indeed, as the curving of the rocks would permit.

Towards noon the sun appeared to him to give more than its usual warmth. Standing upon the powerful frame which he had built up, he paused again to survey the wide expanse.

The sea was more than tranquil. It was a dull dead calm. No sail was visible. The sky was everywhere clear; but from blue it had become white. The whiteness was singular. To the west, and upon the horizon, was a little spot of a sickly hue. The spot remained in the same place, but by degrees grew larger. Near the breakers the waves shuddered; but very gently.

Gilliatt had done well to build his breakwater.

A tempest was approaching.

The elements had determined to give battle.

Gilliatt ascended to the summit of the Great Douvre. From hence he could see around the horizon. The western side was appalling. A wall of cloud spread across it, barring the wide expanse from side to side, and ascending slowly from the horizon towards the zenith. This wall, straight lined, vertical, without a crevice in its height, without a rent in its structure, seemed built by the square and measured by the plumb-line. It was cloud in the likeness of granite. Its escarpment, completely perpendicular at the southern extremity, curved a little towards the north, like a bent sheet of iron, presenting the steep, slippery face of an inclined plane. The dark wall enlarged and grew; but its entablature never ceased for a moment to be parallel with the horizon line, which was almost indistinguishable in the gathering darkness. Silently, and altogether, the airy battlements ascended. No undulation, no wrinkle, no projection changed its shape or moved its place. The aspect of this immobility in movement was impressive. The sun, pale in the midst of a strange sickly transparence, lighted up this outline of the Apocalypse. Already the cloudy bank had blotted out one half the space of the sky; shelving like the fearful talus of the abyss. It was the uprising of a dark mountain between earth and heaven.

It was night falling suddenly upon midday.

There was a heat in the air as from an oven door, coming from that mysterious mass on mass. The sky, which from blue had become white, was now turning from white to a slatey grey. The sea beneath was leaden-hued and dull. There was no breath, no wave, no noise. Far as eye could reach, the desert ocean. No sail was visible on any side. The birds had disappeared. Some monstrous treason seemed abroad.

Gilliatt stood there motionless a few moments, his eye fixed upon the cloud bank, as if mentally taking a sounding of the tempest. His *galérienne* was in the pocket of his jacket; he took it out and placed it on his head. He put on his overalls, and his waterproof overcoat, like a knight who puts on his armour at the moment of battle. He had no shoes; but his naked feet had become hardened to the rocks.

This preparation for the storm being completed, he looked down upon his breakwater, grasped the knotted cord hurriedly, descended from the plateau of the Douvres, stepped on to the rocks below and hastened to his store cavern. A few moments later he was at work. The vast silent cloud might have heard the strokes of his hammer. With the nails, ropes, and beams which still remained, he constructed for the eastern gullet, a second frame, which he succeeded in fixing at ten or twelve feet from the other.

Suddenly an immense peal of thunder burst upon the air. Gilliatt himself felt the shock. No electric flash accompanied the report. It was a blind peal. The silence was profound again. There was an interval, as when combatants take up their position. Then appeared slowly, one after the other, great shapeless flashes; these flashes were silent. The wall of cloud was now a vast cavern, with roofs and arches. Outlines of forms were traceable among them; monstrous heads were vaguely shadowed forth; rocks seemed to stretch out; elephants bearing turrets, seen for a moment, vanished. Sheets of clouds undulated like folds of giant flags.

Suddenly Gilliatt felt a breath moving his hair. Two or three large spots of rain fell heavily around him on the rock. Then there was a second thunder clap. The wind was rising.

The terror of darkness was at its highest point. The first peal of thunder had shaken the sea; the second rent the wall of cloud from top to base; a breach was visible; the pent up deluge rushed towards it; the rent became like a gulf filled with rain. The outpouring of the tempest had begun.

Rain, wind, lightnings, thunder, waves swirling upwards to the clouds, foam, hoarse noises, whistlings, mingled together like monsters suddenly unloosened.

For a solitary man, imprisoned with an over-loaded vessel, between two dangerous rocks in mid-ocean, no crisis could have been more menacing. The danger of the tide, over which he had triumphed, was nothing compared with the danger of the tempest.

Surrounded on all sides by dangers, Gilliatt, at the last moment, and before the crowning peril, had developed an ingenious strategy. He had secured his basis of operations in the enemies' territory; had pressed the rock into his service. The Douvres, originally his enemy, had become his second in that immense duel. Out of that sepulchre he had constructed a fortress. He was built up among those formidable sea ruins. He was blockaded, but well defended. He had, so to speak, set his back against the wall, and stood face to face with the hurricane. He had barricaded the narrow strait, that highway of the waves. The sloop might be considered secure on three sides. Closely wedged between the two interior walls of the rock, made fast by three anchorings, she was sheltered from the north by the Little Douvre, on the south by the Great one; terrible escarpments more accustomed to wreck vessels than to save them. On the western side she was protected by the frame of timbers made fast and nailed to the rocks—a third barrier which had withstood the rude flood-tide of the sea; a veritable citadel gate, having for its sides the columns of the rock—the two Douvres themselves. Nothing was to be feared from that side. It was on the eastern side only that there was danger.

On that side there was no protection but the breakwater. A breakwater requires at least two frames. Gilliatt had only had time to construct one. He was compelled to build the second in the very presence of the tempest.

The wildness of the storm went on increasing. All the tumult of the wide expanse rushed towards the Douvres. Voices were heard in the darkness. What could they be? The ancient terror of the sea was there. At times they seemed to speak as if some one was uttering words of command. There were clamours, strange trepidations, and then that majestic roar which the mariners call the "Ocean cry." The indefinite and flying eddies of the wind whistled, while curling the waves and flinging them like giant quoits, cast by invisible athletes, against the breakers. The enormous surf streamed over all the rocks; torrents above; foam below. Then the roaring was redoubled. No uproar of men or beasts could yield an idea of that din which mingled with the incessant breaking of the sea. The clouds cannonaded, the hailstones poured their volleys, the surf mounted to the assault. As far as eye could reach, the sea was white; ten leagues of yeasty water filled the horizon.

Meanwhile Gilliatt seemed to pay no attention to the storm. His head was bent over his work. The second framework began to approach completion. To every clap of thunder he replied with a blow of his hammer, making a cadence which was audible even amidst that tumult. He was bare-headed, for a gust had carried away his *galérienne*. He suffered from a burning thirst. Little pools of rain had formed in the rocks around him. From time to time he took some water in the hollow of his hand and drank. Then, without even looking upward to observe the storm, he applied himself anew to his task.

All might depend upon a moment. He knew the fate that awaited him if his breakwater should not be completed in time. Of what avail could it be to lose a moment in looking for the approach of death?

The storm had now rotated to the west, and was expending its fury upon the barricades of the two Douvres. But Gilliatt had faith in his breakwaters, and with good reason. These barricades, made of a great portion of the fore-part of the *Durande*, took the shock of the waves easily. To demolish them it would have been necessary to overthrow the Douvres themselves.

The second frame of the eastern barrier was nearly completed. A few more knots of rope and ends of chains and this new rampart would be ready to play its part in barring out the storm.

Suddenly there was a great brightness; the rain ceased; the clouds rolled asunder; the wind had just shifted; a sort of high, dark window opened in the zenith, and the lightnings were extinguished. The end seemed to have come.

It was but the commencement. The change of wind was from the north-west to the north-east. The storm was preparing to burst forth again with a new legion of hurricanes. The north was about to mount to the assault. Sailors call this dreaded moment of transition the "Return storm." The southern wind brings most rain, the north wind most lightning.

The attack, coming now from the east, was directed against the weak point of the position.

This time Gilliatt interrupted his work and looked around him. He stood erect upon a curved projection of the rock behind the second barrier, which was nearly finished. If the first frame had been carried away, it would have broken down the second, which was not yet consolidated, and must have crushed him. Gilliatt, in the place that he had chosen, must in that case have been destroyed before seeing the sloop, the machinery, and all his work shattered and swallowed up in the gulf. Such was the possibility which awaited him. He accepted it, and contemplated it sternly.

In that wreck of all his hopes, to die at once would have been his desire; to die first, as he would have regarded it—for the machinery produced in his mind the effect of a living being. He moved aside his hair, which was beaten over his eyes by the wind, grasped his trusty mallet, drew himself up in a menacing attitude, and awaited the event.

He was not kept long in suspense.

A flash of lightning gave the signal; the livid opening in the zenith closed; a driving torrent of rain fell; then all became dark, save where the lightnings broke forth once more. The attack had recommenced in earnest.

A heavy swell, visible from time to time in the blaze of the lightning, was rolling in the east beyond "The Man" rock. It resembled a huge wall of glass. It was green and without foam, and it stretched across the wide expanse. It was advancing towards the breakwater, increasing as it approached.

The great wave struck "The Man" rock, broke in twain, and passed beyond. The broken wave, rejoined, formed a mountain of water, and instead of advancing in parallel line as before, came down perpendicularly upon the breakwater. The shock was terrific: the whole wave became a roaring surf.

For some moments the sea drowned everything. Nothing was visible except the furious waters, an enormous breadth of foam, the whiteness of a winding sheet blowing in the draught of a sepulchre; nothing was heard but the roaring storm working devastation around.

When the foam subsided, Gilliatt was still standing at his post.

The barrier had stood firm.

Suddenly a crash was heard, resounding and prolonging itself through the defile at some distance behind him: a crash more terrible than any he had yet heard.

It came from the direction of the sloop.

Something disastrous was happening there.

Gilliatt hastened toward it.

From the eastern gullet where he was, he could not see the sloop on account of the sharp turns of the pass. At the last turn he stopped and waited for the lightning.

The first flash revealed to him the position of affairs.

The rush of the sea through the eastern entrance had been met by a blast of wind from the other end. A disaster was near at hand.

The sloop had received no visible damage; anchored as she was, the storm had little power over her, but the carcase of the *Durande* was distressed. It was entirely out of the sea in the air, exposed. The breach which Gilliatt had made, and which he had passed the engine through, had rendered the hull still weaker. The keelson was snapped, the vertebral column of the skeleton was broken.

The hurricane had passed over it. Scarcely more than this was needed to complete its destruction. The planking of the deck had bent like an open book. The square opening which he had cut in the keel had become a gaping wound. The wind had converted the smooth cut hole into a ragged fracture. This transverse breach separated the wreck in two. The after-part, nearest to the sloop, had remained firm in its bed of rocks. The forward portion which faced him was hanging. The whole mass oscillated, as the wind moved it, with a doleful noise. Fortunately the sloop was no longer beneath it. But this swinging movement shook the other portion of the hull, still wedged and immovable as it was between the two Douvres. Under the obstinate assaults of the gale, the dislocated part might suddenly carry away the other portion, which almost touched the sloop. In this case, the whole wreck, together with the sloop and the engine, must be swept into the sea and swallowed up.

Gilliatt was one of those who are accustomed to snatch the means of safety out of danger itself. He collected his ideas for a moment. Then he hastened to his arsenal and brought his hatchet. He mounted upon the wreck, got a footing on that part of the planking which had not given way, and leaning over the precipice of the pass between the Douvres, he began to cut away the broken joists and the planking which supported the hanging portion of the hull.

His object was to effect the separation of the two parts of the wreck, to disencumber the half which remained firm, to throw overboard what the waves had seized, and thus share the prey with the storm. Five or six pieces of the planking only, bent and started but not broken, still held. Their fractures creaked and enlarged at every gust, and the axe, so to speak, had but to help the labour of the wind.

The tempest had reached its highest point. Hitherto the storm had seemed to work its own imperious will, to give the impulse, to drive the waves to frenzy. Below was fury—above anger. But the intoxication of its own horrors had confused it. It had become a mere whirlwind; it was a blindness leading to night. There are times when tempests become frenzied, when the heavens are attacked with a sort of delirium; when the firmament raves and hurls its lightnings blindly. It is at that instant that in the blackest spot of the clouds, a circle of blue light appears, which the Spanish sailors of ancient times called the eye of the tempest, *el ojo de la tempestad*. That terrible eye looked down upon Gilliatt.

Gilliatt raised his head. After every stroke of his hatchet he stood erect and gazed upwards, almost haughtily. He was watchful as well as bold. He planted his feet only where the wreck was firm. He ventured his life, and yet was careful; for his determined spirit, too, had reached its highest point. The strokes of his hatchet were like blows of defiance. It was a contest with the elements for the prize at his feet.

He passed to and fro upon the tottering wreck, making the deck tremble under his steps, striking, cutting, hacking with the hatchet in his hand, pallid in the gleam of the lightning, his long hair streaming, his feet naked, in rags, his face covered with the foam of the sea, but grand still amid that maelstrom of the thunderstorm.

Against these furious powers man has no weapon but his invention. Invention was Gilliatt's triumph. His object was to allow all the dislocated portions of the wreck to fall together. For this reason he cut away the broken portions without entirely separating them, leaving some parts on which they still swung.

Suddenly he stopped, holding his axe in the air. The operation was complete. The entire portion went with a crash. The mass rolled down between the two Douvres, just below Gilliatt. It fell perpendicularly into the water, struck the rocks, and stopped in the defile before touching the bottom. Enough remained out of the water to rise more than twelve feet above the waves. The vertical mass of planking formed a wall between the two Douvres; like the rock overturned crosswise higher up the defile, it allowed only a slight stream of foam to pass through at its two extremities, and thus was a fifth barricade improvised by Gilliatt against the tempest in that passage of the seas. The hurricane itself, in its blind fury, had assisted in the construction of this last barrier. Henceforth, let the storm do what it might, there was nothing to fear for the sloop or the machinery. Between the barrier of the Douvres, which covered them on the west, and the barricade which protected them from the east, no heavy sea or wind could reach them.

Gilliatt had plucked safety out of the catastrophe itself. The storm had been his fellow-labourer in the work. This done, he took a little water in the palm of his hand from one of the rain-pools, and drank: and then, looking upward at the storm, said with a smile,

"Bungler."

THE GUNNER'S FIGHT WITH THE CARRONADE[1]

Victor Hugo

(1802–1885)

ONE of the carronades of the battery, a twenty-pounder, had got loose.

This is perhaps the most formidable of all ocean accidents. Nothing more terrible can happen to a vessel in open sea and under full sail.

[1] From *Ninety-three.*

A gun that breaks its moorings becomes suddenly some indescribable supernatural beast. It is a machine which transforms itself into a monster. This mass turns upon its wheels, has the rapid movements of a billiard ball; rolls with the rolling, pitches with the pitching; goes, comes, pauses, seems to meditate; resumes its course, rushes along the ship from end to end like an arrow, circles about, springs aside, evades, rears, breaks, kills, exterminates. It is a battering ram which assaults a wall at its own caprice. Moreover, the battering ram is of metal, the wall wood. It is the entrance of matter into space. One might say that this eternal slave avenges itself. It seems as if the power of evil hidden in what we call inanimate objects finds a vent and bursts suddenly out. It has an air of having lost patience, of seeking some fierce, obscure retribution; nothing more inexorable than this rage of the inanimate. The mad mass has the bounds of a panther, the weight of the elephant, the agility of the mouse, the obstinacy of the axe, the unexpectedness of the surge, the rapidity of lightning, the deafness of the tomb. It weighs ten thousand pounds, and it rebounds like a child's ball. Its flight is a wild whirl abruptly cut at right angles. What is to be done? How to end this? A tempest ceases, a cyclone passes, a wind falls, a broken mast is replaced, a leak is stopped, a fire dies out; but how to control this enormous brute of bronze? In what way can one attack it?

You can make a mastiff hear reason, astound a bull, fascinate a boa, frighten a tiger, soften a lion; but there is no resource with that monster, a cannon let loose. You cannot kill it—it is dead; at the same time it lives. It lives with a sinister life bestowed on it by Infinity.

The planks beneath it give it play. It is moved by the ship, which is moved by the sea, which is moved by the wind. This destroyer is a plaything. The ship, the waves, the blasts, all aid it; hence its frightful vitality. How to assail this fury of complication? How to fetter this monstrous mechanism for wrecking a ship? How foresee its comings and goings, its returns, its stops, its shocks? Any one of these blows upon the sides may stave out the vessel. How divine its awful gyrations? One has to deal with a projectile which thinks, seems to possess ideas, and which changes its direction at each instant. How stop the course of something which must be avoided? The horrible cannon flings itself about, advances, recoils, strikes to the right, strikes to the left, flees, passes, disconcerts, ambushes, breaks down obstacles, crushes men like flies. The great danger of the situation is in the mobility of its base. How combat an inclined plane which has caprices? The ship, so to speak, has lightning imprisoned in its womb which seeks to escape; it is like thunder rolling above an earthquake.

In an instant the whole crew were on foot. The fault was the chief gunner's; he had neglected to fix home the screw-nut of the mooring chain, and had so badly shackled the four wheels of the carronade that the play given to the sole and frame had separated the platform and ended by breaking the breeching. The cordage had broken, so that the gun was no longer secure on the carriage. The stationary breeching which prevents recoil was not in use at that period. As a heavy wave struck the port, the carronade, weakly attached, recoiled, burst its chain, and began to rush wildly about. Conceive, in order to have an idea of this strange sliding, a drop of water running down a pane of glass.

At the moment when the lashings gave way the gunners were in the battery, some in groups, others standing alone, occupied with such duties as sailors perform in expectation of the command to clear for action. The carronade, hurled forward by the pitching, dashed into this knot of men and crushed four at the first blow; then, flung back and shot out anew by the rolling, it cut in two a fifth poor fellow, glanced off to the larboard side and struck a piece of the battery with such force as to unship it. The men rushed towards the ladder; the gun-deck emptied in the twinkling of an eye. The enormous cannon was left alone. She was given up to herself. She was her own mistress, and mistress of the vessel. She could do what she willed with both. This whole crew, accustomed to laugh in battle, trembled now. To describe the universal terror would be impossible.

Captain Boisberthelot and Lieutenant La Vieuville, although both intrepid men, stopped at the head of the stairs, and remained mute, pale, hesitating, looking down on the deck. Someone pushed them aside with his elbow and descended.

It was their passenger—the peasant—the man of whom they had been speaking a moment before.

When he reached the foot of the ladder he stood still.

The cannon came and went along the deck. One might have fancied it the living chariot of the Apocalypse. The marine lantern oscillating from the ceiling added a dizzying whirl of lights and shadows to this vision. The shape of the cannon was indistinguishable from the rapidity of its course; now it looked black in the light, now it cast weird reflections through the gloom.

It kept on its work of destruction. It had already shattered four other pieces, and dug two crevices in the side, fortunately above the waterline, though they would leak in case a squall should come on. It dashed itself frantically against the framework. The solid tie-beams resisted, their curved form giving them great strength; but they creaked ominously under the assaults of this terrible club, which seemed endowed with a sort of appalling ubiquity, striking on every side at once. The strokes of a bullet shaken in a bottle would not be madder or more rapid. The four wheels passed and repassed above the dead men, cut, carved, slashed them, till the five corpses were a score of stumps rolling about the deck; the heads seemed to cry out; streams of blood twisted in and out the planks with every pitch of the vessel. The ceiling, damaged in several places, began to gape. The whole ship was filled with the awful tumult.

The captain promptly recovered his composure, and at his orders the sailors threw down into the deck everything which could deaden and check the mad rush of the gun—mattresses, hammocks, spare sails, coils of rope, extra equipments, and the bales of false assignats of which the corvette carried a whole cargo; an infamous deception which the English considered a fair trick in war.

But what could these rags avail? No one dared descend to arrange them in any useful fashion, and in a few instants they were mere heaps of lint.

There was just sea enough to render the accident as complete as possible. A tempest would have been desirable; it might have thrown the gun upside down, and the four wheels once in the air, the monster could have been mastered. But the devastation increased. There were gashes and even fractures in the masts, which, embedded in the woodwork of the keel, pierce the decks of ships like great round pillars. The mizzenmast was cracked, and the mainmast itself was injured under the convulsive blows of the gun. The battery was being destroyed. Ten pieces out of the thirty were disabled; the breaches multiplied in the side, and the corvette began to take in water.

The old passenger who had descended to the gun-deck, looked like a form of stone stationed at the foot of the stairs. He stood motionless, gazing sternly about upon the devastation. Indeed, it seemed impossible to take a single step forward.

Each bound of the liberated carronade menaced the destruction of the vessel. A few minutes more and shipwreck would be inevitable.

They must perish or put a summary end to the disaster—a decision must be made; but how?

What a combatant—this cannon! They must check this mad monster. They must seize this flash of lightning. They must overthrow this thunderbolt.

Boisberthelot said to La Vieuville, "Do you believe in God, chevalier?"

La Vieuville replied, "Yes—no—sometimes."

"In a tempest?"

"Yes, and in moments like this."

"Only God can aid us here," said Boisberthelot.

All were silent—the cannon kept up its horrible fracas.

The waves beat against the ship, their blows from without responded to the strokes of the cannon.

It was like two hammers alternating.

Suddenly into the midst of this sort of inaccessible circus, where the escaped cannon leaped and bounded, there sprang a man with an iron bar in his hand. It was the author of this catastrophe, the gunner whose culpable negligence had caused the accident—the captain of the gun. Having been the means of bringing about the misfortune, he desired to repair it. He had caught up a handspike in one fist, a tiller-rope with a slipping noose in the other, and jumped down into the gun-deck. Then a strange combat began, a Titanic strife—the struggle of the gun against the gunner; a battle between matter and intelligence; a duel between the inanimate and the human.

The man was posted in an angle, the bar and rope in his two fists; backed against one of the riders, settled firmly on his legs as on two pillars of steel; livid, calm, tragic, rooted as it were in the planks, he waited.

He waited for the cannon to pass near him.

The gunner knew his piece, and it seemed to him that she must recognize her master. He had lived a long while with her. How many times he had thrust his hand between her jaws! It was his tame monster. He began to address it as he might have done his dog.

"Come!" said he. Perhaps he loved it.

He seemed to wish that it would turn towards him.

But to come towards him would be to spring upon him. Then he would be lost. How to avoid its crush? There was the question. All stared in terrified silence.

Not a breast respired freely, except perchance that of the old man who alone stood in the deck with the two combatants, a stern second.

He might himself be crushed by the piece. He did not stir.

Beneath them the blind sea directed the battle.

At the instant when, accepting this awful hand-to-hand contest, the gunner approached to challenge the cannon, some chance fluctuation of the waves kept it for a moment immoveable as if suddenly stupefied. "Come on!" the man said to it. It seemed to listen.

Suddenly it darted upon him. The gunner avoided the shock.

The struggle began—struggle unheard of—the fragile matching itself against the invulnerable; the thing of flesh attacking the brazen brute; on the one side blind force, on the other a soul.

The whole passed in a half-light. It was like the indistinct vision of a miracle.

A soul—strange thing; but you would have said that the cannon had one also—a soul filled with rage and hatred. The blindness appeared to have eyes. The monster had the air of watching the man. There was— one might have fancied so at least—cunning in this mass. It also chose its moment. It became some gigantic insect of metal, having, or seeming to have the will of a demon. Sometimes this colossal grasshopper would strike the low ceiling of the gun-deck, then fall back on its four wheels like a tiger upon its four claws, and dart anew on the man. He, supple, agile, adroit, would glide away like a snake from the reach of these lightning-like movements. He avoided the encounters; but the blows which he escaped fell upon the vessel, and continued the havoc.

An end of broken chain remained attached to the carronade. This chain had twisted itself, one could not tell how, about the screw of the breech-button. One extremity of the chain was fastened to the carriage. The other, hanging loose, whirled wildly about the gun, and added to the danger of its blows.

The screw held it like a clenched hand, and the chain, multiplying the strokes of the battering-ram by its strokes of a thong, made a fearful whirlwind about the cannon—a whip of iron in a fist of brass. This chain complicated the battle.

Nevertheless the man fought. Sometimes, even, it was the man who attacked the cannon. He crept along the side, bar and rope in hand, and the cannon had the air of understanding, and fled as if it perceived a snare. The man pursued it, formidable, fearless.

Such a duel could not last long. The gun seemed suddenly to say to itself, "Come, we must make an end!" and it paused. One felt the approach of the crisis. The cannon, as if in suspense, appeared to have, or had—because it seemed to all a sentient being—a furious premeditation. It sprang unexpectedly upon the gunner. He jumped aside, let it pass, and cried out with a laugh, "Try again!" The gun, as if in fury, broke a carronade to larboard; then, seized anew by the invisible sling which held it, was flung to starboard towards the man, who escaped.

Three carronades gave way under the blows of the gun; then, as if blind and no longer conscious of what it was doing, it turned its back on the man, rolled from the stern to the bow, bruising the stem and making a breach in the plankings of the prow. The gunner had taken refuge at the foot of the stairs, a few steps from the old man, who was watching.

The gunner held his handspike in rest. The cannon seemed to perceive him, and without taking the trouble to turn itself, backed upon him with the quickness of an axe-stroke. The gunner, if driven back against the side, was lost. The crew uttered a simultaneous cry.

But the old passenger, until now immovable, made a spring more rapid than all those wild whirls. He seized a bale of the false assignats, and at the risk of being crushed, succeeded in flinging it between the wheels of the carronade. This manœuvre, decisive and dangerous, could not have been executed with more adroitness and precision by a man trained to all the exercises set down in Durosel's *Manual of Sea Gunnery*.

The bale had the effect of a plug. A pebble may stop a log, a tree branch turn an avalanche. The carronade stumbled. The gunner, in his turn, seizing this terrible chance, plunged his iron bar between the spokes of one of the hind wheels. The cannon was stopped. It staggered. The man, using the bar as a lever, rocked it to and fro. The heavy mass turned over with a clang like a falling bell, and the gunner, dripping with sweat, rushed forward headlong and passed the slipping noose of the tiller-rope about the brazen neck of the overthrown monster.

It was ended. The man had conquered. The ant had subdued the mastodon; the pigmy had taken the thunderbolt prisoner.

The marines and the sailors clapped their hands.

The whole crew hurried down with cables and chains, and in an instant the cannon was securely lashed.

The gunner saluted the passenger.

"Sir," he said to him, "you have saved my life."

HOW DANTÈS ESCAPED FROM THE CHÂTEAU D'IF[1]

Alexandre Dumas

(1806–1870)

ON THE bed, at full length, and faintly lighted by the pale ray that penetrated the window, was visible a sack of coarse cloth, under the large folds of which were stretched a long and stiffened form; it was Faria's last winding-sheet—a winding-sheet which, as the turnkey said, cost so little. All, then, was completed. A material separation had taken place between Dantès and his old friend; he could no longer see those eyes which had remained open as if to look even beyond death; he could no longer clasp that hand of industry which had lifted for him the veil that had concealed hidden and obscure things. Faria, the usual and the good companion, with whom he was accustomed to live so intimately, no longer breathed. He seated himself on the edge of that terrible bed, and fell into a melancholy and gloomy reverie.

Alone!—he was alone again!—again relapsed into silence! he found himself once again in the presence of nothingness! Alone!—no longer to see, no longer to hear the voice of the only human being who attached him to life! Was it not better, like Faria, to seek the presence of his Maker, and learn the enigma of life at the risk of passing through the mournful gate of intense suffering? The idea of suicide, driven away by his friend, and forgotten in his presence whilst living, arose like a phantom before him in presence of his dead body.

"If I could die," he said, "I should go where he goes, and should assuredly find him again. But how to die? It is very easy," he continued, with a smile of bitterness; "I will remain here, rush on the first person that opens the door, will strangle him, and then they will guillotine me."

But as it happens that in excessive griefs, as in great tempests, the abyss is found between the tops of the loftiest waves, Dantès recoiled from the idea of this infamous death, and passed suddenly from despair to an ardent desire for life and liberty.

"Die! Oh no!" he exclaimed, "not die now, after having lived and suffered so long and so much! Die! yes, had I died years since; but now it would be, indeed, to give way to my bitter destiny. No, I desire to live; I desire to struggle to the very last; I wish to reconquer the happiness of which I have been deprived. Before I die I must not forget that I have

---

[1] From *The Count of Monte Cristo*.

my executioners to punish, and perhaps, too, who knows, some friends to reward. Yet they will forget me here, and I shall die in my dungeon like Faria."

As he said this, he remained motionless, his eyes fixed like a man struck with a sudden idea, but whom this idea fills with amazement. Suddenly he rose, lifted his hand to his brow as if his brain were giddy, paced twice or thrice round his chamber, and then paused abruptly at the bed.

"Ah! ah!" he muttered, "who inspires me with this thought? Is it thou, gracious God? Since none but the dead pass freely from this dungeon, let me assume the place of the dead."

Without giving himself time to reconsider his decision, and, indeed, that he might now allow his thoughts to be distracted from his desperate resolution, he bent over the appalling sack, opened it with the knife which Faria had made, drew the corpse from the sack, and transported it along the gallery to his own chamber, laid it on his couch, passed round its head the rag he wore at night round his own, covered it with his counterpane, once again kissed the ice-cold brow, and tried vainly to close the resisting eyes, which glared horribly; turned the head towards the wall, so that the gaoler might, when he brought his evening meal, believe that he was asleep, as was his frequent custom; returned along the gallery, threw the bed against the wall, returned to the other cell, took from the hiding-place the needle and thread, flung off his rags, that they might feel naked flesh only beneath the coarse sackcloth, and getting inside the sack, placed himself in the posture in which the dead body had been laid, and sewed up the mouth of the sack withinside.

The beating of his heart might have been heard, if by any mischance the gaolers had entered at that moment. Dantès might have waited until the evening visit was over, but he was afraid the governor might change his resolution, and order the dead body to be removed earlier. In that case his last hope would have been destroyed. Now his project was settled under any circumstances, and he hoped thus to carry it into effect. If during the time he was being conveyed the grave-diggers should discover that they were conveying a live instead of a dead body, Dantès did not intend to give them time to recognize him, but with a sudden cut of the knife, he meant to open the sack from top to bottom, and, profiting by their alarm, escape; if they tried to catch him, he would use his knife.

If they conducted him to the cemetery and laid him in the grave, he would allow himself to be covered with earth, and then, as it was night, the grave-diggers could scarcely have turned their backs, ere he would have worked his way through the soft soil and escape, hoping that the weight would not be too heavy for him to support. If he was deceived in this, and the earth proved too heavy he would be stifled, and then, so much the better, all would be over. Dantès had not eaten since the previous evening, but he had not thought of hunger or thirst, nor did he now think of it. His position was too precarious to allow him even time to reflect on any thought but one.

The first risk that Dantès ran was that the gaoler, when he brought him his supper at seven o'clock, might perceive the substitution he had effected; fortunately, twenty times at least, from misanthropy or fatigue, Dantès had received his gaoler in bed, and then the man placed his bread and soup on the table, and went away without saying a word. This time the gaoler might not be silent as usual, but speak to Dantès, and seeing that he received no reply, go to the bed, and thus discover all.

When seven o'clock came, Dantès' agony really commenced. His hand placed upon his heart was unable to repress its throbbings, whilst, with the other, he wiped the perspiration from his temples. From time to time shudderings ran through his whole frame, and collapsed his heart as if it were frozen. Then he thought he was going to die. Yet the hours passed on without any stir in the *château*, and Dantès felt he had escaped this first danger: it was a good augury. At length, at about the hour the governor had appointed, footsteps were heard on the stairs. Edmond felt that the moment had arrived, and summoning up all his courage, held his breath, happy if at the same time he could have repressed in like manner the hasty pulsation of his arteries.

They stopped at the door—there were two steps, and Dantès guessed it was the two grave-diggers who came to seek him—this idea was soon converted into certainty, when he heard the noise they made in putting down the hand-bier. The door opened, and a dim light reached Dantès' eyes through the coarse sack that covered him; he saw two shadows approach his bed, a third remaining at the door with a torch in his hand. Each of these two men, approaching the ends of the bed, took the sack by its extremities.

"He's heavy though for an old and thin man," said one, as he raised the head.

"They say every year adds half a pound to the weight of the bones," said another, lifting the feet.

"Have you tied the knot?" inquired the first speaker.

"What would be the use of carrying so much more weight?" was the reply; "I can do that when we get there."

"Yes, you're right," replied the companion.

"What's the knot for?" thought Dantès.

They deposited the supposed corpse on the bier. Edmond stiffened himself in order to play his part of a dead man, and then the party, lighted by the man with the torch, who went first, ascended the stairs. Suddenly he felt the fresh and sharp night air, and Dantès recognized the *Mistral*. It was a sudden sensation, at the same time replete with delight and agony. The bearers advanced twenty paces, then stopped, putting their bier down on the ground. One of them went away, and Dantès heard his shoes on the pavement.

"Where am I then?" he asked himself.

"Really, he is by no means a light load!" said the other bearer, sitting on the edge of the hand-barrow. Dantès' first impulse was to escape, but fortunately he did not attempt it.

"Light me, you!" said the other bearer, "or I shall not find what I am looking for."

The man with the torch complied, although not asked in the most polite terms.

"What can he be looking for?" thought Edmond. "The spade perhaps."

An exclamation of satisfaction indicated that the grave-digger had found the object of his search.

"At last," said the other, "not without some trouble though."

"Yes," was the answer, "but it has lost nothing by waiting."

As he said this, the man came towards Edmond, who heard a heavy and sounding substance laid down beside him, and at the same moment a cord was fastened round his feet with sudden and painful violence.

"Well, have you tied the knot?" inquired the grave-digger who was looking on.

"Yes, and pretty tight too, I can tell you," was the answer.

"Move on, then." And the bier was lifted once more, and they proceeded.

They advanced fifty paces farther, and then stopped to open a door, then went forward again. The noise of the waves dashing against the rocks on which the *château* is built, reached Dantès' ears distinctly as they progressed.

"Bad weather!" observed one of the bearers; "not a pleasant night for a dip in the sea."

"Why, yes, the abbé runs a chance of being wet," said the other; and then there was a burst of brutal laughter.

Dantès did not comprehend the jest, but his hair stood erect on his head.

"Well, here we are at last," said one of them.

"A little farther—a little farther," said the other. "You know very well that the last was stopped on his way, dashed on the rocks, and the governor told us next day that we were careless fellows."

They ascended five or six more steps, and then Dantès felt that they took him one by the head and the other by the heels, and swung him to and fro.

"One!" said the grave-diggers. "Two! Three!"

And at the same instant Dantès felt himself flung into the air like a wounded bird falling, falling with a rapidity that made his blood curdle. Although drawn downwards by the same heavy weight which hastened his rapid descent, it seemed to him as if the time were a century. At last, with a terrific dash, he entered the ice-cold water, and as he did so he uttered a shrill cry, stifled in a moment by his immersion beneath the waves.

Dantès had been flung into the sea, into whose depths he was dragged by a thirty-six pound shot tied to his feet.

The sea is the cemetery of Château d'If.

Dantès, although giddy and almost suffocated, had yet sufficient presence of mind to hold his breath; and as his right hand (prepared as he was for every chance) held his knife open, he rapidly ripped up the sack, extricated his arm, then his head; but in spite of all his efforts to free himself from the shot, he felt it dragging him down still lower. He then bent his body, and by a desperate effort severed the cord that bound his legs, at the moment he was suffocating. With a vigorous spring he rose to the surface of the sea, whilst the shot bore to its depths the sack that had so nearly become his shroud.

Dantès merely paused to breathe, and then dived again, in order to avoid being seen. When he arose a second time, he was fifty paces from where he had first sunk. He saw overhead a black and tempestuous sky, over which the wind was driving the fleeting vapours that occasionally suffered a twinkling star to appear; before him was the vast expanse of waters, sombre and terrible, whose waves foamed and roared as if before the approach of a storm. Behind him, blacker than the sea, blacker than the sky, rose like a phantom the giant of granite, whose projecting crags seemed like arms extended to seize their prey; and on the highest rock was a torch that lighted two figures. He fancied these two forms were looking at the sea; doubtless these strange grave-diggers had heard his cry. Dantès dived again, and remained a long time beneath the water. This manœuvre was already familiar to him, and usually attracted a crowd of spectators in the bay before the lighthouse at Marseilles when he swam there, and who, with one accord, pronounced him the best swimmer in the port. When he reappeared the light had disappeared.

It was necessary to strike out to sea. Ratonneau and Pomègue are the nearest isles of all those that surround the Château d'If; but Ratonneau and Pomègue are inhabited, together with the islet of Daume; Tiboulen or Lemaire were the most secure. The isles of Tiboulen and Lemaire are a league from the Château d'If. Dantès, nevertheless, determined to make for them. But how could he find his way in the darkness of the night? At this moment he saw before him, like a brilliant star, the lighthouse of Planier. By leaving this light on the right, he kept the isle of Tiboulen a little on the left; by turning to the left, therefore, he would find it. But, as we have said, it was at least a league from the Château d'If to this island. Often in prison Faria had said to him, when he saw him idle and inactive, "Dantès, you must not give way to this listlessness; you will be drowned if you seek to escape, and your strength has not been properly exercised and prepared for exertion." These words rang in Dantès' ears, even beneath the waves; he hastened to cleave his way through them to see if he had not lost his strength. He found with pleasure that his captivity had taken away nothing of his power, and that he was still master of that element on whose bosom he had so often sported as a boy.

Fear, that relentless pursuer, clogged Dantès' efforts. He listened if any noise was audible; each time that he rose over the waves his looks scanned the horizon, and strove to penetrate the darkness. Every wave seemed a boat in his pursuit, and he redoubled exertions that increased his distance from the *château*, but the repetition of which weakened his strength. He swam on still, and already the terrible *château* had disappeared in the darkness. He could not see it, but he *felt* its presence. An hour passed, during which Dantès, excited by the feeling of freedom, continued to cleave the waves.

"Let us see," said he, "I have swum above an hour, but as the wind is against me, that has retarded my speed; however, if I am not mistaken, I must be close to the isle of Tiboulen. But what if I were mistaken."

A shudder passed over him. He sought to tread water, in order to rest himself; but the sea was too violent, and he felt that he could not make use of this means of repose.

"Well," said he, "I will swim on until I am worn out, or the cramp seizes me, and then I shall sink."

And he struck out with the energy of despair.

Suddenly the sky seemed to him to become still darker and more dense, and compact clouds lowered towards him; at the same time he felt a violent pain in his knee. His imagination told him a ball had struck him, and that in a moment he would hear the report; but he heard nothing. Dantès put out his hand, and felt resistance; he then extended his leg, and felt the land, and in an instant guessed the nature of the object he had taken for a cloud.

Before him rose a mass of strangely-formed rocks, that resembled nothing so much as a vast fire petrified at the moment of its most fervent combustion. It was the isle of Tiboulen.

Dantès rose, advanced a few steps, and, with a fervent prayer of gratitude, stretched himself on the granite, which seemed to him softer than down. Then, in spite of the wind and rain, he fell into the deep sweet sleep of those worn out by fatigue.

At the expiration of an hour Edmond was awakened by the roar of the thunder. The tempest was unchained and let loose in all its fury; from time to time a flash of lightning stretched across the heavens like a fiery serpent, lighting up the clouds that rolled on like the waves of an immense chaos.

Dantès had not been deceived—he had reached the first of the two isles, which was, in reality, Tiboulen. He knew that it was barren and without shelter; but when the sea became more calm, he resolved to plunge into its waves again, and swim to Lemaire, equally arid, but larger, and consequently better adapted for concealment.

An overhanging rock offered him a temporary shelter, and scarcely had he availed himself of it when the tempest burst forth in all its fury.

Edmond felt the rock beneath which he lay tremble, the waves, dashing themselves against the granite rock, wetted him with their spray. In safety, as he was, he felt himself become giddy in the midst of this war of the elements and the dazzling brightness of the lightning. It seemed to him that the island trembled to its base, and that it would, like a vessel at anchor, break her moorings and bear him off into the centre of the storm.

He remembered then that he had not eaten or drunk for four and twenty hours. He extended his hands, and drank greedily of the rainwater that had lodged in a hollow of the rock.

As he rose, a flash of lightning that seemed as if the whole of the heavens were opened, illumined the darkness. By its light, between the isle of Lemaire and Cape Croiselle, a quarter of a league distant, Dantès saw, like a spectre, a fishing-boat driven rapidly on by the force of the winds and waves. A second after, he saw it again, approaching nearer. Dantès cried at the top of his voice to warn them of their danger, but they saw it themselves. Another flash showed him four men clinging to the shattered mast and the rigging, while a fifth clung to the broken rudder. The men he beheld saw him doubtless, for their cries were carried to his ears by the wind. Above the splintered mast a sail rent to tatters was waving; suddenly the ropes that still held it gave way, and it disappeared in the darkness of the night like a vast sea-bird.

At the same moment a violent crash was heard, and cries of distress. Perched on the summit of the rock, Dantès saw, by the lightning, the vessel in pieces; and amongst the fragments were visible the agonized features of the unhappy sailors.

Then all became dark again.

Dantès ran down the rocks at the risk of being himself dashed to pieces; he listened, he strove to examine, but he heard and saw nothing—all human cries had ceased, and the tempest alone continued to rage.

By degrees the wind abated, vast grey clouds rolled towards the west, and the blue firmament appeared studded with bright stars. Soon a red streak became visible in the horizon, the waves whitened, a light played over them, and gilded their foaming crests with gold.

It was day.

Dantès stood silent and motionless before this vast spectacle, for since his captivity he had forgotten it. He turned towards the fortress, and looked both at the sea and the land. The gloomy building rose from the bosom of the ocean with that imposing majesty of inanimate objects that seems at once to watch and to command.

It was about five o'clock. The sea continued to grow calmer.

"In two or three hours," thought Dantès, "the turnkey will enter my chamber, find the body of my poor friend, recognize it, seek for me in vain, and give the alarm. Then the passage will be discovered; the men who cast me into the sea, and who must have heard the cry I uttered, will be questioned. Then boats filled with armed soldiers will pursue the wretched fugitive. The cannon will warn every one to refuse shelter to a man wandering about naked and famished. The police of Marseilles will be on the alert by land, whilst the government pursues me by sea. I am cold, I am hungry. I have lost even the knife that saved me. Oh, my God! I have suffered enough surely. Have pity on me, and do for me what I am unable to do for myself."

As Dantès (his eyes turned in the direction of the Château d'If) uttered this prayer, he saw appear, at the extremity of the isle of Pomè-gue, like a bird skimming over the sea, a small bark, that the eye of a sailor alone could recognize as a Genoese tartane. She was coming out of Marseilles harbour, and was standing out to sea rapidly, her sharp prow cleaving through the waves.

"Oh!" cried Edmond, "to think that in half an hour I could join her, did I not fear being questioned, detected, and conveyed back to Marseilles! What can I do? What story can I invent? Under pretext of trading along the coast, these men, who are in reality smugglers, will prefer selling me to doing a good action. I must wait. But I cannot—I am starving. In a few hours my strength will be utterly exhausted; besides, perhaps I have not been missed at the fortress. I can pass as one of the sailors wrecked last night. This story will pass current, for there is no one left to contradict me."

As he spoke, Dantès looked towards the spot where the fishing-vessel had been wrecked, and started. The red cap of one of the sailors hung to a point of the rock, and some beams that had formed part of the vessel's keel, floated at the foot of the crags.

In an instant Dantès' plan was formed. He swam to the cap, placed it on his head, seized one of the beams, and struck out so as to cross the line the vessel was taking.

"I am saved!" murmured he.

And this conviction restored his strength.

He soon perceived the vessel, which, having the wind right ahead, was tacking between the Château d'If and the tower of Planier. For an instant he feared lest the bark, instead of keeping inshore, should stand out to sea; but he soon saw by her manœuvres that she wished to pass, like most vessels bound for Italy, between the islands of Jaros and Calaseraigne. However, the vessel and the swimmer insensibly neared one another, and in one of its tacks the bark approached within a quarter of a mile of him. He rose on the waves, making signs of distress; but no one on board perceived him, and the vessel stood on another tack. Dantès would have cried out, but he reflected that the wind would drown his voice.

It was then he rejoiced at his precaution in taking the beam, for without it he would have been unable, perhaps, to reach the vessel—certainly to return to shore, should he be unsuccessful in attracting attention.

Dantès, although almost sure as to what course the bark would take, had yet watched it anxiously until it tacked and stood towards him. Then he advanced; but before they had met, the vessel again changed her direction.

By a violent effort he rose half out of the water, waving his cap, and uttering a loud shout peculiar to sailors.

This time he was both seen and heard, and the tartane instantly steered towards him. At the same time he saw they were about to lower a boat.

An instant after, the boat, rowed by two men, advanced rapidly towards him. Dantès abandoned the beam, which he thought now useless, and swam vigorously to meet them. But he had reckoned too much upon his strength, and then he felt how serviceable the beam had been to him. His arms grew stiff, his legs had lost their flexibility, and he was almost breathless.

He uttered a second cry. The two sailors redoubled their efforts, and one of them cried in Italian, "Courage!"

The word reached his ear as a wave which he no longer had the strength to surmount passed over his head. He rose again to the surface, supporting himself by one of those desperate efforts a drowning man makes, uttered a third cry, and felt himself sink again, as if the fatal shot were again tied to his feet. The water passed over his head, and the sky seemed livid. A violent effort again brought him to the surface. He felt as if something seized him by the hair, but he saw and heard nothing. He had fainted.

When he opened his eyes, Dantès found himself on the deck of the tartane. His first care was to see what direction they were pursuing. They were rapidly leaving the Château d'If behind.

Dantès was so exhausted that the exclamation of joy he uttered was mistaken for a sigh.

As we have said, he was lying on the deck. A sailor was rubbing his limbs with a woollen cloth; another, whom he recognized as the one who had cried out "Courage!" held a gourd full of rum to his mouth; whilst the third, an old sailor, at once the pilot and captain, looked on with that egotistical pity men feel for a misfortune that they have escaped yesterday and which may overtake them to-morrow.

"Who are you?" said the pilot, in bad French.

"I am," replied Dantès in bad Italian, "a Maltese sailor. We were coming from Syracuse laden with grain. The storm of last night overtook us at Cape Morgiou, and we were wrecked on these rocks. You have saved my life, and I thank you."

"Now what are we to do with you?" said the captain.

"Alas! anything you please. My captain is dead; I have barely escaped; but I am a good sailor. Leave me at the first port you make; I shall be sure to find employment."

"Do you know the Mediterranean?"

"I have sailed over it since my childhood."

"You know the best harbours?"

"There are few ports that I could not enter or leave with my eyes shut."

"I say, captain," said the sailor who had cried "Courage!" to Dantès, "if what he says is true, what hinders his staying with us?"

"If he says true," said the captain doubtingly. "But in his present condition he will promise anything, and take his chance of keeping it afterwards."

"I will do more than I promise," said Dantès.

"We shall see," returned the other, smiling.

"As you will!" said Dantès, getting up. "Where are you going?"

"To Leghorn."

"Then why, instead of tacking so frequently, do you not sail nearer the wind?"

"Because we should run straight on to the island of Rion."

"You shall pass it by twenty fathoms."

"Take the helm then, and let us see what you know."

The young man took the helm, ascertaining by a slight pressure if the vessel answered the rudder, and seeing that, without being a first rate sailer, she yet was tolerably obedient:

"To the braces!" said he.

The four seamen who composed the crew, obeyed, whilst the pilot looked on.

"Haul taut!"

They obeyed.

"Belay!"

This order was also executed, and the vessel passed, as Dantès had predicted, twenty fathoms to the right.

"Bravo!" cried the captain.

"Bravo!" repeated the sailors.

And they all regarded with astonishment this man whose eye had recovered an intelligence and his body a vigour they were far from suspecting.

"You see," said Dantès, quitting the helm, "I shall be of some use to you at least during the voyage. If you do not want me at Leghorn, you can leave me there, and I will pay you out of the first wages I get, for my food and the clothes you lend me."

"Ah," said the captain, "we can agree very well, if you are reasonable."

"Give me what you give the others," returned Dantès.

"That's not fair," said the seaman who had saved Dantès, "for you know more than we do."

"What's that to you, Jacopo?" returned the captain. "Every one is free to ask what he pleases."

"That's true," replied Jacopo, "I only made a remark."

"Well, you would do much better to lend him a jacket and a pair of trousers, if you have them."

"No," said Jacopo, "but I have a shirt and a pair of trousers."

"That is all I want," interrupted Dantès. "Thank you, my friend."

Jacopo dived into the hold and soon returned with what Edmond wanted.

"Now, then, do you wish for anything else?" said the captain.

"A piece of bread and another glass of the capital rum I tasted, for I have not eaten or drunk for a long time."

He had not, in truth, tasted food for forty hours. They brought him a piece of bread, and Jacopo offered him the gourd.

"Larboard your helm!" cried the captain to the helmsman.

Dantès glanced to the same side as he lifted the gourd to his mouth.

"Halloa! what's the matter at the Château d'If?" said the captain.

A small white cloud, which had attracted Dantès' attention, crowned the summit of the bastion of the Château d'If. A moment later the far-off report of a gun was heard. The sailors looked at one another.

"What does it mean?" asked the captain.

"A prisoner has escaped from Château d'If, and they are firing the alarm gun," replied Dantès.

The captain glanced at him, but he had lifted the rum to his lips, and was drinking it with so much composure that his suspicions, if he had any, died away.

"At any rate," murmured he, "if it be, so much the better, for I have made a rare acquisition."

Under pretence of being fatigued, Dantès asked to take the helm. The helmsman, enchanted to be relieved, looked at the captain who, by a nod, indicated that he might abandon it to his new comrade. Dantès could thus keep his eye on Marseilles.

"What is the day of the month?" asked he of Jacopo, who sat down beside him.

"The 28th of February."

"In what year?" asked Dantès.

"In what year! You ask me in what year!"

"Yes," replied the young man, "I ask you in what year."

"You have forgotten?"

"I was so frightened last night," said Dantès, laughing, "that I have almost lost my memory. I ask you what year is it?"

"1829," said Jacopo.

It was fourteen years, day for day, since Dantès' arrest.

He was nineteen when he entered the Château d'If; he was thirty-three when he escaped. A sorrowful smile passed over his face; he asked himself what had become of Mercédès, who must believe him dead. Then his eyes lighted up with hatred as he thought of the three men who had caused him so long and wretched a captivity. He renewed against Danglars, Fernand, and Villefort the oath of implacable vengeance he had made in his dungeon. This oath was no longer a vain menace; for the fastest sailer in the Mediterranean would have been unable to overtake the little tartane, that with every stitch of canvas set, was flying before the wind to Leghorn.

A WHALE OF UNKNOWN SPECIES[1]

Jules Verne

WE WERE at last on the scene of the last frolics of the monster; and the truth was, no one lived really on board. The entire crew were under the influence of such nervous excitement as I could not give the idea of. They neither ate nor slept. Twenty times a day some error of estimation, or the optical delusion of a sailor perched on the yards, caused intolerable frights; and these emotions, twenty times repeated, kept us in a state too violent not to cause an early reaction.

And, in fact, the reaction was not slow in coming. For three months—three months, each day of which lasted a century—the *Abraham Lincoln* ploughed all the waters of the North Pacific, running down all the whales signalled, making sharp deviations from her route, veering suddenly from one tack to another, and not leaving one point of the Chinese or Japanese coast unexplored. And yet nothing was seen but the immense waste of waters—nothing that resembled a gigantic narwhal, nor a submarine islet, nor a wreck, nor a floating reef, nor anything at all supernatural.

The reaction, therefore, began. Discouragement at first took possession of all minds, and opened a breach for incredulity. A new sentiment was experienced on board, composed of three-tenths of shame and seven-tenths of rage. They called themselves fools for being taken in by a chimera, and were still more furious at it. The mountains of arguments piled up for a year fell down all at once, and all every one thought of was to make up the hours of meals and sleep which they had so foolishly sacrificed.

With the mobility natural to the human mind, they threw themselves

---

[1]From *Twenty Thousand Leagues Under the Sea*. By permission of W. Collins, Sons & Co., Ltd.

from one excess into another. The warmest partisans of the enterprise became finally its most ardent detractors. The reaction ascended from the depths of the vessel, from the coal-hole, to the officers' ward-room, and certainly, had it not been for very strong determination on the part of Captain Farragut, the head of the frigate would have been definitely turned southward,

However, this useless search could be no further prolonged. No crew of the American navy had ever shown more patience or zeal; its want of success could not be imputed to it. There was nothing left to do but to return.

A representation in this sense was made to the commander. The commander kept his ground. The sailors did not hide their dissatisfaction, and the service suffered from it. I do not mean that there was revolt on board, but after a reasonable period of obstinacy the commander, like Columbus before him, asked for three days' patience. If in three days the monster had not reappeared, the man at the helm should give three turns of the wheel, and the *Abraham Lincoln* should make for the European seas.

Two days passed. The frigate kept up steam at half-pressure. Large quantities of bacon were trailed in the wake of the ship, to the great satisfaction of the sharks. The frigate lay to, and her boats were sent in all directions, but the night of the 4th of November passed without unveiling the submarine mystery.

Japan lay less than 200 miles to leeward. Eight bells had just struck as I was leaning over the starboard side. Conseil, standing near me, was looking straight in front of him. The crew, perched in the ratlins, were keeping a sharp look-out in the approaching darkness. Officers with their night-glasses swept the horizon.

Looking at Conseil, I saw that the brave fellow was feeling slightly the general influence—at least it seemed to me so. Perhaps for the first time, his nerves were vibrating under the action of a sentiment of curiosity.

"Well, Conseil," said I, "this is your last chance of pocketing 2000 dollars."

"Will monsieur allow me to tell him that I never counted upon the reward, and if the Union had promised 100,000 dollars it would never be any the poorer."

"You are right, Conseil. It has been a stupid affair, after all. We have lost time and patience, and might just as well have been in France six months ago."

"Yes, in monsieur's little apartments, classifying monsieur's fossils, and monsieur's babiroussa would be in its cage in the Jardin des Plantes, attracting all the curious people in Paris."

"Yes, Conseil, and besides that we shall get well laughed at."

"Certainly," said Conseil tranquilly. "I think they will laugh at monsieur. And I must say——"

"What, Conseil?"

"That it will serve monsieur right! When one has the honour to be a *savant* like monsieur, one does not expose——"

Conseil did not finish his compliment. In the midst of general silence Ned Land's voice was heard calling out,—

"Look out, there! The thing we are looking for is on our weather beam!"

At this cry the entire crew rushed towards the harpooner. Captain, officers, masters, sailors, and cabin-boys, even the engineers left their engines, and the stokers their fires. The order to stop her had been given, and the frigate was only moving by her own momentum. The darkness was then profound, and although I knew the Canadian's eyes were very good, I asked myself what he could have seen, and how he could have seen it. My heart beat violently.

At two cables' length from the *Abraham Lincoln* on her starboard quarter, the sea seemed to be illuminated below the surface. The monster lay some fathoms below the sea, and threw out the very intense but inexplicable light mentioned in the reports of several captains. This light described an immense and much-elongated oval, in the centre of which was condensed a focus the over-powering brilliancy of which died out by successive gradations.

"It is only an agglomeration of phospheric particles," cried one of the officers.

"No, sir," I replied with conviction. "Never did pholas or salpæ produce such a light as that. That light is essentially electric. Besides—see! look out! It moves—forward—on to us!"

A general cry rose from the frigate.

"Silence!" called out the captain. "Up with the helm! Reverse the engines!"

The frigate thus tried to escape, but the supernatural animal approached her with a speed double her own.

Stupefaction, more than fear, kept us mute and motionless. The animal gained upon us. It made the round of the frigate, which was then going at the rate of fourteen knots, and enveloped her with its electric ring like luminous dust. Then it went two or three miles off, leaving a phosphoric trail like the steam of an express locomotive. All at once, from the dark limits of the horizon, where it went to gain its momentum, the monster rushed towards the frigate with frightful rapidity, stopped suddenly at a distance of twenty feet, and then went out, not diving, for its brilliancy did not die out by degrees, but all at once, as if turned off. Then it reappeared on the other side of the ship, either going round her or gliding under her hull. A collision might have occurred at any moment, which might have been fatal to us.

I was astonished at the way the ship was worked. She was being attacked instead of attacking; and I asked Captain Farragut the reason.

On the captain's generally impassive face was an expression of profound astonishment.

"M. Aronnax," he said, "I do not know with how formidable a being I have to deal, and I will not imprudently risk my frigate in the darkness. We must wait for daylight, and then we shall change parts."

"You have no longer any doubt, captain, of the nature of the animal?"

"No sir. It is evidently a gigantic narwhal, and an electric one too."

"Perhaps," I added, "we can no more approach it than we could a gymnotus or a torpedo."

"It may possess as great blasting properties, and if it does it is the most terrible animal that ever was created. That is why I must keep on my guard."

All the crew remained up that night. No one thought of going to sleep. The *Abrahan Lincoln* not being able to compete in speed, was kept under half-steam. On its side the narwhal imitated the frigate, let the waves rock it at will, and seemed determined not to leave the scene of combat.

Towards midnight, however, it disappeared, dying out like a large glowworm. At seven minutes to one in the morning a deafening whistle was heard, like that produced by a column of water driven out with extreme violence.

The captain, Ned Land, and I were then on the poop, peering with eagerness through the profound darkness.

"Ned Land," asked the commander, "have you often heard whales roar?"

"Yes, captain, often; but never such a whale as I earned 2000 dollars by sighting."

"True, you have a right to the prize; but tell me, is it the same noise they make?"

"Yes, sir; but this one is incomparably louder. It is not to be mistaken. It is certainly a cetacean there in our seas. With your permission, sir, we will have a few words with him at daybreak."

"If he is in a humour to hear them, Mr Land," said I, in an unconvinced tone.

"Let me get within a length of four harpoons," answered the Canadian, "and he will be obliged to listen to me."

"But in order to approach him," continued the captain, "I shall have to put a whaler at your disposition."

"Certainly sir."

"But that will be risking the lives of my men."

"And mine too," answered the harpooner simply.

About 2 A.M. the luminous focus reappeared, no less intense, about five miles to the windward of the frigate. Notwithstanding the distance and the noise of the wind and sea, the loud strokes of the animal's tail were distinctly heard, and even its panting breathing. When the enormous narwhal came up to the surface to breathe, it seemed as if the air rushed into its lungs like steam in the vast cylinders of a 2000 horse-power engine.

"Hum!" thought I, "a whale with the strength of a cavalry regiment would be a pretty whale!"

Until daylight we were all on the *qui-vive*, and then the fishing tackle was prepared. The first mate loaded the blunderbusses, which throw harpoons the distance of a mile, and long duck-guns with explosive bullets, which inflict mortal wounds even upon the most powerful animals. Ned Land contented himself with sharpening his harpoon—a terrible weapon in his hands.

Day began to break, and with the first glimmer of dawn the electric light of the narwhal disappeared. At 7 A.M. a very thick sea-fog obscured the atmosphere, and the best glasses could not pierce it.

I climbed the mizenmast and found some officers already perched on the mast-heads.

At 8 A.M. the mist began to clear away. Suddenly, like the night before, Ned Land's voice was heard calling,—

"The thing in question on the port quarter!"

All eyes were turned towards the point indicated. There, a mile and a half from the frigate, a large black body emerged more than a yard above the waves. Its tail, violently agitated, produced a considerable eddy. Never did caudal appendage beat the sea with such force. An immense track, dazzlingly white, marked the passage of the animal, and described a long curve.

The frigate approached the cetacean, and I could see it well. The accounts of it given by the *Shannon* and *Helvetia* had rather exaggerated its dimensions, and I estimated its length at 150 feet only. As to its other dimensions, I could only conceive them to be in proportion.

Whilst I was observing it, two jets of vapour and water sprang from its vent-holes and ascended to a height of fifty yards, thus fixing my opinion as to its way of breathing. I concluded definitely that it belonged to the vertebrate branch of mammalia, order of cetaceans, family. . . . Here I could not decide. The order of cetaceans comprehends three families—whales, cachalots, and dolphins—and it is in the last that narwhals are placed.

The crew were waiting impatiently for their captain's orders. Farragut, after attentively examining the animal, had the chief engineer called.

"Is your steam up?" asked the captain.

"Yes, captain," answered the engineer.

"Then make up your fires and put on all steam."

Three cheers greeted this order. The hour of combat had struck. Some minutes afterwards the funnels of the frigate were giving out torrents of black smoke, and the deck shook under the trembling of the boilers.

The *Abraham Lincoln*, propelled by her powerful screw, went straight at the animal, who let her approach to within half a cable's length, and then, as if disdaining to dive, made a little attempt at flight, and contented itself with keeping its distance.

This pursuit lasted about three-quarters of an hour, without the frigate gaining four yards on the cetacean. It was quite evident she would never reach it at that rate.

The captain twisted his beard impatiently.

"Ned Land!" called the captain, "do you think I had better have the boats lowered?"

"No, sir," answered Ned Land, "for that animal won't be caught unless it chooses."

"What must be done, then?"

"Force steam if you can, captain, and I, with your permission, will post myself under the bowsprit, and if we get within a harpoon length I shall hurl one."

"Very well," said the captain. "Engineer, put on more pressure."

Ned Land went to his post, the fires were increased, the screw revolved forty-three times a minute, and the steam poured out of the valves. The log was heaved, and it was found that the frigate was going eighteen miles and five-tenths an hour. But the animal went eighteen and five-tenths an hour too.

During another hour the frigate kept up that speed without gaining a yard. It was humiliating for one of the quickest vessels in the American navy. The crew began to get very angry. The sailors swore at the animal, who did not deign to answer them. The captain not only twisted his beard, he began to gnaw it too. The engineer was called once more.

"Have you reached your maximum of pressure?" asked the captain.

"Yes sir."

The captain ordered him to do all he could without absolutely blowing up the vessel, and coal was at once piled up on the fires. The speed of the frigate increased. Her masts shook again. The log was again heaved, and this time she was making nineteen miles and three-tenths.

"All steam on!" called out the captain.

The engineer obeyed. The manometer marked ten degrees. But the cetacean did the nineteen miles and three-tenths as easily as the eighteen and five-tenths.

What a chase! I cannot describe the emotion that made my whole being vibrate again. Ned Land kept at his post, harpoon in hand. The animal allowed itself to be approached several times. Sometimes it was so near that the Canadian raised his hand to hurl the harpoon, when the animal rushed away at a speed of at least thirty miles an hour, and even during our maximum of speed it bullied the frigate, going round and round it.

A cry of fury burst from all lips. We were not further advanced at twelve o'clock than we had been at eight. Captain Farragut then made up his mind to employ more direct means.

"Ah!" said he, "so that animal goes faster than my ship! Well, we'll see if he'll go faster than a conical bullet. Master, send your men to the forecastle."

The forecastle gun was immediately loaded and pointed. It was fired, but the ball passed some feet above the cetacean, which kept about half a mile off.

"Let some one else try!" called out the captain. "Five hundred dollars to whomsoever will hit the beast!"

An old gunner with a grey beard—I think I see now his calm face as he approached the gun—put it into position and took a long aim. A loud report followed and mingled with the cheers of the crew.

The bullet reached its destination; it struck the animal, but, gliding off the rounded surface, fell into the sea two miles off.

"Malediction!" cried the captain; "that animal must be clad in six-inch iron plates. But I'll catch it, if I have to blow up my frigate!"

It was to be hoped that the animal would be exhausted, and that it would not be indifferent to fatigue like a steam-engine. But the hours went on, and it showed no signs of exhaustion.

It must be said, in praise of the *Abraham Lincoln*, that she struggled on indefatigably. I cannot reckon the distance we made during this unfortunate day at less than 300 miles. But night came on and closed round the heaving ocean.

At that minute, I believed our expedition to be at an end, and that we should see the fantastic animal no more.

I was mistaken, for at 10.50 P.M. the electric light reappeared, three miles windward to the frigate, clear and intense as on the night before.

The narwhal seemed motionless. Perhaps, fatigued with its day's work, it was sleeping in its billowy cradle. That was a chance by which the captain resolved to profit.

He gave his orders. The *Abraham Lincoln* was kept up at half-steam, and advanced cautiously so as not to awaken her adversary. It is not rare to meet in open sea with whales fast asleep, and Ned Land had harpooned many a one in that condition. The Canadian went back to his post under the bowsprit.

The frigate noiselessly approached, and stopped at two cables' length from the animal. No one breathed. A profound silence reigned on deck. We were not 1000 feet from the burning focus, the light of which increased and dazzled our eyes.

At that minute, leaning on the forecastle bulwark, I saw Ned Land below me, holding the martingale with one hand and with the other brandishing his terrible harpoon, scarcely twenty feet from the motionless animal.

All at once he threw the harpoon, and I heard the sonorous stroke of the weapon, which seemed to have struck a hard body.

The electric light suddenly went out, and two enormous waterspouts fell on the deck of the frigate, running like a torrent from fore to aft, upsetting men, and breaking the lashing of the spars.

A frightful shock followed. I was thrown over the rail before I had time to stop myself, and fell into the sea.

Although I was surprised by my unexpected fall, I still kept a very distinct impression of my sensations. I was at first dragged down to a depth of about twenty feet. I was a good swimmer, and this plunge did not make me lose my presence of mind. Two vigorous kicks brought me back to the surface.

My first care was to look for the frigate. Had the crew seen me disappear? Had the *Abraham Lincoln* veered round? Would the captain have a boat lowered? Might I hope to be saved?

The darkness was profound. I perceived a black mass disappearing in the east, the beacon lights of which were dying out in the distance. It was the frigate. I gave myself up.

"Help! help!" cried I, swimming towards the frigate with desperate strokes.

My clothes embarrassed me. The water glued them to my body. They paralysed my movements. I was sinking.

"Help!" rang out again in the darkness.

This was the last cry I uttered. My mouth filled with water. I struggled not to be sucked into the abyss.

Suddenly my clothes were seized by a vigorous hand, and I felt myself brought back violently to the surface of the water, and I heard—yes, I heard these words uttered in my ear,—

"If monsieur will have the goodness to lean on my shoulder, monsieur will swim much better."

I seized the arm of my faithful Conseil.

"You!" I cried—"you!"

"Myself," answered Conseil, "at monsieur's service."

"Did the shock throw you into the sea too?"

"No; but being in the service of monsieur, I followed him."

The worthy fellow thought that quite natural.

"What about the frigate?" I asked.

"The frigate!" answered Conseil, turning on his back; "I think monsieur will do well not to count upon the frigate."

"Why?"

"Because, as I jumped into the sea, I heard the man at the helm call out, 'The screw and the rudder are broken.'"

"Broken?"

"Yes, by the monster's tusk. It is the only damage she has sustained, I think, but without a helm she can't do anything for us."

"Then we are lost!"

"Perhaps," answered Conseil tranquilly. "In the meantime we have still several hours before us, and in several hours many things may happen."

The *sang-froid* of Conseil did me good. I swam more vigorously, but encumbered by my garments, which dragged me down like a leaden weight, I found it extremely difficult to keep up. Conseil perceived it.

"Will monsieur allow me to make a slit?" said he. And, slipping an open knife under my clothes, he slit them rapidly from top to bottom. Then he quickly helped me off with them whilst I swam for both. I rendered him the same service, and we went on swimming near each other.

In the meantime our situation was none the less terrible. Perhaps our disappearance had not been remarked, and even if it had, the frigate could not tack without her helm. Our only chance of safety was in the event of the boats being lowered.

The collision had happened about 11 P.M. About 1 A.M. I was taken with extreme fatigue, and all my limbs became stiff with cramp. Conseil was obliged to keep me up, and the care of our preservation depended upon him alone. I heard the poor fellow breathing hard, and knew he could not keep up much longer.

"Let me go! Leave me!" I cried.

"Leave monsieur? Never!" he answered. "I shall drown with him."

Just then the moon appeared through the fringe of a large cloud that the wind was driving eastward. The surface of the sea shone under her rays. I lifted my head and saw the frigate. She was five miles from us, and only looked like a dark mass, scarcely distinguishable. I saw no boats.

I tried to call out, but it was useless at that distance. My swollen lips would not utter a sound. Conseil could still speak, and I heard him call out "Help!" several times.

We suspended our movements for an instant and listened. It might be only a singing in our ears, but it seemed to me that a cry answered Conseil's.

"Did you hear?" I murmured.

"Yes, yes!"

And Conseil threw another despairing cry into space. This time there could be no mistake. A human voice answered ours. Was it the voice of some other victim of the shock, or a boat hailing us in the darkness? Conseil made a supreme effort, and, leaning on my shoulder whilst I made a last struggle for us both, he raised himself half out of the water, and I heard him shout. Then my strength was exhausted, my fingers slipped, my mouth filled with salt water, I went cold all over, raised my head for the last time, and began to sink.

At that moment I hit against something hard, and I clung to it in desperation. Then I felt myself lifted up out of the water, and I fainted.

I soon came to, thanks to the vigorous friction that was being applied to my body, and I half opened my eyes.

"Conseil!" I murmured.

"Did monsieur ring?" answered Conseil.

Just then, by the light of the moon that was getting lower on the horizon, I perceived a face that was not Conseil's, but which I immediately recognized.

"Ned!" I cried.

"The same, sir, looking after his prize," replied the Canadian.

"Were you thrown into the sea when the frigate was struck?"

"Yes, sir, but, luckier than you, I soon got upon a floating island."

"An island?"

"Yes, or if you like better, on our giant narwhal."

"What do you mean, Ned?"

"I mean that I understand now why my harpoon did not stick into the skin, but was blunted."

"Why, Ned, why?"

"Because the beast is made of sheet-iron plates."

I wriggled myself quickly to the top of the half-submerged being or object on which we had found refuge. I struck my foot against it. It was evidently a hard and impenetrable body, and not the soft substance which forms the mass of great marine mammalia. But this hard body could not be a bony carapace like that of antediluvian animals. I could not even class it amongst amphibious reptiles, such as tortoises and alligators, for the blackish back that supported me was not scaly but smooth and polished.

The blow produced a metallic sound, and, strange as it may appear, seemed caused by being struck on riveted plates. Doubt was no longer possible. The animal, monster, natural phenomenon that had puzzled the entire scientific world, and misled the imagination of sailors in the two hemispheres, was, it must be acknowledged, a still more astonishing phenomenon, a phenomenon of man's making. The discovery of the existence of the most fabulous and mythological being would not have astonished me in the same degree. It seems quite simple that anything prodigious should come from the hand of the Creator, but to find the impossible realized by the hand of man was enough to confound the imagination.

We were lying upon the top of a sort of submarine boat, which looked to me like an immense steel fish. Ned Land's mind was made up on that point, and Conseil and I could only agree with him.

"But then," said I, "this apparatus must have a locomotive machine, and a crew inside of it to work it."

"Evidently," replied the harpooner, "and yet for the three hours that I have inhabited this floating island, it has not given sign of life."

"The vessel has not moved?"

"No, M. Aronnax. It is cradled in the waves, but it does not move."

"We know, without the slightest doubt, however, that it is endowed with great speed, and as a machine is necessary to produce the speed, and a mechanician to guide it, I conclude from that that we are saved."

"Hum," said Ned Land in a reserved tone of voice.

At that moment, and as if to support my arguments, a boiling was heard at the back of the strange apparatus, the propeller of which was evidently a screw, and it began to move. We only had time to hold on to its upper part, which emerged about a yard out of the water. Happily its speed was not excessive.

"As long as it moves horizontally," murmured Ned Land, "I have nothing to say. But if it takes it into its head to plunge, I would not give two dollars for my skin!"

The Canadian might have said less still. It therefore became urgent to communicate with whatever beings were shut up in the machine. I looked on its surface for an opening, a panel, a "man hole," to use the technical expression; but the lines of bolts, solidly fastened down on the joints of the plates, were clear and uniform.

Besides, the moon then disappeared and left us in profound obscurity. We were obliged to wait till daybreak to decide upon the means of penetrating to the interior of this submarine boat.

Thus, then, our safety depended solely upon the caprice of the mysterious steersmen who directed this apparatus, and if they plunged we were lost! Unless that happened I did not doubt the possibility of entering into communication with them. And it was certain that unless they made their own air they must necessarily return from time to time to the surface of the ocean to renew their provision of breathable molecules. Therefore there must be an opening which put the interior of the boat into communication with the atmosphere.

As to the hope of being saved by Commander Farragut, that had to be completely renounced. We were dragged westward, and I estimated that our speed, relatively moderate, attained twelve miles an hour. The screw beat the waves with mathematical regularity, sometimes emerging and throwing the phosphorescent water to a great height.

About 4 A.M. the rapidity of the apparatus increased. We resisted with difficulty this vertiginous impulsion, when the waves beat upon us in all their fury. Happily Ned touched with his hand a wide balustrade fastened on to the upper part of the iron top, and we succeeded in holding on to it solidly.

At last this long night slipped away. My incomplete memory does not allow me to retrace all the impressions of it. A single detail returns to my mind. During certain lullings of the sea and wind, I thought several times I heard vague sounds, a sort of fugitive harmony produced by far-off chords. What, then, was the mystery of this submarine navigation, of which the entire world vainly sought the explanation? What beings lived in this strange boat? What mechanical agent allowed it to move with such prodigious speed?

When daylight appeared the morning mists enveloped us, but they soon rose, and I proceeded to make an attentive examination of the sort of horizontal platform we were on, when I felt myself gradually sinking.

"*Mille diables!*" cried Land, kicking against the sonorous metal, "open, inhospitable creatures!"

But it was difficult to make oneself heard amidst the deafening noise made by the screw. Happily the sinking ceased.

Suddenly a noise like iron bolts being violently withdrawn was heard from the interior of the boat. One of the iron plates was raised, a man appeared, uttered a strange cry, and disappeared immediately.

Some moments after, eight strong fellows, with veiled faces, silently appeared, and dragged us down into their formidable machine.

ATLANTIS[1]

Jules Verne

AS SOON as I was dressed I went into the saloon. The compass was not reassuring. The direction of the *Nautilus* was S. S. W. We were turning our backs on Europe.

I waited impatiently for our bearings to be taken. About 11.30 A.M. the reservoirs were emptied, and our apparatus went up to the surface of the ocean. I sprang upon the platform. Ned Land preceded me there.

There was no land in sight. Nothing but the immense sea. A few sails on the horizon, doubtless those that go as far as San Roque in search of favourable winds for doubling the Cape of Good Hope. The weather was cloudy. A gale was springing up.

Ned, in a rage, tried to pierce the misty horizon. He still hoped that behind the mist stretched the land so much desired.

At noon the sun appeared for an instant. The first officer took advantage of the gleam to take the altitude. Then, the sea becoming rougher, we went down again, and the panel was closed.

An hour afterwards, when I consulted the map, I saw that the position of the *Nautilus* was indicated upon it by 16° 17′ long, and 33° 22′ lat., at 150 leagues from the nearest coast. It was no use to dream of escaping now, and I leave Ned Land's anger to be imagined when I informed him of our situation.

On my own account I was not overwhelmed with grief. I felt relieved from a weight that was oppressing me, and I could calmly take up my habitual work again.

---

[1]From *Twenty Thousand Leagues Under the Sea.* Reprinted by permission of W. Collins, Sons & Co., Ltd.

That evening, about 11 P.M., I received the very unexpected visit of Captain Nemo. He asked me very graciously if I felt fatigued from sitting up so late the night before. I answered in the negative.

"Then, M. Aronnax, I have a curious excursion to propose to you."

"What is it, captain?"

"You have as yet only been on the sea-bottom by daylight. Should you like to see it on a dark night?"

"I should like it much."

"It will be a fatiguing walk, I warn you. You will have to go far, and climb a mountain. The roads are not very well kept in repair."

"What you tell me makes me doubly curious. I am ready to follow you."

"Come, then, professor. We will go and put on our diving dresses."

When we reached the ward-room I saw that neither my companions nor any of the crew were to follow us in our excursion. Captain Nemo had not even asked me to take Ned or Conseil.

In a few minutes we had put on our apparatus. They placed on our backs the reservoirs full of air, but the electric lamps were not prepared. I said as much to the captain.

"They would be of no use to us," he answered.

I thought I had not heard aright, but I could not repeat my observation, for the captain's head had already disappeared under its metallic covering. I finished harnessing myself, felt that some one placed an iron spiked stick in my hand, and a few minutes later, after the usual manœuvre, we set foot on the bottom of the Atlantic, at a depth of 150 fathoms.

Midnight was approaching. The waters were in profound darkness, but Captain Nemo showed me a reddish point in the distance, a sort of large light shining about two miles from the *Nautilus*. What this fire was, with what fed, why and how it burnt in the liquid mass, I could not tell. Anyway it lighted us, dimly it is true, but I soon became accustomed to the peculiar darkness, and I understood, under the circumstances, the uselessness of the Ruhmkorff apparatus.

Captain Nemo and I walked side by side directly towards the light. The flat soil ascended gradually. We took long strides, helping ourselves with our sticks, but our progress was slow, for our feet often sank in a sort of mud covered with seaweed and flat stones.

As we went along I heard a sort of pattering above my head. The noise sometimes redoubled, and produced something like a continuous shower. I soon understood the cause. It was rain falling violently and crisping the surface of the waves. Instinctively I was seized with the idea that I should be wet through. By water, in water! I could not help laughing at the odd idea. But the truth is that under a thick diving dress the liquid element is no longer felt, and it only seems like an atmosphere rather denser than the terrestrial atmosphere, that is all.

After half an hour's walking the soil became rocky. The medusæ, the microscopic crustaceans, the pennatules slightly lighted us with their phosphorescent gleams. I caught a glimpse of heaps of stones covered by some millions of zoophytes and thickets of seaweed. My foot often slipped upon this viscous carpet of seaweed and without my stick I should have fallen several times. Turning, I still saw the white light of the *Nautilus* beginning to gleam in the distance.

The heaps of stones of which I have just spoken were heaped on the bottom of the ocean with a sort of regularity I could not explain to my-self. I perceived gigantic furrows which lost themselves in the distant darkness, the length of which escaped all valuation. Other peculiarities presented themselves that I did not know how to account for. It seemed to me that my heavy leaden shoes were crushing a litter of bones that cracked with a dry noise. What then was this vast plain I was thus moving across. I should have liked to question the captain, but his language by signs, that allowed him to talk to his companions when they followed him in his submarine excursions, was still incomprehensible to me.

In the meantime the reddish light that guided us increased and in-flamed the horizon. The presence of this fire under the seas excited my curiosity to the highest pitch. Was it some electric effluence? Was I going towards a natural phenomenon still unknown to the *savants* of the earth? Or—for this thought crossed my mind—had the hand of man any part in the conflagration? Had it lighted this fire? Was I going to meet in this deep sea companions and friends of Captain Nemo living the same strange life, and whom he was going to see? All these foolish and in-admissible ideas pursued me, and in that state of mind, ceaselessly excited by the series of marvels that passed before my eyes, I should not have been surprised to see at the bottom of the sea, one of the submarine towns Captain Nemo dreamed of.

Our road grew lighter and lighter. The white light shone from the top of a mountain about eight hundred feet high. But what I perceived was only a reflection made by the crystal of the water. The fire, the source of the inexplicable light, was on the opposite side of the mountain.

Amidst the stony paths that furrowed the bottom of the Atlantic Captain Nemo went on without hesitating. He knew the dark route, had doubtless often been along it, and could not lose himself in it. I followed him with unshaken confidence. He appeared, whilst walking before me, like one of the sea genii, and I admired his tall stature like a black shadow on the luminous background of the horizon.

It was one o'clock in the morning. We had reached the first slopes of the mountain. But the way up led through the difficult paths of a vast thicket.

Yes, a thicket of dead trees, leafless, sapless, mineralized under the action of the water, overtopped here and there by gigantic pines. It was like a coal-series, still standing, holding by its roots to the soil that had given way, and whose branches, like fine black paper-cuttings, stood out against the watery ceiling. My readers may imagine a forest on the side of the Hartz Mountains, but forest and mountain sunk to the bottom of the sea. The paths were encumbered with seaweed and fucus, amongst which swarmed a world of crustaceans. I went on climbing over the rocks, leaping over the fallen trunks, breaking the sea-creepers that balanced from one tree to another, startling the fish that flew from branch to branch. Pressed onwards I no longer felt any fatigue. I followed my guide, who was never fatigued.

What a spectacle! How can I depict it? How describe the aspect of the woods and rocks in this liquid element, their lower parts sombre and wild, the upper coloured with red tints in the light which the reverberating power of the water doubled? We were climbing rocks which fell in enormous fragments directly afterwards with the noise of an avalanche. Right and left were deep dark galleries where sight was lost. Here opened vast clearings that seemed made by the hand of man, and I asked myself sometimes if some inhabitant of these submarine regions was not about to appear suddenly.

But Captain Nemo still went on climbing. I would not be left behind. My stick lent me useful aid. A false step would have been dangerous in these narrow paths, hollowed out of the sides of precipices; but I walked along with a firm step without suffering from vertigo. Sometimes I jumped over a crevice the depth of which would have made me recoil on the glaciers of the earth; sometimes I ventured on the vacillating trunks of trees thrown from one abyss to another without looking under my feet, having only eyes to admire the savage sites of that region. There, monumental rocks perched on these irregularly-cut bases seemed to defy the laws of equilibrium. Between their stony knees grew trees like a jet of water under strong pressure, sustaining and sustained by the rocks. Then, natural towers, large scarps cut perpendicularly like a fortress curtain, inclining at an angle which the laws of gravitation would not have authorized on the surface of the terrestrial regions.

And did I not myself feel the difference due to the powerful density of the water, when, notwithstanding my heavy garments, my brass headpiece, my metal soles, I climbed slopes impracticably steep, clearing them, so to speak, with the lightness of an isard or a chamois?

I feel that this recital of an excursion under the sea cannot sound probable. I am the historian of things that seem impossible, and that yet are real and incontestable. I did not dream. I saw and felt.

Two hours after having quitted the *Nautilus* we had passed the trees, and a hundred feet above our heads rose the summit of the mountain, the projection of which made a shadow on the brilliant irradiation of the opposite slope. A few petrified bushes were scattered hither and thither in grimacing zigzags. The fish rose in shoals under our footsteps like birds surprised in the tall grass. The rocky mass was hollowed out into impenetrable confractuosities, deep grottoes, bottomless holes, in which I heard formidable noises. My blood froze in my veins when I perceived some enormous antennæ barricading my path, or some frightful claw shutting up with noise in the dark cavities. Thousands of luminous points shone amidst the darkness. They were the eyes of gigantic crustaceans, giant lobsters setting themselves up like halberdiers, and moving their claws with the clanking sound of metal; titanic crabs pointed like cannon on their carriages, and frightful poulps, intertwining their tentacles like a living nest of serpents.

What was this exorbitant world that I did not know yet? To what order belonged these articulates to which the rock formed a second carapace? Where had Nature found the secret of their vegetating existence, and for how many centuries had they lived thus in the lowest depths of the ocean?

But I could not stop. Captain Nemo, familiar with these terrible animals, paid no attention to them. We had arrived at the first plateau, where other surprises awaited me. There rose picturesque ruins which betrayed the hand of man, and not that of the Creator. They were vast heaps of stones in the vague outlines of castles and temples, clothed with a world of zoophytes in flower, and, instead of ivy, seaweed and fucus clothed them with a vegetable mantle.

But what, then, was this portion of the globe swallowed up by cataclysms? Who had placed these rocks and stones like dolmens of antihistorical times? Where was I? Where had Captain Nemo's whim brought me to?

I should have liked to question him. As I could not do that, I stopped him. I seized his arm. But he, shaking his head, and pointing to the last summit, seemed to say to me,—

"Higher! Still higher!"

I followed him with a last effort, and in a few minutes I had climbed the peak that overtopped for about thirty feet all the rocky mass.

I looked at the side we had just climbed. The mountain only rose seven or eight hundred feet above the plain; but on the opposite side it commanded from twice that height the depths of this portion of the Atlantic. My eyes wandered over a large space lighted up by a violent fulguration. In fact, this mountain was a volcano. At fifty feet below the peak, amidst a rain of stones and scoriæ, a wide crater was vomiting forth torrents of lava which fell in a cascade of fire into the bosom of the liquid mass. Thus placed, the volcano, like an immense torch, lighted up the lower plain to the last limits of the horizon.

I have said that the submarine crater threw out lava, but not flames. The oxygen of the air is necessary to make a flame, and it cannot exist in water; but the streams of red-hot lava struggled victoriously against the liquid element, and turned it to vapour by its contact. Rapid currents carried away all this gas in diffusion, and the lava torrent glided to the foot of the mountain like the eruption of Vesuvius on another Torre del Greco.

There, before my eyes, ruined, destroyed, overturned, appeared a town, its roofs crushed in, its temples thrown down, its arches dislocated, its columns lying on the ground, with the solid proportions of Tuscan architecture still discernible upon them; further on were the remains of a gigantic aqueduct; here, the encrusted base of an Acropolis, and the outlines of a Parthenon; there, some vestiges of a quay, as if some ancient port had formerly sheltered, on the shores of an extinct ocean, merchant vessels and war triremes; farther on still, long lines of ruined walls, wide deserted streets, a second Pompeii buried under the waters, raised up again for me by Captain Nemo.

Where was I? Where was I? I wished to know at any price. I felt I must speak, and tried to take off the globe of brass that imprisoned my head.

But Captain Nemo came to me and stopped me with a gesture. Then picking up a piece of clayey stone he went up to a black basaltic rock and traced on it the single word—

"ATLANTIS."

What a flash of lightning shot through my mind! Atlantis, the ancient Meropis of Theopompus, the Atlantis of Plato, the continent disbelieved in by Origen, Jamblichus, D'Anville, Malte-Brun, and Humboldt, who placed its disappearance amongst legendary tales; believed in by Possidonius, Pliny, Ammianus, Marcellinus, Tertullian, Engel, Sherer, Tournefort, Buffon, and D'Avezac, was there before my eyes bearing upon it the unexceptionable testimony of its catastrophe! This, then, was the engulfed region that existed beyond Europe, Asia, and Lybia, beyond the columns of Hercules, where the powerful Atlantides lived, against whom the first wars of Ancient Greece were waged!

The historian who put into writing the grand doings of the heroic times was Plato himself. His dialogue of Timotheus and Critias was, thus to speak, written under the inspiration of Solon, poet and legislator.

One day Solon was talking with some wise old men of Saïs, a town already eight hundred years old, as the annals engraved on the sacred walls of its temples testified. One of these old men related the history of another town, a thousand years older. This first Athenian city, nine hundred centuries old, had been invaded and in part destroyed by the Atlantides. These Atlantides, said he, occupied an immense continent, larger than Africa and Asia joined together, which covered a surface between the twelfth and fortieth degree of north latitude. Their dominion extended even as far as Egypt. They wished to impose it upon Greece, but were obliged to retire before the indomitable resistance of the Hellenes. Centuries went by. A cataclysm occurred with inundations and earthquakes. One night and one day sufficed for the extinction of this Atlantis, of which the highest summits, the Madeiras, Azores, Canaries, and Cape Verde Islands still emerge.

Such were the historical souvenirs that Captain Nemo's inscription awoke in my mind. Thus, then, led by the strangest fate, I was treading on one of the mountains of this continent! I was touching with my hand these ruins a thousand times secular and contemporaneous with the geological epochs. I was walking where the contemporaries of the first man had walked. I was crushing under my heavy soles the skeletons of animals of fabulous times, which these trees, now mineralized, formerly covered with their shade.

Ah! why did time fail me? I should have liked to descend the abrupt sides of this mountain, and go over the whole of the immense continent that doubtless joined Africa to America, and to visit the great antediluvian cities. There, perhaps, before my gaze, stretched Makhinios the warlike, Eusebius the pious, whose gigantic inhabitants lived entire centuries, and who were strong enough to pile up these blocks which still resisted the action of the water. One day, perhaps, some eruptive phenomenon would bring these engulfed regions back to the surface of the waves. Sounds that announced a profound struggle of the elements have been heard, and volcanic cinders projected out of the water have been found. All this ground, as far as the Equator, is still worked by underground forces. And who knows if in some distant epoch, increased by the volcanic dejections and by successive strata of lava, the summits of ignivome mountains will not appear on the surface of the Atlantic?

Whilst I was thus dreaming, trying to fix every detail of the grand scene in my memory, Captain Nemo, leaning against a moss-covered fragment of ruin, remained motionless as if petrified in mute ecstasy. Was he dreaming about the long-gone generations and asking them the secret of human destiny? Was it here that this strange man came to refresh his historical memories and live again that ancient existence?—he who would have no modern one. What would I not have given to know his thoughts, to share and understand them!

We remained in the same place for a whole hour, contemplating the vast plain in the light of the lava that sometimes was surprisingly intense. The interior bubblings made rapid tremblings pass over the outside of the mountain. Deep noises, clearly transmitted by the liquid medium, were echoed with majestic amplitude.

At that moment the moon appeared for an instant through the mass of waters and threw her pale rays over the engulfed continent. It was only a gleam, but its effect was indescribable. The captain rose, gave a last look at the immense plain, and then, with his hand, signed to me to follow him.

We rapidly descended the mountain. When we had once passed the mineral forest I perceived the lantern of the *Nautilus* shining like a star.

The captain walked straight towards it, and we were back on board as the first tints of dawn whitened the surface of the ocean.

THE OCEAN CHRIST[1]

Anatole France

(1844–1924)

THAT year many of the fishers of Saint-Valéry had been drowned at sea. Their bodies were found on the beach cast up by the waves with the wreckage of their boats; and for nine days, up the steep road leading to the church were to be seen coffins borne by hand and followed by widows, who were weeping beneath their great black-hooded cloaks, like women in the Bible.

Thus were the skipper Jean Lenoël and his son Désiré laid in the great nave, beneath the vaulted roof from which they had once hung a ship in full rigging as an offering to Our Lady. They were righteous men and God-fearing. Monsieur Guillaume Truphème, priest of Saint-Valéry, having pronounced the Absolution, said in a tearful voice:

"Never were laid in consecrated ground, there to await the judgment of God, better men and better Christians than Jean Lenoël and his son Désiré."

And while barques and their skippers perished near the coast, in the high seas great vessels foundered. Not a day passed that the ocean did not bring in some flotsam of wreck. Now one morning some children who were steering a boat saw a figure lying on the sea. It was a figure of Jesus Christ, life-size, carved in wood, painted in natural colouring, and looking as if it were very old. The Good Lord was floating upon the sea with arms outstretched. The children towed the figure ashore and brought it up into Saint-Valéry. The head was encircled with the crown of thorns. The feet and hands were pierced. But the nails were missing as well as the cross. The arms were still outstretched ready for sacrifice and blessing, just as he appeared to Joseph of Arimathea and the holy women when they were burying Him.

The children gave it to Monsieur le Curé Truphème, who said to them:

"This image of the Saviour is of ancient workmanship. He who made it must have died long ago. Although to-day in the shops of Amiens and Paris excellent statues are sold for a hundred francs and more, we must admit that the earlier sculptors were not without merit. But what delights me most is the thought that if Jesus Christ be thus come with open arms to Saint-Valéry, it is in order to bless the parish, which has been so

[1]From Winifred Stephens's translation of *Crainquebille and Other Tales*. Reprinted by permission of John Lane, the Bodley Head, Ltd., and of Dodd, Mead & Company, Inc.

cruelly tried, and in order to announce that He has compassion on the poor folk who go a-fishing at the risk of their lives. He is the God who walked upon the sea and blessed the nets of Cephas."

And Monsieur le Curé Truphème, having had the Christ placed in the church on the cloth of the high altar, went off to order from the carpenter Lemerre a beautiful cross in heart of oak.

When it was made, the Saviour was nailed to it with brand new nails, and it was erected in the nave above the churchwarden's pew.

Then it was noticed that His eyes were filled with mercy and seemed to glisten with tears of heavenly pity.

One of the churchwardens, who was present at the putting up of the crucifix, fancied he saw tears streaming down the divine face. The next morning when Monsieur le Curé with a choir-boy entered the church to say his mass, he was astonished to find the cross above the churchwarden's pew empty and the Christ lying upon the altar.

As soon as he had celebrated the divine sacrifice he had the carpenter called and asked him why he had taken the Christ down from His cross. But the carpenter replied that he had not touched it. Then, after having questioned the beadle and the sidesmen, Monsieur Truphème made certain that no one had entered the church since the crucifix had been placed over the churchwarden's pew.

Thereupon he felt that these things were miraculous, and he meditated upon them discreetly. The following Sunday in his exhortation he spoke of them to his parishioners, and he called upon them to contribute by their gifts to the erection of a new cross more beautiful than the first and more worthy to bear the Redeemer of the world.

The poor fishers of Saint-Valéry gave as much money as they could and the widows brought their wedding rings. Wherefore Monsieur Truphème was able to go at once to Abbeville and to order a cross of ebony, highly polished and surmounted by a scroll with the inscription I.N.R.I. in letters of gold. Two months later it was erected in the place of the former and the Christ was nailed to it between the lance and the sponge.

But Jesus left this cross as He had left the other; and as soon as night fell He went and stretched Himself upon the altar.

Monsieur le Curé, when He found Him there in the morning, fell on his knees and prayed for a long while. The fame of this miracle spread throughout the neighbourhood, and the ladies of Amiens made a collection for the Christ of Saint-Valéry. Monsieur Truphème received money and jewels from Paris, and the wife of the Minister of Marine, Madame Hyde de Neuville, sent him a heart of diamonds. Of all these treasures, in the space of two years, a goldsmith of La Rue St Sulpice, fashioned a cross of gold and precious stones which was set up with great pomp in the church of Saint-Valéry on the second Sunday after Easter in the year 18—. But He who had not refused the cross of sorrow, fled from this cross of gold and again stretched Himself upon the white linen of the altar.

For fear of offending Him, He was left there this time; and He had lain upon the altar for more than two years, when Pierre, son of Pierre Caillou, came to tell Monsieur le Curé Truphème that he had found the true cross of Our Lord on the beach.

Pierre was an innocent; and, because he had not sense enough to earn a livelihood, people gave him bread out of charity; he was liked because he never did any harm. But he wandered in his talk and no one listened to him.

Nevertheless Monsieur Truphème, who had never ceased meditating on the Ocean Christ, was struck by what the poor imbecile had just said. With the beadle and two sidesmen he went to the spot, where the child said he had seen a cross, and there he found two planks studded with nails, which had long been washed by the sea and which did indeed form a cross.

They were the remains of some old shipwreck. On one of these boards could still be read two letters painted in black, a J and an L; and there was no doubt that this was a fragment of Jean Lenoël's barque, he who with his son Désiré had been lost at sea five years before.

At the sight of this, the beadle and the sidesmen began to laugh at the innocent who had taken the broken planks of a boat for the cross of Jesus Christ. But Monsieur le Curé Truphème checked their merriment. He had meditated much and prayed long since the Ocean Christ had arrived among the fisherfolk, and the mystery of infinite charity began to dawn upon him. He knelt down upon the sand, repeated the prayer for the faithful departed, and then told the beadle and the sidesmen to carry the flotsam on their shoulders and to place it in the church. When this had been done he raised the Christ from the altar, placed it on the planks of the boat and himself nailed it to them, with the nails that the ocean had corroded.

By the priest's command, the very next day this cross took the place of the cross of gold and precious stones over the churchwarden's pew. The Ocean Christ has never left it. He has chosen to remain nailed to the planks on which men died invoking His name and that of His Mother. There, with parted lips, august and afflicted, He seems to say:

"My cross is made of all men's woes, for I am in truth the God of the poor and the heavy-laden."

HOW ST MAËL VOYAGED TO THE ISLAND OF THE PENGUINS[1]

Anatole France

(1844–1924)

MAËL, a scion of a royal family of Cambria, was sent in his ninth year to the Abbey of Yvern so that he might there study both sacred and profane learning. At the age of fourteen he renounced his patrimony and took a vow to serve the Lord. His time was divided, according to the rule, between the singing of hymns, the study of grammar, and the meditation of eternal truths.

A celestial perfume soon disclosed the virtues of the monk throughout the cloister, and when the blessed Gal, the Abbot of Yvern, departed from this world into the next, young Maël succeeded him in the government of the Monastery. He established therein a school, an infirmary, a guest-house, a forge, workshops of all kinds, and sheds for building ships, and he compelled the monks to till the lands in the neighbourhood. With his own hands he cultivated the garden of the Abbey, he worked in metals, he instructed the novices, and his life was gently gliding along like a stream that reflects the heavens and fertilizes the fields.

At the close of the day this servant of God was accustomed to seat himself on the cliff, in the place that is to-day called still St Maël's chair. At his feet the rocks bristling with green seaweed and tawny wrack seemed like black dragons as they faced the foam of waves with their monstrous breasts. He watched the sun descending into the ocean like a red Host whose glorious blood gave a purple tone to the clouds and to the summits of the waves. And the holy man saw in this the image of the mystery of the Cross, by which the divine blood has clothed the earth with a royal purple. In the offing a line of dark blue marked the shores of the island of Gad, where St Bridget, who had been given the veil by St Malo, ruled over a convent of women.

Now Bridget, knowing the merits of the venerable Maël, begged from him some work of his hands as a rich present. Maël cast a hand-bell of bronze for her and, when it was finished, he blessed it and threw it into the sea. And the bell went ringing towards the coast of Gad, where St Bridget, warned by the sound of the bell upon the waves, received it piously, and carried it in solemn procession with singing of psalms into the chapel of the convent.

Thus the holy Maël advanced from virtue to virtue. He had already passed through two-thirds of the way of life, and he hoped peacefully to reach his terrestial end in the midst of his spiritual brethren, when he

[1]From A. W. Evans's translation of *Penguin Island*. Reprinted by permission of John Lane, the Bodley Head, Ltd., and of Dodd, Mead & Company, Inc.

knew by a certain sign that the Divine wisdom had decided otherwise, and that the Lord was calling him to less peaceful but not less meritorious labours.

One day as he walked in meditation to the furthest point of a tranquil beach, for which rocks jutting out into the sea formed a rugged dam, he saw a trough of stone which floated like a boat upon the waters.

It was in a vessel similar to that St Guirec, the great St Columba, and so many holy men from Scotland and from Ireland had gone forth to evangelize Armoria. More recently still, St Avoye having come from England, ascended the river Auray in a mortar made of rose-coloured granite into which children were afterwards placed in order to make them strong; St Vouga passed from Hibernia to Cornwall on a rock whose fragments, preserved at Penmarch, will cure of fever such pilgrims as place these splinters on their heads. St Samson entered the Bay of St Michael's Mount in a granite vessel which will one day be called St Samson's basin. It is because of these facts that when he saw the stone trough the holy Maël understood that the Lord intended him for the apostolate of the pagans who still peopled the coast of the Breton Islands.

He handed his ashen staff to the holy Budoc, thus investing him with the government of the monastery. Then, furnished with bread, a barrel of fresh water, and the book of the Holy Gospels, he entered the stone trough which carried him gently to the island of Hœdic.

This island is perpetually buffeted by the winds. In it some poor men fished among the clefts of the rocks and laboriously cultivated vegetables in gardens full of sand and pebbles that were sheltered from the wind by walls of barren stone and hedges of tamarisk. A beautiful fig-tree raised itself in a hollow of the island and thrust forth its branches far and wide. The inhabitants of the island used to worship it.

And the holy Maël said to them: "You worship this tree because it is beautiful. Therefore you are capable of feeling beauty. Now I come to you to reveal the hidden beauty." And he taught them the Gospel. And having instructed them he baptized them with salt and water.

The islands of Morbihan were more numerous in those times than they are to-day. For since then many have been swallowed up by the sea. St Maël evangelized sixty of them. Then in his granite trough he ascended the river Auray. And after sailing for three hours he landed before a Roman house. A thin column of smoke went up from the roof. The holy man crossed the threshold on which there was a mosaic representing a dog with its hind legs outstretched and its lips drawn back. He was welcomed by an old couple, Marcus Combabus and Valeria Mœrens, who lived there on the products of their lands. There was a portico round the interior court the columns of which were painted red, half their height upwards from the base. A fountain made of shells stood against the wall and under the portico there rose an altar with a niche in which the master of the house had placed some little idols made of baked earth and whitened with whitewash. Some represented winged children, others Apollo or Mercury, and several were in the form of a naked woman twisting her hair. But the holy Maël, observing those figures discovered among them the image of a young mother holding a child upon her knees.

Immediately pointing to that image he said:

"That is the Virgin, the mother of God. The poet Virgil foretold her in Sibylline verses before she was born, and in angelical tones he sang 'Jam redit et virgo.' Throughout heathendom prophetic figures of her have been made, like that which you, O Marcus, have placed upon this altar. And without doubt it is she who has protected your modest household. Thus it is that those who faithfully observe the natural law prepare themselves for the knowledge of revealed truths."

Marcus Combabus and Valeria Mœrens having been instructed by this speech were converted to the Christian faith. They received baptism together with their young freedwoman Caelia Avitella, who was dearer to them than the light of their eyes. All their tenants renounced paganism and were baptized on the same day.

Marcus Combabus, Valeria Mœrens, and Caelia Avitella led henceforth a life full of merit. They died in the Lord and were admitted into the canon of the saints.

For thirty-seven years longer the blessed Maël evangelized the pagans of the inner lands. He built two hundred and eighteen chapels and seventy-four abbeys.

Now on a certain day in the city of Vannes, where he was preaching the Gospel, he learned that the monks of Yvern had in his absence declined from the rule of St Gal. Immediately, with the zeal of a hen who gathers her brood, he repaired to his erring children. He was then towards the end of his ninety-seventh year; his figure was bent, but his arms were still strong, and his speech was poured forth abundantly like winter snow in the depths of the valleys.

Abbot Budoc restored the ashen staff to St Maël and informed him of the unhappy state into which the Abbey had fallen. The monks were in disagreement as to the date on which the festival of Easter ought to be celebrated. Some held for the Roman calendar, others for the Greek calendar, and the horrors of a chronological schism distracted the monastery.

There also prevailed another cause of disorder. The nuns of the island of Gad, sadly fallen from their former virtue, continually came in boats to the coast of Yvern. The monks received them in the guest-house and from this there arose scandals which filled pious souls with desolation.

Having finished his faithful report, Abbot Budoc concluded in these terms:

"Since the coming of these nuns the innocence and peace of the monks are at an end."

"I readily believe it," answered the blessed Maël. "For woman is a cleverly constructed snare by which we are taken even before we suspect the trap. Alas! the delightful attraction of these creatures is exerted with even greater force from a distance than when they are close at hand. The less they satisfy desire the more they inspire it. This is the reason why a poet wrote this verse to one of them:

'When present I avoid thee, but when away I find thee,'

Thus we see, my son, that the blandishments of carnal love have more power over hermits and monks than over men who live in the world. All through my life the demon of lust has tempted me in various ways, but his strongest temptations did not come to me from meeting a woman, however beautiful and fragrant she was. They came to me from the image of an absent woman. Even now, though full of days and approaching my ninety-eighth year, I am often led by the enemy to sin against chastity, at least in thought. At night when I am cold in my bed and my frozen old bones rattle together with a dull sound I hear voices reciting the second verse of the third Book of Kings: 'Wherefore his servants said unto him, Let there be sought for my lord the king a young virgin; and let her stand before the king, and let her cherish him, and let her lie in thy bosom, that my lord the king may get heat,' and the devil shows me a girl in the bosom of a youth who says to me: 'I am thy Abishag; I am thy Shunamite. Make, O my lord, room for me in thy couch.'

"Believe me," added the old man, "it is only by the special aid of Heaven that a monk can keep his chastity in act and in intention."

Applying himself immediately to restore innocence and peace to the monastery, he corrected the calendar according to the calculations on chronology and astronomy, and he compelled all the monks to accept his decision; he sent the women who had declined from St Bridget's rule back to their convent; but far from driving them away brutally, he caused them to be led to their boat with singing of psalms and litanies.

"Let us respect in them," he said, "the daughters of Bridget and the betrothed of the Lord. Let us beware lest we imitate the Pharisees who affect to despise sinners. The sin of these women and not their persons should be abased, and they should be made ashamed of what they have done and not of what they are, for they are all creatures of God."

And the holy man exhorted his monks to obey faithfully the rule of their order.

"When it does not yield to the rudder," said he to them, "the ship yields to the rock."

The blessed Maël had scarcely restored order in the Abbey of Yvern before he learned that the inhabitants of the Island of Hœdic, his first catechumens and the dearest of all to his heart, had returned to paganism, add that they were hanging crowns of flowers and fillets of wool to the branches of the sacred fig-tree.

The boatman who brought this sad news expressed a fear that soon these misguided men might violently destroy the chapel that had been built on the shore of their island.

The holy man resolved forthwith to visit his faithless children, so that he might lead them back to the faith and prevent them from yielding to such sacrilege. As he went down to the bay where his stone trough was moored, he turned his eyes to the sheds, then filled with the noise of saws and of hammers, which, thirty years before, he had erected on the fringe of that bay for the purpose of building ships.

At that moment the Devil, who never tires, went out from the sheds and, under the appearance of a monk called Samson he approached the holy man and tempted him thus:

"Father, the inhabitants of the island of Hœdic commit sins unceasingly. Every moment that passes removes them further from God. They are soon going to use violence towards the chapel that you have raised with your own venerable hands on the shore of their island. Time is pressing. Do you not think that your stone trough would carry you more quickly towards them if it were rigged like a boat and furnished with a rudder, a mast, and a sail, for then you would be driven by the wind? Your arms are still strong and able to steer a small craft. It would be a good thing too, to put a sharp stem in front of your apostolic trough. You are much too clear-sighted not to have thought of it already."

"Truly time is pressing," answered the holy man. "But to do as you say, Samson, my son, would it not be to make myself like those men of little faith who do not trust the Lord? Would it not be to despise the gifts of Him who has sent me this stone vessel without rigging or sail?"

This question the Devil, who is a great theologian, answered by another.

"Father, is it praiseworthy to wait, with our arms folded, until help comes from on high, to ask everything from Him, who can do all things, instead of acting by human prudence and helping ourselves?"

"It certainly is not," answered the holy Maël, "and to neglect to act by human prudence is tempting God."

"Well," urged the Devil, "is it not prudence in this case to rig the vessel?"

"It would be prudence if we could not attain our end in any other way."

"Is your vessel then so very speedy?"

"It is as speedy as God pleases."

"What do you know about it? It goes like Abbot Budoc's mule. It is a regular old tub. Are you forbidden to make it speedier?"

"My son, clearness adorns your words, but they are unduly over-confident. Remember that this vessel is miraculous."

"It is, Father. A granite trough that floats on the water like a cork is a miraculous trough. There is not the slightest doubt about it. What conclusions do you draw from that?"

"I am greatly perplexed. Is it right to perfect so miraculous a machine by human and natural means?"

"Father, if you lost your right foot and God restored it to you, would not that foot be miraculous?"

"Without doubt, my son."

"Would you put a shoe on it?"

"Assuredly."

"Well, then, if you believe that one may cover a miraculous foot with a natural shoe, you should also believe that we can put a natural rigging on a miraculous boat. That is clear. Alas! Why must the holiest persons have their moments of weakness and despondency? The most illustrious of the apostles of Brittany could accomplish works worthy of eternal glory. . . . But his spirit is tardy and his hand is slothful. Farewell then, father! Travel by short and slow stages and when at last you approach the coast of Hœdic you will see the smoking ruins of the chapel that was built and consecrated by your own hands. The pagans will have burned it and with it the deacon you left there. He will be as thoroughly roasted as a black pudding."

"My trouble is extreme," said the servant of God, drying with his sleeve the sweat that gathered upon his brow. "But tell me, Samson, my son, would not rigging this stone trough be a difficult piece of work? And if we undertook it might we not lose time instead of gaining it?"

"Ah! Father," exclaimed the Devil, "in one turning of the hourglass the thing would be done. We shall find the necessary rigging in this shed that you have formerly built here on the coast and in those storehouses abundantly stocked through your care. I will myself regulate all the ship's fittings. Before being a monk I was a sailor and a carpenter and I have worked at many other trades as well. Let us to work."

Immediately he drew the holy man into an out-house filled with all things needful for fitting out a boat.

"That for you, Father!"

And he placed on his shoulders the sail, the mast, the gaff, and the boom.

Then, himself bearing a stem and a rudder with its screw and tiller, and seizing a carpenter's bag full of tools, he ran to the shore, dragging the holy man after him by his habit. The latter was bent, sweating and breathless, under the burden of canvas and wood.

The Devil, having tucked his clothes up to his armpits, dragged the trough on the sand, and fitted the rigging in less than an hour.

As soon as the holy Maël had embarked, the vessel, with all its sails set, cleft through the water with such speed that the coast was almost immediately out of sight. The old man steered to the south so as to

double the Land's End, but an irresistible current carried him to the
south-west. He went along the southern coast of Ireland and turned
sharply towards the north. In the evening the wind freshened. In vain
did Maël attempt to furl the sail. The vessel flew distractedly towards
the fabulous seas.

By the light of the moon the immodest sirens of the North came around
him with their hempen-coloured hair, raising their white throats and
their rose tinted limbs out of the sea; and beating the water into foam
with their emerald tails, they sang in cadence:

> "Whither goest thou, gentle Maël,
> In thy trough distracted?
> All distended is thy sail
> Like the breast of Juno
> When from it gushed the Milky Way."

For a moment their harmonious laughter followed him beneath the
stars, but the vessel fled on, a hundred times more swiftly than the red
ship of a Viking. And the petrels, surprised in their flight, clung with
their feet to the hair of the holy man.

Soon a tempest arose full of darkness and groanings, and the trough,
driven by a furious wind, flew like a sea-mew through the mist and the
surge.

After a night of three times twenty-four hours the darkness was suddenly rent and the holy man discovered on the horizon a shore more
dazzling than diamond. The coast rapidly grew larger, and soon by the
glacial light of a torpid and sunken sun, Maël saw, rising above the
waters, the silent streets of a white city, which, vaster than Thebes with
its hundred gates, extended as far as the eye could see the ruins of its
forum built of snow, its palaces of frost, its crystal arches, and its iri-
descent obelisks.

The ocean was covered with floating icebergs around which swam
men of the sea of a wild yet gentle appearance. And Leviathan passed
by hurling a column of water up to the clouds.

Moreover, on a block of ice which floated at the same rate as the stone
trough there was seated a white bear holding her little one in her arms,
and Maël heard her murmuring in a low voice this verse of Virgil,
"*Incipe parve puer.*"

And full of sadness and trouble, the old man wept.

The fresh water had frozen and burst the barrel that contained it.
And Maël was sucking a piece of ice to quench his thirst, and his food
was bread dipped in dirty water. His beard and hair were broken like
glass. His habit was covered with a layer of ice and cut into him at every
movement of his limbs. Huge waves rose up and opened their foaming
jaws at the old man. Twenty times the boat was filled by masses of sea.

And the ocean swallowed up the book of the Holy Gospels which the apostle guarded with extreme care in a purple cover marked with a golden cross.

Now on the thirtieth day the sea calmed. And lo! with a frightful clamour of sky and waters a mountain of dazzling whiteness advanced towards the stone vessel. Maël steered to avoid it, but the tiller broke in his hands. To lessen the speed of his progress towards the rock he attempted to reef the sails, but when he tried to knot the reef-points the wind pulled them away from him and the rope seared his hands. He saw three demons with wings of black skin having hooks at their ends, who, hanging from the rigging, were puffing with their breath against the sails. Understanding from this sight that the enemy had governed him in all these things, he guarded himself by making the sign of the Cross. Immediately a furious gust of wind filled with the noise of sobs and howls struck the stone trough, carried off the mast with all the sails, and tore away the rudder and the stem.

The trough was drifting on the sea, which had now grown calm. The holy man knelt and gave thanks to the Lord who had delivered him from the snares of the demon. Then he recognized, sitting on a block of ice, the mother bear who had spoken during the storm. She pressed her beloved child to her bosom, and in her hand she held a purple book marked with a golden cross. Hailing the granite trough, she saluted the holy man with these words:

"*Pax tibi Maël.*"

And she held out the book to him.

The holy man recognized his evangelistary, and, full of astonishment, he sang in the tepid air a hymn to the Creator and his creation.

After having drifted for an hour the holy man approached a narrow strand, shut in by steep mountains. He went along the coast for a whole day and a night, passing around the reef which formed an insuperable barrier. He discovered in this way that it was a round island in the middle of which rose a mountain crowned with clouds. He joyfully breathed the fresh breath of the moist air. Rain fell, and this rain was so pleasant that the holy man said to the Lord:

"Lord, this is the island of tears, the island of contritions."

The strand was deserted. Worn out with fatigue and hunger he sat down on a rock in the hollow of which there lay some yellow eggs, marked with black spots, and about as large as those of a swan. But he did not touch them, saying:

"Birds are the living praises of God. I should not like a single one of these praises to be lacking through me."

And he munched the lichens which he tore from the crannies of the rocks.

The holy man had gone almost entirely round the island without meeting any inhabitants, when he came to a vast amphitheatre formed of black and red rocks whose summits became tinged with blue as they rose towards the clouds, and they were filled with sonorous cascades.

The reflection from the polar ice had hurt the old man's eyes, but a feeble gleam of light still shone through his swollen eyelids. He distinguished animated forms which filled the rocks, in stages, like a crowd of men on the tiers of an amphitheatre. And at the same time, his ears, deafened by the continual noises of the sea, heard a feeble sound of voices. Thinking that what he saw were men living under the natural law, and that the Lord had sent him to teach them the Divine law, he preached the gospel to them.

Mounted on a lofty stone in the midst of the wild circus:

"Inhabitants of this island," he said, "although you be of small stature, you look less like a band of fishermen and mariners than like a senate of a judicious republic. By your gravity, your silence, your tranquil deportment, you form on this wild rock an assembly comparable to the Conscript Fathers at Rome deliberating in the temple of Victory, or rather, to the philosophers at Athens disputing on the benches of the Areopagus. Doubtless you possess neither their science nor their genius, but perhaps in the sight of God you are their superiors. I believe that you are simple and good. As I went round your island I saw no image of murder, no sign of carnage, no enemies' heads or scalps hung from a lofty pole or nailed to the doors of your villages. You appear to me to have no arts and not to work in metals. But your hearts are pure and your hands are innocent, and the truth will easily enter into your souls."

Now what he had taken for men of small stature but of grave bearing were penguins whom the spring had gathered together, and who were ranged in couples on the natural steps of the rock, erect in the majesty of their large white bellies. From moment to moment they moved their winglets like arms, and uttered peaceful cries. They did not fear men, for they did not know them, and had never received any harm from them; and there was in the monk a certain gentleness that reassured the most timid animals and that pleased these penguins extremely. With a friendly curiosity they turned towards him their little round eyes lengthened in front by a white oval spot that gave something odd and human to their appearance.

Touched by their attention, the holy man taught them the Gospel.

"Inhabitants of this island, the earthly day that has just risen over your rocks is the image of the heavenly day that rises in your souls. For I bring you the inner light; I bring you the light and heat of the soul. Just as the sun melts the ice of your mountains so Jesus Christ will melt the ice in your hearts."

Thus the old man spoke. As everywhere throughout nature voice calls to voice, as all which breathes in the light of day loves alternate strains, these penguins answered the old man by the sounds of their throats. And their voices were soft for it was the season of their loves.

The holy man, persuaded that they belonged to some idolatrous people and that in their own language they gave adherence to the Christian faith, invited them to receive baptism.

"I think," said he to them, "that you bathe often, for all the hollows of the rocks are full of pure water, and as I came to your assembly I saw several of you plunging into these natural baths. Now purity of body is the image of spiritual purity."

And he taught them the origin, the nature, and the effect of baptism.

"Baptism," said he to them, "is Adoption, New Birth, Regeneration, Illumination."

And he explained each of these points to them in succession. Then, having previously blessed the water that fell from the cascades, and recited the exorcisms, he baptized those whom he had just taught, pouring on each of their heads a drop of pure water and pronouncing the sacred words.

And thus for three days and three nights he baptized the birds.

ICELAND FISHERMEN[1]

Pierre Loti

(1850–1923)

I

THEIR smack was named *La Marie*, and her master was Captain Guermeur. Every year she set sail for the big dangerous fisheries, in the frigid regions where the summers have no night. She was a very old ship, as old as the statuette of her patron saint itself. Her heavy oaken-built planks were rough and worn, impregnated with ooze and brine, but still strong and stout, and smelling strongly of tar. At anchor she looked an old unwieldy tub from her so massive build, but when blew the mighty western gales, her lightness returned, like a sea-gull awakened by the wind. Then she had her own style of tumbling over the rollers, and rebounding more lightly than many newer ones, launched with all your new fangles.

As for the crew of six men and the boy, they were "Icelanders" the valiant race of seafarers whose homes are at Paimpol and Tréguier, and who from father to son are destined for the cod fisheries.

They had hardly ever seen a summer in France. At the end of each winter, they, with other fishers, received the parting blessing in the harbour of Paimpol. And for that *fête* day an altar, always the same, and imitating a rocky grotto, was erected on the quay; and over it, in the midst of anchors, oars, and nets, was enthroned the Virgin Mary, calm,

---

[1] Reprinted from Clara Cadiot's translation of *An Iceland Fisherman*

and beaming with affection, the patroness of sailors; she would be brought from her chapel for the occasion, and had looked upon generation after generation with her same lifeless eyes, blessing the happy for whom the season would be lucky, and the others who would never return.

The Host, followed by a slow procession of wives, mothers, sweethearts, and sisters, was borne round the harbour, where the boats bound for Iceland, bedecked in all colours, saluted it on its way. The priest halted before each, giving them his holy blessing; and then the fleet started, leaving the country desolate of husbands, lovers, and sons; and as the shores faded from their view, the crews sang together in low, full voices, the hymns sacred to "the Star of the Ocean."

II

About a month later, around Iceland, the weather was of that rare kind which the sailors call a dead calm; in other words, in the air nothing moved, as if all the breezes were exhausted and their task done.

The sky was covered with a white veil, which darkened towards its lower border near the horizon, and gradually passed into dull grey leaden tints; over this the still waters threw a pale light, which fatigued the eyes and chilled the gazer through and through. All at once, liquid designs played over the surface, such light evanescent rings as one forms by breathing on a mirror. The sheen of the waters seemed covered with a net of faint patterns, which intermingled and reformed, rapidly disappearing. Everlasting night, or everlasting day, one could scarcely say what it was; the sun, which pointed to no special hour of the day, remained fixed, as if presiding over the fading glory of dead things; it appeared but as a mere ring, being almost without substance, and magnified enormously by a shifting halo.

Yann and Sylvestre, leaning against one another, sang "Jean-François de Nantes," the song without an end, amused by its very monotony, looking at one another from the corner of their eyes as if laughing at the childish fun, with which they recommenced the verses over and over again, trying to put fresh spirit into them each time. Their cheeks glowed ruddily under the sharp freshness of the morning; the pure air they breathed was strengthening, and they inhaled it deep down in their chests, the very fountain of all vigorous existence. And yet, around them, was a semblance of non-existence, of a world either finished or not yet created; the light itself had no warmth; all things seemed without motion, and as if chilled for eternity under the great ghostly eye which represented the sun.

The *Marie* projected over the sea a shadow long and black as night, or rather appearing deep green in the midst of the polished surface, which reflected all the purity of the heavens; in this shadowed part, which had no glitter, could be plainly distinguished through the transparency, myriads upon myriads of fish, all alike, gliding slowly in the same direction, as if bent towards the goal of their perpetual travels. They were cods, performing their evolutions all as parts of a single body, stretched full length in the same direction, exactly parallel, offering the effect of grey streaks, unceasingly agitated by a quick motion which gave a look of fluidity to the mass of dumb lives. Sometimes, with a sudden quick movement of the tail, all turned round at the same time, showing the sheen of their silvered sides; and the same movement was repeated throughout the entire shoal by slow undulations, as if a thousand metal blades had each thrown a tiny flash of lightning from under the surface.

The sun, already low, lowered further; so night had decidedly come.

As the great ball of flame descended into the leaden-coloured zones which surrounded the sea, it grew yellow, and its outer rim became more clear and solid. Now it could be looked straight at, as if it were but the moon. Yet it still gave out light, and looked quite near in the immensity; it seemed that by going in a ship, only as far as the edge of the horizon, one might collide with the great mournful globe, floating in the air just a few yards above the water.

Fishing was going on well; looking into the calm water, one could see exactly what took place; how the cods came to bite, with a greedy spring, then feeling themselves hooked, wriggled about, as if to hook themselves still firmer. And every moment, with rapid action, the fishermen hauled in their lines, hand over hand, throwing the fish to the man who was to clean them and flatten them out.

The Paimpol fleet was scattered over the quiet mirror, animating the desert. Here and there appeared distant sails, unfurled for mere form's sake, considering there was no breeze. They were like clear white outlines upon the greys of the horizon. In this dead calm, fishing off Iceland seemed so easy and tranquil a trade that ladies' yachting was no name for it.

> "Jean François de Nantes;
> Jean François,
> Jean François!"

So they sang, like a couple of children. . . .

A slight breeze sprang up, fresher yet to inhale, and began to tarnish the surface of the still waters in patches; it traced designs in a bluish green tint over the shining mirror, and scattering in trails, these fanned out or branched off like a coral tree; all very rapidly with a low murmur; it was like a signal of awakening foretelling the end of this intense torpor. The sky, its veil being rent asunder, grew clear; the vapours fell down on the horizon, massing in heaps like slate-coloured wadding, as if to form a soft bank to the sea. The two ever-during mirrors between which the fishermen lived, the one on high and the one beneath, recovered their deep lucidity, as if the mists tarnishing them had been brushed away.

The weather was changing in a rapid way which foretold no good. . . .
Far-off Iceland also reappeared, as if she would fain come near them;
showing her great mountains of bare stones more distinctly than ever.

And there arose a new Iceland of similar colour, which little by little
took a more definite form, and none the less was purely illusive, its
gigantic mountains merely a condensation of mists. The sun, sinking low,
seemed incapable of ever rising again over all things, though glowing
through this phantom island so tangibly that it seemed placed in front of
it. Incomprehensible sight! no longer was it surrounded by a halo, but
its disc had become firmly spread, rather like some faded yellow planet
slowly decaying and suddenly checked there in the heart of chaos. . . .

III

The Northern sun had taken another aspect and changed its colour,
opening the new day by a sinister morn. Completely free from its veil,
it gave forth its grand rays, crossing the sky in fitful flashes, foretelling
nasty weather. During the last few days it had been too fine to last. The
winds blew upon that swarm of boats, as if to clear the sea of them; and
they began to disperse and flee, like an army put to rout, before the
warning written in the air, beyond possibility to misread. Harder and
harder it blew, making men and ships quake alike.

And the still tiny waves began to run one after another and to melt
together; at first they were frosted over with white foam spread out in
patches; and then, with a whizzing sound, arose smoke as though they
burned and scorched, and the whistling grew louder every moment.
Fish-catching was no longer thought of; it was their work on deck. The
fishing-lines had been drawn in, and all hurried to make sail and some
to seek for shelter in the fjords, whilst yet others preferred to round the
southern point of Iceland, finding it safer to stand for the open sea,
with the free space about them, and run before the stern wind. They
could still see each other a while: here and there, above the trough of the
sea, sails wagged as poor wearied birds fleeing; the masts tipped, but
ever and anon righted, like the weighted pith figures which similarly
resumed an erect attitude when released after being blown down.

The illimitable cloudy roof, erstwhile compacted towards the western
horizon, in an island form, began to break up on high and sent its fragments over the surface. It seemed indestructible, for vainly did the winds
stretch it, pull and toss it asunder, continually tearing away dark strips,
which they waved over the pale yellow sky, gradually becoming intensely
and icily livid. Ever more strongly grew the wind which threw all things
in turmoil.

The waves, curling up in scrolls, continued to run after each other,
to re-assemble and climb on one another, and between them the hollows
deepened.

In a few hours, everything was belaboured and overthrown in these regions which had been so calm the day before, and instead of the past silence, the uproar was deafening. The present agitation was a dissolving view, unconscientious and useless, and quickly accomplished. What was the object of it all? What a mystery of blind destruction it was!

The clouds continued to stream out on high, out of the west continually, racing and darkening all. A few yellow clefts remained, through which the sun shot its last rays in volleys. And the now greenish water was striped more thickly with snowy froth.

By midday the *Marie* was made completely snug for dirty weather; her hatches battened down, and her sails storm-reefed; she bounded lightly and elastic; for all the horrid confusion, she seemed to be playing, like the porpoises, also amused in storms. With her foresail taken in, she simply scudded before the wind.

It had become quite dark overhead, where stretched the heavily crushing vault. Studded with shapeless gloomy spots, it appeared a set dome, unless a steadier gaze ascertained that everything was in the full rush of motion; endless grey veils were drawn along, unceasingly followed by others, from the profundities of the sky-line—draperies of darkness, pulled from a never-ending roll.

The *Marie* fled faster and faster before the wind; and time fled also— before some invisible and mysterious power. The gale, the sea, the *Marie*, and the clouds were all lashed into one great madness of hasty flight towards the same point. The fastest of all was the wind; then the huge seething billows, heavier and slower, toiling after; and, lastly, the smack, dragged into the general whirl. The waves tracked her down with their white crests, tumbling onward in continual motion, and she—though always being caught up to and outrun—still managed to elude them by means of the eddying waters she spurned in her wake, upon which they vented their fury. In this similitude of flight the sensation particularly experienced was of buoyancy, the delight of being carried along without effort or trouble, in a springy sort of way. The *Marie* mounted over the waves without any shaking, as if the wind had lifted her clean up; and her subsequent descent was a slide. She almost slid backwards, though, at times, the mountains lowering before her as if continuing to run, and then she suddenly found herself dropped into one of the measureless hollows which evaded her also; without injury she sounded its horrible depths, amid a loud splashing of water, which did not even sprinkle her decks, but was blown on and on like everything else, evaporating in finer and finer spray until it was thinned away to nothing. In the trough it was darker, and when each wave had passed the men looked behind them to see if the next to appear were higher; it came upon them with furious contortions, and curling crests, over its transparent emerald body, seeming to shriek: "Only let me catch you, and I'll swallow you whole!"

But this never came to pass, for, as a feather, the billows softly bore them up and then down as gently; they felt it pass under them, with all its boiling surf and thunderous roar. And so on continually, but the sea getting heavier and heavier. One after another rushed the waves, more and more gigantic, like a long chain of mountains, with yawning valleys. And the madness of all this movement, under the ever-darkening sky, accelerated the height of the intolerable clamour.

Yann and Sylvestre stood at the helm, still singing "Jean François de Nantes"; intoxicated with the quiver of speed, they sang out loudly, laughing at their inability to hear themselves in this prodigious wrath of the wind.

"I say, lads, does it smell musty up here too?" called out Guermeur to them, passing his bearded face up through the half-open hatchway, like a Jack-in-box.

Oh, no! it certainly did not smell musty on deck. They were not at all frightened, being quite conscious of what man can cope with, having faith in the strength of their bark and their arms. And they furthermore relied upon the protection of that china virgin, which had voyaged forty years to Iceland, and so often had danced the dance of this day, smiling perpetually between her branches of artificial flowers.

Generally speaking, they could not see far around them; a few hundred yards off, all seemed entombed in the fearfully big billows, with their frothing crests shutting out the view. They felt as if in an enclosure, continually altering shape; and, besides, all things seemed drowned in the aqueous smoke, which fled before them like a cloud with the greatest rapidity over the heaving surface. But from time to time a gleam of sunlight pierced through the north-west sky, through which a squall threatened; a shuddering light would appear from above, a rather spun-out dimness, making the dome of the heavens denser than before, and feebly lighting up the surge. This new light was sad to behold; far off glimpses as they were, that gave too strong an understanding that the same chaos and the same fury lay on all sides, even far, far behind the seemingly void horizon; there was no limit to its expanse of storm, and they stood along in its midst!

A tremendous tumult arose all about, like the prelude of an apocalypse, spreading the terror of the ultimate end of the earth. And amidst it thousands of voices could be heard above, shrieking, bellowing, calling, as from a great distance. It was only the wind, the great motive breath of all this disorder, the voice of the invisible power ruling all. Then came other voices, nearer and less indefinite, threatening destruction, and making the water shudder and hiss as if on burning coals; the disturbance increased in terror.

Notwithstanding their flight, the sea began to gain on them, to "bury them up," as they phrased it: first the spray fell down on them from behind, and masses of water thrown with such violence as to break everything in their course. The waves were ever increasing, but the tempest tore off their ridges and hurled them, too, upon the poop, like a demon's game of snowballing, till dashed to atoms on the bulwarks. Heavier masses fell on the planks with a hammering sound, till the *Marie* shivered throughout, as if in pain. Nothing could be distinguished over the side, because of the screen of creamy foam; and when the winds soughed more loudly, this foam formed into whirling spouts, like the dust of the way in summer time. At length a heavy rain fell crossways, and soon straight up and down, and how all these elements of destruction yelled together, clashed and interlocked, no tongue can tell.

Yann and Sylvestre stuck staunchly to the helm, covered with their waterproofs, hard and shiny as shark-skin; they had firmly secured themselves at the throat by tarred strings, and likewise at wrists and ankles to prevent the water from running in, and the rain only poured off them; when it fell too heavily, they arched their backs, and held all the more stoutly, not to be thrown over board. Their cheeks burned, and every minute their breath was beaten out or stopped.

After each sea was shipped and rushed over, they exchanged glances, grinning at the crust of salt settled in their beards.

In the long run, though, this became tiresome, an unceasing fury, which always promised a worse visitation. The fury of men and beasts soon falls and dies away; but the fury of lifeless things, without cause or object, is as mysterious as life and death, and has to be borne for very long.

"Jean François de Nantes—"

Through their pale lips still came the refrain of the old song, but as from a speaking automaton, unconsciously taken up from time to time. The excess of motion and uproar had made them dumb, and despite their youth their smiles were insincere, and their teeth chattered with cold; their eyes, half-closed under their raw, throbbing eyelids, remained glazed in terror. Lashed to the helm, like marble cariatides, they only moved their numbed blue hands, almost without thinking, by sheer muscular habit. With their hair streaming and mouths contracted, they had become changed, all the primitive wildness in man appearing again. They could not see one another truly, but still were aware of being companioned. In the instants of greatest danger, each time that a fresh mountain of water rose behind them, came to overtower them, and crash horribly against their boat, one of their hands would move as if involuntarily, to form the sign of the cross. They no more thought of Gaud than of any other woman, or any marrying. The travail was lasting too long, and they had no thoughts left. The intoxication of noise, cold, and fatigue drowned all in their brain. They were merely two pillars of stiffened human flesh, held up by the helm; two strong beasts, cowering, but determined they would not be overwhelmed.

ITALY

THE LAST VOYAGE OF ULYSSES[1]

Dante Alighieri

(1265–1321)

WE DEPARTED thence; and, by the stairs which the rocky bourns had given us to descend before, my Guide remounted and drew me up. And pursuing our solitary way among the jaggs and branches of the cliff, the foot without the hand sped not.

I sorrowed then, and sorrow now again when I direct my memory to what I saw; and curb my genius more than I am wont, lest it run where Virtue guides it not; so that, if kindly star or something better have given to me the good, I may not grudge myself that gift.

As many fire-flies as the peasant—who is resting on the hill at the time that he who brightens the world least hides his face from us, when as the fly yields to the gnat—sees down along the valley, there perchance where he gathers grapes and tills: with flames thus numerous the eighth chasm was all gleaming; as I perceived so soon as I came to where the bottom showed itself. And as he who was avenged by the bears, saw Elijah's chariot at its departure, when the horses rose erect to heaven; for he could not so follow it with his eyes as to see other than the flame alone, like a little cloud, ascending up: thus moved each of those flames along the gullet of the foss, for none of them shews the theft, and every flame steals a sinner.

I stood upon the bridge, having risen so to look that, if I had not caught a rock, I should have fallen down without being pushed. And the Guide, who saw me thus intent, said:

"Within those fires are the spirits; each swathes himself with that which burns him."

"Master," I replied, "from hearing thee I feel more certain; but had already discerned it to be so, and already wished to say to thee: Who is in that fire, which comes so parted at the top, as if it rose from the pile where Eteocles was put with his brother?"

He answered me: "Within it there, Ulysses is tortured, and Diomed; and thus they run together in punishments, as erst in wrath. And in their flame they groan for the ambush of the horse that made the door by which the noble seed of the Romans came forth. Within it they lament the artifice whereby Deidamia in death still sorrows for Achilles; and there they suffer penalty for the Palladium."

---

[1]From *The Divine Comedy*. Translated by John A. Carlyle.

"If they within those sparks can speak," said I, "Master! I pray thee much, and repray that my prayer may equal a thousand, deny me not to wait until the horned flame comes hither. Thou seest how with desire I bend me towards it."

And he to me: "Thy request is worthy of much praise, and therefore I accept it. But do thou refrain thy tongue. Let me speak, for I have conceived what thou wishest; and they, perhaps, because they were Greeks, might disdain thy words."

After the flame had come where time and place seemed fitting to my Guide, I heard him speak in this manner:

"O ye, two in one fire! If I merited of you whilst I lived, if I merited of you much or little, when on earth I wrote the High Verses, move ye not; but let the one of you tell where he wandering went to die."

The greater horn of the ancient flame began to shake itself, murmuring, just like a flame that struggles with the wind. Then carrying to and fro the top, as if it were the tongue that spake, threw forth a voice, and said:

"When I departed from Circe, who beyond a year detained me there near Gaeta, ere Æneas thus had named it, neither fondness for my son, nor reverence for my aged father, nor the due love that should have cheered Penelope, could conquer in me the ardour that I had to gain experience of the world, and of human vice and worth: I ventured into the deep open sea, with but one ship, and with that small company which had not deserted me. Both the shores I saw as far as Spain, far as Morocco; and saw Sardinia and the other isles which that sea bathes round.

"I and my companions were old and slow, when we came to that narrow pass where Hercules assigned his landmarks to hinder man from venturing farther. On the right hand, I left Seville; on the other, had already left Ceuta.

"'O brothers!' I said, 'who through a hundred thousand dangers have reached the West, deny not, to this the brief vigil of your senses that remains, experience of the unpeopled world behind the Sun. Consider your origin: ye were not formed to live like brutes, but to follow virtue and knowledge.'

"With this brief speech I made my companions so eager for the voyage that I could hardly then have checked them. And, turning the poop towards morning, we of our oars made wings for the foolish flight, always gaining on the left. Night already saw the other pole, with all its stars; and ours so low that it rose not from the ocean floor. Five times the light beneath the Moon had been rekindled and quenched as oft, since we had entered on the arduous passage, when there appeared to us a Mountain, dim with distance; and to me it seemed the highest I had ever seen. We joyed, and soon our joy was turned to grief; for a tempest rose from the new land, and struck the forepart of our ship. Three times it made her whirl round with all the waves; at the fourth, made the poop rise and the prow go down, as pleased Another, till the sea was closed above us."

THE LEGEND OF ST MARK AND THE FISHERMEN OF VENICE[1]

Anna Jameson

(1794–1860)

O N THE 25th of February, 1340, there fell out a wonderful thing in this land; for during three days the waters rose continually, and in the night there was fearful rain and tempest, such as had never been heard of. So great was the storm that the waters rose three cubits higher than had ever been known in Venice; and an old fisherman being in his little boat in the canal of St Mark, reached with difficulty the Riva di San Marco, and there he fastened his boat, and waited the ceasing of the storm.

And it is related that at the time this storm was at the highest, there came an unknown man, and besought him that he would row him over to San Giorgio Maggiore, promising to pay him well; and the fisherman replied:

"How is it possible to go to San Giorgio? We shall sink by the way."

But the man only besought him the more that he should set forth. So, seeing that it was the will of God, he arose and rowed over to San Giorgio Maggiore, and the man landed there, and desired the boatman to wait.

In a short while he returned with a young man; and they said:

"Now row towards San Nicolò di Lido."

And the fisherman said:

"How can one possibly go so far with one oar?"

And they said,

"Row boldly, for it shall be possible to thee, and thou shalt be well paid."

And he went; and it appeared to him as if the waters were smooth. Being arrived at San Nicolò di Lido, the two men landed, and returned with a third, and having entered into the boat, they commanded the fisherman that he should row beyond the two castles. And the tempest raged continually.

Being come to the open sea, they beheld approaching with such terrific speed that it appeared to fly over the waters, an enormous galley full of demons (as it is written in the Chronicles, and Marco Sabellino also makes mention of this miracle): the said bark approached the castles to overwhelm Venice, and to destroy it utterly; anon the sea, which had hitherto

---

[1]From *Sacred and Legendary Art.*

been tumultuous, became calm; and these three men, having made the sign of the cross, exorcized the demons, and commanded them to depart, and immediately the galley or the ship vanished: then these three men commanded the fisherman to land them, the one at San Nicolò di Lido, the other at San Giorgio Maggiore, and the third at San Marco. And when he had landed the third, the fisherman, notwithstanding the miracle he had witnessed, desired that he would pay him; and he replied:

"Thou art right; go now to the Doge, and to the Procuratore of St Mark, and tell them what thou hast seen, for Venice would have been overwhelmed had it not been for us three. I am St Mark the evangelist, the protector of this city; the other is the brave knight St George; and he whom thou didst take up at the Lido is the holy bishop St Nicholas. Say to the Doge and the Procuratore that they are to pay you; and tell them likewise that this tempest arose because of a certain schoolmaster dwelling at San Felice, who did sell his soul to the devil, and afterwards hanged himself."

And the fisherman replied:

"If I should tell them this, they will not believe me."

Then St Mark took off a ring which was on his finger, which ring was worth five ducats; and he said:

"Show them this, and tell them when they look in the sanctuary they will not find it."

And thereupon he disappeared.

The next morning, the said fisherman presented himself before the Doge, and related all he had seen the night before, and showed him the ring for a sign. And the Procuratore having sent for the ring, and sought in the usual place, found it not, by reason of which miracle the fisherman was paid, and a solemn procession was ordained, giving thanks to God, and to the relics of the three holy saints, who rest in our land, and who delivered us from this great danger. The ring was given to Signor Marco Loredano and to Signor Andrea Dandolo the procuratore, who placed it in the sanctuary; and, moreover, a perpetual provision was made for the aged fisherman above mentioned.

A "POETIC TEMPEST"[1]

Francesco Petrarca

(1304–1374)

WHEN Horace wished to describe a great storm, he called it a "poetic tempest," and methinks he could not have more tersely expressed its grandeur, for neither the angry heavens, nor the tempestu-

---

[1]From a letter to Cardinal Colonna. Translated by Althea M. Wollaston.

ous sea, can present any sight so stupendous or so utterly beyond the genius of poets to describe. You may already see this truth in Homer's description of the storm at Cæsarea, but the storm which I saw yesterday could neither be painted with the brush nor described in words. It was a phenomenon unique and unheard of in any age, and beyond the power of any poet to depict, unless we except Homer's description of a storm in Greek waters, Virgil's of that off Sicily, and Lucan's of one on the coast of Epirus. If ever I have time, the Neapolitan storm will be the subject of my poem. One cannot, however, rightly call it Neapolitan, for it was universal on the Tyrrhenian coast, and in the Adriatic; but to me it seems natural to speak of it thus, since it found me once again, and much against my will, in Naples.

To be brief, if, owing to the haste of the bearer of this letter to leave the city, I have too little time to write to you fully of the event, I beg you to believe that a more horrible catastrophe was never seen.

Many days ago, the Bishop of a small island near Naples, had foretold this scourge of God by astrological signs, but as usual, the astrologers did not arrive at the exact truth, and they predicted a most terrible earthquake for the twenty-fifth of November, which was to cause the destruction of the whole of Naples. This prophecy had gained so much credence that the greater part of the townsfolk put aside every other consideration, and thought only of imploring mercy from God and pardon for their sins, being convinced that very shortly they must die. On the other hand, many scoffed at the prediction, declaring that little faith was to be put in astrologers, especially as only a few days before there had been several earthquake shocks.

Between fear and hope, but rather more hopeful than fearful, I went back to my dwelling before sunset on the evening of the twenty-fourth, having seen nearly all the women of the city, more mindful of the danger which threatened them than of modesty, with bare feet, flowing hair, their children in their arms, going round from church to church, weeping and calling upon God for mercy. When night fell the sky was more serene than usual, so my servants went to bed soon after supper. I myself, determined to wait, in order to observe the setting of the moon which I thought was in the seventh phase, so I opened the window looking to the west, and before midnight, saw her hide herself behind the hill of San Martino, her face covered with darkness and clouds. Then I shut the window, and lay down on my bed, and, having lain awake for a good long time, I was just beginning to sleep when I was awakened by a rumbling noise and an earthquake, which not only flung open the windows, and put out the light which I am accustomed to keep burning at night, but shook my room to its foundations. Wakened thus suddenly from sleep, I was assailed by the fear of immediate death, and went out into the cloister of the monastery where I was living. There, in the darkness, unable to see except by the chance light of some lamp, we sought our friends, and tried to bring comfort to each other. Meanwhile, terrified at such an awful storm, the monks and the Prior, a man of great sanctity, had gone into the church to sing Matins; and presently, carrying the crucifix and relics of the Saints with numbers of lighted tapers, weeping as they devoutly chanted the prayers, they came to the cloister where we were. At this point I plucked up a little spirit, and went into the church with them, and there, all of us prone on the ground, we did not cease to call aloud upon the mercy of God, expecting from moment to moment that the church would fall in upon us.

It would be much too long a story if I were to try to tell the full horror of that infernal night, and although the truth is more astounding than I can say, I suspect that my words will seem exaggerated. What mountains of waves! What awful winds! What thunder! What ghastly crashing sounds in the sky! What horrible earth tremors! What a fearful roaring of the sea, and what cries from all that great concourse of people! It seemed as if by some magic art the length of the night were doubled, but, at length, came the dawn. Even then, so black was the sky that we could only guess from a faint glimmer of light that day was at hand. Then the priests vested themselves for Mass, and we, who had not yet sufficient courage to raise our eyes to heaven, still prostrate, persevered in our laments and our prayers.

Now when the day broke, although it was still so dark that it seemed more like night, the tumult of the people in the upper part of the town began to diminish, and there arose a much greater clamour down near the sea, and we soon heard horses galloping along the street, and could not conceive the cause thereof. At last, my despair giving place to audacity, I too mounted my horse, and set forth to see what was going forward, or die!

Great God! Who had ever heard tell of such things! Aged sailors say that nothing like it had ever been seen or heard of. In the midst of the harbour, one could see floating the bodies of great numbers of unfortunate men who, while struggling desperately to reach the shore, had been so battered and dashed by the furious violence of the sea, that they looked like a flock of helpless sheep, all getting in each other's way. The whole great harbour was full of drowned or drowning people; some with their heads cut open, some with broken arms, and others with their entrails gushing out. Meanwhile the shrieks of the men and women who lived in the houses near the shore were not less awful than the terrific roar of the sea itself, and where only the day before we had walked along the sand, we saw tremendous waves, more dangerous than the breakers round the lighthouse at Messina. A thousand Neapolitan horsemen, nay, more than a thousand, had ridden down to this spot, as if to follow the obsequies of their native land, and I, having joined their troop, began to be in better heart, knowing that at least I should die in their company. But suddenly there arose an appalling sound, and, as the very ground under our feet began to sink into a chasm that opened beneath the waters, we fled, and went further up from the sea.

In truth to see the heavens in that angry mood and the sea so fierce and cruel was a horrible and amazing sight for mortal eye! The waves were like thousands of huge mountains, and not black or blue, as they usually are in a storm, but of an intense white hue, as they rushed across the bay from Capri. The young Queen, bare-footed, and followed by a great company of ladies, went to pray in all the churches dedicated to the Blessed Virgin. There was not a ship in the harbour which could stand against the terrific storm, and to our great sorrow we saw three galleys which had come from Cyprus and passed through so many dangerous waters, and which were to have sailed the next morning, founder before our very eyes, without a single man being saved. In the same way, the other great ships which had anchored in the harbour, were hurled against each other with such violence that they were dashed to pieces with the loss of all hands.

Of all the ships in the harbour only one was saved. This was a vessel on which were four hundred criminals condemned to the galleys, and lately serving in the Sicilian War: she was able to resist the fury of the sea until late in the evening, thanks to the efforts of these ruffians, who held death at bay until nightfall, when, contrary to their expectations and the general opinion, the sky became clear and the fury of the sea abated. But by this time many of them were already exhausted, and so it came about that those who were saved were among the worst, either because the saying of Lucan is true that Fortune helps the ungodly, or because it so pleased God, or because those are safest in danger, who hold life lightly.

Here then is the story of yesterday, and I should like to beg you never again to ask me to commit my life to the sea and the winds, for in such a case I should not be able to obey either you, or the Pope, or even my father, if he were alive. Let us leave the air to the birds, and the sea to the fish, for I, as a terrestial creature prefer to move on the earth. If you should order me to go to Mauritania, to Sarmatia or to India, I protest that I should assert my liberty, and if you should say to me: "I will see that you have a good ship, navigated by experienced sailors, and you may go into the harbour before night, and you may, if you like, hug the shore,"—I shall answer: "I have not heard from others, or read of it in books, but have actually seen the most gallant ships manned by famous sailors, sunk in harbour before my very eyes, and for this cause your reasonableness must pardon my fear; and you will see that it will be better to allow me to die on land since I was born on land! Moreover-having made several safe voyages in the Mediterranean, I do not wish people to be able to quote to me the proverb that he who tempts the sea

by making another voyage, when once he has been nearly drowned, does
wrong to complain of the sea!"

Farewell. Be in good health.

HOW RANDOLFO RUFFOLO TURNED PIRATE[1]

Giovanni Boccaccio

(1313–1375)

IT IS generally admitted, that the sea coast from Reggio to Gaeta
is the pleasantest part of Italy; that part of it near Salerno, which
the inhabitants call the Coast of Malfi, is full of little towns, gardens,
rivulets, and abounds with rich people expert at merchandize. Amongst
the rest there is a town called Ravello, in which were many wealthy
persons, and one especially, called Landolfo Ruffolo who, not content
with his great store, but willing to make it double, was near losing all he
had, and his life also. This man, having settled his affairs, as other merchants are used to do, bought a large ship, and freighting it all on his own
account, set sail for the island of Cyprus. He there found many ships
laden with the very same commodities as his own, consequently it was
necessary for him not only to make a quick market of his goods, but also,
if he meant to dispose of them at all, to sell them for a trifle, to his great
loss and almost ruin. Grieving much thereat, and hardly knowing what
to do, seeing that from great wealth he was reduced almost to poverty,
he resolved either to die, or to repair his losses by plunder, rather than
go back a poor man to the home from which he had come away so wealthy.
Meeting with a purchaser for his great ship, with the money made of
that and his merchandise he bought a light little vessel fit for a pirate,
and armed and furnished it with everything suitable, intending to make
other people's goods his own, and especially those of the Turks. Fortune
was abundantly more favourable to him in this way of life than she
had been in trade; for, in the space of a year, he took so many Turkish
prizes, that he found he had not only got his own again, but made it
more than double.

Being now comforted for his former loss, and thinking he had enough,
he resolved, for fear of a second disaster, to make the best of his way
home with what he had acquired; and, as he was still fearful of trade,
he had no mind to employ any more of his money that way, but set sail
in the little vessel in which he had gained it. He was now in the Archipelago, when at nightfall a sirocco, or great south-east wind, arose,
directly contrary to their intended course, which made such a sea that

---

[1]From W. R. Kelly's translation of *The Decameron*.

the ship could not bear up against it, and they were glad to get into a bay under the cover of a little island, to wait for better weather.

Landolfo had just entered the harbour when two Genoese carracks came in from Constantinople to avoid the same storm; and, as soon as the men in them saw the small bark, they blocked her in, and on ascertaining that she belonged to an owner whom they knew to be very rich, as men addicted to plunder and rapine, they resolved to make her their prize. Landing some of their men, therefore, well armed with crossbows and other weapons, they posted them so as to prevent any of the crew issuing out of the bark, unless at the cost of their lives; whilst the rest getting into the long-boat, and the sea being favourable, soon boarded Landolfo's vessel, and took all his people, and everything in it, without the loss of a man, leaving him nothing but a waistcoat; and after they had cleared out the vessel, they sank her. The day following, the wind having shifted, they made sail for the west, and had a good voyage all that day; but night coming on, the wind became boisterous again, and the storm was such that the two carracks were parted, whilst that wherein poor Landolfo was, drove with the utmost violence upon the coast of Cephalonia, and was smashed like a glass flung against the wall. The sea being covered in a moment with all sorts of merchandise, and with chests, tables, and fragments of the wreck, all those of the crew who could swim strove, in spite of the darkness and the fury of the waves, to lay hold of such things as chanced to float near them. Amongst these was the unfortunate Landolfo, who, though he had wished for death a thousand times the day before, rather than return home a beggar, was terrified now that he saw death at hand, and got hold of a plank, like the rest, in hopes that if his fate were delayed, God would send him some means for his escape. Bestriding the plank as well as he could, and driven to and fro by the wind, he supported himself till daylight; and then looking round him he could see nothing but clouds and water, and a chest driving towards him, to his great alarm, for sometimes it came so near that he was afraid it would dash against him, and then he would endeavour, with the little strength he had left, to put it by with his hand; at length a great blast of wind sent it with such violence against the plank on which he floated, as to overset it, and plunge him over head and ears into the water. He rose again, however, and swimming with the strength of fear rather than with his own, he found himself at such a distance from the plank that he was afraid he could not recover it. Getting therefore to the chest, which was nearer, he laid his breast upon it as well as he could, and used his arms for paddles. In this manner was he carried up and down, with nothing to eat, but drinking more than he desired, neither knowing where he was, nor seeing anything but water for a day and a night.

The next morning (whether it was through God or the force of the winds) Landolfo who was well nigh become a sponge, grappling the chest with both arms, with the usual tenacity of drowning men, drew near to the island of Corfu, at a spot where, by good fortune, a poor woman was scouring her dishes with salt water and sand. When she saw him approach, and could discover in him nothing in the shape of a man, she screamed, and started back in terror. He was too exhausted to be able to speak, and scarcely could he see much; but as the waves carried him towards the shore, the woman could distinguish the shape of the chest. Looking more narrowly, she saw an arm laid over it, and then a face, and knew at once what was the matter. Moved by compassion, she stepped a little way into the sea, which was now calm, and seizing the half-drowned wretch by the hair of his head, drew both him and the chest to land, where, with much trouble, she unfolded his arms from the chest, which she set upon the head of her daughter, who was with her. She herself carried Landolfo like a little child to the town, put him on a stove, and chafed and washed him with warm water, by which means the vital warmth began to return, and his strength partially revived. In due time she took him from the stove, comforted him with wine and good cordials, and kept him some days till he knew where he was; she then restored him his chest, and told him he might now provide for his departure.

He had forgotten all about the chest, but took it from the hands of the woman, supposing that, small as its worth might be, it might serve for his support for a short time. Finding it very light, he was somewhat disheartened; however, whilst the good woman was out of the way, he broke it open, and found a great quantity of precious stones, some of which were polished and set. Having some judgment of such matters, and seeing that these gems were of immense value, he was now thoroughly comforted, and praised God for not having yet forsaken him. However, as he had been twice buffeted by fortune already, and was fearful of a third mishap, he judged that great caution was requisite to bring these things safe home; he wrapped them up, therefore, in old rags, as well as he could, and told the woman that he had no further use for the chest, but that she might keep it if she would give him a sack in its stead, which she was very glad to do. And now, returning her a thousand thanks, he departed with his sack over his shoulder, and passed over in a bark to Brindisi, and thence to Trani, where he met with merchants of his own town, who clothed him out of charity, after he had told them all that had befallen him, only omitting all mention of the cask of jewels. They also lent him a horse, and sent company with him to Ravello, whither he said he wished to return. Arriving there in safety, he gave thanks to God; and now he inquired more narrowly into his sack than he had done before, and found so many valuable jewels, that, rating them at the lowest prices, he was twice as rich as when he left home. Finding means, therefore, to dispose of them, he sent a sum of money to the woman at Corfu, who had taken him out of the sea, and treated him so kindly; and also to the merchants at Trani for clothing him; the remainder he kept, without having any more mind to trade, and lived handsomely upon it the rest of his life.

HOW PRINCE GERBINO FOUGHT THE GALLEY OF THE KING OF TUNIS[1]

Giovanni Boccaccio

(1313–1375)

GUIGLIELMO, the second king of Sicily (as their histories relate) had two children, a son named Ruggieri, and a daughter called Constantia. Ruggieri died before his father, leaving a son, called Gerbino, whom his grandfather took care to bring up, and he became a most accomplished prince; nor did his fame confine itself within the bounds of his own country, but was echoed through numerous parts of the world, especially in Barbary, which was then tributary to the King of Sicily. Amongst others, who had heard of his singular worth and character, was a daughter of the king of Tunis, who, in the opinion of all that ever saw her, was as beautiful a woman as ever lived, with a soul equally noble and perfect. The lady, inquiring always after people of worth, received from all hands a most extraordinary account of Gerbino's merit and noble exploits, which were so pleasing to her, that, conceiving within her own mind the idea of his person, she became violently in love, and was never more pleased than when he was the subject of discourse. On the other hand, no less had her fame reached Sicily, as well as other countries, and was particularly agreeable to the prince, who had conceived the same love for her. Being desirious of all things of seeing her, he charged some of his friends, till he could obtain leave from his grandfather to go himself to Tunis, to make his love known privately to her, in the best manner they were able, and to bring him some tidings concerning her. This was managed very dexterously by one of them, who went under the character of a jeweller. The princess received him with great cheerfulness and satisfaction, declaring a mutual regard for the prince, and as a proof of it, she sent him a present of one of her richest jewels. He received it with great joy, and wrote several letters, presenting her with things of great value, and pledging himself to wait upon her in person, when fortune afforded him an opportunity.

Things being carried so far, and farther than ought to have been, it happened, that the princess's father promised her in marriage to the King of Granada, to her infinite sorrow, and could she have found opportunity, she would gladly have fled from her father to the prince. He, in like manner, hearing of this contract, was afflicted beyond measure,

---

[1] From W. R. Kelly's translation of *The Decameron*.

and resolved, if it should happen that she was sent by sea, to take her away by force. The King of Tunis, hearing something of Gerbino's love, and what he designed, and well knowing his resolution and great valour, when the time came that she was to depart, sent to the King of Sicily to acquaint him with his design, and to desire a safe conduct; and that monarch, knowing nothing of his grandson's affections towards the lady, nor thinking that the safe conduct was desired upon that account, readily granted it, in token whereof he sent one of his gloves to the King of Tunis. The latter then fitted out a stately ship at Carthage, and providing it with everything necessary to transport his daughter to Granada, waited only for the time that had been appointed. The young lady, who was aware of all this, sent one of her servants in secret to Palermo, to acquaint the prince that she was to sail in a few days, and that it would now appear whether he was a person of such valour as had been always reported, or had that love for her which he had often declared. The message was faithfully delivered; and the prince knowing, at the same time, that his grandfather had granted a safe conduct, was at a loss how to act; but reflecting upon the lady's words, and that he might not appear a dastard, he hired two light ships at Messina, which he took care to have well manned, and sailed with them to the coast of Sardinia, expecting that the ship which had his mistress on board must take that course. In a few days that expectation was answered, and he saw the ship sailing with a light wind near the place where he was stationed. Thereupon he thus addressed his companions:

"Gentlemen, if you are the men I take you to be, there is none of you, I imagine, but must have felt the extraordinary power of love, without which, as I judge by myself, there can be no valour or worth in mortal. If then you have ever been, or are now, in love, you will the more easily comprehend the nature of my design. It is love that makes me call upon you; and the object of it is in the ship before you. Besides that, there is store of riches, which, if you fight manfully, you may easily obtain. For my part I desire nothing but the lady, for whose sake I have taken up arms; everything else shall be yours. Let us go then boldly to the attack; fortune seems to favour our undertaking; they lie still, unable to get along for want of wind."

The prince had no occasion to make use of such an exhortation; for his people, eager for rapine, were ready enough to his orders. They declared their approbation then with a great shout, whilst the trumpets sounded, and they all armed themselves, and rowed towards the ship. In like manner, the other ship's crew, seeing two galleys come towards them, and that there was no possibility of escaping by flight, stood resolutely upon their defence. The prince being come sufficiently near, ordered that the masters of the vessel should come on board, unless they meant to fight. The Saracens, understanding who the assailants were, and what their demand was, told them, that it was contrary to treaty, to the royal faith plighted to them, in token of which they showed King Guiglielmo's glove; and they flatly declared, that they would neither surrender themselves, nor part with anything in the ship till they were forced to do so. The prince, now seeing the lady upon deck, whose charms exceeded all he had dreamed of them, replied, "Show your glove to your hawks when you fly them, it is of no use here; either deliver up the lady, or prepare for fight." Then they began slinging darts and stones on both sides; battering one another for a considerable time, to the great damage of both. At length, when the prince saw that little good was to be done that way, he took a small pinnace which he had brought with him from Sardinia, and setting it on fire, towed it with his two galleys alongside of the ship. The Saracens being now assured that they must either surrender or perish, had the lady brought from below, where she was all in tears; then they shouted to Gerbino, and murdered her before his face, whilst she begged in vain for mercy and help, and threw her into the sea, saying, "Take her, such as we now give her to thee: and such as thy breach of faith has deserved." He, seeing their cruelty, and not caring now what became of his own life, in spite of all the darts and stones that were thrown at him, came up close with the ship, and boarded her; and, as a famished lion, when he gets among a herd of cattle, gives a loose to his fury before he satisfies his hunger, so did the prince slay all that came in his way, whilst the fire getting a-head in the ship, he ordered the sailors to save what booty they were able for themselves, and returned to his galley little pleased with so dear a conquest. Afterwards, having recovered the lady's body out of the sea, and lamenting heartily over it, he returned to Sicily, and had it buried in Ustria, a little island over against Trapani, and then he came home the saddest man on earth.

The King of Tunis, upon hearing the news, sent ambassadors all in deep mourning to the King of Sicily, complaining of the breach of faith, and relating in what manner it had been done. Guiglielmo was much concerned at this, and seeing no way by which he could deny them the justice they demanded, he had his grandson seized, and notwithstanding the intercession of every one of his barons, ordered his head to be struck off in his presence; choosing rather to be without a grandson, than to be thought a king without honour. So miserable was the end of these two lovers within a few days of each other, without tasting the least fruit of their loves.

HOW THE *GALLEON OF VENICE* WON GLORY AT THE BATTLE OF PREVESA (1538)[1]

Jurien de la Gravière

AT LAST, on the 5th of September, Doria's squadron was sighted by the look-outs of the island. As yet the squadron consisted of no more than forty-nine galleys. Delayed by the calm and by the variable winds, the sailing ships only arrived off Corfu on the twenty-second. Since the discovery of the New World Spain had made considerable advances in her sailing craft, and Doria set great store by his unwieldy vessels, confident that a few volleys of their big guns were going to sweep the enemy from the seas. The Venetian fleet was made up of fourteen sailing ships, to which Doria had generously offered to add fourteen of his own. There would thus be thirty-six remaining to the Spanish fleet, and these thirty six were to be under the command of Franco Doria, the Generalissimo's nephew and lieutenant. The Venetian sailing ships were commanded by a very gallant gentleman—Alessandro Condalmiero, Captain of the *Galleon of Venice*. This galleon, bristling from stern to prow with guns, seemed, by its vast bulk, a floating citadel, a sort of *helepole*, behind which the flotilla of galleys could manœuvre in safety. Condalmiero's *Galleon* had, moreover, been well caulked the year before, and the fleet trusted as much to its sailing capacity as to its guns. She was known as a good sailer.

The Christian fleet, when once Grimani and Doria had joined, consisted of about two hundred sail, carrying, with the land forces, nearly sixty thousand men. Such a force has at all times been reckoned an imposing armament: William the Conqueror and Saint Louis crossed the sea with fewer men. As for Barbarossa, he had been unable to get together more than one hundred and twenty two ships, but, on the other hand, he came to meet the enemy accompanied by the most famous Corsairs of the day: Torghoud, known to Christians as Dragut, Tabach, Mourad, Guzeldje, Sinan, Sinan Reis.

The waters of Santa Maura, at an interval of fifteen hundred and sixty nine years, have witnessed the joining of the same battle, repeating in some sort its phases: once, on September 2nd, 31 B. C. under the name of Actium, between Octavius and Antony: a second time, between Andrea Doria and Barbarossa, on September 27th, 1538, under the name of Prevesa. On both occasions ships of a light draught easy to manœuvre, overcame the massive vessals rendered immovable by the state of the sea, irregular depths and the caprice of the wind.

On the 22nd of September, Charles V's admiral, reinforced by the

---

[1]Translated by Elizabeth D'Oyley, expressly for this collection, from *Doria et Barberousse*, by permission of the *Librairie Plon*.

last of his ships, ordered the galleys to take in water, wood and fresh
provisions: on the 25th, at the sound of the commander-in-chief's
trumpet, the fleet of two hundred sail weighed anchor, and sped southward before the wind. Grimani, with the galleys, led the van; Doria held
the centre; Vincenzo Cappello, with the Venetians, brought up the rear.
Formed in two squadrons of two columns, the sailing ships followed the
galleys in open order, the *Galleon* of Condalmiero, a veritable squadron
in herself, preceding them.

From the roadstead of Corfu to the entrance to the Gulf of Arta is a
distance of about fifty-five to sixty miles. That same evening the fleet
anchored off the Cape of Prevesa, the *Galleon*, the rallying point and
guide of the other ships, dropping her anchor in sixteen feet of water,
barely enough to keep her afloat.

A strong swell was running shorewards: all through the night ships
and galleys rolled side by side. On the morning of the 26th, the west
wind dropped, giving place to a light wind from the north.

During the night of the 26-27th of September, the Christian fleet
had made some thirty miles to the southward. A few hours before daybreak the wind freshened and entirely changed its direction. Doria put
in towards the Island of Santa Maura and cast anchor off the little isle
of Sessola. The *Galleon* and some of the other ships were sighted afar off,
making all sail in order to join the fleet. Barbarossa, before proceeding
upon a sortie the danger of which he well knew, called together his captains for the last time.

"Let each one of you," said he, to these old seafarers, many of whom
had been the companions of his first cruise, "Let each one of you get his
ship into line. I have only one order to give you: watch my manœuvres,
and by mine, regulate your own."

With fustas, brigantines, galliots, and galleys, the Ottoman fleet
counted a hundred and forty sail. According to their usual plan, they
were divided into three squadrons. The first rays of the rising sun revealed this crowd of vessels, this swiftly-moving host, with wide-spread
sails, to the look-outs of the Christian fleet. Doria meant to lure the fleet
of Barbarossa out: he did not expect to see his wishes so promptly
realized. The battleground to which the impatience of his enemy called
him, was not of a surety the one he sought. To join battle on a coast
where there was no harbourage, where the least storm was far more to
be feared than the guns of the enemy, had nothing to recommend it to
a leader endowed with any foresight.

It is easy to understand how Doria, with this idea in his mind, should
have hesitated for three hours before facing the foe. The weight of public
opinion, the warlike ardour of Vincenzo Cappello and Grimani at last
won him over. Unwillingly he gave orders to weigh anchor and to make
northward. He counted upon being reinforced *en route* by the *Galleon*
of Condalmiero and by the rest of the delayed ships; but the *Galleon*

had been suddenly becalmed when rounding Cape Zuana, an abrupt headland formed by a high hill. She was then about four miles from the coast, nine from the entrance to Prevesa which lay hard-by to the north-east, and ten from the anchorage of Sessola, to the south-south-west.

The enormous hulk, deserted by the wind, came to an abrupt stand-still, to remain immovable as a tower. Condalmiero at once despatched a light frigate which served him as long boat, asking Doria for orders and for aid.

"Begin the fight," was the admiral's reply, "Support shall be sent you quickly."

As soon as the Turkish ships were beyond the shoals, they deployed with a nicety worthy of their customary skill: they formed into a single line slightly concave, a line which either by design or accident took the form of a crescent. Sixteen great fustas commanded by Bragut led the van—the fusta being, like the galliot and the brigantine, a smaller type of galley. The left wing stood in to the coast as close as possible.

The end Barbarossa had in view is evident: he meant to surround the sailing ships thus becalmed before the galleys could bring them succour. Santa Marau, like Epirus, was at this time in the hands of the Turks, so that Barbarossa's fleet had a double advantage in fighting with the coast at its back. A number of Turkish galleys threw themselves between the *Galleon* and the land which, at this spot, a ship can sail so close to as almost to touch it. Beyond range of her guns, these galleys circled about Condalmiero's *Galleon*, and turning back as soon as they had passed her, came up to starboard. Were they going to sweep down on this lonely fortress and carry her by boarding?

The roll of drums, the shrill of war's clarions, mingled with the savage cries which, with the Turks, always precede the attack, for a moment made them fear so. Happily for Condalmiero, however, the galleys, impelled onward by swiftest oars, the white foam falling back before their prows, suddenly, and simultaneously, became motionless. A volley of guns, followed by a dense cloud of smoke, made clear the fact that they meant to engage at a distance. Beneath this storm of shot, the crew of the *Galleon* remained calm and unmoved. Condalmiero had given orders that not a single shot was to be fired until the Turks were within range of grape-shot. Complete silence reigned on board; the Turks might well have doubted it upon this enemy vessel, buoyed up by the remains of the swell, there existed a single gun.

Yet already the mainmast had been carried away by a ball, dragging down in its fall the topmast from which a moment ago had floated the Standard of St Mark. Encouraged by the fact that their fire was not returned, little by little the Turks drew nearer, until they could use their arquebuses. Condalmiero seized the opportunity. With voice and with gesture he gave the signal. He had ordered the gunners not to waste time in seeking to make a direct hit:

"Fire low!" said this gallant Venetian Captain. "The balls will ricochet and skim over the water."

The first broadside from the *Galleon* was terrible: a ball of one hundred and twenty pounds fired by the chief of the bombardiers himself, Francesco d'Arba, struck the prow of one of the galleys with such dire effect that the terrified crew rushed in a body to the poop in the hope of preventing the water pouring in astern. So huge and deep was the hole that the galley filled in a few minutes and went down as in a whirlpool. The rest of the Turkish vessels did not wait for a second volley: the order to withdraw had already been given and was obeyed with unusual promptness. When once the galleys, their poops driving back through the waves had got beyond range of the guns, the bombardiers made haste to reload. The *Galleon* was not to wait long for a fresh attack—but this time the attack would be more cautious and more methodical—an attack *en échelon*.

A squadron of fifteen to twenty galleys led the advance, delivered its fire, and withdrew as swiftly as it had come: a second squadron followed and repeated the manœuvre; and at once a third took its place. From one in the afternoon until sunset the roll of the guns continued, scarcely ceasing for a moment. Thirteen of the *Galleon's* crew were killed and forty wounded in this encounter. She was so full of splintered wood that to move about her decks seemed impossible. One ball passed from end to end of the vessel, poop-high, smashing on its way the stanchions of the forecastle, the maintop, and the mizzen yards; others carried away the binnacle, a case full of arrows, both the pumps, the longboat, the anchors, part of the windlass, penetrating to the storeroom and passing out beneath the water. Most of the balls were of powerful calibre. After the battle, thirty sixty-pounders were picked up in the bridge of the *Galleon* or from among her timbers. Twice fire broke out aboard: the ammunition cases which had been left between decks covered with wool, exploded and started the fire.

Covered with blood, wounded in the right side and in the face by the flying splinters, Captain Condalmiero never for a moment lost his imperturbable coolness. The shattered crew rallied each time to his call: the fire from the *Galleon* had never been surer or more deadly. Numbers of the Ottoman galleys, pierced by a thousand holes, only kept themselves afloat thanks to the activity of the carpenters: slung over the side in their rope seats, these gallant workmen, with nothing to shelter them, drove in the wooden plugs prepared beforehand to stop the leaks, with strong blows of their mallets.

At the hour when the sun plunges his red disk into the mists of the horizon, the whole of the Turkish fleet seemed gathered together to give the *coup de grâce* to this colossus which for six hours had borne the fire of the Ottomans without flinching. Condalmiero had foreseen this final effort. The *Galleon's* guns were loaded to the muzzle with ball and splintered stone; the gunners, linstock in hand, with strained ears, awaited in silence the signal from the bridge. Another few minutes and the fate of the Venetian ship would be decided.

Aboard his Captain's Galley which for this great day had been hung with scarlet banners, Barbarossa led in person the line of attack. Did his heart fail him in the very moment of casting the spear? Did he recoil as a reckless hunter recoils before the wounded lion he has tracked to its lair? Or did the approach of Doria cause the Captain-Pasha to change his mind in a moment? Historians have left the point doubtful. However it may be, in the very instant when the boarding of the *Galleon* seemed imminent, and hand to hand fighting inevitable, the Venetians saw the Captain's Galley haul off, and heading southward, bear down upon some of the less important ships—transport vessels carrying scarcely any artillery—which the caprice of the wind had separated from the main body of the fleet.

HOW IL SOLITARIO ESCAPED FROM CAPRERA[1]

Giuseppe Garibaldi

(1807–1882)

ON THE evening of the 14th October, 1867, three men left the farm of Caprera, and whilst they were threading their way along the path which leads to Fontanaccia (in water, trees, and plants the richest part of the island), a fourth man came out by the gate of the wooden fence which joins the little iron house to the main building, and followed the road leading to the Bay of Stagnatello. The characteristic dress of this last, as well as his southern physiognomy and his dark complexion, betrayed him to be a Sardinian. It was Giovanni, our sailor, the captain of the yacht for which the "Solitario" [Garibaldi himself] has to thank the generous English nation.

The three first individuals wore a suspicious garment, viz., a red shirt, which, in the case of Barberini and Frusciante, was only partly hidden by an overcoat, while their companion concealed his with a poncho, that well-known South-American cloak. Barberini was not favoured by nature from a physical point of view, but he was not the less a man of parts. Small and active, he had a lion's courage and an arm of iron in combination with a rather weak voice. As for Frusciante, he possessed the same qualities, and was besides strong and imposing in appearance. I dare not describe the man in the poncho: he is the object of the most miserable fears and most forcible measures of precaution of a Govern-

---

[1]Translated by Charles Edwardes. From Elphis Melena's *Garibaldi: Recollections of His Public and Private Life*. Reprinted by permission of Kegan Paul Trench, Trubner & Co., Ltd.

ment unworthy of the Italian nation, which allows to act cruelly in its name people whose lives ought to be ruled by a higher standard.

With a melancholy howl the sirocco whistled over the small but vigorous shrubs of Caprera, that volcanic daughter of the sea. Dark clouds, lashed by the storm, hid the Teggialone, which is the loftiest point of the island, and so high that if they had massed upon its topmost peaks they would have been changed into frozen snow-flakes.

Silently the three men pursued their way. When the undulating ground allowed them to see to a distance, they directed a searching gaze over the Bay of Stagnatello, where they descried three ships rising gracefully on the waves. The unarmed and unmanned yacht presented a striking contrast with the war-sloop, furnished with its threatening artillery, and the gun-boat filled with soldiers and sailors. The sun had set, and if the advancing night did not menace a complete storm, it at least indicated that strong kind of sirocco, which, saturated with an unhealthy humidity, and blowing from the marshes of Sardinia, is often fatal.

When the three fugitives had reached the fields of Fontanaccia, Frusciante said to the others, "I am going to leave you here, and turn to the left towards Arcaccio."

The two friends continued on their way. They opened and shut after them the four gates, through which one must pass to reach *Muro a secco*. This wall, made of nothing but pieces of rock undressed, divides the cultivated lands of Fontanaccia from the uncultivated lands, which extend to the seashore. Once there, the "Solitario" took off his poncho, and exchanged his white hat for a cap of his son Menotti's. He gave Barberini the hat and cloak he had just taken off, and then, having assured himself that there was no one on the other side of the wall, he mounted and cleared it with astonishing agility.

A remembrance of his adventurous youth gave him wings, and he felt himself twenty years younger. Besides, were not his sons and his comrades-in-arms already engaged in a struggle against the mercenaries of a monkish power? Could he keep quiet, and content himself with the pruning of his trees and the disgraceful existence of the "Moderati"?

When the "Solitario" had successfully cleared the wall, he said to Barberini: "It is still too light; let us stay here a moment, and smoke half a cigar."

Thereupon he drew from his pocket a match-box, a valued souvenir of the kind Lady Shaftesbury, lit a Cavour, and handed the match to his companion, who held a cigarette in readiness. This long and black Tuscan cigar, which costs about a half-penny, the "Solitario" generally cuts in two, and smokes but half at a time.

The shades of night soon began to fall; but in the east there appeared a feeble brightness, forerunner of the queen of night, then silently approaching.

"In three-quarters of an hour the moon will rise behind the moun-

tains!" remarked the "Solitario." "We must not delay any longer."
The two companions set out again, and proceeded to the harbour.
There Giovanni was at his post. Aided by Barberini he got the *becca-cino* afloat. The *beccacino* is our smallest kind of boat, used only for duck-shooting. It is so shallow that the one person who gets into it must lie down so as to make it go with a single oar.

The "Solitario" got into this at once, and stretched himself upon his poncho. When Giovanni had launched the canoe, and was assured that all was safe, he himself got into his *becca* a boat built exactly like the *beccacino*, only larger, and, humming an air, he rowed towards the yacht.

"Stop! who goes there?" shouted to the Sardinian the soldiers of the gunboat, who were thus degraded to the *rôle* of police subordinates. But Giovanni paused neither in his patriotic song nor his progress.

At length, at the third summons, he replied, "I am going on board." For though in the darkness he could hardly be hit by a musket-shot, yet, to a man unaccustomed to them, bullets are somewhat alarming; and Giovanni, though else brave and courageous enough, was such a man. Besides, he would certainly have been hit sooner or later if he had not answered.

The "Solitario," in the meantime making his *beccacino* go, now with the pole, and now (like the American canoes) with the paddle, proceeded by the shore of Paviano, between the harbour of Stagnatello and the headland of Arcaccio; and, in truth, the humming-bird (when he flies about the perfumed flowers of the torrid zone, and, like the busy bee, sucks their sweets) makes more noise than was made by the *beccacino* rapidly gliding, light as a feather, over the waves of the Tyrrhenian Sea.

When he reached the headland of Arcaccio, the "Solitario" distinguished among the huge boulders the form of his faithful Frusciante, fantastic in the twilight.

"Nothing new as far as the rocks of Arcaccio," cried Frusciante, speaking as softly as possible.

"Then I am safe!" replied the "Solitario," propelling his boat with increasing rapidity towards the steep cliffs, until he reached a certain point, whence he threw a piercing look over the little Isle of Rabbits, the most southern of the three islands which compose the harbour of Stagnatello. Then he promptly urged his barque in a north-westerly direction towards the high seas.

When the "Solitario" observed how strong the light of the moon had become, he rowed vigorously, and, helped by the sirocco, the little canoe passed the strait "Della Moneta" with a speed which would have excited the envy of a steamer.

By moonlight, and at a certain distance, every rock which rises above the sea level looks more or less like a boat, and as the commander of Rattazzi's squadron, to increase the number of the boats of the warships with which he was besieging Caprera, had seized all the small craft of Maddalena, it seemed as if the little archipelago "Della Moneta" swarmed with sloops and skiffs, all engaged solely in the hindering of *one* man from doing his duty.

As soon as the "Solitario" had reached the little island[1] situated near the north-east coast of Maddalena, he steered the *beccacino* into the labyrinth of reefs which guard the shore like a bulwark, and, from his hiding-place, he carefully scrutinized the coast-line, which was well illumined by the moon.

It is a fact that the majority of the *employés* of nearly all Governments, in the daytime, and when they are, or think they are, in the presence of their employers, display the utmost zeal in the fulfilment of their duties, but at night, when their superiors have made a good supper, and offered copious libations to Bacchus, or are resting or amusing themselves, these same *employés* allow their zeal to die away, and their sense of duty to become deadened in an extraordinary manner.

When the "Solitario" found himself in front of the island Dei Giardinelli, he had to choose between three different ways of reaching the ford which separates it from Maddalena. He could go by sea, rounding the island either to the south or the north, or he might land there at once, and cross it on foot. After mature reflection he chose the last alternative.

Was it due to the skill of the steersman of the *beccacino* or to the negligence of the sentinels, who were sleeping peacefully? I will not determine this point. Enough to say that the "Solitario" set foot on shore not only safe and sound, but without having been challenged by a single "Who goes there?" However, as soon as he had drawn up his canoe on to the shore, he saw that he was still confronted by several obstacles; for the island Dei Giardinelli, on which the flocks of Maddalena are sent to graze, is divided into a number of enclosures, all surrounded by high walls garnished with prickly boughs.

After making many detours and breakneck scrambles, the "Solitario" surmounted the last of these walls, and was preparing to climb a gate studded with pointed stones, when on the other side he thought he saw a file of sailors, lying close to the ground. It was an optical illusion, but he would not have been surprised had it been otherwise, for at Caprera he had learnt that several marines and soldiers had landed that day on the island Dei Giardinelli. The loss of time occasioned by this circumstance accounted to the "Solitario" for his not finding at their posts two of those friends who ought to have been waiting for him not far from the ford.

It was not until ten o'clock that, having looked well about him to assure himself that no inimical sentry was near, the "Solitario" prepared to cross the fordable place which separates the island Dei Giardinelli from Maddalena. But he had scarcely gone ten paces when he heard a "Who goes there?" from the ships on guard, followed by a number of gun shots.

---

[1] The island Dei Giardinelli.

None the less, however, he continued his bold walk through the waves. Soon he had left behind him the dangerous passage, and set foot upon the island of Maddalena. But he had still a tiresome piece of work before him, for his water-logged boots made it difficult to proceed over the unlevel ground.

When at length the sight of Mrs Collins's house told the "Solitario" that he was approaching hospitable shelter, he continued on his way with redoubled precautions, fearing lest the villa should be surrounded by spies; and then he selected a moment when the moon was hidden by a cloud, to venture to knock softly with his Scotch stick at the window looking south. Mrs Collins had believed in the star of the "Solitario." Warned of his project, she had listened for the sound of his footsteps with lively anxiety; thus, as soon as she heard the knock, she hurried to the door to welcome her former neighbour, and receive him with her own kindly smile.

"What a boon is such a reception as this, in a sure refuge after surmounting a storm of dangers! How peaceful and delicious!"

The "Solitario" felt very happy in his friend's abode, where he was the subject of the most loving and delicate attentions.

UGLY WEATHER[1]

Giovanni Verga

(1840–1922)

'NTONI went out to sea every blessed day, and had to row, tiring his back dreadfully. But when the sea was high, and fit to swallow them all at one gulp—them, the *Providenza*, and everything else—that boy had a heart as brave as the sea itself—"Malavoglia blood!" said his grandfather; and it was fine to see him at work in a storm, with the wind whistling through his hair, while the bark sprang over the big waves like a porpoise in the spring.

The *Providenza* often ventured out into blue water, old and patched though she was, after that little handful of fish which was hard to find, now that the sea was swept from side to side as if with brooms. Even on those dark days when the clouds hung low over Agnone, and the horizon to the east was full of black shadows, the sail of the *Providenza* might be seen like a white handkerchief against the leaden-coloured sea, and everybody said that Padron 'Ntoni's people went out to look for trouble, like the old woman with a lamp.

Padron 'Ntoni replied that he went out to look for bread; and when the corks disappeared one by one in the wide sea, gleaming green as

---

[1] From Mary A. Craig's translation of *I Malavoglia* (*The House by the Medlar Tree*). Reprinted by permission of Harper & Brothers.

grass, and the houses of Trezza looked like a little white spot, so far off were they, and there was nothing all around them but water, he began to talk to his grandsons in sheer pleasure. La Longa and the others would come down to the beach to meet them on the shore as soon as they saw the sail rounding the Fariglione; and when they too had been to look at the fish flashing through the nets, and looking as if the bottom of the boat were full of molten silver; and Padron 'Ntoni replied before any one had asked, "Yes, a quintal or a quintal twenty-five" (generally right, even to an ounce); and then they'd sit talking about it all the evening, while the women pounded salt in the wooden mortars; and when they counted the little barrels one by one, and Uncle Crucifix came in to see how they had got on, to make his offer, so, with his eyes shut; and Goosefoot came, too, screaming and scolding about the right price, and the just price, and so on; then they didn't mind his screaming, because, after all, it was a pity to quarrel with old friends; and then La Longa would go on counting out sou by sou the money which Goosefoot had brought in his handkerchief, saying, "These are for the house; these are for the every-day expenses," and so on. Mena would help, too, to pound the salt and to count the barrels, and she should get back her blue jacket and her coral necklace that had been pawned to Uncle Crucifix; and the women could go back to their own church again, for if any young man happened to look after Mena, her dowry was getting ready.

"For my part," said 'Ntoni, rowing slowly, slowly round and round, so that the current should not drive him out of the circle of the net, while the old man pondered silently over all these things, "for my part, all I wish is that hussy Barbara may be left to gnaw her elbows when we have got back our own again, and may live to repent shutting the door in my face."

"In the storm one knows the good pilot," said the old man. "When we are once more what we have always been, every one will bear a smooth face for us, and will open their doors to us once more."

"There were two who did not shut their doors," said Alessio, "Nunziata and our cousin Anna."

"In prison, in poverty and in sickness one finds one's friends; for that may the Lord help them, too, and all the mouths they have to feed!"

"When Nunziata goes out on the downs to gather wood, or when the rolls of linen are too heavy for her, I go and help her too, poor little thing," said Alessio.

"Come and help now to pull in this side, for this time Saint Francis has really sent us the gift of God!" And the boy pulled and puffed, with his feet braced against the side of the boat, so that one would have thought he was doing it all himself.

Meanwhile 'Ntoni lay stretched on the deck singing to himself, with his hands under his head, watching the white gulls flying against the blue sky, which had no end, it rose so pure and so high, and the *Providenza* rushed on the green waves rolling in from farther than the eye could see.

"What is the reason," said Alessio, "that the sea is sometimes blue and sometimes green and then white, then again black as the sand of the beach, and is never all one colour, as water should be?"

"It is the will of God," replied the grandfather, "so the mariner can tell when he may safely put out to sea, and when it is best to stay on shore."

"Those gulls have a fine time of it, flying in the air; they need not fear the waves when the wind is high."

"But they have nothing to eat, either, poor beasts."

"So every one has need of good weather, like Nunziata, who can't go to the fountain when it rains," concluded Alessio.

"Neither good nor bad weather lasts forever," observed the old man.

But when bad weather came, and the mistral blew, and the corks went dancing on the water all day long as if the devil were playing the violin for them, or if the sea was white as milk, or bubbling up as if it were boiling, and the rain came pouring down upon them until evening, so that no wraps were proof against it, and the sea went frying all about them like oil in the pan, then it was another pair of shoes—and 'Ntoni was in no humour for singing, with his hood down to his nose, bailing out the *Providenza*, that filled faster than he could clear out the water, and the grandpapa went on repeating, "White sea, sirocco there'll be!" or "Curly sea, fresh wind!" as if he had come there only to learn proverbs; and with these blessed proverbs, too, he'd stand in the evening at the window looking out for the weather, with his nose in the air, and say, "When the moon is red it means wind; when it is clear, fine weather; when it is pale it means rain."

"If you know it is going to rain," said 'Ntoni, one day, "why do we go out, while we might stay in bed an hour or two longer?"

"'Water from the sky, sardines in the net,'" answered the old man.

Later on 'Ntoni began to curse and swear, with the water half up to his knees.

"This evening," said his grandfather, "Maruzza will have a good fire ready for us, and we shall soon be quite dry."

And at dusk when the *Providenza*, with her hull full of the gifts of God, turned towards home, with her sail puffing out like Donna Rosolina's best petticoat, and the lights of the village came twinkling one by one from behind the dark rocks as if they were beckoning to each other, Padron 'Ntoni showed his boys the bright fire which burned in La Longa's kitchen at the bottom of the tiny court in the narrow black street; for the wall was low, and from the sea the whole house was visible, with the tiles built into a shed for the hens, and the oven on the other side of the door.

"Don't you see what a blaze La Longa has got up for us?" said he, in high spirits; and La Longa was waiting for them, with the baskets ready. When they were brought back empty, there wasn't much talking; but instead, if there were not enough, and Alessio had to run up to the house for more, the grandfather would put his hands to his mouth and shout, "Mena! Oh, Mena!" And Mena knew well what it meant, and they all came down in procession—she, Lia, and Nunziata, too, with all her chicks behind her; then there was great joy, and nobody minded cold or rain, and before the blazing fire they sat talking of the gifts of God which Saint Francis had sent them, and of what they would do with the money.

But in this desperate game, men's lives are risked for a few pounds of fish; and once the Malavoglia were within a hair's-breadth of losing theirs all at once, as Bastianazzo had, for the sake of gain, when they were off Agnone as the day drew to a close, and the sky was so dark that they could not even see Etna, and the winds blew and swept up the waves so close about the boat that it seemed as if they had voices and could speak.

"Ugly weather," said Padron 'Ntoni. "The wind turns like a silly wench's head, and the face of the sea looks like Goosefoot's when he is hatching some hateful trick."

The sea was as black as the beach, though the sun had not yet gone down, and every now and then it hissed and seethed like a pot.

"Now the gulls have all gone to sleep," said Alessio.

"By this time they ought to have lighted the beacon at Catania," said 'Ntoni, "but I can't see it."

"Keep the rudder always north-east," ordered the grandfather, "in half an hour it will be darker than an oven."

"On such evenings as this it is better to be at Santuzza's tavern."

"Or asleep in your bed, eh?" said the old man; "then you should be a clerk, like Don Silvestro."

The poor old fellow had been groaning all day with pain. "The weather is going to change," he said, "I feel it in my bones."

All of a sudden it grew so black that one couldn't even see to swear. Only the waves, as they rolled past the *Providenza*, shone like grinning teeth ready to devour her; and no one dared to speak a word in presence of the sea, that moaned over all its waste of waters.

"I've an idea," said 'Ntoni, suddenly, "that we had better give the fish we've caught to-day to the devil."

"Silence!" said his grandfather; and the stern voice out of that darkness made him shrink together like a leaf on the bench where he sat.

They heard the wind whistle in the sails of the *Providenza* and the ropes ring like the strings of a guitar. Suddenly the wind began to scream like the steam-engine when the train comes out from the tunnel in the mountain above Trezza, and there came a great wave from nobody knew where, and the *Providenza* rattled like a sack of nuts, and sprang up into the air and then rolled over.

"Down with the sail—down!" cried Padron 'Ntoni. "Cut away, cut away!"

'Ntoni, with the knife in his mouth, scrambled like a cat out on the yard, and standing on the very end to balance himself, hung over the howling waves that leaped up to swallow him.

"Hold on, hold on!" cried the old man to him, through all the thunder of the waves that strove to tear him down, and tossed about the *Providenza* and all that was inside her, and flung the boat on her side, so that the water was up to their knees. "Cut away, cut away!" called out the grandfather again.

"Sacrament!" exclaimed 'Ntoni; "and what shall we do without the sail, then?"

"Stop swearing; we are in the hands of God now."

Alessio, who was grasping the rudder with all his force, heard what his grandfather said, and began to scream, "Mamma, mamma, mamma!"

"Hush!" cried his brother, as well as he could for the knife in his teeth. "Hush, or I'll give you a kick."

"Make the holy sign, and be quiet," echoed the grandfather so that the boy dared not make another sound.

Suddenly the sail fell all at once in a heap, and 'Ntoni drew it in, furling it light, quick as a flash.

"You know your trade well, as your father did before you," said his grandfather. "You, too, are a Malavoglia."

The boat righted and gave one leap, then began to leap about again among the waves.

"This way the rudder, this way; now it wants a strong arm," said Padron 'Ntoni; and though the boy, too, clung to it like a cat, the boat still sprang about, and there came great waves sweeping over it that drove them against the helm, with force enough nearly to knock the breath out of them both.

"The oars!" cried 'Ntoni; "Pull hard, Alessio; you're strong enough when it comes to eating; just now the oars are worth more than the helm."

The boat creaked and groaned with the strain of the oars pulled by those strong young arms; the boy, standing with his feet braced against the deck, put all his soul into his oar as well as his brother.

"Hold hard!" cried the old man, who could hardly be heard at the other side of the boat, over the roaring of the wind and the waves. "Hold on, Alessio!"

"Yes, grandfather, I do," replied the boy.

"Are you afraid?" asked 'Ntoni.

"No, he's not," answered his grandfather for him; "but we must commend ourselves to God."

"Holy devil!" exclaimed 'Ntoni. "Here one ought to have arms of iron, like the steam-engine. The sea is getting the best of it."

The grandfather was silent, listening to the blast.

"Mamma must by this time have come to the shore to watch for us."

"Don't talk about Mamma now," said the old man; "it is better not to think about her."

"Where are we now?" asked 'Ntoni after some time, hardly able to speak for fatigue.

"In God's hands," answered the grandfather.

"Then let me cry!" exclaimed Alessio, who could bear it no longer; and he began to scream aloud and to call for his mother at the top of his voice, in the midst of the noise of the wind and of the sea, and neither of them had the heart to scold him.

"It's all very well your howling, but nobody can hear you, and you had best be still," said his brother at last, in a voice so changed and strange that he hardly knew it himself. "Now hush!" he went on; "it is best for you and best for us."

"The sail!" ordered Padron 'Ntoni. "Put her head to the wind, and then leave it in the hands of God."

The wind hindered them terribly, but at last they got the sail set, and the *Providenza* began to dance over the crests of the waves, leaning to one side like a wounded bird.

The Malavoglia kept close together on one side, clinging to the rail. At that moment no one spoke, for when the sea speaks in that tone no one else dares to utter a word.

Only Padron 'Ntoni said, "Over there they are saying the rosary for us."

And no one spoke again, and they flew along through the wild tempest and the night, that had come on as black as pitch.

"The light on the mole!" cried 'Ntoni; "do you see it?"

"To the right!" shouted Padron 'Ntoni; "to the right! It is not the light on the mole. We are driving on shore! Furl, furl!"

"I can't," cried 'Ntoni; "the rope's too wet." His voice was hardly to be heard through the storm, so tired he was. "The knife, the knife! Quick, Alessio!"

"Cut away, cut away!"

At that moment a crash was heard; the *Providenza* righted suddenly, like a still spring let loose, and they were within one of being flung into the sea; the spar with the sail fell across the deck, snapped like a straw. They heard a voice which cried out as if some one were hurt to death.

"Who is it? Who called out?" demanded 'Ntoni, aiding himself with his teeth and the knife to clear away the rigging of the sail, which had fallen with the mast across the deck, and covered everything. Suddenly a blast of wind took up the sail and swept it whistling away into the night. Then the brothers were able to disengage the wreck of the mast, and to fling it into the sea. The boat rose up, but Padron 'Ntoni did not rise, nor did he answer when 'Ntoni called to him.

THE END[1]

Guido Milanesi

(1875–   )

I

We have strowed our best to the weed's unrest,
To the shark, and the sheering gull . . .

RUDYARD KIPLING, *The Seven Seas*

THERE he stood, in full dress, and wearing all his decorations, leaning against the doorway of the Admiral's Office, surrounded by a small group of comrades who had come up one after the other to shake him by the hand. He lingered over the greetings and farewells, and had a smile for every one, but there was something weary and remote about his smile, and his gaze wandered absently from the great gates of the Arsenal to the tablet opposite, on which was written in large black letters "Admiral's Office." But all these familiar objects were shadowy and confused: they seemed to flicker before his eyes, and then to fade in a sudden darkness which disturbed and distressed him. . . .

"Well, good-bye! The gig's waiting, and I must get back aboard," said a Captain, embracing him. "Don't forget us," he added, and walked off hastily to the Arsenal gates.

He gazed after the retreating figure in silence, and only answered with a sad nod.

Meanwhile from within they heard an electric bell, rung twice.

"That's the Admiral summoning me," said another. "Good-bye, Commander." And he went straight off to the office.

At last, after numerous other farewells, interspersed with good advice, and old jokes which lighted up the weather-beaten faces with flashes of boyish fun, he found himself alone.

Then he pulled himself together, hastily readjusted his cap, and, erect and calm, turned his steps resolutely towards the gate and passed the guards and *carabinieri* who lined up to salute him.

"Free! Free!" he said to himself, as he crossed the iron bridge which separates the Arsenal from the city, and he forced himself to repeat the word again, for it seemed suddenly to have lost its ordinary meaning, and to have become an empty sound.

[1] Translated by Althea M. Wollaston from *Thalatta*. By permission of the Casa Editrice Alberto Stock.

Like a flash there passed before him the countless times he had crossed the bridge during his long service: when he had to present himself to the Admiral before embarking: on his return from a campaign; on his daily visits to the workshops, when he was serving at the Arsenal: in answer to innumerable chance calls: to receive orders: on a thousand other occasions when, in constant fear of being late, he had hurried across the iron footway. He saw himself buttoned up to the chin in his oilskins, in torrents of rain when it was quite difficult to walk on the wet iron, especially where it was worn and polished by the feet of thousands of workmen crossing it daily. Then he had a vision of the dog-days, himself in white from head to foot, the iron scorching now, almost red-hot, the sound of his footsteps drowned by the shouting of the cicalas in the great trees of the avenue. From his youth till now, at every stage of his career, he saw himself crossing the bridge, and realized that there, during the strain of those long years, his steps had lost their speed and spring.

Only yesterday he had crossed it again, after settling his accounts with the authorities for the last time. He had then learnt the exact figure at which they valued his life's work, and the amount of cash which represented all the physical and mental energy of his best years. The very essence and marrow of his being had passed into the wide waters and the salt breezes, in the service of his country, and under the stern strain of responsibility. He now received the reward of his devotion.

The money was enough to ensure him rest from his labours, and the enjoyment of his little estate on the Adriatic. He had managed to buy this with his savings, and for years the building of his villa had been one of his chief pleasures, so yesterday, with this in mind, he had crossed the bridge with buoyant step, and hopeful heart, s..ying to himself: "To-morrow." But to-day, only twenty-four hours later, an eternity seemed to have gone by;—a vast span of time, in which the most insignificant events seemed of immense importance, and in which he seemed to have lost all sense of proportion.

From a dark background of confused memories, now one, now another emerged: stood out and took shape, sharply outlined by the ever-recurring words: "The last—" "Never again—" "No more of that job!" "That's over too!"

While all this was passing through his mind, he was vaguely aware that, as they saluted him, both officers and men showed some surprise at seeing a Captain in full dress in the morning without any notification in the Order of the Day, and he returned the salute mechanically and out of sheer force of habit, conscious of a sudden incongruity between himself and his uniform. Indeed, he almost felt as if he were wearing a strange dress to which he had no right, and it seemed to hang about him like a weight. The gold braid and the decorations certainly did not belong to him, but to some Captain who had vanished when his superannuation took effect yesterday. He was merely the man (Heaven alone knew why!)

charged to wear the uniform which was to be packed up and put away. A feeling of acute discomfort, almost of alarm, came over him, a feeling which he instinctively and instantly resisted by a more rigid and martial bearing and a swifter step.

But this self-control cost him such an effort that he arrived at his hotel exhausted and bathed in sweat. He scarcely knew how he replied to the greeting of his servant who was on the look-out for him, and of his little dog (a Pekinese bought the year before at Tientsin—when he was in command of the *Stromboli*) who rushed to meet him, jumping up, pawing his uniform and spoiling the gold braid on his trousers.

. . . .

Once again he saw the *Stromboli:* he saw her from the window of his compartment as the train wound its way along between Migliarina and Val di Lochi: he suddenly recognized her masts and funnels in the midst of the forest of ships lying in Spezia harbour. His first glance was vague and uncomprehending, but presently he looked more carefully, and deliberately paused to recognize the chart house which he had had built on the bridge, the wireless aerial put up by his instructions, and the pennant, which, at his orders, had been hoisted at the masthead; but this he did not succeed in making out, and it suddenly struck him that no sooner had he left the ship than some one had had it removed. He felt as if his very soul had been pierced: he was cut to the quick. This gave the clearest reflection of his disappearance, of his annihilation, the final proof of the utter and complete end of his career. . . .

Then he shut his eyes and tried to sleep, humming to himself to the accompaniment of the monotonous rhythm of the train. He only succeeded in concentrating his thoughts more and more upon himself, and his weary brain reconstructed an endless series of pictures of life on board, against an unchanging background of blue sea. As if photographed on his retina, he saw, most clearly of all, the last time he handled the *Stromboli* in bringing her inside the breakwater at Spezia. Then the familiar sounds of the ship re-echoed in his ears, and the rhythmical jolt of the train became the thud of the propeller. Why were they going on stoking the furnaces without his orders?

Too much smoke from the funnels!

Why so much shouting on board? Names of Stations? No! Of course not! What the deuce did the Second-in-Command mean by allowing such a noise? Perfectly inexplicable how they dared to vary the speed of the engines like that! What about his instructions in the Chiesuola Journal? Did no one read them any more? Bad discipline somewhere! Where then? On his ship? No, not there! That at any rate he knew to be out of the question! . . . And, after all, there were the engines working steadily again . . . and at last there was calm and silence, at last he could really sleep.

His breathing grew quiet, his limbs relaxed, and he fell into a deep and heavy slumber.

II

In the stifling heat of a summer afternoon he reached his country house, accompanied by his servant and his Pekinese dog, and followed at a respectful distance by a rough-looking fellow who seemed to be even more in awe of the severe aspect of the master than fascinated by the sailor and his bright blue collar.

Meanwhile, the captain, with head still bent, with hardly a glance at the rooms of which he had dreamt during so many weary hours at sea, entered the house, overcome by a sudden depression at the thought that here, in this very house, in one or other of these rooms, he must one day die.

His thoughts, however, speedily began to wander far afield, yielding to the insistent claim of old days and other surroundings. He was surprised to find the rooms so high and the windows so wide. He found the walls and shutters too highly coloured, and altogether, the place struck him as too lavish. It seemed pointless and tiresome, and he felt vaguely irritated by it all.

Finally he established himself in one of the rooms, less distasteful to him than the rest by reason of the faint familiar smell of varnish which still hung about it. Here he sat and watched his servant dealing with his chests, and silently unpacking possessions collected in all parts of the world, strange metals and brilliant coloured silks, about which the tang of the sea still lingered.

He followed the familiar process—repeated with every change of ship, and found some colace in remembering the exact position which every object had occupied on board.

"Commander," said the sailor suddenly, "where shall we put the carpet which used to lie under the 57 cm. gun?"

"In my bedroom."

"And the one from the door?"

"There too."

"And the Mogador rugs which you liked beside your bunk?"

"Beside my bed."

"All there?"

"All there."

"As on board. Everything under his eye," thought his servant.

And so he re-created around him the familiar atmosphere, exotic, and somewhat oriental, the atmosphere of cabins which have been in every part of the world.

Meanwhile, on the road outside stood a handful of villagers, peering through the shrubs on the other side of the wall which enclosed his little property. They just saw the sailor at work, passing and repassing the wide open window: they saw, too, a severe-looking elderly man who appeared for a moment and cast an indifferent glance in their direction.

"Who is it that's come to live here?" was the question they were asking each other.

"A commander, they say."

"Rubbish! A commander! Not a bit of it! He's an admiral: the postman told me so this morning."

The man at the window heard the words, and a strange ironical smile came over his face: his mouth hardened into a bitter line, and with a hasty movement he pulled the shutters to, and withdrew from the window.

III

His sailor servant was also on the retired list, and had, in fact, finished his service at the end of the previous year, on the *Stromboli*, but in accordance with the regulations, had had to stay on board until the end of the campaign. Then he had followed his captain ashore, and had come with him to the home of his choice, without ever, for a moment, considering any other possible course.

When the captain with his fine sense of honour, had asked him what his plans were, he answered: "Yours, sir." And so he stayed: this was his duty, and there was no more to be said.

In an empty room upstairs, he slung his hammock, now perfectly shapeless thanks to frequent and furious scrubbing on deck. He laid out his clothes with extreme care, on a towel spread on the floor, as if he were putting them out for the regular Saturday airing. He left his uniform carefully folded and sprinkled with naphthaline at the bottom of his empty oilcloth bag, and finally put on his ordinary clothes, still creased from lying for four years put away in the family wardrobe in the little house in Sicily: but a hat he simply could not abide, so he went on wearing his service cap with black ribbon, bearing the name *Stromboli* in gold letters.

IV

A few hundred yards from the house, huddled between the hills and the shore, lay a fishing village. Every morning it sent out to sea its fleet of boats with their gay painted sails, and every evening, called them home again: then, from some point on the horizon below which they had been hidden all day, they slowly reappeared. The whole life of the village was summed up in this daily departure and return. By day the streets were deserted: the only sounds, the monotonous singing of the women as they worked at the nets hanging along the lower walls of the houses, and the cries of the half-naked children left alone in the great arched doorways. But, after sunset, when the low light fell across the village from the western hills, smoke rose from all the house-tops in honour of the returning men-folk, and a rhythmic cry, half-chant, half-shout, rose from the shore as they dragged the boats up, over the sand. The streets were full of life and movement while the great cases of fish were carried through the village, from the shore to the station, and the whole population turned out to share in the only event of the day.

This happened without fail every evening. Every evening, too, without fail there appeared on the road between the sea and the railway, the solitary figure of the old officer, going home after a walk on the shore, and with him his faithful companion, the little Pekinese. By this time the people had grown accustomed to see him appear thus, like a sad ghost, and then disappear beyond the bridge. For a moment, as he crossed it, his erect figure stood out against the sky, then he descended the steep slope on the further side, and vanished utterly, just as the evening bells began to ring, and the sea, too, faded from sight.

There was plenty of talk about "The Admiral" in the evening down at the Pharmacy on the Piazza, and not a little gossip and scandal. A somewhat bitter note characterized the remarks about the old man, chiefly because the villagers vaguely resented his craze for holding aloof from the narrow life and petty affairs of his neighbours. They seemed to be really annoyed with him for not properly appreciating his position as a stranger and a guest in their midst.

"Too high and mighty, too high and mighty!" reiterated the Mayor, a Socialist who managed the "Fishermen's Co-operative," and made ten per cent out of it. Moreover there were sound reasons for their dissatisfaction! Certainly there were! The recluse had obstinately refused to take into his service two village girls who had gone up to his house and asked for the place. This was the grievance of the local tobacconist, the uncle of one of them.

"Yes, quite true, but that's not all!" repeated the Mayor. "Although the second floor of his villa is empty, he refused to let it to a family who wanted to spend the summer here, and of course, it's the village, and all of us who are the losers. What I say is, that he ought to have more consideration for us."

Besides all this, there was indeed another reason, but the Mayor carefully refrained from alluding to it. The fact was that the fishermen had by degrees got into the habit of taking off their caps to "The Admiral" as he passed: moreover, it happened that two old sailors who had served under him in the Navy recognized him, and one day, cap in hand, had approached him and greeted him with the greatest deference and pleasure. Then, for once forgetting his customary reserve, he got them to go home with him and walked off between them, a hand on the shoulder of each. Once at the villa, he took them upstairs and kept them for a long talk, and when he said good-bye at the garden gate, made them promise to come and see him again.

"Well, we have got a strange fellow come to live here!" said the village gossips, when they heard what had happened.

"Who knows what reason brought him to this particular place?"

V

And what was the reason?

The story goes back to 1865, the year before the war with Austria. He often recalled a number of rather confused pictures of those days, and they always brought a smile to his lips. They came back to him in the long, lonely hours when he stood at the window, leaning on his elbows, gazing out beyond the horizon towards the Dalmatian coast straight across the Adriatic.

In those days he was in the Coastguards: only eighteen, no more than a boy.

When he was on his first ship the *Vedetta*, at Ancona, he met a little Austrian girl, travelling in Italy with an old aunt who seemed to be there for the express purpose of encouraging all her niece's whims and fancies.

"Hanzy"—"Hanzy Salter." The name was hardly visible now on the corner of an old photograph which had travelled all over the world with him and now stood on the table beside his bed.

She came from Czernowitz: a graceful little figure with a big hat, and her fair hair hanging over her shoulders in long plaits. She looked for all the world like a Dresden china figure suddenly come to life, and, bored at being alone, stepping down from her pedestal and smiling her china smile, she set off to find a companion figure for her group.

And when the lovely Dresden figure at last found the little "Page" of her dreams, she clung to him closely and secured him firmly at her side. The charming pair arranged themselves gracefully beneath a fine gilded clock, which all too soon began to strike the happy hours, and to tick away the blissful moments.

Thus passed the winter of '65, and the early months of '66, the fatal year, were upon them!

How often, alone, free and happy, had they roamed together along the coast, and explored its hamlets, making the most of the liberty granted by the obliging aunt who, herself, stayed in Ancona, writing letters or looking after her rheumatism. The last of these happy excursions had been to this very fishing village, which had attracted them by its wonderful peace and quiet, and where the old hostess of the little restaurant had called them "betrothed."

Quite soon after this the *Vedetta* left Ancona, recalled to the Squadron at Taranto, for the war.

The porcelain group, cruelly dashed to the ground, was shattered, and the clock stopped.

His grief was overwhelming, and came upon him like a thunderbolt.

Suddenly, one day, he received a long letter from Austria, the letter of a despairing child, stunned by the first cruel blow of the lash of life. But he did not answer it: to write to an enemy of his country during the war, was unthinkable, impossible:—and later, when peace was signed; the mere idea struck him as outrageous. . . .

In the meantime, one day in Vienna, it happened that a Magyar nobleman came across our little Dresden figure, still weeping, and took pity on her. The upshot was that not long afterwards she meekly followed him to Hungary and made no serious protest when he offered to make her the mistress of several huge feudal estates, of which one, his favourite summer residence, was in Dalmatia, just opposite to the fishing village to the south of Ancona.

Long years after this, the Italian officer, already an elderly man, saw in a newspaper, an advertisement of the sale of a piece of land, not far from the village. He bought it; bought it to satisfy a fancy to end his life where it had really begun, and because the little cemetery on the hill, facing the sea, and looking towards the Dalmatian coast, had always remained in his memory as a picture of the most utter peace, as the place for real rest for him, when at last the sea had taken toll of all his strength, and cast up his worn-out body on the shore.

Beyond this romantic sentiment, however, there was a deeper reason; his fine spirit preferred the dignity of solitude to the crowd and confusion of the city where he would have dragged himself wearily from *café* to *café*, to escape the wretched hours spent in furnished rooms or in hotels, and to save his tortured mind from still greater misery.

VI

This step was, in fact, to condemn him to spend the rest of his life in memories and regrets, in silence, and in a deadly monotony.

Must he then resign himself to endless empty months devoid of interest, with no object in life, and no work? Was it inevitable that henceforth he must accept the bitter fact that he was useless, and that all that made life worth living was over?

No! This was impossible. He could not accept it. . . . A letter from a brother officer hardly junior to himself, telling him that he had been given the command of a ship just put in commission; notices in the newspapers of promotion to the rank of Admiral of Captains only just below him in the Navy List, roused his gloomy soul to fierce passion, and nearly broke his heart. For the hundredth time, and with a bitter laugh, he compared these favoured mortals with himself. Before him on his writing table, lay the big portfolio of official correspondence which contained the story of his distinguished career. Papers, now yellow with age, full of praise and congratulations and thanks from ambassadors and admirals and Foreign Ministers, who wrote to him as an equal: letters couched in the most flattering terms, written in many languages, and on paper bearing most impressive coats-of-arms. Here, too, were souvenirs of royal receptions, and banquets in his honour in all parts of the world, where he had tasted the food and drunk the beverages of every race, from the most exquisite European cooking to the humble dishes of Java, from the "puddings" of the English to fish-jam, and goose cooked in oil; from portwine to vodka and fermented honey.

On those occasions he proceeded to the place of entertainment with great ceremony, and an escort of officers, crowds thronging round the carriage to see him pass, and not infrequently to cheer him: in many countries, the streets along which he drove, had been lined with troops who presented arms as he passed.

There were hundreds more letters: from authorities of all sorts, diplomatic and consular, military and religious, from "Consortia," associations, clubs and commercial institutions; from obscure compatriots in all sorts of countries, from emigrants and from people of every condition and rank: from the highest to the humblest. In the files, too, there were the rough drafts of his replies, scribbled in pencil, to be handed over to his secretary. He had only to glance at the first line of any of them, to recall the whole transaction, so familiar were all these events, and so much attention had he devoted to them.

He lingered with special satisfaction over some of these documents. On one there was a note in the vigorous handwriting of those days. "Je ne vous reconnais pas, Monsieur le Gouverneur, le droit de m'intérroger. . . ."

He had the most lively recollection of this episode. It was a squabble he had had in a distant colony over the absurd airs of an official, and he had written to remonstrate in this strain, and taken the risk of paying dearly for it. He smiled when he remembered the excuses which had speedily followed, and which he had accepted somewhat haughtily!

Another reply began—"We are not accustomed to refuse. . . ." and was addressed to the Commander of the *Indiana*, U. S. A. This officer had challenged the Italian sailors to a *regatta* of six thousand yards, at Shang Hai, proposing that both sides should put down a very large sum; and the Italians had beaten the American sailors by a good thousand yards, and won the money!

On a particularly bulky envelope he had noted "Warlike operations on the coast of Zanzibar. R. N. *Volturno.*" On another "Blockade of Candia. R. N. *Aretusa.*"

There were also voluminous manuscripts on all sorts of subjects: complicated studies of electrical machines, of new methods in gunnery, of hydrographic operations and tactical plans.

All these old papers constituted, so to speak, a *résumé* of his life's work —a life of energy and industry, of devotion to duty, a life animated by a fine sense of honour and inspired by a spirit of self-sacrifice. And the end of all this was the dreary existence of the old recluse whose name was never mentioned now, except perhaps by the Mayor and his friends in a village pharmacy!

Others, a little junior to himself had supplanted his name in the Navy List, and were now Admirals, solely by virtue of being those few months younger than he: for no other reason at all.

These gloomy reflections often ended in sudden gusts of passion which left him exhausted in body and mind. Then, without calling his servant, he used to get out one of the big bottles of "Canadian whiskey," of which, in old days at sea, he used now and then to drink a few drops to warm himself after a night on the bridge. Now, however, he took it hoping to distract himself and dull these sad memories, thankful for the drowsiness which calmed his nerves, and careless of the fever which heated his blood.

After such a night, his servant would find him with teeth and hands clenched, and the table on which his head had fallen, shaken by his heavy, spasmodic breathing, the old papers scattered around him in confusion.

VII

Thus began a strange old age spent in utter isolation.

He had moments of something like spiritual annihilation, when the whole world was abhorrent to him, and man, his enemy. At such moments, in the stifling heat of July and August, all the shutters of the little house remained closed, and it was as inscrutable, and unapproachable as its master. The garden was overgrown with weeds, and the leaves of plants and shrubs were grey with dust. Death seemed already to have visited it, and the desolation was terrible.

But, in winter, when the north wind lashed the shore and tore up the trees on the hills, when the fishing boats could not put out to sea, and remained drawn up on the sand, then he walked in the teeth of the gale, stooping to meet the rain, and striding along the shore, where the waves beat, and broke. He would spend hours staring at the raging waters, calmly letting himself be battered by the fury of wind and wave, as if impelled by the urgent need of proving to himself that he could still struggle, that he was still "captain of his soul," and that, as of old he had steered his ship through dangerous seas, so now he could weather the storms of misfortune.

At last, a violent shiver of cold would shake his frame and force him to leave the shore. Then he used to turn homewards, letting himself be carried along by the force of the wind, glad of his aching limbs and weary body, proud of asking help and service from none, feeling as he used to feel when he sought his cabin alone after a rough night spent on the bridge. But now, after such an exhausting day, his eyes were hollow, and his face the livid colour which had shocked him twenty-five years ago, in the Colonial Hospital at Gibraltar, when he first got up and saw himself after months of typhoid. Round his mouth and on his temples were heavy lines, traced in skin and tissue powerless now to resist the cruel hand of age. Then there came over him a sudden terror at finding himself old, hopelessly old. He became conscious that, after thirty-eight years at sea, he was gradually breaking up both mentally and physically, and he was overcome by a feeling of vague terror, when there passed through his mind strange horrible visions from which he strove to free his thoughts and turn his eyes.

VIII

A family?

Certainly. Even he had possessed a family. Witness some ancient portraits which had accompanied him on all his wanderings. But at last they seemed to have lost all power of calling up any clear memories. One might almost imagine that so much had he gazed at them that the likeness had lost all vitality, and that having long since delivered their message, they had grown dumb, and were now but yellow bits of cardboard in their shabby frames.

From the time of his childhood, he had only known his home in short spells of leave, separated by long months and years at sea. Even letters, after following him in vain to many ports, used finally to reach him at the other end of the world, in envelopes covered with postmarks and addresses and corrections of addresses, only to give him news of things which had happened many months before, and of events which had no connection whatever with the actual moment.

One day, at Buenos Aires, he learnt that he was an orphan, his parents having died within a few days of each other. He went home, but by that time it seemed an old story, and his brother was fighting the lawyers over the will. He was soon at sea again, and then he was pursued for months by legal documents, unearthed from family archives, to be signed and resigned. These were occasionally accompanied by cold and unfriendly letters from his brother. Even now, after so many years, the memory of those days hurt him. It was almost a relief to him to learn at last that he was all but ruined, and that the indignation with which he always thought of his brother, was perfectly justified.

His extreme loneliness made him very unhappy for many years, but little by little, he schooled himself to self-dependence, and he so thoroughly assumed the mask of indifference, that his features seemed to be indelibly impressed by it.

But there were moments, when he plunged passionately back into life, sudden kindling of affection when he formed violent and ill-judged friendships with anyone whose temperament struck some sympathetic chord in tune with his own.

Marriage?

Yes, of course! He too had thought of it, when, one by one, all his friends got married and fired him with a desire to do likewise. He, too, had had a definite "affair," this time *not* with a china figure, and this devotion he had carried with him over the whole face of the earth, in the secrecy of his cabin. In those days, when they arrived in distant ports, the ship's postman used to bring him a mail which was the envy of his brother officers—a big bundle of letters in a firm upright feminine hand. But from that episode he emerged wounded, and sore.

One day she deserted him without warning, for the sake of a great name, and a great fortune, and he was left the wreck of himself, shattered and bleeding.

After this, he gave himself up to the sea, and dedicated himself entirely to his profession, perfectly determined to create no ties which could wound or hurt him in any part of the world, in any "destination," however remote, to which he might be ordered.

This was the will of the sea! There must be no regrets for any place or person, left behind, all one's possessions must be concentrated in one's cabin. This period saw him become the energetic, resolute man, the first-rate officer, the commander remembered and talked of by old sailors, long years after they had served under him. Alas! here, too, was disappointment: even his profession betrayed him!

At fifty-five, full of vigour and vitality, he had been cast aside, and declared useless, in accordance with regulations! These two betrayals, of his love, and of his life, left him with little: a few bundles of dusty letters, a book written by himself, entitled *Naval Strategy in the Mediterranean*, which he had dreamt of putting into practice some day, when, as Admiral of the Fleet, he should lead it to victory! There were papers and maps. . . .

Here were the ashes, the embers of his life, which refused to die out or grow cold, despite the bitter tears, the heart's blood which had been shed over them, and which, in all conscience, should have extinguished every spark!

IX

A sailor would have recognized in a moment the hand of a sailor, by the way in which a very tall flag-staff had been put up on the roof of "The Admiral's" house. The shrouds and pulleys had needed a vast amount of patience and hard work, and then it had taken almost a month to replace the tiles on the roof, but finally it looked exactly like the real thing on a ship, and the sailor could not only be proud of his idea, but could survey his work with satisfaction, as not unworthy of one who had been formerly the servant of the Captain of R. N. *Stromboli*.

On national festivals, at 8 o'clock precisely, the tricolour was hoisted on the villa, and remained flying till sunset, when it was lowered slowly, according to naval tradition.

The seaman never failed to ask leave first, standing at attention, and repeating the correct formula of the Officer of the Watch, "May the Colours be hoisted, sir?"

The Captain himself, having given permission, used always to go out to feast his eyes once more on the lovely sight of the flag waving in the wind and standing out bravely against the sky.

Even at sea he used to watch it with delight as it was swung to and fro, like everything else on board, by the immense speed of the ship, or when, in a violent gale, its edges began to tear into ribbons.

There was always some good reason for having a look at the colours, and often it was a positive necessity, especially when one considered how carelessly those wretched signalmen hoisted it, often even letting it foul. One really had to keep an eye upon it!

X

There followed a series of barren years, marked only by the changing seasons: spells of north-east winds—the fierce heat of the dog-days—south-west winds and fog.

Little by little his upright figure grew bent, the veins on his face grew heavy and dark, his bones stood out under the dry and shrivelled skin, which seemed merely a taut covering for his frame.

Sleepless nights, torrid heat, years of living on tinned foods, nervous strain, acute and prolonged, frequent sudden changes of climate, disease contracted from reckless embraces in all parts of the world;—all this was a debt of long standing which had to be all too hastily paid off: painfully paid off in enfeebled limbs, a poisoned system, clots of blood shifting slowly in his veins, strange spasms in his eyes, and sharp pains at the back of his neck.

In the early days of his retirement, his strength had failed rapidly, and now there were no means of retarding this break-up. It was the complete collapse of his vitality, the heavy hand of death laid upon him, suddenly and swiftly.

At this time, the approach of night was a fresh torment. The most violent sensations experienced in real life returned to him in the form of terrifying dreams, dreams so ghastly that, bathed in sweat, he used to leap from his bed in mad fear and grope about in the darkness till he touched the walls and so convinced himself that he was really still in his room.

One night he had this dream.

Scarcely had he fallen asleep when his bed began to rock; gently at first, and then more violently in long swinging movements as if supported by a mass of water. And, indeed, there evidently *was* water, for, on either side of him, white specks dashed past him like spray at the side of a boat.

So they were moving! But where? Ah! now he saw! They were in one of those lonely seas where there is nothing in sight, and where there is no life, nothing real except the planks under one's feet. On this lonely ocean whose waters moaned a wild lament, the night came down, dark and swift: a night of such darkness that all objects vanished without trace, and were swallowed up utterly.

Presently he found that he was standing up, and grasping something solid with his eyes turned towards the gloom whither they were moving, terrified at being able to see nothing. But no! there was something! and beside him he became aware of the form of a man, who, with a steady hand was moving a circular object very much like a wheel. He saw that it actually was a wheel, a steering wheel; and then he stooped to look at the man until he actually touched him, and asked him in a low voice: "How's the helm?"

"Starboard fifteen degrees," answered the other in a strange whisper, "and the ship's not answering the helm, won't alter course. This cursèd *Fulmine*."

Fulmine? ah! so that was it, they were on the destroyer, steaming madly through the darkness! . . . But suddenly, the man at the helm gave a cry and pointed out a huge red light which in a flash emerged from the blackness a few metres away, and came sailing across their bows.

"Starboard! Starboard! all—" he shouted.

"She doesn't answer, she doesn't answer, Sir."

He wanted to shout: "Engines starboard reverse! Reverse at full steam." But to his dismay he found that he could utter no sound—his lips would not move.

At that moment, there was a terrible shock in the darkness and the night was filled with desperate cries. He felt the deck sinking beneath his feet, but it was impossible for him to move, for the helmsman had his arms firmly round his neck, and was dragging him down with him, forcing him down with more violence every moment,—down into an atmosphere, which by degrees was becoming light, and warm, and filled with a strange arid odour. Then he looked steadily at the man who had brought him here, whose fierce hold was now relaxing and becoming a gentle caress! Man! There was no man!—it was a little Geisha! smiling into his face, clinging to him in a close embrace, and whispering words of love in Pidgin-English. She wore a cherry-coloured kimono, fantastically embroidered in gold, and loosely fastened at the waist, so that at every movement of her lissom body the rosy flesh of her limbs, showed through the crimson silk.

Yes! It all came back to him. Nagasaki. The Tea-house, the Maison des fleurs. Once more he saw around him the screens, with the strange beasts and fantastic flowers. On the floor the fine mats and lacquer stools, laden with tea-cups exquisitely painted with clouds of butterflies, each a gem of beaten gold.

His companion was the loveliest Geisha, Tsuki-San whom he had known in the far off days of real life, thirty-five years ago. And here she was, kissing his shoulder, the touch of her lips leaving just such a mark, as that old scar of the burn, which he had thought quite healed. Then her warm mouth passed down his arm, giving him a dull ache, and then a sharp, and ever sharper pain, till it penetrated his very flesh, and her kisses seemed like the pricking of a thousand needles, piercing skin and bone to the marrow. In vain did he try to push away the face which seared and tormented him. He was powerless, and had to resign himself to the torture of those burning kisses, in every limb.

Meanwhile, there was a smiling witness of this scene: another woman lay naked, like a sculptured figure, face downwards on the floor, supporting herself on her elbows, her chin between her hands, and her eyes upon his face. "Marika! You are Marika? My lovely Athenian from the Epirus?" he asked her eagerly. She nodded in assent, smiling the while with a quiet little smile—which slowly, slowly, became sinister and malicious.

Then she began to move slowly towards him, moving along on her elbows and knees, until she laid her golden head between his knees. Her touch gave him the most agonizing pain, as if his legs, held in a vice between two rough stones, were being slowly wrenched and crushed.

Then the violence of the pain woke him. He found himself in bed—streaming with perspiration and in anguish. His hands were resting on his legs, and he had acute shooting pains in all his bones, while he felt as if his heart were in the grip of an icy hand. His lungs were incapable of breathing, and so nearly did he choke, that there was a rattle in his throat.

Roused by his moans his dog came up to the bed—the poor beast was crying and whining because he was too old to climb up.

In a flash, in that moment of waking, he had a clear vision of himself, awaiting the bier, and the grave. He saw the contortion of his limbs, the pain on his face, the final impress which would have remained, had he died in that unspeakable agony.

XI

In the rosy dawn of a certain August day, the fishing fleet with its red and yellow sails, was drifting out to sea with the last breeze from the shore, a breeze which had gathered the fragrance of the grass on the hillsides, and was still cool with the freshness of the dew.

Pale and fairy-like in the early light, the boats still half-asleep, seemed to have set themselves in a fantastic group on the horizon, as if for some "*festa*" of their own, planned in secret, and arranged in silence, seizing the early hours of the morning, so that no stranger should be present.

With this intent, and still better to ward off any unwanted spectators, the boats nearest the shore had left their great square sails spread, and the strange host of grotesque figures, roughly painted on them, seemed to be laughing silently at the world on shore, in mischievous delight at having stolen a march upon it!

But they had not altogether succeeded. . . .

Far away, were silhouetted, clear and sharp, the slender masts of the distant ships casting delicate reflections in long vertical lines into the depths of the motionless water, where they melted into one another in a series of streamers, amber and violet, shot with gold. In the background, merging into one another, sea and sky, both lighted up by a tremulous iridescence and by sudden flashes of the far-off flaming dawn, formed a single brilliant setting, framed by the last shadows of the night. Against this wonderful light the most distant boats looked dark, and were hardly visible; they seemed to be suspended in mid-air in some strange element, unseen—and yet navigable.

It was in truth a village afloat! A village which, in its compact groups, its wide spaces, its haughty aloofness reproduced at sea, all the sympathies, antipathies and rivalries of its original on shore. Here, by shouting, one could carry on a discussion, interrupted on the Piazza the evening before, and could repeat the popular jokes of the Inn, which would be greeted, as they were passed from boat to boat, by the hearty laughter which well-worn jokes never fail to provoke. Now and then was heard a gruff order from some sleepy master, promptly followed by the obedient sound of the pulleys. There were loud yawns, and heavy unmelodious snores from the men, while the boys lying in the bows whistled with maddening persistency the latest tunes picked up at the local cinema.

They had to get further out to sea before casting the nets, and the breeze was so delicious, the memory of conjugal delights so recent, that to take to the oars, and wear out one's arms with rowing at daybreak seemed positive torture.

So the secret *"festa"* of the boats went on, as they sailed further and further away, all their colours melting into the gold, catching here and there shafts of deep blue as they approached the rising sun, while the surrounding shadows gradually faded and vanished in the flaming glory.

But their success was not complete: their secret not inviolate.

Among the dim specks of the ships on the farthest horizon, an intruder had found her way, an intruder who, like themselves, had managed to assume the calm unreal aspect of the most distant objects, on which, moreover, one only cast the most fleeting glances, since one wished to avoid thinking about the tiresome work which awaited one "out there!"

And so from the beginning no one had noticed it; no one had heeded the strange fact that the "speck" had grown rapidly larger, making its way towards the shore, moving in and out among the groups of boats, as if driven by a strong wind unperceived by themselves. It was a slender column of smoke rising from the grey speck itself which revealed the astonishing nature of the intruder! And then, from boat to boat, right through the motionless fleet as the boys eagerly got to their feet in the bows, rose the cry of surprise and warning.

"Ahoy! A torpedo-boat!"

"A torpedo-boat—Ahoy!"

There was very soon a sort of wild roar, animated by that fear which always seizes fishermen, in the presence of these swift vessels, with their sharp, fierce bows, whose rapid racking to avoid the boats at the last moment only adds to their panic.

"Ahoy! Aho-o-y! Ahoy!!"

"Keep out, there! Ahoy! Keep out!"

Only those who had lately returned from serving in the Navy were silent, and stood instinctively in the rigid attitude prescribed for the close passing of another ship. Their faces wore the look of those who know, and will not impart their knowledge. In their eyes were visions of events past and buried, of sad, but suddenly glorious memories.

An ex-boatswain's mate however, was more articulate:

"Two funnels, two masts, immensely long, high in the bows! An ocean-going torpedo-boat!" he shouted with pride, and the information was handed on among old sailors, and the young ones who had lately done their service.

"It's an A. like mine," he continued to an old man who stood at the helm. "Look! like mine, like the *Albatross!*"

The torpedo-boat was by this time in the thick of the fishing boats. With superb nonchalance, her sharp bows ploughed her way between two great walls of water gushing behind her in a mass of white foam, as she darted along the great furrow, and the unaccustomed sea heaved all round in long waves which made the boats roll heavily and the loose sails beat against the masts.

In a few moments, it was possible to see clearly the shining objects on board, and almost instantly the lovely grey form had passed, moving rhythmically to the swift pulsation of her engines, throwing aloft its breath of flame, vibrating with life, full of daring and power, piercing the calm air with the shriek of her siren, and leaving behind her the trace of her unerring course, in the furrow of surging water churned and foaming, and—like all lovely things, soon lost.

Then the old sailor at the helm looked up to the bridge, and called out to the young Commander who was examining the coast with his glasses.

"Look out my lad! Go slow! Go slow!"

The helmsman of the *Albatross* took his eyes for a moment from the compass, and gave a hasty glance of utter astonishment, down at the boat alongside, while a smile fluttered over the face of the young officer who was still looking ahead through his glasses.

With immense speed the ship gained the shore, steered unhesitatingly to the best anchorage opposite the village. Then the propeller was reversed and the anchor cast. At the hollow, rattling sound of the chain, the windows of the houses were, one after another, thrown open. Sleepy figures appeared, with faces screwed up in the sudden light, after the stuffy darkness within, and, with dazzled eyes, stood there, trying to make out what that huge grey form could be,—motionless and silent, there at their very doors, come from Heaven knew where! They all began to shout from window to window and then up and down the streets:

"A torpedo-boat! A big torpedo-boat! Hurry up, and come along down to see her!"

What excitement! What a rush! Hasty dressing, getting ready the boats, warning the food shops, and the laundresses. What an unexpected holiday! My word! Perhaps they'd be allowed on board. Anyhow, they must get off to the beach as soon as possible, and then who knows? With luck. . . .

XII

He had leapt from his bed when he heard the shriek of the distant siren which had roused melancholy echoes like the moans of dying monsters among the houses and the hills.

Accustomed to dreams compact of memories, to uneasy sleep punctuated by sudden starts, filled with nameless horror, and often to finding himself muttering and whispering when he woke, he feared that once again he was the prey of one of those phantasms and distorted visions of his old life which still haunted him. A vision possibly more vivid, more realistic, but still—only a vision. And, standing there motionless, he gazed in bitterness of spirit at his empty bed, and, in a moment of strange lucidity of mind, was filled with a feeling of infinite pity for himself.

But, no; was it after all only a dream? What about that metallic sound? Was that hallucination again? Wasn't it really the blessed sound of the cable of the anchor being let out?

No sailor could be mistaken: first the regular sound of the links of the cable being let out from the locker: then the slackening of speed caused by the anchor touching bottom and by the stopping of the engines: then the pauses between the harsh sound of the cable being hauled in in short jerks: then again the slow letting out, link by link; and finally—silence.

He heard the whole rugged music of arrival in harbour, familiar to sailors, and only to sailors, all the world over; the ancient liturgy celebrated everywhere with the same rites, the same clang of steel, the same passionate movements of the ships, their glad nuptials with the shore, and then the joy of repose! No! This was no dream, but the real thing at last! Convinced of this, he strode to the window, flung it open, half-closed his eyes, and slowly, slowly opened them, greedily drinking in every detail of the alert grey form. She was an ocean-going torpedo-boat, one of the latest type of ship such as had not existed in his day. He had never seen one, and at the first glance had taken her for a destroyer. With the help of his old binoculars, he was able to distinguish the details, to count her guns, and to read her name, sparkling on the poop. But it took him a long time to make out everything, for, to his dismay, he could not control the shaking of his hands.

As soon as he had looked his fill, he began to dress, with something of the anxious joy of a child summoned to look at his presents on his birthday. He still stood in front of the window, so as not to lose sight of the ship, and to be able to watch her every movement, for fear of a sudden departure.

When he reached the road, the sun was already up, and numbers of people were already hurrying down to the shore, summoned by the unwonted excitement. His first feeling was one of distaste at having become of the common herd, a casual sight-seer hurrying to the beach, and obliged to dispute a seat in a boat with loafers and washerwomen. Dispute a place in a boat! He! accustomed to go on board a battle-ship in a six-oared gig, or in an immaculate launch, gleaming and swift, reserved for his use, and to be received when he came on the quarter-deck by the Second-in-command, the Officers of the Watch, by a line of motionless sailors presenting arms, and by the whole crew on deck standing at attention at the spot where they were occupied when the bugle sounded the attention.

And now, to dispute a place in the boats? This was unthinkable. Getting ahead of the crowd, he hastened to the beach, shouted to a boatman offering him a big fare, and pushed off, alone. When he came alongside the torpedo-boat, the warrant-officer of the watch was pacing slowly up and down the deck between the conning-tower and the bows with a weary step. A seaman of the watch was on deck preparing to hoist the tricolour at 8 o'clock. There was no one else on deck. Every one was below, asleep.

Neither of them showed the smallest sign of having noticed the arrival of the boat, and they both let the old man approach the Jacob's ladder without a word. Only when the boatman losing patience asked: "Can we come on board?" in an unnecessarily loud voice, they both rushed up and warned him not to make such a noise, especially there, near the poop close to where the Commander was sleeping.

"But, look here! tell us all the same, if we can come on board?" asked the boatman again, this time in a low voice.

"No! you can't!" answered the warrant-officer. "In any case, it's never allowed before the colours are hoisted, and even then I should have to ask the Commander, and he's asleep. Besides, we're off directly, and shall get up steam, as soon as the stores are taken on board."

Meanwhile, other boats, heavily laden, had come alongside; their occupants were already disputing over the ladder, and in their determina-

tion to be first on board they began quarrelling. Their bows began banging against the smooth sides of the torpedo-boat, and the sailor on watch
had to shout orders to them to hold off.

But no one obeyed. Mutual threats, emphasized by uplifted oars
roused them all. Moreover to begin a scuffle and to be the first to defy the
law is[1] a distinction dear to the hearts of an Italian crowd. In these circumstances the officer was compelled to interfere, and he shouted to the
seaman on watch, to draw up the Jacob's ladder and to shove off the
boats with all possible force: their bows were still knocking the sides of
the ship, just against the Commander's cabin, and only a few centimetres
from his head.

But it was too late! Bad luck to them! Suddenly they heard the sound
of an electric bell, rung loud and long. It was, as the officer expected, the
Commander, wakened with a start after two sleepless nights spent on
the bridge, and wanting to know from the warrant-officer, what in thunder was the meaning of all this noise and confusion round the ship, and
why he had not put a stop to it immediately.

When the warrant-officer reappeared on deck, he was beside himself
with rage.

"See that they all clear out, and at once," he said furiously to the seaman, repeating word for word what the Commander had just said to
him, "and if you don't carry out the order, you'll pay for it!"

"Clear out! Get off with you!" shouted the seaman turning to the
crowd of boats still close to the ship. "Be off, and leave us to sleep in
peace. Goodness knows we need it badly enough."

Thereupon the boats began slowly to row away. Only one, whose occupants had apparently not heard the order, remained close to the ladder.
In this boat an old man was standing alone in the stern, gazing at the
torpedo-boat with a strange look of passionate longing and infinite sadness.

"Hi! you, there!" shouted the young sailor, turning towards the
lonely figure. "Didn't you hear? Do you want me to get my leave stopped
on your account?"

In a faint voice in which some echoes of the old tones of command were
strangely blended with a note of almost timid entreaty, the old man replied gently:

"I am a Captain. Tell the warrant-officer of the watch this."

Then an extraordinary thing happened.

The sailor began to look the man before him up and down, carefully
examined his shabby clothes, scrutinized his tragic face, and marked his
bent shoulders; finally noticed the humble boat in which he had come:—
and then burst into a roar of laughter.

"Don't tell *me* your tales," he said, "None of your bluff! If you're

---

[1]To-day it would be more accurate to say "was" than "is."—*Italian editor's note.*

mad, go and get shut up! Off with you! Do you understand a plain order?
Yes or No?"

... The boat was rowed away....

"A fine story. Full-blown Captain indeed! What a yarn!" and the
seaman went off still laughing to tell the warrant-officer what had
happened.

"Do you see him? Over there, going away. Of course he must be mad.
Look! Just look at him now! What on earth is he doing? Why! I believe
the fellow's crying! What a lunatic!"

And he went back on deck to get ready to hoist the colours.

XIII

One grey December day, the postman brought up to the villa, a large
yellow envelope, bearing the Admiralty stamp.

It was absolutely saturated with sleet, and when the Captain took it a
shudder of cold seemed to run right through him. What could they want
with him now? Why disturb him again in his solitude? He read the address a second time. His name, followed by the words, "Captain. Retired."

Retired! *A riposo?* Repose! The word struck him as a piece of cruel
irony. His actual life, a sequence of days of unutterable grief, described
as rest, "repose?"

A strange laugh echoed through the room. Such a laugh as one sometimes hears if one chances to pass a mad-house.

He spent a long time in reading the letter. Without preamble or final
greeting, with formal official phrases, it announced to him the bare fact
that the *Stromboli* was to be put out of commission and sold. In going
through the various inventories they had found certain discrepancies.
They inquired whether he recalled any important changes in the material equipment of the ship when it was under his command; changes of
which they could find no trace in the Admiralty documents. Then followed a list and they finally begged him to answer without delay, as it
was not possible to proceed to the sale of the ship, without the desired
information. The words were unsteady under his eyes, shook, and
danced, till they were hopelessly confused: then they began to move
round in innumerable little circles, like insects when one disturbs them
by lifting a stone. Only one word remained fairly clear at the foot of the
page:—the signature of the Minister; and that seemed to remain clear
and steady, expressly for the purpose of reminding him that the man now
at the head of the Admiralty had been under him as Gunnery-officer
when he was second-in-command on the *Affondatore.*

For a considerable time his mind was entirely occupied with this fact:
then he suddenly turned his thoughts to the real significance of the
communication. His head dropped- his eyes closed, his hand uncon-

sciously relaxed its hold, and the letter fell on to the table. The picture of his splendid cruiser rose before him, white, gleaming, and immaculate: the iron sinews of his fatherland, controlled by him, and held in readiness for a mighty blow in the hour of battle. Again he saw himself inspiring the little world of the battle-ship by his own untiring energy, and making use of the absolute obedience and perfect discipline of the men trained by him, to secure the absolute order and perfect working of that same microcosm.

If they had asked of him another anxious strenuous day, another sleepless night, another moment of tense mental strain, he could have answered with pride: "I can give no more. I have loyally given all that a man can give. Put me to the test. My ship will obey your orders, and carry out your will, whenever, and wherever you may impose them. But if you ask more of me, I can only give my life, my breast to be riven by shot and shell, my brain which has served you so well to be destroyed by deadly explosives."

And now his lovely and beloved ship was to be robbed of her soul: she had grown old, and was dying. She was dying in the midst of the clamour of speculators with their banknotes, fighting over her body, a sinister band of birds of prey already wrangling over the steel ribs and fittings, and carrying them off to be melted down in the furnaces. He saw her already in dock being broken up under the sad slow blows of the ship-breaker's hammer, so different from the eager, joyous sounds of the shipyards.

She would die a sad death, with laments and cries, and like himself, would lose her strength and see herself breaking up. Her iron frame, no doubt, would resist and bend before it broke, as his nerves had resisted before utterly giving way: and, just as the ship would at last be destroyed by the ship-breaker's hammer, so he too would perish, as a bunch of seaweed thrown far up on the shore, above the waves, is dried and withered in the sun.

Then he smiled an enigmatic smile. A strange idea flashed through his mind: an idea which suddenly obsessed him, and he brooded on it with the erratic tenacity peculiar to such a temperament as his.

So they could not sell the ship until he had given them the information? Well, at least he would delay her death; he would not answer:—and, in forming this strange plan there was in his mind some vague idea that he would thereby prolong his own life.

XIV

The following night, the Geisha of Nagasaki, Tsuki-San appeared. She wore a black kimono figured with golden dolphins, strange, twisted creatures, each trying to bite his own tail.

The girl had the same expression as the women in Michael Angelo's

"Last Judgment." The very spirit of voluptuousness, exhaling corruption and death, seemed to gleam in her eyes. In her gestures there was something hideously sensual, as if she were sent to slay, and would draw out his very life, by the deadly passion of her lips.

She dropped her kimono, and stood there, naked. Then, with her undulating sensuous gait, she approached, and said, in a tongue unknown to him, and yet intelligible: "I am that vitality, that life, which you lavished on the sea. But you promised them to me, your manhood, and your vigour! Why did you flee from me?"

At the same moment, from the floor beside him, came the sinister laugh of Marika, the Greek, who had also reappeared, and in the same classic attitude as before.

"Hear me!" she said. "I am the manhood and vitality which you wasted and dissipated."

Of both these claims, he recognized the truth. His mind was in dire confusion; his body bathed in sweat. He could utter no word of excuse.

The Geisha continued, deliberately:

"I am here to claim all that remains of your manhood. You owe it to me—not to her—" pointing, as she spoke, to the Greek.

Again she approached him, with her blood-red lips open to meet his, and laid her hand on his brow.

At that touch, he felt a sudden terrible sensation of weight upon his chest. His lungs seemed to be in the clutch of a mighty grip, and he experienced a terrifying sensation of suffocation, and pain.

Gasping for breath, he was just able to cry:

"Air! Air! For God's sake give me air!" and he made a desperate effort to tear those hands from his breast, and to free his mouth from those greedy lips. In vain: he was helpless: he had a spasm of agonizing pain in his arms, especially in the left: he felt as if a heavy rope were firmly tied round his heart, tugging and pulling as if to tear it asunder.

With a shriek of pain, he rolled his eyes horribly—and became perfectly cold.

"Angina pectoris," whispered the doctor called in by the sailor-servant who had rushed off to fetch him in the night. "A very bad case, very bad," he added.

During the days that followed, the whole life of the sick man seemed to be concentrated in his brain, and he saw with uncanny clearness the destruction of his own body, and the gradual dissolution of his whole being.

The Geisha of the black kimono now appeared every night, amazed at meeting such resistance to her deadly kiss, but nevertheless, diabolically arrogant.

And, ultimately, one night, she prevailed. The tortured man fell to the floor between his bed and the wall—his arms distorted by the desperate struggle, and his nails dug into the flesh on his temples.

The Pekinese who had slept on the Mogador rug, set up a desolate howl, while he licked one of his master's cold feet.

In the morning the flag was hoisted at half-mast, as on board ship; an expression of grief sent up—not to unthankful men—but to the sky, to the sea breezes, to all things lovely and pure.

The next day, a strange letter reached the Admiralty. There was nothing official about it. The letters had been traced with difficulty, and the words were all uneven, and were obviously barely kept in some sort of line by an effort which ultimately broke down. "Your excellency," it said, "I cannot give the required information about the *Stromboli* because . . . I am dying."

It was signed: "Captain. Retired." (*Capitano di vascello a riposo.*)

SPAIN

HOW DON PERO NIÑO CAPTURED THE MOORISH GALLEY AND HOW THE SEA FOUGHT FOR THE ENGLISH[1]

Gutierre Diaz de Gomez

(c. 1378 – ?)

I

AFTER he had taken the sailing ship the captain had news that the King of Tunis had manned certain galleys, and he went to look for them.

Our galleys set out towards Tunis and crept along the Coast of Barbary, as secretly as they could. They drew near to the island which is called Zimbre; it lies near another little island named Zimbrot. Both are towards the Cape of Africa, five leagues from Tunis. Zimbrot is a desert island; there are in it many springs of sweet water, much game, and many birds that nest there. The galleys cast anchor there, and our men rested there for several days, for they were much wearied by the sea, hoping that some Moorish sailing ship or carrack should pass; but none were seen. Thence the land was clearly seen, and one night, in bright moonlight, they left the island and steered straight for the Port of Tunis. For the ten days that the galleys had been in that place, never had they lighted a fire, and the Captain, no more than his men, had eaten boiled or roast meats. And if they had stayed there longer, they would have had good fortune, for the Moorish galleys were not long in coming thither.

The galleys rowed along very quietly, that neither noise of oar striking water, nor any speech might be heard, as must be done by whosoever would make his way into so fair a haven as is the harbour before this city of Tunis, where lives one of the most mighty of all the Moorish kings, and where there are ever sailing ships and light galleys lying manned. Thus rowing and keeping watch on every side, about a league before the entrance into the harbour, they sighted a galley lying at anchor. The captain ordered that they should make for her and grapple her. The masters of the oarsmen said:

"My lord, if we lay our grappling irons upon her, it may hap that other galleys shall come upon us; and then we should wish to free ourselves and we could not."

The captain answered: "At this hour I see no other in sight. Grapple

[1]Reprinted from Joan Evans's translation of *El Victorial* by permission of George Routledge & Sons, Ltd.

with her; then when the others come, if it please God, we shall have finished with this one."

Thereupon the trumpets sounded and they drew near to the ship The Moors had not seen the captain's galleys until they were upon them: nevertheless they defended themselves a good time. Finally, we took the galley, and killed or captured all the men we encountered.

The prisoners, having confessed all they knew, and having told that there was yet another galley manned, very great (it was the great galeasse of the King of Tunis), our galleys began to enter the harbour, that they might seek it out. They would have surprised it like the other, but that there was in those parts a Genoese carrack, which by day anchored at the harbour mouth and left it at night. The Genoese had heard the noise of the fight at the taking of the first galley, and thinking that it was they that we were after, they stood to arms and sounded a trumpet. The Moors on the galeasse caught the sound; they weighed anchor and sighted the captain's galleys swooping down upon them, as bold as eagles that fall upon their prey. So soon as they saw us they bore away to the land and threaded their way into the channel of a river which flows into the harbour. The captain's galley followed them, fighting its way by dint of pulling into this same channel, which was so narrow that perforce one galley had to go behind the other. At last, the captain's galley drew close in to their poop, and as they drew close he leapt across on to it. But at the shock of striking his galley was thrown back and he found himself alone in the galley of the Moors.

The arms that he bore were these: a cuirass, vambraces, a steel cap, a sword, and a targe: and eagerly did he begin his battle against the Moors. The galley of Fernando Niño could not get near. In the captain's galley so great was the press to bear off the galeasse of the Moors, which had run aground, and to attack, and to defend themselves (for the Moorish galley was higher than ours) that men took no thought for the captain, for only those who were on the poop had seen him leap across. He cried out to them for help, but in so great a noise he was not heard. Every moment more men came up on the land side, where there were already many folk. They came into the sea to fight and their number grew so great that our men could no longer make any resistance.

The good knight, seeing that he would have no help unless it were from God and that he must go through with this undertaking to its end by himself, fought so lustily that it is a matter hard to believe except for those who saw him. He struck such good blows, killed and wounded so many, that in a short time he had fought himself free of them all and had driven them before him into the middle of the ship. There he laid hands on the Arraez of the galley (who is the Admiral) and having wounded him he made him stay stock still in one place, without daring to move.

Already day was breaking, and the Moors saw that all this havoc was wrought by one single man in their midst. They turned upon him like mad dogs and struck at him so hard that he could offer no resistance and they bore him backwards almost to the poop. The good knight, when he saw himself in such a pass, called upon St Mary to help him and there made a solemn vow. Then he hurled himself upon them, fierce as a lion who throws himself upon his prey striking, killing, driving them before him on to the deck, which he swept clean up to the prow. Then his own galley came up, and his men climbed in to the Moorish galley, and she remained in their hands; but she was still aground.

There, on the prow, he found himself face to face with a Moorish knight, of whom he had much to tell later, and he swore that this Moor struck him so hard on the head with his sword, that his knees bent beneath the blow. Here did Pero Niño receive several great wounds.

As soon as the day had dawned our men saw that Moorish troops were mustering near the city in such a press that they covered all the ground as they passed. None the less we went on labouring to get the great galley off again, that we might carry her away with us. We were near enough to land to touch it, and the shore in this place is flat; the Moors came into the water on their horses and fought with the men in the captain's galleys. There were already more than ten thousand Moors in the sea, of whom many died therein. The conflict and the cries from one side and another passed all description; so great was the multitude that an arrow could not have been loosed among them without finding a mark, nor a blow struck that did not strike home.

Our men's desire to bear off the Moorish galley led them to forget the captain's galley, and she was all but lost, for the Moors laid hands on her side in such numbers that they dragged her to the shore. Seeing this, the captain leapt on to his galley with some of his folk; but it was a miracle that any man could yet save her from the hands of the Moors. So great a massacre was made there that the water round the galleys was all red with blood. While they fought, the Moors removed some of the timbers beneath the prow of their galley, and the water flowed in and filled her. When they saw the water coming in, they told the captain to labour no longer to take her, for it was no longer possible to bear her thence; and then they sacked her. Thereat the captain went back to his own galleys; but when they tried to row his own galley out they could not move her, for she had run aground at the prow. They asked his cousin's galley that was nearer the mouth of the channel to give them a tow, which she did. Thus rowing, they got themselves out of this pass.

When the fight was ended and the captain had recognized that he could not float the galeasse off, likewise that he could not carry off the other galley that he had taken, for he had not men enough and was far distant from any Christian land, he caused everything to be removed that could be taken out of her, and then ordered them to set fire to her, and thus both were burnt. There was found therein fair booty of cross-bows and arms and other things which pertain to the armament of a war galley; and on the galeasse they took two great banners of silk and gold, the fairest in the world. Then the galleys drew off from the shore, and anchored, and they set about tending their wounded, of whom there were enough. The captain on that day received many blows from stones, lances, and arrows. He was very weary and much bruised; but what made him suffer most was a wound from an arrow that had gone through his leg, which galled him much; but so long as the battle lasted he felt nothing. His men then ate and rested: they had need.

While the galleys were anchored, there came to them in a rowing boat a Moorish knight sent by the King of Tunis to discover what men they were and to what country the galleys belonged. They told him that they were galleys of Castille. The Moor did not know what meant Castille. He asked if they were "Alfonsis." They told him, Yes. (By that it must be understood that this name is still used for Castillians in that country, since the time of the good kings who were named Alfonso, such as were Don Alfonso the Chaste, and Don Alfonso the Catholic, and Don Alfonso the Great, and Don Alfonso son of Don Pedro, lord of Cantabria, and the Emperor Don Alfonso and Don Alfonso that gained the victory of Benamarin and others named Don Alfonso, all noble and saintly kings, who wrought great destruction among the Moors and won back the country where now we live, that before them had been lost; by reason of the nobility of these kings were the Castillians called Alfonsis.)

When the Moor had learnt what they were, he went back to the King, and thence returned again and said to the captain that the King had sent him to ask wherefore he had wrought such havoc in his harbour; that if he had been warned in time, he would have given him better than he received; that there dwelt with this King men of our country to whom he shewed kindness and gave of his goods; and that he would do as much to our captain, if he would take what was offered him with a good grace; and that he besought him to do no more damage than had already been done.

The captain answered:

"Say to the King that I thank him and give him grace for his good words, but that I do not go coursing up and down the seas to receive gifts in such wise of any man, but only to fulfil the orders of my lord, the King; howsoever, tell him that to do him pleasure I will shortly go hence, and that I have no intent to molest him more at this present."

II

While Pero Niño was at La Rochelle, there came thither, with two galleys, a French knight called Messire Charles de Savoisy. He was a noble knight, an officer of the household of the King of France. For some of those matters which may befall knights of great estate, he had been banished from the Court for two years. This lord was brave, enterprising, courteous, well equipped, and rich. Some said he was in love with a great lady, and he certainly appeared to be, and gave it to be understood by his badges. He had come to Marseilles and had there built at his own expense two good galleys, which he had fully manned with gentlemen and picked crossbowmen; and they were the best furnished and fairest galleys ever seen in our time. Well do I believe that the banners alone were worth as much as the fittings of an ordinary galley. Messire Charles had already had news of Pero Niño, who for his part had also heard tell of Messire Charles. They met, and had great pleasure in each other's company.

Chance had well arranged things in thus bringing them together; for the qualities that each valued were found abundantly in the other. They agreed to sail together, to bear each other good company and not to leave each other during this war. They were likewise both resolved to go to England and to make first for the islands of Ouessant. But Messire Charles and his mariners then said that there would be great danger in making for the Cape of Ouessant, for they might strike the English fleet on the high seas; and that if the weather became bad, they would be in great danger from them; that, if the captain thought it good, it would be better to coast along Brittany, and that then they would not have so long a crossing. This pleased the captain, and the more since he knew that the Castillian ships were already off the Brittany coast. As for Messire Charles, he was so courteous a knight that it ever pleased him to recognize Pero Niño as captain; and he asked him to light the lantern on the poop of his galley, according to the custom of a captain at sea, assuring him that he would follow him even as his own galleys did.

Sailing from port to port along the coasts of Brittany, they rounded the Cape of St Matthew, and entered the Race, which is twenty miles long. This Race is very dangerous. A man would think that the sea was boiling there in great bubbles, like water in a cauldron over the fire; not, however, that it is hot, but the sea there is such that it is all whirlpools. In heavy weather the peril there is extreme, and the ship that is dragged towards the coast is sunk in an instant. Neither oars nor sails serve there; there must be good auxiliary rudders, for the currents are so strong and bear so hard upon the ship that, when God guards her from reefs, she may do these twenty leagues in three or four hours, and when the Race is passed, the sailors give thanks to God, Who has saved them. There the Flanders channel begins, which continues up to the Watch Tower in Flanders.

After they had passed the Race, the galleys came to a port of Brittany and passed the night there. The next day they left there and passed through the Race of Blanchart. This is not so long as the Race of St

Matthew. On the morrow they passed through another, which is called
the Race of St Malo. Thus sailing each day they reached the port of
Brest, which is a town of Brittany. There they met the fleet of Castille
of which Martin Ruiz de Avendaño was captain. Pero Niño and Messire
Charles spoke of the voyage to England with the captain of the ships, but
they could come to no agreement with him, for, as was clearly manifest
thereafter, he and his company wished to do nothing but make a profit
with the merchants that they had brought.

When Pero Niño and Messire Charles saw that the captain of the
ships was not willing to help them and to fight, they resolved between
themselves to cross the sea and pass over to England.

That very night the sailors made everything seaworthy. They observed the sky and the signs were favourable: the sunset was clear and
the moon was five days old; she had one of her horns turned towards
the sea. The galleys left the port at nightfall. During the whole of the
first watch they rowed out into the open sea, their lantern lit on the
stern of the captain's galley, and lay to on a grapnel until the dawn
watch to let the men rest. Then they set their course west-north-
west, the wind blowing from the west on the galley's cheek; they hoisted
sail and the weather was good. When day broke the wind dropped;
they unshipped the oars and rowed all day until evening; then the wind
freshened and became contrary, blowing on the prow; they hoisted
storm trysails and fixed the auxiliary rudders. The weather promised ill.
The ship's captain looked on every side, pale, sighing, consulting compass
and chart; he spoke low with the sailors, and these had already bestirred
themselves to work the vessel. The captain watched them and saw in all
this signs of a tempest. He summoned the sailors to a council and asked
them what these changes signified; the pilot said to him:

"My lord, leave all cares to us others who have to do the work; it will
serve no purpose of yours to learn them."

But the captain insisted, saying that he wished to know; and they answered that a great storm was gathering.

"The moon is new and already well on in her quarter: the wind is
veering to the west-north-west, and blows on our prow, so that we cannot
get to England. On this course, if we return to France we shall be across
the Race: if we steer to the west, we can find no harbour. If the wind still
freshens we must make once more for Spain. The passage is long and
dangerous, and furthermore, we may meet the English fleet on our way.
There is then danger on every side, so we ought to make ready in time."

The captain ordered the signal to be made to Messire Charles and to
the captains of the other galleys to come near his ship for a council. They
were asked what they thought of the weather and of the look of things.
Their conclusion was to continue the voyage as they had begun it, to try
with all their might to get near the coast of England, and, if they could
not achieve it, to turn, but for them all to follow the guiding lantern as

long as they could. This resolution taken, the wind freshened, and blew
so hard and so fierce, and raised such a sea, that the waves came aboard
over the prow up to the middle of the galleys and forced them round.
The waves were mountain high and the sea all hollowed. The galleys
were separated, each pursuing its course, so that there were no longer
any two together. In a few hours they were all scattered, and lost to view,
so that none of them had any sight of the others, and they were several
days without meeting.

All this night the captain's galley hugged the wind, until the gale mastered it and then they had to run before it and send all the crew below
decks and batten down all the hatches. There was no sail hoisted higher
than the height of a man. The waves were so strong that as they struck
the ship's quarter they threatened to break her, and made her sides ring
again. And such high seas came over the poop that some came right into
the galley. Such waves are the most dangerous; they carried off the long
boat from the place where she was lashed and cast her into the sea. All
the crew despaired of their lives and prayed God to have pity on their
souls. So passed the whole night in a great gale; and moreover it rained,
which is a thing which is very troublesome to sailors.

When dawn came one of the galleys appeared, but so far off that they
could only see her sail against the main. The moon then went into her
first quarter, and it happened that several times she disappeared and one
would have said that she was swallowed up; this disappearance was
wrought by the height of the waves. Land was still not in sight on any
quarter. Nevertheless continuing to head for France; at midday they
sighted the spires of the churches of France; for in this part the coast
of France is flat and low, and affords no bearings. It pleased God that
towards the hour of nones the wind fell in great part; they hoisted a sail
and took their bearings along the land and the galley came to an island
that is called Barbarac. The captain's galley rode there and cast anchor;
the crew had great need of rest. It was already the hour of vespers and
the sun was going down.

Thither too came one of the galleys of Messire Charles; it was the one
they had sighted at dawn; but it was fifteen days before all five ships
were once more together. It pleased God that none of them should perish,
and all thus going in search of the captain in the divers ports of Brittany,
ended by finding themselves together. The men on each ship imagined
that the other galleys had gone down; great therefore was their joy
when they saw Pero Niño, Messire Charles, and all their other comrades.

Certain knights of Brittany came to visit them, and the captain had
his tent set up in the Island and invited them all to eat with him, and
gave then a most noble feast. Each recounted the adventures that had
befallen him during the night of the tempest. Messire Charles said that
his galley climbed into the clouds and dropped into the abyss; that
sometimes she went with head aloft and sometimes head down; that he

thought so much about his soul that the world no longer mattered to him; and that the sea had carried away everything upon the deck up to the oarsmen's benches, which for the most part had been torn out. His shipmaster told that so many and strong were the blows of the waves against his galley that they nearly capsized her; that many times he thought he saw the decks go under and the keel come atop; and that once he saw the stars in the sky between the deck and the hull of the galley. He likewise said that his galley would have been opened by the force of the waves if he had not had her frapped with cables and mats. Others said that several men had died stifled in the hold, so close pressed were they therein.

Each thus recounted the toils and labours that he had had to endure. The captain said to them:

"My friends, we owe many thanks to God who has delivered us. We had to pass through this trial and God has saved us that we may do some good. Let us try to make up for lost time." He further said: "See how God protects this evil nation of the English. He protects them not because they are righteous, but because of our sins, for if they are evil, we are sinful. If God was this time against us, yet another time we shall find Him favourable, for He is full of mercy, and if we have found the sea enraged, another time we shall see her kind. Let no man, therefore, despair; men should know how to endure evil fortune; man is born to labour. Those who have conquered lands and won kingdoms have had to go through many hardships and bear heavy labours."

When Pero Niño had finished his discourse, Messire Charles said that these were words of a good knight and that all should be done as he should order.

THE FIRST VOYAGE TAKEN BY THE ADMIRAL DON CRISTOBAL COLON WHEN HE DISCOVERED THE INDIES[1]

Christopher Columbus

(c. 1446–1506)

BECAUSE, O most Christian, and very high, very excellent and puissant Princes, King and Queen of the Spains and of the islands of the Sea, our Lords, in this present year of 1492, acting on the information that I had given to your Highnesses touching the lands of India, resolved to send me, Cristobal Colon, to the said parts of India, and ordered that I should not go by land to the eastward, but by way of the

---

[1]From Sir Clements R. Markham's translation of The Journal of Christopher Columbus. Reprinted by permission of the Hakluyt Society.

west, whither up to this day we do not know for certain that any one has gone.

Thus, in the month of January, your Highnesses gave orders to me that with a sufficient fleet I should go to the said parts of India, and for this they made great concessions to me, and ennobled me, so that henceforward I should be called Don, and should be chief Admiral of the Ocean Sea, perpetual Viceroy and Governor of all the islands and continents that I should discover and gain, and that I might hereafter discover and gain in the Ocean Sea, and that my eldest son should succeed, and so on from generation to generation for ever.

I left the city of Granada on the 12th of May, in the same year of 1492, being Saturday, and came to the town of Palos which is a seaport; where I equipped three vessels well suited for such service; and departed from that port, well supplied with provisions and with many sailors, on the 3rd day of August of the same year, being Friday, half an hour before sunrise, taking the route to the islands of Canaria, belonging to your Highnesses, which are in the said Ocean Sea, that I might thence take my departure for navigating until I should arrive at the Indies. As part of my duty I thought it well to write an account of all the voyage very punctually, noting from day to day all that I should do and see, that should happen, as will be seen further on. Also, Lords Princes, I resolved to describe each night what passed in the day, and to note each day how I navigated at night. I propose to construct a new chart for navigating, on which I shall delineate all the sea and lands of the Ocean in their proper positions under their bearings; and further, I propose to prepare a book, and to put down all as it were in a picture, by latitude from the equator, and western longitude. Above all, I shall have accomplished much, for I shall forget sleep, and shall work at the business of navigation, that so the service may be performed; all which will entail great labour.

Friday, 3rd of August. We departed on Friday, the 3rd of August, in the year 1492, from the bar of Saltes, at 8 o'clock, and proceeded with a strong sea breeze until sunset, towards the south, for 60 miles, equal to 15 leagues; afterwards S.W. and W.S.W., which was the course for the Canaries.

Saturday, 4th of August. They steered S.W. $\frac{1}{4}$ S.

Sunday, 5th of August. They continued their course day and night more than 40 leagues.

Monday, 6th of August. The rudder of the caravel *Pinta* became unshipped, and Martin Alonso Pinzon, who was in command, believed or suspected that it was by contrivance of Gomes Rascon and Cristobal Quintero, to whom the caravel belonged, for they dreaded to go on that voyage. The Admiral says that before they sailed, these men had been displaying a certain backwardness, so to speak. The Admiral was much disturbed at not being able to help the said caravel without danger, and he says that he was eased of some anxiety when he reflected that Martin Alonso Pinzon was a man of energy and ingenuity. They made, during the day and night, 29 leagues.

Tuesday, 7th of August. The rudder of the *Pinta* was shipped and secured, and they proceeded on a course for the island of Lanzarote, one of the Canaries. They made, during the day and night, 25 leagues.

Wednesday, 8th of August. Opinions respecting their position varied among the pilots of the three caravels; but that of the Admiral proved to be nearer the truth. He wished to go to Gran Canaria, to leave the caravel *Pinta*, because she was disabled by the faulty hanging of her rudder, and was making water. He intended to obtain another there if one could be found. They could not reach the place that day.

Thursday, 9th of August. The Admiral was not able to reach Gomera until the night of Sunday, while Martin Alonso remained on that coast of Gran Canaria by order of the Admiral, because his vessel could not be navigated. Afterwards the Admiral took her to Canaria, and they repaired the *Pinta* very thoroughly through the pains and labour of the Admiral of Martin Alonso and the rest. Finally they came to Gomera. They saw a great fire issue from the mountain of the island of Tenerife, which is of great height. They rigged the *Pinta* with square sails, for she was lateen rigged; and the Admiral reached Gomera on Sunday the 2nd of September, with the *Pinta* repaired.

The Admiral says that many honourable Spanish gentlemen who were at Gomera with Doña Ines Peraza, mother of Guillen Peraza (who was afterwards the first Count of Gomera), and who were natives of the island of Hierro, declared that every year they saw land to the west of the Canaries; and others, natives of Gomera, affirmed the same on oath. The Admiral here says that he remembers, when in Portugal in the year 1484, a man came to the King from the island of Madeira, to beg for a caravel to go to this land that was seen, who swore that it could be seen every year, and always in the same way. He also says that he recollects the same thing being affirmed in the islands of the Azores; and all these lands were described as in the same direction, and as being like each other, and of the same size. Having taken in water, wood, and meat, and all else that the men had who were left at Gomera by the Admiral when he went to the island of Canaria to repair the caravel *Pinta*, he finally made sail from the said island of Gomera, with his three caravels, on Thursday the 6th day of September.

Thursday, 6th of September. He departed on that day from the port of Gomera in the morning, and shaped a course to go on his voyage; having received tidings from a caravel that came from the island of Hierro that three Portuguese caravels were off that island with the object of taking him. There was a calm all that day and night, and in the morning he found himself between Gomera and Tenerife.

Friday 7th of September. The calm continued all Friday and Saturday, until the third hour of the night.

Saturday, 8th of September. At the third hour of Saturday night it began to blow from the N.E., and the Admiral shaped a course to the west. He took in much sea over the bows, which retarded progress, and 9 leagues were made in that day and night.

Sunday, 9th of September. This day the Admiral made 19 leagues, and he arranged to reckon less than the number run, because if the voyage were of long duration, the people would not be so terrified and disheartened. In the night he made 120 miles, at the rate of 12 miles an hour, which are 30 leagues. The sailors steered badly, letting the ship fall off to N.E., and even more, respecting which the Admiral complained many times.

Monday, 10th of September. In this day and night he made 60 leagues, at the rate of 10 miles an hour, which are $2\frac{1}{2}$ leagues; but he only counted 48 leagues, that the people might not be alarmed if the voyage should be long.

Tuesday, 11th of September. That day they sailed on their course, which was west, and made 20 leagues and more. They saw a large piece of the mast of a ship of 120 tons, but were unable to get it. In the night they made nearly 20 leagues, but only counted 16, for the reason already given.

Wednesday, 12th of September. That day, steering their course, they made 33 leagues during the day and night, counting less.

Thursday, 13th of September. That day and night, steering their course, which was west, they made 33 leagues, counting 3 or 4 less. The currents were against them. On this day, at the commencement of the night, the needles turned a half point to north-west, and in the morning they turned somewhat more north-west.

Friday, 14th of September. That day they navigated, on their westerly course, day and night, 20 leagues, counting a little less. Here those of the caravel *Niña* reported that they had seen a tern and a boatswain bird, and these birds never go more than 25 leagues from the land.

Saturday, 15th of September. That day and night they made 27 leagues and rather more on their west course; and in the early part of the night there fell from heaven into the sea a marvellous flame of fire, at a distance of about 4 or 5 leagues from them.

Sunday, 16th of September. That day and night they steered their course west, making 39 leagues, but the Admiral only counted 36. There were some clouds and small rain. The Admiral says that on that day, and ever afterwards, they met with very temperate breezes, so that there was great pleasure in enjoying the mornings, nothing being wanted but the song of nightingales. He says that the weather was like April in Andalusia. Here they began to see many tufts of grass which were very

green, and appeared to have been quite recently torn from the land.
From this they judged that they were near some island, but not the
main land, according to the Admiral, "because," as he says, "I make the
main land to be more distant."

Monday, 17th of September. They proceeded on their west course, and
made over 50 leagues in the day and night, but the Admiral only counted
47. They were aided by the current. They saw much very fine
grass and herbs from rocks, which came from the west. They,
therefore, considered that they were near land. The pilots observed
the north point, and found that the needles turned a full point to
the west of north. So the mariners were alarmed and dejected,
and did not give their reason. But the Admiral knew, and ordered that
the north should be again observed at dawn. They then found that the
needles were true. The cause was that the star makes the movement, and
not the needles. At dawn, on that Monday, they saw much more weed
appearing, like herbs from rivers, in which they found a live crab, which
the Admiral kept. He says that these crabs are certain signs of land.
The sea-water was found to be less salt than it had been since leaving the
Canaries. The breezes were always soft. Every one was pleased, and the
best sailers went ahead to sight the first land. They saw many tunny
fish, and the crew of the *Niña* killed one. The Admiral here says that
these signs of land came from the west, "in which direction I trust in
that high God in whose hands are all victories that very soon we shall
sight land." In that morning he says that a white bird was seen which
has not the habit of sleeping on the sea, called *rabo de junco* (boatswain-
bird).

Tuesday, 18th of September. This day and night they made over 55
leagues, the Admiral only counting 48. In all these days the sea was very
smooth, like the river at Seville. This day Martin Alonso, with the *Pinta*,
which was a fast sailer, did not wait, for he said to the Admiral, from his
caravel, that he had seen a great multitude of birds flying westward,
that he hoped to see land that night, and that he therefore pressed onward. A great cloud appeared in the north, which is a sign of the proximity of land.

Wednesday, 19th of September. The Admiral continued on his course,
and during the day and night he made but 25 leagues because it was
calm. He counted 22. This day, at 10 o'clock, a booby came to the ship,
and in the afternoon another arrived, these birds not generally going
more than 20 leagues from the land. There was also some drizzling rain
without wind, which is a sure sign of land. The Admiral did not wish to
cause delay by beating to windward to ascertain whether land was near,
but he considered it certain that there were islands both to the north
and south of his position. For his desire was to press onwards to the
Indies, the weather being fine. For on his return, God willing, he could
see all. These are his own words. Here the pilots found their positions.

He of the *Niña* made the Canaries 440 leagues distant, the *Pinta* 420. The pilot of the Admiral's ship made the distance exactly 400 leagues.

Thursday, 20th of September. This day the course was W. b. N., and as her head was all round the compass owing to the calm that prevailed, the ships made only 7 or 8 leagues. Two boobies came to the ship, and afterwards another, a sign of the proximity of land. They saw much weed, although none was seen on the previous day. They caught a bird with the hand, which was like a tern. But it was a river-bird, not a sea-bird, the feet being like those of a gull. At dawn two or three land-birds came singing to the ship, and they disappeared before sunset. Afterwards a booby came from W.N.W., and flew to the S.W., which was a sign that it left land in the W.N.W.; for these birds sleep on shore, and go to sea in the mornings in search of food. not extending their flight more than 20 leagues from the land.

Friday, 21st of September. Most of the day it was calm, and later there was a little wind. During the day and night they did not make good more than 13 leagues. At dawn they saw so much weed that the sea appeared to be covered with it, and it came from the west. A booby was seen. The sea was very smooth, like a river, and the air the best in the world. They saw a whale, which is a sign that they were near land, because they always keep near the shore.

Saturday, 22nd of September. They shaped a course W.N.W. more or less, her head turning from one to the other point, and made 30 leagues. Scarcely any weed was seen. They saw some sandpipers and another bird. Here the Admiral says: "This contrary wind was very necessary for me, because my people were much excited at the thought that in these seas no wind ever blew in the direction of Spain." Part of the day there was no weed, and later it was very thick.

Sunday, 23rd of September. They shaped a course N.W., and at times more northerly; occasionally they were on their course, which was west, and they made about 22 leagues. They saw a dove and a booby, another river-bird, and some white birds. There was a great deal of weed, and they found crabs in it. The sea being smooth and calm, the crew began to murmur, saying that here there was no great sea, and that the wind would never blow so that they could return to Spain. Afterwards the sea rose very much, without wind, which astonished them. The Admiral here says: "Thus the high sea was very necessary to me, such as had not appeared but in the time of the Jews when they went out of Egypt and murmured against Moses, who delivered them out of captivity."

Monday, 24th of September. The Admiral went on his west course all day and night, making 14 leagues. He counted 12. A booby came to the ship, and many sandpipers.

Tuesday, 25th of September. This day began with a calm, and afterwards there was wind. They were on their west course until night. The

Admiral conversed with Martin Alonso Pinzon, captain of the other caravel *Pinta*, respecting a chart which he had sent to the caravel three days before, on which, as it would appear, the Admiral had certain islands depicted in that sea. Martin Alonso said that the ships were in the position on which the islands were placed, and the Admiral replied that so it appeared to him; but it might be that they had not fallen in with them, owing to the currents which had always set the ships to the N.E., and that they had not made so much as the pilots reported. The Admiral then asked for the chart to be returned, and it was sent back on a line. The Admiral then began to plot the position on it, with the pilot and mariners. At sunset Martin Alonso went up on the poop of his ship, and with much joy called to the Admiral, claiming the reward as he had sighted land. When the Admiral heard this positively declared, he says that he gave thanks to the Lord on his knees, while Martin Alonso said the *Gloria in excelsis* with his people. The Admiral's crew did the same. Those of the *Niña* all went up on the mast and into the rigging, and declared that it was land. It so seemed to the Admiral, and that it was distant 25 leagues. They all continued to declare it was land until night. The Admiral ordered the course to be altered from W. to S.W., in which direction the land had appeared. That day they made 4 leagues on a west course, and 17 S.W. during the night, in all 21; but the people were told that 13 was the distance made good; for it was always feigned to them that the distances were less, so that the voyage might not appear so long. Thus two reckonings were kept on this voyage, the shorter being feigned, and the longer being the true one. The sea was very smooth, so that many sailors bathed alongside. They saw many *dorados* and other fish.

Wednesday, 26th of September. The Admiral continued on the west course until after noon. Then he altered course to S.W., until he made out that what had been said to be land was only clouds. Day and night they made 31 leagues, counting 24 for the people. The sea was like a river, the air pleasant and very mild.

Thursday, 27th of September. The course west, and distance made good during day and night 24 leagues, 20 being counted for the people. Many *dorados* came. One was killed. A boatswain bird came.

Friday, 28th of September. The course was west, and the distance, owing to calms, only 14 leagues in day and night, 13 leagues being counted. They met with little weed; but caught two *dorados*, and more in the other ships.

Saturday, 29th of September. The course was west, and they made 24 leagues, counting 21 for the people. Owing to calms, the distance made good during day and night was not much. They saw a bird called *rabiforcado* (man-o'-war bird), which makes the boobies vomit what they have swallowed, and eats it, maintaining itself on nothing else. It is a sea-bird, but does not sleep on the sea, and does not go more than 20 leagues from the land. There are many of them at the Cape Verde Islands. Afterwards they saw two boobies. The air was very mild and agreeable, and the Admiral says that nothing was wanting but to hear the nightingale. The sea smooth as a river. Later, three boobies and a man-o'-war bird were seen three times. There was much weed.

Sunday, 30th of September. The western course was steered, and during the day and night, owing to calms, only 14 leagues were made, 11 being counted. Four boatswain-birds came to the ship, which is a great sign of land, for so many birds of this kind together is a sign that they are not straying or lost. They also twice saw four boobies. There was much weed. *Note* that the stars which are called *las guardias* (the Pointers), when night comes on, are near the western point, and when dawn breaks they are near the N.E. point; so that, during the whole night, they do not appear to move more than three lines or 9 hours, and this on each night. The Admiral says this, and also that at nightfall the needles vary a point westerly, while at dawn they agree exactly with the star. From this it would appear that the north star has a movement like the other stars, while the needles always point correctly.

Monday, 1st of October. Course west, and 25 leagues made good, counted for the crew as 20 leagues. There was a heavy shower of rain. At dawn the Admiral's pilot made the distance from Hierro 578 leagues to the west. The reduced reckoning which the Admiral showed to the crew made it 584 leagues; but the truth which the Admiral observed and kept secret was 707.

Tuesday, 2nd of October. Course west, and during the day and night 39 leagues were made good, counted for the crew as 30. The sea always smooth. Many thanks be given to God, says the Admiral, that the wind is coming from east to west, contrary to its usual course. Many fish were seen, and one was killed. A white bird was also seen that appeared to be a gull.

Wednesday, 3rd of October. They navigated on the usual course, and made good 47 leagues, counted as 40. Sandpipers appeared, and much weed, some of it very old and some quite fresh and having fruit. They saw no birds. The Admiral, therefore, thought that they had left the islands behind them which were depicted on the charts. The Admiral here says that he did not wish to keep the ships beating about during the last week, and in the last few days when there were so many signs of land, although he had information of certain islands in this region. For he wished to avoid delay, his object being to reach the Indies. He says that to delay would not be wise.

Thursday, 4th of October. Course west, and 63 leagues made good during the day and night, counted as 46. More than forty sandpipers came to the ship in a flock, and two boobies, and a ship's boy hit one with a stone. There also came a man-o'-war bird, and a white bird like a gull.

Friday, 5th of October. The Admiral steered his course, going 11 miles an hour, and during the day and night they made good 57 leagues, as the wind increased somewhat during the night: 45 were counted. The sea was smooth and quiet. "To God," he says, "be many thanks given, the air being pleasant and temperate, with no weed, many sandpipers, and flying-fish coming on the deck in numbers."

Saturday, 6th of October. The Admiral continued his west course, and during day and night they made good 40 leagues, 33 being counted. This night Martin Alonso said that it would be well to steer south of west, and it appeared to the Admiral that Martin Alonso did not say this with respect to the island of Cipango. He saw that if an error was made the land would not be reached so quickly, and that consequently it would be better to go at once to the continent and afterwards to the islands.

Sunday, 7th of October. The west course was continued; for two hours they went at the rate of 12 miles an hour, and afterwards 8 miles an hour. They made good 23 leagues, counting 18 for the people. This day, at sunrise, the caravel *Niña*, which went ahead, being the best sailer, and pushed forward as much as possible to sight the land first, so as to enjoy the reward which the Sovereigns had promised to whoever should see it first, hoisted a flag at the mast-head and fired a gun, as a signal that she had sighted land, for such was the Admiral's order. He had also ordered that, at sunrise and sunset, all the ships should join him; because those two times are most proper for seeing the greatest distance, the haze clearing away. No land was seen during the afternoon, as reported by the caravel *Niña*, and they passed a great number of birds flying from N. to S.W. This gave rise to the belief that the birds were either going to sleep on land, or were flying from the winter which might be supposed to be near in the land whence they were coming. The Admiral was aware that most of the islands held by the Portuguese were discovered by the flight of birds. For this reason he resolved to give up the west course, and to shape a course W.S.W. for the two following days. He began the new course one hour before sunset. They made good, during the night about 5 leagues, and 23 in the day, altogether 28 leagues.

Monday, 8th of October. The course was W.S.W., and 11½ or 12 leagues were made good in the day and night; and at times it appears that they went at the rate of 15 miles an hour during the night (if the handwriting be not deceptive[1]). The sea was like the river at Seville. "Thanks be to God," says the Admiral, "the air is very softlike the April at Seville; and it is a pleasure to be here, so balmy are the breezes." The weed seemed to be very fresh. There were many land-birds, and they took one that was flying to the S.W. Terns, ducks, and a booby were also seen.

Tuesday, 9th of October. The course was S.W., and they made 5 leagues. The wind then changed, and the Admiral steered W. by N. 4 leagues.

---

[1]Note by Las Casas.

Altogether, in day and night, they made 11 leagues by day and 20½ by night; counted as 17 leagues altogether. Throughout the night birds were heard passing.

Wednesday, 10th of October. The course was W.S.W., and they went at the rate of 10 miles an hour, occasionally 12 miles, and sometimes 7. During the day and night they made 59 leagues, counted as no more than 44. Here the people could endure no longer. They complained of the length of the voyage. But the Admiral cheered them up in the best way he could, giving them good hopes of the advantages they might gain from it. He added that, however much they might complain, he had to go to the Indies, and that he would go on until he found them, with the help of the Lord.

Thursday, 11th of October. The course was W.S.W. and there was more sea than there had been during the whole of the voyage. They saw sandpipers, and a green reed near the ship. Those of the caravel *Pinta* saw a cane and a pole, and they took up another small pole which appeared to have been worked with iron; also another bit of cane, a land-plant, and a small board. The crew of the caravel *Niña* also saw signs of land, and a small branch covered with berries. Every one breathed afresh and rejoiced at these signs. The run until sunset was 26 leagues.

After sunset the Admiral returned to his original west course and they went along at the rate of 12 miles an hour. Up to two hours after midnight they had gone 90 miles, equal to 22½ leagues. As the caravel *Pinta* was a better sailer, and went ahead of the Admiral, she found the land, and made the signals ordered by the Admiral. The land was first seen by a sailor named Rodrigo de Triana. But the Admiral, at ten in the previous night, being on the castle of the poop, saw a light, though it was so uncertain that he could not affirm it was land. He called Pero Gutierrez, a gentleman of the King's bed-chamber, and said that there seemed to be a light, and that he should look at it. He did so, and saw it. The Admiral said the same to Rodrigo Sanchez of Segovia, whom the King and Queen had sent with the fleet as inspector, but he could see nothing because he was not in a place whence anything could be seen. After the Admiral had spoken he saw the light once or twice, and it was like a wax candle rising and falling. It seemed to few to be an indication of land; but the Admiral made certain that land was close. When they said the *Salve*, which all the sailors were accustomed to sing in their way, the Admiral asked and admonished the men to keep a good look-out on the forecastle, and to watch well for land; and to him who should first cry out that he saw land, he would give a silk doublet, besides the rewards promised by the Sovereigns, which were 10,000 maravedis to him who should first see it. At two hours after midnight the land was sighted at a distance of two leagues. They shortened sail, and lay under the mainsail without the bonnets. The vessels were hove to, waiting for daylight; and on Friday they arrived at a small island of the

Lucayos, called, in the language of the Indians, *Guanahani*. Presently they saw naked people. The Admiral went on shore in the armed boat, and Martin Alonso Pinzon, and Vicente Yañez, his brother, who was captain of the *Niña*. The Admiral took the royal standard, and the captains went with two banners of the green cross, which the Admiral took in all the ships as a sign, with an F and a Y and a crown over each letter, one on one side of the cross and the other on the other. Having landed, they saw trees very green, and much water, and fruits of diverse kinds. The Admiral called to the two captains and to the others who leaped on shore, and to Rodrigo Escovedo, secretary of the whole fleet, and to Rodrigo Sanchez of Segovia, and said that they should bear faithful testimony that he, in presence of all, had taken, as he now took, possession of the said island for the King and for the Queen, his Lords.

HOW VASCO NUÑEZ DE BALBOA DISCOVERED THE PACIFIC[1]

TO FURTHER what the Admiral Columbus had begun, God raised an instrument in the person of Vasco Nuñez de Balboa, one of the first discoverers of this new world; a man of good understanding, as he showed upon the occasion which I shall now relate.

He was with others, upon the discovery with General Enrisco, the Governor: they came to a place called Uraba, and as they entered the port, by negligence of the steersman, the Governor's ship struck upon a sand, and was lost, nothing being saved out of her but the lives of the men, who got into the boats, but naked, and in danger of perishing for want of provisions. Vasco de Nuñez said, that he remembered there was not far off a river, the banks of which were inhabited by much people: he guided them thither: and the thing being found to be as he had said, he gained great reputation among them all. They came thither, and found the Indians in arms against the Castilians, whose name was already become odious to those nations: they made a vow to Our Lady, to dedicate to her the first settlement and church to the honour of her image, under the title of Sancta Maria la Antigua, or the Ancient St Mary, which to this day is venerated in Seville; and to send her many rich gifts of gold and silver, which one of them, as a pilgrim, should carry in the name of the rest. Being encouraged by this vow, they fell upon the Indians, and obtained the victory.

Presently they made a settlement, and built a town dedicated to the Virgin, calling it Sancta Maria el Antigua of Dairen, because that was the name of that river. After this, to accomplish their vow, they sent the promised presents to the devout image of the Virgin.

The good opinion of Vasco de Nuñez increasing, thus daily, and having cunningly ordered it so, that Encisco resigned his governorship, they

[1]From *Pinkerton's Voyages*.

chose Vasco Nuñez in his room: at first with an associate; but he found means in time to be alone, as it was necessary he should, in point of command, being to overcome such difficulties as were to be met with at every turn: and, indeed, he knew how to make himself be both feared and beloved, having a very good spirit of government.

In the new discoveries he undertook, he came first to the lands of the Cacique Ponea, and not finding him at home, he destroyed them: he passed on to the lands of the Cacique Careta, who not caring to enter into war, received him peacefully, and treated him as a friend. This Cacique Careta had a kinsman, who was a lord, that lived further in the country, and his name was Suran; who persuaded another neighbouring Prince, called Comagre, to make a friendship with the Castilians: this Prince had a very fine palace, which astonished them; and particularly when they saw, in a kind of chapel or oratory, some dead bodies lying, covered with rich mantles, and many jewels of gold and pearls; and being asked, whose bodies these were, they answered, of their predecessors; and that, to preserve them from corruption, they had dried them with fire.

The King caressed the Castilians, and gave them great presents: he had seven sons, and one of them, more liberal, gave the Spaniards a present of near four thousand pesos of fine gold, and some pieces of rare workmanship: they weighed it, and taking the King's fifths, they began to divide the remainder. In the division, two soldiers fell out about their shares; the Cacique's son, who had made the present, hearing the noise, could not bear it, but coming to them, struck the balance where the gold was weighing, and threw it all upon the ground, saying:

"Is it possible you should value so much a thing that so little deserves your esteem? and that you should leave the repose of your houses, and pass so many seas, exposed to such dangers, to trouble those who live quiet in their own country? Have some shame, Christians, and do not value these things: but if you are resolved to search gold, I will show you a country where you may satisfy yourselves."

And, pointing with his finger to the south, he told them they should see there another sea, when they had passed over certain high mountains where they should see other people, who could go with sails and oars as they did: and that passing that sea, they should meet with vast quantities of gold, whereof the natives made all their utensils; and that he would be their guide, and conduct them with his father's vassals: but that it would be requisite they should be more in number, because they were powerful kings, who could hinder their passage: giving them by this the first notice of Peru and its riches.

This was the first knowledge and light which the Spaniards got of the South Sea, and of the gold and riches of its coasts, which gave them all great joy; so that they were impatient to see the hour of breaking through all obstacles, to see that sea never before heard of, and enjoy the riches of it. Vasco Nuñez immediately disposed all things, and went out of Dairen, in the beginning of September in the year 1513, and going along the seaside, to the habitation of the friendly Cacique Careta, he went towards the mountains by the lands of the Cacique Ponea, who, though at first he endeavoured to oppose their passage, yet being advised by the Indians of Careta who accompanied the Castilians, he presented them with gold and provisions, and gave them guides; they, in return, giving him looking-glasses, needles, knives, and other baubles, which they valued very much.

Then they began to mount the mountain, through the country of a Cacique called Quareca, who appeared in arms, and attacked the Spaniards: he had a long robe of cotton, but all his men were naked. They began to skirmish, and threaten, by their actions, to hinder the passage; but no sooner did they hear the noise, and feel the effects of the muskets, and find some to fall, but they turned their backs, flying like a herd of deer, frighted to see the fire, and hear the sound of the vollies, which appeared thunder to them, and thought the Spaniards had thunderbolts at their command: so they left the passage free to them.

The Indians of Careta had said, that from their country to the top of the highest mountain, there was the time of six suns: for by that they meant so many days' journey; but the ways were so bad, that they employed five and twenty days to get to the top.

A little before they were at the highest, Vasco Nuñez de Balboa, caused a halt to be made, desiring to have the glory of having himself been the first man that ever saw the South Sea. And so it was: he goes alone, discovers that vast ocean, and the large bays of the South Sea, called Pacifick: and upon his knees, with tears in his eyes, lifts up his eyes to Heaven, giving thanks to the great Creator of all things, for having brought him from such remote parts to contemplate that which none of his ancestors had ever seen: he made a sign after this to his companions to come up, and so they all run in haste, pushing one another on; and when they were on the top, where there is a full prospect of the sea, it is not to be imagined the content they all received in admiring that vast and smooth liquid chrystal, which not being animated, did not on its side give leaps of joy, nor go out of its bed to the tops of the mountains, to welcome those who came to deliver it from the tyranny the devil exercised over it, by infesting it with storms and tempests, and infecting the air with the breath of idolatry, which was breathed in all those parts, both east, west, and north, and south.

Vasco Nuñez de Balboa, having performed his devotions, and thanked Our Lord with all his companions, for so great a favour done him, as to bring them to that place, he then bethought himself of his second obligation, which was to his King; in conformity to which, he took possession, in His Majesty's name, for the Crowns of Castile and Leon, of the place where he was and of the sea which he discovered from thence; cutting for this purpose many trees and making great crosses which he set up, and writ upon them the names of Their Majesties.

HOW FERNAN DE MAGALHAES SAILED INTO THE SOUTHERN SEA AND THE MANNER OF HIS DEATH[1]

Anthony Pigapheta

(1491–1535)

I

ANTHONY PIGAPHETA, *Patrician of Vicenza, and Knight of Rhodes, to the very illustrious and very excellent* Lord Philip de Villers Lisleaden, *the famous Grand Master of Rhodes, his most respected Lord.*

Since there are several curious persons (very illustrious and very reverend lord) who not only are pleased to listen to and learn the great and wonderful things which God has permitted me to see and suffer in the long and perilous navigation, which I have performed (and which is written hereafter), but also they desire to learn the methods and fashions of the road which I have taken to go thither, therefore, my lord, it will please you to hear that finding myself in Spain in the year of the Nativity of our Lord, one thousand five hundred and nineteen, at the court of the most serene king of the Romans, and knowing both by the reading of many books and by the report of many lettered and well informed persons, the very great and awful things of the ocean, I deliberated, with the favour of the Emperor to experiment and go and see with my eyes a part of these things.

Now in order to decypher the commencement of my voyage (very illustrious lord); having heard that there was in the city of Seville, a small armade to the number of five ships, ready to perform this long voyage, that is to say, to find the islands of Maluco, from whence the spices come: of which armade the captain-general was Fernand de Magaglianes, a Portuguese gentleman, commander of *St James of the Sword*, who had performed several voyages in the ocean sea (in which he had behaved very honourably as a good man), I set out from Barcelona and came by sea as far as Malaga, and thence I went away by land until I arrived at the said city of Seville. There I remained for the space of three months, waiting till the said armade was in order and readiness to perform its voyage.

Finally (very illustrious lord), after all provisions had been made, and the vessels were in order, the captain-general, a discreet and virtuous man, careful of his honour, would not commence his voyage without

---

[1]From Lord Stanley of Alderley's translation of *The First Voyage Round the World of Magellan.* Reprinted by permission of the Hakluyt Society.

first making some good and wholesome ordinances, such as it is the good custom to make for those who go to sea. Nevertheless he did not entirely declare the voyage which he was going to make, so that his men should not from amazement and fear be unwilling to accompany him. These ordinances he made over in writing to each master of the ships, and commanded them to be observed and inviolably kept.

Firstly, the said captain-general willed that the vessel in which he himself was should go before the other vessels, and that the others should follow it; therefore he carried by night on the poop of his ship a torch or faggot of burning wood, which they called farol, which burned all the night, so that his ships should not lose sight of him. Sometimes he set a lantern, sometimes a thick cord of reeds was lighted, which was called trenche. When the captain had made one of his signals to his people, they answered in the same way. In that manner they knew whether the ships were following and keeping together or not. And when he wished to take a tack on account of the change of weather, or if the wind was contrary, or if he wished to make less way, he had two lights shown; and if he wished the others to lower their small sail, which was a part of the sail attached to the great sail, he showed three lights. Also by the three lights, notwithstanding that the wind was fair for going faster, he signalled that the studding sail should be lowered; so that the great sail might be quicker and more easily struck and furled when bad weather should suddenly set in, on account of some squall or otherwise. Likewise when the captain wished the other ships to lower the sail he had four lights shown which shortly after he had put out and then showed a single one, which was a signal that he wished to stop there and turn, so that the other ships might do as he did. Withal, when he discovered any land, or shoal, that is to say, a rock at sea, he made several lights to be shown or had a bombard fired off. And to know whether all the ships followed him and were coming together, he showed one light only besides the farol, and then each of the ships showed another light, which was an answering signal.

Besides the above-mentioned ordinances for carrying on seamanship as is fitting, and to avoid the dangers which may come upon those who do not keep watch, the said captain ordered that three watches should be kept at night. The first was at the beginning of the night, the second at midnight, and the third towards break of day, which is commonly called *La diane*, otherwise the star of the break of day.

Monday, the day of St Lawrence, the 10th of August, in the year above mentioned, the fleet, provided with what was necessary for it, and carrying crews of different nations, to the number of two hundred and thirty-seven men in all the five ships, was ready to set sail from the mole of Seville; and firing all the artillery, we made sail only on the foremast, and came to the end of a river named Betis, which is now called Guadalcavir. And passing by many little villages along the said river, at last we arrived at a castle, which belongs to the Duke of Medina Sidonia, named St Lucar, where there is a port from which to enter the ocean sea.

Tuesday, the 20th September of the said year, we set sail from St Lucar, making the course of the south-west otherwise named Labeiche; and on the twenty-sixth of the said month we arrived at an island of great Canaria, named Teneriphe, which is in twenty-eight degrees latitude; there we remained three days and a half to take in provisions and other things which were wanted. After that we set sail thence and came to a port named Monterose, where we sojourned two days to supply ourselves with pitch, which is a thing necessary for ships.

Monday, the third of October of the said year, at the hour of midnight, we set sail, making the course auster, which the lavantine mariners call Siroc, entering into the ocean sea. We passed the Cape Verd and the neighbouring islands in fourteen-and-a-half degrees, and we navigated for several days by the coast of Guinea or Ethiopia; where there is a mountain called Sierra Leona, which is in eight degrees latitude according to the art and science of cosmography and asytology. Sometimes we had the wind contrary and at other times sufficiently good, and rains without wind. In this manner we navigated with rain for the space of sixty days until the equinoctial line, which was a thing very strange and unaccustomed to be seen, according to the saying of some old men and those who had navigated here several times. Nevertheless, before reaching this equinoctial line we had in fourteen degrees a variety of bad weather and bad winds, as much on account of squalls as for the head winds and currents which came in such a manner that we could no longer advance. In order that our ships might not perish nor broach to (as it often happens when the squalls come together), we struck our sails, and in that manner we went about the sea hither and thither until the fair weather came. During the calm there came large fishes near the ships which they called *Tiburoni* (sharks), which have teeth of a terrible kind, and eat people when they find them in the sea either alive or dead. During these storms the body of St Anselme appeared to us several times; amongst others, one night that it was very dark on account of the bad weather, the said saint appeared in the form of a fire lighted at the summit of the mainmast, and remained there near two hours and a half, which comforted us greatly, for we were in tears, only expecting the hour of perishing; and when that holy light was going away from us it gave out so great a brilliancy in the eyes of each, that we were near a quarter-of-an-hour like people blinded, and calling out for mercy. For without any doubt nobody hoped to escape from that storm. It is to be noted that all and as many times as that light which represents the said St Anselme shows itself and descends upon a vessel which is in a storm at sea, that vessel never is lost.

After that we had passed the equinoctial line, towards the south, we lost the star of the tramontana, and we navigated between the south and Garbin, which is the collateral wind (or point) between south and west; and we crossed as far as a country named Verzin, which is in twenty-four degrees and a half of the Antarctic sky. At this place we had refreshments of victuals, like fowls and meat of calves, also a variety of fruits, called *battate, pigne* (pine-apples), sweet, of singular goodness, and many other things, which I have omitted mentioning, not to be too long.

We entered into this port the day of Saint Lucy (13th December) before Christmas, and departing from it, and following our course, we went as far as thirty-four degrees and a third towards the antarctic pole; there we found, near a river, men whom they call "cannibals," who eat human flesh, and one of these men, great as a giant, came to the captain's ship to ascertain and ask if the others might come. This man had a voice like a bull, and whilst this man was at the ship his companions carried off all their goods which they had to a castle further off, from fear of us. Seeing that, we landed a hundred men from the ships, and went after them to try and catch some others; however they gained in running away. This kind of people did more with one step than we could do at a bound.

This place was formerly called the Cape of St Mary, and it was thought there that from thence there was a passage to the Sea of Sur; that is to say, the South Sea. And it is not found that any ship has ever discovered anything more, having passed beyond the said cape. And now it is no longer a cape, but it is a river which has a mouth seventeen leagues in width, by which it enters into the sea.

Afterwards following the same course towards the Antarctic pole, going along the land, we found two islands full of geese and goslings, and sea wolves.

Departing thence as far as forty-nine degrees and a half in the Antarctic heavens (as we were in the winter), we entered into a port to pass the winter, and remained there two whole months without ever seeing anybody. However, one day, without anyone expecting it, we saw a giant, who was on the shore of the sea, quite naked, and was dancing and leaping, and singing, and whilst singing he put the sand and dust on his head. Our captain sent one of his men towards him, whom he charged to sing and leap like the other to reassure him, and show him friendship. This he did, and immediately the sailor led this giant to a little island where the captain was waiting for him; and when he was before us he began to be astonished, and to be afraid, and he raised one finger on high, thinking that we came from heaven. He was so tall that the tallest of us only came up to his waist; however he was well built. He had a large face, painted red all round, and his eyes also were painted yellow around them, and he had two hearts painted on his cheeks; he had but little hair on his head, and it was painted white. When he was brought before the captain, he was clothed with the skin of a certain beast, which skin was very skilfully sewed. This beast has its head and ears the size of a mule, and the neck and body of the fashion of a camel, the legs of a deer, and the tail like that of a horse, and it neighs like a horse. The captain caused food and drink to be given to this giant, then they showed him some things, amongst others a steel mirror. When the giant saw his likeness in it, he was greatly terrified, leaping backwards, and made three or four of our men fall down.

We remained in this port, which was called the Port of St Julian, about five months, during which there happened to us many strange things, of which I will tell a part. One was, that immediately that we entered into this port, the masters of the other four ships plotted treason against the captain-general, in order to put him to death. These were thus named: John of Carthagine, conductor of the fleet; the treasurer, Loys de Mendoza; the conductor, Anthony Cocha; and Gaspar de Casada. However, the treason was discovered, for which the treasurer was killed with stabs of a dagger, and then quartered. This Gaspar de Casada had his head cut off, and afterwards was cut into quarters; and the conductor having a few days later attempted another treason, was banished with a priest, and was put in that country called Pattagonia. The captain-general would not put this conductor to death, because the Emperor Charles had made him captain of one of the ships.

Departing thence, we found in fifty-one degrees less one third (50° 40′ S.), in the Antarctic, a river of fresh water, which was near causing us to be lost, from the great winds which it sent out; but God, of his favour, aided us. We were about two months in this river, as it supplied fresh water and a kind of fish an ell long, and very scaly, which is good to eat. Before going away, the captain chose that all should confess and receive the body of our Lord like good Christians.

After going and taking the course to the fifty-second degree of the said Antarctic sky, on the day of the Eleven Thousand Virgins (October 21), we found, by a miracle, a strait which we called the Cape of the Eleven Thousand Virgins, this strait is a hundred and ten leagues long, which are four hundred and forty miles, and almost as wide as less than half a league, and it issues in another sea; which is called the peaceful sea; it is surrounded by very great and high mountains covered with snow. In this place it was not possible to anchor with the anchors, because no bottom was found, on which account they were forced to put the moorings of twenty-five or thirty fathoms length on shore. This strait was a round place surrounded by mountains, as I have said, and the greater number of the sailors thought that there was no place by which to go out thence to enter into the peaceful sea. But the captain-general said that there was another strait for going out, and said that he knew it well, because he had seen it by a marine chart of the King of Portugal, which map had been made by a great pilot and mariner named Martin of Bohemia. The captain sent on before two of his ships, one named *St*

Anthony, and the other the *Conception*, to seek for and discover the outlet of this strait, which was called the Cape de la Baya. And we, with the other two ships, that is to say, the flagship named *Trinitate*, and the other the *Victory*, remained waiting for them within the bay, where in the night we had a great storm, which lasted till the next day at midday, and during which we were forced to weigh the anchors and let the ships go hither and thither about the bay. The other two ships met with such a head wind that they could not weather a cape which the bay made almost at its extremity; wishing to come to us, they were near being driven to beach the ships. But, on approaching the extremity of the bay, and whilst expecting to be lost, they saw a small mouth, which did not resemble a mouth but a corner, and (like people giving up hope) they threw themselves into it, so that by force they discovered the strait. Seeing that it was not a corner, but a strait of land, they went further on and found a bay, then going still further they found another strait and another bay larger than the first two, at which, being very joyous, they suddenly returned backwards to tell it to the captain-general. Amongst us we thought that they had perished: first because of the great storm; next, because two days had passed that we had not seen them. And being thus in doubt we saw the two ships under all sail, with ensigns spread, come towards us: these, when near us, suddenly discharged much artillery, at which we, very joyous, saluted them with artillery and shouts. Afterwards, all together, thanking God and the Virgin Mary, we went to seek further on.

After having entered inside this strait we found that there were two mouths, of which one trended to the Sirocco (S.E.) and the other to the Garbin (S.W.). On that account the captain again sent the two ships, *St Anthony* and *Conception*, to see if the mouth which was towards Sirocco had an outlet beyond into the said peaceful sea. One of these two ships, named *St Anthony*, would not wait for the other ship, because those who were inside wished to return to Spain: this they did, and the principal reason was on account of the pilot of the said ship being previously discontented with the said captain-general, because that before this armament was made, this pilot had gone to the Emperor to talk about having some ships to discover countries. But, on account of the arrival of the captain-general, the Emperor did not give them to this pilot. The other ship, named the *Conception*, not being able to follow that one, was always waiting for it, and fluttered hither and thither. But it lost its time, for the other took the road by night for returning.

When this happened, at night the ship of the captain and the other ship went together to discover the mouth to Garbin (S.W.), where, on always holding on our course, we found the same strait. But at the end we arrived at a river which we named the River of Sardines, because we found a great quantity of them. So we remained there four days to wait for the other two ships. A short time after we sent a boat well supplied with men and provisions to discover the cape of the other sea; these remained three days in going and coming. They told us that they had found the cape, and the sea great and wide. At the joy which the captain-general had at this he began to cry, and he gave the name of the Cape of Desire to this cape, as a thing which had been much desired for a long time.

Having done that we turned back to find the two ships which were at the other side, but we only found the *Conception*, of which ship we asked what had become of her companion. To this the captain of the said ship, named John Serrano, replied that he knew nothing of her, and that he had never seen her since she entered the mouth. However, we sought for her through all the strait, as far as the said mouth, by which she had taken her course to return. Besides that, the captain-general sent back the ship named the *Victory* as far as the entrance of the strait to see if the ship was there, and he told the people of this ship that if they did not find the ship they were looking for, they were to place an ensign on the summit of a small hill, with a letter inside a pot placed in the ground near the ensign, so that if the ship should by chance return, it might see that ensign, and also find the letter which would give information of the course which the captain was holding. This manner of acting had been ordained by the captain from the commencement, in order to effect the junction of any ship which might be separated from the others. So the people of the said ship did what the captain had commanded them, and more; for they set two ensigns with letters; one of the ensigns was placed on a small hill at the first bay, the other on an islet in the third bay, where there were many sea wolves and large birds. The captain-general waited for them with the other ship near the river named Isles: and he caused a cross to be set upon a small island in front of that river, which was between high mountains covered with snow. This river comes and falls into the sea near the other river of the Sardines.

If we had not found this strait the captain-general had made up his mind to go as far as seventy-five degrees towards the Antarctic pole; where at that height in the summer time there is no night, or very little: in a similar manner in the winter there is no day-light, or very little, and so that every one may believe this, when we were in this strait the night lasted only three hours, and this was in the month of October.

The land of this strait on the left-hand side looked towards the Sirocco wind, which is the wind collateral to the Levant and South; we called this strait Pathagonico. In it we found at every half league a good port and place for anchoring, good waters, wood all of cedar, and fish like sardines, missiglioni, and a very sweet herb named *appio* (celery). There is also some of the same kind which is bitter. This herb grows near the springs, and from not finding anything else we ate of it for several days. I think that there is not in the world a more beautiful country, or better strait than this one.

Wednesday, the twenty-eighth of November, 1520, we came forth out of the said strait, and entered into the Pacific Sea, where we remained three months and twenty days without taking in provisions or other refreshments, and we only ate old biscuit reduced to powder, and full of grubs, and stinking from the dirt which the rats had made on it when eating the good biscuit, and we drank water that was yellow and stinking. We also ate the ox hides which were under the main-yard, so that the yard should not break the rigging: they were very hard on account of the sun, rain, and wind, and we left them for four or five days in the sea, and then we put them a little on the embers, and so ate them; also the sawdust of wood, and rats which cost half-a-crown each, moreover enough of them were not to be got. Besides the above-named evils, this misfortune which I will mention was the worst, it was that the upper and lower gums of most of our men grew so much that they could not eat, and in this way so many suffered that nineteen died. Besides those who died, twenty-five or thirty fell ill of divers sicknesses, both in the arms and legs, and other places, in such manner that very few remained healthy. However, thanks be to the Lord, I had no sickness. During those three months and twenty days we went in an open sea, while we ran fully four thousand leagues in the Pacific sea. This was well named Pacific, for during this same time we met with no storm, and saw no land except two small uninhabited islands, in which we found only birds and trees. We named them the Unfortunate Islands; they are two hundred leagues apart from one another, and there is no place to anchor, as there is no bottom. There we saw many sharks, which are a kind of large fish which they call *Tiburoni*. The first Isle is in fifteen degrees of austral latitude, and the other island is in nine degrees. With the said wind we ran each day fifty or sixty leagues, or more; now with the wind astern, sometimes on a wind or otherwise. And if our Lord and his Mother had not aided us in giving us good weather to refresh ourselves with provisions and other things, we should all have died of hunger in this very vast sea, and I think that never man will undertake to perform such a voyage.

II

Friday, the 26th of April, Zula, who was one of the principal men or chiefs in the island of Matan, sent to the captain a son of his with two goats to make a present of them, and to say that if he did not do all that he had promised, the cause of that was another chief named Silapulapu, who would not in any way obey the King of Spain, and had prevented him from doing so: but that if the captain would send him the following night one boat full of men to give him assistance, he would fight and subdue his rival. On the receipt of this message, the captain decided to go himself with three boats. We entreated him much not to go to this enterprise in person, but he as a good shepherd would not abandon his flock.

We set out from Zubu at midnight, we were sixty men armed with corslets and helmets; there were with us the Christian king, the prince, and some of the chief men, and many others divided among twenty or thirty balangai. We arrived at Matan three hours before daylight. The captain before attacking wished to attempt gentle means, and sent on shore the Moorish merchant to tell those islanders who were of the party of Cilapulapu, that if they would recognize the Christian king as their sovereign, and obey the King of Spain, and pay us the tribute which had been asked, the captain would become their friend, otherwise we should prove how our lances wounded. The islanders were not terrified, they replied that if we had lances, so also had they, although only of reeds, and wood hardened with fire. They asked however that we should not attack them by night, but wait for daylight, because they were expecting reinforcements, and would be in greater number. This they said with cunning, to excite us to attack them by night, supposing that we were ready; but they wished this because they had dug ditches between their houses and the beach, and they hoped that we should fall into them.

We however waited for daylight; and then we leaped into the water up to our thighs, for on account of the shallow water and the rocks, the boats could not come close to the beach, and we had to cross two good crossbow shots through the water before reaching it. We were forty-nine in number, the other eleven remained in charge of the boats. When we reached land we found the islanders fifteen hundred in number, drawn up in three squadrons; they came down upon us with terrible shouts, two squadrons attacking us on the flanks, and the third in front. The captain then divided his men in two bands. Our musketeers and crossbow-men fired for half an hour from a distance, but did nothing, since the bullets and arrows, though they passed through their shields made of thin wood, and perhaps wounded their arms, yet did not stop them. The captain shouted not to fire, but he was not listened to. The islanders seeing that the shots of our guns did them little or no harm would not retire, but shouted more loudly, and springing from one side to the other to avoid our shots, they at the same time drew nearer to us, throwing arrows, javelins, spears hardened in fire, stones, and even mud, so that we could hardly defend ourselves. Some of them cast lances pointed with iron at the captain-general.

He then, in order to disperse this multitude and to terrify them, sent some of our men to set fire to their houses, but this rendered them more ferocious. Some of them ran to the fire, which consumed twenty or thirty houses, and there killed two of our men. The rest came down upon us with greater fury; they perceived that our bodies were defended, but that the legs were exposed, and they aimed at them principally. The captain had his right leg pierced by a poisoned arrow, on which account he gave orders to retreat by degrees; but almost all our men took to precipitate flight, so that there remained hardly six or eight of us with him. We were oppressed by the lances and stones which the enemy hurled at us, and could make no more resistance. The bombards which we had in the boat were of no assistance to us, for the shoal water kept them too far from the beach. We went thither, retreating little by little, and still fighting, and we had already got to the distance of a crossbow shot from the shore, having the water up to our knees, the islanders following and picking up again the spears which they had already cast, and they threw the same spear five or six times; as they knew the captain they aimed specially at him, and twice they knocked the helmet off his head. He, with a few of us, like a good knight, remained at his post without choosing to retreat further. Thus we fought for more than an hour, until an Indian succeeded in thrusting a cane lance into the captain's face. He then, being irritated, pierced the Indian's breast with his lance, and left it in his body, and trying to draw his sword, he was unable to draw it more than half way, on account of a javelin wound which he had received in the right arm. The enemies seeing this, all rushed against him, and one of them with a great sword, like a great scimetar gave him a great blow on the left leg, which brought the captain down on his face; then the Indians threw themselves upon him, and ran him through with lances and scimetars, and all the other arms which they had, so that they deprived of life our mirror, light, comfort, and true guide. Whilst the Indians were thus overpowering him, several times he turned round towards us to see if we were all in safety, as though his obstinate fight had no other object than to give an opportunity for the retreat of his men. We who fought to extremity, and who were covered with wounds, seeing that he was dead, proceeded to the boats which were on the point of going away. This fatal battle was fought on the 27th of April of 1521, on a Saturday; a day which the captain had chosen himself, because he had a special devotion to it. There perished with him eight of our men, and four of the Indians, who had become Christians; we had also many wounded, amongst whom I must reckon myself. The enemy lost only fifteen men.

He died; but I hope that your illustrious highness will not allow his memory to be lost, so much the more since I see revived in you the virtue of so great a captain, since one of his principal virtues was constance in the most adverse fortune. In the midst of the sea he was able to endure hunger better than we. Most versed in nautical charts, he knew better than any other the true art of navigation, of which it is a certain proof that he knew by his genius, and his intrepidity, without anyone having given him the example, how to attempt the circuit of the globe, which he had almost completed.

THE BATTLE OF LEPANTO (1571)[1]

W. H. Prescott

(1796–1859)

ON THE third of October, Don John put to sea, and stood for the gulf of Lepanto. As the fleet swept down the Ionian Sea, it passed many a spot famous in ancient story. None, we may imagine, would be so likely to excite an interest at this time as Actium, on whose waters was fought the greatest naval battle of antiquity. But the mariner, probably, gave little thought to the past, as he dwelt on the conflict that awaited him at Lepanto. On the fifth, a thick fog enveloped the armada, and shut out every object from sight. Fortunately the vessels met with no injury, and passing by Ithaca, the ancient home of Ulysses, they safely anchored off the eastern coast of Cephalonia. For two days their progress was thwarted by head-winds. But on the seventh, Don John, impatient of delay, again put to sea, though wind and weather were still unfavourable.

It was two hours before dawn, on Sunday, the memorable seventh of October, when the fleet weighed anchor. The wind had become lighter; but it was still contrary, and the galleys were indebted for their progress much more to their oars than their sails. By sunrise they were abreast of the Curzolari,—a cluster of huge rocks, or rocky islets, which on the north defends the entrance of the gulf of Lepanto. The feet moved laboriously along, while every eye was strained to catch the first glimpse of the hostile navy. At length the watch on the foretop of the *Real* called out "A sail!" and soon after declared that the whole Ottoman fleet was in sight. Several others, climbing up the rigging, confirmed his report; and in a few moments more, word was sent to the same effect by Andrew Doria, who commanded on the right. There was no longer any doubt; and Don John, ordering his pennant to be displayed at the mizzen-peak, unfurled the great standard of the League, given by the pope, and directed a gun to be fired, the signal for battle. The report, as it ran along the rocky shores, fell cheerily on the ears of the confederates, who, raising their eyes towards the consecrated banner, filled the air with their shouts.

The principal captains now came on board the *Real*, to receive the last orders of the commander-in-chief. Even at this late hour, there were some who ventured to intimate their doubts of the expediency of engaging the enemy in a position where he had a decided advantage. But Don John cut short the discussion. "Gentlemen," he said, "this is the time for combat, not for counsel." He then continued the dispositions he was making for the attack.

He had already given to each commander of a galley written instruc-

[1] From *History of Philip II.*

tions as to the manner in which the line of battle was to be formed in case of meeting the enemy. The armada was now disposed in that order. It extended on a front of three miles. Far on the right, a squadron of sixty-four galleys was commanded by the Genoese admiral, Andrew Doria,—a name of terror to the Moslems. The centre, or *battle*, as it was called, consisting of sixty-three galleys, was led by John of Austria, who was supported on the one side by Colonna, the captain-general of the pope, and on the other by the Venetian captain-general, Veniero. Immediately in the rear was the galley of the Grand-Commander Requesens who still remained near the person of his former pupil; though a difference which arose between them on the voyage, fortunately now healed, showed that the young commander-in-chief was wholly independent of his teacher in the art of war.

The left wing was commanded by the noble Venetian, Barbarigo, whose vessels stretched along the Aetolian shore, to which he approached as near as, in his ignorance of the coast, he dared to venture, so as to prevent his being turned by the enemy. Finally, the reserve, consisting of thirty-five galleys, was given to the brave marquis of Santa Cruz, with directions to act in any quarter where he thought his presence most needed. The smaller craft, some of which had now arrived, seem to have taken little part in the action, which was thus left to the galleys.

Each commander was to occupy so much space with his galley as to allow room for manœuvring it to advantage, and yet not enough to allow the enemy to break the line. He was directed to single out his adversary, to close with him at once, and board as soon as possible. The beaks of the galleys were pronounced to be a hindrance rather than a help in action. They were rarely strong enough to resist a shock from an antagonist, and they much interfered with the working and firing of the guns. Don John had the beak of his vessel cut away. The example was followed throughout the fleet, and, as it is said, with eminently good effect. It may seem strange that this discovery should have been reserved for the crisis of a battle.

When the officers had received their last instructions, they returned to their respective vessels; and Don John, going on board of a light frigate, passed rapidly through the part of the armada lying on his right, while he commanded Requesens to do the same with the vessels on his left. His object was to feel the temper of his men, and to rouse their mettle by a few words of encouragement. The Venetians he reminded of their recent injuries. The hour for vengeance, he told them, had arrived. To the Spaniards and other confederates he said: "You have come to fight the battle of the Cross; to conquer or to die. But whether you are to die or conquer, do your duty this day, and you will secure a glorious immortality." His words were received with a burst of enthusiasm which went to the heart of the commander, and assured him that he could rely on his men in the hour of trial. On returning to his vessel, he saw Veniero on his quarter-deck; and they exchanged salutations in as friendly a manner as if no difference had existed between them. At this solemn hour both these brave men were willing to forget all personal animosity in a common feeling of devotion to the great cause in which they were engaged.

The Ottoman fleet came on slowly and with difficulty. For, strange to say, the wind, which had hitherto been adverse to the Christians, after lulling for a time, suddenly shifted to the opposite quarter, and blew in the face of the enemy. As the day advanced, moreover, the sun, which had shone in the eyes of the confederates, gradually shot its rays into those of the Moslems. Both circumstances were of good omen to the Christians, and the first was regarded as nothing short of a direct interposition of Heaven. Thus ploughing its way along, the Turkish armament, as it came more into view, showed itself in greater strength than had been anticipated by the allies. It consisted of nearly two hundred and fifty royal galleys, most of them of the largest class, besides a number of smaller vessels in the rear, which, like those of the allies, appear scarcely to have come into action. The men on board, of every description, were computed at not less than a hundred and twenty thousand. The galleys spread out, as usual with the Turks, in the form of a regular half-moon, covering a wider extent of surface than the combined fleets, which they somewhat exceeded in number. They presented, indeed, as they drew nearer, a magnificent array, with their gilded and gaudily-painted prows, and their myriads of pennons and streamers, fluttering gaily in the breeze; while the rays of the morning sun glanced on the polished scymitars of Damascus, and on the superb aigrettes of jewels which sparkled in the turbans of the Ottoman chiefs.

In the centre of the extended line, and directly opposite to the station occupied by the captain-general of the League, was the huge galley of Ali Pasha. The right of the armada was commanded by Mahomet Sirocco, viceroy of Egypt, a circumspect as well as courageous leader; the left, by Uluch Ali, dey of Algiers, the redoubtable corsair of the Mediterranean. Ali Pasha had experienced a difficulty like that of Don John, as several of his officers had strongly urged the inexpediency of engaging so formidable an armament as that of the allies. But Ali, like his rival, was young and ambitious. He had been sent by his master to fight the enemy; and no remonstrances, not even those of Mahomet Sirocco, for whom he had great respect, could turn him from his purpose.

He had, moreover, received intelligence that the allied fleet was much inferior in strength to what it proved. In this error he was fortified by the first appearance of the Christians; for the extremity of their left wing, commanded by Barbarigo, stretching behind the Aetolian shore, was hidden from his view. As he drew nearer and saw the whole extent of the Christian lines, it is said his countenance fell. If so, he still did not abate one jot of his resolution. He spoke to those around him with the same confidence as before, of the result of the battle. He urged his rowers to strain every nerve. Ali was a man of more humanity in his nature than often belonged to his nation. His galley-slaves were all, or nearly all, Christian captives; and he addressed them in this brief and pithy manner:—"If your countrymen are to win this day, Allah give you the benefit of it: yet if I win it, you shall certainly have your freedom. If you feel that I do well by you, do then the like by me."

As the Turkish admiral drew nearer, he made a change in his order of battle, by separating his wings farther from his centre, thus conforming to the dispositions of the allies. Before he had come within cannon-shot, he fired a gun by way of challenge to his enemy. It was answered by another from the galley of John of Austria. A second gun discharged by Ali was as promptly replied to by the Christian commander. The distance between the two fleets was now rapidly diminishing. At this solemn moment a death-like silence reigned throughout the armament of the confederates. Men seemed to hold their breath, as if absorbed in the expectation of some great catastrophe. The day was magnificent. A light breeze, still adverse to the Turks, played on the waters, somewhat fretted by the contrary winds. It was nearly noon; and as the sun, mounting through a cloudless sky, rose to the zenith, he seemed to pause, as if to look down on the beautiful scene, where the multitude of galleys, moving over the water, showed like a holiday spectacle rather than a preparation for mortal combat.

The illusion was soon dispelled by the fierce yells which rose on the air from the Turkish armada. It was the customary war-cry with which the Moslems entered into battle. Very different was the scene on board of the Christian galleys. Don John might be there seen, armed *cap-à-pie*, standing on the prow of the *Real*, anxiously awaiting the conflict. In this conspicuous position, kneeling down, he raised his eyes to Heaven, and humbly prayed that the Almighty would be with his people on that day. His example was followed by the whole fleet. Officers and men, all prostrating themselves on their knees, and turning their eyes to the consecrated banner which floated from the *Real*, put up a petition like that of their commander. They then received absolution from the priests, of whom there were some in every vessel; and each man, as he rose to his feet, gathered new strength, as he felt assured that the Lord of Hosts would fight on his side.

When the foremost vessels of the Turks had come within cannon-shot, they opened their fire on the Christians. The firing soon rang along the whole of the Turkish line, and was kept up without interruption as it advanced. Don John gave orders for trumpet and atabal to sound the signal for action; which was followed by the simultaneous discharge of such of the guns in the combined fleet as could be brought to bear on the enemy. The Spanish commander had caused the *galeazzas*, those mammoth warships, to be towed half a mile ahead of the fleet, where they might intercept the advance of the Turks. As the latter came abreast of them, the huge galleys delivered their broadsides right and left, and their heavy ordnance produced a startling effect. Ali Pasha gave orders for his galleys to open their line and pass on either side, without engaging these monsters of the deep, of which he had had no experience. Even so their heavy guns did considerable damage to several of the nearest vessels, and created some confusion in the pacha's line of battle. They were, however, but unwieldy craft, and having accomplished their object, seem to have taken no further part in the combat.

The action began on the left wing of the allies, which Mahomet Sirocco was desirous of turning. This had been anticipated by Barbarigo, the Venetian admiral, who commanded in that quarter. To prevent it, as we have seen, he lay with his vessels as near the coast as he dared. Sirocco, better acquainted with the soundings, saw there was space enough for him to pass, and darting by with all the speed that oars could give him, he succeeded in doubling on his enemy. Thus placed between two fires, the extreme of the Christian left fought at terrible disadvantage. No less than eight galleys went to the bottom, and several others were captured. The brave Barbarigo, throwing himself into the heat of the fight, without availing himself of his defensive armour, was pierced in the eye by an arrow, and, reluctant to leave the glory of the field to another, was borne to his cabin. The combat still continued with unabated fury on the part of the Venetians. They fought like men who felt that the war was theirs, and who were animated not only by the thirst for glory, but for revenge.

Far on the Christian right a manœuvre similar to that so successfully executed by Sirocco was attempted by Uluch Ali, the dey of Algiers. Profiting by his superiority in numbers, he endeavoured to turn the right wing of the confederates. It was in this quarter that Andrew Doria commanded. He had foreseen this movement of his enemy, and he succeeded in foiling it. It was a trial of skill between the two most accomplished seamen in the Mediterranean. Doria extended his line so far to the right indeed, to prevent being surrounded, that Don John was obliged to remind him that he left the centre too much exposed. His depositions were so far unfortunate for himself, that his own line was thus weakened, and afforded some vulnerable points to his assailant. These were soon detected by the eagle eye of Uluch Ali; and, like the king of birds swooping on his prey, he fell on some galleys separated by a considerable interval from their companions, and, sinking more than one, carried off the great *Capitana* of Malta in triumph as his prize.

While the combat opened thus disastrously to the allies both on the right and on the left, in the centre they may be said to have fought with doubtful fortune. Don John had led his division gallantly forward. But the object on which he was intent was an encounter with Ali Pasha, the foe most worthy of his sword. The Turkish commander had the same combat no less at heart. The galleys of both were easily recognized, not only from their position, but from their superior size and richer decoration. The one, moreover, displayed the holy banner of the League; the other, the great Ottoman standard. This, like the ancient standard of the caliphs, was held sacred in its character. It was covered with texts from the Koran, emblazoned in letters of gold, and had the name of Allah inscribed upon it no less than twenty-eight thousand nine hundred times. It was the banner of the sultan, having passed from father to son since the foundation of the imperial dynasty, and was never seen in the field unless the grand seigneur or his lieutenant was there in person.

Both the chiefs urged on their rowers to the top of their speed. Their galleys soon shot ahead of the rest of the line, driven through the boiling surges as by the force of a tornado, and closed with a shock that made every timber crack, and the two vessels to quiver to their very keels. So powerful, indeed, was the impetus they received, that the pacha's galley, which was considerably the larger and loftier of the two, was thrown so far upon his opponent, that the prow reached the fourth bench of rowers. As soon as the vessels were disengaged from each other, and those on board had recovered from the shock, the work of death began. Don John's chief strength consisted in some three hundred Spanish arquebusiers, culled from the flower of his infantry. Ali, on the other hand, was provided with an equal number of janizaries. He was followed by a smaller vessel, in which two hundred more were stationed as a *corps de reserve*. He had, moreover, a hundred archers on board. The bow was still as much in use with the Turks as with the other Moslems.

The pacha opened at once on his enemy a terrible fire of cannon and musketry. It was returned with equal spirit and much more effect; for the Turks were observed to shoot over the heads of their adversaries. The Moslem galley was unprovided with the defences which protected the sides of the Spanish vessels; and the troops, crowded together on the lofty prow, presented an easy mark to their enemy's balls. But though numbers of them fell at every discharge, their places were soon supplied by those in reserve. They were enabled, therefore, to keep up an incessant fire, which wasted the strength of the Spaniards; and as both Christian and Mussulman fought with indomitable spirit, it seemed doubtful to which side victory would incline.

The affair was made more complicated by the entrance of other parties into the conflict. Both Ali and Don John were supported by some of the most gallant captains in their fleets. Next to the Spanish commander, as we have seen, were Colonna and the veteran Veniero, who, at the age of seventy-six, performed feats of arms worthy of a paladin of romance. In this way a little squadron of combatants gathered round the principal leaders, who sometimes found themselves assailed by several enemies at the same time. Still the chiefs did not lose sight of one another; but, beating off their inferior foes as well as they could, each, refusing to loosen his hold, clung with mortal grasp to his antagonist.

Thus the fight raged along the whole extent of the entrance to the gulf of Lepanto. The volumes of vapour rolling heavily over the waters effectually shut out from sight whatever was passing at any considerable distance, unless when a fresher breeze dispelled the smoke for a moment, or the flashes of the heavy guns threw a transient gleam on the dark canopy of battle. If the eye of the spectator could have penetrated the cloud of smoke that enveloped the combatants, and have embraced the whole scene at a glance, he would have perceived them broken up into small detachments, separately engaged one with another, independently of the rest, and indeed ignorant of all that was doing in other quarters. The contest exhibited few of those large combinations and skilful manœuvres to be expected in a great naval encounter. It was rather an assemblage of petty actions, resembling those on land. The galleys, grappling together, presented a level arena, on which soldier and galley-slave fought hand to hand, and the fate of the engagement was generally decided by boarding. As in most hand-to-hand contests, there was an enormous waste of life. The decks were loaded with corpses, Christian and Moslem lying promiscuously together in the embrace of death. Instances are recorded where every man on board was slain or wounded. It was a ghastly spectacle, where blood flowed in rivulets down the sides of the vessels, staining the waters of the gulf for miles around.

It seemed as if a hurricane had swept over the sea, and covered it with the wreck of the noble armaments which a moment before were so proudly riding on its bosom. Little had they now to remind one of their late magnificent array, with their hulls battered, their masts and spars gone or splintered by the shot, their canvas cut into shreds and floating wildly on the breeze, while thousands of wounded and drowning men were clinging to the floating fragments, and calling piteously for help. Such was the wild uproar which succeeded the Sabbath-like stillness that two hours before had reigned over these beautiful solitudes.

The left wing of the confederates, commanded by Barbarigo, had been sorely pressed by the Turks, as we have seen, at the beginning of the fight. Barbarigo himself had been mortally wounded. His line had been turned. Several of his galleys had been sunk. But the Venetians gathered courage from despair. By incredible efforts they succeeded in beating off their enemies. They became the assailants in their turn. Sword in hand, they carried one vessel after another. The Capuchin was seen in the thickest of the fight, waving aloft his crucifix, and leading the boarders to the assault. The Christian galley-slaves, in some instances, broke their fetters, and joined their countrymen against their masters. Fortunately, the vessel of Mahomet Sirocco, the Moslem admiral, was sunk; and though extricated from the water himself, it was only to perish by the

sword of his conqueror, Giovanni Contarini. The Venetian could find
in his heart no mercy for the Turk.

The fall of their commander gave the final blow to his followers.
Without further attempt to prolong the fight they fled before the avenging swords of the Venetians. Those nearest the land endeavoured to
escape by running their vessels ashore, where they abandoned them as
prizes to the Christians. Yet many of the fugitives, before gaining the
land, perished miserably in the waves. Barbarigo, the Venetian admiral,
who was still lingering in agony, heard the tidings of the enemy's defeat,
and, uttering a few words expressive of his gratitude to Heaven, which
had permitted him to see this hour, he breathed his last.

During this time the combat had been going forward in the centre
between the two commanders-in-chief, Don John and Ali Pasha, whose
galleys blazed with an incessant fire of artillery and musketry, that
enveloped them like "a martyr's robe of flames." The parties fought with
equal spirit, though not with equal fortune. Twice the Spaniards had
boarded their enemy, and both times they had been repulsed with loss.
Still their superiority in the use of fire-arms would have given them a
decided advantage over their opponents, if the loss they had inflicted
had not been speedily repaired by fresh reinforcements. More than once
the contest between the two chieftains was interrupted by the arrival of
others to take part in the fray. They soon, however, returned to each
other, as if unwilling to waste their strength on a meaner enemy. Through
the whole engagement both commanders exposed themselves to danger
as freely as any common soldier. In such a contest even Philip must
have admitted that it would be difficult for his brother to find, with
honour, a place of safety. Don John received a wound in the foot. It was
a slight one, however, and he would not allow it to be dressed till the
action was over.

Again his men were mustered, and a third time the trumpets sounded
to the attack. It was more successful than the preceding. The Spaniards
threw themselves boldly into the Turkish galley. They were met with the
same spirit as before by the janizaries. Ali Pasha led them on. Unfortunately, at this moment, he was struck in the head by a musket-ball,
and stretched senseless in the gangway. His men fought worthily of their
ancient renown. But they missed the accustomed voice of their commander. After a short but ineffectual struggle against the fiery impetuosity of the Spaniards, they were overpowered and threw down their
arms. The decks were loaded with the bodies of the dead and the dying.
Beneath these was discovered the Turkish commander-in-chief, severely
wounded, but perhaps not mortally. He was drawn forth by some Castilian soldiers, who, recognizing his person, would at once have dispatched
him. But the disabled chief, having rallied from the first effects of his
wound, had sufficient presence of mind to divert them from their purpose, by pointing out the place below where he had deposited his money

and jewels; and they hastened to profit by the disclosure, before the treasure should fall into the hands of their comrades.

Ali was not so successful with another soldier, who came up soon after, brandishing his sword, and preparing to plunge it into the body of the prostrate commander. It was in vain that the latter endeavoured to turn the ruffian from his purpose. He was a convict, one of those galley-slaves whom Don John had caused to be unchained from the oar and furnished with arms. He could not believe that any treasure would be worth so much as the head of the pacha. Without further hesitation, he dealt him a blow which severed it from his shoulders. Then, returning to his galley, he laid the bloody trophy before Don John. But he had miscalculated on his recompense. His commander gazed on it with a look of pity mingled with horror. He may have thought of the generous conduct of Ali to his Christian captives, and have felt that he deserved a better fate. He coldly inquired "of what use such a present could be to him"; and then ordered it to be thrown into the sea. Far from the order being obeyed, it is said the head was stuck on a pike, and raised aloft on board of the captured galley. At the same time the banner of the Crescent was pulled down; while that of the Cross, run up in its place, proclaimed the downfall of the pacha.

The sight of the sacred ensign was welcomed by the Christians with a shout of "Victory!" which rose high above the din of battle. The tidings of the death of Ali soon passed from mouth to mouth, giving fresh heart to the confederates, but falling like a knell on the ears of the Moslems. Their confidence was gone. Their fire slackened. Their efforts grew weaker and weaker. They were too far from shore to seek an asylum there, like their comrades on the right. They had no resource but to prolong the combat or to surrender. Most preferred the latter. Many vessels were carried by boarding, others were sunk by the victorious Christians. Ere four hours had elapsed, the centre, like the right wing, of the Moslems might be said to be annihilated.

Still the fight was lingering on the right of the confederates, where, it will be remembered, Uluch Ali, the Algerine chief, had profited by Doria's error in extending his line so far as greatly to weaken it. Uluch Ali, attacking it on its most vulnerable quarter, had succeeded, as we have seen, in capturing and destroying several vessels, and would have inflicted still heavier losses on his enemy had it not been for the seasonable succor received from the marquis of Santa Cruz. This brave officer, who commanded the reserve, had already been of much service to Don John when the *Real* was assailed by several Turkish galleys at once during his combat with Ali Pasha; for at this juncture the marquis of Santa Cruz arriving, and beating off the assailants, one of whom he afterwards captured, enabled the commander-in-chief to resume his engagement with the pacha.

No sooner did Santa Cruz learn the critical situation of Doria, than, supported by Cardona, "general" of the Sicilian squadron, he pushed forward to his relief. Dashing into the midst of the *mêlée*, the two commanders fell like a thunderbolt on the Algerine galleys. Few attempted to withstand the shock. But in their haste to avoid it, they were encountered by Doria and his Genoese galleys. Thus beset on all sides, Uluch Ali was compelled to abandon his prizes and provide for his own safety by flight. He cut adrift the Maltese *Capitana*, which he had lashed to his stern, and on which three hundred corpses attested the desperate character of her defence. As tidings reached him of the discomfiture of the centre, and of the death of Ali Pasha, he felt that nothing remained but to make the best of his way from the fatal scene of action, and save as many of his own ships as he could. And there were no ships in the Turkish fleet superior to his, or manned by men under more perfect discipline. For they were the famous corsairs of the Mediterranean, who had been rocked from infancy on its waters.

Throwing out his signals for retreat, the Algerine was soon to be seen, at the head of his squadron, standing towards the north, under as much canvas as remained to him after the battle, and urged forward through the deep by the whole strength of his oarsmen. Doria and Santa Cruz followed quickly in his wake. But he was borne on the wings of the wind, and soon distanced his pursuers. Don John, having disposed of his own assailants, was coming to the support of Doria, and now joined in the pursuit of the viceroy. A rocky headland, stretching far into the sea, lay in the path of the fugitive; and his enemies hoped to intercept him there. Some few of his vessels were stranded on the rocks. But the rest, near forty in number, standing more boldly out to sea, safely doubled the promontory. Then, quickening their flight, they gradually faded from the horizon, their white sails, the last thing visible, showing in the distance like a flock of Arctic seafowl on their way to their native homes. The confederates explained the inferior sailing of their own galleys on this occasion by the circumstances of their rowers, who had been allowed to bear arms in the fight, being crippled by their wounds.

The battle had lasted more than four hours. The sky, which had been almost without a cloud through the day, began now to be overcast, and showed signs of a coming storm. Before seeking a place of shelter for himself and his prizes, Don John reconnoitred the scene of action. He met with several vessels too much damaged for further service. These, mostly belonging to the enemy, after saving what was of any value on board, he ordered to be burnt. He selected the neighbouring port of Petala, as affording the most secure and accessible harbour for the night. Before he had arrived there, the tempest began to mutter and darkness was on the water. Yet the darkness rendered only more visible the blazing wrecks, which, sending up streams of fire mingled with showers of sparks, looked like volcanoes on the deep.

THE CAPTIVE'S ESCAPE[1]

Miguel de Cervantes Saavedra

(1547–1616)

IN LESS than fifteen days our renegado had bought a very good bark, capable of holding above thirty persons; and, to make sure work, and give the business a colour, he made a short voyage to a place called Sargel, thirty leagues from Algiers towards Oran, to which there is a great trade for dried figs. Two or three times he made this trip, in company of the Tagarin. You must know, that each time he passed with his bark, he cast anchor in a little creek, not two bow-shots distant from the garden, where Zoraida expected us: and there the renegado designedly set himself, together with the Moors that rowed, either to perform the zala, or to practise by way of jest what he intended to execute in earnest; and with this view he would go to Zoraida's garden, and beg some fruit, which her father would give him, without knowing who he was. His design was, as he afterwards told me, to speak to Zoraida and tell her that he was the person, who, by my direction, was to carry her to Christendom, and that she might be easy and secure: but it was impossible for him to do it, the Moorish women never suffering themselves to be seen either by Moor or Turk, unless when commanded by their husbands and fathers. But I should have been sorry if he had talked to her, because it might have frightened her, to see that the business was intrusted to a renegado. But God, who ordered it otherwise, gave the renegado no opportunity of effecting his good design: who, finding how securely he went to and from Sargel, and that he lay at anchor, when, how, and where, he pleased, and that the Tagarin, his partner, had no will of his own, but approved whatever he directed; that I was ransomed, and that there wanted nothing but to find some Christians to help to row; he bid me consider who I would bring with me, besides those already ransomed, and bespeak them for the first Friday; for that was the time he fixed for our departure. Upon this I spoke to twelve Spaniards, all able men at the oar, and such as could most easily get out of the city unsuspected: and it was no easy matter to find so many at that juncture; for there were twenty corsairs out pirating, and they had taken almost all the rowers with them; and these had not been found, but that their master did not go out that summer, having a galiot to finish, that was then upon the stocks. I said nothing more to them, but that they should steal out of the town one by one, the next Friday in the dusk of the evening, and wait for me somewhere about Agimorato's garden. I gave this direction to each of them separately, with this caution, that, if they

---

[1]From the translation of *Don Quixote* by Charles Jarvis.

should see any other Christians there, they should only say, I ordered them to stay for me in that place.

"This point being taken care of, one thing was yet wanting, and that the most necessary of all; which was, to inform Zoraida how matters stood, that she might be in readiness, and on the watch, so as not to be frightened if we rushed upon her on a sudden, before the time she could think that the vessel from Christendom could be arrived. And therefore I resolved to go to the garden, and try if I could speak to her: and under pretence of gathering some herbs, one day before our departure I went thither, and the first person I met was her father, who spoke to me in a language, which all over Barbary, and even at Constantinople, is spoken among captives and Moors, and is neither Morisco nor Castilian, nor of any other nation, but a medley of all languages, and generally understood. He, I say, in that jargon, asked me what I came to look for in that garden, and to whom I belonged? I answered him, I was a slave of Arnauté Mamai, who, I knew, was a very great friend of his; and that I came for a few herbs of several sorts to make a sallad. He then asked me if I was upon ransom or not, and how much my master demanded for me? While we were thus talking, the fair Zoraida, who had espied me some time before, came out of the house: and, as the Moorish women make no scruple of appearing before the Christians, nor are at all shy towards them, as I have already observed, she made no difficulty of coming where I stood with her father, who, seeing her walking slowly towards us, called to her, and bid her come on. It would be too hard a task for me, at this time, to express the great beauty, the finery and richness of attire, with which my beloved Zoraida appeared then before my eyes. More pearls, if I may say so, hung about her beauteous neck, and more jewels were in her ears and hair, than she had hairs on her head. In short, she came extremely adorned, and extremely beautiful; to me at least she seemed the most so of any thing I had ever beheld: which, together with my obligations to her, made me think her an angel from heaven, descended for my pleasure and relief.

"When she was come up to us, her father told her, in her own tongue, that I was a captive belonging to his friend Arnauté Mamai, and that I came to look for a sallad. She took up the discourse, and in the aforesaid medley of languages, asked me whether I was a gentleman, and why I did not ransom myself. I told her I was already ransomed, and by the price she might guess what my master thought of me, since he had got fifteen hundred pieces of eight for me. To which she answered:'Truly, had you belonged to my father, he should not have parted with you for twice that sum: for you Christians always falsify in your accounts of yourselves, pretending to be poor, in order to cheat the Moors.' —'It may very well be so, madam,' answered I; 'but in truth, I dealt sincerely with my master, and ever did and shall do the same by everybody in the world.' 'And when you go away?' said Zoraida. 'To-morrow

I believe,' said I: 'for there is a French vessel which sails to-morrow, and I intend to go in her.'—'Would it not be better,' replied Zoraida, 'to stay until some ships come from Spain, and go with them, and not with those of France, who are not your friends?'—'No, madam,' answered I; 'but should the news we have of a Spanish ship's coming suddenly prove true, I would perhaps stay a little for it, though it is more likely I shall depart to-morrow: for the desire I have to be in my own country, and with the persons I love, is so great, that it will not suffer me to wait for any other conveniency, though ever so much better.' —'You are married, doubtless, in your own country?' said Zoraida, 'and therefore you are so desirous to be gone, and be at home with your wife?'—'No,' replied I, 'I am not married; but I have given my word to marry as soon as I get thither.'—'And is the lady whom you have promised beautiful?' said Zoraida. 'So beautiful,' answered I, 'that to compliment her, and tell you the truth, she is very like yourself.' Her father laughed heartily at this, and said: 'Really, Christian, she must be beautiful indeed, if she resembles my daughter, who is accounted the handsomest woman in all this kingdom: observe her well, and you will see I speak the truth.' Zoraida's father served us as an interpreter to most of this conversation, as understanding Spanish; for though she spoke the bastard language in use there, as I told you, yet she expressed her meaning more by signs than by words.

"While we were thus engaged in discourse, a Moor came running to us, crying aloud that four Turks had leaped over the pales or wall of the garden, and were gathering the fruit, though it was not yet ripe. The old man was put into a fright, and so was Zoraida: for the Moors are naturally afraid of the Turks, especially of their soldiers, who are insolent and imperious. Therefore Zoraida's father said to her; 'Daughter, retire into the house, and lock yourself in, while I go and talk to these dogs; and you, Christian, gather your herbs, and be gone in peace, and Alla send you safe to your own country.' I bowed myself, and he went his way to find the Turks, leaving me alone with Zoraida, who also made as if she was going whither her father bid her. But scarcely was he got out of sight among the trees of the garden, when she turned back to me, with her eyes full of tears, and said: 'Amexi, Christiano, amexi?' that is, '*Are you going away, Christian, are you going away?*' I answered, 'Yes, madam, but not without you: expect me the next Juma, and be not frightened when you see us; for we shall certainly get to Christendom.' I said this in such a manner, that she understood me very well; and throwing her arm about my neck, she began to walk softly and trembling towards the house: and fortune would have it, which might have proved fatal, if heaven had not ordained otherwise, that, while we were going in the posture and manner I told you, her arm being about my neck, her father returning from driving away the Turks, saw us in that posture, and we were sensible that he discovered us. But Zoraida had the discretion and presence of mind not to take her arm from about my neck, but rather held me closer; and leaning her head against my breast, and bending her knees a little, gave plain signs of fainting away: and I also made as if I held her up only to keep her from falling. Her father came running to us, and seeing his daughter in that posture, asked what ailed her. But she not answering, he said: 'Without doubt, these dogs have frightened her into a swoon': and taking her from me, he inclined her gently to his bosom. And she fetching a deep sigh, and her eyes still full of tears, said again: 'Amexi, Christiano, amexi': *Begone, Christian, Begone.* To which her father answered: 'There is no occasion, child, why the Christian should go away: he has done you no harm, and the Turks are gone off: let nothing frighten you; there is no danger.' 'Sir,' said I to her father, 'they have frightened her, as you say; but, since she bids me be gone, I will not disturb her: God be with you, and with your leave, I will come again, if we have occasion for herbs.' I now took my leave of them both, and she, seeming as if her soul had been rent from her, went away with her father. And I, under pretence of gathering herbs, walked over and took a view of the whole garden at my leisure, observing carefully all the inlets and outlets, and the strength of the house, and every conveniency which might tend to facilitate our business.

"When I had so done, I went and gave an account to the renegado and my companions of all that had passed, longing eagerly for the hour when, without fear of surprise, I might enjoy the happiness which fortune presented me in the beautiful Zoraida. In a word, time passed on, and the day appointed, and by us so much wished for, came; and we all observing the order and method which after mature deliberation and long debate we had agreed on, had the desired success. For the Friday following the day when I talked with Zoraida in the garden, Morrenago, for that was the renegado's name, at the close of the evening cast anchor with the bark almost opposite to where Zoraida dwelt. The Christians who were to be employed at the oar were ready and hidden in several places thereabouts. They were all in suspense, their hearts beating in expectation of my coming, being eager to surprise the bark which lay before their eyes: for they knew nothing of what was concerted with the renegado, but thought they were to regain their liberty by mere force, and by killing the Moors who were on board the vessel. As soon, therefore, as I and my friends appeared, all they that were hidden came out and joined us one after another. It was now the time when the city gates were shut, and nobody appeared abroad in all that quarter. Being met together, we were in some doubt whether it would be better to go first to Zoraida, or secure the Moors who rowed the vessel. While we were in this uncertainty, our renegado came to us, asking us what we staid for; for now was the time, all his Moors being thoughtless of danger, and most of them asleep. We told him what we demurred about, and he said, that the thing of the most importance was, first to seize the vessel, which might be done with all imaginable ease, and without any manner of danger; and then we might presently go and fetch Zoraida. We all approved of what he said, and so, without further delay, he being our guide, we came to the vessel; and he leaping in first, drew a cutlass, and said in Morisco: 'Let not one man of you stir, unless he has a mind it should cost him his life.' By this time all the Christians were got on board; and the Moors, who were timorous fellows, hearing the master speak thus, were in a great fright; and, without making any resistance, for indeed they had few or no arms, silently suffered themselves to be bound, which was done very expeditiously, the Christians threatening the Moors that if they raised any manner of cry, or made the least noise, they would in that instant put them all to the sword.

"This being done, and half our number remaining on board to guard them, the rest of us, the renegado being still our leader, went to Agimorato's garden, and as good luck would have it, the door opened as easily to us as if it had not been locked: and we came up to the house with great stillness and silence, and without being perceived by anyone. The lovely Zoraida was expecting us at a window, and when she knew it was I, she staid not a moment, but came down in an instant, and opening the door, appeared to us all so beautiful and richly attired that I cannot easily express it. As soon as I saw her I took her hand and kissed it: the renegado did the same, and my two comrades also, and the rest, who knew not the meaning of it, followed our example, thinking we only meant to express our thanks and acknowledgments to her as the instrument of our deliverance. The renegado asked her in Morisco, whether her father was in the house: she answered he was, and asleep. 'Then we must awaken him,' replied the renegado, 'and carry him with us, and all that he has of value in this beautiful villa.'—'No' said she, 'my father must by no means be touched, and there is nothing considerable here but what I have with me, which is sufficient to make you all rich and content: stay a little, and you shall see.' And so saying, she went in again, and bid us be quiet, and make no noise, for she would come back immediately. I asked the renegado what she said: he told me, and I bid him be sure to do just as Zoraida would have him, who was now returned with a little trunk so full of gold crowns, that she could hardly carry it.

"Ill fortune would have it, that her father in the meantime happened to awake, and hearing a noise in the garden, looked out at the window, and presently found there were Christians in it. Immediately he cried out as loud as he could in Arabic, 'Christians, Christians, thieves, thieves!' which outcry put all into the utmost terror and confusion. But the renegado seeing the danger we were in and considering how much it imported him to go through with the enterprise before it was discovered, ran up with the greatest speed to the room where Agimorato was;

and with him ran up several others: but I did not dare to quit Zoraida, who had sunk into my arms almost in a swoon. In short, they that went up acquitted themselves so well, that in a moment they came down with Agimorato, having tied his hands, and stopped his mouth with a handkerchief, so that he could not speak a word, and threatening, if he made the least noise, that it should cost him his life. When his daughter saw him she covered her eyes, that she might avoid his sight, and her father was astonished at finding her, not knowing how willingly she had put herself into our hands. But at that time, it being of the utmost consequence to us to fly, we got as speedily as we could to the bark, where our comrades already expected us with impatience, fearing we had met with some cross accident. Scarcely two hours of the night were passed, when we were all got on board, and then we untied the hands of Zoraida's father, and took the handkerchief out of his mouth: but the renegado warned him again not to speak a word; for if he did they would take away his life. When he saw his daughter there, he began to weep most tenderly, and especially when he perceived that I held her closely embraced, and that she, without making any show of opposition, complaint, or coyness, sat so still and quiet: nevertheless he held his peace, lest we should put the renegado's threats in execution.

"Zoraida now finding herself in the bark, and that we began to handle our oars, and seeing her father there, and the rest of the Moors, who were bound, spoke to the renegado, to desire me to do her the favour to loose those Moors, and set her father at liberty; for she would sooner throw herself into the sea, than see a father, who loved her so tenderly, carried away captive before her eyes, and upon her account. The renegado told me what she desired, and I answered that I was entirely satisfied it should be so: but he replied it was not convenient; for should they be set on shore there, they would presently raise the country and alarm the city, and cause some light frigates to be sent out in quest of us, and so we should be beset both by sea and land, and it would be impossible for us to escape: but what might be done was, to give them their liberty at the first Christian country we should touch at. We all came into this opinion, and Zoraida also was satisfied when we told her what we had determined, and the reasons why we could not at present comply with her request. And then immediately, with joyful silence and cheerful diligence, each of our brave rowers handled his oar, and recommending ourselves to God with all our hearts, we began to make toward the island of Majorca, which is the nearest Christian land. But the north wind beginning to blow fresh, and the sea being somewhat rough, it was not possible for us to steer the course of Majorca, and we were forced to keep along shore towards Oran, not without great apprehensions of being discovered from the town of Sargel, which lies on that coast, about sixty miles from Algiers. We were afraid, likewise, of meeting in our passage with some of those galiots which came usually

with merchandise from Tetuan; though, each relying on his own courage and that of his comrades in general, we presumed that, if we should
meet a galiot, provided it were not a cruiser, we should be so far from
being ruined, that we should probably take a vessel in which we might
more securely pursue our course. While we proceeded in our voyage,
Zoraida kept her head between my hands, that she might not look on her
father; and I could perceive she was continually calling upon Lela
Marien to assist us.

"We had rowed about thirty miles, when day-break came upon us,
and we found ourselves not above three musket-shot distant from the
shore, which seemed to be quite a desert, and without any creature to
discover us: however, by mere dint of rowing, we made a little out to
sea, which was by this time become more calm; and when we had advanced about two leagues, it was ordered they should row by turns,
whilst we took a little refreshment, the bark being well provided, but
the rowers said, that it was not a time to take any rest, and that they
would by no means quit their oars, but would eat and row, if those who
were unemployed would bring the victuals to them. They did so; and
now the wind began to blow a brisk gale, which forced us to set up our
sails, lay down our oars, and steer directly to Oran, it being impossible
to hold any other course. All this was done with great expedition; and
we sailed above eight miles an hour, without any other fear than that of
meeting some corsair. We gave the Moorish prisoners something to eat,
and the renegado comforted them, telling them they were not slaves,
and that they should have their liberty given them the first opportunity,
and he said the same to Zoraida's father, who answered: 'I might, perhaps, expect or hope for any other favour from your liberality and generous usage, O Christians; but as to giving me my liberty, think me not
so simple as to imagine it; for you would never have exposed yourselves
to the hazard of taking it from me, to restore it me so freely, especially
since you know who I am, and the advantage that may accrue to you
by my ransom; which do but name, and from this moment I promise
you whatever you demand for myself and for this my unhappy daughter, or else for her alone, who is the greater and better part of my soul.'
In saying this he began to weep so bitterly, that it moved us all to
compassion, and forced Zoraida to look up at him; who seeing him weep
in that manner, was so melted, that she got up from me, and ran to embrace her father; and laying her face to his, they began so tender a
lamentation that many of us could not forbear keeping them company.
But when her father observed that she was adorned with her best attire,
and had so many jewels about her, he said to her in his language: 'How
comes it, daughter, that yesterday evening, before this terrible misfortune befell us, I saw you in your ordinary household dress, and now, I
see you set off with the best clothes that I could possibly give you, when
fortune was more favourable to us?' The renegado interpreted to us

all that the Moor said to his daughter, who answered him not a word: but when he saw in a corner of the vessel the little trunk in which she used to keep her jewels, which he knew very well he had left in Algiers, and had not brought with him to the garden, he was still more confounded, and asked her how that trunk had come to our hands, and what was in it; to which the renegado, without staying until Zoraida spoke, answered; 'Trouble not yourself, Signor, about asking your daughter so many questions; for with one word I can satisfy them all: and therefore be it known to you, that she is a Christian, and has been the instrument to file off our chains, and give us the liberty we enjoy: she is here with her own consent, and well pleased, I believe, to find herself in this condition, like one who goes out of darkness into light, from death to life, and from suffering to glory.'—'Is this true, daughter?' said the Moor. 'It is,' answered Zoraida. 'In effect then,' replied the old man, 'you are become a Christian, and are she who has put her father into the power, of his enemies?' To which Zoraida answered: 'I am indeed a Christian; but not she who has reduced you to this condition: for my desire never was to do you harm, but only myself good.' 'And what good have you done yourself, my daughter?' 'Ask that,' answered she, 'of Lela Marien, who can tell you better than I can.'

"The Moor had scarcely heard this when, with incredible precipitation, he threw himself headlong into the sea, and without doubt had been drowned, if the wide and cumbersome garments he wore had not kept him a little while above water. Zoraida cried out to save him: and we all presently ran, and laying hold of his garments dragged him out, half drowned and senseless; at which sight Zoraida was so affected, that she set up a tender and sorrowful lamentation over him, as if he had been dead. We turned him with his mouth downward, and he voided a great deal of water, and in about two hours came to himself.

"In the mean time the wind being changed, we were obliged to ply our oars to avoid running upon the shore: but by good fortune we came to a creek by the side of a small promontory, or head, which by the Moors is called the cave of Cava Rumia, that is to say, in our language, *The Wicked Christian Woman*; for the Moors have a tradition, that Cava, who occasioned the loss of Spain, lies burried there; Cava signifying in their language a *wicked woman*, and Rumia, *a Christian*; and farther, they reckon it an ill omen to be forced to anchor there; and otherwise they never do so: though to us it proved, not the shelter of a wicked woman, but a safe harbour and retreat, considering how high the sea ran. We placed scouts on shore, and never dropped our oars: we eat of what the renegado had provided, and prayed to God and to Our Lady very devoutly for assistance and protection, that we might give a happy ending to so fortunate a beginning. Order was given, at Zoraida's entreaty, to set her father on shore with the rest of the Moors, who, until now, had been fast bound; for she had not the heart, nor could her tender feelings brook, to see her father and her countrymen carried off prisoners before her face. We promised her it should be done at our going off, since there was no danger in leaving them in so desolate a place. Our prayers were not in vain: heaven heard them; for the wind presently changed in our favour, and the sea was calm, inviting us to return and prosecute our intended voyage.

"Seeing this, we unbound the Moors, and set them one by one on shore, at which they were greatly surprised: but when we came to disembark Zoraida's father, who was now perfectly in his senses, he said: 'Why, Christians, think you, is this wicked woman desirous of my being set at liberty? Think you it is out of any filial piety she has towards me? No, certainly, but it is on account of the disturbance my presence would give her when she has a mind to put her evil inclinations in practice. And think not that she is moved to change her religion because she thinks yours is preferable to ours: no, but because she knows that libertinism is more allowed in your country than in ours.' And turning to Zoraida, whilst I and another Christian held him fast by both arms, lest he should commit some outrage, he said: 'O infamous girl, and ill-advised maiden! whither goest thou blindfold and precipitate, in the power of these dogs, our natural enemies? Cursed be the hour in which I begat thee, and cursed be the indulgence and luxury in which I brought thee up!' But perceiving he was not likely to give over in haste, I hurried him ashore, and from thence he continued his execrations and wailings, praying to Mahomet that he would beseech God to destroy, confound, and make an end of us: and when, being under sail, we could no longer hear his words, we saw his actions; which were, tearing his beard, plucking off his hair, and rolling himself on the ground: and once he raised his voice so high, that we could hear him say: 'Come back, beloved daughter, come back to shore; for I forgive thee all: let those men keep the money they already have, and do thou come back, and comfort thy disconsolate father, who must lose his life in this desert land, if thou forsakest him.' All this Zoraida heard; all this she felt and bewailed; but could not speak nor answer him a word. So I comforted Zoraida, and we all minded our voyage, which was now made so easy to us by a favourable wind, that we made no doubt of being next morning upon the coast of Spain.

"But as good seldom or never comes pure and unmixed, without being accompanied or followed by some ill, it happened, that being now got far out to sea, and the third hour of the night well nigh past; being under full sail, and the oars being lashed, for the fair wind eased us of the labour of making use of them,—by the light of the moon, which shone very bright, we discovered a round vessel with all her sails out a little ahead of us, but so very near that we were forced to strike sail to avoid running foul of her; and they also put the helm hard up to give us room to go by. The men had posted themselves on the quarter-deck to ask who we were, whither we were going, and from whence we came: but asking us in French, our renegado said, 'Let no one answer; for these, without doubt, are French corsairs, to whom all is fish that comes to net.' Upon this caution nobody spoke a word: and having sailed a little on, their vessel being under the wind, on a sudden they let fly two pieces of artillery, and both, as it appeared, with chain-shot, for one cut our mast through the middle, which, with the sail, fell into the sea, and the other at the same instant came through the middle of our bark, so as to lay it quite open without wounding any of us. But finding ourselves sinking, we all began to cry aloud for help, and to beg of those in the ship to take us in, for we were drowning. They then struck their sails, and hoisting out the boat or pinnace, with about twelve Frenchmen in her, well armed with muskets, and their matches lighted, they came up close to us, and seeing how few we were, and that the vessel was sinking, they took us in, telling us, that this had befallen us because of our incivility in returning them no answer. Our renegado took the trunk, in which was Zoraida's treasure, and without being perceived by any one, threw it overboard into the sea. In short, we all passed into the French ship, where, after they had informed themselves of whatever they had a mind to know concerning us, immediately, as if they had been our capital enemies, they stripped us of every thing, and Zoraida even of the bracelets she wore upon her ancles: but the uneasiness they gave her, gave me less than the apprehension I was in, lest they should proceed from plundering her of her rich and precious jewels, to the depriving her of the jewel of most worth, and that which she valued most. But the desires of this sort of men seldom extend farther than money, with which their avarice is never satisfied, as was evident at that time; for they would have taken away the very clothes we wore as slaves, if they had thought they could have made anything of them. Some of them were of opinion it would be best to throw us all overboard, wrapped up in a sail: for their design was to trade in some of the Spanish ports, pretending to be of Brittany; and should they carry us with them thither, they would be seized on and punished, upon discovery of the robbery. But the captain, who had rifled my dear Zoraida, said he was contented with the prize he had already got, and that he would not touch at any port of Spain, but pass the Straits of Gibraltar by night, or as he could, and make the best of his way for Rochelle, from whence he came; and therefore, in conclusion, they agreed to give us their ship-boat, and what was necessary for so short a voyage as we had to make: which they did the next day in view of the Spanish coast; at which sight all our troubles and miseries were forgotten as entirely as if they had never happened to us; so great is the pleasure of regaining one's lost liberty. It was about noon when they put us into the boat, giving us two barrels of water and some biscuit; and the captain, moved by I know not what compassion, gave the beautiful Zoraida at her going off,

about forty crowns in gold, and would not permit his soldiers to strip
her of these very clothes she has now on.

"We went on board, giving them thanks for the favour they did us,
and showing ourselves rather pleased than dissatisfied. They stood out
to sea, steering towards the Straits; and we, without minding any other
north-star than the land before us, rowed so hard that we were at sunset
so near it that we might easily, we thought, get thither before the night
should be far spent: but the moon not shining, and the sky being cloudy,
as we did not know the coast we were up on, we did not think it safe
to land, as several among us would have had us, though it were among
the rocks, and far from any town; for by that means they said, we
should avoid the danger we ought to fear from the corsairs of Tetuan,
who are over-night in Barbary, and the next morning on the coast of
Spain, where they commonly pick up some prize, and return to sleep
at their own homes. However, it was agreed at last that we should row
gently towards the shore, and if the sea proved calm, we should land
wherever we could. We did so; and a little before midnight we arrived
at the foot of a very large and high mountain, not so close to the shore
but there was room enough for our landing commodiously. We ran our
boat into the sand; we all got on shore and kissed the ground, and, with
tears of joy and satisfaction, gave thanks to God our Lord for the unparalleled mercy he had shown us in our voyage.

THE BEAUTIFUL MORISCA[1]

Miguel de Cervantes Saavedra

(1547–1616)

THAT evening Don Antonio Moreno and his two friends, Don Quixote and Sancho, went to the gallies. The commodore of the four
gallies, who had notice of the coming of the two famous personages,
Don Quixote and Sancho, no sooner perceived them approach the shore,
but he ordered all the gallies to strike their awnings, and the waits to
play: and immediately he sent out the pinnace, covered with rich
carpets, and furnished with cushions of crimson velvet; and just as
Don Quixote set his foot into it, the captain-galley discharged her forecastle piece, and the other gallies did the like; and at his mounting the
ladder on the starboard side, all the crew of slaves saluted him, as the
custom is when a person of rank comes on board, with three "Hu, hu,
hu's." The general, for so we shall call him, who was a gentleman of
quality of Valencia, gave Don Quixote his hand, and embraced him, saying:

"This day will I mark with a white stone, as one of the best I ever wish

[1]From the translation of *Don Quixote* by Charles Jarvis.

to see, while I live, having seen Don Señor Quixote de la Mancha, in whom is composed and abridged the whole worth of knight-errantry."

Don Quixote answered him in expressions no less courteous, being overjoyed to find himself treated so like a lord. All the company went to the poop, which was finely adorned, and seated themselves upon the lockers. The boatswain passed along the middle gangway, and gave the signal with his whistle for the slaves to strip; which was done in an instant. Sancho seeing so many men in buff, was frightened; and more so, when he saw them spread an awning so swiftly over the galley, that he thought all the devils in hell were there at work. But all this was tarts and cheese cakes to what I am going to relate.

Sancho was seated near the stern, on the right hand, close to the hindmost rower, who, being instructed what he was to do, laid hold on Sancho, and lifted him up in his arms. Then the whole crew of slaves standing up, and beginning from the right side, passed him from bank to bank, and from hand to hand, so swiftly, that poor Sancho lost the very sight of his eyes, and verily thought the devils themselves were carrying him away; and they had not done with him, till they brought him round by the left side, and replaced him at the stern. The poor wretch remained bruised, out of breath, and in a cold sweat, without being able to imagine what had befallen him. Don Quixote, who beheld Sancho's flight without wings, asked the general if that was a ceremony commonly used at people's first coming aboard the gallies: for, if so, he, who had no intention of making profession in them, had no inclination to perform the like exercise, and vowed to God, that if anyone presumed to lay hold of him to toss him, he would kick their souls out. And, saying this, he stood up, and laid his hand on his sword.

At that instant they struck the awning, and with a great noise let fall the main-yard from the top of the mast to the bottom. Sancho thought the sky was falling off its hinges, and tumbling upon his head, and shrinking it down, he clapped it for fear between his legs. Don Quixote knew not what to think of it, and he too quaked, shrugged his shoulders, and changed countenance. The slaves hoisted the main-yard with the same swiftness and noise they had struck it; and all this without speaking a word, as if they had neither voice nor breath. The boatswain made a signal for weighing anchor, and jumping into the middle of the forecastle, with his whip, he began to flyflap the shoulders of the slaves at the oar, and by little and little to put off to sea. Sancho, seeing so many red feet (for such he took the oars to be) move all together, said to himself:

"Aye, these are enchanted things indeed, and not those my master talks of. What have these unhappy wretches done to be whipped at this rate? And how has this one man, who goes whistling up and down, the boldness to whip so many? I maintain it, this is hell, or purgatory at least."

Don Quixote seeing with what attention Sancho observed all that passed, said:

"Ah, friend Sancho, how quickly and how cheaply might you, if you would strip to the waist, and, placing yourself among these gentlemen, put an end to the enchantment of Dulcinea! for, having so many companions in pain, you would feel but little of your own: besides, perhaps, the sage Merlin would take every lash of theirs, coming from so good a hand, upon account for ten of those you must, one day or other, give yourself."

The general would have asked what lashes he spoke of, and what he meant by the disenchantment of Dulcinea; when a mariner said:

"The fort of Montjuy makes a signal, that there is a vessel with oars on the coast, on the western side."

The general hearing this, leaped upon the middle gangway, and said:

"Pull away, my lads, let her not escape us: it must be some brigantine belonging to the corsairs of Algiers that the fort makes the signal for."

Then the other three gallies came up with the captain to receive his orders. The general commanded that two of them should put out to sea as fast as they could, and he with the other would go along shore, and so the vessel could not escape. The crew plied the oars, impelling the gallies with such violence that they seemed to fly. Those that stood out to sea, about two miles off discovered a sail, which they judged to carry about fourteen or fifteen banks of oars: and so it proved to be. The vessel discovering the gallies, put herself in chase, with design and in hope to get away by her swiftness. But, unfortunately for her, the captain-galley happened to be one of the swiftest vessels upon the sea, and therefore gained upon the brigantine so fast, that the corsairs saw they could not escape; and so the master of her ordered his men to drop their oars, and yield themselves prisoners, that they might not exasperate the captain of our gallies. But fortune, that would have it otherwise, so ordered, that just as the captain-galley came so near that the corsairs could hear a voice from her, calling to them to surrender, two Toraquis, that is to say two Turks, that were drunk, who came in the brigantine with twelve others, discharged two muskets, with which they killed two of our soldiers upon the prow. Which the general seeing, he swore not to leave a man alive he should take in the vessel, and coming up with all fury to board her, she slipped away under the oars of the galley. The galley ran ahead a good way: they in the vessel, perceiving they were got clear, made all the way they could while the galley was coming about, and again put themselves in chase with oars and sails. But their diligence did them not so much good as their presumption did them harm; for the captain-galley, overtaking them in little more than half a mile, clapped her oars on the vessel, and took them all alive.

By this time the two other gallies were come up, and all four returned with their prize to the strand, where a vast concourse of people stood expecting them, desirous to see what they had taken. The general cast anchor near the land, and knowing that the viceroy was upon the shore, he ordered out the boat to bring him on board, and commanded the main-yard to be let down, immediately to hang thereon the master of the vessel, and the rest of the Turks he had taken in her, being about six and thirty persons, all brisk fellows, and most of them Turkish musqueteers. The general inquired which was the master of the brigantine; and one of the captives, who afterwards appeared to be a Spanish renegado, answered him in Castilian:

"This youth, Sir, you see here, is our master"; pointing to one of the most beautiful and most graceful young men that human imagination could paint. His age, in appearance, did not reach twenty years.

The general said to him:

"Tell me, ill-advised dog, what moved you to kill my soldiers, when you saw it was impossible to escape? Is this the respect paid to captain-gallies? Know you not, that temerity is not valour, and that doubtful hopes should make men daring, but not rash?"

The youth would have replied; but the general could not hear him then, because he was going to receive the viceroy, who was just then entering the galley; with whom there came several of his servants, and some people of the town.

"You have had a fine chase of it, Señor-General," said the viceroy.

"So fine," answered the general, "that your excellency shall presently see the cause of it hanged up at the yard-arm."

"How so?" said the viceroy.

"Because," replied the general, "against all law, against all reason, and the custom of war, they have killed me two of the best soldiers belonging to the gallies, and I have sworn to hang every man I took prisoner, especially this youth here, who is master of the brigantine"; pointing to one who had his hands already tied, and a rope about his neck, and stood expecting death.

The viceroy looked at him, and, seeing him so beautiful, and so humble (his beauty giving him, in that instant, a kind of letter of recommendation), he had a mind to save him, and therefore he asked him:

"Tell me, Sir, are you a Turk, a Moor, or a renegado?"

To which the youth answered in the Castilian tongue;

"I am neither a Turk, nor a Moor, nor a renegado."

"What are you then?" replied the viceroy.

"A Christian woman," answered the youth.

"A Christian woman in such a garb, and in such circumstances," said the viceroy, "is a thing rather to be wondered at than believed."—

"Gentlemen," said the youth, "suspend the execution of my death: it will be no great loss to defer your revenge, while I recount the story of my life."

What heart could be so hard as not to relent at these expressions, at least so far as to hear what the sad and afflicted youth had to say? The general bid him say what he pleased, but not to expect pardon for his notorious offence. With this license the youth began his story in the following manner.

"I was born of Moorish parents, of that nation more unhappy than wise, so lately overwhelmed under a sea of misfortunes. In the current of their calamity, I was carried away by two of my uncles into Barbary, it availing me nothing to say I was a Christian, as indeed I am, and not of the feigned or pretended, but of the true and catholic ones. The discovery of this truth had no influence on those who were charged with our unhappy banishment; nor would my uncles believe it, but rather took it for a lie, and an invention of mine, in order to remain in the country where I was born; and so, by force rather than by my good-will, they carried me with them. My mother was a christian, and my father a discreet man, and a christian too. I sucked in the catholic faith with my milk. I was virtuously brought up, and, neither in my language nor my behaviour, did I, as I thought, give any indication of being a Morisca. My beauty, if I have any, grew up, and kept equal pace with these virtues; for such I believe them to be: and, though my modesty and reserve were great, I could not avoid being seen by a young gentleman, called Don Gaspar Gregorio, eldest son of a person of distinction, whose estate joins to our town. How he saw me, how we conversed together, how he was undone for me, and how I was little less for him, would be tedious to relate, especially at a time when I am under apprehensions that the cruel cord which threatens me may interpose between my tongue and my throat; and therefore I will only say, that Don Gregorio resolved to bear me company in our banishment. And so, mingling with the Moors, who came from other towns (for he spoke the language well), in the journey he contracted an intimacy with my two uncles, who had the charge of me; for my father being a prudent and provident person, as soon as he saw the first edict for our banishment, left the town, and went to seek some place of refuge for us in foreign kingdoms. He left a great number of pearls, and precious stones of great value, hid and buried in a certain place, known to me only, and some money in crusadoes and pistoles of gold, commanding me in nowise to touch the treasure he left, if peradventure we should be banished before he returned. I obeyed, and passed over into Barbary with my uncles and other relations and acquaintance, as I have already said; and the place we settled in was Algiers, or rather hell itself. The king heard of my beauty, and fame told him of my riches, which partly proved my good fortune. He sent for me, and asked me of what part of Spain I was, and what money and jewels I had brought with me. I told him the town, and that the jewels and money were buried in it; but that they might easily be brought off, if I myself went to fetch them. All this I told him, in hopes that his own covetousness, more than my beauty, would blind him.

"While he was thus discoursing with me, information was given him, that one of the handsomest youths imaginable came in my company. I presently understood, that they meant Don Gaspar Gregorio, whose beauty is beyond all possibility of exaggeration. I was greatly disturbed when I considered the danger Don Gregorio was in; for, among those barbarous Turks, a beautiful boy or youth is more valued and esteemed, than a woman, be she never so beautiful. The king commanded him to be immediately brought before him, that he might see him, and asked me, if it was true, what he was told of the youth. I, as if inspired by heaven, answered, Yes, it was; but that I must inform him, he was not a man, but a woman as I was: and I requested that he would let me go and dress her in her proper garb, that she might shine in full beauty, and appear in his presence with less concern. He said I might go in a good hour, and that next day he would talk with me of the manner how I might conveniently return to Spain, to get the hidden treasure.

"I consulted with Don Gaspar; I told him the danger he ran in appearing as a man: and I dressed him like a Morisca, and that very afternoon introduced him as a woman to the king, who was in admiration at the sight of her, and proposed to reserve her for a present to the Grand Signior: and, to prevent the risk she might run in the seraglio among his own wives, and distrusting himself, he ordered her to be lodged in the house of a Moorish lady of quality, there to be kept and waited upon: whither she was instantly conveyed. What we both felt (for I cannot deny that I love him) I leave to the consideration of those who mutually love each other, and are forced to part.

"The king presently gave order for my returning to Spain, in this brigantine, accompanied by two Turks, being those who killed your soldiers. There came with me also this Spanish renegado (pointing to him who spoke first) whom I certainly know to be a christian in his heart, and that he comes with a greater desire to stay in Spain, than to return to Barbary. The rest of the ship's crew are Moors and Turks, who serve for nothing but to row at the oar. The two drunken and insolent Turks disobeying the orders given them to set me and the renegado on shore in the first place of Spain we should touch upon, in the habit of christians, with which we came provided, would needs first scour the coast, and make some prize, if they could; fearing, if they should land us first, we might be induced by some accident or other to discover, that such a vessel was at sea, and, if perchance there were any gallies abroad upon this coast, she might be taken. Last night we made this shore, and not knowing anything of these four gallies, were discovered ourselves, and what you have seen has befallen us. In short, Don Gregorio remains among the women, in woman's attire, and in manifest danger of being undone; and I find myself, with my hands tied, expecting, or rather fearing, to lose that life, of which I am already weary. This, Sir, is the conclusion of my lamentable story, as true as unfortunate. What I beg of you, is, that you will suffer me to die like a christian, since, as I have told you, I am nowise chargeable with the blame, into which those of my nation have fallen."

Here she held her peace, her eyes pregnant with tender tears, which were accompanied by many of those of the standers-by.

The viceroy being of a kind and compassionate disposition, without speaking a word, went to her, and with his own hands unbound the cord that tied the beautiful ones of the fair Morisca. While the Moriscan christian was relating her strange story, an old pilgrim, who came aboard the galley with the viceroy, fastened his eyes on her, and, scarcely had she made an end, when, throwing himself at her feet, and embracing them, with words interrupted by a thousand sobs and sighs, he said: "O Anna Felix! my unhappy daughter! I am thy father Ricote, who am returned to seek thee, not being able to live without thee, who art my very soul."

At which words Sancho opened his eyes, and lifted up his head, which he was holding down, ruminating upon his late disgrace; and looking at the pilgrim, he knew him to be the very Ricote he met with upon the day he left his government, and was persuaded this must be his daughter: who, being now unbound, embraced her father, mingling her tears with his.

Ricote said to the general and the viceroy:

"This, Sirs, is my daughter, happy in her name alone: Anna Felix she is called, with the surname of Ricote, as famous for her own beauty, as for her father's riches. I left my native country, to seek, in foreign kingdoms, some shelter and safe retreat: and having found one in Germany, I returned in this pilgrim's weed, in the company of some Germans, in quest of my daughter, and to take up a great deal of wealth I had left buried. My daughter I found not, but the treasure I did, and have it in my possession: and now, by the strange turn of fortune you have seen, I have found the treasure which most enriches me, my beloved daughter. If our innocence, and her tears and mine, through the uprightness of your justice, can open the gates of mercy, let us partake of it, who never had a thought of offending you, nor in any ways conspired with the designs of our people, who have been justly banished."

Sancho then said:

"I know Ricote very well, and am sure what he says of Anna Felix's being his daughter is true: but as for the other idle stories of his going and coming, and of his having a good or bad intention, I meddle not with them."

All that were present wondered at the strangeness of the case; and the general said:

"Each tear of yours hinders me from fulfilling my oath: live, fair Anna Felix, all the years heaven has allotted you, and let the daring and the insolent undergo the punishment their crime deserves."

Immediately he ordered that the two Turks who had killed his soldiers should be hanged at the yard-arm. But the viceroy earnestly entreated him not to hang them, their fault being rather the effect of madness than of valour. The general yielded to the viceroy's request: for it is not easy to execute revenge in cold blood. Then they consulted how to deliver Don Gaspar Gregorio from the danger he was left in. Ricote offered above two thousand ducats, which he had in pearls and jewels, towards it. Several expedients were proposed, but none so likely to succeed as that of the Spanish renegado aforementicned, who offered to return to Algiers in a small bark of about eight banks, armed with christian rowers: for he knew where, how, and when he might land; nor was he ignorant of the house in which Don Gaspar was kept. The general and the viceroy were in doubt whether they should rely on the renegado, or trust him with the christians, who were to row at the oar. Anna Felix answered for him, and her father Ricote said, he would be answerable for the ransom of those christians, if they should be betrayed. Matters being thus settled, the viceroy went ashore, and Don Antonio Moreno took the Morsica and her father along with him, the viceroy charging him to regale and welcome them as much as possible, offering, on his own part, whatever his house afforded for their better entertainment; so great was the kindness and charity that the beauty of Anna Felix infused into his breast.

THE INVINCIBLE ARMADA[1]

James Anthony Froude

(1818–1894)

ALL being thus in order, the Duke of Medina Sidonia sailed from Lisbon on the 19th-29th of May. The northerly breeze which prevails on the coast of Portugal was unusually strong. The galleons standing high out of the water, and carrying small canvas in proportion to their size, worked badly to windward. They were three weeks in reaching Finisterre where, the wind having freshened to a gale, they were scattered, some standing out to sea, some into the Bay of Biscay. Their orders, in the event of such a casualty, had been to make for Ferrol. The wind shifting suddenly to the west, those that had gone into the Bay could not immediately reach it, and were driven into Santander. The officers, however, were, on the whole, well satisfied with the qualities which the ships had displayed. A mast or two had been sprung, a few yards and bowsprits had been carried away; but beyond loss of time there had been no serious damage.

[1]From *The History of England.* Reprinted by permission of Longmans, Green & Co., Ltd., and of Charles Scribner's Sons.

The weather moderating, the fleet was again collected in the Bay of Ferrol by the 6th-16th of July. All repairs were completed by the 11th-21st, and the next day, the 12th-22nd, the Armada took leave of Spain for the last time.

The scene as the fleet passed out of the harbour must have been singularly beautiful. It was a treacherous interval of real summer. The early sun was lighting the long chain of the Gallician mountains, marking with shadows the cleft defiles, and shining softly on the white walls and vineyards of Coruña. The wind was light, and falling towards a calm; the great galleons drifted slowly with the tide on the purple water, the long streamers trailing from the trucks, the red crosses, the emblem of the crusade, shewing bright upon the hanging sails. The fruit boats were bringing off the last fresh supplies, and the pinnaces hastening to the ships with the last loiterers on shore. Out of thirty thousand men who that morning stood upon the decks of the proud Armada, twenty thousand and more were never again to see the hills of Spain. Of the remnant who in two short months crept back ragged and torn, all but a few hundred returned only to die.

The Spaniards, though a great people, were usually over conscious of their greatness, and boasted too loudly of their fame and prowess; but among the soldiers and sailors of the doomed expedition against England, the national vainglory was singularly silent. They were the flower of the country, culled and chosen over the entire Peninsula, and they were going with a modest nobility upon a service which they knew to be dangerous, but which they believed to be peculiarly sacred. Every one, seaman, officer, and soldier, had confessed and communicated before he went on board. Gambling, swearing, profane language of all kinds had been peremptorily forbidden. Private quarrels and differences had been made up or suspended. The loose women who accompanied Spanish armies, and sometimes Spanish ships to sea, had been ordered away, and no unclean thing or person permitted to defile the Armada; and in every vessel, and in the whole fleet, the strictest order was prescribed and observed. Medina Sidonia led the way in the *San Martin*, showing lights at night, and firing guns when the weather was hazy. Mount's Bay was to be the next place of rendezvous if they were again separated.

On the first evening the wind dropped to a calm. The morning after, the 13th-23rd, a fair fresh breeze came up from the south and southwest; the ships ran flowingly before it; and in two days and nights they had crossed the bay, and were off Ushant. The fastest of the pinnaces was dispatched from thence to Parma, with a letter bidding him expect the Duke's immediate coming.

But they had now entered the latitude of the storms which through the whole season had raged round the English shore. The same night a south west gale overtook them. They lay to, not daring to run further. The four galleys unable to keep the sea were driven in upon the French coast, and wrecked. The *Santa Ana*, a galleon of eight hundred tons, went down, carrying with her ninety seamen, three hundred soldiers, and fifty thousand ducats in gold. The weather was believed to be under the peculiar care of God, and this first misfortune was of evil omen for the future. The storm lasted two days, and then the sky cleared, and again gathering into order, they proceeded on their way. On the 19th-29th, they were in the mouth of the Channel. At daybreak on the morning of the 20th-30th the Lizard was under their lee, and an English fishing-boat was hanging near them, counting their numbers. They gave chase; but the boat shot away down wind and disappeared. They captured another an hour or two later, from which they learnt the English fleet was in Plymouth, and Medina Sidonia called a council of war, to consider whether they should go in, and fall upon it while at anchor. Philip's orders, however, were peremptory that they should turn neither right nor left, and make straight for Margate roads and Parma. The Duke was unenterprising, and consciously unequal to his work; and already bending under his responsibilities he hesitated to add to them.

Had he decided otherwise it would have made no difference, for the opportunity was not allowed him. Long before the Spaniards saw the Lizard they had themselves been seen, and on the evening of the 19th-29th, the beacons along the coast had told England that the hour of its trial was come.

THE RETURN[1]

James Anthony Froude

(1818-1894)

THE dawn found them dragging heavily into the North Sea. The north-west wind was blowing hard, and setting them bodily on the banks. The bad sailors could not go to windward at all. Those which had been in the fight could not bear sail enough to hold a course which, when sound, they might have found barely possible. The crews were worn out. On the Sunday they had been dinnerless and supperless. All Monday they had been fighting, and all Monday night plugging shot-holes and fishing spars. The English fleet hung dark and threatening a mile distant on the weather quarter. The water was shoaling every moment. They could see the yellow foam where the waves were breaking on the banks. To wear round would be to encounter another battle, for which they had neither heart nor strength, while the English seemed to be contented to let the elements finish the work for them. The English vessels drew more water, and would have grounded while the gal-

[1]From *The Spanish Story of the Armada*. Reprinted by permission of Longmans, Green & Co., Ltd., and of Charles Scribner's Sons.

leons were still afloat. It was enough for them if they could prevent the Armada from turning round, and could force it to continue upon a course of which an hour or two would probably see the end. The *San Martin* and Oquendo's ship, the *San Juan*, were furthest out. The sounding-line on the *San Martin* gave at last but six fathoms; the vessels to leeward had only five. Some one, perhaps Diego Flores, advised the Duke to strike his flag and surrender. Report said that a boat was actually lowered to go off to Howard and make terms, and that Oquendo had prevented it from pushing off, by saying savagely that he would fling Diego Flores overboard. . . .

With death staring them in the face and themselves helpless, men and officers betook themselves to prayer as the only refuge left, and apparently the prayer was answered. Somewhere about noon, "God was pleased to work a miracle." The wind shifted, backing to the south-west, and ceased to jam them down upon the sands. With eased sheets they were able to point their heads northwards and draw out into the deep water. The enemy followed, still keeping at the same distance, but showed no further disposition to meddle with them; and the Armada breathed again, though huddled together like a flock of frightened sheep. . . . This Tuesday, August 9th, was the day of Philip's patron saint, St Lawrence, whose arm he had lately added to his sacred treasures in the Escurial. In the afternoon a council of war was held on board the flag-ship, consisting of the Duke, Alonso de Leyva, Recalde, Don Francisco de Bobadilla and Diego Flores. They had little pleasant to say to each other. Oquendo was at first absent, but came in while they were still deliberating.

"O Señor Oquendo," they cried, "*que haremos?*" (what shall we do?)
"Do," he replied. "Bear up and fight again."

It was the answer of a gallant man who preferred death to disgrace. But the Duke had to consider how to save what was left of his charge, and the alternatives had to be considered. They were before the wind, running right up the North Sea. The Duke explained that every cartridge had been spent in the vessels which had been engaged, and that, although some were left in the rest of the fleet, the supply was miserably short. Their ships were leaking. Half the sailors and half the artillery-men were killed or wounded. The Duke's own opinion was that they ought to make haste back, and by the sea route round the North of Scotland and Ireland. . . .

Flight, for it was nothing else, after such high expectations and loud prayers and boastings, flight after but a week's conflict, seemed to the old companion of Santa Cruz an intolerable shame. De Leyva was doubtful. He admitted, as the Duke said, that the English were too strong for them. They had done their best and it had not availed. His own ship would hardly float, and he had not thirty cartridges left. Recalde and Bobadilla supported Oquendo, and insisted that, at whatever risk, they must endeavour to recover Calais Roads. They were old sailors, who had weathered many a storm, and fought in many a battle. The chances of war had been against them so far, but would not be against them always. If the English fleet could go down Channel, it was not to be supposed that a Spanish fleet could not, and if they were to return home the Channel was the nearest road. If the worst came, an honourable death was better than a scandalous retreat . . .

The bolder course was rejected . . . Forlorn and miserable, the great Armada was set upon its course for the Orkneys, from thence to bear away to the West of Ireland, and so round to Spain . . . The Duke himself was short and sullen, shut himself in his state-room, and refused to see or speak with any one. Diego Flores became the practical commander, and had to announce the alarming news that the provisions taken in at Corunna had been wholly inadequate, and that at the present rate of consumption they would all be starving in a fortnight. The state of the water supply was worst of all, for the casks had most of them been destroyed by the English guns. The salt meat and fish were gone or spoilt. The rations were reduced to biscuit. Half a pound of biscuit, a pint of water, and half a pint of wine were all that each person could be allowed. Men and officers fared alike; and on this miserable diet, and unprovided with warm clothing, which they never needed in their own sunny lands, the crews of the Armada were about to face the cold and storms of the northern latitudes. . . .

The high-built, broad and shallow galleons were all execrable sailers, but some sailed worse than others, and some were in worse condition than others. They passed the Orkneys together, and were then separated in a gale. The nights were lengthening, the days were thick and misty, and they lost sight of each other. Two or three went north as far as the Faroe Islands, suffering pitifully from cold and hunger. Detachments, eight or ten together, made head as they could, working westward. against wind and sea, the men dying daily in hundreds. The *San Martin.* with sixty ships in company, kept far out into the Atlantic, and they rolled down towards the south dipping their mainyards in the tremendous seas. On August 21st they were two hundred miles west of Cape Wrath, amidst the tumult of the waters. . . .

The weather grew wilder and wilder. The number of vessels which could bear up against the gales diminished daily, and one by one they fell to leeward on the fatal Irish shore . . . The Spaniards were excellent seamen. They had navigated ships no worse than those which were lumbering through the Irish Seas, among West Indian hurricanes and through the tempests at Cape Horn. But these poor wretches were but shadows of themselves; they had been poisoned at the outset with putrid provisions; they were now famished and sick, their vessels' sides torn to pieces by cannon-shot and leaking at a thousand holes, their wounded spars no longer able to bear the necessary canvas; worst of all their spirits broken. The superstitious enthusiasm with which they started had turned into a fear that they were the objects of a malignant fate with which it was useless to struggle. Some had been driven among the Western Islands of Scotland; the ships had been lost; the men who got on shore alive made their way to the Low Countries. But these were the few. Thirty or forty other vessels had attempted in scattered parties to beat their way into the open sea. But, in addition to hunger, the men were suffering fearfully for want of water, and perhaps forced the pilots either to make in for the land, or else to turn south before they had gained sufficient offing. Thus, one by one all these drove ashore, either on the coast of Sligo or Donegal, on in Clew Bay or Galway Bay, or the rocks of Clare and Kerry, and the wretched crews who escaped the waves found a fate only more miserable. . . .

The sixty galleons which remained with the Duke till the end of August were parted again by a south-westerly gale, off the point of Kerry. The Duke himself passed so far out to sea that he did not see the Irish coast at all. Recalde, with two large ships besides his own, had come round Dunmore Head, near the land. His crews were dying for want of water. He seems to have known Dingle. At all events, he was aware that there was a harbour in Dingle Bay, and he made for it with his consorts. One of them, *Our Lady of the Rosary*, was wrecked in Blasket Sound. She carried seven hundred men when she sailed out of Lisbon. Two hundred out of the seven were alive in her when she struck the rock, and every one of them perished, save a single lad. Recalde, with the other galleon, anchored in the Dingle estuary, and sent in to the town a passionate entreaty to be allowed to fill his water-casks. The English account states that Recalde had to sail as he was, to live or die. The belief in Spain was that he took the water that he wanted by force. Perhaps the inhabitants were not entirely inhuman, and did not interfere. He saved the lives for the moment of the wretched men under his charge, though most of them perished when they reached their homes; he brought back his ship to Corunna, and there died himself two days after his arrival, worn out by shame and misery.

Oquendo also reached Spain alive. The persevering west winds drove him down the Bay of Biscay, and he made his way into St Sebastian, where he had a wife and children; but he refused to see them; he shut himself into a solitary room, turned his face to the wall, and ended like Recalde, unable to outlive the disgrace of the gallant navy which he had led so often into victory. They had done all that men could do. On the miserable day when their commander decided to turn his back and fly they would have forced him upon a more honourable course, and given the forlorn adventure an issue less utterly ignominious. But their advice had been rejected. They had sailed away from an enemy whose strength at most was not greater than theirs. They had escaped from a battle with a human foe to a more fatal war with the elements, and they had seen their comrades perish round them, victims of folly and weakness. The tremendous catastrophe broke their hearts, and they lay down and died. Oquendo's *Capitana* had been blown up after the fight at Plymouth. By a strange fatality the ship which brought him home blew up also in the harbour of St Sebastian. The explosion may have been the last sound which reached his failing sense.

The stragglers came in one by one; sixty-five ships only of the hundred and thirty who, in July, had sailed out of Corunna full of hope and enthusiasm. In those hundred and thirty had been twenty-nine thousand human creatures, freshly dedicated to what they called the service of the Lord. Nine or ten thousand only returned; a ragged remnant, shadows of themselves, sinking under famine and fever and scurvy, which carried them off like sheep with the rot. When they had again touched Spanish soil, a wail of grief rose over the whole peninsula, as of Rachel weeping for her children; yet above it all rose the cry, Where was Alonso de Leyva? Where was the flower of Spanish chivalry?

Weeks, even months, passed before certain news arrived, and rumour invented imaginary glories for him. He had rallied the missing galleons, he had fallen in with Drake, had beaten and captured him, and had sunk half the English fleet. Vain delusion. De Leyva, like Oquendo and Recalde, had done all which could be done by man, and God had not interposed to help him! He had fought his *Rata Coronada* till her spars were shot away and her timbers pierced like a sieve. She became waterlogged in the gales on the Irish coast. A second galleon and a surviving galeass were in his company. The *Rate* and the galleon drove ashore. De Leyva, in the galeass, made Killybegs harbour, and landed there with fourteen hundred men. It was the country of the O'Neil. They were treated with the generous warmth which became the greatest of the Irish chieftains. But their presence was known in Dublin. O'Neil was threatened, and De Leyva honourably refused to be an occasion of danger to him. He repaired the galeass at Killybegs. The October weather appeared to have settled at last, and he started again with as many of his people as the galeass would carry to make the coast of Scotland. She had passed round the north of Donegal, she had kept along the land and had almost reached the Giant's Causeway, when she struck a rock and went to pieces, and De Leyva and his companions went the way of the rest.

THE RETURN OF THE FISHING BOATS[1]

José María de Pereda

(1833–1906)

AT LAST there was a sound on the quay of rough voices and the heavy tramp of feet: a troop of fishermen arrived, laden with their nets, their food, their oilskins, and many of them with articles belonging to the boats. Andrés saw to his joy that Reñales' boat was soon ready with all its crew. They took their oars, and the skipper of the boat stood at his oar at the stern to steer. They shoved off and the boat received the first impulse of its fourteen oarsmen: it made for the open sea, and its thin keel began to cleave the level, tranquil, gleaming surface of the bay. The first light now began to show the outlines of what had hitherto been a confused blackness, from Cape Quintres to Mount Cabarga; the coast of St Martin was reflected in the transparent water, and in the neighbouring fields and meadows began once more the ordered round of rural life, the most remote of the battles of the world. To the right reddened the sand-dunes of the Quebrantas, crowned with a green hill, and plunging their feet into the gently fawning sea. They looked like two tigers playing, waiting for their prey.

In order to take advantage of the fresh land wind which now began to blow, the boat hoisted its sails, and advancing with twofold speed, was soon outside the bar.

"See what a shoal of sardines," said Reñales, calling Andrés' attention to a long dark streak of water above which a cloud of seagulls hovered. "Good for those who have come out for sardines. As for me, when I fish for sardines, I get nothing but cod: such is one's luck."

The boat kept advancing farther and farther out to sea, the greater part of her idle crew asleep in the prow; and presently the land was but a narrow brown line, above which stood a white dot which was the lighthouse of Cabo Mayor. For cod, the boats go fifteen or eighteen miles from land, and for tunny, twelve or fourteen leagues, so that they carry a compass to steer their way back. At last the order was given to furl the sails, for the boat had reached her destination. The whole of that vast expanse was dotted with tiny black specks which appeared and disappeared every instant in the rise and fall of the waves. Those nearest the coast were the rowing boats, which never went more than three or four miles from land. Of the boats fishing for cod, that of Reñales was the nearest of all to the land.

A long time went by without any of the lines which they had laid down showing the least movement. Suddenly Cole, in the prow, cried out: "Praise be to God!" It was the announcement of the first bite. Cole,

---

[1] Translated from *Sotileza* by Aubrey Fitzgerald Bell expressly for this collection.

hauling in the line little by little with a strong wrist, landed a fine cod; a minute later came another and then another, and then two together. Presently, however, they ceased to be lured by the bait offered them in those serene depths or had departed to some more congenial prey; and the rest of the morning was spent in fruitless endeavour. They therefore spoke of going yet farther out to sea, but Reñales, after scanning the horizon, remarked:

"It's not a day for pleasure-rides: we'll have our meal and be thankful."

The wind meanwhile had died down, and along the northern horizon extended a thick leaden haze, which between the east and south changed to great irregular belts of intense blue, with a background of most brilliant orange; huge chains of great clouds were massed above the Urrieles or Picos de Europa; and the sun in the zenith shone with more than its wonted heat. The scouts of the boats farthest out at sea had set an oar upright, the signal of precaution; but in none could be seen the flag which means a warning to return. Reñales had an eye on the haze and the signals as he ate his meal; but his companions, although likewise watchful, did not appear to give them so much importance as he did. Andrés asked him what he thought of it all.

"I don't like the look of it when so far from land," was his answer. Suddenly, pointing towards Cabo Mayor, he said, as he rose to his feet: "See, lads, what Falagán is telling us."

They saw a smoke rise three times over the headland: it was the signal that the south wind was blowing strong in the bay. Twice only would have meant that the surf was breaking on the coast. A furious south wind is dangerous for sailing boats, but its worst danger of all consists in its sudden veerings to the northwest. In view of these dangers, Reñales ordered an immediate return. The rowing boats were already entering the harbour, and the boats which had been fishing for bream were about to follow their example. Without an instant's loss of time he commanded them to hoist sail, and as there was little wind they fell to rowing as well. All the boats far out at sea did the same. An hour passed thus, the only sound in the boat being the creaking of the rowlocks, the measured fall of the oars on the water, and the quick breathing of the men toilfully assisting the flapping sails. At times the wind freshened and the rowers rested; no great change could be seen in the haze on the horizon. Both ahead and astern were other boats following the same course as that of Reñales. All was therefore well, and so it continued for another half hour, when they could discern plainly the Urros de Liencres and the rocks of the Virgin of the Sea.

Suddenly they heard a terrible distant sound, as though gigantic battle trains were rolling over a hollow ground; a damp cold gust of wind blew in their faces; the sun was darkened; and in the north west, great lines of an almost black green advanced across the sea. At the same moment, Reñales shouted:

"Down with the mainsail!"

And those brave men grew pale as with hurried movements they obeyed his command. An instant's delay would have meant the loss of all, for scarcely had the small sail been hoisted when a furious squall charged with rain burst against it, and dashed the boat into a raging whirlwind. A dense mist blotted out the horizon, and the coast, rather than seen, could be guessed from the roaring of the seas breaking over it and the seething of the foam against the cliffs. On every side could be seen nothing but an awful waste of waves pursuing one another in a mad race, their white manes flying in the wind. To run before this raging fury without allowing oneself to be overtaken by it was the only chance of safety; but it was a poor chance, for the only impetus was given by the sail, and even the little sail they carried was sufficient to capsize the boat. The mast creaked in its step, bent like a willow; the sail cracked; the boat plunged and reeled and shipped heavy seas; and Reñales gave the order to furl the small sail and run up a tiny bit of sail half-way up a short mast fixed at the prow. This sail was known by the terrible name of "The unction," that is to say, between life and death.

Fortunately the boat resisted well and sped before the raging waters; but the waves grew mightier as the hurricane lashed them, and the danger that they would swamp the weak boat increased every instant. Everything they could do was done to prevent this. The fish they had caught were thrown overboard at the stern, where also a sail was trailed; but this was only of slight avail. The only hope, if they were not to perish, was to keep running before the storm. So the boat rose on the foaming crests and fell into the gulf between; rose again to fall into a deeper pit; and kept gaining ground and avoiding being broadside on to the breaking seas. The seamen, sometimes in the throes of despair, sometimes with stoic serenity, kept baling out the boat as the waves broke over her stern, or, in a momentary breathing-space, obeyed a silent order of Reñales.

The storm continued unchecked, and the boat, half swamped, continued to run madly before it. In one of its lurches it came within a few inches of a shape tossing between two waves, its tufts of unkempt hair floating upon the water.

"*Muergo!*" cried Reñales, and at the same time attempted with one hand to seize the corpse. But he lost his balance and fell, knocking his head against the side of the boat. The boat, deprived of its helm, lay broadside on to the oncoming seas; the mast snapped; the sail was torn away by the wind. Andrés then, realizing how terrible was this new danger, called out "To your oars" to the dismayed seamen, and himself seized the steering oar—which Reñales had let fall from his hands as he fell,—and righted the boat with such rapidity and skill that it was the saving of them. They were then passing Cabo Menor, over whose rocks the seas were breaking and falling on the other side in a raging torrent.

From there, or rather from Cabo Mayor to the mouth of the harbour, past the island of Mouro to Cape Quintres and Cape Ajo, the whole coast was one long fringe of roaring boiling foam, rushing up to the assault of the cliffs and falling back to attack anew, impelled by the mountains of water at its back to dash itself ceaselessly upon those unyielding barriers. Andrés, as he clutched the oar, his feet nailed, as it were, to the floor of the boat, and strove like his brave companions with superhuman efforts to ward off the death that threatened them on every side, began to feel the sublimity of all this horror, and praised God at the sight of this tremendous sign of His might.

Meanwhile, Reñales moved neither hand nor foot, and at a sign from Andrés, Cole and another comrade who were incessantly baling, interrupted their important task to raise the fallen helmsman, who had been stunned by his fall and was losing much blood from the wound in his head. They attended to him as best they could, and presently he regained consciousness, and was even anxious to return to his post, as the boat, passing like lightning along the Sardinero, arrived in front of the Caleta del Caballo. But extraordinary strength as well as calmness and intelligence were now required in the helmsman, and this Reñales lacked; whereas Andrés possessed all three.

"On then," said Reñales, crouching in the boat, since his head was too painful to buffet with the gale, "and may God's will be done."

On to attempt to enter the harbour, to risk the last and most hazardous throw of life or death; for the harbour was closed by a series of walls of immense waves which, on finding themselves hemmed in the narrow entrance, partly rushed to the assault of the rocks of Mouro and partly dashed into the dark pass, filling it and rearing their huge backs in the narrow space, till the immense walls of granite trembled. What escape or refuge was there left? It was a miracle every minute that the boat was not swamped in its dreadful course. At least they would soon know their fate now; a conviction which could be read on the faces of the crew, fixed and still as they gazed at Andrés, as though one common thought had turned them all to stone.

"As you know, Don Andrés," said Reñales, "the course lies exactly midway between the height of Rubayo and the Codío de Solares."

"Yes," answered Andrés bitterly, without removing his eyes from the harbour's neck, or his hands from the steering oar, "but when one can see neither the height of Rubayo nor the Codío de Solares, what then, Reñales?"

"Go in where best you can," he answered after a brief pause, plunging his eyes into the dreadful gulf which was now but a stone's throw from the boat.

Up to now to advance had been to come nearer to safety, but from now on it was as dangerous to advance rapidly as to pause, since the boat was between the hurricane which drove it on and the entrance which must be passed when the seas were not breaking in it. Andrés, who knew this well, stood like a stone statue with eyes of fire; the oarsmen were like machines ready to move at his merest glance; Reñales held his breath. On the heights of Hano a crowd of people, battling against the tempest, gazed in horror at the doomed boat; but fortunately for himself and the rest Andrés did not look up, his attention riveted on the ground where the decisive battle must be fought.

Suddenly he shouted to the oarsmen:

"Now, now: more."

And the rowers, in a miracle of strength after their long toil, rose rigidly aloft, their feet fixed against the thwarts, their hands hanging on the oars. A gigantic wave, curved, gleaming, roaring, was then advancing down the neck of the harbour, and on the wave's very crest was perched the boat, the men rowing with all their might. The crest reached from side to side of the entrance, rolling like the coil of a colossal serpent, and advancing towards the Quebrantas; it passed under the boat's keel, and the boat began to slide down by the stern, as down a waterfall, to the bottom of the gulf left behind by the wave in its onward course. The danger was that the boat would "go to sleep" there; but Andrés vigilantly demanded another heroic effort of the oarsmen. And they answered to his call; as they rowed against the recoil of the wave that had passed, another larger wave passed in without breaking in the entrance, raised the boat's stern, lifted it on its crest and impelled it towards the harbour. It was a dreadful height, and Andrés felt dizzy as on a precipice, but he did not yield to fear nor lose his balance in that strange angle.

"More, more!" he shouted to the weary crew.

And the oars creaked, the men gasped for breath, and the boat remained on the wave's crest, gaining a little ground. When it was about to receive the last favouring impulse from the wave, Andrés, luffing with all his strength, shouted in accents of intense and fiery fervour the solemn:

"*Jesus adentro!*"

And this wave too passed on towards the Quebrantas, and again the boat began to slide down a hill of water into a new abyss; but this time, the abyss meant salvation, for they had rounded the point of la Cerda, and were in the shelter of the harbour.

TRAFALGAR[1]

Beneto Perez Galdós

(1845–1920)

IT WAS the 18th of October. I can have no doubt as to the date because the fleet sailed out of the bay next day. We rose very early and went down to the quay, where a boat was waiting to carry us on board.

Imagine, if you can, my surprise—nay, surprise do I say?—my enthusiasm, my rapture, when I found myself on board the *Santísima Trinidad*, the largest vessel on the main, that floating fortress of timber which, seen from a distance, had appeared to my fancy some portentous and supernatural creature; such a monster as alone was worthy of the majesty of the seas. Each time our boat passed under the side of a ship I examined it with a sort of religious astonishment, wondering to see the hulls so huge that from the ramparts had looked so small; and in the wild enthusiasm that possessed me I ran the greatest danger of falling into the water as I gazed in ecstasy at a figurehead—an object which fascinated me more than anything else.

At last we reached the *Santísima Trinidad*. As we approached, the colossal mass loomed larger and larger, and when the launch pulled up alongside, lost in the black transparent void made where its vast shadow fell upon the water—when I saw the huge hulk lying motionless on the dark waves which gently plashed against the side—when I looked up and saw the three tiers of cannon with their threatening muzzles thrust through the portholes—my excitement was changed to fear; I turned pale and sat silent and motionless by my master's side.

But when we went up the side and stood on deck my spirits rose. The intricate and lofty rigging, the busy scene on the quarter-deck, the open view of the sky and bay, the perfect order of everything on deck, from the hammocks lashed in a row to the bulwarks, to the capstans, shells, windsails, and hatchways; the variety of uniforms—everything I saw, in short, amazed me to such a degree that for some time I stood blankly gazing at the stupendous structure, heedless of all else. . . .

The *Santísima Trinidad* had four decks; the largest ships in the world had but three. This giant, constructed in Havana, in 1769, of the finest woods of Cuba, could reckon thirty-six years of honourable service. She measured 220 feet from stem to stern, 58 feet in the waist, that is to say in width, and 28 feet deep from the keel to the deck, measurements which no other vessel at the time could approach. Her huge ribs, which were a perfect forest, supported four decks. When she was first built

---

[1]From Clara Bell's translation of *Trafalgar*. Reprinted by permission of Kegan Paul Trench, Trubner and Co., Ltd.

116 portholes gaped in her sides which were thick walls of timber; after she was enlarged in 1796 she had 130, and when she was newly fitted in 1805 she was made to carry 140 guns, cannons and carronades. The interior was a marvel of arrangement; there were decks for the guns, the forecastle for the crew, holds for stores of all kinds, state-cabins for the officers, the galley, the cock-pit and other offices. I was quite bewildered as I ran through the passages and endless nooks of this floating fortress. The stern cabins on the main deck were a little palace within, and outside like some fantastic castle; the galleries, the flag-turrets at the corners of the poop—exactly like the oriels of a Gothic tower—looked like huge cages open to the sea, whence the eye could command three quarters of the horizon.

Nothing could be grander than the rigging—those gigantic masts thrust up to heaven like a menace to the storm. It was difficult to believe that the wind could have strength enough to fill those vast sails. The eye lost its way and became weary in gazing at the maze of the rigging with the shrouds, stays, braces, halyards, and other ropes used to haul and reef the various sails. . . .

In the cabin I found my master eagerly conversing with the captain in command of the ship, Don Francisco Xavier de Uriarte, and the commander of the squadron, Don Baltasar Hidalgo de Cisneros. From what I overheard I could have no doubt that the French admiral had ordered the fleets to put to sea the next morning. . . .

The fleet was to sail out of the bay next morning—what joy! To ride the seas in this immense vessel—the largest in the world; to witness a fight at sea; to see what a battle was like, how cannon were fired, how the enemy's ships were taken—what a splendid triumph! and then to return to Cadiz covered with glory. To say afterwards to all who cared to hear: "Yes, I was there, I was on board, I saw it all . . ." To tell Rosita too, describing the glorious scene, winning her attention, her curiosity, her interest. To say to her: "Oh yes! I was in the most dangerous places and I was not afraid:"—and to see her turn pale with alarm, or faint, as she heard my tale of the horrors of the battle—and then to look down in contempt on all who would ask me: "Tell us, Gabrielito, was it so terrible after all?" All this was more than enough to fire my imagination, and I may frankly say that I would not, that day, have changed places with Nelson himself.

The morning of the 19th dawned, the day I hailed so eagerly; indeed it had not yet dawned when I found myself at the stern of the vessel with my master, who wanted to look on at the working of the ship. After clearing the decks the business of starting the ship began. The huge topsails were hoisted, and the heavy windlass, turning with a shrill clatter, dragged the anchor up from the bottom of the bay. The sailors clambered along the yards, while others handled the braces, obedient to the boatswain's call; and all the ship's voices, hitherto mute, filled the air with threatening outcries. The whistles, the bell, the discordant medley of men's voices, mixed with the creaking of the blocks, the humming of the ropes, the flapping of the sails as they thrashed the mast before they caught the wind—all these various sounds filled the air as the huge ship got under way. The bright ripples seemed to caress her sides, and the majestic monster made her way out of the bay without the slightest roll or even lurch, with a slow and solemn advance which was only perceptible to those on board by watching the apparent motion of the merchantmen lying at anchor and the landscape beyond.

At this moment I stood looking back at the scene behind us. And what a scene it was! Thirty-two men-of-war, five frigates, and two brigantines, Spanish and French together—some in front, some behind, and some abreast of us—were bursting into sail, as it were, and riding before the light breeze. I never saw a lovelier morning. The sun flooded those lovely shores with light; a faint purple tinge coloured the sea to the east, and the chain of hills which bound the horizon on the side of the town seemed to be on fire in the sunrise; the sky was perfectly clear excepting where, in the east, a few rose and golden clouds floated above the horizon. The blue sea was calm, and over that sea and beneath that sky the forty ships with their white sails rode forward, one of the noblest fleets that human eyes ever rested on.

The vessels did not all sail with equal speed. Some got ahead, others were slow to get under way; some gained upon us, while we passed others. The solemnity of their advance, the height of their masts, covered with canvas, and a vague and obscure harmony which my childish ears fancied they could detect proceeding from those glorious hulls—a kind of hymn, which was no doubt the effect of my own imagination— the loveliness of the day, the crispness of the air, the beauty of the sea, which seemed to be dancing with joy outside the gulf at the approach of the vessels—all formed the grandest picture that the mind of man can conceive of.

Cadiz, itself, like a moving panorama, unfolded itself before our eyes, displaying in turn every aspect of its vast amphitheatre. The low sun, illuminating the glass in its myriad windows, sprinkled it with living sparks of gold, and its buildings lay so purely white above the blue water that it looked as if it might have been that moment called into being, or raised from the sea like the fanciful city of San Genaro. I could see the wall extending from the mole as far as the fort of Santa Catalina; I could distinguish the bastions of Bonete and Orejon, and recognize the *Calete;* and my pride rose as I reflected what I had risen from and where I now was. At the same time the sound of the bells of the waking city came to my ears like some mysterious music, calling the inhabitants to early mass, with all the confused clamour of the bells of a large town. Now they seemed to me to ring gladly, and send good wishes after us—I listened to them as if they were human voices bidding us

God-speed; then again they tolled sadly and dolefully—a knell of misfortune; and as we sailed further and further away their music grew fainter till it was lost in space.

The fleet slowly made its way out of the bay—some of the ships taking several hours in getting fairly to sea. Marcial meanwhile made his comments on each, watching their behaviour, laughing them to scorn if they were clumsy, and encouraging them with paternal advice if they were swift and well-handled.

"What a lump that Don Federico is!" he exclaimed as he looked at the *Príncipe de Asturias* commanded by Gravina. "There goes Mr Corneta,[1]" he exclaimed as he saw the *Bucentaure* with Villeneuve on board. "He was a clever man that called you the *Rayo!*" (Thunderbolt) he cried ironically, as he watched the ship so named, which was the least manageable of all the fleet. "Well done *Papá Ignacio!*" he added, pointing to the *Santa Ana* commanded by Alava.

"Hoist your topsail properly, senseless oaf!" he went on, addressing Dumanoir's ship, *Le Formidable*. "That Frenchman keeps a hairdresser to crimp the topsail and to clew up the sails with curling tongs."

Towards evening the sky clouded over, and as night fell we could see Cadiz, already at a great distance, gradually vanish in the mist till the last faint outline became one with the darkness. The fleet then steered to the southward.

All night I kept close to Marcial, as soon as I had seen my master comfortably settled in his cabin. The old sailor, eagerly listened to by a couple of veteran comrades and admirers, was explaining Villeneuve's plan of battle.

"*Mr Corneta*," said he, "has divided the fleet into four lines. The vanguard led by Alava consists of six vessels; the centre, likewise of six, is commanded by *Mr Corneta* in person; the rear, again of six, is under Dumanoir, and the reserve of twelve ships is led by Don Federico. This seems to me not badly planned. I imagine that the French and Spanish ships are mixed, in order that they may not leave us impaled on the bull's horns, as they did at Finisterre.

"From what Don Alfonso tells me the Frenchman says that if the enemy comes up to leeward we are to form in line of battle and attack at once . . . This is very pretty talk in the state-room; but do you think the *Señorito*[2] will be such a booby as to come up to leeward of us? Oh yes—his lordship has not much brains in his figure-head and is sure to let himself be caught in that trap! Well! we shall see—if we see, what the Frenchman expects.—But do you just tell me: if we Spanish want to scuttle a few of those English ships, are we not strong enough and many enough to do it? Then why in the world need we ally ourselves with the

[1]Admiral Villeneuve.
[2]Nelson.

French, who would not allow us to do anything we had a mind to, but would have us dancing attendance at the end of their tow-line? Whenever we have had to work with them they have got us into mischief and we have had the worst of it. Well—may God and the Holy Virgin *del Cármen* be on our side, and rid us of our French friends for ever and ever, Amen.". . .

On the morning of the 20th there was a stiff breeze blowing and the vessels kept at some distance from each other; but as the wind had moderated soon after noon the admiral signalled that the ships were to form in five lines—the van, centre, and rear, and two lines of reserve. I was enchanted with watching the docile monsters, obediently taking their places; for, although the conditions of naval manœuvres did not admit of great rapidity nor of perfect uniformity in the line, it was impossible to see them without admiration. The wind was from the south west, according to Marcial, and the fleet, catching the breeze on the starboard quarter, ran towards the straits. During the night a few lights were seen, and by dawn on the 21st we saw twenty-seven ships to windward, among which Marcial pointed out three as three-deckers. By eight o'clock the thirty-three vessels of the enemy's fleet were in sight, forming two columns. Our fleet displayed a wide front, and to all appearance Nelson's two columns, advancing in a wedge, were coming down upon us so as to cut our lines through the centre and rear.

This was the position of the hostile fleets when the *Bucentaure* signalled that we were to put about; maybe you do not understand this. It means that we were to turn completely round and that whereas the wind was on our port side it would now be on the starboard, so that we should sail in the opposite direction. The ships' heads were now turned northwards and this manœuvre, which was intended to place us to windward of Cadiz so that we might reach it in case of disaster, was severely criticized on board the *Trinidad*, especially by Marcial, who said:

"The line of battle is all broken up; it was bad before and is worse now."

In point of fact what had been the vanguard was now in the rear and the reserve ships, which, as I heard said, were the best, were hindmost of all. The wind had fallen and the ships, being of various tonnage and inefficiently manned, the new line could not form with due precision; some of the vessels moved quickly and rushed forward; others went slowly, hanging back or losing their course, and forming a wide gap that broke the line before the enemy took the trouble of doing it.

"Reform the line," was now the signal; but, though a good ship answers her helm with wonderful docility, it is not so easy to manage as a horse. As he stood watching the movements of the ships nearest to us, Marcial observed:

"The line is wider than the Milky Way. If the *Señorito* cuts through it,

Heaven help us! we shall not be able to sail in any sort of order; they will shave our heads for us if they fire upon us. They are going to give us a dose through the centre, and how can the *San Juan* and the *Bahama* come up to support us from the rear—or the *Neptuno* and the *Rayo* which are in front. Besides, here we are to leeward, and the 'great-coats' can pick and choose where they will attack us, while all we can do is to defend ourselves as best we may. All I have to say is: God get us well out of the scrape and deliver us from the French for ever and ever, Amen."

The sun had now nearly reached the meridian and the enemy was coming down upon us.

"And is this a proper hour to begin a battle?" asked the old sailor indignantly. "Twelve o'clock in the day!"

But he did not dare to express his views publicly and these discussions were confined to a small circle into which I, with my eternal and insatiable curiosity, had squeezed myself. I do not know why, but it seemed to me that there was an expression of dissatisfaction on every face. The officers on the quarter-deck, and the sailors and non-commissioned officers at the bows, stood watching the ships to leeward, quite out of the line of battle, four of which ought to have been in the centre.

I forgot to mention one preliminary in which I myself had borne a hand. Early in the morning the decks were cleared for action, and when all was ready for serving the guns and working the ship, I heard someone say: "The sand—bring the sand." Marcial pulled me by the ear, and taking me to one of the hatchways set me in a line with some of the pressed men, ship's boys, and other supernumeraries. A number of sailors were posted on the ladders from the hatchway to the hold and between decks, and in this way were hauling up sacks of sand. Each man handed one to the man next to him and so it was passed on without much labour. A great quantity of sacks were thus brought up from hand to hand, and to my great astonishment they were emptied out on the upper deck, the poop, and the forecastle, the sand being spread about so as to cover all the planking; and the same thing was done between decks. My curiosity prompted me to ask the boy who stood next to me what this was for.

"For the blood," he said very coolly.

"For the blood!" I exclaimed unable to repress a shudder. I looked at the sand—I looked at the men who were busily employed at this task —and for a moment I felt I was a coward. However, my imagination reverted to the ideas which had previously filled it, and relieved my mind of its alarms; I thought no more of anything but victory and a happy issue.

Everything was ready for serving the guns, and the ammunition was passed up from the store-rooms to the decks by a chain of men, like that which had brought up the sand-bags.

The English advanced to attack us in two sections. One came straight down upon us, and at its head, which was the point of the wedge, sailed a large ship carrying the admiral's flag. This, as I afterwards learned, was the *Victory*, commanded by Nelson. At the head of the other line was the *Royal Sovereign*, commanded by Collingwood. All these names, and the strategical plan of the battle, were not known to me till later. . . .

It was now a quarter to twelve. The fatal moment was approaching. The anxiety was general, and I do not speak merely from what was going on in my own mind, for I was absorbed in watching the ship which was said to contain Nelson, and for some time was hardly aware of what was going on round me.

Suddenly a terrible order was given by our captain—the boatswains repeated it; the sailors flew to the tops; the blocks and ropes creaked, the topsails flapped in the wind.

"Take in sail!" cried Marcial, with a good round oath. "The infernal idiot is making us work back."

And then I understood that the *Trinidad* was to slacken her speed so as to run alongside of the *Bucentaure*, because the *Victory* seemed to be taking measures to run in between those two ships and so cut the line in the middle. . . .

So far as I am concerned, in all my life my soul has never gone through any experiences to compare with those of that hour. In spite of my youth, I was quite capable of understanding the gravity of the occasion, and for the first time in my life, my mind was filled with grand ideas, lofty aspirations, and heroic thoughts. A conviction that we must conquer was so firmly rooted in my mind that I felt quite pitiful towards the English, and wondered to see them so eagerly advancing to certain destruction. For the first time too I fully understood the ideal of patriotism, and my heart responded to the thought with a glow of feeling such as I had never experienced before. Until now my mother country had been embodied in my mind in the persons of its rulers—such as the King and his famous minister, for whom I felt different degrees of respect. As I knew no more of history than I had picked up in the streets, it was to me a matter of course that everybody's enthusiasm must be fired by knowing that the Spaniards had, once upon a time, killed a great number of Moors, and, since then, swarms of French and of English. I considered my countrymen as models of valour; but valour, as I conceived of it, was as like barbarity as one egg is like another; and with such ideas as these, patriotism had been to me nothing more than boastful pride in belonging to a race of exterminators of Moors.

But in the pause that preceded the battle I understood the full significance of that divine word; the conception of nationality, of devotion to a mother-country, was suddenly born in my soul, lighting it up, as it were, and revealing a thousand wonderful possibilities—as the rising sun dissipates the darkness that has hidden a beautiful landscape.

thought of my native land as a vast place full of people all united in brotherly regard—of society as divided into families, married couples to be held together, and children to be educated—of honour, to be cherished and defended; I imagined an unspoken agreement among all these human beings to help and protect each other against any attack from without, and I understood that these vessels had been constructed by them all for the defence of their native land; that is to say, for the soil on which they lived, the fields watered by their sweat, the homes where their ancestors had dwelt, the gardens where their children played, the colonies discovered and conquered by their forefathers, the harbours where their ships found shelter after long voyages—the magazines where they stored their wealth—the Church which was the mausoleum of those they had loved, the dwelling-place of their saints, and the ark of their belief—the public places where they might take their pleasure, the private homes where the venerable household gods, handed down from generation to generation, seemed to symbolize the perpetuity of the nation—their family hearth round which the smoke-dyed walls seem still to re-echo with the time-honoured legends with which the grand dame soothes the flightiness or the naughtiness of the little ones, the street where friendly faces meet and smile—the field, the sea, the sky—everything which from the moment of birth makes up the sum of existence, from the crib of a pet animal to the time-honoured throne of the king; every object into which the soul seems to go forth to live, as if the body that clothes it were too narrow a shell.

I believed too that the disputes between Spain and France or England were always about something that those countries ought to give up to us, and in which Spain could not, on the whole, be wrong. Her self-defence seemed to me as legitimate as the aggression was brutal; and as I had always heard that justice must triumph, I never doubted of victory. Looking up at our red and yellow flag—the colours nearest to that of fire—I felt my bosom swell, and could not restrain a few tears of enthusiasm and excitement; I thought of Cadiz, of Vejer, of the whole Spanish nation assembled, as it were, on a vast platform and looking on with eager anxiety; and all this tide of emotion lifted up my heart to God to whom I put up a prayer, which was neither a *Paternoster* nor an *Ave*, but a gush of inspiration that came to me at the moment.

A sudden shock startled me from my ecstasy, terrifying me with its violent vibration. The first broadside had been fired.

A vessel in the rear had been the first to fire on the *Royal Sovereign*, commanded by Collingwood, and while that ship carried on the fight with the *Santa Ana* the *Victory* came down on us. On board the *Trinidad* every one was anxious to open fire; but our captain would not give the word till he saw a favourable opportunity. Meanwhile, as if the ships were in such close communication that a slow-match was lighted from one to the other, the fire ran along from the *Santa Ana* in the middle, to each end of the line.

The *Victory* fired first on the *Redoubtable*, and being repulsed, came up to the windward of the *Trinidad*. The moment had come for us; a hundred voices cried "Fire!"—loudly echoing the word of command, and fifty round-shot were hurled against the flank of the English man-of-war. For a minute I could see nothing of the enemy for the smoke, while he, as if blind with rage, came straight down upon us before the wind. Just within gun-shot he put the ship about and gave us a broad-side. In the interval between our firing and theirs, our crew, who had taken note of the damage done to the enemy, had gained in enthusiasm. The guns were rapidly served, though not without some hitches owing to want of experience in some of the gunners. Marcial would have been only too glad to undertake the management of one of the cannon, but his mutilated body was not equal to the heroism of his spirit. He was forced to be satisfied with superintending the delivery of the charges and encouraging the gunners by word and gesture.

The *Bucentaure*, just at our stern, was, like us, firing on the *Victory*, and the *Téméraire*, another powerful English vessel. It seemed as though the *Victory* must fall into our hands, for the *Trinidad's* fire had cut her tackle to pieces, and we saw with pride that her mizzen-mast had gone by the board.

In the excitement of this first onslaught I scarcely perceived that some of our men were wounded or killed. I had chosen a place where I thought I should be least in the way, and never took my eyes off the captain who stood on the quarter-deck, issuing his orders with heroic coolness; and I wondered to see my master, no less calm though less enthusiastic, encouraging the officers and men in his quavering voice.

"Ah!" said I to myself, "if only Doña Francisca could see him now!"

I am bound to confess that at times I felt desperately frightened, and would gladly have hidden myself at the very bottom of the hold, while at others I was filled with an almost delirious courage, when I longed to see the glorious spectacle from the most dangerous posts. However, I will set aside my own insignificant individuality and relate the most terrible crisis of our fight with the *Victory*. The *Trinidad* was doing her immense mischief when the *Téméraire*, by a wonderfully clever manœuvre, slipped in between the two vessels thus sheltering her consort from our fire. She then proceeded to cut through the line behind the *Trinidad*, and as the *Bucentaure*, under fire, had got so close alongside of the *Trinidad* that their yards touched, there was a wide space beyond into which the *Téméraire* rushed down and, going about immediately, came up on our lee and delivered a broadside on that quarter, till then untouched. At the same time the *Neptune*, another large English ship, ran in where the *Victory* had previously been, while the *Victory* veered round so that, in a few minutes, the *Trinidad* was surrounded by the enemy and riddled on all sides.

From my master's face, from Uriarte's heroic fury, and from a volley of oaths delivered by Marcial and his friends, I understood that we were lost and the idea of defeat was anguish to my soul. The line of the combined fleets was broken at several points, and the bad order in which they had formed after turning round, gave place to the most disastrous confusion. We were surrounded by the enemy whose artillery kept up a perfect hail of round and grape-shot on our ship, and on the *Bucentaure* as well. The *Augustin*, the *Héros*, and the *Leandro* were engaged at some distance from us where they had rather more sea-room, while the *Trinidad*, and the Admiral's ship, utterly hemmed in and driven to extremities by the genius of the great Nelson, were fighting heroically—no longer in hopes of a victory which was impossible, but anxious, at any rate, to perish gloriously.

The white hairs which now cover my old head almost stand on end as I remember those terrible hours, from two to four in the afternoon. I think of those five ships, not as mere machines of war obeying the will of men, but as living giants, huge creatures fighting on their own account, carried into action by their sails as though they were active limbs and using the fearful artillery they bore in their sides for their personal defence. As I looked at them then, my fancy could not help personifying them, and to this hour I feel as though I could see them coming up, defying each other, going about to fire a broadside, rushing furiously up to board, drawing back to gather more force, mocking or threatening the enemy; I can fancy them expressing their sufferings when wounded or loftily breathing their last, like a gladiator who in his agony forgets not the dignity which beseems him;—I can imagine that I hear the voices of the crews like the murmur of an oppressed sufferer, sometimes eager with enthusiasm, sometimes a dull roar of desperation the precursor of destruction, sometimes a hymn of triumph in anticipation of victory, or a hideous storm of voices lost in space and giving way to the awful silence of disgrace and defeat.

The scene on board the *Santísima Trinidad* was nothing short of infernal. All attempt at working the ship had been abandoned, for it did not and could not move. The only thing to be done was to serve the guns with the utmost rapidity, and to do as much damage to the enemy as they had done to us. The English small-shot rent the sails just as if huge and invisible nails were tearing slits in them. The splinters of timber and of masts, the stout cables cut through as if they were straws, the capstans, spindles, and other heavy machinery torn from their place by the enemy's fire, strewed the deck so that there was scarcely room to move. Every minute men, till then full of life, fell on deck or into the sea; the blasphemy of those who were fighting mingled with the cries of the wounded till it was impossible to say whether the dying were defying God or the living crying to him for mercy while they fought. . . .

Blood was flowing in rivulets on the upper and lower decks and in spite of the sand the motion of the ship carried it from side to side making sinister patterns on the boards. The cannon-balls, fired at such a short range, mutilated those they killed in a terrible manner, and I saw more than one man still standing with his head blown away, the force of the shock not having been great enough to fling the victim into the sea, whose waters would have extinguished almost painlessly the last sensation of existence. Other balls struck a mast or against the bulwarks, carrying off a hail of hot splinters that pierced and stung like arrows. The rifle-shots from the tops and the round-shot from the carronades dealt a more lingering and painful death, and there was hardly a man to be seen who did not bear the marks, more or less severe, of the foe's iron and lead.

The crew—the soul of the ship—being thus thrashed by the storm of battle and utterly unable to deal equal destruction saw death at hand though resolved to die with the courage of despair; and the ship itself—the glorious body—shivered under the cannonade. I could feel her shudder under the fearful blows; her timbers cracked, her beams creaked, her ribs groaned like limbs on the rack, and the deck trembled under my feet with audible throbs, as though the whole huge creature was indignant at the sufferings of her crew. Meanwhile the water was pouring in at a hundred holes in the riddled hull, and the hold was fast filling.

The *Bucentaure*, the Admiral's vessel, surrendered before our very eyes. Villeneuve struck to the *Victory*. When once the leader of the fleet was gone, what hope was there for the other ships? The French flag vanished from the gallant vessel's mast and she ceased firing. The *San Augustin* and the *Héros* still persevered, and the *Rayo* and *Neptuno*, of the van, made an effort to rescue us from the enemy that was battering us. I could see what was going on in the immediate neighbourhood of the *Trinidad*, though nothing was to be seen of the rest of the line. The wind had fallen to a calm and the smoke settled down over our heads shrouding everything in its dense white wreaths which it was impossible for eye to pierce. We could catch a glimpse now and then of a distant ship, mysteriously magnified by some inexplicable optical effect; I believe indeed that the terror of that supreme moment exaggerated every impression.

Presently this dense cloud was dispersed for an instant—but in what a fearful manner! A tremendous explosion, louder than all the thousand guns of the fleet fired at once, paralysed every man and filled every soul with dread; and just as the ear was stunned by the terrific roar an intense flash lighted up the two fleets, rending the veil of smoke and revealing the whole panorama of the battle. This catastrophe had taken place on the side towards the South where the rear line had been posted.

"A ship blown up!" said one to another. But opinion differed as to whether it was the *Santa Ana*, the *Argonauta*, the *Ildefonso*, or the *Bahama*. We afterwards learnt that it was a Frenchman, the *Achille*. The explosion scattered in a myriad fragments what had a few moments before been a noble ship of 74 guns and 600 men. But a few seconds after we had already forgotten the explosion in thinking only of ourselves.

The *Bucentaure* having struck, the enemy's fire was directed on us, and our fate was sealed. The enthusiasm of the first hour was by this extinct in my soul; my heart quaked with terror that paralysed my limbs and smothered every other emotion excepting curiosity. This I found so irresistible that I could not keep away from places where the danger was greatest. My small assistance was of no great use now, for the wounded were too numerous to be carried below and the guns had to be served by those who had some little strength left. Among these was Marcial who was here, there, and everywhere, shouting and working to the best of his small ability, acting as boatswain, gunner, sailor, and carpenter all at once, doing everything that happened to be needed at this awful moment. No one could have believed that, with hardly more than half a body, he could have done the work of so many men. A splinter had struck him on the head and the blood had stained his face and given him a most horrible appearance. I could see his lips move as he licked the blood from them and then he spit it out viciously over the side, as if he thought he could thus punish the enemy.

What astonished me most, and indeed shocked me somewhat, was that Marcial even in this scene of horror could still cut a good-humoured joke; whether to encourage his dejected comrades or only to keep his own courage up I do not know. The foremast fell with a tremendous crash, covering the whole of the fore-deck with rigging, and Marcial called out to me:

"Bring the hatchets, boy; we must stow this lumber in Davy Jones' locker," and in two minutes the ropes were cut and the mast went overboard.

Then, seeing that the enemy's fire grew hotter, he shouted to the purser's mate, who had come up to serve a gun:

"Daddy, order up some drink for those 'great coats,' and then they will let us alone."

To a soldier, who was lying like a dead creature with the pain of his wounds and the misery of sea-sickness, he exclaimed as he whisked the slow-match under his nose:

"Take a whiff of orange-flower, man, to cure your faintness. Would you like to take a turn in a boat? Nelson has invited us to take a glass of grog with him."

This took place amidships; looking up at the quarter-deck I saw that Cisneros was killed; two sailors hastily carried him down into his cabin. My master remained immoveable at his post, but his left arm was bleeding severely. I ran up to help him, but before I could reach the spot an officer had gone to him to persuade him to retire to his state-room. He had not spoken two words when a ball shot away half his head and his blood sprinkled my face. Don Alonso withdrew, as pale as the corpse which fell on the quarter-deck. When my master had gone down the commander was left standing alone, so perfectly cool that I could not help gazing at him for a few minutes, astounded by such courage. His head was uncovered, his face very white, but his eyes flashed and his attitude was full of energy, and he stood at his post, commanding the desperate strife, though the battle was lost past retrieval. Even this fearful disaster must be conducted with due order, and the captain's duty was still to keep discipline over heroism. His voice still controlled his men in this struggle between honour and death. An officer who was serving in the first battery came up for orders, and before he could speak he was lying dead at the feet of his chief; another officer of marines who was standing by his side fell wounded on the deck, and at last Uriarte stood quite alone on the quarter-deck, which was strewn with the dead and wounded. Even then he never took his eyes off the English ships and the working of our guns—the horrible scene on the poop and in the roundhouse, where his comrades and subalterns lay dying, could not quell his noble spirit nor shake his firm determination to face the fire till he too should fall. As I recall the fortitude and stoical calmness of Don Francisco Xavier de Uriarte, I understand all that is told us of the heroes of antiquity. At that time the word Sublime was as yet unknown to me, but I felt that there must be, in every language under heaven, some human utterance to express that greatness of soul which I here saw incarnate and which revealed itself to me as a special grace vouchsafed by God to miserable humanity.

By this time most of our guns were silenced, more than half of our men being incapable of serving them. I might not, however, have been aware of the fact, but that being impelled by curiosity I went out of the cabin once more and heard a voice saying in a tone of thunder:

"Gabrielillo, come here."

It was Marcial who was calling me; I ran to his side and found him trying to work one of the guns which had been left silent for lack of men. A ball had shot away the half of his wooden leg, which made him exclaim:

"Well! so long as I can manage to keep the one of flesh and bone. . . .!"

Two sailors lay dead by the gun; a third, though horribly wounded, still tried to go on working it.

"Let be, mate!" said Marcial. "You cannot even light the match," and taking the linstock from his hand, he put it into mine, saying, "Take it, Gabrielillo. If you are afraid you had better jump overboard."

He loaded the cannon as quickly as he was able, helped by a ship's boy who happened to come up; we ran it forward: "Fire!" was the word, I applied the match and the gun went off.

We repeated this operation a second and a third time, and the roar of the cannon fired by my own hand produced an extraordinary effect on my nerves. The feeling that I was no longer a spectator but an actor in this stupendous tragedy for the moment blew all my alarms to the winds; I was eager and excited or at any rate determined to appear so. That moment revealed to me the truth that heroism is often simply the pride of honour. Marcial's eye—the eyes of the world were upon me; I must bear myself worthy of their gaze.

"Oh!" I exclaimed to myself with an impulse of pride, "If only my young mistress could see me now!.... Bravely firing cannon like a man!" Two dozen of English were the least I might have sent to the other world.

These grand visions, however, did not last long for Marcial, enfeebled by age, was beginning to sink with exhaustion; he breathed hard as he wiped away the blood which flowed profusely from his head, and at last his arms dropped by his side, and closing his eyes, he exclaimed:

"I can do no more; the powder is rising to my head. Gabrielillo, fetch me some water."

I ran to obey him, and when I had brought the water he drank it eagerly. This seemed to give him fresh energy; we were just about to load once more when a tremendous shock petrified us as we stood. The main-mast, cut through by repeated shots, fell amidships and across the mizzen; the ship was completely covered with the wreck, and the confusion was appalling.

I happily was so far under shelter that I got no harm but a slight blow on the head which, though it stunned me for a moment, did not prevent my thrusting aside the fragments of rope and timber which had fallen above me. The sailors and marines were struggling to clear away the vast mass of lumber, but from this moment only the lower deck guns could be used at all. I got clear as best I could and went to look for Marcial, but I did not find him, and casting my eyes up at the quarter-deck, I saw that the captain was no longer at his post. He had fallen senseless, badly wounded in the head by a splinter, and two sailors were just about to carry him down to the stateroom. I was running forward to assist when a piece of shell hit me on the shoulder, terrifying me excessively, for I made sure my wound was mortal and that I was at my last gasp. My alarm did not hinder me from going into the cabin; I tottered from loss of blood and for a few minutes lay in a dead faint. I was roused from my short swoon by hearing the rattle of the cannon below and then a voice shouting vehemently:

"Board her! bring pikes!—axes!"

And then the confusion was so complete that it was impossible to distinguish human voices from the rest of the hideous uproar. However, somehow—I know not how—without thoroughly waking from my drowsy state, I became aware that all was given up for lost and that the officers had met in the cabin to agree to strike; nor was this the work of my fancy, bewildered as I was, for I heard a voice exclaiming: "The *Trinidad* never strikes!" I felt sure that it was Marcial's voice; but at any rate some one said it.

When I recovered perfect consciousness, I saw my master sunk on one of the sofas in the cabin, his face hidden in his hands, prostrate with despair, and paying no heed to his wound.

I went to the heart-broken old man, who could find no way of expressing his grief but by embracing me like a father, as if we were both together on the brink of the grave. He, at any rate, was convinced that he must soon die of grief, though his wound was by no means serious. I comforted him as best I might, assuring him that if the battle were indeed lost it was not because I had failed to batter the English to the best of my power; and I went on to say that we should be more fortunate next time—but my childish arguments failed to soothe him.

Going out presently in search of water for my master, I witnessed the very act of lowering the flag which was flying at the gaff, that being one of the few spars, with the remains of the mizzen-mast that remained standing. The glorious flag, the emblem of our honour, pierced and tattered as it was, which had gathered so many fighting-men under its folds, ran down the rope never to be unfurled again. The idea of stricken pride, of a brave spirit giving way before a superior force, can find no more appropriate symbol to represent it than that of a flying standard which sinks and disappears like a setting sun. And our flag thus slowly descending that fatal evening, at the moment when we surrendered, seemed to shed a parting ray of glory.

The firing ceased, and the English took possession of the conquered vessel.

THE FISHERMEN OF RODILLERO[1]

Armando Palacio Valdes

THE weather became so bad, and the men so mistrustful of it, that the skippers met together and decided that three of them should keep watch each night to note carefully the state of sea and sky, and, according to their observations, decide whether to call out the men or not. Moreover, as they usually went out before daybreak, it was agreed that the boat which went out first or was ahead of the others, should set a light at the prow in case it seemed dangerous to go on; this would serve as a signal to the other boats to put back to harbour.

---

[1]From *José*. Translated by Elizabeth D'Oyley with the author's permission.

Two nights before the event we are about to tell of, it fell to José to keep watch with two of the others. The sky, they saw, gave promise of bad weather, and they did not want to call out the men. But as it was now some days since they had been out, and the pinch of hunger was beginning to be felt, there was some murmuring in the inn at this decision. During the day the weather improved a little, but not much. That night three other skippers kept watch, who hesitated a long time before giving the boy the order for calling out the crews, for the outlook had seldom been less promising. At last they did give it, thinking of the people's misery, or, maybe, in fear of the grumblers.

José was one of the first to reach the shore.

"Ave Maria, how awful!" he cried, looking at the sky. "What a night to put to sea!"

Too wise to alarm his fellows, and too brave to refuse to go out, he kept silent, and, helped by his men, launched the boat. As it was the nearest, it was the first ready and afloat. And the crew, once aboard, took the oars. There were more men in the boat than there would be in summer; as always happened, firstly, because in winter there was no other work for them, and secondly, because more oars were needed on account of the frequent calms. In José's boat there were fourteen.

A mile from shore José gave the order to hoist sail. Asturian boats always carry five sails, which are—in order of size—the mainsail, spritsail, foresail, foretopsail, and the *uncion* which are differently grouped according to the force of the wind. The *uncion*, the smallest, bears this terrible name, because it is the only one hoisted when the boat is on the point of being lost.

"What sail shall we set, José?" one of the men asked.

"Foresails," he answered, shortly.

Amidships the seamen ran up the spritsail, and the foresail at the prow, which was the meaning of José's order.

The night was dark, but not impenetrable. Here and there the sky was clear. Big dark clouds sailed swiftly, plainly showing that on high the wind blew strongly, though they felt little of it below. It was this that made José—whose eyes were fixed upon the sky—uneasy and preoccupied. The men, too, were silent and apprehensive; the cold paralysed their hands and dread—which they could not hide—their tongues. They cast frequent glances aloft and each time saw the clouds racing with greater fury. The sea was oily and sinister.

A quarter of an hour went by, and then José broke the silence with a sudden exclamation.

"What a filthy night! Not fit for a dog to be out!"

"You're right!" three or four of the men made haste to say. "Dirty weather—more fit for pigs than Christians."

"Don't go on for us, José," one of them ended. "Put back, if you want to."

José did not answer. He was silent for a few minutes: then, raising himself suddenly, he said with decision.

"Light that lantern, boy! About ship!"

The boy lit the lantern and set it in the prow with evident relief; and with equal relief the men obeyed the order.

The boat tacked, bearing towards Rodillero. And at once, far off, they saw the lanterns of the boats come alight, one after the other, signifying that all had seen the signal and were putting back to harbour.

"As if we could do anything else!" said one of the men.

"Who on earth would go to sea of his own free will to-day?" another exclaimed.

"Why the devil did those fools Nicholas and Toribio call us out?"

The tongues of all were loosened, and, as they talked, making for home, José saw to leeward the shape of a boat, passing not far from his, without a light at the prow.

"Easy, lads!" he said. "What the devil's that? Where's that boat making for?"

"You may well ask!"

The skipper got to his feet, and making a trumpet of his hands, shouted:

"Ahoy there!"

"What d'you want, José?" the skipper of the other boat answered, recognizing him by his voice.

"Where are you making for, Hermanegildo?" asked José, who had recognized him too.

"The fishing ground," the other answered, coming as near as he could.

"Why didn't you light your lantern when I did?"

"Because I know these folks well. They'll show you their lights and pay no damn heed to you. How much d'you bet me all the boats will be at the fishing ground at daybreak?"

"Damn his cheek!" muttered José, and turning to his crew:—"Go about! Some day when we least expect it we'll have to pay for this folly."

With a bad grace the seamen obeyed the command.

"Haven't I told you many a time, José," said Bernardo, "that in these parts anyone will willingly lose one eye as long as his neighbour loses two?"

The skipper did not answer.

"The best of it is," said another, "those fools yonder think we'll cheat them, when the truth is we're all wanting to know what the other fellow's up to."

"The joke'll be when we meet at dawn!" a third added.

"You'll see! When something happens one of these days," said José again, "they'll soon find somebody to blame."

"Always the way!" Bernardo answered with mock gravity.

Silence reigned in the boat after that. The men scanned the horizon.

The skipper kept a close watch upon the weather and with more and more uneasiness, despite the fact that for one moment the sky seemed to clear entirely. But it soon clouded over again. Yet even now the wind did not blow hard, except up above. Towards daybreak it grew quieter. The dawn was sadder and greyer than usual. With difficulty the light filtered through a threefold bank of clouds.

When they reached the fishing ground, they saw in fact nearly all the Rodillero boats, which had already thrown their lines into the sea and were fishing not very far from one another. As soon as they had furled their sails, they, too, made one of them, and in two hours' time they had caught a few bream; but not many. About ten o'clock the sky darkened and a shower fell, bringing with it a little wind. Half an hour later came another, and the wind grew stronger. Then a few of the boats gathered in their tackle, and hoisting sail, headed for land. One after the other the rest followed.

"We didn't need baggage for this trip," said one of José's men sullenly, clewing up the fore-topsail.

They were some ten or twelve leagues from the coast. Before they had covered two miles, over in the west they saw the sky darkening ominously. So dark it was that the men looked from one to the other apprehensively.

"*Madre del alma*, look what's coming," cried one.

For safety, José had at the start ordered the hoisting of the foresails only, that is, the foresail amidships and the foretopsail at the prow. He gazed steadily westward. The blackness was coming closer rapidly. When he felt upon his cheek the coolness that foreruns a squall, he jumped to his feet, shouting:

"Let go sheets and halyards!"

Quickly the men obeyed, though they did not realize how great the danger was. The sails fell heavily on to the thwarts—in the nick of time, for a violent gust of wind went whistling between the masts and hurled the boat forward. The men threw a grateful look at José.

"How did you smell the damned blast?" said one. Then looking seaward, they saw that one of the boats had foundered, and once again they turned their glance upon José, pale as the dead.

"Did you see, José?" one of them asked in a husky shaken voice.

The skipper closed his eyes as a sign of assent. But the boy in the bow, seeing what had happened, began to cry aloud:

"Holy Virgin! what's to become of us? Holy Mother! what's to become of us?"

José, faced him, his eyes flashing with anger.

"Stow that, you little devil, or I'll pitch you overboard!"

And the little lad, terrified, fell silent.

"Up with the foretops'l and the *uncion*!" José ordered.

Quickly it was done. As much as possible José let the boat fall off to leeward, taking care not to lose sight of the coast line of Rodillero; and with extraordinary swiftness the boat gathered way, for the wind blew fiercely, growing stronger each moment. Not many minutes had gone when a heavy sea got up, so that they could no longer see the direction the other boats were taking. Now and again it rained heavily. The boat shipped a good deal of water, and several of the men had to be always baling. But José paid more heed to the wind, than to the water. It blew so fitfully and treacherously that should he relax his attention for a moment the boat would most surely capsize. Twice again he had to strike sail hastily to prevent it: and at last seeing the impossibility of carrying even the two sails, he gave orders for the hoisting of the *uncion* only. The men looked at him in consternation and the hands of many of them trembled as they obeyed.

"We must put her before the wind," said José, his voice already hoarse with shouting. "We can't make Rodillero. We'll put into Sarrio."

"It looks to me as if we won't make Sarrio either," an old man answered in a low voice.

"Don't lose heart, lads! Courage! This is nothing!" the skipper answered with energy.

From the moment when they gave up all idea of making Rodillero and put the boat before the wind, he could do no more, especially as they were carrying so very little sail. But the sea began to alarm them. Helped by the oily swell of the night before, it had become in truth a mountainous sea, terrible and awe-inspiring. The waves broke so heavily and so unceasingly against the stern that at last José was forced to bear away a little. In spite of this the men never ceased to bale. The sea grew heavier. The waves every moment higher. The boat disappeared beneath them and by a miracle rose again. One sea carried away the rudder. Quickly José seized the one they had in reserve, but even as he was hooking it in place, another blow wrenched it from his hands and the boat shipped a heavy sea.

The boy broke into sobs, crying out again;

"*Madre de mi alma*, we're lost!"

José threw the tiller—which still remained on board—at his head.

"Shut up, you young fool, or I'll kill you!"

And seeing signs of fear in the faces of some of the crew, he flung a fierce look at them;

"The first man who cries out—I'll wring his neck!"

This roughness was needed: if panic fell upon them and they ceased for one moment to bale, they would most surely founder.

In place of the rudder, José put an oar over the stern. With sails set, it is utterly impossible to steer with an oar, but as they were carrying nothing but the *uncion*, he could, by dint of great effort, make the boat answer to it. At each buffet of the sea they shipped a great quantity of water, and in spite of the fact that one man, working steadily, could with a bucket bale out a pipe of water in eight or ten minutes, it was impossible to clear the boat; almost always the water remained knee-high. And José never ceased for a moment to shout with the little voice left him:

"Bale, lads! Bale! Courage, lads! Bale! Bale!"

One wave carried away Bernardo's cap.

"Go on!" he cried angrily. "My head 'll go next!"

Their case was desperate. And although they tried to hide it, fear had taken hold of them all. Then it was that José, seeing their strength must soon give out, said:

"Boys, we're in a tight corner. Would you like to call upon the Holy Christ of Rodillero to save us?"

"Yes, José," they all answered with the haste of despair.

"Very well; if you like, we'll offer to go barefooted to hear Mass. But this must give us courage. There must be no cowardice. Courage! And bale, lads, bale!"

The vow put new heart into them and in faith they went on with their work. In a few minutes they had flung out most of the water and the boat rode easier. Then José noticed that the mainmast was hampering them.

"We must unship the mainmast," he said, and pushed forward in haste to grasp it.

But in that instant they saw with terror an immense wave coming down on them, high as a mountain and black as a cave.

"José, this is beyond a joke!" cried out Bernardo, resigning himself to death.

The wave struck the boat with such force that it flung José upon his face and hurled him against the thwarts. The boat was awash, almost swamped. But José, nearly stunned as he was, struggled doggedly to his feet, crying out:

"Bale! Bale! It's nothing!"

What was passing in Rodillero?

The few boats that had obeyed José's signal returned to harbour before morning. Their crews felt shamed and disheartened when they saw how miserably they had been taken in, especially when their women-folk bantered them.

"Must you always play the fool? When will you know the kind of people you have to deal with? *Hombre de Dios!* You'll see what sort of a sea we get to-day! You'll see!"

The men held their tongues as usual, knowing that right was on their side. But they swore within themselves not to fall again into the same snare.

At daybreak they changed their opinion a little. The sea had so drear an aspect and the weather looked so bad that their idleness did not greatly trouble them. When, shrouded in a shower, the first blast of the

North East wind was felt in the village, some of them went back to their wives, with a smile.

"What d'you think of it now? You'd like me to be at sea now, would you?"

It was the women's turn then to hold their tongues. The second blast, much fiercer than the first, put the whole neighbourhood in commotion. Men and women hurried to the shore, and from there, despite the rain that fell in torrents, mounted to San Esteban. Fear showed itself so quickly that the superstitious unrest which had reigned in the place all winter was easy to be seen. From the corners of their eyes the women watched the old seamen screwing up their faces anxiously.

"Is there any danger, Uncle Pepe?" some of them thrust forward to ask.

"It's not up to much . . . But the sea hasn't yet said 'Here I am!'"

It said it, nevertheless, sooner than they expected. The storm broke suddenly, furiously. In an instant the sea rose in a way truly terrifying, and began to break upon the Hoesos de San Pedro, the reefs nearest to the coast. Soon it was breaking also on the Cobanin, the nearest reefs on the other side of the bay. The crowd standing on the heights of San Esteban, watched the progress of the storm in terror. Some of the women began to cry.

Nevertheless there was no need to worry as yet—so said the experienced seamen. The harbour was quite open. As long as the boats did not capsize (and this was the men's own lookout; they must trust to their own skill to avoid it) they could put into Rodillero without danger. But some one cried out:

"And what about the great waves? Will they have time to bale?"

"Time enough!" a dour-looking fisherman said. "One would think we'd never seen a high sea before! There never was a village like this for getting excited over nothing!"

The energy with which he said these words silenced the doubters and a little lightened the hearts of the women. Unhappily his triumph was short lived: a few minutes later the waves broke over the Tornio, another of the reefs that formed the bar.

Near the chapel of San Esteban stood a hut in which lived a peasant who was employed by the coastguard service for a very small yearly wage, to light the beacons which served as signals on days or nights of danger. This peasant, although he had been to sea only a few times, knew it as well as any sailor. After watching it closely for some time and often hesitating, he took from the hut yard a load of furze and dry broom, put it on the highest part of the headland and set fire to it. It was the first signal for the fishermen.

Elisa who was among the crowd, close to her godmother, felt her heart contract at sight of the beacon. She called to mind the terrible curse of the sacristan's wife; and all the sad forebodings and superstitious fears that lay sleeping in her soul awoke suddenly. Yet for shame's sake she managed to control herself; but she began to hasten from group to group, listening with ill-concealed anxiety to the remarks of the seamen. What she heard terrified her.

Little was said; all watched intently. The wind whipped their faces with the last raindrops of the squall. The sea grew rapidly. After breaking over the Huesos de San Pedro, the Cobanin and the Torno, it burst upon another reef further from the coast.

"It's breaking on the Furada! . . . Manuel, you can light your perch beacon," cried one of the seamen.

Manuel ran to the hut once again, brought out another load of furze and set fire to it close to the first. This was the signal of immediate danger. If those at sea did not make haste to harbour, they ran the risk of its being closed against them.

"Any boat in sight, Rafael?" asked a young girl, two large tears rolling down her cheeks.

"Not yet. We can't see much for the spray."

Not a sail showed on the horizon. Anguish so held the watchers that some minutes passed before a voice was raised among them. Every gaze was riveted upon the Carrero, a short space left free by the bar of Rodillero, where the boats had safe entry when the sea was choppy. Elisa's forehead was cold and damp with sweat, and she clung tightly to her godmother to prevent herself from falling.

A quarter of an hour went by. Suddenly a cry went up from the crowd, a cry weaker, but more mournful than the roar of the sea. A wave had just broken upon the Carrero. The bar was now nothing but a fringe of foam. The harbour was closed.

Manuel, pale and silent, went in search of another load of furze and set fire to it, beside the other two. The rain had ceased and the beacons, fanned by the wind, flared up.

Elisa trembled at the sound of that cry, and urged by an irresistible impulse, she hurried away, ran down the pathway through the pines, crossed the deserted village, mounted the avenue to the church and came, spent and panting, to the door. For a moment she paused to take breath; then, making the sign of the cross, she dropped to her knees, and so made her way up to the high altar; but instead of halting there, she turned to the right and began to mount painfully the winding stairway which led to the chapel of the Christ. It was the stairway of penitence and its steps were worn by the knees of the devout. Elisa's when she reached the top were dropping blood.

The chapel was a dusky place, its walls covered with images and offerings, with a grated window opening upon the church, through which the faithful could see the venerated image on the days when Mass was said at its altar. The Holy Christ was there, covered as usual by a velvet curtain. With a hand that trembled Elisa drew aside the curtain and prostrated herself. A little while later many of the other women came in, and in like manner knelt down in silence. From time to time, an irrepressible sob broke upon the mystery and majesty of the place.

The sea grew calmer by the afternoon. Thanks to this, a good many of the boats managed, though at great risk, to put into Rodillero. Later, others came in, but when night fell there were still five missing. One of them was José's. The seamen who had no doubt as to their fate—for they had seen one boat founder, dared not utter a word; the countless questions put to them they answered evasively. No one knew anything; no one had seen anything. The shore remained thronged with people late into the night, but as the hours went by, despair grew. Little by little the beach was deserted, only the families of the men still at sea remaining. At last these, too, almost gave up hope, and leaving the shore went back to the village utterly heart-broken.

That awful night! There still rings in my ears the heart-rending sobs of unhappy wives and of children crying for their father. The village looked drear—terrible. People hastened through the street in groups, gathering about the house doors, all talking with raised voices. The inns were open, and there the men argued hotly, blaming one another for this disaster. From time to time a dishevelled woman, stricken with grief, would cross the street, uttering cries so horrible as to make one's hair stand on end. Even from within the houses came the sound of groans and sobs.

The first moment of dismay and anguish was followed by one of calm, more sorrowful yet, if that were possible. The people were shut within doors, and grief had now more the look of resignation. Within those humble homes how many tears were shed! In one, a poor old woman, whose two sons were out at sea, uttered such piercing shrieks that the few who passed along the street stood still in horror. In another, an unhappy wife who had lost her husband was sobbing in a corner while two little children of three or four were playing and eating nuts. When day dawned, the village seemed a place of the dead. The priest had the bells rung, calling all to church, and he arranged to celebrate next day a requiem mass for the repose of the souls of those who had been lost.

But towards midday a rumour went about—though none knew who brought it—that some of the Rodillero boats had put into the port of Banzones, some seven leagues away. Such tidings caused an immense sensation in the neighbourhood. Hope, already dead, was born again in every heart. Bustle and noise filled the street once again. Swift messengers were sent to find out the truth, and many were the comments and surmises that went about. The day and night passed in anguish and pitiful anxiety. Pale and weeping, the poor women ran from group to group, longing to find in the men's talk something that might give them hope.

At last, at twelve o'clock, came the news that the boats which had reached Banzones were no more than two. Which? The messengers did not know or did not want to say. Nevertheless in a little while news began to leak out that one of them was José's and the other Toribio's.

Then, in the afternoon, came a boy, breathless, bare-headed, covered with sweat.

"Here they are! Here they are!"

"Who?"

"Lots of them! Lots of them! Lots are coming!" he managed to say, with difficulty for breath failed him. "They must be in Antromero now."

Then a change indescribable swept over the village. Without a single exception every one came out of doors, made a great uproar in the street for a few moments, and then in one body hastened from the place. They took the way to Antromero, along the seashore, in a state of excitement and anguish it is impossible to describe. The men talked busily, speculating upon the way their comrades had managed to save themselves. The women went in silence, dragging along the children who in vain pleaded that they were tired. Half a league further on they came upon an opening from where they could see in the distance a group of fishermen coming towards them with their oars on their shoulders. A loud cry went up from the crowd. Waving their caps, the fishermen gave an answering Hurrah! From one to the other the cries went, until, hastening towards each other, they met.

It was a sight both joyous and terrible. As the large and small groups mingled, cries of joy and cries of grief broke out together. The women, wide-eyed, sought their lost ones and not finding them, burst into piteous sobs, and dropping to the ground, wrung their hands in agony. Others, more fortunate, finding much loved husbands and sons, flung themselves fiercely upon them, and remained pressed against their breasts as if nothing on earth could ever tear them away. The men, the centre of this fervent welcome, strove to hide their emotion with a smile, but the tears rolled down their cheeks in spite of them.

Elisa who was among the crowd, felt such a tightening in her throat when she saw José that she thought she would stifle. She covered her face with her hands and burst into sobs, striving to make no sound. José, nearly strangled by his mother's arms, sought eagerly over her shoulder for his betrothed. Elisa lifted her face to his, and looking into each other's eyes their lips met.

The first moments of emotion passed, and the great crowd of people turned with slow step towards the village. Each one of the men was surrounded by a group of his comrades, all eager to learn every detail of the boat's fortune. Behind came the women; sometimes, just to assure themselves that they were still alive, they would call their men by name and when they turned in answer, found nothing to say to them.

That same afternoon it was arranged that they should give thanks to God on the day following by a solemn *fiesta*. It chanced that almost all the rescued men had made the same vow—to hear Mass barefooted at the altar of the Christ. It was a vow very common in Rodillero in moments of danger and one which had come down from father to son. And so, upon the following morning they met upon the seashore, and from there each crew with its skipper at the head, set out slowly for the church, all bare-footed and bare-headed. They went in silence, their faces grave, their quiet eyes showing the simple and ardent faith of those who know little of this life save its sorrows. Behind came the women, the children and the few gentlefolk of the village, silent too, overcome by emotion at the sight of these men, so strong and so rugged, thus humbling themselves like children. The widows and orphans of those who had been lost went, too, to pray for the repose of their dead. They had put on whatever bit of black they had been able to find at the moment—a kerchief, an apron, a cap.

And in the little church of Rodillero the miraculous Christ awaited them, hanging from the cross, with open arms. He too had suffered shipwreck and had been saved from the sea by the piety of a few fishermen; he too had experienced the sadness and loneliness of the ocean and the bitterness of its waves. They knelt down, dropping their heads upon their breasts while their lips murmured prayers learnt in childhood and never said with more fervour. The candles surrounding the sacred image flickered sadly. From the crowd came a soft murmur. The voice of the officiating priest, shaken and tremulous, broke from time to time the majestic silence of the church.

When Mass was ended, Elisa and José met in the church porch and smiled tenderly upon each other; and with that innocent and pardonable egoism which belongs to love, forgot in a moment all the sadness that was about them; side by side, in eager and happy talk, they went down the village street, and before they had reached the house, had fixed upon the day of their wedding.

THE TRITON[1]

Vicente Blasco Ibañez

(1867–1928)

THE first things that Ulysses admired upon entering the doctor's house were the three frigates adorning the ceiling of the dining-room—three marvellous vessels in which there was not lacking a single sail nor pulley rope, nor anchor, and which might be made to sail over the sea at a moment's notice.

They were the work of his grandfather Ferragut. Wishing to release his two sons from the marine service which had weighed upon the family

[1]Reprinted from Charlotte Brewster Jordan's translation of *Mare Nostrum*, by permission of Ernest Benn, Ltd., and E. P. Dutton & Company Inc.

for many centuries, he had sent them to the University of Valencia in order that they might become inland gentlemen. The older, Esteban, had scarcely terminated his career before he obtained a notaryship in Catalunia. The younger one, Antonio, became a doctor so as not to thwart the old man's wishes, but as soon as he acquired his degree he offered his services to a transatlantic steamer. His father had closed the door of the sea against him and he had entered by the window.

And so, as Ferragut senior began to grow old, he lived completely alone. He used to look after his property—a few vineyards scattered along the coast in sight of his home—and was in frequent correspondence with his son, the notary. From time to time there came a letter from the younger one, his favourite, posted in remote countries that the old Mediterranean seaman knew only by hearsay. And during his long, dull hours in the shade of his arbour facing the blue and luminous sea, he used to entertain himself constructing these little models of boats. They were all frigates of great tonnage and fearless sail. Thus the old skipper would console himself for having commanded during his lifetime only heavy and clumsy merchant vessels like the ships of other centuries, in which he used to carry wine from Cette or cargo prohibited in Gibraltar and the coast of Africa.

Ulysses was not long in recognizing the rare popularity enjoyed by his uncle, the doctor—a popularity composed of the most antagonistic elements. The people used to smile in speaking of him as though he were a little touched, yet they dared to indulge in these smiles only when at a safe distance, for he inspired a certain terror in all of them. At the same time they used to admire him as a local celebrity, for he had traversed all seas, and possessed, besides, a violent and tempestuous strength which was the terror and pride of his neighbours. The husky youths when testing the vigour of their fists, boxing with crews of the English vessels that came there for cargoes of raisins, used to evoke the doctor's name as a consolation in case of defeat. "If only the *Doctor* could have been here! . . . Half a dozen Englishmen are nothing to him!"

There was no vigorous undertaking, however absurd it might be, that they would not believe him capable of. He used to inspire the faith of the miracle-working saints and audacious highway captains. On calm, sunshiny winter mornings the people would often go running down to the beach, looking anxiously over the lonely sea. The veterans who were toasting themselves in the sun near the overturned boats, or scanning the broad horizon, would finally discern an almost imperceptible point, a grain of sand dancing capriciously on the waves.

They would all break into shouts and conjectures. It was a buoy, a piece of masthead, the drift from a distant shipwreck. For the women it was somebody drowned, so bloated that it was floating like a leather bottle, after having been many days in the water.

Suddenly the same supposition would arise in every perplexed mind.

"I wonder if it could be the *Doctor!*" A long silence . . . The bit of wood was taking the form of a head; the corpse was moving. Many could now perceive the bubble of foam around his chest that was advancing like the prow of a ship, and the vigorous strokes of his arms. . . . Yes, it surely was the *Doctor!* . . . The old sea dogs loaned their telescopes to one another in order to recognize his beard sunk in the water and his face, contracted by his efforts or expanded by his snortings.

And the *Doctor* was soon treading the dry beach, naked and as serenely unashamed as a god, giving his hand to the men, while the women shrieked, lifting their aprons in front of one eye—terrified, yet admiring the dripping vision.

All the capes of the promontory challenged him to double them, swimming like a dolphin; he felt impelled to measure all the bays and coves with his arms, like a proprietor who distrusts another's measurements and rectifies them in order to affirm his right of possession. He was a human bark who, with the keel of his breast, cut the foam, whirling through the sunken rocks and the pacific waters in whose depth sparkled fishes among mother-of-pearl twigs and stars moving like flowers.

He used to seat himself to rest on the black rocks with overskirts of seaweed that raised or lowered their fringe at the caprice of the wave, awaiting the night and the chance vessel that might come to dash against them like a piece of bark. Like a marine reptile he had even penetrated certain caves of the coast, drowsy and glacial lakes illuminated by mysterious openings where the atmosphere is black and the water transparent, where the swimmer has a bust of ebony and legs of crystal. In the course of these swimming expeditions he ate all the living beings he encountered fastened to the rocks by antennae and arms. The friction of the great, terrified fish that fled, bumping against him with the violence of a projectile, used to make him laugh.

In the night hours passed before his grandfather's little ships, Ulysses used to hear the *Triton* speak of the *Peje Nicolao*, a man-fish of the Straits of Messina mentioned by Cervantes and other authors, who lived in the water maintaining himself by the donations from the ships. His uncle must be some relative of this *Peje Nicolao*. At other times this uncle would mention a certain Greek who in order to see his lady-love swam the Hellespont every night. And he, who used to know the Dardanelles, was longing to return there as a simple passenger merely that a poet named Lord Byron might not be the only one to imitate the legendary crossing. . . .

"All this is yours," he said, showing the house to his nephew.

His also the boat, the books and the antique furniture in whose drawers the money was so openly hid that it invited attention.

In spite of seeing himself lord of all that surrounded him, a rough and affectionate despotism kept nevertheless weighing the child down.

He was very far from his mother, that good lady who was always closing the windows near him and never letting him go out without tying his neck-scarf around him with an accompaniment of kisses.

Just when he was sleeping soundest, believing that the night would still be many hours longer, he would feel himself awakened by a violent tugging at his leg. His uncle could not touch him in any other way. "Get up, cabin boy!" In vain he would protest with the profound sleepiness of youth. . . . Was he, or was he not the "ship's cat" of the bark of which his uncle was the captain and only crew? . . .

His uncle's hands bared him to the blasts of salt air that were entering through the windows. The sea was dark and veiled by a light fog. The last stars were sparkling with twinkles of surprise, ready to flee. A crack began to appear on the leaden horizon, growing redder and redder every minute, like a wound through which the blood is flowing. The ship's cat was loaded up with various empty baskets, the skipper marching before him like a warrior of the waves, carrying the oars on his shoulders, his feet rapidly making hollows on the sand. Behind him the village was beginning to awaken and, over the dark waters, the sails of the fishermen, fleeing the inner sea, were slipping past like ghostly shrouds.

Two vigorous strokes of the oar sent their boat out from the little wharf of stones, and soon he was untying the sails from the gunwales, and preparing the ropes. The unfurled canvas whistled and swelled in bellying whiteness. "There we are! Now for a run!" The water was beginning to sing, slipping past both sides of the prow. Between it and the edge of the sail could be seen a bit of black sea, and coming little by little over its line, a great red streak. The streak soon became a helmet, then a hemisphere, then an Arabian arch confined at the bottom, until finally it shot up out of the liquid mass as though it were a bomb sending forth flashes of flame. The ash-coloured clouds became stained with blood and the large rocks of the coast began to sparkle like copper mirrors. As the last stars were extinguished, a swarm of fire-coloured fishes came trailing along before the prow, forming a triangle with its point in the horizon. The mist on the mountain tops was taking on a rose colour as though its whiteness were reflecting a submarine eruption. "*Bon dia!*" called the doctor to Ulysses, who was occupied in warming his hands stiffened by the wind.

And, moved with childlike joy by the dawn of a new day, the *Triton* sent his bass voice booming across the maritime silence, several times intoning sentimental melodies that in his youth he had heard sung by a vaudeville prima donna dressed as a ship's boy, at other times carolling in Valencian the chanteys of the coast—fishermen's songs invented as they drew in their nets, in which most shameless words were flung together on the chance of making them rhyme. In certain windings of the coast the sail would be lowered, leaving the boat with no other motion than a gentle rocking around its anchor rope.

Upon seeing the space which had been obscured by the shadow of the boat's hulk, Ulysses found the bottom of the sea so near that he almost believed that he could touch it with the point of his oar. The rocks were like glass. In their interstices and hollows the plants were moving like living creatures, and the little animals had the immovability of vegetables and stones. The boat appeared to be floating in the air and athwart the liquid atmosphere that wraps this abysmal world, the fish hooks were dangling, and a swarm of fishes was swimming and wriggling toward its encounter with death.

It was a sparkling effervescence of yellowing flames, of bluish blacks and rosy fins. Some came out from the caves silvered and vibrant as lightning flashes of mercury; others swam slowly, big-bellied, almost circular, with a golden coat of mail. Along the slopes, the crustaceans came scrambling along on their double row of claws attracted by this novelty that was changing the mortal calm of the under-sea where all follow and devour, only to be devoured in turn. Near the surface floated the medusae, living parasols of an opaline whiteness with circular borders of lilac or red bronze. Under their gelatinous domes was the skein of filaments that served them for locomotion, nutrition, and reproduction.

The fishermen had only to pull in their lines and a new prisoner would fall into their boat. Their baskets were filling up so fast that the *Triton* and his nephew grew tired of this easy fishing. . . . The sun was now near the height of its curve, and every wavelet was carrying away a bit of the golden band that divided the blue immensity. The wood of the boat appeared to be on fire.

"We've earned our day's pay," said the *Triton*, looking at the sky, and then at the baskets. "Now let's clean up a little bit."

And stripping off his clothing, he threw himself into the sea. Ulysses saw him descend from the centre of the ring of foam opened by his body, and could gauge by it the profundity of that fantastic world composed of glassy rocks, animal plants, and stone animals. As it went down, the tawny body of the swimmer took on the transparency of porcelain. It appeared of bluish crystal—a statue made of a Venetian mirror composition that was going to break as soon as it touched the bottom.

Like a god he was passing through the deeps, snatching plants out by the roots, pursuing with his hands the flashes of vermilion and gold hidden in the cracks of the rocks. Minutes would pass by; he was going to stay down for ever; he would never come up again. And the boy was beginning to think uneasily of the possibility of having to guide the bark back to the coast all alone. Suddenly the body of white crystal began taking on a greenish hue, growing larger and larger, becoming dark and coppery, until above the surface appeared the head of the swimmer, who, spouting and snorting, was holding up all his submarine plunder to the little fellow.

"Now then, your turn!" he ordered in an imperious tone.

All attempts at resistance were useless. His uncle either insulted him with the harshest kind of words or coaxed him with promises of safety. He never knew certainly whether he threw himself into the water or whether a tug from the doctor jerked him from the boat. The first surprise having passed, he had the impression of remembering some long forgotten thing. He was swimming instinctively, divining what he ought to do before his master told him. Within him was awakening the ancestral experience of a race of sailors who had struggled with the sea and, sometimes, had remained forever in its bosom.

Recollection of what was existing beyond his feet suddenly made him lose his serenity—his lively imagination making him shriek, "Uncle!... Uncle!"

And he clutched convulsively at the hard island of hairy and shining muscles. His uncle came up immovable, as though his feet of stone were fastened to the bottom of the ocean. He was like the nearby promontory that was darkening and chilling the water with its ebony shadow.

MARE NOSTRUM[1]

Vicente Blasco Ibañez

(1867–1928)

THE *Triton* and his nephew used to eat their supper under the arbour in the long summer twilights. After the cloth was removed Ulysses would manipulate his grandfather's little frigates, learning the technical parts and names of the different apparatus, and the management of the sets of sails. Sometimes the two would stay out on the rustic porch until a late hour gazing out over the luminous sea sparkling under the splendour of the moon, or streaked with a slender wake of starry light in the murky nights.

All that mankind had ever written or dreamed about the Mediterranean, the doctor had in his library and could repeat to his eager little listener. In Ferragut's estimation the *mare nostrum* was a species of blue beast, powerful and of great intelligence—a sacred animal like the dragons and serpents that certain religions adored, believing them to be the source of life. The rivers that threw themselves impetuously into its bosom in order to renew it were few and scanty. The Rhone and the Nile appeared to be pitiful little rivulets compared with the river courses of other continents that empty into the oceans.

Losing by evaporation three times more liquid than the rivers bring to it, this sunburnt sea would soon have been converted into a great salt desert were not the Atlantic sending it a rapid current of renewal

---

[1]Reprinted from Charlotte Brewster Jordan's translation of *Mare Nostrum*, by permission of Ernest Benn, Ltd., and E. P. Dutton & Company Inc.

that was precipitated through the Straits of Gibraltar. Under this super-ficial current existed still another, flowing in an opposite direction, that returned a part of the Mediterranean to the ocean, because the Mediterranean waters were more salt and dense than those of the Atlantic. The tide scarcely made itself felt on its strands. Its basin was mined by subterranean fires that were always seeking extraordinary out-lets through Vesuvius and Ætna, and breathed continually through the mouth of Stromboli. Sometimes these Plutonic ebullitions would come to the surface, making new islands rise up upon the waters like tumours of lava.

In its bosom exist still double the quantity of animal species that abound in other seas, although less numerous. The tunny fish, playful lambs of the blue pasture lands, were gamboling over its surface or passing in schools under the furrows of the waves. Men were setting netted traps for them along the coasts of Spain and France, in Sardinia, the Straits of Messina and the waters of the Adriatic. But this whole-sale slaughter scarcely lessened the compact, fishy squadrons. After wandering through the windings of the Grecian Archipelago, they passed the Dardanelles and the Bosphorus, stirring the two narrow passage-ways with the violence of their invisible gallopade and making a turn at the bowl of the Black Sea, swimming back, decimated but impetuous, to the depths of the Mediterranean.

Red coral was forming immovable groves on the substrata of the Balearic Islands, and on the coasts of Naples and Africa. Ambergris was constantly being found on the steep shores of Sicily. Sponges were growing in the tranquil waters in the shadow of the great rocks of Mallorca and the Isles of Greece. Naked men without any equipment what-ever, holding their breath, were still descending to the bottom as in primitive times, in order to snatch these treasures away.

The doctor gave up his geographic descriptions to discourse on the history of his sea, which had indeed been the history of civilization, and was more fascinating to him. At first miserable and scanty tribes had wandered along its coasts seeking their food from the crustaceans drawn from the waves—a life similar to that of the rudimentary people that Ferragut had seen in the islands of the Pacific. When stone saws had hollowed out the trunks of trees and human arms had ventured to spread the first rawhides to the forces of the atmosphere, the coasts became rapidly populated.

On this landlocked sea mankind had learned the art of navigation. Every one looked at the waves before looking at the sky. Over this blue highway had arrived the miracles of life, and out of its depths the gods were born. The Phoenicians—Jews, become navigators—abandoned their cities in the depths of the Mediterranean sack, in order to spread the mysterious knowledge of Egypt and the Asiatic monarchies all along the shores of the interior sea. Afterwards the Greeks of the maritime republics took their place.

Then Rome, terrestrial Rome, in order to hold its own . . . against the superiority of the Semitic navigators of Carthage, had to teach the management of the oar and marine combat to the inhabitants of Latium, to their legionaries with faces hardened by the chin straps of their helmets, who did not know how to adjust their world-dominating iron-shod feet to the slippery planks of a vessel.

The divinities of *mare nostrum* always inspired a most loving devotion in the doctor. He knew that they had not existed, but he, nevertheless, believed in them as poetic phantasms of natural forces.

The ancient world only knew the immense ocean in hypothesis, giving it the form of an aquatic girdle around the earth. Oceanus was an old god with a long beard and horned head who lived in a maritime cavern with his wife, Tethys, and his three hundred daughters, the Oceanides. No Argonaut had ever dared to come in contact with these mysterious divinities. Only the grave Æschylus had dared to portray the Oceanides —virgins fresh and demure, weeping around the rock to which Prometheus was bound. . . .

A brother of the Oceanides, the prudent Nereus, used to reign in the depths of the Mediterranean. This son of Oceanus had a blue beard, green eyes, and bunches of sea rushes on his eyebrows and breast. His fifty daughters, the Nereids, bore his orders across the waves or frolicked around the ships, splashing in the faces of the rowers the foam tossed up by their arms. But the sons of Father Time, on conquering the giant, had reapportioned the world, determining its rulers by lot. Zeus remained lord of the land, the obscure Hades, lord of the underworld, reigned in the Plutonic abysses, and Poseidon became master of the blue surfaces.

Nereus, the dispossessed monarch, fled to a cavern of the Hellenic sea in order to live the calm existence of the philosopher-counsellor of mankind, and Poseidon installed himself in the mother-of-pearl palaces with his white steeds tossing helmets of bronze and manes of gold.

His amorous eyes were fixed on the fifty Mediterranean princesses, the Nereids, who took their names from the aspect of the waves—the Blue, the Green, the Swift, the Gentle . . . "Nymphs of the green abysses with faces fresh as a rosebud, fragrant virgins that took the forms of all the monsters of the deep," sang the Orphic hymn of the Grecian shore. And Poseidon singled out among them all the Nereid of the Foam, the white Amphitrite who refused to accept his love.

She knew about this new god. The coasts were peopled with cyclops like Polyphemus, with frightful monsters born of the union of Olympian goddesses and simple mortals; but an obliging dolphin came and went, carrying messages between Poseidon and the Nereid, until, overwhelmed by the eloquence of this restless rover of the wave, Amphitrite agreed to become the wife of the god, and the Mediterranean appeared to take on still greater beauty.

She was the aurora that shows her rosy finger-tips through the immense cleft between sky and sea, the warm hour of midday that makes the waters drowsy under its robe of restless gold, the bifurcated tongue of foam that laps the two faces of the hissing prow, the aroma-laden breeze that like a virgin's breath swells the sail, the compassionate kiss that lulls the drowned to rest, without wrath and without resistance, before sinking forever into the fathomless abyss.

Her husband—Poseidon on the Greek coast and Neptune on the Latin—on mounting his chariot, used to awaken the tempest. The brazen-hoofed horses with their stamping would paw up the huge waves and swallow up the ships. The tritons of his cortege would send forth from their white shells the bellowing blasts that snap off the masts like reeds.

O, mater Amphitrite! . . . and Ferragut would describe her as though she were just passing before his eyes. Sometimes when swimming around the promontory, feeling himself enveloped like primitive man in the blind forces of Nature, he used to believe that he saw the white goddess issuing forth from the rocks with all her smiling train after a rest in some marine cave.

A shell of pearl was her chariot and six dolphins harnessed with purpling coral used to draw it along. The tritons, her sons, handled the reins. The Nereids, their sisters, lashed the sea with their scaly tails, lifting their mermaid bodies wrapped in the magnificence of their sea-green tresses between whose ringlets might be seen their heaving bosoms. White seagulls, cooing like the doves of Aphrodite, fluttered around their nude sea-queen, serenely contemplating them from her movable throne, crowned with pearls and phosphorescent stars drawn from the depths of her dominion. White as the cloud, white as the sail, white as the foam, entirely, dazzlingly white was her fair majesty except where a rosy blush tinted the petal-like skin of her heels or her bosom.

The entire history of European man—forty centuries of wars, emigrations, and racial impact—was due, according to the doctor, to the desire of possessing this harmoniously framed sea, of enjoying the transparency of its atmosphere and the vivacity of its light.

The men from the North who needed the burning log and alcoholic drink in order to defend their life from the clutches of the cold, were always thinking of these Mediterranean shores. All their warlike or pacific movements were with intent to descend from the coasts of the glacial seas to the beaches of the warm *mare nostrum*. . . .

The South had replied to the invasion from the North with defensive wars that had extended even into the centre of Europe. And thus history had gone on repeating itself with the same flux and reflux of human waves

—mankind struggling for thousands of years to gain or hold the blue vault of Amphitrite.

The Mediterranean peoples were to Ferragut the aristocracy of humanity. Tanned and bronzed by the profound absorption of the sun and the energy of the atmosphere, its navigators were transmuted into pure metal. The men from the North were stronger, but less robust, less easily acclimatized than the Catalan sailor, the Provençal, the Genoese, or the Greek. The sailors of the Mediterranean made themselves at home in all parts of the world. Upon their sea man had developed his highest energies. . . .

Every type of human vigour had sprung from the Mediterranean race—fine, sharp, and dry as flint, doing good and evil on a large scale with the exaggeration of an ardent character that discounts half-way measures and leaps from duplicity to the greatest extremes of generosity. Ulysses was the father of them all, a discreet and prudent hero, yet at the same time complex and malicious. So was old Cadmus with his Phoenician mitre and curled beard, a great old sea-wolf, scattering by means of his various adventures the art of writing and the first notions of commerce.

In one of the Mediterranean islands Hannibal was born, and twenty centuries after, in another of them, the son of a lawyer without briefs embarked for France, with no other outfit than his cadet's uniform, in order to make famous his name of Napoleon.

Over the Mediterranean waves had sailed Roger de Lauria, knight-errant of vast tracts of sea, who wished to clothe even the fishes with the colours of Aragon. A visionary of obscure origin named Columbus had recognized as his country the republic of Genoa. A smuggler from the coasts of Laguria came to be Massena, the marshal beloved by Victory, and the last personage of this stock of Mediterranean heroes associated with the heroes of fabulous times was a sailor from Nice, simple and romantic, a warrior called Garibaldi, an heroic tenor of all seas and lands who cast over his century the reflection of his red shirt, repeating on the coast of Marseilles the remote epic of the Argonauts.

PORTUGAL

HOW THE PAGE OF PRINCE HENRY THE NAVIGATOR BROUGHT HOME THE SHIP[1]

Gomez Eannes de Zurara

AH, IN what brief words did I find enregistered the record of the death of such a noble knight as was this Nuno Tristam, of whose sudden end I purpose to speak. And of a surety I could not pass it by without tears, did I not know, almost by divine forecast, the eternal delight his soul tasteth, for it seemeth to me that I should be reckoned as covetous by all true Catholics were I to bewail the death of one whom it hath pleased God to make a sharer in His immortality. . . .

Now this noble knight was perfectly informed of the great desire and purpose of our virtuous Prince, being one who from such an early youth had been brought up in his household; and seeing how the Prince was toiling to send his ships to the land of the Negroes and much further yet, if he might accomplish it; and hearing that some caravels had already passed the river of Nile, and the things that were reported from there; it seemed to him that if he were not to make himself one of that elect company and to render service to the Infant his lord in that land in any good thing that might be done or encountered there, he could not obtain the name of a good man and true.

Wherefore he straightway made him ready a caravel, and having it armed, he began his voyage and stayed not in any part, but pursued his course toward the land of the Negroes. And passing by Cape Verde, he went sixty leagues further on and came unto a river, in the which it seemed to him that there ought to be some inhabited places. Wherefore he caused to be launched two small boats he was carrying, and in them there entered twenty-two men, to wit, ten in one and twelve in the other. And as they began to take their way up the river, the tide was rising with the which they entered, and they made for some habitations that they espied on the right hand. And it came to pass that before they went on shore, there appeared from the other side twelve boats, in the which there would be as many as seventy or eighty Guineas, all Negroes, with bows in their hands. And because the water was rising, one of the boats of the Guineas crossed to the other side and put on shore those it was carrying, and thence they began to shoot arrows at our men in the boats. And the others who remained in the boats bestirred them-

[1]From the translation of *The Chronicle of the Discovery and Conquest of Guinea* by C. R. Beazley and Edgar Prestage. Reprinted by permission of the translators and of the Hakluyt Society.

selves as much as they could to get at our men, and as soon as they perceived themselves to be within reach, they discharged that accursed
ammunition of theirs all full of poison upon the bodies of our countrymen. And so they held on in pursuit of them until they had reached the
caravel which was lying outside the river in the open sea; and they were
all hit by those poisoned arrows in such wise that before they came on
board four of them died in the boats.

And so, wounded as they were, they made fast their small boats to
the ship, and commenced to make ready for their voyage, seeing their
case how perilous it was; but they were not able to lift their anchors for
the multitude of arrows with which they were attacked, and they were
constrained to cut the cables so that not one remained. And so they
began to make sail, leaving the boats behind, for they could not hoist
them up. And it came to pass that of the twenty-two men that left the
ship only two escaped, to wit, one André Diaz and another Alvaro da
Costa, both esquires of the Infant and natives of the City of Evora;
and the remaining nineteen died, for that poison was so artfully composed that a slight wound, if it only let blood, brought men to their last
end. And there died that noble Knight Nuno Tristam, very desirous as
he was of this present life, in that there was no place left him to buy his
death like a brave man. And there died also another Knight called John
Correa, and one Duarte Dollanda, and Estevam Dalmeida, and Diego
Machado, men of noble birth and young in years, brought up by the
Infant in his household; as well as other esquires and foot-soldiers of the
same upbringing; and seamen and others of the ship's company.

Suffice it to say that they numbered in all twenty-one, for of the seven
that had remained in the caravel, two were also wounded as they were
trying to raise the anchors. But whom will you have to make ready this
ship that she may pursue her voyage and depart from among that evil
race? For the two esquires who remained, as we said, did not wholly
escape from that peril, for being wounded they came near unto death,
and lay ill quite twenty days, not being able to render any aid to the
others who were toiling to direct the caravel. And these latter were not
more than five in number, to wit, a sailor lad very little acquainted with
the act of navigating, and a boy of the Infant's household called Airas
Tinoco, who went as purser, and a Guinea boy who had been captured
with the first prisoners taken in that land, and two other boys, both
quite young, who were living with some of those esquires that died
there. Of a surety, compassion is due to their great toil at that hour.
They went weeping and sorrowing for the death of such a captain and
of the others their comrades and friends, and were from that time in
fear of the hateful enemies they knew to be near them, from whose
deadly wounds so many and such brave men had died in a very brief
space. And especially they sorrowed because they found so slight a remedy whereby to seek their safety; for the sailor lad in whom they were all

putting their hope, confessed openly his scant knowledge, saying that he knew not how to direct the course of a ship or to work at anything of that kind in such wise as to be serviceable; but only if directed by another he would do what he could, as he was bidden.

O Thou great and supreme succour of all the forsaken and afflicted who dost never desert those that cry out to Thee in their most great necessity, and who now didst hear the cries of these men who made their moan to Thee, fixing their eyes on the height of the clouds and calling upon Thee to hasten to their aid; clearly didst Thou show that Thou heardest their prayers when in such a brief space Thou didst send them heavenly aid. For Thou didst give courage and understanding to a youth who had been born and brought up in Olivenca, an inland town far removed from the sea; and he, enlightened by divine grace, piloted the ship, and bade the seamen steer directly to the North, declining a little to the East, namely, to the wind that is called North-east, for he thought that there lay the kingdom of Portugal, towards which they wished to make their voyage. And as they were going thus on their way, after a part of the day was over, they went to see Nuno Tristam and the other wounded men, and they found them dead, so that they were obliged to throw them into the sea; and on that day they threw in fifteen, and four remained in the boats, and two they threw in the next day. But I write not of the feelings that would be theirs when they cast those bodies upon the multitude of waters, burying their flesh in the bellies of fish. For what importeth it to us if our bodies lack sepulture? since in our flesh we shall see our Saviour, according to the determination of Holy Scripture, for it is the same thing whether we lie in the sea or the land, and whether we be eaten of fishes or of birds. Our chief concern is in those works of ours by which after our death we shall find the truth of all these matters that here we see in figure. . . . Therefore we can say with justice to these men: "Beati mortui qui in Domino moriuntur." And moreover, all who read this history will obtain a reward from God, if they make a memorial of the death of these men in their prayers, for inasmuch as they died in the service of God and their lord, their death is happy.

Now this youth whom I have mentioned was that same Airas Tinoco of whom I spoke above, and in him God put such grace that for two months together he directed the course of that ship; but all were doubtful what their end would be, for in all those two months they never caught sight of land. And at the end of this time they sighted a pinnace which was on warlike business, and they had great fear at the sight, for they thought it belonged to Moors; but after they found it pertained to a Galician pirate whose name was Pero Falcom, a new joy came upon them, and much more so when they were told that they were off the coast of Portugal, opposite a place belonging to the Mastership of Santiago, called Sines. And so they arrived at Lagos, and thence they went to the Infant to tell him of the tragical fortune of their voyage, and laid before him a multitude of arrows by the which their companions had died.

THE STORY OF GASPAR AND MIGUEL CORTE REAL[1]

Damiao de Goes

GASPAR CORTE REAL, son of Joam Vaz Corte Real, was an enterprising man, valorous, and eager to gain honour. He proposed to undertake the discovery of lands towards the north, because many discoveries had been made to the south. Thus he obtained favour for his undertaking from the King, whose servants he was when Duke of Beja, and armed one ship which was well supplied with men and all necessaries. He sailed from the port of Lisbon in the beginning of the summer of 1500. In this voyage he discovered, in that direction of the north, a land which was very cool and with great woods, as are all lands that lie in that direction. He gave it the name of Green Land. The people are very barbarous and wild, almost like those of the land of Sancta Cruz. At first they are white, but they are so cut up by the cold that they lose their whiteness with age, and remain brown. They are of medium height, very agile, and great archers, using sticks hardened by fire instead of darts, with which they make as good a cast as if it was tipped with fine steel. They dress in the skins of animals which abound in that land. . . .

Returning to Gaspar Corte Real, after he had discovered that land, and coasted along a great part of it, he returned to this kingdom. Presently, in the year 1501, being desirous of discovering more of this province, and of becoming better acquainted with its advantages, he departed from Lisbon on the 15th of May; but it is not known what happened to him in this voyage, for he never more appeared, nor were there any tidings of him.

The delay and the suspicion that began to arise of his fate caused Miguel Corte Real, Chief Porter of the King, for the great love he bore his brother, to determine to go in search of him. He left Lisbon on the 10th of May, 1502, with two ships, but there were never any tidings of them. The King felt the loss of these two brothers very much, and, of his own royal and pious motion, in the year 1503, he ordered two armed ships to be fitted out at his own cost, to go in search of them. But it could never be ascertained how either the one or the other was lost. To that part of the province of Green Land where it was believed that the brothers were lost the name was given of the Land of the Corte Reals.

These two brothers, Gaspar and Miguel Corte Real, had another

---

[1]From Sir Clements R. Markham's translation of *The Journal of Christopher Columbus*. Reprinted by permission of the Hakluyt Society.

brother, whose name was Vasque Anes Corte Real, who was Controller of the King's Household, of his Council, Captain-Governour of the Islands of St George and Terceira, and Alcalde Mayor of the city of Tavilla. He was a very good knight and Christian, a man of exemplary life, and one who dispensed many charities, both publicly and in secret. His son and heir is Emanuel Corte Real, also of the King's Council and Captain of the same islands, who now lives. This Vasque Anes Corte Real, unable to persuade himself that his brothers were dead, determined to fit out ships at his own cost, and go in search of them, in the year 1503. But, on requesting the King to excuse his absence, His Majesty could not consent that he should proceed further in that business, holding that it was useless, and that all had been done that could be done.

HOW FERDINAND MENDEZ PINTO SOUGHT FORTUNE ON THE SEA AND OF SOME MISCHANCES THAT BEFELL HIM THERE[1]

Ferdinand Mendez Pinto

(1510–1583)

I

SO OFTEN as I represent unto myself the great and continual Travels that have accompanied me from my Birth, and amidst the which I have spent my first years, I find that I have a great deal of reason to complain of Fortune, for that she seemeth to have taken a particular care to persecute me, and to make me feel that which is most insupportable in her, as if her glory had no other foundation then her cruelty. For not content to have made me be born, and to live miserably in my Country during my Youth, she conducted me, notwithstanding the fear I had of the dangers that menaced me, to the East-Indies where, instead of the relief which I went thither to seek, she made me find an increase of my pains, according to the increase of my age. Since then it hath pleased God to deliver me from so many dangers, and to protect me from the fury of that adverse Fortune, for to bring me into a Port of safety and assurance; I see that I have not so much cause to complain of my Travels past, as I have to render him thanks for the benefits which until now I have received of him; seeing that by his Divine bounty he hath preserved my life, to the end I might have means to leave this rude and unpolished Discourse unto my Children for a memorial and an inheritance. For my intention is no other, but to write it for them, that they may behold what strange fortunes I have run for the space of one and twenty years, during the which I was thirteen times a captive, and

[1]From *The Voyages and Adventures of Ferdinand Mendez Pinto*. Done into English by H. C., Gent., 1663.

seventeen times sold in the Indies, in Æthiopia, in Arabia, in China, in Tartaria, in Madagascar, in Sumatra, and in divers other Kingdoms and Provinces of that Oriental Archipelago upon the Confines of Asia, which the Chinese, Siames, Guaos, and Lecquios name, and that with reason, in their Geography, the eye-lids of the world.

Now that others may help me to praise the Lord Almighty for the infinite mercy he hath shewed me, without any regard to my sins, which I confess were the cause and original of all my mis-fortunes, and that from the same Divine Power I received strength and courage to resist them, escaping out of so many dangers, with my live saved, I take from the beginning of my Voyage the time which I spent in this Kingdom of Portugal, and say, That after I had lived there till I was about eleven or twelve years old, in the misery and poverty of my Fathers house within the Town of Monte-mor Ovelho, an Uncle of mine, desirous to advance me to a better fortune then that whereunto I was reduced at that time, and to take me from the caresses and cockerings of my Mother, brought me to this City of Lisbon, where he put me into the service of a very honourable Lady: the which he was carried out of the hope he had, that by the favour of her self and her friends he might attain to his desire for my advancement; and this was in the same year that the funeral pomp of the deceased King Emanuel of happy memory was celebrated at Lisbon, namely St Lucies day, the 13 of December, 1521, which is the furthest thing I can remember. In the meantime my Uncles design had a success clean contrary to that which he hath promised to him in favour of me: For having been servant of this Lady, about a year and a half, an accident befel me, that cast me into manifest peril of Life, so that to save my self I was constrained to abandon her house with all the speed that possibly I could. Flying away then in very great fear, I arrived before I was aware at the Ford of Pedra, which is a small Port so called. There I found a Carvel of Alfama, that was laden with the horses and stuff of a Lord, who was going to Setuval, where at that instant King James the Third kept his Court, by reason of a great plague that reigned in divers parts of the Kingdom.

Perceiving then that this Carvel was ready to put to Sea, I imbarqued my self in her, and departed the next day. But alas! a little after we had set sail, having gotten to a place named Cezmibra, we were set upon by a French Pirate, who having boarded us, caused fifteen or sixteen of his men to leap into our Vessel, who finding no resistance made themselves Masters of her: now after they had pillaged every one of us, they emptied all the Merchandise wherewithal ours was laden, which amounted to above six thousand Duckats, into their ship, and then sunk her; so that of seventeen of us that remained alive, not so much as one could escape slavery, for they clap'd us up all bound hand and foot under hatches, with an intent to go and sell us at La Rache in Barbary, whither also, as we found by being amongst them, they carried Arms to the Mahometans in way of Trade; for this purpose they kept us thirteen days together, continually whipping us; but at the end thereof it fortuned that about Sun set, they discovered a Ship, unto which they gave chase all the night, following her close, like old Pirates long used to such Thieveries; having fetched her up by break of day, they gave her a volley of three pieces of Ordnance, and presently invested her with a great deal of courage; Now though at first they found some resistance yet they quickly rendred themselves Masters of her, killing six Portugals, and ten or eleven slaves. This was a goodly Vessel, and belonged to a Portugal Merchant of the Town of Conde, named Silvestre Godinho, which divers other Merchants of Lisbon had laden at Saint Tome, with great store of Sugar and Slaves; in such sort that those poor people seeing themselves thus taken and robbed fell to lament their loss, which they estimated to be forty thousand Duckats.

Whereupon these Pirates having gotten so rich a booty, changed their design for going to La Rache, and bent their course for the Coast of France, carrying with them such of ours for slaves, as they judged fit for the service of their Navigation. The remainder of us they left at night in the Road, at a place called *Melides*, where we were landed miserably naked, our bodies covered with nothing but with the stripes of the lashes which so cruelly we had received the dayes before. In this pitiful case we arrived the next morning at St Jago de Caten, where we were relieved by the inhabitants of the place, especially by a Lady that was there at that time, named Donna Beatrix, daughter to the Earl of Villanova, and wife to Alonso Perez Pantoia, Commander and grand Provost of the Town.

Now after the sick and wounded were recovered, each of us departed, and got him where he hoped to find the best assistance; for my self, poor wretch, I went with 6 or 7 that accompanied me in my misery to Setuval: Thither I was no sooner come, but my good fortune placed me in the service of Francisco de Faria, a Gentleman belonging to the great Commander of S. Jago, who in recompence of four years service I did him, put me to the said Commander to wait on him in his Chamber, which I performed for an year and an half after. But in regard the entertainment which was given at that time in Noble-mens houses was so small as I was not able to live on it, necessity constrained me to quit my Master, with a design to imbarque my self by his favour to go to the Indies; for that I thought was the best way I could take to free me of my poverty. So albeit I were but meanly accommodated, I imbarqued my self notwithstanding, submitting my self to whatsoever fortune should arrive unto me in those far Countries, either good or bad.

II

It was in the year 1537, and the eleventh of March, that I parted from this Kingdom in a Fleet of five ships, whereof there was no General; for each of those Vessels was commanded by a particular Captain: For example, in the ship named the *Queen*, commanded Don Pedro de Silva, surnamed the Cock, son to the Admiral Don Vasco de Gama. In the ship called *S. Rock* commanded Don Fernando de Lima, son to Diego Lopez de Lima, grand Provost of the Town of Guimaranes, who died valiantly in defence of the Fortress of Ormuz, whereof he was Captain the year following, 1538. In the *S. Barba*, commanded Don Fernando de Lima who was the Governor of the Town of Chaul; of that which was called the *Flower of the Sea*, Lope Vaz Vagado was Captain; And in the fifth and last ship, named *Galega*, commanded Martin de Freitas, born in the Isle of Maddra, who the same year was slain at Damao, together with five and thirty men that followed him.

These Vessels sailing different wayes, arrived at length at a great Port called Mozambique. There we met with the *Saint Michael*, that wintered there, and was commanded by Duart Tristao, who parted thence richly laden for to return unto Portugal; Howbeit I believe she was taken, or suffered shipwrack, as it happens but too often in this Voyage to the Indies, for he was never heard of since.

After our five Vessels were equipped with all that was necessary for them, and ready to set sail from Mozambique, the Lieutenant of the Fortress, called Vincent Pegado, shewed the Captains of the said five ships a Mandate from the Governour, named Nunho de Cunha, whereby he expressly commanded that all Portugal ships, which did arrive in that Port this year should go to Diu, and leave their men there for the guard of the Fortress, because of the fear they were in of the Turkish Army. The Captains assembled together to deliberate thereupon, at length concluded that three of those five ships appertaining to the King, should go to Diu, conformable to the contents of the said Mandate, and that the other two, which belonged to particular Merchants, should pursue their course to Goa. The Kings three ships sailing to Diu, and the other two Merchants towards Goa, it pleased God to conduct them safe thither.

Seventeen days after we were arrived at the Fortress of Diu, where at that time two Foists were ready prepared to go to the Streight of Mecqua, for to discover and find out the design of the Turkish Army, whose coming was greatly feared in the Indies, because one of those Foists was commanded by a Captain that was a great friend of mine, who gave me good hope of the Voyage he was bound for, I imbarqued my self with him.

Relying then on the promises which the Captain made me, that by his favour and means I should quickly be rich, the only thing in the world that I most desired, and suffered my self to be deceived by my hopes, I imagined that I was already Master of great wealth, never considering how vain and uncertain the promises of men are, and that I could not reap much benefit by the Voyage I was going to undertake, by reason it was dangerous, and unseasonable for Navigation in that Country.

Now being departed from Diu, we sailed in a time full of storms, because it was about the end of Winter, which seemed to begin anew, so impetuous were the winds and so great was the rain. Nevertheless, how violent soever the Tempest was, and dark the weather, we letted not to discover the Isle of Curia, Muria, and Avedalcuria, at the sight whereof we thought our selves quite lost, and without hope of life. Whereupon, to decline the danger, we turned the prow of our Vessel to the South-east, knowing no other mean then that to avoid shipwrack. But by good fortune for us, it pleased God that we let fall an Anchor at the point of the Island of Socotora: there we presently anchored, a League below the place where Don Francisco d'Almeyda caused a Fortress to be built in the year 1507, when he came from Portugal as the first Vice-roy that ever was in the Indies. In the said place we took in Fresh water, and some provision of Victuals that we bought of the Christians of the Country, which are the descendants of those whom the Apostle S. Thomas converted in those parts.

Being refreshed thus, we parted from thence with a purpose to enter the Streightes, so that after we had sailed nine dayes with a favourable wind, we found our selves right against Mazua. There about Sun-set we descried a Sail at Sea, whereunto we gave so hard chace that before the first watch of the night we came up close to her; and then to satisfie the desire we had for to learn something of the Captain by gentleness touching the Turkish Army, we demanded of him whether it was parted from Sues, or whether he had not met with it in any place; and that we might be the better informed, we spake aloud to all those that were in the ship.

But instead of answer, without speaking a word, and in contempt of us, they gave us 12 pieces of Ordnance, whereof five were small, and the other seven field Pieces, together with good store of Musquet shot. And withall, in a kind of jollity, and as it were believing that we were already theirs, they made all the air about resound again with their confused cries. After this, to brave and terrifie us the more, they flourished a many flags and streamers up and down, and from the top of their poop they brandished a number of naked Scymitars, commanding us with great threatening to come aboard and yield our selves unto them.

At the first view of so many Rhodomontados and bravings we were in some doubt and amaze, which caused the Captains of our Foists to call the Souldiers to Councel, for to know what they should do; and the conclusion was, to continue shooting at them till the next morning, that so by day-light they might be the better fought withal and invested, it being agreed upon of all sides that they were not to be let go unpunished for their presumption: which accordingly was performed, and all the rest of the night we gave them chace, plying them with our Ordnance. So morning come, their ship being shot thorow and thorow in many places, and cruelly battered all over, they render themselves into our hands. In the encounter there were 64 of their men killed, and of 80 that remained, the most part, feeling themselves reduced to extremity, cast themselves into the Sea, choosing rather there to be drowned then to be burnt in their ship with the artificial fires that we had hurled into her; so that of all the forescore there escaped but five, very sore hurt, whereof one was the Captain. The same, by force of torture, whereunto he was exposed by the Command of our two Captains, confessed that he came from Judea, and that the Turkish Army was already departed from Sues, with a design to take in Adem, and then to build a Fortress there before they attempted anything in the Indies, according to an express charge sent by the great Turk from Constantinople to the Bassa of grand Cairo who was going to be General of the Army. Besides this, he confessed many other things conformable to our desire, amongst the which he said that he was a renegado Christian, a Maliorquin by Nation born at Cerdenha, and son to one named Paul Andrez, a Merchant of that Island, and that about four years before growing enamoured of a very fair Greekish Mahumetan, that was then his wife, for the love of her he had adjured Christianity, and embraced the Law of Mahomet. Our Captains much amazed hereat, gently perswaded him to acquit this abominable belief, and become a Christian again, whereunto the wicked Caytiff made answer with a brutish obstinacy, that at no hand he would yield to forsake his Law, shewing himself so hardened in the resolution to continue therein, as if he had been born in it, and never had posest any other. By these speeches of his, the Captains, perceiving there was no hope of recalling him from his damnable error, caused him to be bound hand and foot, and so with a great stone tyed about his neck to be cast alive into the Sea, sending him to participate with the torments of this Mahomet, and to be his companion in the other world, as he had been his confident in this. This Infidel being executed in this sort, we put the other prisoners into one of our Foists, and then sunk their Vessel, with all the goods that were in her, which consisted most in packs of stained Cloths, whereof we had no use, and a few pieces of Chamlet that the soldiers got to make them apparel.

III

The season being now fit for Navigation, and Antonio de Faria furnished with all that was necessary for this new Voyage, which he had undertaken to make on Munday the fourteenth of May, in the year one thousand five hundred forty and two, he departed from this Port to go to the Island of Calempluy; For which purpose he imbarqued in two Panoures resembling small Gallies, but that they were a little higher, by reason he was counselled not to use Junks, as well to avoid discovery, as in regard of the great currents of water that descended from the Bay

of Nanquin, which great Vessels with all their Sails were not able to
stem, especially at the time wherein he set forth, for then the Snows of
Tartaria and Njxihumflao dissolving ran all the months of May, June,
and July into these Seas with a most violent impetuosity. In these two
Vessels were fifty Portugals, one Priest to say Mass, and forty-eight
Mariners, all Natives of Patana, as also two and forty Slaves, so that the
whole number of our company amounted to an hundred forty and one
persons, for the Pirate Similau, who was our Pilot, would have no more
men nor Vessels for fear of being known, because he was to traverse the
streight of Nanquin, and to enter into Rivers that were much frequented,
whereby we might probably be subject to great hazard.

That day and all the night following we imployed in getting out from
amongst the Islands of Augitur, and pursued our course through the
Seas, which the Portugals had neither seen nor sailed on till then. The
first five days we had the winde favourable enough, being still within
sight of land till we came to the mouth of the River of the Fishings of
Nanquin. There we crost over a Gulf of forty leagues, and discovered a
very high Mountain, called Nangofo, towards the which bending North-
wardly, we sailed fifty days. At length the wind abated somewhat, and
because in that place the Tides were very great, Similau put into a little
River, where was good anchoring and riding, inhabited by men that
were white and handsome, having very little eyes like the Chineses, but
much different from them, both in language and attire. Now during the
space of 3 days, that we continued there, the Inhabitants would have no
manner of communication with us, but contrariwise they came in troops
to the shore, by which we anchored, and running up and down like madmen they howled in a most hideous fashion, and shot at us with slings
and cross-bows.

As soon as the weather and the Sea would permit us, Similau by whom
all was then governed, began to set sail, directing his course East-North-
East, and so proceeded 7 days in sight of land; then traversing another
Gulf, and turning more directly to the East, he past through a streight,
10 leagues over, called Sileupaquin. There he sailed five days more, still
in view of many goodly Cities and Towns, this River being frequented
with an infinite company of Vessels; whereupon Antonia de Faria,
knowing that if he hapned to be discovered, he should never escape with
life, resolved to get from thence, and continue this course no longer,
which Similau perceiving, and opposing the advice that every one gave
him;

"Signior," said he unto him, "I do not think that any of your company can accuse me for misperforming my duty hitherto, you know how
at *Liampoo* I told you publickly in the General Council that was held in
the Church before an hundred Portugals at the least, that we were to
expose our selves to great dangers, and chiefly my self, because I was a
Chinese and a Pilot, for all you could be made to endure but one death,

whereas I should be made to endure two thousand if it were possible, whereby you may well conclude that setting apart all Treason, I must of necessity be faithful unto you, as I am, and ever will be, not only in this Voyage, but in all other Enterprises, in despight of those that murmur and make false reports unto you of me. Howbeit if you fear the danger so much as you say, and are therefore pleased that we should take some other way less frequented with men and vessels, and where we may sail without dread of any thing, then you must be contented to bestow a far longer time in this Voyage; wherefore resolve with your company upon it without any further delay, or let us return back, for lo I am ready to do whatsoever you will."

Antonio de Faria, embracing, and giving him many thanks, fell to discourse with him about that other safer way of which he spake: whereupon Similau told him that some hundred and forty leagues further forwards to the North, there was a River somewhat larger by half a league, called Sumhepadano, where he should meet with no obstacle, for that it was not peopled like the streight of Nanquin, wherein they now were, but that then they should be retarded a moneth longer by the exceeding much wynding of this River. Antonio de Faria thinking it far better to expose himself to a length of time then to hazard his life for abridgement of way, followed the counsel that Similau gave him; so that going out of the streight of Nanquin, he coasted the land 5 days, at the end whereof we discovered a very high Mountain towards the East, which Similau told us was called Fanius. Approaching somewhat near unto it, we entred into a very fair Port, 40 fathoms deep, that extending it self in the form of a Crescent was sheltered from all sorts of winds, so spacious withall as 2000 Vessels how great soever might ride there at ease.

Antonio de Faria went ashore with some 10 or 11 Souldiers, and rounded this Haven, but could not meet with any one body that could instruct him in the way he pretended to make, whereat he was very much vext, and greatly repented him for that without any kinde of consideration, or taking advice of any one, he had rashly, and out of a capacious humour, undertaken this Voyage. Howbeit he dissembled this displeasure of his the best he could for fear lest his company should tax him with want of courage. In this Haven he discoursed again with Similau before every one concerning this our Navigation, which he told him was made but by ghess; whereunto the Chinese answered,

"Signior Captain, If I had any thing I could engage to you of more value then my head, I protest unto you I would most willingly do it, for I am so sure of the course I hold, that I would not fear to give you my very Children in Hostage of the promise I made you at Liampoo. Nevertheless I advertise you again, that if repenting the undertaking of this enterprise you fear to proceed any further, in regard of the tales your people are ever tatling in your ear, as I have often observed, do but command, and you shall finde how ready I am to obey your pleasure. And whereas they would make you believe that I spin out this Voyage longer then I promised you at Liampoo, the reason thereof you know well enough, which seemed not amiss when I propounded it unto you, seeing then you once allowed of it, let me intreat you to set your heart at rest for that matter, and not to break off this Design by returning back, whereby at length you shall finde how profitable this patience of yours will prove."

This speech somewhat quieted Antonio de Faria's minde, so that he bid him go on as he thought best, and never trouble himself with the murmuring of the Souldiers, whereof he complained, saying, that it was ever the manner of such as were idle, to finde fault with other mens actions, but if they did not mend their errour the sooner, he would take a course with them to make them to do it; wherewith Similau rested very well satisfied and contented.

After we were gone from this Haven, we sailed along the Coast above thirteen days together, always in sight of land, and at length arrived at a Port called Buxipalem, in the height of forty nine Degrees. We found this Climate somewhat colder than the rest. Here we saw an infinite company of Fishes and Serpents, of such strange forms, as I cannot speak of them without fear. Similau told Antonio de Faria incredible things concerning them, as well of what he had seen himself, having been there before, as of that had been reported unto him, especially in the full Moons of the moneths of November, December, and January, when the storms reign there most, as indeed this Chinese made it appear to our own eyes, whereby he justified unto us the most of that which he had affirmed.

For in this place we saw Fishes in the shape of Thornbacks, that were four fathoms about, and had a Muzzle like an Ox; likewise we saw others resembling great Lizards, spotted all over with green and black, having three rows of prickles on their backs, that were very sharp, and of the bigness of an arrow; their bodies also were full of the like, but they were neither so long, nor so great as the others. These Fishes would ever and anon bristle up themselves like Porcupines, which made them very dreadful to behold; they had Snouts that were very sharp and black, with two crooked teeth out of each jaw-bone, two spans long, like the tusks of a wild Boar. We also saw Fishes whose bodies were exceeding black, so prodigious and great, that their heads onely were above six spans broad. I will pass over in silence many other Fishes of sundry sorts, which we beheld in this place, because I hold it not fit to stand upon things that are out of my discourse; let it suffice me to say, that during two nights we stayed here we did not think our selves safe, by reason of Lizards, Whales, Fishes, and Serpents, which in great numbers shewed them selves to us.

Having left this Haven of Buxipalem, by us called the River of Serpents, which in great numbers shewed themselves to us, Similau sailed fifteen leagues further to another Bay named Calindano, which was in form of a Crescent, six leagues in circuit, and invironed with high Mountains, and very thick Woods, in the midst whereof divers Brooks of fresh waters descended, which made up four great Rivers that fell all unto this Bay. There Similau told us that all those prodigious creatures we had seen and heard of, as well in this Bay as in that where we were before, came thither to feed upon such Ordure and Carrion as the overflowing of these Rivers brought to this place. Antonio de Faria demanding of him thereupon, whence those Rivers should proceed, he answered that he knew not, but it was said that the Annals of China affirmed, how two of those Rivers took their beginnings from a great Lake, called Moscombia, and the other two from a Province, named Alimania, where there are high Mountains, that all the year long are covered with Snow, so that the Snow coming to dissolve, these Rivers swelled in that manner as we then beheld them, for now they were bigger then at any other time of the year. Hereunto he added, that entring into the mouth of the River, before the which we rode at anchor, we should continue our course, steering Easteward, for to find out the Port of Nanquin again, which we had left two hundred and threescore leagues behind us, by reason that in all this distance we had multiplied a greater height then that of the Island was, which we were in quest of.

Now although this was exceeding grievous unto us, yet Similau desired Antonia de Faria to think the time we had past well spent, because it was done for the best, and for the better securing of our lives; being asked then by Antonio de Faria how long we should be in passing through this River, he answered that we should be out of it in fourteen or fifteen days, and that in five days after he would promise to land him and his Souldiers in the Island of Calempluy, where he hoped fully to content his desire, and to make him think his pains well bestowed, whereof he now so complained. Antonio de Faria, having embraced him very lovingly thereupon, vowed to be his friend for ever, and reconciled him to his Souldiers, who were very much out with him before.

Being thus reconfirmed by Similaus speeches, and certified of this new course we were to take, he incouraged his company, and put all things in order convenient for his design, to that end preparing his Ordnance which till then had never been charged; he caused also his Arms to be made ready, ordained Captains, and Sentinels to keep good watch, together with all besides that he thought necessary for our defence, in case of any attempt upon us. This done, he spake unto Diego Lobato, who was the Priest that we carried along with us, and one that we much respected, as a man of the Church, to make a Sermon unto his company for to animate them against all dangers that might happen, which he worthily performed, and by the efficacy of his words, full of sweetness, and excellent examples, he so revived our spirits, that before were much dejected through the apprehension of the dangers that menaced us, as there was not one amongst us but presently took fresh heart, boldly to execute the enterprise we had undertaken: Whereupon with great devotion and zeal we sung a *Salvo* before an Image of our Lady, every man promising without any future fear to finish the Voyage we had begun. That done, we joyfully hoysted sail, and entring into the mouth of the River, steering directly East, and with tears in our eyes, invoked from the bottome of our hearts the assistance of that Sovereign Lord which sits at the right hand of the Father everlasting, to preserve us by his Almighty power.

HOW VASCO DA GAMA CAME TO THE LAND OF CALICUT[1]

Luiz de Camoës

(1524–1579)

THE heathen king eagerly welcomed the hardy navigators, anxious to win the friendship of the Christian king and so powerful a people, and sad that fate had not made him a nearer neighbour to the fertile land of Europe. With dances and games and other festivities and rich banquets, he daily entertained the Portuguese.

But their Captain, seeing that he made too long a stay, and that now a favourable wind invited him to depart on the long sea voyage that was still before them, took leave of the king with many expressions of friendship. So they set sail for the lands of the East, which they had sought so long, and his new pilot showed him the true course without any treacherous design.

And now they sailed in Indian seas and came in sight of the region where the sun rose, and had almost attained their goal; but cruel Bacchus enraged by the good fortune of the Portuguese, gave free rein to his fierce wrath. He saw that Heaven had determined to make of Lisbon another Rome, and he was unable to prevent what had been decreed by an omnipotent power. In despair he left Olympus, and descended to earth in search of a remedy, and entered the watery realm of the God of the Sea.

In the lowest depths of the deep-sunk caverns, where the sea lies hid and whence the waves issue when the sea answers to the wind's fury, dwell Neptune and the festive Nereids and other ocean Gods. There, in a plain of finest sand, rise lofty towers of transparent crystal or diamond, so brightly do they gleam. The doors are of fine gold inlaid with pearls and wrought with lovely sculpture. Angry Bacchus entered this palace, and Neptune, warned of his coming, received him at the gate, accom-

[1]Translated from *The Lusiad* by Aubrey Fitzgerald Bell.

panied by the Nymphs who marvel at the coming of the God of Wine to this watery realm.

"Neptune," said he, "be not amazed at this my visit, for fortune plagues even the great and powerful; but bid the Gods of the Sea assemble before I say more, if you are willing to hear me; they will hear of great misfortunes, and indeed it concerns them nearly."

Neptune, considering that it must be indeed some strange event, at once sent Triton to call the Gods of the farther and the nearer seas— Triton, the son of King Neptune and Salacia, a dark and uncouth youth of large stature, his father's messenger; his hair and beard fell over his shoulders unkempt, matted with slime and mussels; on his head for cap he wore a lobster's shell. His naked limbs were rough with innumerable shells and crabs, oysters and crayfish. And now as he blew his curving shell, his voice sounded from sea to sea, and all the company of the Gods began to come towards the palace of the God.

Oceanus came with all his sons and daughters; Nereus, who married Doris and peopled all the sea with Nymphs; and the seer Proteus also came, leaving his sea-flocks to graze in their bitter pastures, although he knew already what was Bacchus' wish. Thither also came the lovely spouse of Neptune, daughter of Heaven and Vesta, of grave and cheerful mien, and so fair that the sea grew calm in wonder: her transparent robe allowed her crystal form to be seen; and Amphitrite, lovely as the flowers, conducted by the dolphin who had introduced her to King Neptune's love: her eyes shine brighter than the sun. Both queens come hand in hand, acknowledging one lord. And she, who fleeing from the rage of Athamas, became a Goddess, brought her son, numbered among the Gods; along the shore he runs, playing with the fair sea-shells, and sometimes lovely Panopaea carried him on her neck. The God, too, who from a man was transformed by powerful herbs into a fish, and attained a glorious divinity, came, still bewailing the evil trick played by Circe upon his love, the lovely Scylla.

At length they are all seated in the great hall, noble and divine, the Goddesses on richest daises, the Gods on seats of crystal. They were welcomed by Poseidon who sat enthroned with the Theban God; and all the house was filled with richest incense of Arabia. When the tumult of the Gods and their reception had subsided, Bacchus began to unfold his troubles to them, with grieved and angry mien, devising violent death for the Portuguese.

"O Prince, who rulest in thy might the angry sea from pole to pole, and hemmest the peoples of all the earth in their appointed bounds; and thou, Father Ocean, who surroundest the whole world and only allowest men to exist outside thy frontier; and you Gods of the Sea, who in your mighty realm permit no injury to pass unavenged: how is it that you are careless now? You see how a weak race of men, called Lusians after one who owns my sovereignty, with proud and lofty heart are overcoming me and you and all the world. You see how they sail across your sea more than ever was done by ancient Rome, and outrage your kingdom and break your laws."

More would he have spoken, but tears impede his speech, tears that from water change the Gods to fire. Their anger permitted no further counsel or delay: they send word from Neptune to great Æolus, bidding him loose the fury of all the winds and drive all navigators from the seas. Proteus, indeed, would gladly have spoken first and uttered some deep prophecy, but so great a tumult of the Gods arose that Tethys cried to him angrily:

"Neptune knows well what order he has sent."

And now the proud son of Hippotes released the raging winds from their prison, and incited them against those brave and daring men. Suddenly the sky grew dark, and the winds with renewed strength and fury begin to overthrow towers and hills and houses.

While this council of the Gods was held in the depths of the ocean, the glad though weary fleet was continuing its long voyage with gentle wind over the tranquil sea. It was night, at the hour when the first watch were about to awake those who were to take their place; yawning and sleepy they stand against the rigging in the bitter cold, and rubbing their eyes tell many a tale to ward off sleep. But suddenly the boatswain, who had been observing the sky, blows his whistle, summoning all the seamen from their sleep: he points to a black cloud, from which the wind blew strongly, and bade them furl the topgallant sails. Hardly had this been done when a fierce and sudden squall fell on them.

"Down with the mainsail," roared the boatswain.

But the furious winds gave them no time to obey; in one fell rush they tear it to pieces with a sound of shattering worlds. A sudden fear and dismay overcame the men, for they were now shipping heavy seas.

"Throw everything overboard," cried the boatswain, "and the rest work the pumps without ceasing."

The brave soldiers ran to the pumps, but the ship, rolling in that dreadful sea, hurled them from side to side. Three strong and seasoned seamen scarce sufficed to hold the helm, and neither strength nor skill availed. The winds could not have been more fierce and cruel if it had been their intent to overthrow the strong tower of Babel: in the towering seas the strong ship is a speck and seems to survive by miracle. The great ship in which Paulo da Gama sailed was full of water; her mast broken in twain, and her crew are imploring the Saviour of the world. Those in Coelho's ship were not in less affliction, although their boatswain had been able to furl the mainsail before the blast struck it.

Now the raging waves carry them up to the clouds; now they seem to see the lowest depths of the abyss; the four winds vied to unhinge the world; the black and dreadful night is lit with lightning flashes. The halcyons along the rocky coast sang again their sorrowful song of old, caused by the raging waters, and the lovelorn dolphins sought their caverns, fleeing from the tempest and relentless winds which gave them no peace even in the ocean depths. Never were such thunderbolts forged against the fierce pride of the giants by the grim smith who wrought gleaming armour for his son-in-law; nor was such lightning hurled athwart the world by the great Thunderer in the mighty flood from which two alone escaped to convert stones into men. Many a mountain was overthrown by the angry waves, many an ancient tree torn up by the roots, and the astonished sand of the depths was hurled to heaven.

Vasco da Gama, when he saw ruin appear as he had nearly reached his goal, and the sea raging heaven-high, hell-deep, in the confusion and danger betook himself to the only remaining refuge, to the Power which can achieve even the impossible.

"O heavenly Power, that rulest over skies and sea and earth, Thou who gavest to Israel a passage through the Red Sea, who didst rescue Paul from wreck and whirlpool, and, with his sons, save the second founder of the flooded empty world; since we have passed safe through a new Scylla and Charybdis, over new shoals and whirlpools, and along fell Acroceraunian cliffs, why after so many dangers dost Thou now forsake us, seeing that this our voyage is undertaken in Thy service? O happy they who fell fighting in Morocco for the faith, whose honoured memory is a new life after death!"

But as he spoke, the raging winds increased the tempest, roaring like angry bulls and whistling in the rigging; fierce lightning flashed without ceasing, and the fell thunder seemed to declare that the very sky had fallen on the earth, and all the elements were waging war.

But now love's morning star shone clear on the horizon, the harbinger of day, and the Goddess who guides it through the Heavens was revisiting with joyous mien the earth and broad seas; the Goddess from whom sword-girt Orion flees; but when she saw the sea and the fleet which she held dear, she felt both fear and anger.

"This," she said, "is the work of Bacchus, but may it be mine always to prevent his fell designs."

So saying, she descends swiftly into the depths of the sea, bidding her Nymphs crown themselves with roses; for she would woo the sullen company of the winds with sight of the fair Nymphs, lovelier even than the stars. And so it was; for at sight of them, their former strength of battle weakened, and they willing are to obey the Nymphs' behests. And fairest Orithia thus addresses Boreas:

"Think not, fierce Boreas, ever to persuade me that thy love to me was a constant love, for that is marked by gentleness, not fury. If thou dost not at once check this raging storm, my love for thee must be changed into fear."

Even so the lovely Galatea spoke to fierce Notus, who in joy at this sign of her love is eager to obey her. In like manner the other Nymphs

tamed their lovers, and all the rage and fury bowed down before fair
Venus, who promised ever to favour their loves in return for their
oath to be loyal to her during this voyage. And now clear morning shone
along the hills where Ganges murmurs to the sea, when from the main-
topmast the seamen discovered land to starboard; and fear departed
from them, since they had escaped the storm and raging seas; and cheerfully the pilot from Melinde said:
"The land must be the land of Calicut."

HOW THE *SÃO THOMÉ* WAS WRECKED OFF THE TERRA DOS FUMOS[1]

Diogo do Couto

(1542–1616)

WHEN Manoel de Sousa Coutinho was Governor of India, Estevam
da Veiga left Cochin in the ship *São Thomé* in January 1589, and
steering a course outside the Shallows, made for the island of Diogo
Rodrigues, twenty degrees south, where he met a south-east wind so
violent, that in great seas the ship rode at the mercy of the wind, and
was so beaten about that she sprang a leak in the prow, so that the tow
of the calking hung out and let some water in; but this was soon reme-
died. The wind now calmed, and they continued their course to a latitude
of twenty-six degrees off the Island of S. Lourenço, and here, ninety or a
hundred leagues from land, the ship began to leak worse and in a more
dangerous place—under the floorheads, where it is more difficult to stop
than in any other place. The seamen cleared this part of the ship, and
found the leak, which was very large, both the tow and the leaden bands
nailed over it having been forced out, owing to the badness of the calking, through which many ships are lost: there is great carelessness in
this respect, and the workmen are very unscrupulous, as though they
were not responsible for the lives and property embarked in these ships.
The force of the leak was such that a man's hand had not strength to
stay it. As it could not be stopped without cutting away the flanks of
the ship, this was done against the opinion of many, but they soon desisted, since this is, as it were, the key of the whole ship, and there were
no nails to mend the hole made (for most of these ships are sent out anyhow in order to save a few shillings). They then stopped the hole as best
they could with knives and large nails and other articles, and pressing
many small sacks of rice against the sides of the ship, and crushing them
together in a mass, threw sand over the sacks of rice to strengthen them
against the force of the water.

With this the ship became easier, and the water less, and they con-

[1]Translated from *Historia Tragico-Maritima* by Aubrey Fitzgerald Bell.

tinued their voyage in good weather to a latitude of thirty-two and a half degrees south, 150 leagues from the Bay of Alagoa and eighty from Natal, the nearest land. Here on the 11th of March a south-west wind struck them, so that they took in the greater part of their sail, and took a northerly direction in great stress of wind and seas, so that the water poured in through the old leak; there were soon three or four feet in the hold and there was great work in throwing overboard everything on the lower deck in order to keep the hatchways clear; and all with their hands on the pumps spent the night without rest; but the water rose another foot, and, flooding the ballast in the hold, reached the barrels and cargo which began to roll from one side of the ship to the other and knock against her side with such force as to shake the whole ship. And as the water was still rising, the seamen placed some lateen yards above the hatchways in prow and stern, and here arranged many small barrels which could be let down and brought up with ease. And there was no one, beginning with Dom Paulo de Lima, who was in the ship with his wife, and Bernardim de Carvalho, Captain Estevam da Veiga, Gregorio Botelho, father-in-law of Guterres de Monroy, who was taking his daughter to be married at home, and other passengers, gentlemen and monks —nobody was exempt from working day and night at the pumps and at the barrels, without leaving them even for meals; for the priests went up and down the deck with biscuits, preserves, and water, giving to all both material and spiritual comfort.

Nevertheless the water kept on rising, and they therefore determined to make for land and cast themselves upon it; and they set the small sails to the prow without daring to touch the mainsail, since to leave the pumps even for an instant would be enough to sink them. And as they made for land, it being now the 14th of March, the hold was entirely filled with water, and the pumps were choked with the pepper that was carried into the hold, and they ceased working them in despair; but those noblemen, monks, and honourable gentlemen kept working with great spirit, and encouraged the rest to do likewise, persuading them not to take their hands off the pumps, for that was their only hope. The seamen spent that day in clearing the pumps, and lining the openings with tin so that they should not again be choked. And as it was necessary to lighten the ship as mush as possible, they entrusted this work to certain persons who threw overboard the wealth in the ship, and the extremely valuable porcelain, all of which had been won with much toil and who knows by what means.

Next day, the fifteenth of the month, the deck above the hold was under water, and the wind blew from the south-west, and from time to time in fearful and violent squalls. Everything indeed was against them; even the helm ceased to steer, and the ship lay like a hulk without sails, for they were all rent, and the seamen attended to nothing so as not to cease work at the pumps, in which lay their only hope. All this night was passed in great trouble and despair, for everything around them seemed to tell of death: beneath them they saw the ship full of water, and above them the sky which seemed to conspire against them, and was shrouded in blackest gloom and darkness. The wind whistled on every side, seeming to pipe out "Death, death"; below, the water came rushing in; above, the sky poured water down on them as though it would drown them in another flood. Inside the ship nothing could be heard but sighs, groans, cries and lamentation and prayers for mercy to God, who appeared to be angered against them on account of the sins of some of those who were in the ship.

Next day at dawn, giving up all hope, they began to set about lowering the boat, and for this it was necessary to make a space by clearing away some of the barrels. And between decks it seemed that all the spirits of the damned were let loose, and with the thud of things floating from side to side and knocking against one another it sounded like the Last Judgment. The seamen and others made ready the boat rapidly, but with great difficulty, owing to the rocking of the ship between sea and sea, the seas entering through the gangway which was open for throwing the cargo overboard. Their direction was now north-east, for the pilot was of opinion that they were very near land, and that day at sunset a sailor declared that he had sighted it, and called out from the maintopmast: "Land! land!" The pilot did not know if there were reefs on that coast, and therefore stood off and took a course north-east in order to make the land in daylight, and save all the people who had come through this night of toil and affliction. At dawn next day they saw no land, and let down the boat with great difficulty, because, before it was clear of the ship, men leapt into it like madmen, in spite of the fact that Dom Paulo de Lima stood in the boat, sword in hand, in order to prevent the crew from going off in it and leaving him; yet for all the ruthless slashing with swords and cutlasses, so many entered the boat that it would have sunk as soon as it touched the water. At length with great pains Dom Paulo was able to make some of those in it return to the ship, promising them that the boat would take off all it possibly could.

The boat was then brought to the stern of the ship to take in over the ship's side women, monks and noblemen; but the ship rolled so that there was danger of the coat capsizing, and it put off a little, and orders were given that the women should be strapped on bales of cloth: they were thus taken into the boat over the ship's side after being plunged in the sea and in pitiable plight.

The ordering of all this and of the ship fell on Bernardim de Carvalho, for as for Dom Paulo de Lima, as a God-fearing Christian, he believed that the wreck was a punishment for his sins, and was so downcast that he did not seem to be the same man who in great risks and danger had never for a minute lost his calm and courage, which now altogether failed him. The first to be taken into the boat was his wife; then Dona Mariana, wife of Guterres de Monroy; and Dona Joana de Mendoça, widow of Gonçalo Gomez de Azevedo, who, though young and with many hopes in the world, was going home to enter a convent; a woman of great virtue, who in all this voyage set an admirable example to every one. She had with her a daughter less than two years old: she had her in her arms and was imploring God for mercy when, in order to strap her to a bale, it became necessary to take the child from her and give it to its nurse. After the women, the priests were taken off, and then Bernardim de Carvalho, and last of all the ship's master and boatswain, who were busy throwing into the boat barrels of biscuit and water: and with that it could contain no more and put off.

Dona Joana de Mendoça, seeing that her child had remained on board, on its nurse's neck, who showed it to her with many tears and cries, spoke imploringly in such affliction that she moved the hearts of all to go back to the ship and ask the nurse for the child, bidding her strap it to a bale and throw it down; but she never would, saying that they must take her too, otherwise she would not give it up; and they were never able to persuade her although her mistress entreated her with tears and prayers which might have moved a tiger if a tiger had held the child in its arms. And because they might not delay and the girl was obstinate and the ship was lurching terribly and threatened to capsize the boat, they were obliged to put off, which they did with great pity for the poor mother, who kept her eyes fixed on her daughter with that sorrowful affection with which men look their last on those they love. And seeing that she must leave her child, although she would rather have remained on board with it in her arms than leave it to the mercy of the cruel waves which seemed ready to swallow it, she turned her back on the ship, and raising her eyes to heaven offered her infant daughter in sacrifice as a second Isaac, praying for mercy for herself since her innocent daughter needed none. This sight filled them all with great sorrow, although each of those in the boat was himself in sore need of his neighbour's pity.

When the boat was some little way from the ship, they waited for the Dominican Frei Nicolao do Rosario, who had refused to enter the boat without confessing all those who remained on the ship, that, having no material comfort, spiritual consolation might not be denied them also; and thus he confessed and comforted them with great charity and absolved them of their sins. It was not possible for the boat to go near and take him off by force, and he was determined to remain and comfort those on board the ship, but at last Dom Paulo de Lima and the others in the boat induced him to jump into the sea and swim to the boat, and he was received by all with joy, since his virtue and example in all that voyage had made them respect and love him. After they had taken him in they made for the land.

After the departure of the boat, those on the ship, placing their hope in God alone, made some rafts as best they could, but God had ordained that they should perish there and they were all sunk, as were two small boats launched from the stern. And really it seemed a punishment of God, for all the people in the ship might easily have been saved if those in the boat had not thought of themselves alone: they could have put everybody, with water and provisions, on great rafts which the boat would then have towed ashore, for the land was so near that they had sight of it next morning; and the ship lasted for twenty-four hours after the pumps had ceased working.

When the boat began to make for land, the seamen found it so full and so low in the water that they began to implore some of those in it to throw themselves into the sea in order to save the rest; the nobles agreed to this course and left the choice of those who must die to the seamen; and they at once threw overboard six persons, who plunged into the depths and were no more seen. The rest looked on amazed, as in a dream; and after these six persons had gone, there remained in the boat one hundred and four. The tide kept pushing the boat out to sea, for it was very heavy and they were too worn out to row; and at midnight they found themselves not far from the ship and rowed up to her, and saw many lights moving on board, for those in the ship spent the night in processions and litanies, holding lighted candles in their hands and imploring the mercy of God with cries and supplications so loud that they could be heard from the boat. At dawn the boat went close up to the ship and had speech with those on board, and encouraged them to make rafts, and offered to wait to accompany them. Those on board answered with loud shouts and lamentation, beseeching for pity with so deep a passion as to fill every one with fear and awe, for the scene was all the more terrible because it was not yet fully light.

When day broke, three or four sailors in the boat swam to the ship to take off food and muskets; they found the deck under water and the people all demented in expectation of death, and in the raised part of the stern there was still a beautiful altar to the Virgin; round it were huddled the slaves with hair dishevelled, supplicating Our Lady for mercy; and in front of them all was Dona Joana's nurse, with the child still in her arms, unwitting of its danger. The sailors threw into the sea some barrels of water and biscuit and one barrel of wine which were taken into the boat. The boat made some efforts to go up to the ship and put on board some of those who made it too heavy to be seaworthy. The sailors returned to the boat without Dona Joana's child, for indeed most of them are inhuman and cruel by nature.

Being unable to reach the ship, they pulled away and left it to the seamen to act as they considered best; and these proceeded to throw certain persons overboard, among them being a certain Diogo Fernandez, a good man of little spirit, who was returning from the post of factor in Ceylon; a soldier named Diogo de Seixas; Diogo Duarte, a merchant; and Diogo Lopes Bayam, who had spent many years in Balagate, where the native ruler had given him an income of three thousand crusados because he was a man of skill and resource, who traded in horses between Goa and Balagate, and brought him secret news; and it was suspected that he was doubtful in the faith, for which reason he was sent home. Before they threw him into the sea, he gave Frei Nicolao a sack of precious stones which were said to be worth ten or twelve thousand crusados. And together with these men they threw into the sea some slaves, who were all immediately swallowed up by those cruel waves.

After this abominable cruelty on the part of the seamen, for which God soon punished them, since all or most of them perished in despair on land, the boat began to row ashore, and when they were some way from the ship, at ten o'clock in the morning, they saw her plunge terribly and disappear in an instant from their sight. The boat hoisted a sail, and made for the nearest land, the wind blowing from the east; and in the afternoon of the 20th of March they came in sight of land with great rejoicing, if hearts so stricken might rejoice.

HOW AFONSO DALBOQUERQUE CAME TO THE END OF HIS VOYAGE[1]

Braz Dalboquerque

AND when all this had been arranged he ... ordered Diogo Fernandez de Béja to get the ship *Flor da Rosa*, of which he was the captain, ready for him, that he might sail away to India, with all the ships which were to go in his company. And thus having settled the manner of his departure, he sent word to the King of Ormuz by Pero Dalpoem and Alexander de Ataide, that he was desirous of going away, for it was absolutely necessary for him (dead or alive) to go and set the affairs of India in order; therefore he begged him earnestly to forgive him not having taken a personal farewell, for his illness had increased to so great a degree that it gave him no opportunity of doing so, but he trusted in God that he would be able very soon to return and visit him; and that he would leave Pero Dalboquerque his nephew as captain of the fortress, and he was assured that that commander would serve him very well. The king replied to Pero Dalpoem that he must declare to his father how grieved he was at his departure, but he would be supported by the hope of speedily seeing him again.

Thereupon Afonso Dalboquerque, being so eagerly desirous of setting out on the way to India, took his leave of Pero Dalboquerque, and the captains who were to remain behind, and went on board on Thursday the eighth day of the month of November of the same year (1515), about

---

[1]From Walter de Gray Birch's translation of *The Commentaries of the Great Afonso Dalboquerque*. Reprinted by permission of the Hakluyt Society.

six o'clock, that no one might take notice of him, and immediately set sail and brought up again at anchor about a league's distance from the city, and there he remained waiting for the two great galleys and the caravela of João Gomez, and the brigantine *Sanctiago* which were to accompany him in the passage. And on Saturday morning Hacem Ali arrived with two native war-boats (*terradas*) laden with refreshments sent to him by the king; so he ordered him to be brought into the chamber where he was. And after Hacem Ali had delivered the king's message, Afonso Dalboquerque replied, thanking him very much for his visit, and saying that he had felt better after he had got out to sea; and that now he was no longer present in Ormuz, he begged the king would pay better attention to the work of the fortress, for it was the best thing he could have in the kingdom for the preservation of his state; and then he bade him farewell, giving him thirty *xerafins*, and to the Moors who navigated the *terradas* forty, and a good supply of wine to drink, which pleased them more than the money did. As soon as they were gone he set sail and steered away direct to India.

Directly that Hacem Ali had taken his leave, the great Afonso Dalboquerque bade Diogo Fernandez de Béja to clap on all sail, and having now got clear out of the throat of the Straits of Ormuz, as far advanced as Galayate, one day in the morning a Moorish *terrada* or native war-boat hove in sight, under full sail; and as Afonso Dalboquerque was very desirous of knowing some news from India, he told Diogo Fernandez, captain of the ship, to send the brigantine *Sanctiago* after her, who chased her so close that she struck sail. And after he had gone on board, Diogo Fernandez enquired of them whence they came? The Moors replied that they came from Diu. Afonso Dalboquerque thereupon ordered that the captain, master, and pilot should be brought before him; and when they were there, he commanded Alexandre de Ataíde, the interpreter, upon his oath, to conceal nothing from him that these Moors should reveal, nor any of the news of India that they might give. The Moors craved pardon of Afonso Dalboquerque because they had not struck sail immediately the brigantine bore down upon them, alleging as an excuse that they did not know that he himself was in the ship. But as the disease with which he was suffering was hastening him to his end, and the mere act of conversation wearied him, he desired Alexandre de Ataíde to make very searching enquiries of them concerning Indian news, and to what port they were bound.

The captain of the *terrada* confessed that Cide Ale, and an ambassador of the Xeque Ismael who was at Diu, had despatched him with letters for his lordship (Afonso Dalboquerque), and in these they might see for themselves the news of India. Then Afonso Dalboquerque ordered Alexandre de Ataíde to read the letters at once. That written by Cide Ale stated that twelve ships had come from Portugal, and with them Lopo Soarez as captain major of India, and Diogo Mendez as captain of the fortress of Cochim, and other captains for all the other fortresses, as they were therein named, and that Miliqueaz had not written to him because he was very much offended at the king having ordered him to leave India.

And in the letter sent by the ambassador of the Xeque Ismael to Afonso Dalboquerque it was written, that inasmuch as the king of Portugal so badly recognized his knightly deeds and his services, he advised him to take service with the Xeque Ismael, for he was sure the Xeque would appreciate his services by making him one of the greatest lords of his land; and he desired a safe-conduct to bring his merchandise to Ormuz and to take it to Persia.

When Afonso Dalboquerque learned that another governor had come out in his stead, and saw how his enemies were in favour with the king, he lifted up his hands, and gave thanks to Our Lord, and cried:

"In bad repute with men because of the king, and in bad repute with the king because of the men. It were well that I were gone."

And having said so he ordered that all the letters which the Moors were carrying to Ormuz should be taken from them, wherein it was advised that if a fortress had not already been given to Afonso Dalboquerque, that it should not be now granted, for another governor had been appointed who would do anything they wished. And in order that those letters should do no harm to the building of the fortress he caused them all to be burned, and bade the Moors begone, and remained alone with his secretary; and having already made his testament, wherein he expressed a desire to be interred in his chapel that he had built in Goa, which he had taken from the Moors, he added a codicil whereby he ordered that his bones, after the flesh had been consumed, should be carried to Portugal; and other matters not necessary to be written here.

And when this was done he wrote a letter to the king D. Manuel after the following words:—"Sire, I am writing this letter to Your Highness while I am suffering from a spasm which is a signal of my dissolution. In the kingdom of Portugal I have a son, and I beg Your Highness to ennoble him for my sake, as a reward for the services which I have performed for Your Highness in accordance with my condition of being your servant; for I command him on pain of forfeiting my blessing to ask this at your hands. And as for the affairs of India I say nothing, for they will speak for themselves and for me."

At this time he had become so weak that he could not stand, ever desiring Our Lord to take him to Goa, and there do with him as should be best for his service; and when the ship was yet distant three or four leagues from the bar, he ordered them to summon Fr. Domingos, the Vicar-General, and Master Afonso, the physician. And as he was so weak that he could not eat anything, he ordered his attendants to give him a little of the red wine which had been sent that year from Portugal. And when the brigantine had sailed away in advance to Goa, the vessel proceeded to cast anchor on the bar, on Saturday night, the fifteenth day of the month of December. When they told Afonso Dalboquerque that he was at the end of his voyage, he lifted up his hands and gave many thanks to Our Lord because he had vouchsafed to grant him that mercy which he had so earnestly desired, and thus he remained all through that night (with the Vicar-General, who had already come off from the shore to the ship, and Pero Dalpoem, Secretary of India, whom he constituted his executor), embracing the crucifix and continually talking; and he desired the Vicar-General, who was his confessor, to recite the Passion of Our Lord, written by St John, to which he was always devoted, for in it, and in that Cross which was made in the likeness of that whereon Our Lord had suffered, and on His Wounds, he rested all the hope of his salvation: and he commanded them to attire him in the habit of Sanctiago, whereof he was a "Commendador," that he might die in it; and on the Sunday, one hour before the morning, he rendered up his soul to God; and there finished all his troubles without seeing any satisfaction of them. And we may well believe that one who thus finished his life could not have so many errors of commission laid to his charge that the king whom he had served very loyally should command him to return to Portugal without rewarding his services; but whereas Afonso Dalboquerque had enemies in the King's Council who were envious of his greatness and of the glorious victories which Our Lord had granted him in those countries, they prevailed upon the king D. Manuel to command his return, and they did not fail to allege reasons for this according to their intent, and to send Lopo Soarez as Governor of India.

Now that the great Afonso Dalboquerque had expired, before any one came from the city he was immediately enshrouded and clothed in the habit of Sanctiago, with some buskins on his legs, and spurs on the boots, and a sword in his belt—after the customary manner of burying the Commendadors—and on his head was placed a velvet cap, and at his neck a stole of the same. And when the body had been thus attired, Pero Dalpoem gave orders to lay down carpets on the quarterdeck of the ship, and there they set out the body upon a bier covered with a pall of black velvet, with a cushion of the same material at the head. And Diogo Fernandez de Béja, who was the captain, ordered a boat to be made ready wherein the body was to be conveyed to land; and when morning came, the people of the city began to assemble in boats with a great outcry to accompany him, but when they learned that he was dead, so great was the crying and weeping on all sides that it seemed as if the very river of Goa was being poured out; and because the people were in a great throng he was immediately put into the boat and so carried to the city.

And when the quay was reached where D. Goterres, captain of the city, and all the Fidalgoes and Cavaliers, and all the populace and clerks and friars were waiting, the body was taken out of the boat to the land on the biers on which it had rested, and thereupon uprose another fresh outbreak of lamentations. And after praying for him, which the clerks and friars could not do without weeping, the Fidalgoes who were standing by took up the bier on their shoulders and beneath the pall bore him to his chapel of "Our Lady of the Conception," where he was interred, while there accompanied the procession all the people of the city, not only Christians but Hindoos and Moors, who filled the streets, demonstrating by the profusion of their tears the great sorrow they felt at his death. As for the Hindoos, when they beheld his body stretched upon the bier, with his long beard reaching down to his waist and his eyes half open, they declared, after their heathen notions, that it could not be that he was dead, but that God had need of him for some war and had therefore sent for him.

MODERN GREECE

SEA[1]

Antrea Karkavitsas

I

MY FATHER—may the wave that buried him be holy oil for him—
never meant to make a sailor of me.

"Keep away, my boy," he said, "keep away from the lying monster!
She has no faith nor mercy. Worship her as you will—honour her—she
never moves from her own aim. Don't look at her deceiving smile, promising her countless wealth. Sooner or later she will dig a grave for you,
or she will cast you on the world a useless ruin, with nothing to own
but your skin and bones. Sea or woman—it's all the same!"

These were the words of a man who had spent a whole life on a ship's
deck, a man whose father and grandfather and great-grandfather had
died by the mast. And he was not alone in this opinion. The other old
men of the island, veterans of the ships, and the younger people whose
hands were still callous, whenever they took their seats in the coffee-
house to smoke their water pipes, would waggle their heads sadly and
say with a sigh:

"There's no more bread to be gained from the sea. Let me have just
a root of vine on the solid earth and I would throw a black stone behind
me."

The truth was that many of them had money enough to own not only
a vine but a whole island. Yet they would spend it all on the sea. They
competed against each other to see who could build the biggest vessel or
who would be a captain first. I, who often heard their words and saw their
acts, contrary to and inconsistent with their words, could not understand
the mystery.

Some God's breath, I said to myself, some power sent from infinity
was coming down to drag with it all those souls and hurl them captives
against their wills into the open sea, just as the raging north wind beating on the bare cliffs bites off the weathered pieces and hurls them down
in a mass of fragments.

But the same impulse was pushing me, too, that way. Ever since my
childhood days, I loved the sea. You might say I took my first steps in
the water. My first toy was a box of beans with a little stick set up in
the centre for a mast, with two pieces of thread for hawsers and a sheet of
paper for a sail and my imagination made of this little box a triple-

[1]Translated by Demetra Vaka and Aristides Phoutrides. Reprinted by permission of
Duffield & Co.

decked bark. I put it to sea with emotion and imagined myself in it. Of course, as soon as I took my hand off, my bark sank to the bottom, but I was not slow in building another of timber. My dockyard was at the little harbour of St Nicholas. I put my boat to sea and I followed it, swimming to the entrance of the harbour, where the current swept it far away from me. Later I became first in rowing and first in swimming. All I lacked was a fish's scales.

"Bravo!" said the old sailors to me with their good-natured smiles as they saw me ripping the water like a dolphin. "You will put us all to shame!"

I was proud because of these words and I hoped that some day I would fulfill their prophecy. I remember it was my seventh year at school when I closed my books forever. I found nothing in them that would respond to my longings, while everything else about me, living or not, whispered to me a thousand tales: The sailors with their faces bronzed by the sun; the old men with their reminiscences; the piled timber with its story told at sight; the lasses with their songs:

How handsome is my little mate when wet with the sea-spray,
He puts on his change of snow-white clothes and takes the helm in hand.

This song I heard ever since my cradle days and it seemed to me like a hymn sung by my island to lure its inhabitants to the life of the sea. My dream, too, was some day to be a mate and wet with the sea-spray, to hold the helm in hand. Surely I would be handsome then and strong— a real man. I would be the pride of my island and I would be loved by every lass.

Yes, I did love the sea! At times I saw her spreading from the headland far away and mingling with the blue firmament, like a sapphire floor, smooth, calm, and silent with a secret that I longed to know. At times I saw her in a fury, spattering the shore angrily with white foam, toppling over the reefs, scaling the caves of the great rocks with a restless thundering roar, as if she sought to penetrate the earth's fiery womb and to extinguish the flames that burned there. This intoxicated me, and I ran to play with her, to make her angry and provoke her, so that she might rush against me and chase me, and lash my body with her spray—tease her as we like to tease wild beasts bound with chains. Then, when I saw a ship lifting anchor and sailing out of the harbour into the open sea, and heard the cheering chanties of the sailors labouring at the capstan sheets and the farewells of the women, my soul would fly like a lonely bird after it. The sails of dark grey, swelling with the wind, the stays stretching like delicate lines against the horizon, the golden trucks leaving behind them a trail of light in the blue sky, called out to me to go with them, promising new lands, new men, riches, joys, strange kisses that, though I knew it not, were stored in my heart as the inherited pleasures of my fathers. So, day and night, my soul longed for nothing else but the day of sailing away. Even when the news of a shipwreck reached the island, and the death of the drowned men lay heavy on everybody's heart, and silent grief spread from the frowning faces to the inanimate pebbles of the beach; even when I met the orphans of the dead in the streets, like gilded pieces of wood among the ruins of a once prosperous home, and saw the women clothed in black, and the bereaved sweethearts left disconsolate, and heard the survivors of the shipwreck tell of their misfortune—even then I was sorry and jealous that I had not been with them to see my own sweetheart in her wild majesty and to wrestle with her, wrestle unto death.

At last I could no longer control myself. My father had sailed away with his schooner. My uncle, Kaligeres, was just about to set sail for the Black Sea. I fell on his neck; and my mother, too, fearing I might get sick, intervened in my behalf. He consented to take me along.

"I will take you," he said, "but you'll have to work. A sailing ship needs care, it's no fishing boat for food and sleep."

I was always afraid of my uncle. He was as rude and mean to me as he was to his sailors. Men avoided working under him.

> Better slaving in Algiers
> Than with Captain Kaligeres,

they would say to show his heartlessness. He would "bake a fish on their lips" not only in the work he exacted but even in the food and the pay he gave them. Whatever there was of old salt junk, mouldy dry cod, bitter flour, weevilly biscuit and chalky cheese could be found in Kaligeres' stores to be used for his sailors. He would never speak, except to command, to swear, or to abuse somebody. Only men who despaired of any other chance would offer themselves to him. So I knew well I was not going to indulge in caresses and good times. But the lure of the sea made me disregard everything.

"Only take me aboard," I said, "and I'll work as much as you want."

To make my word good, I plunged into work. I made the futtock-shrouds my play. The higher I had to go the more eager I was to climb up first. Perhaps my uncle wished to make it especially hard for me from the beginning, and to acquaint me with the endless trials of a sailor's life in order to make me change my mind. He surely kept me going, from deck-washing to deck-scrubbing, from sail-mending to rope-twisting, from letting go and clewing up the sails to stowing them; from the quay to the capstan, from loading to unloading, from caulking to painting. I had to be first in everything. First be it! What did I care? I was satisfied to climb high to the topyard and with my big toes grasping the backstay to look down into space and watch the sea open a way and retreat before me as my humble subject. Drunk with joy, I compared myself to a proud bird winging its way triumphantly across the skies. I was in a magic trance. I looked with pity on the rest of the world, on the men who lived on dry land. They seemed to me like ants, creeping snakes, or slow-moving tortoises condemned to wear their shells forever as a useless burden.

"Bah!" I would say with contempt. "They think they live!" On such a surge of enthusiasm I heard one day the Captain's voice roar like a peal of thunder beside me:

"Let go the sails! Clew up and let go all!"

I was frightened, and ran to follow the other sailors without understanding exactly what the trouble was. Every one to his post, and I to mine. They flew to the jibs; I followed them. They climbed up to the yards. I was among them, making fast and stowing every sail. Within five minutes the bark was a skeleton of spars. In front of his cabin the captain stood shouting and abusing and cursing. I looked at him, but damned if I knew what he was talking about.

"What in hell is the matter?" I asked the man next to me as we were making the sky-sail fast.

"The squall—don't you see? The water spout!"

The waterspout! A shiver ran down my back. I had often heard of its awful wonders; how it sweeps everything away in its path, how it makes tatters of sails, breaks down masts, and downs all things that sail the sea. There was not only one, but three or four. Two of them rose towards Batum. The others were on our port bow, sweeping over the waters from grey distance where sky and sea met. Ahead, Caucasus, a frowning monstrous mass, showing his darkened coast walled with great cliffs like bare teeth ready to tear a world. Above us, the sky draped with thick heavy curtains of clouds; below, the sea, blackish-grey, trembling from end to end like a living thing shuddering with fear. For the first time I saw my sweetheart frightened.

The one waterspout was high and arched like an elephant's proboscis, and hung over the waters, a black, motionless monster. The other, at first like an immense thick pillar rising straight up, was suddenly broken in two like a column of smoke; its lower half was shattered into a thousand fragments, while the upper half hung from the clouds like a many-forked serpent's tongue. I saw the serpent moving on, stretching his neck, now this way and now that, brandishing his tongues as if seeking something on the face of the waters, and then suddenly flinging his body backward and gathering it in coils to nestle among the clouds. But a third one, black and grey and as thick as the trunk of a plane-tree a thousand years old, stood motionless for some time sucking up the water and swelling in size; and then, tottering like a menacing beast, it started sweeping against us, a monstrous mass of terror.

"Down, there! Get down!" I heard a voice from the deck calling to me.

Turning around, I saw that all the others had climbed down while I had been clinging fast to the topmast, watching the strange miracle. I slid down to the captain. With bulging eyes he was glaring at the apparition. In his right hand he held a black-handled knife, and stood behind the mainmast as if it were a bulwark. Nearby the mate was hurriedly filling up the rusty "trompone"[1], and around him stood the stunned sailors, staring now at the sea, now at the sky.

The waterspout was approaching on winged feet, sucking up the water and then spitting it out skyward in a black roaring fog. It seemed as if it would sweep everything off the boat, or as if it would lift it up bodily. It came within two fathoms of us—cylindrical, luminous, golden and green like smoked crystal, its piston working inside its heart, as if it were endeavouring to extinguish some huge conflagration up in heaven.

"Now!" commanded the captain.

The mate sent the contents of the "trompone" into it. Old nails, lead, oakum all were absorbed in it. It seemed to totter. That stopped: it tried to move. Twice it swooped about, and again stood, uniting sea and sky.

"We failed," the captain said bitterly to the mate.

"Yes, we did. And now draw the pentagram, captain, and let the sin be upon my head."

"God forgive me!" murmured the captain, making the sign of the cross.

With the black-handled knife he traced the pentagram upon the mast, saying thrice: "In the beginning was the Word, and the Word was God, and God was the Word."

He stuck the knife in the middle of the pentagram as if he were nailing it to the very entrails of the monster.

A blast was heard as if a cannon had been discharged, and a gigantic wave broke over our deck. At the same instant the Caucasus was illuminated by a lightning flash, and reverberated thunderously as the monster broke. And the frightened sea foamed and raged over its whole immense surface.

"Aloft the sails!" commanded the captain quickly. "Top-sails! Jibs! Top-gallants! Royals!"

We spread our sails, and soon the bark was on its course again.

II

Three weeks later we anchored at Constantinople, with a cargo on board. There I received the first letter from my mother, a first letter that came like a first stab at my inexperienced heart.

"Yanne, my boy," said the old woman, "when you come back to the

---

[1] An ancient Turkish term for a bell-mouthed gun or small cannon was a "tromboni."

island with St Nicholas' help and my blessing, you will not be any longer a captain's son as you were on the day you sailed away—your father is gone with his schooner and all our fortune! The Black Sea has swallowed them all. Now you have nothing left but this one-story house, me, a helpless woman, and God. May your arms be strong. Work, my boy, and respect your uncle. If you have anything left over from your earnings, send it to me to buy oil and burn a candle before the Saint for your father's soul."

I crossed my hands and looked with tearful eyes at the sea. The words of the letter seemed to me like an echo of my father's words. He had been a captain, owner of his own vessel for many years, and now his widow had to depend on my savings to make a wheat offering[1] for the dead man's soul! His wheat offering, not to speak of the poor widow's own needs! Meanwhile, who knows against what reefs, his iron-strong arms are dashing, what gulls are tearing his flesh, or what waves are bleaching his fleshless bones!

How significant were his last words! We had met for the last time just as we were sailing into the port of Theodosia, when he saw me high on the top-yard stowing the skysail. He crossed himself and stood dumb with emotion. He had not expected such a thing.

"Why do you look at him, Captain Angele?" Kaligeres shouted to him as we sailed by. "I wouldn't exchange him for your best hand."

At the same moment I was praying earnestly that the sea might open and swallow me. I could not rest so long as I felt his stern eyes fixed on me. I ran hurriedly from one end to another, as if I were too busy to stop. Down into the forecastle I would go, and up the futtock-shrouds; or I would pass from the capstan to the poop and do anything to avoid him. He understood my confusion, and did not rise from his seat; but from the place where he sat he followed me with a sad, complaining eye as if he was looking on a deathbed.

Next day he met me as I was going to town with the other men. As soon as I caught sight of him, I tried to hide, but he nodded, and even from the distance his nod was so commanding that my legs refused to obey my will.

"My boy, whatever was the matter with you? Have you thought over what you are trying to do?"

For the first time I knew there was gentleness in my father's voice; but I did not hesitate.

"Father," I said with courage, "I did think it over. Maybe my act is foolish and bad; but I can't help it. I can't live otherwise. The sea calls me; don't try to stop me. Else I might go where you will never see me again."

---

[1]Boiled wheat seasoned with sugar, cinnamon, burned flour nuts, etc., and placed on a tray before the altar. The priest prays for the forgiveness of the dead person's sins and the wheat is distributed among all present, who take it saying, "God forgive him," and eat it.

He made the sign of the cross, puzzled by my determination. He looked straight into my eyes for some time, then he shook his head and said:

"Very well, my boy; do whatever God prompts you to. I have done my part. Remember, I have spared neither words nor money. You will have no reason to curse me in the future. Go with my blessing."

His last blessing was my first regret. The sea did not reward my love on my first trip.

I was now truly a hired man for Captain Kaligeres, to earn my own bread and my mother's, who had been a captain's wife. Yet in spite of her advice, I could neither respect him nor work for my uncle any longer. If I must be a hired sailor, I thought, thank God there are other vessels. I would much rather get a shower of abuse from a stranger than from my own kin. A stranger would be more likely to respect my name. And so I made up my mind, if all was well, to disembark at the first port.

"Out for a better job? You will see!" said Kaligeres, who guessed my thoughts.

One day I went to ask a little olive oil for my food.

"No," he said, "that's for the man who stands by the wheel."

I went a second time and a third. The same answer. It wasn't enough for him to feed us with every decaying thing; he had to strike even olive oil off our rations. His avarice and his heartlessness were his most detestable traits. I decided to get back at him once, and one day when I was at the wheel and he was out of sight, I took the picture of St Nicholas from the chart-house, where a lamp filled with olive oil burned before it, tied it to the wheel and left the deck. The bark, like a crazy person, wandered all over the sea.

"Yanne!" shouted the captain, "who is at the wheel?"

"He who eats the oil!" I answered.

All the crew split themselves laughing and that angered him.

"Get out!" he said. "Pack your things and go!"

"All right. Give me my pay."

He took me into the chart-house and opened his account book. He reckoned up my dues in his usual manner.

"I hired you on such a day. The next day you came aboard; the day after, you brought your clothes, and one day later you started work. Not so?"

He cheated me, altogether, out of five days' pay. Still, it might have been worse.

"Just as you say," I said.

And so, with two pounds in my pocket, I landed in Messene.

III

From now on I lived like a real sailor. A life of toil and turmoil. Ant-like as far as being always busy, but never ant-like in saving. How could you ever save with such living from hand to mouth? One pair of shoes took one month's wages. A water-proof, another month's pay. One good time on shore, a third month. One month out of a job, six months in debt. How could you save and support a home? My home did not last long. Merciful death sealed its door. Within a year my mother died and her care was taken off my shoulders.

Wandering from ship to ship, from captain to captain, and from trip to trip, I wasted ten years on the sea. It was a troubled life; one pleasure, three misadventures. Before you could say "praise God," you had to yell "God help us!" Day and night my father's words resounded in my ears. What was the use? You might knock your fist against a knife or your head against a mast; the mast can't break. If I had a root of grapevine on land I might throw a black stone behind me and leave the sea forever. But where was the vine? I had one of two fates coming to me: either some wave would bury me, or I might fare forth into the world a beggar. Very well, then. I might stick to the job and have a good time. I wasn't alone, was I? Every sailor in the world has the same bad luck. I was a hired hand on many vessels, and worked with many foreigners, too, but never did I envy anyone. A sailor's life is the same everywhere; abuse from the captain, contempt from the super-cargo, threats from the sea, kicks from the land. Wherever he turns, he faces an enemy.

Once, when I had come to Piraeus, on an English brig, I thought of going to my island, which I had never seen since the day I had sailed away with Captain Kaligeres. Fate had taken me on her wings and made me spin about the earth like a top. On my return I found my home a ruin, my mother's grave overgrown with weeds and my young sweetheart a grown-up girl. I had the priest read prayers for my mother, I burned a taper for my father's soul, and cast two glances on my sweetheart. I shivered all over.

"Who knows?" I thought bitterly. "If I had listened to my father's words might I not now be Mary's husband?"

Her father, Captain Parares, was an ancient ship-owner, of the same age as my father. He was lucky with the sea. He struck it at the proper time, and so he reaped a rich harvest from it. Then he sold his bark, *St Stephanos*, bought some dry fields, turned them into a garden, and ceased his travels forever.

I did not leave on the next day, as I had planned. Nor the day after. A week went by and I was still there. Something held me back, though I had nothing more to do. But the same thought came again and again to my mind, putting out, like an extinguisher, all other thoughts.

"If I had listened to my father's words, might I not now be Mary's husband?"

At the same time I kept passing and repassing her home, and toward evening I would take the road to the village—well, just to catch a glimpse of her. In other words, I was in love with Mary. Whenever she passed with lowered eyes and light step before me and I saw her full breast and her hair banging in black waves down her back, I felt a desire to run to her and lock her in my arms with unfailing passion. Her black, almond-shaped eyes seemed to promise to me a calm, happy, and restful nest, and her bosom looked like a harbour of tranquil waters and smooth sands where a mariner might, without any fear, moor his boat.

It was like the vision that always haunts me. Waves, sky, earth and its crops, men, life itself always transitory and changing, tire our souls. As a balance of necessity nature must seek stability; and our mind looks for a place where it can rest by day and by night while the body goes on with its endless trials and struggles. So a woman is found and a marriage is sought. Do you think it of small importance while you wander over the world to know that there is a little corner for you some-where, where love burns for you and awaits your return anxiously? The same magnet that once had lured me, an inexperienced lad, to the sea, was now drawing me a full-grown man, toward the woman—only with much greater force. With the same blind passion, I followed the foot-prints of my fair one. I first sent Captain Kaligeres as messenger of my love. Then Kalomoira, "the Good Fortune," an old woman famous throughout the island as a matchmaker.

"I will not go," I thought, "until I have an answer."

But Kalomoira brought everything to a happy end. There was honey in her words, and she won both the girl and her father.

"I want to speak to you," said Captain Parares to me one evening after taking me aside. "Your purpose is good and your way is honest. There is nobody I would like to have in my house better than the son of a friend who was like a brother to me. Mary will be yours. But on one condition; you will have to give up the sea. I stand by your father's words. The sea has no faith nor mercy. You must give it up."

"But what am I to do?" I asked. "How can I live? You know I have learned no other trade."

"I know it. But Mary has a fortune of her own."

It came like a slap to me and I turned all red.

"Then am I to take a wife to support me?"

"No, she will not support you. Don't be angry. I did not mean to offend you. You will work together. There is the orchard, the vineyard, the field. They need workers."

The truth was I needed nothing better. I was ready to give up the sea forever. I felt like St Elias, who shouldered his oar and took to the mountains, looking for a place to live where men had never heard of his name. He didn't care either to look on the sea or to hear of it any longer. I felt exactly the same. Her name, her colour, her charms had no more secrets for me. The spell had been broken.

"Agreed!" I said, "you have my word for it."

IV

Three years went by, spent with Mary up in Trapi, my father-in-law's village. Three years of real life. I learned how to handle a pick, and worked with my wife in the orchard, the vineyard and the field. With work and love, I never felt the passing of time. When we did not dig together we chased each other under the citron trees like birds just learning how to fly. Her word followed on my word; her kiss on mine. I learned how to dig around the citron trees, how to prune the vines, and how to plough the field. Then I knew how to pick the citrons in the fall, how to gather the grapes when vintage time came in August, and how to reap the wheat-field in the month of harvest. I earned fifty talera from my citrons yearly, twenty from my vine, and forty from my wheat, besides the seed I kept for next year's crop and the provisions for my own home use. It was the first time that I really knew what earning was, and realized that my labour was received gratefully and rewarded with plenty. The speechless earth tried in a thousand manners, colours, shapes, fragrances, fruits, and flowers to speak and thank me for taking care of it.

If I ploughed, the furrow remained faithfully where I opened it. It would receive the seed and hide it diligently from the flying things; then it would keep it warm and damp until the day when it would show it before my eyes fresh with dew, green with living sap, and finally mature with gold. The earth seemed to say: "See how I have brought it up!" If I lightened the burden of a vine by pruning it, the vine would seem to burst into tears with emotion, and shaking with delight would open its eyes like bright butterflies and suddenly bring forth its heavy burden of new clusters. If I trimmed the citron tree, it would rise lithe with grace and dazzling with beauty, and with its tufted branches would build wonderful shady arches to cool our bodies from the noon-day heat and to shower fragrances on our sleep at night, while its light golden fruit would refresh our very being.

Yes, it is the earth God has blessed with feeling, and not that senseless monster which effaces your track as soon as the keel has opened it, jealous of the least sign that anyone might try to leave on eternity. Praise the sea all you may; flatter it, sing of it; its answer is a thrust for you to get away, a murmur of discontent at your presence, or an untamed tiger's roar when it tries to open a grave for you. Cain, after his crime, should have been condemned to a seaman's life.

At sunset we would walk back to the village. Mary would go ahead in the midst of her playful goats, who shook their bells as they frisked about merrily. I would follow with the pick on my shoulder, leading behind me the mule loaded with logs for fuel. Then, at home, while Mary lighted the fire to make supper, I would light my pipe and sit down comfortably at the threshold in the midst of a gay honeysuckle that spread lustily over the walls in the midst of scented royal mints and spearmints and sweet marjorams, generous little plants that asked for nothing but a handful of proper earth and a drop of water to bathe us with fragrance and grace.

From this place I would exchange greetings with passing neighbours, greetings that trickled from the very heart.

"Good evening!"

"Good evening to you!"

"Good night!"

"Good luck to you!"

I did not have to look anxiously at the sky any longer. I did not have to consider the position of the moon, the trembling light of the stars, the course of the wind, the rise of the Pleiades. And late at night, when I cast anchor in my love's arms, what bay or what luring port could ever give me such happiness!

So two years passed, and now we were in the third. One Sunday in February I went with my wife to my old town of St Nicholas by the sea. Her cousin, Captain Malamos, was christening his brig, and had invited us to the joyful occasion. It was a beautiful day, which was the first awakening of my old longing. The dock was covered with timber, masts, beams, splinters, and wood-shavings. The air was filled with the smell of the sea brine, the scent of freshly cut timber, the heavy odour of tar, pitch, and ropes. There were hills of hemp and piles of steel pieces. From one end of the beach to the other there was an array of little row-boats beautifully painted, brigs careened, luggers stripped of all rigging and old hulls covered with barnacles and seaweed. There were skeletons of cutters, schooners, and brigantines, some with just the keel and the sea-steps, others ribbed and planked up to the gunwale, others only half-way up. Any tool a seaman might wish for was there; and any seaman's dreams, ambitions, simple longings, and great hopes could be found on that gold-sanded beach, expressed vividly in some wooden structure by some ship-builders' hands. The guests—the whole island, it seemed—old men and young boys, old women and young girls, moved in their Sunday clothes from one ship's frame to another. The boys hopped from place to place. The men handled their parts with knowing pride, and often they spoke to them as if they were living things. The veterans of the sea sized up each ship's worth, estimated its speed, measured its tonnage, re-counted the profits it might bring, and gave their advice to the master builder on everything. At last, they concluded by wishing the owner of each ship that its nails might turn to gold for him.

Captain Malamos' brig was in its dock; its fine and lovely hull, with its many props on both sides, looked like a huge centipede sleeping on the sandy beach. Its prow curved like a delicately wrought sabre; its stern was girded with garlands of flowers. A glistening meadow of pure azure, the sea, spread before it, shimmering playfully and reaching for the ship's feet with little tongues of rippling water. She sprinkled it with her lukewarm spray, made it fragrant with her salt breath, and sang to it a secret confiding song: "Come," she sang, "come and lie on my bosom. I will give you life with my kiss; I will breathe a soul into you and will make you fly on strong wings. Why do you lie there, a mass of soulless timber, like something heavy with sleep? Are you not weary of the torpor of the forest and its life of no will? Shame on you! Come out into the sun, and the air, and the light! Come to wrestle with the wave and ride victor over it! With raised breast meet the strong wind and tear him into tatters. You will be the whale's envy, the dolphin's mate, the sea-gulls' comfort, the sailor's song, your captain's pride. Come, my golden one, come!" and the ship seemed to feel the spell of the sea and began to creak, eager to leave its bed where it lay in idleness.

All about, the guests were crowding. Captain Malamos stood by with a smooth-shaved, smiling face, dressed in his best, with a broad scarf about his waist. Near him, his wife, in a dress of silk, looked like a bride. They seemed to live their wedding-day once more, while a violin, a mandolin, and a drum played their gay melodies, with a spirit that seemed determined to carry the glad tidings to the ends of the earth.

Would you believe it? I was not happy in the least. As I sat toward the end nearest the sea, I would see the water's little ripples reaching at my feet, and a certain sadness wrung my heart. My first sweetheart, whom I had not seen for years, was now facing me again, young and beautiful, clothed in her raiment of sapphire blue. Her face smiled with perfect gladness; and I thought that she had her eyes fixed on me and that she spoke words of regretful complaint:

"Faithless one! Deceiver! Coward!"

"Get thee behind me, Satan!" I said to myself, and made the sign of the cross.

I wanted to get away but my feet refused. My body seemed like a mass of lead that was stuck to the rock; and my eyes, my ears, my soul were a helpless prey to the wave which continued to sing its sad complaint:

"Faithless one! Deceiver! Coward!"

Tears almost came to my eyes. My hatred for the sea, her tyranny, her crimes, the sleepless nights and my fruitless labour, all, vanished from my mind like bad dreams. I remembered only my first joys, the glad intoxication of the sea, the charm of wandering over her, the magic shiver of her dangers, the sheer enjoyment of escaping them, the recklessness of a sailor's life. All these joys I had abandoned for the sake of a woman.

"Well, what makes you so thoughtful, life of mine?" I heard a voice beside me. I turned and saw Mary, beautiful and smiling, with her lithe body, her fresh lips, her full breast, her shining eyes, and her coal-black hair. I felt confused and guilty as if I had been caught in the act of deceiving her.

"Nothing," I murmured; "nothing! Lend me a hand to get up. I feel dizzy."

I took her hand and grasped her with intense eagerness as if I were in danger of falling into the cold darkness of an abyss. The priest, in his vestments, was reading his prayers over the new ship. The ship-builder began giving his commands:

"Let go the stern prop! Let go the prow! Loosen the sides, now!"

One after another the props fell from the hull and the brig began to shake as if still stiff from sleep and hesitating to plunge forward into its new life. The boys who had climbed on deck were running from stern to prow and from starboard to port, making a noise like a flock of sheep.

The hands had taken their places beside the hull in order to push it into the sea. The master-builder commanded again:

"Let go!"

At the united effort of so many breasts, the ship groaned, shook once more, and finally glided, like a duck, into the water with its youthful crew on deck.

"Good luck to it, Captain Malamos! Good luck to it. May her nails turn to gold for you!" the crowd of seamen shouted, and sprinkled the captain and his wife with handfuls of spray.

But at that moment one of the boys on deck stumbled as he ran and fell senseless overboard. On the same instant, I plunged into the sea with my clothes on. With the second dive I pulled the boy to the surface. I saved the boy, but the meshes of the sea were tight about me, and none could save me. From that time on I could neither sleep nor rest. Joy had left me forever. That plunge into the sea, her warm water that had embraced me, was now dragging my soul a slave behind it. I remembered its touch was like warm kisses that sent an electric current down my back. With my open eyes I saw before me a bride clothed in blue; young, glad, and tender, nodding to me from the distance to follow her. I could hear her call: "Come! Come!"

I could not work any longer. I tried to go back to my orchard, field and vineyard, but all seemed to me walled-in and narrow. The shade of the citron tree was heavy and cold. The vine-twigs with their knots seemed disgustingly ugly, like a lobster's legs. The furrows of the field, cheap. So I spent day after day on the beach plunging into the water. I felt its touch with shivers of delight. I caught hungrily its salt breath, and I wallowed in bliss among the seaweeds as on a bed of soft feathers and silk. I would spend hours picking sea-urchins and crabs. Often I would go down to the harbour, and with some hesitation draw near the groups of sailors to hear them talk about their rigs, and travels, and storms, and shipwrecks. They would hardly look at me. You see, I was only a peasant, an old farmer, while they were sailors, dolphins of the sea. What could a poplar have to do with rhubarb? How could it stoop from its height to see the little weed at its feet? They could not even count me as present in their company. The younger sailors would look at me with wonder, as if to say: "Where does this ghost come from?" The older men who once had been my friends and my mates would occasionally deign to address me with a jest:

"Now, Yanne, you have your hawsers pretty tight. You don't have to worry about wind or sea. You've cast anchor for good!"

Their eyes had such an expression of pity that I could read in them what they did not speak in words: "You are a dead man! You don't belong to the living world any longer!" So I turned to the beach to tell my troubles to the waves. In the end, I turned back to my early years and consoled myself with little ships which I built with my hands. My skill was mature now, and I could make them with oak masts and actual stays and sails, while my imagination was again aflame and made triple-decked barks out of them. I was a child again.

Mary watched me and wondered about my change. Often she thought I was turning insane and prayed to Virgin Mary to help me. She made more than one vow to the Holy Virgin of Tenos, and went with bare feet on many pilgrimages to the neighbouring country shrines. She had prayers read over my clothes, and often, beating her breast with anxiety, she called on the saints and tried to secure their help in bringing me back to my senses again.

"Mary," I said to her once, "there's nothing that will help. Neither saints nor vows can cure my trouble. I am a child of the sea. It calls and I must go. Sooner or later I must return to my old trade. Else I cannot live."

As soon as she heard it she put on mourning. At last she knew the serpent that had been biting her so long in secret.

"Your trade!" she cried; "to be a sailor—and poor again!"

"Yes, a sailor! I can't help it. The sea is calling me!"

But she could not understand. She would not hear of it. She cried and prayed. She threw her arms about me, pressed me to her bosom, and covered me with kisses, clinging to me with despair, anxious in her jealousy to make me see the toil of the sea, its dangers, and shipwrecks. She would abuse the sea, find a thousand faults with it, and curse it as if it were her rival. But all was in vain. Neither her arms nor her kisses could bind me any longer. Everything seemed cold and wearisome, even my bed.

One evening, about sunset, as I was sitting on the rocks by the sea, plunged in my usual thought, I saw before me a brig sailing by, with all her sails drawing. It looked like a cliff of light rising suddenly from the midst of the sea. All her spars and stays were painted with wonderful distinctness against the blue sky. I saw the jibs, the courses, the top-sails, the top-gallants, the trucks. I believed I could even see the billet-head. My eyes seemed to get a supernatural power, so that they could turn timber to crystal and reach the very depths of the ship. I could see the captain's cabin adorned with the picture of St Nicholas and his never-failing candle. I could see the sailors' bunks, hear their simple talk, and sense their sour smell. I could see the galley, the water-barrels, the pump, the capstan. My soul, like a homesick bird, had perched on the full-rigged ship. I heard the wind whistling through the stays and shrouds, singing with a harmony more than divine of a seaman's life; and before my eyes passed on winged feet virgins with fair hair and black hair, virgins with blue eyes and dark eyes, and virgins with flowers, showing their bare breasts and sending me distant kisses. Then I saw noisy ports, taverns filled with smoke and wine-cups and resounding with sweet-voiced guitars and tambourines. Suddenly I saw a sailor pointing at me and heard him say to his companion:

"There goes one who renounced the sea for fear of it!"

I sprang up like a madman. Never for fear! Never, I thought, and ran back to the house. Mary had gone out to the brook. So much the better. I took a purse from under my pillow, cast a last glance on the bed, and with a pack of clothes on my shoulder, I disappeared like a thief. It was dark when I reached St Nicholas, but without losing any time I jumped into a boat and rowed to the brig.

Life has been a phantom for me ever since. If you ask me if I regret it, I would not know what to answer. But even should I go back to my island now, I could never rest.

The sea claims me.

BELGIUM

THE BEGGARS OF ZEALAND[1]

Charles De Coster

(1827–1879)

BEING at Heyst, upon the dunes, Ulenspiegel and Lamme see, coming from Ostend, from Blanckenberghe, from Knokke, many fishing boats full of armed men, adherents of the Beggars of Zealand, who wear in their headgear the silver crescent with this inscription: "Better to serve the Turk than the Pope."

Ulenspiegel is glad; he whistles like the lark; from all sides answers the warlike clarion of the cock.

The boats, sailing or fishing and selling their fish, come to land, one after the other, at Emden. There William of Blois is detained, who is equipping a ship under commission from the Prince of Orange.

Très-Long, having been at Emden for eleven weeks, was bitterly sick of waiting. He went from his ship to land and from the land to his ship, like a bear on a chain.

Ulenspiegel and Lamme, wandering about on the quays, saw there a lord of a jovial visage, somewhat melancholy and at a loss to heave up one of the paving-stones of the quay with a pikestaff. Not succeeding in this he still bent every effort to carry out his undertaking, while a dog gnawed at a bone behind him.

Ulenspiegel came to the dog and pretended to want to rob him of his bone. The dog growls; Ulenspiegel does not stop: the dog makes a great uproar of doggish wrath.

The lord, turning at the noise, said to Ulenspiegel:

"What good does it do thee to torment this beast?"

"What good does it do you, Messire, to torment this pavement?"

"It is not the same thing at all," said the lord.

"The difference is not extreme," replied Ulenspiegel; "if the dog sets store by his bone and wants to keep it, this pavement holds to its quay and is fain to remain on it. And it is the very least that folk like us, may do, turning to busy ourselves about a dog when folk like you busy yourselves about a paving stone."

Lamme remained behind Ulenspiegel, not daring to speak.

"Who art thou?" asked the lord.

"I am Thyl Ulenspiegel, the son of Claes, who died in the flames for his faith."

[1]From F. M. Atkinson's translation of *The Legend of Ulenspiegel*. Reprinted by permission of the translator and of William Heinemann, Ltd.

And he whistled like the lark and the lord crowed like the cock.

"I am Admiral Très-Long," said he; "what wouldst thou with me?"

Ulenspiegel narrated to him his adventures, and gave him five hundred carolus.

"Who is this big man?" asked Très-Long, pointing a finger at Lamme.

"My comrade and friend," replied Ulenspiegel: "he desires, like myself, to sing on your ship, with the fine voice of a musket, the song of deliverance for the land of our fathers."

"Ye are brave men both," said Très-Long, "and ye shall go on my ship."

They were then in the month of February; sharp was the wind, keen the frost. After three weeks of grudging waiting Très-Long left Emden under protest. Thinking to enter the Texel, he went out from Vlie, but was forced to go in to Wieringen, where his ship was locked up in the ice. . . .

One morning in March, since the wind, that was blowing sharp and cutting, ceased not to thicken the ice, and Très-Long's ship could not leave, the sailors and the soldiers of the vessel were holding feasting and revel on sledges and on skates.

Ulenspiegel was at the inn, and the pretty woman said to him, all woeful, and as if bereft of her wits:

"Poor Lamme! poor Ulenspiegel!"

"Why do you lament?" asked he.

"Alas! Alas!" said she, "why do ye not believe in the mass? Ye would go to paradise without a doubt, and I could save you in this life."

Seeing her go to the door and listen attentively, Ulenspiegel said to her:

"It is not the snow falling that you are listening to?"

"No," said she.

"It is not the moaning wind that you give ear to?"

"No," she said again.

"Nor to the merry din that our valiant sailors are making in the tavern close by?"

"Death cometh as a thief," she said.

"Death!" said Ulenspiegel. "I do not understand thee; come inside and speak."

"They are there," she said.

"Who?"

"Who?" she answered. "The soldiers of Simonen-Bol, who are to come, in the name of the duke, to throw themselves on all of you; if you are so well treated here, it is like the bullocks that are meant for the slaughter. Ah! why," said she all in tears, "why did I not know it save but just now."

"Do not weep, nor cry out," said Ulenspiegel, "and stay where you are."

"Do not betray me," said she.

Ulenspiegel went out from her house, ran, made his way to all the booths and taverns, whispering into the ears of the seamen and the soldiers these words: "The Spaniard is coming."

All ran to the ship, preparing with the utmost haste all that was needed for battle, and they awaited the enemy. . . .

Meanwhile had come up the men of Simonen-Bol, with a great artillery.

They fired against the ship, which replied to them. And their cannon balls broke the ice all about it. Towards evening a warm rain fell.

The wind blowing from the west, the sea grew angry under the ice, and heaved it up in immense blocks, which were seen rising up on high, falling back again, clashing against one another, one mounting on top of another, not without peril to the ship, which, when dawn broke through the clouds of night, opened out its canvas wings like a bird of freedom and sailed towards the free ocean.

There they joined up with the fleet of Messire de Lumey de la Marche, admiral of Holland and Zealand, and chief and captain-general, and as such carrying a lantern at his ship's peak.

"Look well at him, my son," said Ulenspiegel; "that one will never spare thee, if thou shouldst wish to leave the ship against orders. Hearest thou his voice breaking forth like thunder? See how broad and strong he is in his great stature! Look at his long hands with the crooked nails! See his round eyes, eagle eyes and cold, and his long pointed beard that he means to leave to grow until he has hanged all the monks and priests to avenge the death of the two counts! See him redoubtable and cruel." . . .

On that day Très-Long's ship took a ship from Biscay laden with mercury, gold dust, wines, and spices. And the ship was emptied of its marrow, men, and booty, as a beef bone under a lion's teeth.

It was at this time also that the duke ordained in the Low Countries cruel and abominable imposts, obliging all the inhabitants who sold real or personal estate to pay one thousand florins in ten thousand. And this tax was a permanent one. All sellers and buyers whatsoever must pay the king the tenth part of the purchase price, and it was said among the people that if goods were sold ten times within a week the king should have all.

And thus commerce and industry took the way towards Ruin and Death.

And the Beggars took Briele, a strong seaboard fortress that was christened the Orchard of Freedom.

In the days of May, under a clear sky, with the ship sailing proudly along the sea, Ulenspiegel sang:

> "Long live the Beggar! Beat upon the drum!
>   Briele is taken,
>   Flessingue, too, the key of the Scheldt;
>   God is good, Camp-Veere is taken,
>   Where Zealand kept her artillery!
>   We have bullets, powder, and shot,
>   Iron shot and leaden shot,
>   God is with us, who them is against?
>
> "Beat upon the drum of war and glory!
>   Long live the Beggar! Beat upon the drum!"

"Aye, good fellows and friends," said Ulenspiegel; "aye, they have set up at Antwerp, before the Town-hall, a dazzling scaffold covered with red cloth; the duke is seated upon it like a king upon his throne in the midst of liverymen and soldiers. Meaning to smile benevolently, he makes a sour grimace. Beat upon the war drum!

"He hath accorded a pardon, make silence, his gilded cuirass shines in the sun; the grand provost is on horseback beside the dais; lo here cometh the herald with his kettledrums; he reads; it is a pardon for all those that have not sinned; the others will be punished cruelly.

"Oyez, good fellows, he reads the edict that orders, on penalty as for rebellion, the payment of the tenth and twentieth deniers."

And Ulenspiegel sang:

> "O Duke! hearest thou the voice of the people,
>   The strong dull clamour? 'Tis the sea that rises
>   In the hour of the mighty surges.
>   Enough of gold, enough of blood.
>   Enough of ruins. Beat upon the drum!
>   The sword is drawn. Beat upon the drum of woe!
>
> "The fair land of Flanders,
>   The gay country of Brabant,
>   Are sad as graveyards.
>   There where of old, in freedom's days,
>   Sang the viols, squealed the fifes,
>   There are silence now and death.
>   Beat upon the drum of war.
>
> "Land of our fathers, sufferer beloved,
>   Stoop not your brow to the murderer's foot,
>   Toilsome bees, rush in your swarms,
>   Upon the hornets of Spain.
>   Corpses of women and girls buried alive
>   Cry out to Christ: 'Vengeance!'

"Wander in the fields by night, poor souls,
Cry unto God! The arm quivers to strike,
The sword is drawn, Duke; we will tear out thy entrails
And flog thy face with them.
Beat upon the drum. The sword is drawn.
Beat upon the drum. Long live the Beggar!"

And all the seamen and the soldiers of Ulenspiegel's ship and of the other ships sang likewise:

"The sword is drawn, long live the Beggar!"

And their voices growled like a thunder of deliverance.

Upon the hulls of Zealand, on *boyers*, on *croustèves*, away goes Thyl Claes Ulenspiegel.

The free sea wafts the valiant flyboats on which are eight ten or twenty guns all of iron: they belch forth death and massacre on the traitor Spaniards.

He is an expert gunner, Thyl Ulenspiegel, son of Claes, lo how he aims straight and true, and pierces like a wall of butter the carcases of the butchers. ·

In his hat he wears the silver crescent, with this legend: "Liever den Turc als den Paus": "Rather to serve the Turk than the Pope."

The sailors that see him climb up upon their ships, agile as a cat, supple as a squirrel, singing some song or other, with some gay jest in his mouth, would ask him curiously:

"Whence is it, little man, that thou hast so young a mien, for they say thou wert born long ago at Damme."

"I am no body, but a spirit," said he, "and Nele, my sweetheart, is like me. Spirit of Flanders, love of Flanders, we shall never die." . . .

And the embroidered banners of the Roman Catholic processions floated from the masts of the ships. And clad in velvet in brocade, in silk, in cloth of gold and of silver, such as abbots wear at solemn masses, bearing mitre and crozier, drinking the monks' wine, the Beggars kept guard on their ships.

And it was a strange sight to behold appearing from out of these rich vestments, those coarse hands that held arquebus or arbalest, halberd or pike, and all men of hard physiognomy, girt about with pistols and cutlasses gleaming in the sun, and drinking from golden chalices the abbots' wine that had become the wine of liberty.

And they sang and they shouted: "Long live the Beggar!" and thus they scoured the ocean and the Scheldt. . . .

On a black night the tempest growled in the depths of the clouds. Ulenspiegel was on the deck of the ship with Nele, and said:

"All our lights are out. We are foxes, watching by night for the pass.

ing of the Spanish poultry, which is to say their two and twenty *assabres*, rich ships with lanterns burning, that will be to them stars of ill fortune. And we shall rush upon them."

Nele said:

"This night is a witches' night. This sky is black as the mouth of hell; these lightnings gleam like the smile of Satan; the distant thunder-storm is growling dully; the sea-mews pass, uttering loud cries; the sea rolls its phosphorescent waves like silver serpents. . . . ."

And Ulenspiegel and Nele saw nothing now save the black sky the surging sea, the dark clouds coming forward on the phosphorescent sea, and close at hand, red stars.

These were the lanterns of the two and twenty *assabres*. The sea and the thunder were growling dully and faintly.

And Ulenspiegel rang the bell for the *wacharm* softly, and cried: "The Spaniard, the Spaniard! He is sailing for Flessingue!" And the cry was repeated throughout the whole fleet.

And Ulenspiegel said to Nele:

"A grey hue is spreading over the sky and over the sea. The lanterns burn now but feebly; the dawn lifts, the wind is freshening, the waves throw their spume over the decks of the ships; a thick rain is falling and speedily ceases; the sun rises radiant, gilding the crest of the waves: it is thy smile, Nele, fresh as the morning, sweet as the sun's ray."

The two and twenty *assabres* pass: on the ships of the Beggars the drums are beating, the fifes are squealing: de Lumey cries: "In the Prince's name, to the chase!" Ewont Pietersen Wort, sub-admiral, cries: "In the name of Monseigneur d'Orange and the admiral, to the chase!" On all the ships, the *Johannah*, the *Swan*, *Anne-Mic*, the *Beggar*, the *Compromise*, the *d'Egmont*, the *de Hoorn*, on the *Willem de Zwyger* (the *William the Silent*), all the captains cry: "In the name of Monseigneur d'Orange and the admiral!"

"To the chase! Long live the Beggar!" cry the soldiers and sailors. Très-Long's *houlque*, on which are Lamme and Ulenspiegel, and called *Briele*, followed closely by the *Johannah*, the *Swan*, and the *Beggar*, take four *assabres*. The Beggars fling everything Spanish into the sea, make the inhabitants of the Low Countries prisoners, empty the ships like eggshells, and leave them to float without masts or sails in the roadstead. Then they pursue the other eighteen. The wind blows vio-lently; coming from Antwerp, the sides of the swift ships bend over in the water of the river beneath the weight of the sails swollen like a monk's cheeks in the wind that comes from kitchens; the *assabres* go swiftly; the Beggars pursue them into the very roadstead of Meddle-burg under the fire from the forts. There a bloody battle joins: the Beg-gars carrying axes rush on the decks of the ships, soon strewn with lopped-off arms and legs, that have to be thrown into the waves after the combat ends. The forts fire on them: they take no heed, and to the shout of "Long live the Beggar!" take from out the *assabres* powder, artillery, bullets, and corn; burn the boats when they have emptied them; and make off to Flessingue, leaving them smoking and flaming in the roadsteads.

From there they will send squadrons to pierce the dykes of Zealand and Holland, to help in the construction of fresh ships, and notably of flyboats of one hundred and forty tons carrying up to twenty cannon of cast iron.

On the ocean, on the Scheldt, in sunshine, in rain, in snow, in hail, winter and summer, glided the ships of the Beggars to and fro.

All sails are out like mantling swans, swans of white freedom.

White for freedom, blue for great heart, orange for the prince, 'tis the standard of the proud ships.

All sails set! all sails set, the stout ships; the billows beat upon them, the waves besprinkle them with foam.

They pass, they run, they fly along the river, their sails in the water, swift as clouds in the north wind, the proud ships of the Beggars. Hear you their prows cleaving the wave? God of freemen? Long live the Beggar!

Hulks, flyboats, *boyers*, *croustèves*, swift as a wind big with tempest, like the cloud that bears the thunderbolt. Long live the Beggar!

Boyers and *croustèves*, flat-bottomed boats, slide along the river. The waters groan as they are cloven through, when the ships go straight on face forwards with the deadly mouth of their long culverin on the point of the bows, Long live the Beggar!

All sail out! all sail out, the gallant ships, the waves toss them, sprinkle them with foam.

Night and day, through rain, hail, and snow, they go on their way! Christ smileth on them in cloud, in sun, in starshine. Long live the Beggar. . . .

On the ships of the Beggars, under the dazzling sky, over the shining waves, squealed the fifes; droned bagpipes, gurgled flasks, chimed glasses, and shone the steel of weapons and armour.

"Ho!" said Ulenspiegel, "let us beat the drum of glory, let us beat the drum of joy. Long live the Beggar! Spain is conquered; the ghoul is beaten down. Ours is the sea, Briele is taken. Ours the coast as far as Nieuport, beyond Ostende and Blanckenberghe, the islands of Zealand, the mouths of the Scheldt, the mouths of the Meuse, the Rhine mouths as far as Helder. Ours are Texel, Vlieland, Ter-Schelling, Ameland, Rottum, Borkum. Long live the Beggar!

"Ours are Delft, and Dordrecht. 'Tis a trail of powder. God holdeth the linstock. The murderers abandon Rotterdam. Free conscience, like a lion with teeth and claws of justice, seizes the county of Zutphen, the towns of Deutecom, Doesburg, Goor, Oldenzeel, and on the Welnuire, Hattem, Elburg, and Harderwyck. Long live the Beggar!

"'Tis lightning, 'tis a thunder bolt: Campen, Zwol, Hassel, Sheenwyck, fall into our hands with Oudewater, Gouda, Leyden. Long live the Beggar!

"Ours are Bueren, Enckhuys! Not yet have we Amsterdan, Schoonhoven, or Middleburg. But all cometh in time to patient blades. Long live the Beggar!

"Drink we the wine of Spain. Drink from the chalice whence they drank the blood of the victims. We shall go by way of the Zuyderzee, by rivers, streams, canals; we have North Holland, South Holland, and Zealand; we shall take East and West Frisia; La Briele shall be the refuge for our ships, the nest of the hens that hatch out liberty. Long live the Beggar!

"Hearken in Flanders, our beloved land, how there bursts forth the cry of avenging. Armour is polishing, the swords are a-whetting. All are astir, a-thrill like the strings of a harp in the warm breeze, the breath of souls that cometh from grave pits, from torture fires, from the bleeding corpses of the victims. All, Hainaut, Brabant, Luxembourg, Namur, Liége the free city, all! Blood sprouts and springs up. The harvest is ripe for the sickle. Long live the Beggar.

"Ours the Noord-Zee, the wide North Sea. Ours are good guns, proud ships, the bold band of redoubted seamen: rogues, robbers, soldier-priests, gentlemen, townsfolk, and artisans fleeing persecution. Ours to all of us joined together for the work of freedom! Long live the Beggar!

"Philip, king of blood, where art thou? D'Alba, where art thou? Thou dost cry out and curse and blaspheme, thou with the holy hat, the Holy Father's gift. Beat the drums of joy. Long live the Beggar! Drink all!

"The wine flows into the golden cups. Drain it with glee. Priestly robes on the backs of rough men are flooded with red liquor; banners, ecclesiastic and Roman, wave in the wind. Eternal music! To you, fifes squealing, bagpipes droning, drums beating, peals of glory. Long live the Beggar!"

HOLLAND

THE FLYING DUTCHMAN[1]

Auguste Jal

ONCE upon a time, a good many years ago, there was a ship's captain who feared neither God nor His Saints. He is said to have been a Dutchman, but I do not know, nor does it greatly matter, from what town he came. He happened once to be making a voyage to the South. All went well until he came near to the Cape of Good Hope, where he ran into a head wind strong enough to blow the horns off a bull. The ship was in great danger, and every one began to say to the Captain:

"Captain, we must turn back. If you insist on continuing to try to round the Cape we shall be lost. We shall inevitably perish, and there is no priest on board to give us absolution."

But the Captain laughed at the fears of his crew and passengers, and began to sing songs so horrible and blasphemous that they might well have attracted the lightning to his mast a hundred times over. Then he calmly smoked his pipe and drank his beer as though he was seated in a tavern at home. His people renewed their entreaties to him to turn back, but the more they implored him the more obstinate he became. His masts were broken, his sails had been carried away, but he merely laughed as a man might who has had a piece of good news.

So the Captain continued to treat with equal contempt the violence of the storm, the protests of the crew and the fears of the passengers, and when his men attempted to force him to make for the shelter of a bay near by, he flung the ringleader overboard. But even as he did so, the clouds opened and a Form alighted on the quarter deck of the ship. This Form is said to have been the Almighty Himself. The crew and passengers were stricken with fear, but the Captain went on smoking his pipe, and did not even touch his cap when the Form addressed him.

"Captain," said the Form, "you are very stubborn."

"And you're a rascal," cried the Captain. "Who wants a peaceful passage? I don't. I'm asking nothing from you, so clear out of this unless you want your brains blown out.?"

The Form gave no other answer than a shrug of the shoulders.

The Captain then snatched up a pistol, cocked it and fired; but the bullet, instead of reaching its target, pierced his hand. His fury knew no bounds. He leaped up to strike the Form in the face with his fist, but his arm dropped limply to his side, as though paralyzed. In his im-

[1]This translation is taken from J. G. Lockhart's *Mysteries of the Sea* and is reprinted by his permission and that of the publishers, Philip Allan & Co., Ltd.

potent rage he cursed and blasphemed and called the good God all sorts of impious names.

But the Form said to him:

"Henceforth you are accursed, condemned to sail on for ever without rest or anchorage or port of any kind. You shall have neither beer nor tobacco. Gall shall be your drink and red-hot iron your meat. Of your crew your cabin-boy alone shall remain with you; horns shall grow out of his forehead, and he shall have the muzzle of a tiger and skin rougher than that of a dog-fish."

The Captain groaned, but the Form continued:

"It shall ever be your watch, and when you wish, you will not be able to sleep, for directly you close your eyes a sword shall pierce your body. And since it is your delight to torment sailors, you shall torment them."

The Captain smiled.

"For you shall be the evil spirit of the sea. You shall traverse all latitudes without respite or repose, and your ship shall bring misfortune to all who sight it."

"Amen to that!" cried the Captain with a shout of laughter.

"And on the Day of Judgment Satan shall claim you."

"A fig for Satan!" was all the Captain answered.

The Almighty disappeared, and the Dutchman found himself alone with his cabin-boy, who was already changed as had been predicted. The rest of his crew had vanished.

From that day forward the Flying Dutchman has sailed the seas, and it is his pleasure to plague poor mariners. He casts away their ship on an uncharted shoal, sets them on a false course and then shipwrecks them. He turns their wine sour and all their food into beans. Sometimes he will send letters on board the ships he meets, and if the Captain tries to read them he is lost. Or an empty boat will draw alongside the Phantom Ship and disappear, a sure sign of ill-fortune. He can change at will the appearance of his ship, so as not to be recognized; and round him he has collected a crew as cursed as himself, all the criminals, pirates and cowards of the sea.

HOW WILLIAM THE SILENT OPENED THE GATES OF THE SEA[1]

John Lothrop Motley
(1814–1877)

ON THE 26th of May, (1574) Valdez reappeared before the place, at the head of eight thousand Walloons and Germans, and Leyden was now destined to pass through a fiery ordeal. This city was one of

[1]From *The Rise of the Dutch Republic.*

the most beautiful in the Netherlands. Placed in the midst of broad and fruitful pastures, which had been reclaimed by the hand of industry from the bottom of the sea, it was fringed with smiling villages, blooming gardens, fruitful orchards. The ancient and, at last, decrepit Rhine, flowing languidly towards its sandy death-bed, had been multiplied into innumerable artificial currents by which the city was completely interlaced. Those watery streets were shaded by lime-trees, poplars, and willows, and crossed by one hundred and forty-five bridges, mostly of hammered stone. Upon an artificial elevation, in the centre of the city, rose a ruined tower of unknown antiquity. By some it was considered to be of Roman origin, while others preferred to regard it as a work of the Anglo-Saxon Hengist raised to commemorate his conquest of England. Surrounded by fruit-trees and overgrown in the centre with oaks, it afforded, from its mouldering battlements, a charming prospect over a wide expanse of level country, with the spires of neighbouring cities rising in every direction. It was from this commanding height, during the long and terrible summer days which were approaching, that many an eye was to be strained anxiously seaward, watching if yet the ocean had begun to roll over the land.

Valdez lost no time. . . . In the course of a few days, Leyden was thoroughly invested, no less than sixty-two redoubts, some of them having remained undestroyed from the previous siege, now girdling the city, while the besiegers already numbered nearly eight thousand, a force to be daily increased. On the other hand, there were no troops in the town, save a small corps of ":free-booters," and five companies of the burgher guard.

The main reliance of the city, under God, was on the stout hearts of its inhabitants within the walls, and on the sleepless energy of William the Silent without. The Prince, hastening to comfort and encourage the citizens, although he had been justly irritated by their negligence in having omitted to provide more sufficiently against the emergency while there had yet been time, now reminded them that they were not about to contend for themselves alone, but that the fate of their country and of unborn generations would, in all human probability, depend on the issue about to be tried. Eternal glory would be their portion if they manifested a courage worthy of their race and of the sacred cause of religion and liberty. He implored them to hold out at least three months, assuring them that he would, within that time, devise the means of their deliverance.

By the end of June, the city was placed on a strict allowance of food, all the provisions being purchased by the authorities at an equitable price. Half a pound of meat and half a pound of bread was allotted to a full-grown man, and to the rest a due proportion. The city being strictly invested, no communication, save by carrier pigeons, and by a few swift and skilful messengers, called jumpers, was possible. Sorties and fierce combats were, however, of daily occurrence, and a handsome bounty was offered to any man who brought into the city gates the head of a Spaniard. The reward was paid many times, but the population was becoming so excited and so apt, that the authorities felt it dangerous to permit the continuance of these conflicts. Lest the city, little by little, should lose its few disciplined defenders, it was now proclaimed, by sound of church bell, that in future no man should leave the gates.

The Prince had his headquarters at Delft and at Rotterdam. Between those two cities, an important fortress, called Polderwaert, secured him in the control of the alluvial quadrangle, watered on two sides by the Yssel and the Meuse. On the 29th June, the Spaniards, feeling its value, had made an unsuccessful effort to carry this fort by storm. They had been beaten off, with the loss of several hundred men, the Prince remaining in possession of the position, from which alone he could hope to relieve Leyden. He still held in his hand the keys with which he could unlock the ocean gates and let the waters in upon the land, and he had long been convinced that nothing could save the city but to break the dykes. Leyden was not upon the sea, but he could send the sea to Leyden, although an army fit to encounter the besieging force under Valdez could not be levied. The battle of Mookerheyde had, for the present, quite settled the question of land relief, but it was possible to besiege the besiegers with the waves of the ocean. The Spaniards occupied the coast from the Hague to Vlaardingen, but the dykes along the Meuse and the Yssel were in possession of the Prince. He determined that these should be pierced, while, at the same time, the great sluices at Rotterdam, Schiedam, and Delftshaven should be opened. The damage to the fields, villages, and growing crops would be enormous, but he felt that no other course could rescue Leyden, and with it the whole of Holland, from destruction. His clear expositions and impassioned eloquence at last overcame all resistance. By the middle of July the estates fully consented to his plan, and its execution was immediately undertaken. "Better a drowned land than a lost land," cried the patriots, with enthusiasm, as they devoted their fertile fields to desolation.

Meantime, Valdez, on the 30th of July, issued most urgent and ample offers of pardon to the citizens, if they would consent to open their gates and accept the King's authority; but his overtures were received with silent contempt, notwithstanding that the population were already approaching the starvation point. Although not yet fully informed of the active measures taken by the Prince, yet they still chose to rely upon his energy and their own fortitude, rather than upon the honeyed words which had formerly been heard at the gates of Harlem and of Naarden. On the 3rd of August, the Prince, accompanied by Paul Buys, chief of the commission appointed to execute the enterprise, went in person along the Yssel, as far as Kappelle, and superintended the rupture of the dykes in sixteen places. The gates at Schiedam and Rotterdam were opened, and the ocean began to pour over the land. While waiting for the waters to rise, provisions were rapidly collected, according to an edict of the Prince, in all the principal towns of the neighbourhood, and some two hundred vessels, of various sizes, had also been got ready at Rotterdam, Delfthaven, and other ports.

The citizens of Leyden were, however, already becoming impatient, for their bread was gone, and of its substitute, malt cake, they had but slender provision. On the 12th of August they received a letter from the Prince, encouraging them to resistance, and assuring them of a speedy relief, and on the 21st they addressed a despatch to him in reply, stating that they had now fulfilled their original promise, for they had held out two months with food, and another month without food. If not soon assisted, human strength could do no more; their malt cake would last but four days, and after that was gone, there was nothing left but starvation. Upon the same day, however, they received a letter, dictated by the Prince, who now lay in bed at Rotterdam with a violent fever, assuring them that the dykes were all pierced, and that the water was rising upon the "Land-scheiding," the great outward barrier which separated the city from the sea. He said nothing, however, of his own illness, which would have cast a deep shadow over the joy which now broke forth among the burghers.

The letter was read publicly in the market-place, and to increase the cheerfulness, Burgomaster Van der Werf, knowing the sensibility of his countrymen to music, ordered the city musicians to perambulate the streets, playing lively melodies and martial airs. Salvos of cannon were likewise fired, and the starving city for a brief space put on the aspect of a holiday, much to the astonishment of the besieging forces, who were not yet aware of the Prince's efforts. They perceived very soon, however, as the water everywhere about Leyden had risen to the depth of ten inches, that they stood in a perilous position. It was no trifling danger to be thus attacked by the waves of the ocean, which seemed about to obey with docility the command of William the Silent. Valdez became anxious and uncomfortable at the strange aspect of affairs; for the besieging army was now in its turn beleaguered, and by a stronger power than man's. He consulted with the most experienced of his officers, with the country people, with the most distinguished among the Glippers, and derived encouragement from their views concerning the Prince's plan. They pronounced it utterly futile and hopeless. The Glippers knew the country well, and ridiculed the desperate project in unmeasured terms.

Even in the city itself, a dull distrust had succeeded to the first vivid gleam of hope, while the few royalists among the population boldly taunted their fellow citizens to their faces with the absurd vision of relief which they had so fondly welcomed. "Go up to the tower, ye Beggars," was the frequent and taunting cry, "go up to the tower, and tell us if ye can see the ocean coming over the dry land to your relief"—and day after day they did go up to the ancient tower of Hengist, with heavy heart and anxious eyes, watching, hoping, praying, fearing, and at last almost despairing of relief by God or man. On the 27th they addressed a desponding letter to the estates, complaining that the city had been forgotten in its utmost need, and on the same day a prompt and warm-hearted reply was received, in which the citizens were assured that every human effort was to be made for their relief. "Rather," said the estates, "will we see our whole land and all our possessions perish in the waves, than forsake thee, Leyden. We know full well, moreover, that with Leyden, all Holland must perish also." They excused themselves for not having more frequently written, upon the ground that the whole management of the measures for their relief had been entrusted to the Prince, by whom alone all the details had been administered, and all the correspondence conducted.

The fever of the Prince had, meanwhile, reached its height. He lay at Rotterdam, utterly prostrate in body, and with mind agitated nearly to delirium, by the perpetual and almost unassisted schemes which he was constructing. Leyden lay, as it were, anxious and despairing at his feet, and it was impossible for him to close his ears to her cry. Therefore, from his sick bed he continued to dictate words of counsel and encouragement to the city; to Admiral Boisot, commanding the fleet, minute directions and precautions.

On the 1st of September, Admiral Boisot arrived out of Zealand with a small number of vessels, and with eight hundred veteran sailors. A wild and ferocious crew were those eight hundred Zealanders. Scarred, hacked, and even maimed, in the unceasing conflicts in which their lives had passed; wearing crescents in their caps, with the inscription, "Rather Turkish than Popish"; renowned far and wide, as much for their ferocity as for their nautical skill; the appearance of these wildest of the "Sea-beggars" was both eccentric and terrific. They were known never to give or to take quarter, for they went to *mortal* combat only and had sworn to spare neither noble nor simple, neither king, kaiser, nor pope, should they fall into their power.

More than two hundred vessels had been now assembled, carrying generally ten pieces of cannon, with from ten to eighteen oars, and manned with twenty-five hundred veterans, experienced both on land and water. The work was now undertaken in earnest. The distance from Leyden to the outer dyke, over whose ruins the ocean had already been admitted, was nearly fifteen miles. This reclaimed territory, however, was not maintained against the sea by these external barriers alone. The flotilla made its way with ease to the Land-scheiding, a strong dyke within five miles of Leyden, but here its progress was arrested. The approach to the city was surrounded by many strong ramparts, one within the other, by which it was defended against its ancient enemy, the ocean, precisely like the circumvallations by means of which it was now assailed by its more recent enemy, the Spaniard. To enable the fleet, however, to sail over the land, it was necessary to break through this two-fold series of defences. Between the Land-scheiding and Leyden were several dykes which kept out the water; upon the level territory, thus encircled, were many villages, together with a chain of sixty-two forts, which completely occupied the land. All these villages and fortresses were held by the veteran troops of the King; the besieging force being about four times as strong as that which was coming to the rescue.

The Prince had given orders that the Land-scheiding, which was still one-and-a-half foot above water, should be taken possession of, at every hazard. On the night of the 10th and 11th of September this was accomplished by surprise, and in a masterly manner. The few Spaniards who had been stationed upon the dyke were all despatched or driven off, and the patriots fortified themselves upon it, without the loss of a man. As the day dawned the Spaniards saw the fatal error which they had committed in leaving this bulwark so freely defended, and from two villages which stood close to the dyke, the troops now rushed in considerable force to recover what they had lost. A hot action succeeded, but the patriots had too securely established themselves. They completely defeated the enemy, who retired, leaving hundreds of dead on the field, and the patriots in complete possession of the Land-scheiding. This first action was sanguinary and desperate. It gave an earnest of what these people, who came to relieve their brethren, by sacrificing their property and their lives, were determined to effect.

The great dyke having been thus occupied, no time was lost in breaking it through in several places, a work which was accomplished under the very eyes of the enemy. The fleet sailed through the gaps; but after their passage had been effected in good order, the Admiral found, to his surprise, that it was not the only rampart to be carried. The Prince had been informed, by those who claimed to know the country, that; when once the Land-scheiding had been passed, the water would flood the country as far as Leyden, but the "Greenway," another long dyke, three-quarters of a mile further inward, now rose at least a foot above the water, to oppose their further progress. Fortunately, by a second and still more culpable carelessness, this dyke had been left by the Spaniards in as unprotected a state as the first had been. Promptly and audaciously Admiral Boisot took possession of this barrier also, levelled it in many places, and brought his flotilla, in triumph, over its ruins. Again, however, he was doomed to disappointment. A large mere, called the Fresh-water Lake, was known to extend itself directly in his path about midway between the Land-scheiding and the city. To this piece of water, into which he expected to have instantly floated, his only passage lay through one deep canal. The sea which had thus far borne him on, now diffusing itself over a very wide surface, and under the influence of an adverse wind, had become too shallow for his ships. The canal alone was deep enough, but it led directly towards a bridge, strongly occupied by the enemy. Hostile troops, moreover, to the amount of three thousand, occupied both sides of the canal. The bold Boisot, nevertheless, determined to force his passage, if possible. Selecting a few of his strongest vessels, his heaviest artillery, and his bravest sailors, he led the van himself, in a desperate attempt to make his way to the mere. He opened a hot fire upon the bridge, then converted into a fortress, while his men engaged in hand-to-hand combat with a succession of skirmishers from the troops along the canal. After losing a few men, and ascertaining the impregnable position of the enemy, he was obliged to withdraw, defeated, and almost despairing.

A week had elapsed since the great dyke had been pierced, and the flotilla now lay motionless in shallow water, having accomplished less than two miles. The wind, too, was easterly, causing the sea rather to sink than to rise. Everything wore a gloomy aspect, when, fortunately, on the 18th, the wind shifted to the north-west, and for three days blew a gale. The waters rose rapidly, and before the second day was closed the armada was afloat again. Some fugitives from Zoetermeer village now arrived, and informed the Admiral that, by making a détour to the right, he could completely circumvent the bridge and the mere. They guided him, accordingly, to a comparatively low dyke, which led between the villages of Zoetermeer and Benthuyzen. A strong force of Spaniards was stationed in each place, but, seized with a panic, instead of sallying to defend the barrier, they fled inwardly towards Leyden, and halted at the village of North Aa. It was natural that they should be amazed. Nothing is more appalling to the imagination than the rising ocean tide, when man feels himself within its power; and here were the waters hourly deepening and closing around them, devouring the earth beneath their feet, while on the waves rode a flotilla, manned by a determined race, whose courage and ferocity were known throughout the world.

Three barriers, one within the other, had now been passed, and the flotilla, advancing with the advancing waves, and driving the enemy steadily before it, was drawing nearer to the beleaguered city. As one circle after another was passed, the besieging army found itself compressed within a constantly contracting field. The *Ark of Delft*, an enormous vessel, with shot-proof bulwarks, and moved by paddle-wheels turned by a crank, now arrived at Zoetermeer, and was soon followed by the whole fleet. After a brief delay, sufficient to allow the few remaining villagers to escape, both Zoetermeer and Benthuyzen, with the fortifications, were set on fire, and abandoned to their fate. The blaze lighted up the desolate and watery waste around, and was seen at Leyden, where it was hailed as the beacon of hope. Without further impediment, the armada proceeded to North Aa, the enemy retreating from this position also, and flying to Zoeterwoude, a strongly-fortified village, but a mile and three quarters from the city walls. It was now swarming with troops, for the bulk of the besieging army had gradually been driven into a narrow circle of forts, within the immediate neighbourhood of Leyden. Besides Zoeterwoude, the two posts where they were principally established were Lammen and Leyderdorp, each within three hundred rods of the town. At Leyderdorp were the head-quarters of Valdez; Colonel Borgia commanded in the very strong fortress of Lammen.

The fleet was, however, delayed at North Aa by another barrier called the "Kirk-way." The waters, too, spreading once more over a wider space, and diminishing under an east wind, which had again arisen, no longer permitted their progress, so that very soon the whole armada was stranded anew. The waters fell to the depth of nine inches, while the vessels required eighteen and twenty. Day after day the fleet lay motionless upon the shallow sea. Orange, rising from his sick bed as soon as he could stand, now came on board the fleet. His presence diffused universal joy; his words inspired his desponding army with fresh hope. He rebuked the impatient spirits who, weary of their compulsory idleness, had shown symptoms of ill-timed ferocity, and those eight hundred mad Zealanders, so frantic in their hatred to the foreigners, who had so long profaned their land, were as docile as children to the Prince. He reconnoitred the whole ground, and issued orders for the immediate destruction of the Kirk-way, the last important barrier which separated the fleet from Leyden. Then, after a long conference with Admiral Boisot, he returned to Delft.

Meantime, the besieged city was at its last gasp. The burghers had been in a state of uncertainty for many days; being aware that the fleet had set forth for their relief, but knowing full well the thousand obstacles which it had to surmount. They had guessed its progress by the illumination from the blazing villages; they had heard its salvos of artillery, on its arrival at North Aa; but since then, all had been dark and mournful again, hope and fear, in sickening alternation, distracting every breast. They knew that the wind was unfavourable, and at the dawn of each day every eye was turned wistfully to the vanes of the steeples. So long as the easterly breeze prevailed, they felt, as they anxiously stood on towers and housetops, that they must look in vain for the welcome ocean. Yet, while thus patiently waiting, they were literally starving; for even the misery endured at Harlem had not reached that depth and intensity of agony to which Leyden was now reduced. Bread, malt-cake, horseflesh, had entirely disappeared; dogs, cats, rats, and other vermin were esteemed luxuries. A small number of cows, kept as long as possible for their milk, still remained; but a few were killed from day to day, and distributed in minute proportions, hardly sufficient to support life among the famishing population. In many a house the watchmen, in their rounds, found a whole family of corpses, father, mother, children, side by side, for a disorder called the plague, naturally engendered of hardship and famine, now came, as if in kindness, to abridge the agony of the people. The pestilence stalked at noonday through the city, and the doomed inhabitants fell like grass beneath its scythe. From six thousand to eight thousand human beings sank before this scourge alone, yet the people resolutely held out—women and men mutually encouraging each other to resist the entrance of their foreign foe—an evil more horrible than pest or famine.

The missives from Valdez, who saw more vividly than the besieged could do, the uncertainty of his own position, now poured daily into the city, the enemy becoming more prodigal of his vows, as he felt that the ocean might yet save the victims from his grasp. The inhabitants, in their ignorance, had gradually abandoned their hopes of relief, but they spurned the summons to surrender. Leyden was sublime in its despair. A few murmurs were, however, occasionally heard at the steadfastness of the magistrates, and a dead body was placed at the door of the burgomaster, as a silent witness against his inflexibility. A party of the more faint-hearted even assailed the heroic Adrian van der Werf with threats and reproaches as he passed through the streets. A crowd had gathered around him, as he reached a triangular place in the centre of the town, into which many of the principal streets emptied themselves, and upon one side of which stood the church of Saint Pancras, with its high brick tower surmounted by two pointed turrets, and with two ancient lime-trees at its entrance. There stood the burgomaster, a tall, haggard, imposing figure, with dark visage, and a tranquil but commanding eye. He waved his broad-leaved felt hat for silence, and then exclaimed, in language which has been almost literally preserved, "What would ye, my friends? Why do ye murmur that we do not break our vows and surrender the city to the Spaniards? a fate more horrible than the agony which she now endures. I tell you I have made an oath to hold the city and may God give me strength to keep my oath! I can die but once; whether by your hands, the enemy's, or by the hand of God. My own fate is indifferent to me, not so that of the city entrusted to my care. I know that we shall starve if not soon relieved; but starvation is preferable to the dishonoured death which is the only alternative. Your menaces move me not; my life is at your disposal, here is my sword, plunge it into my breast, and divide my flesh among you. Take my body to appease your hunger, but expect no surrender, so long as I remain alive."

The words of the stout burgomaster inspired a new courage in the hearts of those who heard him, and a shout of applause and defiance arose from the famishing but enthusiastic crowd. They left the place after exchanging new vows of fidelity with their magistrate, and again ascended tower and battlement to watch for the coming fleet. From the ramparts they hurled renewed defiance at the enemy. "Ye call us rat-eaters and dog-eaters," they cried, "and it is true. So long, then, as ye hear dog bark or cat mew within the walls, ye may know that the city holds out. And when all has perished but ourselves, be sure that we will each devour our left arms, retaining our right to defend our women, our liberty, and our religion, against the foreign tyrant. Should God, in his wrath, doom us to destruction, and deny us all relief, even then will we maintain ourselves for ever against your entrance. When the last hour has come, with our hands we will set fire to the city, and perish, men, women, and children together, in the flames, rather than suffer our homes to be polluted, and our liberties to be crushed."

Such words of defiance, thundered daily from the battlements, sufficiently informed Valdez as to his chance of conquering the city, either by force or fraud, but at the same time, he felt comparatively relieved by the inactivity of Boisot's fleet, which still lay stranded at North Aa. "As well," shouted the Spaniards, derisively, to the citizens, "as well can the Prince of Orange pluck the stars from the sky as bring the ocean to the walls of Leyden for your relief."

On the 28th of September, a dove flew into the city, bringing a letter from Admiral Boisot. In this despatch, the position of the fleet at North Aa was described in encouraging terms, and the inhabitants were assured that in a very few days at furthest, the long-expected relief would enter their gates. The letter was read publicly upon the market-place, and the bells were rung for joy. Nevertheless, on the morrow, the vanes pointed to the east, the waters, so far from rising, continued to sink, and Admiral Boisot was almost in despair. He wrote to the Prince, that if the springtide, now to be expected, should not, together with a strong and favourable wind, come immediately to their relief, it would be in vain to attempt anything further, and that the expedition would, of necessity, be abandoned. The tempest came to their relief. A violent equinoctial gale, on the night of the 1st and 2nd of October, came storming from the north-west, shifting after a few hours full eight points, and then blowing still more violently from the south-west. The waters of the North Sea were piled in vast masses upon the southern coast of Holland, and then dashed furiously landward, the ocean rising over the earth, and sweeping with unrestrained power across the ruined dykes.

In the course of twenty-four hours the fleet at North Aa, instead of nine inches, had more than two feet of water. No time was lost. The Kirk-way, which had been broken through according to the Prince's instructions, was now completely overflowed, and the fleet sailed at midnight, in the midst of the storm and darkness. A few sentinel vessels of the enemy challenged them as they steadily rowed towards Zoeterwoude. The answer was a flash from Boisot's cannon, lighting up the black waste of waters. There was a fierce naval midnight battle; a strange spectacle among the branches of those quiet orchards, and with the chimney stacks of half-submerged farm-houses rising around the contending vessels. The neighbouring village of Zoeterwoude shook with the discharges of the Zealanders' cannon, and the Spaniards assembled in that fortress knew that the rebel Admiral was at last afloat and on his course. The enemy's vessels were soon sunk, their crews hurled into the waves. On went the fleet, sweeping over the broad waters which lay between Zoeterwoude and Zwieten. As they approached some shallows, which led into the great mere, the Zealanders dashed into the sea, and with sheer strength shouldered every vessel through. Two obstacles lay still in their path—the forts of Zoeterwoude and Lammen, distant from the city five hundred and two hundred and fifty yards respectively. Strong redoubts, both well supplied with troops and artillery, they were likely to give a rough reception to the light flotilla, but the panic, which had hitherto driven their foes before the advancing patriots, had reached Zoeterwoude. Hardly was the fleet in sight when the Spaniards in the early morning, poured out from the fortress, and fled precipitately to the left, along a road which led in a westerly direction towards the Hague. Their narrow path was rapidly vanishing in the waves, and hundreds sank beneath the constantly-deepening and treacherous flood. The wild Zealanders, too, sprang from their vessels upon the crumbling dyke and drove their retreating foes into the sea. They hurled their harpoons at them, with an accuracy acquired in many a polar chase; they plunged into the waves in the keen pursuit, attacking them with boat-hook and dagger. The numbers who thus fell beneath these corsairs, who neither gave nor took quarter, were never counted, but probably not less than a thousand perished. The rest effected their escape to the Hague.

The first fortress was thus seized, dismantled, set on fire, and passed, and a few strokes of the oars brought the whole fleet close to Lammen. This last obstacle rose formidable and frowning directly across their path. Swarming as it was with soldiers, and bristling with artillery, it seemed to defy the armada either to carry it by storm or to pass under its guns into the city. It appeared that the enterprise was, after all, to founder within sight of the long expecting and expected haven. Boisot anchored his fleet within a respectful distance, and spent what remained of the day in carefully reconnoitring the fort, which seemed only too strong. In conjunction with Leyderdorp, the headquarters of Valdez, a mile and a half distant on the right, and within a mile of the city, it seemed so insuperable an impediment that Boisot wrote in despondent tones to the Prince of Orange. He announced his intention of carrying the fort, if it were possible, on the following morning, but if obliged to retreat, he observed, with something like despair, that there would be nothing for it but to wait for another gale of wind. If the waters should rise sufficiently to allow them to make a wide détour, it might be possible, if, in the meantime, Leyden did not starve or surrender, to enter its gates from the opposite side.

Meantime, the citizens had grown wild with expectation. A dove had been despatched by Boisot, informing them of his precise position, and a number of citizens accompanied the burgomaster, at nightfall, toward the tower of Hengist—"Yonder," cried the magistrate, stretching out his hand towards Lammen, "yonder, behind that fort, are bread and meat, and brethren in thousands. Shall all this be destroyed by the Spanish guns, or shall we rush to the rescue of our friends?" "We will tear the fortress to fragments with our teeth and nails," was the reply, "before the relief, so long expected, shall be wrested from us." It was resolved that a sortie, in conjunction with the operations of Boisot, should be made against Lammen with the earliest dawn. Night descended upon the scene, a pitch dark night, full of anxiety to the Spaniards, to the armada, to Leyden. Strange sights and sounds occurred at different moments to bewilder the anxious sentinels. A long procession of lights issuing from the fort was seen to flit across the black face of the waters, in the dead of night, and the whole of the city wall, between the Cow-gate and the Tower of Burgundy, fell with a loud crash. The horror-struck citizens thought that the Spaniards were upon them at last; the Spaniards imagined the noise to indicate a desperate sortie of the citizens. Everything was vague and mysterious.

Day dawned, at length, after the feverish night, and the Admiral prepared for the assault. Within the fortress reigned a death-like stillness, which inspired a sickening suspicion. Had the city, indeed, been carried in the night; had the massacre already commenced; had all this labour and audacity been expended in vain? Suddenly a man was descried, wading breast-high through the water from Lammen towards the fleet, while at the same time, one solitary boy was seen to wave his his cap from the summit of the fort. After a moment of doubt, the happy mystery was solved. The Spaniards had fled, panic-struck, during the darkness. Their position would still have enabled them, with firmness, to frustrate the enterprise of the patriots, but the hand of God, which had sent the ocean and the tempest to the deliverance of Leyden, had struck her enemies with terror likewise. The lights which had been seen moving during the night were the lanterns of the retreating Spaniards, and the boy who was now waving his triumphant signal from the battlements had alone witnessed the spectacle. So confident was he in the conclusion to which it led him, that he had volunteered at daybreak to go thither all alone. The magistrates, fearing a trap, hesitated for a moment to believe the truth, which soon, however, became quite evident. Valdez, flying himself from Leyderdorp, had ordered Colonel Borgia to retire with all his troops from Lammen. Thus, the Spaniards had retreated at the very moment that an extraordinary accident had laid bare a whole side of the city for their entrance. The noise of the wall, as it fell, only inspired them with fresh alarm; for they believed that the citizens had sallied forth in the darkness, to aid the advancing flood in the work of destruction. All obstacles being now removed, the fleet of

Boisot swept by Lammen, and entered the city on the morning of the 3rd of October. Leyden was relieved.

THE MAN WHO FIRST ROUNDED THE HORN[1]

John Callander

(d. 1789)

THE States General of the United Provinces having granted to the East-India Company an exclusive charter, prohibiting thereby all their subjects, except the said Company, from carrying on any trade to the eastward beyond the Cape of Good Hope, or westward through the Streights of Magellan, in any countries either known or unknown, under very high penalties; this prohibiton gave very great distaste to many rich merchants, who were desirous of fitting out ships and making discoveries at their own costs, and could not help thinking it a little hard, that the Government should thus, against the laws of nature, bar those passages which Providence had left free. Amongst the number of these merchants, there was one of Amsterdam, who then resided at Egmont, very rich, well-acquainted with business, and who had an earnest desire to employ a part of that wealth, which he had acquired by trade, in acquiring fame as a discoverer. With this view he applied himself to William Cornelison Schouten, of Horn, a man in easy circumstances, and who was deservedly famous for his great skill in maritime affairs, and for his perfect knowledge in the trade to the Indies, having been thrice there himself, in the different characters of master, pilot, and supercargo, or, as the phrase in those days was, of Merchant. The great question proposed by Mr le Maire to this intelligent man was, Whether he did not think it possible to find another passage into the South Seas than by the Streights of Magellan; and whether, if this was possible, it was not highly likely, that the countries to the south of that passage might afford as rich commodities as either the East or West Indies? Mr Schouten answered, That there was great reason to believe such a passage might be found, and still stronger reason to confirm what he conjectured as to the riches of these southern countries.

After many conversations upon this subject, they came at last to a resolution of attempting such a discovery, from a full persuasion, that the States General could not intend, by their exclusive charter to the East-India Company, to preclude their subjects from discovering countries on the south by a new route, distinct from either of those mentioned in that charter. In consequence of this agreement, it was stipulated, that le Maire and his friends should advance one moiety towards the necessary expence of the voyage, and Schouten and his friends the

[1]From *Callander's Voyages.*

other. In pursuance of this scheme, Isaac le Maire advanced his part of the money; and Cornelison Schouten, with the assistance of the following persons, viz. Peter Clementson, Burgomaster of Horn; John Janson Molenwert, one of the Schepen or Aldermen of the same place; John Clementson Keis, Senator of the said town; and Cornelius Segetson, a merchant of Horn, laid down the rest. It is certain that so many people of substance would never have embarked in such a project if they had so much as suspected that the East-India Company had a right to confiscate their vessels and effects whenever they had it in their power.

As soon therefore as these matters were adjusted, which was in the spring of the year 1615, the Company, engaged in this undertaking, began to apply themselves to the carrying it into execution, proposing to equip for that purpose a larger and a less vessel, to sail from Horn at the proper season of the year. And that all parties might be thoroughly satisfied, it was determined, that William Cornelison Schouten, on account of his age and experience, should have the command of the larger ship, with the sole direction of the voyage, and that James le Maire, the eldest son of Isaac le Maire, should be the first supercargo. The Company were so eager in the prosecution of their design, and so attentive to whatever might be necessary to promote it, that in the space of two months all things were ready, and a sufficient number of men engaged for navigating both ships. But, as secrecy was absolutely necessary, the seamen were articled in general terms to go wherever their masters and supercargoes should require; and, in consideration of so unusual a condition, their wages were advanced considerably; which was a circumstance of such consequence, and there were in those days so many adventurous spirits, that they did not find it at all difficult to make up their intended compliment; which gave them an opportunity of chusing none but experienced mariners, on whose skill and fidelity they could depend; a circumstance of the utmost consequence in a voyage of this nature, where the tempers of men were sure to be thoroughly tried.

These extraordinary preparations, but, above all, the mighty secrecy that was observed, caused a great noise, not only at Amsterdam, but all over Holland, where people reasoned on the intention of this voyage, according to the several degrees of their capacity and experience, some fancying they were bound to one place, some to another; but the common people thought they hit upon the proper title, in calling them the Goldfinders; whereas the merchants, who were better versed in such matters, called them, with greater propriety, the South Company, and indeed that was their true designation; for the real design of Isaac le Maire, was to discover those southern regions, to which few people had hitherto travelled even in imagination, and which, by an unaccountable indolence, remain, in a great measure, undiscovered to this day.

In the beginning of the month of May 1615, the South Company drew their men together; and, on the 16th of that month, they were mustered before the magistrates of Horn, took their leave of their friends and relations, and prepared to embark on board their ships.

The biggest of these vessels was called *The Unity*, of the burden of 360 tons, carrying nineteen pieces of cannon, and twelve swivels. She had on board likewise a pinnace to sail, and another to row, a launch for landing of men, and a small boat, with all other necessaries whatever for so long a voyage; and of this vessel William Cornelison Schouten was master and pilot, and Jaques le Maire supercargo. The lesser ship was called *The Horn*, of the burden of 110 tons, carrying eight cannon and four swivels, John Cornelison Schouten master, and Aris Clawson supercargo. The crew of the former consisted of sixty-five men, and the latter of twenty-two only. The *Unity* sailed May 25th, for the Texel, where the *Horn* likewise arrived June 3rd following, that being judged the properest season of the year for them to proceed on their voyage. On June 14th they sailed out of the Texel, and passing, in sight of Dunkirk, between Dover and Calais, anchored on the 17th in the Downs, when William Cornelison Schouten went on shore at Dover, in order to get fresh water, and to hire an English gunner; which accordingly he did, and that day sent him on board. They sailed again in the evening, and met with several large Dutch ships laden with salt. In the night between the 21st and 22d, they were grievously ruffled by a storm; which obliged them to put into the Isle of Wight for shelter, where Captain Schouten endeavoured, if possible, to have hired a carpenter, but without success, which obliged them to sail on the 25th for Plymouth, where he arrived on the 27th, and there hired a carpenter of Maydenblick.

On July 28th, they sailed from Plymouth with a north-north-east wind, and very fair weather. On the 29th, Captain Schouten made a signal for all officers to come on board; when it was resolved in a council, to settle the rate of their sea-allowance in such a manner, as that the men might have no reason to complain, and their officers be in no apprehensions of their wanting provisions during the course of so long a voyage. The rate they fixed in the following proportions; viz, a can of beer a man every day, four pounds of biscuit, half a pound of butter, and as much sweet suet, for the week, together with five large Dutch cheeses, that were to serve them the whole voyage. This was exclusive of flesh or fish: And we may, from hence, form some notion of the frugality the Dutch victualled with in those days, and from which they have deviated very little ever since. They likewise made the necessary orders for the due regulation of the voyage, directing, that, in case of landing men, one of the masters should always command; that, in ports where they went to trade, the supercargo should go on shore, and have the sole direction of the commerce: That, on board, every officer should be strict in the execution of his duty; but without putting unnecessary hardships on the men, or interfering with other officers in their commands: That none of the officers should hold any conversation with the seamen, in relation to the design of the voyage, which being solely in the breast of the first captain and supercargo, conjectures must be fruitless, and might be dangerous; that any embezzlement of provisions, stores, or merchandize, should be severely punished; and, in case of their being reduced to short allowance, then offences of this nature to be punished with death; that the two supercargoes should keep clear and distinct journals of all proceedings, for the use of the Company, that it might plainly appear, how far every man had done his duty, and to what degree the end of the voyage had been answered. All these rules were very exactly observed, and particularly the last; so that, from these journals, kept by the super-cargoes, this account has been taken. On July 8th, being in the latitude of 39 degrees 25 minutes, their carpenter's mate died. On the 9th and 10th, with a north-north-east wind, and a stiff gale, they stood on their course, without putting in to Porto Santo, or Madeira, of which they had sight on the 11th. The reason was, that having, as they conceived, victuals sufficient for the voyage, they determined not to lose time, by going needlessly on shore, especially since hitherto their men were vigor-ous, and in good health; which resolution was founded on an observa-tion made by Captain Schouten, that many voyages had been lost, by lingering in port without any urgent cause, when the winds and seasons were fair, and their course might have been prosecuted without delay.

On July 13, they sailed between the island Teneriff and the grand Canary, with a stiff north-north-east wind, and a swift current. About the 15th, the same wind and current following them still, they passed the Tropic of Cancer. The 20th, in the morning, they fell in with the north side of Cape Verd. At sun-rising the Cape lay west by south from them; so that the north-north-east wind would not suffer them to get beyond it; but kept them there at anchor all that night. The 25th, the Moorish Alcaid came on board them, with whom they agreed at the price of eight states of iron for a supply of fresh water. They left the Cape Au-gust 1, and the 21st of the same month they saw the high land of Sierra Leona, and also the island of Madrabomba, which lies on the south point of the high land of Sierra Leona, and north from the shallows of St Anne's island. This land of Sierra Leona is the highest of all that lies between Cape Verd and the coast of Guinea, so that the point is very easy to be known. Here they would have landed, running up to the point over the baixos, or shallows, of St Anne's at ten, nine, eight, seven, and five fathoms water, it being still deeper to the north, but shallower to the east; so that in the evening, they anchored with a high-water at four fathoms and a half soft ground, and at night at three fathoms and a half.

The 22nd, William Schouten, in the Horn, led the way off the shal-lows, steering north-north-east, with a north-west wind, by which course they were intirely disengaged from the Baixos, and got into thirteen fathoms water. From hence they went to the islands of Madra-bomba, which are very high, and lie all three on a row south-west and north-east, half a league from Sierra Leona, to the seaward. Here they had shallow water at four and five fathoms, and soft muddy ground. They anchored a league from the island, which appeared to be very full of bogs and marshes, and all over waste like a wilderness, scarce fit to entertain any other inhabitants than wild beasts, and indeed not seem-ing to have any other. Going ashore on the 23rd, they found a river there, the mouth of which was so stopped up with sands, and cliffs of rocks, that no ship could get into it; yet, within, the water was sufficiently deep, and the breadth such too, as to give a ship free scope to turn and wind herself about, as she should have occasion. Here they saw tortoises, crocodiles, monkies, wild oxen, and a sort of birds, which made a noise, barking like dogs. They met with no fruit but lemons, some few trees of which they found after a tedious search. The 29th, about noon, they got above the islands of Madrabomba westward, along to the north part of the high land, till they had twelve and fifteen fathoms water, and, in the evening, got about the point.

On the 30th, being assisted both by wind and current, they arrived before the village that looks upon the road of Sierra Leona, where they anchored at eight fathoms water, a little from the shore, in a very sandy bottom. The village consisted of about eight or nine poor houses covered with straw: The Moors, that dwelt there, were willing to come aboard, only demanding pledges to be left ashore, to secure their safe return; because a French ship that came thither before, had perfidiously carried off two of them: So Aris Clawson the merchant went ashore, and staid there amongst them, driving a small trade with them for lemons and bananas, which they exchanged for glass-beads; and in the mean time they came on board, bringing an interpreter with them, who spoke all sorts of languages. Here they had good opportunity of furnishing them-selves with fresh water, which pouring down in large quantities from a very high hill, they had nothing to do but to place their barrels under the fall of the water to receive it. There were also vast woods of lemon-trees here, which made lemons so cheap to them, that, for a few beads and knives, they might have had 10,000. September 1, they drove away before the stream, and anchored that evening at the mouth of the sea, before a small river. Here they took an antelope in the woods, with lemons and palmitoes; and had good success in their fishing. The third the master brought in a great shoal of fish, that were of the shape of a shoemaker's knife, and as many lemons as came to 150 for every man's share.

The 4th, they sailed from Sierra Leona, early in the morning. October 5, they made 4 degrees 27 minutes south latitude; and the same day at noon, they were strangely surprised with a very violent stroke given to one of their ships in the lower part of it. No adversary appeared, no rock was in the way to be encountered with; but, while this amused them, the sea all about them began to change its colour, and looked as if some great fountain of blood had been opened into it; this sudden alteration of the water being no less surprising to them, than the striking of the ship; but the cause both of the one and the other they were equally ignorant of, till they came to Port Desire, and there set the ship upon the strand to make her clean; for then they found a large horn, both in form and magnitude resembling an elephant's tooth, sticking fast in the bottom of the ship. A very firm and solid body it was, and seemed to be equally so all over, there being nothing of a cavity, or a light and spungy matter in the midst of it, but all over as dense and compact a substance, as that in the exterior parts. It had pierced through three very stout planks of the ship, and razed one of the ribs of her; so that it stuck at least half a foot deep in the planks; and there was about as much that appeared without the great hole up to the place where it was broken off. And now the riddle was completely solved, this horn being the spoil of some sea-monster, that had thus rudely assaulted the ship with that piercing weapon; and, after the thrust, not being able to draw it out again, had there broke it, which was attended with such a plentiful effusion of blood, as had discoloured the sea to that degree.

Having now sailed so far, that none in the ships, but the master, knew where they were, or whither they intended, upon the 25th, they discovered their designs to the rest of the company, of going to find out a new southern passage into the great Pacific Sea. This they had kept very close to themselves before, but now thought it time to reveal the scheme, there being no danger of defeating it; and the company seemed to be very well pleased with it, hoping to light on some golden country or other, to make them amends for all their trouble and danger. The 26th, they made 6 degrees 25 minutes south latitude, sailing mostly southwards, till they had made 10 degrees 30 minutes. November 1, they had the sun north of them at noon. The 3rd, in the afternoon, they had sight of Martin Vad's island, called Ascension, under 20 degrees; and here they observed the compass to vary to the north-east 12 degrees. The 21st, they came under 38 degrees 25 minutes, and had a deep water, whose bottom they could reach with their lead. Here the variations of the compass was 17 degrees to the north-east. December 6, they had a prospect of land, not very high, but flat and white; and, quickly after, fell in with the north side of Port Desire, and, that night, anchored within one league and an half from the shore, in ten fathoms water, with an ebb that ran southwards as strongly as the sea runs between Flushing Heads.

The 7th, keeping a south course, at noon they came before the haven of Port Desire, which lies under 47 degrees 40 minutes. At the entry of it they had very high water; neither did any of those cliffs appear, which Van Noort had described, and which he left northwards in sailing into the haven. If there were any, they were all under water; but the cliffs lay open and visible enough towards the south point, which therefore, might be those which Noort intended. Upon this they went on, sailing so far southward, as to miss the right channel. They came into a crooked bay, where, at high-water, they had but four fathoms and a half, and at low water but fourteen feet; by which means the *Unity* lay with her stern fast aground, and, if a brisk gale from the north-east had blown, she must infallibly have been lost; but, the wind blowing west from the land, she recovered again. Here they found plenty of eggs, amongst the cliffs: and the bay afforded them muscles, and smelts of sixteen inches in length, and therefore they called it Smelt-Bay. Their shallop went to the Penguin islands, and came back with 150 penguins, and two sea-lions.

The 8th, before noon, they sailed out of the Smelt-Bay, and anchored just before Port Desire. The shallop was employed before hand to sound the depth of the channel; which proving to be twelve or thirteen fathoms, they boldly entered, having a north-east wind to carry them along: But after a little more than a league's sailing, the wind began to veer about, and they anchored at twenty fathoms; but the bottom they were upon being only slippery stones, and the wind now blowing hard at north-west, their anchors could not preserve them from driving with that rough wind upon the southern shore; so both these ships were likely to be wrecked together. The *Unity* lay with her side upon the cliffs; but still kept the water, and, by the fall of the sea, was gradually slidden down lower and lower into it; but the *Horn* stuck so that her keel was above a fathom out of water, and a man might have walked dry under it at low water. She was, for some time, obliged to the north-west wind, that, by blowing hard upon her side, kept her from falling over; but, that support being gone, with the wind that gave it, she sunk down upon that side at least three feet lower than the keel: Upon which sight they gave her over for lost; and yet the succeeding flood, which came on with still weather, set her upright again; and both she and her companion got clear of that danger. The 9th, they went farther into the river, and came to King's island, which they found full of black sea-mews, and almost covered over with their eggs. A man, without straining to reach, might have taken between fifty and sixty nests with his hand, each of which have three or four eggs a-piece; so that they were quickly furnished with some thousands of them. The 11th the boat went in search of good water lower down the river, on the south-side; but found it all of a brackish unpleasant taste. They saw ostriches here, and a sort of beasts like harts, with wonderful long necks, and extremely wild. Upon the high hills they found great heaps of stones, under which some monstrous carcases had been buried. There were bones of ten and eleven feet long. In all probability they were (if of rational creatures) some bones of the giants of that country. No water was to be found here for several days together; so that, though they had plenty of good fish and fowl, they could meet with no drink to wash it down.

On the 17th, they laid the *Unity* dry upon King's Island in order to clean her, which they performed very successfully. On the 18th, they likewise hauled the *Horn* on shore, for the same purpose, and placed her about 200 yards from the other ship. On the 19th, a very dreadful accident happened; for, while they were busy cleaning both ships, in order to which it was necessary to light a fire of dry reeds under the *Horn*, it so fell out, that the flame got into the ship, and set it on fire; and, as they were fifty feet from the water-side, they were forced to stand still and see her burn, without being able to do anything towards extinguishing it. On the 20th, at high water, they launched the *Unity*, and the next day carried on board her all the wood, iron-work, anchors, and pieces of cannon, and whatever else they could save out of the *Horn*. On the 25th, the sailors found certain holes full of fresh water, which was white and thick, but well tasted, a great quantity of which they carried on board in small casks upon their shoulders. They met here with great numbers of sea-lions; the young ones they eat, and found them pretty good food. The sea-lion is a creature as big as a small horse; their heads resemble lions exactly; on their necks they have long manes of a tough strong hair; but this is to be understood of the he-lions only: For the she-lion is without hair and not above half as big as the male. They are a bold fierce animal, not to be destroyed but by musket-shot.

January 13, they sailed out of Port Desire; but having a calm, they anchored before the haven, till the rising of the wind invited them to pursue their voyage. The 18th, being in 51 degrees, they saw the Sebaldin islands; which they observed to lie in that position and distance from the Strait, that De Weert had determined. The 20th, being then in 53 degrees, they observed the great current that runs south-west; and now they reckoned about twenty leagues to the southwards of the Magellanic Straits. The 23rd they had an uncertain shifting wind, and the water appeared white, as if they had been within the land. They held their course south by west, and the same day saw land, bearing west and west-south-west from them, and quickly after to the south. Then attempting, by an east-south-east course, to get beyond the land, the hard north wind, that blew then, constrained them to take in their topsails. The 24th, in the forenoon, they saw land a starboard, about a league's distance, stretching out east and south, with very high hills, all covered with ice; and then other land bearing east from it, high and rugged as the former. They guessed the lands they had in these two prospects lay about eight leagues asunder, and that there might be a good passage between them, because of a pretty brisk current, that ran southward along by them. About noon, they made 54 degrees 46 minutes, and then began to make towards the aforementioned opening; but the succeeding calm prevented it. Here they saw an incredible number of penguins, and such huge shoals of whales, that they were forced to proceed with great caution for fear they should run their ship upon them.

The 25th, in the forenoon, they got up close by the east land, which, upon the north side, reaches east-south-east as far as the eye can follow it. This they called States Land; and to that which lay west, they gave the name of Maurice Land. They observed there were good roads and sandy bays, good store of fish, penguins, and porpoises, and some sorts of fowls; but the land adjacent seemed quite bare of trees and woods. They had a north wind at their entrance into this passage, and directed their course south-south-west; so that, going pretty briskly on, at noon they made 55 degrees 36 minutes, and then held a south-west course, having a good stiff gale to blow them forwards. The land upon the south side of the passage, at the west end of Maurice Land, appeared to run west-south-west, and south-west as far as they could see it, and all very craggy uneven ground.

In the evening, having a south-west wind, they steered southwards, meeting with mighty waves, that came rolling along before the wind, and the depth of the water to the leeward from them, which appeared by some very evident signs, gave them a full assurance, that the great South Sea was now before them, into which they had almost made their way by a passage of their own discovering. The sea-mews thereabouts were larger than swans, and their wings, when extended to the full length, spread about the compass of a fathom. They would come and very tamely sit down upon the ship, and suffer themselves to be taken by hand, without any endeavours to fly away. The 26th, they made 57 degrees, and were there ruffled by a brisk storm out of the west and south-west. The water was also very high, and blue. They still held all this day their course to the southward, but changed it at night for a north-west one; in which quarter they discovered very high land. The 27th, they were under 56 degrees 51 minutes, the weather very cold, with hail and rain, the wind west and west by south. They went a southern course, and then crossed northwards with their main-sails. The 28th, they hoisted up their topsails, and had great billows out of the west, with a west and then a north-east wind, and therewith held their course south and then west and west by south, which brought them under 56 degrees 48 minutes.

The 29th they had a north-east wind, and held their course south-west which gave them the prospect of two islands, beset round with cliffs, and lying west-south-west from them; they got up to them at noon, but could not sail above them, and therefore held their course to the north. They gave them the name of Barnevelt's Islands, and found their latitude to be 57 degrees south. Taking a north-west course, from hence in the evening, they saw land again, lying north-west, and north-north-west from them; this was the high hilly land, covered with snow.

that lay southward from the Magellanic Straits, ending in a sharp point, which they called Cape Horn, and lying in 57 degrees 48 minutes. They held their course now westward, in which course they found a strong current which ran that way too, yet had the wind in the north, and great billows rolling out of the west upon them. The 30th, the billows and the current still ran as before; and now they gathered a full assurance from hence, that the way was open into the South Sea: This day they made the latitude of 57 degrees, 34 minutes. The 31st, they sailed west, with the wind in the north, and made 58 degrees; but the wind turning to the west and west-south-west, they passed Cape Horn, losing all sight of land, and still meeting the billows rolling out of the west, which, together with the blueness of the water, made them quickly expect the main South Sea. February 1, a storm blowing out of the south-west, they sailed with their main-sails north-west and west-north-west. The 2d, with a westerly wind, they sailed to the southward, and made 57 degrees 58 minutes, the variation being there 12 degrees northward. The 3rd, they made 59 degrees 25 minutes, with a hard west wind, but saw no signs of any land to the south: and the next day 56 degrees 43 minutes, turning to and fro with very uncertain south-west winds, and finding 11 degrees of north-east variation. The 5th, by reason of a strong westerly current, and a hollow water, they could bear no sail, but were forced to drive with the wind.

The 12th they plainly discerned the Magellanic Streights, lying east of them; and therefore, now being secure of their happy new discovery, they rendered thanks to good Fortune in a cup of wine, which went three times round the company. And now this new-found passage had a name given it, which was that of Maire's Streights, though that honour (in justice) ought to have been done to William Schouten, by whose happy conduct the Streights were discovered.

THE DUTCH STORY OF THE FOUR DAYS' BATTLE[1]

THE Holland Fleet having spent from the 1st of June to the fifth of the same month of the year 1666, in getting out of the Texel by reason of several cross Winds and Calms that hindered them, it was impossible for them because of contrary Winds, to pursue their designed Course, and to go towards the Coasts of England, according to the Orders they had received for that purpose, before the 8th of the Month. On the 11th in the morning, they with much ado got as far as 7 or 8 miles to the East-South-East-ward of the North Foreland, which is a part of England that extends between the Channel and the Thames where by a South West Wind that blew very fiercely they were forced to anchor.

[1] From *The Life of Cornelius Van Tromp.*

The English Fleet being come some days before to Anchor in the Downs, unmoor'd from thence on the 11th of June, probably upon the advice they had heard of the approach of the Dutch Fleet. And about noon, the two Fleets met. That of Holland was composed of 83 men of War, or Frigats, besides Advice-Boats, Fire-Ships, and other small Tenders on the Fleet. As for the English Fleet, they were 80 Sail strong as they were counted by the Hollanders, at the very time of Fight. About 1 a Clock Afternoon, they began to play their Guns. Some moments before, the Hollanders, had cut their Anchor-cables to make the more haste, and to Accomodate themselves to the Season, and the violence of the Waves which would not permit them to weigh.

The two Fleets being then met, they both of them made a tack to the South ward, the Wind being then turned West-South-West. That motion was the cause that Lieutenant Admiral Tromp and Van Meppelen, who were before placed in the Rear, found themselves in the Van, and were forced to bear the brunt of the most furious and terrible shock that hapned during the whole fight, which they did most valiantly. The fight being thus begun, the Squadron of Admiral de Ruiter and of Lieutenant Admiral Van Nes, followed by their other Officers, fell thundering upon the Enemies with an undauntedness without Example. A little while after, an English Frigat of the Blue Squadron, carrying 50 Guns, sunk, after she had received a Farewell Broadside from de Ruiter. The Squadron of Lieutenant Admiral Cornelius Evertsz and Tierk Hiddes de Vries had all the difficulty in the World to get to engage at first, because they were to Leeward, and at a pretty distance from the Enemies.

In the mean while, the two Fleets charged one another vigorously, making always the same motion, which lasted till 5 a Clock in the afternoon; when the English tracked to the North-westward, as well to keep the Weather-gage, as to avoid the sand Banks of Flanders. That motion engaged the Squadron of Lieutenant Admiral Evertsz and Tierk Hiddes de Vries in a Bloody Fight, in which the undaunted Valour and Courage of those two Generals were seen to shine with equal Luster. The English, being thus tackt about, the Dutch Fleet found means thereby to intercept some of their biggest Ships which were presently boarded and taken by 2 Dutch Men of War, and afterwards carried into Holland. One of them called the *Swiftsure*, carried 70 Guns, most of them Brass. Commanded by Barkley, Vice-Admiral of the White Squadron, who lost his life there after he had Signalized himself against Captain Henry Adriansz's Ship carrying likewise 70 Guns; another called the *7 Wonders*, of 60 Guns was taken by Captain Vander Zaan's Frigat which carried 52 Guns; and the third called the *Loyal George*, of 44 Guns, fell into the hands of Captain Andrew Swart, whose Ship called the *Deventer*, carried 66 Guns: All those Captains belonged to the Admiralty of Amsterdam. And on the Contrary, in the first attack, there were two Dutch Ships burnt, viz. the *Duivenvoorde* of 46 Guns, and Commanded by Otto Van

Treslong; the second called the *Court of Zealand*, had on board 58 Guns, and was commanded by Captain Blok. These two Ships were unhappily burnt to Ashes by some stopples blown back on board by the force of the Wind, just at the time that their own Guns were discharging.

In the first attack, the Sails, Masts and in General all the Tackle of Lieutenant Admiral Tromp's Ship were so damaged, that another Ship, falling foul of him in passing by, all his Masts were tumbled thereby into the Sea. Rear Admiral Van Nes's Ship came off at a not much better rate, since almost at the same time his Mizzen-Mast was shot by the Board. Upon which those two General Officers were forced to remove into other Ships, for the security of their Persons. In which as soon as they had put up their Flags they were seen again to renew the Fight, and to Signalize themselves. Their unmasted Ships being carried out of the Fray, were towed away into Holland.

The English Fleet having advanced above the Hollanders, their Chief Admiral followed by some Ships of his Squadron, cast Anchor; but a little while after, seeing de Ruiter coming towards him at the head of the Dutch Fleet, he cut his Cables at his approach, so that they engaged again afresh, and the fight was furious and very bloody on that occasion, and yet, God be thanked, without the loss of any of the Dutch Ships; whereas about 7 or 8 a clock in the evening, a great English Ship of the Blew Squadron carrying between 60 and 70 Guns, sank within Musket shot of the Admiral de Ruiter. The two aforesaid English Ships sinking in the view of the Officers and Sea men of the whole Dutch Fleet.

At the beginning of the Night, the Rear Admiral of the White, whose Ship was a First Rate, having been vigorously attackt by De Ruiter, and some other Ships of his Squadron, and being already very much shattered, de Ruiter sent out a Fire Ship from his Squadron, which fastned upon her and set her on fire, but the first Fire-Ship being put off, sunk, and the Flames in the said Rear Admiral were quencht. Then another Fire-Ship of the Zealand Squadron was sent to burn her; and set the English Ship again in Flames, but that was likewise Repulsed, and the fire quencht. A third Fire-Ship under the Covert of Lieutenant Admiral Evertsz's Guns was once more sent to try to repair the ill success of the others, but was not a whit luckier than they, for fastning upon the English Rear Admiral, he set fire to him indeed, but a moment after, that was quencht, and the Fire Ship was sunk with Cannon shot, so that according to the Testimony of all the Dutch Officers which were present, and were spectators of that Glorious Action, the Undaunted Bravery of that English Rear-Admiral cannot but be admired, which was so much the more Remarkable, because some of his men having saved themselves by swiming, and got on board a Dutch Ship, assured us, that near 300 of his men leapt into the Sea, at the approach of the two first Fire Ships, choosing rather to perish by Water than by Fire. The same Rear-Admiral performed likewise at the end of the fight, an Action

Glorious to him, but Fatal to us, by a Cannon shot, that took away the
life of the Illustrious Cornelius Evertsz Lieutenant Admiral, whose good
Conduct and great Courage had made him to be Admired not only in
that fight, but in many other rencounters besides. The night then
parted the Combatants, it being impossible for us to see, by reason of
the darkness, or the thick smoak, whether the aforesaid Rear-Admiral,
being shrewdly battered scap'd away and saved himself, or whether he
sunk to the bottom of the Sea.

When the night was past, the English Fleet found itself on the 12th
of June at break of day, having the Weather-gage, about half a mile off
that of Holland, the Wind at West-South-West. The two Fleets made
a motion, viz. the Hollanders towards the North-West, and the English
toward the South, with design to follow one the other; But the English
having the Advantage of the Wind, disputed their Enemies passage,
and without waiting any longer, advanced to them, and fell upon them.
The Hollanders, without changing their Course or their Countenance,
stood firm in Luffing, so that the two Hostile Fleets broke through one
another and began a most furious fight; yet there was not so much as
one Dutch Ship that was so unfortunate as to be lost in it, according
to the Testimony of all the Officers, both General and Inferior of the
Holland Fleet, given in to the said Deputies and Plenipotentiaries of the
States. The Fleets then having broke in upon one another in that manner, their Guns made strange Havock: For the most part of the Ships
of the two Fleets had their Masts, their Sails and their Tackling either
shot away, or shattered to Pieces. And as each party was endeavouring
with all speed to repair their damages, there hapned a Calm, which produced a Cessation of Arms, so that the two Fleets floated about in
presence of one another, till about 11 a Clock before noon, and then
the Wind rising, they charged again, and renewed the Engagement more
hotly than ever.

The Hollanders had then the Weather-gage, De Ruiter, having penetrated to the very center of the Enemies Fleet, heard a most horrid
Noise of both great Guns and Muskets which made him believe, that
some of his Ships being surrounded by the Enemies, were making their
last efforts, and were in danger of being lost without speedy assistance,
so that without any longer hesitation, he advanced with his Squadron,
and falling upon that part of them, he forced a Passage through the
Storms of the Enemies shot and fire, and found Lieutenant Admiral
Tromp, whose Flag was then hoisted in de Swart's Ship in the last extremity, but yet fighting with all imaginable intrepidity, as likewise did
Vice Admiral Vander Hulst, and the Captains Solomonsz, de Haan, and
Van Amstel, their Ships being surrounded and battered on all sides by
the English, were able to hold out no longer, and were at the point of
being burnt or sunk, without the assistance of de Ruiter. At his approach, Captain Solomonsz's Ship was already all on fire, which 'twas

impossible to Quench. That Captain and a good part of his men had very much ado to save themselves on board another Dutch Ship. Solomonsz as soon as he was got out of that danger, went on board Captain Schey's Ship, where after he had farther Signalized his Bravery, and given great Proofs of his Courage, during the whole time of the fight, he dies at last in the Bed of Honour. Captain Swart's Ship on board which was Lieutenant Admiral Tromp, as likewise the Ships of all the three other Captains above named, were reduced into so pitifull a Condition, by the loss of all their Masts, that Lieutenant Admiral Tromp was again obliged to change Ship, and those which were Commanded by Vice-Admiral Vander Hulst, and the Captains de Haan, Swart, and Van Amstel, being quite disabled for fight, had Order to go out of the fight and seek shelter into the first Harbour they came to.

The fight of the 12th of June was terrible and Bloody, especially afternoon, so that there were few Ships of either Fleet but sufficiently felt the effects of it by the loss of their Masts, Round-Tops, Top-Masts, Sails and Rigging: Amongst others, the Top-Mast and Admirals Flag of de Ruiter's Ship was shot away, about 3 or 4 a Clock, which obliged him to give Order to Lieutenant Admiral Van Nes, till such time as he could repair it, to put the Admirals Flag on board his Ship, and to Command in Chief in his absence, according to the Orders before given: Which he did with so much Courage and Conduct, that after the two Fleets had broke through one another three times, as the Hollanders were ready to fall on the fourth time, the English tackt about and made with all the Sail they could for their own Coasts. Their Fleet was then weakned by the loss of 8 or 9 men of War. The Hollanders seeing them flie made all the sail they could, to pursue them; But their flight was favoured by the obscurity of the night, and the Calms that then begun to come on, which obliged the Hollanders to veer back towards their own Admiral again.

In the mean while, de Ruiter having Repaired his damages, put up the Admirals Flag again, and re-assumed the Chief Command of the Fleet on the 13th of June. But the English discovering at break of Day, the mischiefs that the obscurity of the night had hidden from them, and seeing a good Number of their Ships much shattered, thought fit to burn them, to prevent the pursuit of their Enemies, and prevent their falling into their hands. After which they did their best to get into the Thames. The Wind was at East, and then turning to the East-South-East, grew so weak that they were forced to crowd all the sail they could. The English continuing thus their retreat all the day came at last so very near the Sand Banks that are at the mouth of the River, that Sir George Ayschew, Admiral of the White Squadron, who was in the *Royal Prince* carrying 90 Brass Guns, one of the most considerable Ships of the English Fleet, run a ground upon the bank called the Galloper.

Near about the same time towards evening a Squadron of 22 English

Men of War appeared towards the West, under the command of Prince
Robert,[1] who according to the advices we had of him, was detached
away the day before to sail towards the Harbours of Plymouth and
Portsmouth, in order to joyne some other Men of War, and to go to
meet the Duke of Beauford, Admiral of France, and to fight him.
Three other great English Ships that were come out of the Thames
likewise joyned him, which altogether made a reinforcement of 25 Men
of War. At the sight and approach of that Succour, the Squadron of
Zealand and Friesland advanced to fight them; but Prince Robert
avoided them, and tackt away to joyn the Body of the English Fleet,
so that he joyned them accordingly about the Dusk of Night. And then
the Enemies Fleet was composed of 60 Men of War, of which the most
part were fresh and in good Condition. The Dutch Fleet was still 64 Men
of War strong, but having maintained already a fight of 3 Days, both
their Ships and Men had suffered very much, and their Forces were in
a manner spent.

Things being in that state, and the Hollanders being still at the Eve
of another Bloody Battle, made a Motion in the night, in order to
avoid the Banks and get more Sea-room. When it was Day, Admiral
de Ruiter fired several Guns to summon the Generals and Captains
of the Dutch Fleet on Board him, where he held a Council of War, and
exhorted every one of them in particular, to have in Recommendation
his own Honour, and the Glory of his Country. So that after he had
given them the necessary Orders, the Fight begun again on the 14th of
June, at 8 in the Morning, and was fought between the Foreland, and the
Banks of Flanders, in the open Sea, about 8 miles from the Shore. The
Wind was South South East, so that the Hollanders having the Weather-
gage, came powring with the Three Squadrons of their Fleet upon the
Enemies Navy, in three several Places, forcing a Passage through them,
by which means some English Ships were separated from the rest.
After which, de Ruiter caused a Motion to be made to the Southward,
with design to charge the Enemy again, who did the same on their
Side; which was renewed three several times. Thus the two Fleets fought
all the Day with much Obstinacy, the Victory all the while seeming
equally balanced, and not to know for which side to declare. In the
Time of this cruel Fight, a Dutch Ship commanded by Captain Vitten-
hout, was burnt and sunk. And an English Fire-Ship seeing the Ship
of Vice-Admiral de Liefde unmasted, was going to grapple him, but was
repulsed by the said Vice-Admiral, and chancing to fall foul upon another Dutch Fireship, they were both reduced to Ashes. On the other
side, one of the Dutch Fireships endeavoured also to fasten upon Prince
Robert's Ship, to burn her, but was grappled her self by an English Fire-
ship that kept by Prince Robert's side, so that they were both burnt

---

[1] Rupert.

together with an English Ship that chanced unfortunately to fall foul upon them, and all perished in the Flames.

In the mean while, Lieutenant Admiral Tromp with Rear Admiral Sweers Ship, which he was in, and some others of his Squadron, after he had maintained a long and furious Fight, found himself reduced into so pitiful a Condition, that he was forced to retire out of the Fray, to refit and repair his Damages, with Design to return again, as soon as was possible, to the Charge. De Ruiter, tho' weakened by the Retreat of several of the most considerable Ships of his Fleet, which had been already disabled, considering, that the Sun begun to decline, resolved to make a last Effort, to force the Victory to declare it self; and accordingly gave the Signal to the Hollanders, to fall on all sides upon the English Fleet. At which Signal the Lieutenant Admirals Van Meppelen and de Vries as also the Vice-Admirals Bankert, Schram, and Koenders, and Rear-Admiral Bruinsveld broke in among the Enemies with all imaginable undauntedness, and it happened, that Lieutenant Admiral Van Nes and Vice-Admiral de Liefde, with the Rear-Admirals Van Nes and Evertsz, followed by several other Ships, finding themselves below the English, and Admiral de Ruiter with the rest of the Fleet, above them, that part of the English Fleet that was between them, was so furiously attack'd, as was likewise their whole Navy in general, afterwards, that in less than Half an Hours Fight, they were put in Confusion and begun to fly the second time. On the one side were to be seen the White Squadron with 8 or 10 Men of War flying right before the Wind, and on the other, the Admirals of the Red and Blue making likewise full Sail, and doing what else they could, to advance their Retreat towards the English Coasts.

In the mean while, the Dutch Ships, at de Ruiter's Signal, took all the English Ships they came near enough to Board. Rear-Admiral Bruinsveld, having with much Courage and Resolution grappled two of the Enemies Frigats, took them, but afterwards, whether it were for want of Order, or by the Fault of those that had the guarding of them, the English retook them again. Some time after, Captain Pauw hearing of that Action, fell vigorously upon them again, and wrested them once more out of the Hands of the English. But one of those Frigats, called the *Bull*, was so shattered that she, no longer able to keep the Sea, soon after sunk. The other, called the *Essex*, carrying 58 Guns, and less endamaged, was carried into the Texel. A like accident happened to another English Frigat, but she was retaken by the Enemies.

It seems that God, after He had so gloriously favoured the Arms of the Victours, was not pleased they should be utterly Defeated by the Destruction of their whole Navy, which appeared as unavoidable: For the shattered Remainder of them miraculously escaped by the Favour of a thick Fog, about 7 a Clock at Night. However, the Dutch Fleet being victorious and triumphant, continued to chace them a long time after their being routed, and would have pursued them into their very Ports, if they had not been afraid their Ships would have lost themselves, and have been scattered. And therefore de Ruiter having fired some Guns for a Signal to advertise all the Ships of his Fleet to veer back towards their Admiral, and the whole Dutch Fleet thereupon assembling together, they sailed away all night leisurely, and with little Sail homewards.

GERMANY

A WHALING VOYAGE INTO SPITZBERGEN[1]

Frederick Martens of Hamburg

I

WE SET sail the 15th of April, 1671, about noon, from the Elbe. The wind was north-east; at night, when we came by the Hilgeland, it bore to north-north-east. The name of the ship was *Jonas in the Whale*, Peter Peterson, of Friseland, master.

The 27th, we had storms, hail and snow, with very cold weather, the wind north-east, and by east; we were in seventy-one degrees, and came to the ice, and turned back again. The Island of John Maien bore from us south-west and by west, as near as we could guess within ten miles. We might have seen the Island plain enough, but the air was haizy, and full of fogs and snow, so that we could not see far. About noon it blew a storm, whereupon we took down our topsails, and, furling our mainsail, drove with the missensail towards south-east.

The 29th, it was foggy all day, the wind north-east, and by north; we came to the ice, and sailed from it again.

The 30th, the first Sunday after Easter, was foggy, with rain and snow, the wind at north; at night we came to the ice, but sailed from it again; the sea was tempestuous, and tossed our ship very much.

The 3rd of May was cold, snowy, with hail, and misty sunshine; the wind north-west and by west; the sun set no more, we saw it as well by night as by day.

The 4th, we had snow, hail, and gloomy sunshine, with cold weather, but not excessive; the wind at north-west; the weather every day unconstant. Here we saw abundance of seales; they jumped out of the water before the ship, and, which was strange, they would stand half out of the water, and, as it were, dance together.

The 5th, in the forenoon, it was moderately cold, and sunshine, but toward noon darkish and cloudy, with snow and great frost; the wind north-west and by north. We saw daily many ships, sailing about the ice; I observed that as they passed by one another, they hailed one another, crying *Holla*, and asked each other how many fish they had caught; but they would not stick sometimes to tell more than they had. When it was windy, that they could not hear one another, they waived their Hats to signifie the number caught. But when they have their full fraight of whales, they put up their great flag as a sign thereof: then if any hath a message to be sent, he delivers it to them.

[1]From an anonymous translation of 1694, of *A Voyage into Spitzbergen and Greenland.*

The 7th we had moderate frosts, clouds, and snow, with rain. In the evening we sailed to the ice, the wind was quite contrary to us, and the ice too small, wherefore we sailed from it. In the afternoon we saw Spitzbergen, the south point of the North Foreland: we supposed it the true Harbour. The land appeared like a dark cloud, full of white streeks; we turned to the West again, that it, according to the compass, which is also to be understood of the ice and harbour.

The 9th was the same weather, and cold as before, the wind south-west and by west. In the afternoon a fin-fish swam by our ship, which we took at first to be a whale, before we saw the high fins of his tail and came near to it. We had let down our sloop from the ship, but that labour was lost, for he was not worth taking.

On the 14th, the wind was north-west, fine weather with sunshine; we were within seventy-five degrees and twenty-two minutes. We told twenty ships about us; the sea was very even, and we hardly felt any wind, and yet it was very cold. In this place the sea becomes smooth presently again after a storm, chiefly when the wind blows from the ice; but when it blows off the sea, it always makes a great sea. The same day we saw a whale, not far off from our ship; we put out four boats from on board after him, but this labour was also in vain, for he run under the water and we saw him no more.

On the 20th, it was exceeding cold, so that the very sea was all frozen over; yet it was so calm and still that we could hardly perceive the wind, which was north; there were nine ships in our company, which sailed about the ice; we found still, the longer we sailed the bigger the ice.

On the 21st (which was the fourth Sunday after Easter), we sailed into the ice in the forenoon, with another Hamburgher-ship called the *Lepeler*, with eight Hollanders. We fixed our ship with ice-hooks to a large ice-field, when the sun was south-west and by south; we numbered thirty ships in the sea; they lay, as it were, in an harbour or haven. Thus, they venture their ships in the ice at great hazard.

On the 30th, it was fair weather in the morning, snowy about noon, the wind was south-west, and very calm. We rowed in the great sloop, before the ship, farther into the ice. In the morning we heard a whale blow when the sun was in the east, and brought the whale to the ship when the sun was at south-west and by east; the same day we cut the Fat from it, and filled with it seventy barrels (which they call kardels). By this fish we found abundance of birds, most of them were mallemucks (that is to say, foolish gnats), which were so greedy of their food, that we killed them with sticks. This fish was found out by the Birds, for we saw everywhere by them in the sea where the whale had been, for he was wounded by an harpooning iron that stuck still in his flesh, and he had also spent himself by hard swimming; he blowed also very hollow.

In the morning, June 4th, we were a-hunting again after a whale, and we came so near unto one, that the harpoonier was just going to fling his harpoon into her, but she sunk down behind and held her head out of the water, and so sunk down like a stone, and we saw her no more; it is very like that the great ice-field was full of holes in the middle, so that the whale could fetch breath underneath the ice. A great many more ships lay about this sheet of ice; one hunted the whales to the other, and so they were frighted and became very shy. So one gets as many fishes as the other, and sometimes they all get one. We were there several times a hunting that very day, and yet we got never a one.

On the 12th, it was cold and stormy all day, at night sunshine; he that takes not exact notice, knows no difference whether it be day or night.

On the 13th, in the afternoon, it was windy and foggy; we were in seventy-seven degrees; we sailed along by the ice somewhat easterly towards Spitzbergen. That night we saw more than twenty whales, that run one after another towards the ice; out of them we got our second fish, which was a male one; and this fish, when they wounded him with lances, bled very much, so that the sea was tinged by it where he swam; we brought him to the ship when the sun was in the north, for the sun is the clock to the seamen in Spitzbergen, or else they would live without order, and mistake in the usual seven weekly days.

We arrived at Spitzbergen June the 14th. First we came to the Foreland thereof, then to the seven Ice-hills or mountains, then we passed the harbours (or bays) of the Hamburghers, Magdalans, of the English men, the Danes, and sailed into the South Bay: we were followed by seven ships, three Hamburghers and four Hollanders.

That night we sailed with three boats into the English harbour or bay, and saw a whale, and flung into him three harpoons, and threw our lances into him; the whale ran underneath the small ice, and remained a great while under water before he came up again; and then ran but a very little way before he came up again; and this he repeated very often, so that we were forced to wait upon him above half an hour before he came from underneath the ice. The harpoons broke out at length, and we lost him.

On the 22nd, we had very fair weather, and pretty warm; we were by Rehenfelt (Deersfield), where the ice stood firm. We saw six whales, and got one of them that was a male and our third fish; he was killed at night when the sun stood westward: this fish was killed by one man who flung the harpoon into him; and killed him also, while the other boats were busy in pursuing or hunting after another whale. This fish run to the ice, and before he died beat about with his tail; the ice settled about him, so that the other boats could not come to this boat to assist him, till the ice separated again that they might row, when they tied one boat behind the other, and so towed the whale to the great ship, where they cut him up into the vessels, and filled with him forty-five barrels. This night the sun shined very brightly.

On the 1st July, about noon, two whales came near to our ship; we saw that they had a mind to couple together; we set our boat for them, and the harpoonier hit the female, which when the other found, he did not stay at all, but made away. The female run all along above the water, straight forward, beating about with her tail and fins, so that we durst not come near to lance her; yet one of our harpooniers was so fool-hardy to venture too near the fish, which saluted him with a stroke of her tail over his back so vehemently, that he had much ado to recover his breath again. Those in the other boat, to show their valour also, hastened to the fish, which overturned their boat, so that the harpoonier was forced to dive for it, and hide his head underneath the water; the rest did the same; they thought it very long before they come out, for it was cold, so that they came quaking to the ship again. In the same morning, a whale appeared near our ship, before the wide harbour: we put out four boats from our ship after him, but two Holland ships were about half a league from us; one of them sent a boat towards us; we used great diligence and care to take him, but the fish came up just before the Dutchman's boat, and was struck by him with the harpoon. Thus he took the bread out of our mouths.

On the 5th July, in the forenoon, it was bright sunshine and pretty warm; in the afternoon it was foggy; at night sunshine again, which lasted all the night. We hunted all that day long, and in the morning we struck a whale before the Weigatt; this fish run round about under the water, and so fastened the line whereon our harpoon was about a rock, so that the harpoon lost its hold, and that fish got away. This whale did blow the water so fiercely, that one might hear it at a league's distance.

On the 6th, we had the same weather, and warm sunshine all night. Hard by us rode a Hollander, and the ship's crew busie in cutting the fat of a whale, when the fish burst with so great a bounce as if a cannon had been discharged, and bespattered the workmen all over.

On the 8th, the wind turned north-west, with snow and rain. We were forced to leave one of our anchors, and thank'd God for getting off from land, for the ice came on fiercely upon us; at night the wind was laid, and it was colder, although the sun shined.

On the 12th, we had gloomy sunshine all day. We saw but very few whales more, and those we did see were quite wild, that we could not come near them. That night it was so dark and foggy, that we could hardly see the ship's length; we might have got sea-horses enough, but we were afraid of losing our ships, for we had examples enough of them that had lost their ships, and could not come to them again, but have been forced to return home in other ships. When after this manner any have lost their ships, and cannot be seen, they discharge a cannon from the ship, or sound the trumpets, or hautboys, according as they are provided in their ships, that the men that are lost may find their ship again.

On the 13th, the ice came afloating down apace, we sailed from the south-east land to the west, and we could but just get through by the north side from the Bear Harbour or Bay. We sailed on to the Rehenfelt (or Deer Field), where the ice was already fixed to the land, so that we could but just get through; we sailed further to the Vogelsanck (bird's-song). Then we turned to the east with a north-east wind, in company with twelve ships more, to see whether there were any more whales left, with *George* and *Cornelius Manglesen*, and *Michael Appel*, who sailed in four fathoms water, and touched upon the wreck of a ship that was lost there.

On the 14th, in the morning, we sailed still among the ice, the wind being north-east and by east; we had a fog all that day with sunshine, with a rainbow of two colours, white and pale yellow, and it was very cold, and we saw the sun a great deal lower.

On the 15th, it was windy, cold, and foggy the whole day; the wind turned north-west, and the ice come on in abundance, so that we could hardly sail, for it was everywhere full of small sheets of ice. At this time there were many ships beset with ice in the Deer or Muscle Bay. We sailed all along near the shoar; at night we entered the South-Harbour, where twenty-eight ships lay at anchor, eight whereof were Hamburgh-ers, the rest Dutchmen. From that time when we sailed out of the South-haven we kept always within sight of the land, and saw it always, ex-cept it was foggy; and so long the skippers stay by the ice to see if there are any more whales to be had.

On the 22nd day of July, in the morning, when the sun was north-east, we waied our anchors, and sailed out of the South-haven.

On the 24th, it was so warm with sunshine, that the tarr wherewith the ship was daubed over melted; we drove, it being calm, before the haven or Bay of Magdalen.

On the 25th, at night we came to the Forelands, the night was foggy, the wind south-west.

On the 28th, we turned from the side of the North Foreland towards the west, when the sun was south-east; and we did sail south-west and by west towards the sea. . . .

II

The fish properly called the whale, for whose sake our ships chiefly undertake the voyage to Spitzbergen, is differing from other whales in his finns and mouth, which is without teeth, but instead thereof long, black, somewhat broad and horny flakes, all jagged like hairs: he differs from the finn-fish in his finns, for the finn-fish hath a great finn on his back: but the whale properly so called, hath none on his back: and there are two finns behind his eyes of a bigness proportionable to the whale, covered with a thick black skin, delicately marbled with white strokes; or as you see in marble, trees, houses or the like things represented. In the tail of one of the fishes was marbled very delicately this number, 1222, very even and exact, as if they had been painted on it on purpose. This marbling on the whale is like veins in a piece of wood, that run streight through, or else round about the center or pith of a tree, and so go both white and yellow strokes, through the thick and the thin strokes, that is like parchment or vellam, and give to the whale an incomparable beauty and ornament. When these finns are cut up, you find underneath the thick skin bones that look like unto a man's hand, when it is opened and the fingers are expanded or spread; between these joynts there are stiff sinews, which flye up and rebound again if you fling them hard against the ground, as the sinews of great fish, as of a sturgeon, or of some four footed beasts generally do.

Their tail doth not stand up as the tails of almost any other fish, but it doth lye horizontal, as that of the finn-fish, butskopf, dolphin, and the like, and it is three, three and a half, and four fathoms broad. The head is the third part of the fish, and some have bigger heads; on the upper and under lip are short hairs before. Their lips are quite plain, somewhat bended like an S, and they end underneath the eyes before the two finns. Above the uppermost bended lip he hath black streaks; some are darkish brown, and they are crooked as the lips are. Their lips are smooth and quite black, round like the quarter of a circle; when they draw them together they lock into one another. Within, on the uppermost lip, is the whale-bone, of a brown, black, and yellow colour, with streaks of several colours, as the bones of a finn-fish. The whale bones of some of the whales are blew, and light blew, which two are reckoned to come from young whales. Just before, on the under lip, is a cavity or hole, which the upper lip fits exactly into, as a knife into a sheath. I do really believe, that he draws the water that he bloweth out through this hole, and so I have been informed also by seamen. Within his mouth is the whalebone, all hairy as horse's hair, as it is also in the finn-fish, and it hangs down from both sides all about his tongue. The whalebone of some whales is bended like unto a cimeter, and others like unto a half-moon. The lower part of the whale's mouth is commonly white: the tongue lyeth amongst the whale-bones; it is very close tyed to the undermost chap or lip; it is very large and white, with black spots at the edges.

Upon his head is the hovel or bump before the eyes and finns: at the top of this bump on each side, is a spout-hole, two over-against one another, which are bended on each side like an S, or as the hole that is cut in a violin, whereout he doth blow the water very fiercely, that it roars like a hollow wind which we hear when the wind bloweth into a cave, or against the corner of a board, or like an organ-pipe. This may be heard at a league's distance, although you do not see him by reason of the thick and foggy air. The whale bloweth or spouts the water fiercest of all when he is wounded, then it sounds as the roaring of the sea in a great storm, and as we hear the wind in a very hard storm. The head of the whale is not round at the top, but somewhat flat. and goeth down sloaping, like unto the tyling of an house, to the under lip. The under lip is broader than the whale is in any part of his body, and broadest in the middle; before and behind it is something narrower, according to the shape of the head. In one word, all the whole fish is shaped like unto a shoemakers last, if you look upon it from beneath. Behind the knob or bump where the finns are, between that and the finns, are his eyes, which are not much bigger than those of a bullock, with eyelids and hair, like men's eyes. The crystal of the eye is not much bigger than a pea, clear, white, and transparent as crystal; the colour of some is yellowish, of others quite white. The seale's are three times as big as those of the whale. The eyes of the whale are placed very low, almost at the end of the upper lip. Some bring along with them from Spitzbergen some bones, which they pretend to be the ears of the whale; but I can say nothing to this, because I never saw any; but thus much I do remember, that I have heard them say that they lye very deep. The whale doth not hear when he spouts the water, wherefore he is easiest to be struck at that time. His belly and back are quite red, and underneath the belly they are commonly white, yet some of them are coal black; most of them that I saw were white. They look very beautiful when the sun shines upon them, the small clear waves of the sea that are over him glisten like silver. Some of them are marbled on their back and tail. Where he hath been wounded there remaineth always a white scar; I understood one of our harpooniers that he once caught a whale at Spitzbergen that was white all over. Half white I have seen some, but one above the rest, which was a female, was a beautiful one; she was all over marbled black and yellow. Those that are as black are not all of the same colour, for some of them are black as velvet, others of a coal black, others of the colour of a tench.

The yard of a whale is a strong sinew, and according as they are in bigness, six, seven, or eight foot long, as I have seen myself. Where this yard is fixed the skin is doubled, so that it lies just like a knife in a sheath, where you can see nothing of the knife, but only a little of the haft. Where the yard doth begin it is four-square, consisting of many strong sinews; if you dry them they are as transparent as fish glew; out of these sinews the seamen make twisted whips. Their bones are hard, like unto them of great four-footed beasts, but porous, like unto a spunge, and filled with marrow; when that is consumed out, they will hold a great deal of water, for the holes are big like unto the wax of a honey-comb.

The other strong sinews are chiefly about the tail, where it is thinnest, for with it he turns and winds himself as a ship is turn'd by the rudder; but his finns are his oars, and according to his bigness he rows himself along with them as swiftly as a bird flies, and doth make a long track in the sea, as a great ship doth when under sail.

BARON MUNCHAUSEN TELLS OF THE PRANKS OF A WHALE AND OF WHAT HAPPENED ON A VOYAGE TO THE INDIES[1]

Rudolf Erich Raspe

1737–1794)

1

I EMBARKED at Portsmouth in a first-rate English man-of-war, of one hundred guns, and fourteen hundred men, for North America; nothing worth relating happened till we arrived within three hundred leagues of the river Saint Lawrence, when the ship struck with amazing force against (as we supposed) a rock; however, upon heaving the lead, we could find no bottom, even with three hundred fathom. What made this circumstance the more wonderful, and indeed beyond all comprehension, was, that the violence of the shock was such that we lost our rudder, broke our bowsprit in the middle, and split all our masts from top to bottom, two of which went by the board; a poor fellow, who was aloft, furling the main-sheet, was flung at least three leagues from the ship; but he fortunately saved his life, by laying hold of the tail of a large sea-gull, who brought him back, and lodged him on the very spot whence he was thrown. Another proof of the violence of the shock was the force with which the people between decks were driven against the floors above them; my head particularly was pressed into my stomach, where it continued some months, before it recovered its natural situation. Whilst we were all in a state of astonishment at the general and unaccountable confusion in which we were involved, the whole was suddenly explained, by the appearance of a large whale, who had been basking asleep within sixteen feet of the surface of the water. This animal was so much displeased with the disturbance which our ship had given him, (for in our passage we had with our rudder scratched his nose,) that he beat in all the gallery and part of the quarter-deck with his tail, and almost at the same instant, took the main sheet-anchor, which was suspended, as it usually is, from the head, between his teeth, and ran away with the ship, at least sixty leagues, at the rate of twelve leagues an hour, when fortunately the cable broke, and we lost both the whale and the anchor. However, upon our return to Europe some months after, we found the same whale, within a few leagues of the same spot, floating dead upon the water; it measured above half a mile in length. As we could take but a small quantity of such a monstrous animal on board, we got our boats out, and, with much difficulty, cut off his head, where, to our great joy, we found the anchor, and above 40 fathom of the cable concealed on the left side of his mouth, just under his tongue. Perhaps

---

[1] From *Gulliver Revived*.

this was the cause of his death, as that side of his tongue was much swelled, with a great degree of inflammation. This was the only extraordinary circumstance that happened on this voyage.

II

In a voyage which I made to the East Indies with Captain Hamilton, I took a favourite pointer with me; he was, to use a common phrase, worth his weight in gold, for he never deceived me. One day, when we were, by the best observations we could make, at least three hundred leagues from the land, my dog pointed; I observed him for near an hour with astonishment, and mentioned the circumstance to the Captain, and every officer on board, asserting, that we must be near land, for my dog smelt game; this occasioned a general laugh; but that did not alter in the least the good opinion I had of my dog. After much conversation pro and con, I boldly told the Captain, I placed more confidence in Tray's nose, than I did in the eyes of every seaman on board, and therefore boldly proposed laying the sum I had agreed to pay for my passage (viz., one hundred guineas) that we should find game within half an hour; the Captain (a good hearty fellow) laughed again, desired Mr Crawford, the surgeon, who was present, to feel my pulse; he did so, and reported me in perfect health: the following dialogue between them took place; I overheard it, though spoken low and at some distance.

CAPTAIN. His brain is turned; I cannot with honour accept his wager.

SURGEON. I am of a different opinion; he is quite sane, and depends more upon the scent of his dog, than he will upon the judgment of all the officers on board; he will certainly lose, and he richly merits it.

CAPTAIN. Such a wager cannot be fair on my side; however, I'll take him up, if I return his money afterwards.

During the above conversation, Tray continued in the same situation, and confirmed me still more in my former opinion. I proposed the wager a second time; it was then accepted.

Done and Done were scarcely said on both sides, when some sailors, who were fishing in the long-boat, which was made fast to the stern of the ship, harpooned an exceedingly large shark, which they brought on board, and began to cut up for the purpose of barrelling the oil, when, behold, they found no less than *six brace of live partridges* in this animal's stomach!

They had been so long in that situation, that one of the hens was sitting upon four eggs, and a fifth was hatching when the shark was opened!!!

This young bird we brought up, by placing it with a litter of kittens that came into the world a few minutes before! The old cat was as fond of it as any of her own four-legged progeny, and made herself very unhappy when it flew out of her reach till it returned again; as to the other partridges, there were four hens amongst them; one or more were, during the voyage, constantly sitting, and consequently we had plenty of game at the Captain's table; and in gratitude to poor Tray (for being the means of winning one hundred guineas) I ordered him the bones daily, and sometimes a whole bird.

THE RIDER ON THE WHITE HORSE[1]

Theodor Storm

(1817–1888)

(Near Husum, on the coast of N. W. Schleswig, Hauke Haien, the young dyke-reeve, despite the taunts of his rival Ole Peters, has been experimenting with a new method of dyke construction. The dyke, when finished, seems success-ful, but dark rumours are abroad about Hauke and the white horse he always rides: some great disaster, it is whispered, will come upon North Friesland.)

IT WAS in October, the eve of All Saints. All day a gale had blown from the south-west, and when evening had fallen, and a half moon shone down from the sky, dark clouds raced across its face, so that shad-ows and fitful light fell on to the earth by turns. The storm was getting up.

In the dyke-reeve's living-room the supper things had not been cleared away. The men had been sent out to the cowsheds to see to the cattle; the maids had had to go round and make sure that doors and shutters were fast in house and lofts so that the storm could do no dam-age there. Hauke stood beside his wife at the window: he had been out on the dyke, and had only just swallowed his supper. He had gone out in the early afternoon, and had had pointed stakes and sacks of clay or earth collected wherever the dyke seemed to show weak places, and he had posted men at all these spots to be ready to ram in the stakes and press down the sacks of clay as soon as a breach seemed to be threatened. But at the corner on the north-west, where the new dyke joined the old, he had posted most men. And he had forbidden them to leave their stations without urgent reason.

So he had left things, and had got in, wet through, scarcely a quarter of an hour ago. Now, with his ear to the blasts of wind that made the leaded window-panes rattle, he stared blankly out into the wild night.

Suddenly the little girl, who was standing by her mother, shuddered and hid her face in her mother's skirt.

"Claus!" she said, weeping. "Where's my Claus?"

And she might well ask, for, as in the previous year, the gull had remained behind when the others migrated. The child's father took no notice of the question, but her mother picked her up.

"Your Claus is in the barn," she said. "He's warm there."

[1]From *Der Schimmelreiter*. Translated by Gertrude M. Cross.

"Warm?" said Wienke. "Is that nice?"

"Yes, that's nice."

The master of the house was still by the window.

"We can't stand this, Elke," he said. "Call one of the maids. The wind will force in the panes. We must have the shutters fastened."

At her mistress's word the girl ran out. From the room they could see how her skirts were blown about by the wind, but she had scarcely unfastened the clamp that held the shutters back when the storm tore them from her hands and dashed them against the windows with such force that a couple of panes clattered in fragments on to the floor, and one of the lamps smoked and went out. Hauke had to go out himself to help, and only after much effort were the shutters gradually closed. When they managed to open the door to come in again, a blast followed them that made the silver and the glass in the cupboard on the wall clatter together. In the house above their heads, the beams trembled and creaked as if the storm would have torn the roof from the walls. But Hauke did not come in. Elke heard him go across the threshing floor to the stable.

"The white horse! The white horse, John! Quick!"

She heard him shout that. Then he re-entered the room, his hair dishevelled, but his grey eyes shining.

"The wind has veered to the north-west," he said, "on a half spring tide. That's bad. We've never had such a storm."

Elke had grown as pale as death.

"And you must go out again?"

He took her two hands and pressed them convulsively in his own.

"I must, Elke."

Slowly she raised her dark eyes to his, and for a few moments, that seemed an eternity, they looked at each other.

"Yes, Hauke," she said, "I know you must go."

There was a trampling outside. She threw her arms round his neck, and for a moment it seemed as if she could not let him go. But that, too, only lasted a moment.

"This is our fight," said Hauke. "You are safe here. No flood has ever reached up to this house. And pray that God will have me too in His keeping."

Hauke wrapped himself in his cloak, and his wife wound a scarf round his neck. She wanted to say something, but her trembling lips refused to obey her. The white horse whinnied, and the sound rang out like the blast of a trumpet amid the howling of the storm.

Elke went out with her husband. The old ash beside the door was creaking as if it would not hold together.

"Mount, Master!" shouted the man. "The white horse is like a mad thing. The reins may break."

Hauke threw his arms round his wife.

"At sun-up I shall be back."

And he sprang on to his horse. The animal reared; then, like a charger rushing into battle, it dashed with its rider down the mound on which the house stood, into the night and the howling of the storm.

"Father, father dear!" a complaining childish voice called to him. Wienke had run after her father, but after a few steps she had stumbled in the darkness and fallen down.

The farm-hand, Iven John, brought the weeping child back to her mother, who was leaning against the trunk of the ash, its branches lashing the air above her head. She stared absently into the night in which her husband had been swallowed up, and when the howling of the storm and the roaring of the sea suddenly ceased for a moment, she shuddered with terror. It seemed to her now that everything was bent solely on his destruction, and that when this had been accomplished the tumult would cease.

"Here's the little one, missus," shouted John. "Hold her tight." And he put the child into her mother's arms.

"The little one? I'd forgotten you, Wienke!" she exclaimed. "God forgive me!" And in a passion of love she clasped the child to her breast and fell on her knees. "Lord God," she prayed, "and thou, dear Jesus, do not make me a widow and her an orphan. Protect him, dear Lord! Thou and I alone know him as he is."

And the storm redoubled its fury. It raged and thundered as if the whole world were doomed to perish in clamorous tumult.

"Go indoors, missus," said John. "Come!" And he helped her to her feet, and took them both into the house, and to the living-room.

Hauke Haien, the dyke-reeve, galloped towards the dyke on his white horse. The narrow path afforded little foothold, for on the previous day heavy rain had fallen; but the horse's hoofs did not stick in the damp, absorbent clay; he galloped as if the ground beneath him were as firm as in summer.

Dark cloud-wrack tore across the sky; below lay the broad marsh, like an unrecognizable desert filled with restless shadows. From the waters outside the dyke, ever more menacing, came a dull roar, as if they were bent on devouring everything before them.

"Forward!" cried Hauke to the white horse. "We've never had to ride like this."

From under the horse's hoofs came a sound like a death-cry. He reined in the animal and looked about him. A flock of white gulls were passing, close to the ground. Half flying, half driven along by the storm, with mocking screaming, they were seeking shelter inland. For a moment the moon shone through the clouds and he saw that one lay crushed in the path. It seemed to him that a piece of red ribbon fluttered round its neck.

"Claus!" he said. "Poor Claus!"

Was it indeed his daughter's pet bird, that had recognized steed and rider, and had tried to find shelter with them? He did not know.

"Forward!" he shouted again, and the white horse's hoofs were raised for a fresh gallop when suddenly the storm ceased, and a stillness as of death took its place. Only for a second: afterwards the storm continued with redoubled fury. But in that moment of calm, Hauke heard human voices, and the distant barking of dogs, and when he turned his head in the direction of the village, he saw, as the moonlight broke through the clouds, that people were moving round laden wagons before the houses, and on the mounds on which the houses stood. He saw other wagons, that seemed to be hurrying to the higher ground beyond the fen, and on his ear fell the lowing of the cattle that were being driven out of their stalls up to safety.

"Thank God!" he exclaimed. "They are saving themselves and their cattle." And then came an anxious exclamation. "My wife! My child! —No, no; the floods have never reached as high as our house!"

But it all swept past in a moment, like a vision.

A terrific blast came roaring from the sea, and in its teeth Hauke Haien and his horse stormed up the narrow path on to the dyke. On the top Hauke reined in his horse with an effort. But where was the sea? Where was Jeverssand, and where was the opposite shore? Before him he saw nothing but mountains of water, piling up towards the night sky. Great billows thundered over each other, as if each would overtop the last, towards the land. Crowned with white foam they rolled in, and it seemed that in their roaring were mingled the voices of all the ravening beasts of the wilderness.

The white horse pawed the ground, and snorted defiantly into the storm; but it seemed to his rider as if here all human power had come to an end, and that night, and death, and chaos could no longer be withstood.

But then he reflected. It was the flood-tide caused by a storm, though it was true that he had never seen anything like it. His wife and child were safe in their solid house on its high ground. But his dyke—and a feeling of pride came over him—the Hauke-Haien Dyke, as people called it—that would show them how dykes should be built.

But what was that? He stopped at the corner between the two dykes. Where were the men he had posted to keep watch here? He looked towards the north, along the old dyke, for there, too, men had been posted. Neither here nor there was anyone to be seen. He rode on a little, but found that he was quite alone. The raging of the storm, and the roaring of the water from far and near fell deafeningly on his ears. He turned his horse, came back to the deserted corner, and looked along the new dyke. He noticed distinctly that up its gently sloping sides the waves rolled more slowly, beat less violently. It was almost as if here were a different sea.

"It will hold," he murmured, and wanted to laugh for joy.

But the laugh was silenced as his eye travelled further along the dyke. What was that at the north-west corner? A dark mass seemed to be swarming there, moving busily hither and thither. There was no doubt about it; he was looking at a crowd of people. What did they want? What were they doing to his dyke? He struck his spurs into his horse's flanks, and dashed towards them. The blasts, now broadside on, were so fierce that horse and rider were almost blown from the dyke down into the new polder, but they knew where they were going. Hauke soon saw that at least a couple of dozen people were busily engaged, and then he saw that they had dug a channel right through the new dyke. He reined in his horse abruptly.

"Stop!" he shouted. "What devil's work are you at?"

A number of the men had stopped their work, frightened, when they saw the dyke-reeve suddenly appear among them; the wind carried his words to them, and he saw that several were trying to answer. But he could catch nothing but their excited gestures, for they were all on his left and their words were carried away. Here the storm was so violent that they could scarcely stand against it, and the men were crowded together for shelter. With a quick eye Hauke measured the channel that had been dug, and the height of the water which, in spite of the outward slope of the dyke wall, was already lapping at its top and wetting horse and rider with spray. Another ten minutes' work, and he saw that the flood-tide would stream through the breach, and the Hauke-Haien polder disappear under the sea.

The dyke-reeve beckoned one of the men to the other side of his horse.

"Now, speak!" he shouted. "What are you doing here? What does this mean?"

And the man shouted back. "We've got to break through the new dyke, master, so that the old dyke will hold."

"What must you do?"

"Break through the new dyke."

"And destroy the polder? What devil told you to do that?"

"Nay, master: it was no devil. Ole Peters has been here: he's on the dyke committee: he gave the order."

Anger flashed into the dyke-reeve's eyes.

"Don't you know me?" he cried. "Where I am, Ole Peters has no orders to give. Clear out of here! Go back to the posts I gave you."

And as they hesitated to obey, he made his horse leap into the midst of the group.

"Clear out! To the devil with you!"

"Look out, master!" shouted some one from the crowd, trying to protect himself with his spade from the maddened horse. But a blow from the animal's hoof struck the spade out of his hand. Another man was thrown to the ground.

All at once a cry came from the group—a cry such as nothing but the fear of death forces from men's throats. For a moment all—even the dyke-reeve and his horse—stood as if turned to stone: only one man stretched out his arm, pointing like a sign-post to the north-west corner where the new dyke joined the old. Nothing could be heard save the raging of the storm and the roaring of the water.

Hauke turned in his saddle. What was the matter there? Then his eyes opened wide.

"Lord God! A breach! A breach in the old dyke!"

"Yours is the guilt, dyke-reeve!" shouted a voice. "Yours! Take it with you to God's judgment seat."

Hauke's face, which had been red with anger, had grown as white as death; not even the moonlight that now fell on it could add to its pallor; his arms hung limply; he scarcely knew that the reins were in his hands. But in a moment he pulled himself together, and a groan escaped him; then silently he turned his horse, which snorted and galloped eastward with him. His eyes turned sharply from side to side, but his thoughts were in a tumult. What had he done for which he must answer before God's judgment seat? The breach in the new dyke—perhaps they would have got it finished if he had not stopped them. But there was something else, of which he was only too well aware. If only he had not let Ole Peters' false tongue hold him back. He alone had discovered the weakness in the old dyke, and in spite of this knowledge he had gone on with the new work.

"Lord God, I acknowledge my fault," he cried suddenly into the storm. "I have been an unfaithful steward."

On his left, close to his horse's hoofs, the sea raged. Before him, and now in complete darkness, lay the old polder, with its mounds and homesteads. The pale moonlight had completely vanished, but one solitary light shone in the blackness. It brought comfort to the man's heart, for he knew that it must come from his home—it was like a greeting from wife and child. Thank God they were safe! And by now the others must have found refuge in the village above the polder. He had never seen so many lights shining from there as he saw now; some were even quite high up—they must be in the church tower.

"Everybody will have gone," he said to himself. "But on many a hillock the homestead will be lying in ruins; bad years are in store for the flooded fens; sluices in the dykes will have to be repaired. But we must bear it. And I will help them, yes, even those who have done me an injury. Only have mercy upon me, O Lord my God."

Then he looked to the side, down on to the new polder which his dyke had reclaimed. Round it foamed the sea, but over it the peace of night seemed to brood. In spite of himself, a cry of rejoicing broke from the white horse's rider.

"The Hauke-Haien-Dyke will hold, and in a hundred years it will be standing firm!"

A noise at his feet like thunder wakened him from these dreams. The white horse would not go on. What was the matter? The horse leapt back, and Hauke felt a piece of the dyke in front of him fall into the water. He roused himself thoroughly, and saw that he had reached the old dyke: the horse's feet had rested on it. Involuntarily he reined the animal back, and at that moment the moon broke through the clouds, and its mild rays lit up the horror of the mass of water that, foaming and hissing, poured down before his eyes into the old polder.

Hauke stared at it as if he had lost his senses. This was a second Flood, sent to swallow up man and beast. A ray of light shone into his eyes: it was the light he had already noticed, still shining from his home. His courage returned, and now, when he looked down into the polder, he could see that on the other side of the whirling flood that raged before him, only about a hundred paces was under water. Beyond he could see the road that led up to the dyke. But he saw more: a wagon—no, a two-wheeled trap, was racing like mad towards the dyke. In it sat a woman —yes, and a child, too. And—was not that the yapping of a little dog that the wind bore past him? Almighty God! It was his wife, his child! They were quite near now, and the foaming whirlpool threatened them. A cry of despair broke from him.

"Elke!" he cried. "Elke! Go back! Go back!"

But sea and storm showed him no mercy. His words could not be heard through their raging. The wind caught his cloak; it had almost torn him from his horse, and still the vehicle dashed on towards the flood. Then he saw that his wife seemed to be holding out her arms to him. Had she recognized him? Had the longing for him, the terrible anxiety, driven her out of the safety of her home? And now—was she calling a last word to him? The questions passed through his mind, but they remained unanswered. From him to her, and from her to him, all words were lost. A roaring as if the end of the world had come filled their ears, and let no other sound enter.

"My child! Elke, my faithful Elke!" cried Hauke into the storm.

At that instant another huge piece of the dyke crumbled down, and the sea thundered after it into the abyss. Once more he saw the horse's head and the wheels of the vehicle rise from that seething horror; then they were whirled round, and disappeared beneath it.

The lonely figure on the white horse stared down from the dyke with eyes that saw nothing.

"The end," he said softly.

Then he rode to the edge of the abyss, while below him the waters, with a sinister sound, were beginning to flood his native village. From his home the light still shone, but now it seemed to him a lifeless thing.

He rose in his saddle, and struck spurs into his horse's flanks. The animal reared, and would have fallen backwards, but his rider's strength held him.

"Forward!" He gave the shout which had so often encouraged the white horse to another effort. "Lord God, take me: spare the others!"

Once more the spurs struck home, and a horse's scream rang out above the howling of the storm and the raging of the waters. Then a dull thud, a short struggle.

The moon shone out from the clouds, but no living thing was left on the dyke; there was only the water that soon nearly covered the old polder. Hauke Haien's house still stood above the flood, and from it the light streamed. From the village above the polder, where the lights were extinguished one by one, the lonely light in the church tower threw its wavering beam over the foaming waves.

HOW THE *BLACK GALLEY* TOOK THE *ANDREA DORIA*[1]

Wilhelm Raabe

(1831–1910)

(The following extract is taken from Raabe's *Die Schwarze Galeere*, a story of the Netherlanders' struggle against Spain. Jan Norris, second in command of the *Black Galley*, has been captured by the captain of the *Andrea Doria* and, with his sweetheart, Myga van Bergen, taken on board the galleon. Jan escapes, leaving Myga on board. But——)

OVER Fort Liefkenhoek the banner with the Lions of Leon and the towers of Castile flutters proudly. The same banner flies over Fort Lillo and over all the other fortifications bristling with cannons' mouths, on both sides of the Scheldt, right up to the massive walls of the citadel of Antwerp. On all these walls and ramparts sharp eyes are keeping watch, and the answering cries of the sentinels to each other do not cease either by day or by night.

But near and ever watchful is the enemy. At any moment he may appear. Who knows the hour of his coming?

"Keep good watch! Keep good watch!"

The cannon on the Brabant shore of the Scheldt, the cannon on the Flanders coast are ready to pour out death and destruction on the mad vessel that in their despite might seek its way upstream to Antwerp.

"Keep good watch! Keep good watch!"

But the night is dark, illumined neither by moonlight nor by the glimmer of stars. It is hard to keep good watch on such a night. How still it is, and how warm! Only the rustling of the mighty stream sounds

[1]Translated by Gertrude M. Cross. Reproduced from William Raabe's *Die Schwarze Galeere*, by kind permission of the Verlagsanstalt Hermann Klemm A.-G., Berlin-Grünewald.

continually through the warning cries of the warriors on the ramparts. "Keep good watch! Keep good watch!"

What is this that is coming from South Beveland, crossing the West Scheldt where sea and river meet and can no longer be distinguished the one from the other. What is this that is gliding over the waves in the black night? A hundred invisible arms propel it; swift as an arrow it darts along: it is like the Ship of Ghosts, like the Flying Dutchman.

A mighty ship cuts its way through the waves: others follow, others less powerful.

What does the darkness trouble the men from Zealand! They know how to find their way on the waters which are their home. One dark shadow follows another; in a line they glide along. No sound is heard on board, even the rowers make no noise as they dip their oars into the waves. The words of command are whispered from mouth to mouth. Every man knows his duty. Every man has sworn a mighty oath to drive his knife into the throat of his neighbour should he by a sound, a thoughtless cry, put the success of the enterprise in jeopardy. Every man will keep his oath, though it were father, brother, son, whom he must cut down . . .

Noiselessly the *Black Galley* with its escort of shadows glides on. The deep, solemn booming of the bell is heard in the distance—the bell from the tower of Our Lady in Antwerp.

Two o'clock!

In his place stands the captain of the *Black Galley*, his naked sword in his hand; but on this night another has charge of the ship and its crew. If but the least ray of light were to fall on the face of this leader, you would behold that face with horror, Jan Norris, the betrothed of Myga, now a prisoner on the *Andrea Doria*; Jan Norris, the Water-Beggar, who has left his betrothed in the power of his deadly enemy; Jan Norris, who leapt, but not to his death, from the deck of the Genoese galleon; Jan Norris it is who commands the *Black Galley* to-night.

Jan Norris's eye can see in the night; it pierces the darkness like the brightest day. Rescue—revenge!

Have a care, Leone della Rota! The night breeds misfortune. This is no time to benumb your senses with love of women and with Sicilian wine. Look to your ship, Leone della Rota, beware—beware of—the *Black Galley!*

On board the *Andrea Doria* all the orders had been given and carried out. In three hours the Genoese ship would start on her way to join the four galleys that had gone on ahead: off Biervliet they were to combine for the chase of the *Black Galley*. The ship's company took advantage of their short respite to go to sleep. Even the watch on deck slept, and the man by the gangplank had let his match go out, like the rest of the matches on board. Was not the ship lying safe enough under the walls of Antwerp and the ramparts of the citadel?

From the mainmast, the ship's lantern throws a flickering, uneasy light over the deck; from the cabin windows a feeble illumination falls on to the dark waters of the Scheldt which are rushing past below.

In the cabin, Lieutenant della Rota rises from the couch of Captain Antonio Valani.

"It is all over," he says. "Do you hear, beautiful Fleming? He is dead, and—Leone della Rota is captain of the *Andrea Doria*. Do you hear, most beautiful? I enter into my inheritance. You, too, are mine; with my friend's last breath you became mine."

Spinola's Lieutenant again filled a beaker with wine. He raised the beaker and drained it.

"To thee, Antonio! Poor old fellow—thou shalt have a noble seaman's grave in the seas. They shall not put thee beneath the earth. Under the merry waves shalt thou sleep, as becomes a son of Genoa. In the arms of the sea maidens shalt thou sleep——"

"Mercy, holy God, send death, save me!" sobbed the despairing girl, but the drunken Leone laughed wild and shrill.

"Don't look at me like that, my queen. To-day to me, to-morrow to another. That's war. That's life. What, do you think I should lament and mutter prayers like a papist by the body of my friend? Were we on the Ligurian strand, we would crown ourselves with roses and myrtle to celebrate this wonderful night. In the name of revenge, in the name of victory, come to my arms, wild Beggar: come and be mine, beautiful heretic!"

With a piercing shriek, Myga van Bergen clung to the posts of the bed on which Antonio Valani's pale bleeding body lay stretched. She sought for protection from the dead. But with wild laughter Leone snatched the unfortunate girl up in his arms. His burning kisses rained on her mouth, on her naked shoulders—

Over his head resounded a dull thud that made the lamp on the ceiling shake. A cry—a wrestling—a second thud—the stamping and trampling of many feet—wild cries, the sharp report of a gun—the shout of terror and alarm:

"The Beggars! The Beggars! The Beggars on board! Treachery! Treachery! To arms! To arms!"

"What's that? Diavolo!" cried the Lieutenant, releasing the girl and reaching for his sword.

The body of Antonio Valani raised itself once more from its bloody couch; once more the staring eyes opened wide and fixed themselves on the Lieutenant.

"Protect the ship—traitor! Despicable." A dark stream burst from his mouth. Antonio Valani sank back. This time death held its booty.

On deck the tumult grew more and more general after the fall of the first watch. The ship's company, confused, taken by surprise, turned out with any weapons they could lay their hands on.

"To arms! Treachery! The Beggars!"

Curses—groans—appeals for quarter.

Myga van Bergen fell on her knees as the Lieutenant, drawing his sword, hurried up the cabin stairs. On deck he stumbled over dead and wounded. The fight was swaying wildly hither and thither, and the Netherlanders' shouts of triumph and the terrible battle-cry of the Beggars: "Better Turk than Papist!" began to overpower the call to arms of the Genoese who had been so rudely awakened from their sleep.

And still more and more men were swarming like cats up the sides of the *Andrea Doria*. The merchant ships, and the small warships lying near seemed also to have been overpowered, for from them, too, the noise of battle resounded, shots were fired, torches shone out.

In despair, Leone della Rota threw himself on the path of his nearest foes, with word and deed encouraging his men to resistance. In the Spanish guard-house on the quay, a drum awakened and sounded the Spanish réveillé.

"The Beggars! The Beggars! The Beggars before Antwerp! Treachery! Treachery! The Beggars in the city!"

Torches moved on the quay; lights appeared in the houses behind the city walls.

"Better Turk than Papist! Victory! Victory! The *Black Galley*—the *Black Galley*," shouted the Beggars on board the *Andrea Doria*, carrying all before them. No quarter was given. Those who were not struck or hacked down were simply thrown overboard. The name of the *Black Galley* filled the Italians' hearts with dread, and broke their courage more than all else. Some fled to the land; many more were cut down in the first surprise of the attack.

Round the mainmast, in the circle of light cast by the ship's lantern, a desperate few still struggled. Here Lieutenant della Rota, with the bravest of his men, held his ground, and at last the whole battle was concentrated at this spot. The deck was slippery with blood, and covered with the dead: many a wild beggar fell to the sword of the Italian Lieutenant.

"Courage, brave comrades! To me! They're sending help from the land. Courage!" cried Leone, striking down a Zealander; but in his place stood a fresh warrior, stepping over the fallen.

"Forward, Water Beggars! Down with the foreign tyrants! Down with the flag of shame! Down from the mast with it! Do you know me, foreign scoundrel? cowardly stealer of girls!"

"Diavolo!" cried the Lieutenant, for a moment paralyzed with fright and amazement. But he pulled himself together. "So you are not drowned, Beggar? So much the better—eat cold steel then—there!"

"Take that! And that! Myga! Myga! Rescue! Revenge! Take that, you dog. Go to hell, and greet your comrades there from Jan Norris, the Water-Beggar!"

Leone della Rota sank to the deck in his blood, and Jan Norris set his foot upon the breast of the fallen man, and shouted in his face:

"Myga is saved! The ship is taken! Spread those tidings in hell!"

With that he thrust his sailor's knife into the throat of his deadly enemy.

By this time, all the Genoese who had not saved themselves by flight had fallen. The fight on the *Andrea Doria* was over, and the Beggars were already at work on the chains that moored the ship to the quay.

In the cabin, Myga lay unconscious in the arms of Jan, who carried his betrothed out of that dreadful place and from the dead captain, Antonio Valani, up into the fresh air.

Fighting was still going on on some of the neighbouring ships; others were already gliding out into the stream, steered by the Beggars; and the wild harmonies of the victors' song rose through the night:

> "Wilhelmus von Nassaue
> Bin ich von deutschem Blut,
> Dem Vaterland getreue
> Bleib' ich bis in den Tod———"[1]

From the stern of the *Andrea Doria*, the trumpeter of the *Black Galley* sounded the same air, and in a wild chorus the victorious seamen joined in:—

> "Dass euch die Spanier kränken
> O Niederlande gut,
> Wenn ich daran tu' denken,
> Mein edel Herz, das blu't."[2]

Even the mortally wounded among the Beggars raised themselves at the sound of the solemn harmonies—those who could no longer sing, moved their lips to the words of the song. And through its power, Myga van Bergen came back to life. Laughing and crying in Jan's arms, she joined in the song of freedom.

"Well, I keep faith! With thunder of cannon and clashing of bells and sounding of trumpets, I am taking you home. Saved! Saved!" rejoiced Jan.

Shot after shot of warning sounded from the citadel, drum after drum joined in the alarm raised by the drum on the quay. Sounds that grew

---

[1] Wilhelmus of Nassaue
Of German blood I come,
To Fatherland most faithful
I'll be till life is done.

[2] That Spaniards you harm bring,
My Netherlands so dear;
When that I think upon it,
My heart it bleedeth sore.

ever louder announced that the great Flemish city was rousing itself
behind its walls and its ramparts, and many an oppressed, angry heart
beat high at the proud, forbidden melody that bade defiance to the
roll of the Spanish drums, and seemed to rise more loudly the more they
tried to drown it. The tocsin sounded now from every tower. There
was a rattling and clashing from the city and the citadel down to the
quay—company after company hurrying down to the river.

But proudly and more proudly rang out over the tumult:—

> "Mein Schild und mein Vertreuen
> Bist du, o Gott, mein Herr,
> Auf dich so will ich bauen,
> Verlass mich nimmermehr,

> "Dass ich doch fromm mag bleiben,
> Dir dienen zu aller Stund',
> Die Tyrannei vertreiben,
> Dir mir mein Herz verwund't."[1]

Thousands upon thousands of hearts, behind the walls that Paciotti
had built round the city of Antwerp, were stirred to sweet trembling by
these tones; thousands upon thousands of eyes grew damp because of
them.

But this was no time for reflection. The *Black Galley* had accomplished its greatest feat of arms, now the fruits of victory must be
brought to safety. Protected by the fire of the *Black Galley*, Jan Norris,
commanding the *Andrea Doria*, reached the middle of the Scheldt, and
sailed slowly downstream past the city. Seven smaller ships which had
been captured, were in front with the Beggars' ships—the *Black Galley*
closed the procession.

How fiercely it lightened and thundered from the forts of Antwerp;
how well the reply came from the ships of the Beggars, and from the
Andrea Doria, which now flying the Beggars' flag, her sails merrily
swollen by the morning breeze, glided down the stream; how Don
Federigo Spinola tore his hair at such an unheard of deed!

Fire from every fort, from every battery beside the river!

The thunder of the cannon had ceased. All the Netherlanders' ships

---

[1] My shield and my sure helper
Art Thou, O Lord my God,
I'll build on that foundation,
Dear Lord, forsake me not.

My prayer, that I may faithful
Be, serve Thee all the day,
The tyranny that wounds me
Drive far and fast away.

with their booty, had safely passed the Spanish forts. But from the distance still echoed the song of 1568:

> "Vor Gott will ich bekennen
> Und seiner ganzen Macht,
> Dass ich zu seinen Zeiten
> Den Konig hab' veracht't,
> Weil dass ich Gott dem Herrn,
> Der höchsten Majestät,
> Hab' müssen obedieren
> In der Gerechtigkeit!"[1]

The sounds died away towards the sea, as the Beggars' proud squadron, with its booty, its bloody wounds, and its glory, glided down stream in the thickening mist.

HOW THE SEA SAVED LEYDEN[2]

Georg Ebers

(1837–1898)

PETER was sitting in front of his writing-table in his Burgomaster's dress, and with his hat on. His face was hidden in his folded arms, the two-branched candlestick stood lighted on the table. He saw nothing, heard nothing; and when she presently called him by his name he started violently, stood bolt upright, and flung his hat angrily on to the table. His hair was in disorder, his gaze unsteady, and in the dull flickering light of the candles his face was as grey as that of a corpse.

"What do you want?" he asked shortly in a hoarse voice; but for some moments she could not answer—her tongue seemed paralyzed with terror. At last she spoke.

"What has happened?" she said, and her voice betrayed her anguish.

"The beginning of the end," he said gloomily.

"They have outvoted you!" cried the young woman. "Baersdorp and the rest of the cowards want to treat?"

He drew himself up.

---

[1]Proclaim will I before God
The Lord, and all His Power,
That I the king disdainèd
And scorn showed, in that hour.
Because I, God the Highest,
In majesty supreme,
For righteousness and conscience
My service whole must bring.

[2]From Clara Bell's translation of *The Burgomaster's Wife*.

"Beware of what you say," he cried, in loud and threatening tones. "A man who holds out till his children die, and corpses bar the way to his own house-door, who is responsible for a thousand deaths, who for weeks has been loaded with curses, and who for more than four months has hoped for succour, who, look where he will, sees nothing but unutterable and constantly increasing wretchedness and then feels that he can no longer thrust back the saving hand held out even by the foe——"

"He is a coward, a traitor, and breaks the solemn oath he has sworn!"

"Maria!" thundered Peter, going close up to her with a threatening glare.

She stood still, drawn up to her full height, and pointing her finger at him, as she went on with keen asperity, though her voice trembled: "You—you voted with Baersdorp! You, Peter van der Werff, you! You have done this, the Prince's friend, the guardian and providence of this brave town; you, the man to whom the citizens pledged their word —the son of the martyr, the champion of freedom!"

"Say no more!" he interrupted, quivering with shame and rage. "Do you know what it is to bear the burden of this woe that cries to Heaven, in the sight of God and man?"

"I do, I do, and again I say, I do. It is to bind your heart to the rack and wheel in order to save Holland and her freedom! That is what it is! Great God! great God! You are lost indeed; you are making terms with Valdez!"

"And if I were?" said the Burgomaster with a haughty wave of his hand as if to dismiss the question.

Maria fixed her eyes on his, and exclaimed with clear decision:

"Then it would be my turn to say, Go to Delft, go to Delft; we want other men here."

Van der Werff turned paler and looked down at the floor, while she stood facing him with a frank and fearless gaze. The light fell full on her glowing countenance, and as he raised his eyes once more to hers he felt that the woman who stood before him was that same Maria, who, as his bride, had sworn to share suffering and danger with him, and stand steadfast to the end in the struggle for freedom; he felt that his "child" Maria had grown up to his own level, ay, and beyond it; he recognized for the first time in the high-souled woman before him his ally in the fight, a worthy helpmate in trouble and in danger. An overpowering yearning, an eager aspiration such as he had never before felt, surged and seethed within him, and drew him to her, and bound utterance in words.

"Maria!" he cried, "Maria, my wife, my guardian angel! We have indeed written to Valdez, but it is yet time; nothing as yet binds me, and with you, with you by my side, I can stand firm to the end." And in the middle of this day of anguish her heart overflowed with the flood of this new, unhoped-for, and unutterable joy. As she flung herself on his breast, she exclaimed: "And I with you—one with you! for ever, through this struggle, and in love beyond the grave!"

Peter felt like a man under a charm. Courage and enthusiasm once more filled his soul, for they overflowed in an unfailing stream from the brave and confident spirit of his wife.

Under the pressure of the fearful responsibility he bore and the urgency of his fellow-citizens, he had agreed in the Council to write to Valdez and crave a safe-conduct for an envoy to be sent to the States-General and the Prince of Orange, to beg them to release the perishing city from its oath. Valdez spared no effort to incite the Burgomaster to farther negotiations, but Van der Werff stood firm, and the demand for release from the sacred duty of resistance never left the town. Both the Van der Does, the Town-Clerk, the Jonker van Warmond, and other staunch men, who, at the great general meeting had opposed all negotiations with the enemy, now ranged themselves on his side against their fellow-officials and the Town-Council, who, with the exception of seven only of their number, perseveringly and violently insisted on the discussion of terms.

Deep as the gloom was, and dark as was the horizon, in the midst of all this cruel misery, there were moments when a bright ray of sunshine fell on these suffering souls, and Hope unfurled her green standard. On the morning of the eleventh of September, the townsfolk of Leyden rose from their beds more radiantly joyful than a bride roused on her wedding-day by the songs of her maiden companions, for in the distance the loud and persistent thunder of cannon could be heard, and the sky was dyed with crimson; to the south-west of the town there must be villages in flames, and each house, each granary, that sank into ashes, burying the hopes of honest men, was a beacon of promise to the despairing Ley-deners.

The Gueux were approaching!

There, out there, where the cannon thundered and the horizon glowed, was the Land-scheiding, the dyke, which for centuries had stoutly protected the plain of Leyden against the incursions of the waves, and which now stopped the advance of the fleet that was to bring them life.

"Fall, sheltering wall! Rise, storms, and thou sea, engulf thy prey! Destroy the peasant's wealth, ruin our fields and pastures, but drown the foe or drive him hence!"

Thus sang Janus Dousa, thus cried Peter's soul, thus prayed Maria, and with her thousands of men and women.

But the blaze in the distance died away, the firing was silent. A second day went by, a third, a fourth; no messenger came, no ship of the Gueux was to be seen, and the lake lay motionless; while another awful power grew and stalked through the city with secret, stealthy, and omnipotent force—Death, with its gaunt helpmates Despair and Famine. Silently and at night the dead were carried to their graves, that the survivors might share their slender ration undiminished. From house to house the Angel of Death winged his way, and laid his hand at last on little Elizabeth, kissing her closed eyes as she slept in the noiseless night.

The faint-hearted, and those who sided with the Spaniards, assembled in mobs, one of which even made its way into the council-room, clamouring for bread. But there was not a crumb left in the stores, the authorities had nothing left to give but a morsel of cow or horse-flesh, or hides—soaked and salted hides.

On one of these days of dire extremity, Van der Werff was going down the Breede Straat; he paid no heed to the fact that a crowd of desperate men and women were following him with threats and abuse, but as he turned a corner to go to Van Hout's house, he suddenly found himself surrounded. A pale woman with a child in her arms at its last gasp, flung herself before him, holding the dying infant up to him, and crying in a hollow, feeble voice:

"Is it not enough, is it not enough? Look here, see this—it is the third! It is enough, enough!"

"Enough, enough! Bread, bread—give us bread!" thundered and growled all round him, and stones and missiles were lifted to throw, while a carpenter whom he knew, and who had always stood by the good cause, stepped close up to him, and said deliberately, in a deep voice: "We can bear it no longer. We have patiently endured famine and suffering to defy the Spaniards and to defend our Bible, but to fight with certain death is sheer madness."

Peter stood still, shocked and silent, and looked at the mother, the child, the stalwart working man, and the shrieking threatening wretches. The common woe which was crushing them and so many starving creatures burdened his soul with tenfold weight. Anguish unutterable clutched his heart, and he longed to open his arms and embrace them all as fellow-sufferers, and brethren in a future and nobler existence. He looked from one to another deeply moved; then pressing his hands to his breast he thus addressed the crowd that thronged round him:

"Here I stand. I have sworn to remain faithful, and you swore it with me. I will never break my oath, but I can die! If my death can do you any good, here I am! Bread I have none, but here is my body—take it; kill me, and tear me in pieces. Here I stand, and I will never break my oath."

The carpenter's head fell on his breast. "Come, good folks," he said; "God's will be done. We have sworn."

The Burgomaster passed on calmly to his friend's house. Dame van Hout had watched the whole scene from a window, and that same day she related it to Maria, and her eyes sparkled with enthusiasm as she added:

"I never saw a man so supremely great as he was at that moment. It is well for us that he commands within these walls; this deed will be remembered by our children and our children's children."

They have, indeed, kept his memory green in faithful remembrance. During the night which followed the day when the Burgomaster had held himself so bravely, a letter arrived from the Prince, full of cheerful and encouraging news. Their illustrious chief was well again, and straining every nerve to save his brave town of Leyden. The Gueux had pierced the Land-scheiding; the ships were advancing; help was approaching; and the devoted men who brought the letter had, with their own eyes, seen the fleet that was bringing supplies and the champions of freedom, fired with zeal and valour for the struggle. The two Van der Does were nominated in the same letter to represent the Prince in the place of Van Bronkhorst. Van der Werff no longer stood alone; and when, next morning, "Father William's" letter was read to the populace, and the messenger's errand had become generally known, the spirits and confidence of the long-suffering townsfolk rose like withered grass under refreshing showers.

But there were still weary weeks of terror and misery to be gone through. In the last days of September they had to kill the cows, which till then had been spared for the benefit of the children and women in child-bed; and then—what next? Succour was at hand, for the sky was often red, and the air shook with the thunder of distant cannon; but the east wind blew steadily, and held back the water which was let in upon the land; and the ships which were trying to reach the town needed a high flood-tide.

Of all the messengers they sent forth not one returned; nothing was certain but their hideous, cruel, and increasing misery.

At last Barbara had succumbed, and was complaining of prostration and loathing for every kind of food. Maria remembered the roast pigeon which had been so welcome to their little lost Liesje, and she went to the musician to ask him whether he could bear to sacrifice another of his pets to save her sister-in-law.

She was received by his mother, who was sitting languid and feeble in an easy-chair. She could still walk, it is true, but all this anxiety and extreme want had brought on a strange shaking palsy in her hands. To Maria's question she shook her head and replied: "Ask him yourself. He has had to keep the poor little creatures shut up, for if they had been seen, they would have been shot down long since by the starving people. He still has three; the rest have flown off with various letters, but have never come back. Thank God! say I, for the scrap of food he still has by him is better in the pot than in their crops. Would you believe it? A fortnight since he paid fifty gülden out of his savings for half a sack of peas, and God only knows where he got them then. Ullrich, take Dame van der Werff up to speak to Wilhelm. I would spare you the stairs, but he is watching up there for the pigeons he has sent out, and will not come down even to meals; and God knows they are not worth coming down to."

The day was clear and sunny. Wilhelm was standing on his balcony, and looking out over the green, well-watered plain that stretched before him to the south. Behind him sat the Captain's orphan son, Andreas, writing music; but his attention was not very steady, for, whenever he had finished a line, he sat gazing into the air and watching, like his master, for the expected pigeons. He was not very much the worse for the dearth, for a certain portion of the pigeons' food had fallen to his share with his small allowance of meat.

Wilhelm was as much surprised as honoured by Maria's visit, and promised to grant her request; but it was plain that he did not find it an easy matter to say "Yes." The young woman went out on to the balcony with him, and he showed her that to the south, where formerly nothing had been visible but miles of green, there was a line—a long, level margin—above which hovered a filmy mist. The noon-day sun seemed to saturate the pale vapour with light and draw it upwards. It was the water that was pouring in through the cuts in the dykes; and the long black patches which might be seen moving on its shore must be the Spanish troops and herds of cattle which were being driven into the outermost forts, villages, and hamlets, by the encroaching tide. The Land-scheiding itself was out of sight, but the Gueux had already cut through that. If the fleet could only reach the Zoetermeer Lake, and from thence——

But Wilhelm suddenly broke off in his explanation, for Andreas sprang up, throwing down his stool and shouting:

"It is coming! the pigeon! By Roland, my former self, there it is!"

It was the first time that Wilhelm had ever heard the father's favourite cry from the lips of the son; something must have excited him strangely; and in fact he was not mistaken, for the speck which his sharp eyes had espied cutting through the air was no longer a speck but already an object of discernible form—a bird—a pigeon.

Wilhelm snatched up a banner that lay on the balcony, and waved it more joyfully than ever a pictor waved his flag after winning a battle. There came the pigeon; it settled, slipped into the dovecot, and in another minute the musician appeared with a tiny letter in his hand.

"To the Burgomaster—quick!" cried Wilhelm. "Carry it at once to your husband, dear Dame, and finish what the pigeon has begun. God be praised! they are already at North Aa. This will save the poor folks from despair; and one thing more, you shall have a bird to cook; but take this corn too—barleymeal porridge is the very best remedy in Barbara's condition;—I have tried it."

In the evening, and after the organist had communicated the good news to his parents, he ordered that the blue pigeon with the white breast should be killed. "Make an end of it outside," he said; "I cannot bear to see it done."

Andreas soon came in with the dead pigeon; his lips were red, and

Wilhelm could guess the reason, but he could not scold the famishing boy, and only said:

"Faugh! you ferret!"

Next morning, quite early, another pigeon flew in. The letters that they brought were read out from the window of the town-hall, and the courage of the Leydeners, now in the utmost extremity of misery, once more flickered into life, and helped them to endure the worst. One of the letters was to Van der Werff, the other to Janus Dousa; they spoke of confidence and hope; and the Prince—the faithful rock of their freedom, the friend and leader of the nation—the Prince himself was well and strong again, and had himself been to see the ships which were being sent to relieve the town. Salvation was so near—but the north-east wind would not change, and the waters did not rise.

On the Burcht and other elevated spots stood the citizens, soldiers, town-councillors and women in great numbers, all gazing into the distance. A thousand hands were uplifted in fervent prayer, and all eyes were fixed in feverish expectation and agonizing longing on the southern horizon; but the line of water did not advance, and the sun broke brightly through the mists of the autumn mornings as if in mockery, tempered the keen air, and sank to rest in the evening in a fiery glow and far-reaching shafts of golden light. A cloudless blue sky o'erarched the town with pitiless calm, and decked itself at night with myriads of bright stars.

On the morning of the 29th, however, the mists seemed to pack more solidly together, the grass was dewless, a fog rose, the sharp air was tempered to a dull mildness, and the great clouds grew dense and gathered blackness. Then a light breeze rose, and rustled in the leafless branches, and suddenly a gust of wind swept over the heads of the watching crowd. It was followed by a second and a third, and at last the gale whistled and roared, and a howling storm whirled through the town, sweeping the tiles from the roofs, bending the fruit-trees in the gardens and the young elms and limetrees in the streets; tearing down the banners which the boys had stuck up on the walls, in defiance of the Spaniards; lashing the dull waters of the canals and the moat. And now—for the Lord forsaketh not his own—the weathercock veered, the blast came down from the north-west, and drove the spring-tide in the storm-tossed sea up the mouth of the Maas; none could see it, but the seamen shouted out the news, and it was caught up and passed on from one to another. The stream was forced violently up its channel and over its banks; rushing through the cuttings made in the dykes to admit it, and through the yawning sluice-gates, and bearing on its mighty shoulders the ships that bore relief.

Rage, rage, thou storm; beat down, thou lashing rain; rush on, ye floods; destroy the land, engulf the houses and farms! Thousands are waiting to welcome you on the walls and towers of Leyden. They see in you the avenging and saving hosts of the Lord, and rejoice and hail you with shouts.

For two successive days the Burgomaster—with Maria and Adria, and the families of Van der Does and Van Hout—has remained, with brief intervals, among the townspeople, who are watching from the Burcht or the Cow Gate; and even Barbara, though hardly recovered, will not be kept at home, for hope has done more to revive her than the barleymeal porridge and the lean pigeon; she has dragged herself up to the musician's eyrie, for every one must see the advancing waters, as the earth gives place to them—see the moisture trickle through the grass, collect in puddles, pools, lakes, till at last it is a broad level, beaten by the thrashing rain into bubbles that break into rings and vanish. Every one wants to see with his own eyes how the Spaniards hurry hither and thither, like sheep fleeing before a wolf. Every one must hear for himself the thunder of the Gueux' cannon, the rattle of their arquebuses and musketry; men and women alike, rejoice more in the storm which threatens to sweep them away, than in the softest zephyr; and the drenching rain that soaks them is more delightful than the sun-lit showers of spring.

Beyond the stronghold of Lammen, defended by some hundred Spanish soldiers, and the tower of Croonesteyn, a keen eye could now detect the ships of the Gueux. All Thursday and Friday Wilhelm had looked in vain for a pigeon, but on Saturday his best carrier came home. It bore a letter from Admiral Boisot, begging that the men-at-arms left in the town would make a sortie on the Friday, and throw themselves upon Lammen. The storm had carried the bird out of its track; it had arrived a day too late. However, on the Saturday evening Janus Dousa and Captain van der Laen prepared to move. All who could bear arms were called out early on Sunday morning. A hapless, pale, and diminished force gathered at their Commander's call; but none would be missing, and all were prepared to yield up their lives for the rescue of the town, and of those dear to them.

The storm had moderated; the firing had ceased; the night was warm and dark. Not an eye was closed, and those who, for a few moments, were overcome by sleep were startled and alarmed by strange and mysterious noises. Wilhelm sat up on his balcony looking and listening towards the south. Now a light gust of wind would whistle round the tall house, now a shout, a cry, a trumpet-call rang through the silent night; and presently there was a crash and roar out by the Cow Gate, as though an earthquake had shaken the foundations of part of the town and hurled it to the gound. There was not a star in the sky, but in the neighbourhood of Lammen dancing lights moved in regular rows across the black darkness. It was an ominous and terrible night.

At dawn it was seen that a part of the town-wall by the Cow Gate had fallen in. and a cry of joy went up to Heaven at the sight of the breach, which was now no longer a source of danger, while the joyful news flew through the streets and alleys. Men and women, old men and children, sick and sound, came out of the houses, crowding down to the Cow Gate; now the fleet of the Gueux was to be seen rapidly coming nearer, and the town-carpenter, Thomassohn, with some others, was tearing up the piles with which the Spaniards had barred the Vliet, till at last the first ship, and then a second and a third, was close under the walls. The wild-looking hairy sailors—men with deeply-scarred, fierce, sun-burnt faces, which for years had felt no touch of any salt water but the sea spray—were laughing to the citizens and crying and sobbing like children; while they threw them up loaves and good things long unknown to them, which the poor creatures on the wall ate and ate, and could not even find a word of thanks. And then the chiefs arrived and met; Admiral Boisot fell into the arms of Van der Does and the Burgo-master, and Van Duykenburg into those of his mother, old Barbara, and many a Leydener hugged the liberators he had never set eyes on till this hour. Many, many a tear was shed, and thousands of hearts over-flowed, and the Sunday bells rang out louder and clearer than was their wont, bidding the rescuer and the rescued alike to church and prayer. The wide vault of the sanctuary was too narrow for the worshippers, and when the preacher Corneliuszoon—filling the place of the worthy Vestroot, who had fallen ill himself while tending so many sufferers—exhorted the devout to thanksgiving, his words had long been antici-pated, for at the very first sound of the organ the thousands who crowded the church in every part had been fired to offer up, as with one voice, thanks—thanks, and again fervent thanks!

Pater Damianus, too, returned thanks to God in the little chapel of the Carmelite Sisters, and with him Nicolas van Wibisma and many another Catholic, to whom freedom and his fatherland were dear.

After church, Adrian, with a piece of bread in one hand and his shoes in the other, waded at the head of his school-fellows across the higher meadows, which were all under water, as far as Leyderdorp, to see the deserted Spanish camp. There stood the handsome tent of the Com-mander-in-chief; over the bedstead hung a map of the Rhineland, which had been drawn by Beeldsnyder, a Dutchman, for the destruction of his own countrymen. The boys stood gazing at it, and a Gueux, who had once sat at a desk, and who now looked like a sea-bear, went up to them.

"See here, lads," he said, "here is the Land-scheiding. We cut through that first, but that was only half our task. We were checked at the Green-way, and here at the third dyke—the Voorweg they call it—we found too hard a nut to crack; we could not get through any way. So back we had to go again, a long round by Zeegwaert and through the canal here, where we had a hard tussle, to North Aa. The Zoetermeer Lake was now behind us, but the water was too shallow, and we could get no farther. Have you seen the great *Ark of Delft?* It is a huge vessel, and is not moved by oars but by wheels which turn and push it on through the water; you will like to see it. At last the Lord sent the storm and the spring-tide, and the ships had water enough to float them. At the Kirkway we again had hot work, but we got to Lammen the day before yesterday. Many a brave man had already fallen on both sides, but when we got to Lammen, we all thought we were to fight it out in good earnest. Early this morning we meant to storm the fort, but when day dawned all was awfully still in the nest, and there was an uncanny sultriness in the air. Then we thought to ourselves, 'It is all over with Leyden; hunger has been too much for them!' But nothing of the kind! You are made of sterner stuff; and a boy came wading out to the ship—about as big as one of you—and said that in the night he had seen a long train of lights come out of the fort and march away. At first we would not believe him, but the boy was right. The crabs had found the water too hot for them, and the lights the youngster had seen were the slow matches of the Spaniards. Look, children, there is Lammen——" Adrian and his companions had gone quite close up to the map, and had interrupted the seaman's story with a loud laugh.

"What have you found there, curly-pate?" asked the Gueux.

"Look here, look here, the great Valdez has immortalized himself; and here is his name too! Our head-master would make him wear a dunce's cap, for he writes *Castelli parvi*! '*Vale civitas, valete Castelli parvi; relicti estis propter aquam et non per vim inimicorum*. Oh, what an ass! *Castelli parvi*!"

"And what does all that mean?" asked the sailor.

"Farewell, Leyden, farewell, ye little *Castelli*! you are abandoned because of the waters and not because of the strength of the enemy. '*Parvi Castelli*'!"

OF THE COMPANY OF THE PRIVATEERS[1]

J. G. Lockhart

(1891-   )

WHEN most of the exploits of the Imperial German Navy are forgotten, men will still recall the adventures of the *Emden*. Daring seamanship and humanity towards non-combatants are no less admirable in an enemy than in a friend: and few will deny to Captain von Müller and his company their due share of all these qualities. Indeed, it is hard to associate them with those others—their comrades—who, later in the war, "sank without a trace," sending defenceless merchantmen—crews, passengers and all—to the bottom of the sea. Rather

[1] From *Strange Adventures of the Sea*. Reprinted by permission of the author and of Philip Allan & Co., Ltd.

should we judge them akin to Francis Drake, Paul Jones, and all the gallant company of privateers, British, French, and American.

The *Emden* was a light cruiser of 3,592 tons, with a speed on trial of 24 knots, and an armament of ten 4.1 inch guns. At the beginning of August 1914, she was lying in Tsingtau, Germany's Naval Base in Far Eastern waters; but on the 3rd of the month—the day before Britain declared war on Germany—she slipped out under orders to join Admiral von Spee's squadron in the south.

She was only just in time. Directly war broke out, Vice-Admiral Jerram, the British Commander-in-Chief in China, made it his first business to close Tsingtau; and between his squadron and that of Captain Fitzmaurice the *Emden* narrowly escaped capture at the very beginning of her career. However, she got away, and, steaming at full speed for the south, reached Pagan Island, not far from the German wireless station at Yapp, in the Caroline group, on August 12th. This was her appointed *rendez-vous* with Admiral von Spee and the South Pacific Squadron. On her arrival, however, she found that the Admiral had changed his plans. In view of the threatening attitude of Japan, who actually declared war some ten days later, it was hopeless to return to Tsingtau; the squadron might get in, but would certainly never get out again. Von Spee had accordingly decided to cross the Pacific to South American waters, where he proposed to deal with Admiral Cradock and generally make himself unpleasant. For such an enterprise the *Emden*, with her light armament, was not likely to prove so useful as if she were left behind to do a little commerce-destroying by herself.

Accordingly, when von Spee turned east on the voyage that was to take him to his victory at Coronel and to a fighting end off the Falkland Islands, he sent the *Emden* west. She was, somehow or other, to break through into the Indian Ocean. Arrived there, she was to do as much damage as she could, for as long as she could. There was, of course, only one possible end to such an adventure—she would be hunted without respite, and sooner or later the avengers would run her down. But in the meantime she would have her crowded hour, and, if her career was short, like that of the old pirates it would also be merry.

With these instructions Captain von Müller left Pagan Island on his desperate enterprise. His first task—since surprise was the essence of his business—was to reach the scene of operations unobserved. This was not so easy as it sounds, for in order to pass into the Indian Ocean from the Pacific it was necessary to enter the frequented waters of the Malay Archipelago, to thread his way circumspectly about a maze of islands, and finally to bolt through one of a number of comparatively narrow passages. However, he contrived to make the journey undetected, and on August 23rd the *Emden* stole through the Molucca Straits and round the south coast of Java. Thus, unexpected and most unwelcome, she burst into the peaceful waters of the Indian Ocean.

Immediately thereafter von Müller's tactics were fairly simple. He would lie off one of the main steamer routes, pounce on a few victims, scuttle them, and before the alarm could be given disappear again into the trackless wastes of the ocean, where he might steam for days without sighting another ship. It sounded feasible. He had secured his surprise; he was within striking distance of the great waterways to Calcutta, to the Far East and to Australia; he had speed; and he was not dependent on the caprices of winds. But if he had certain advantages over the old privateers, there were also drawbacks which they had never had to face. There was the wireless telegraph, by which his presence could be made known and a concentration of his pursuers effected in an incredibly short time. Also there was the coal question. On the kind of work in front of her the *Emden's* fuel consumption was certain to be enormous. With luck she might obtain—as, in fact, she did—fresh supplies from some of her victims. But, as this source was doubtful, it had been necessary to arrange meetings in mid-ocean or off secluded islands with a number of German colliers that had been equipped and sent out for the purpose. This was bound to affect her movements, to compel her to be in certain specified spots on specified dates; nor could her own wireless be used to alter arrangements once made, since her whereabouts would thus be betrayed to the enemy.

We may be sure that von Müller set about his task with a clear idea of both his advantages and his difficulties; and it must be owned that from the outset he made excellent use of his opportunities. His first objective was Ceylon, where he hoped to intercept vessels bound for the Bay of Bengal. In the whole of the Bay there was not a single British cruiser, and so secure from enemy interference was the area thought to be that none of the precautions that afterwards became customary were observed by passing vessels. They kept to the old routes; at night they steamed along with all their lights ablaze; and as a result the *Emden* began her career with some very easy victims. The first was a Greek collier, the *Pontoporos*, carrying 6,000 tons of Indian coal; and, though Greece was a neutral, von Müller had no compunction in capturing and retaining her—and her coal. Afterwards, in quick succession, she stopped the *Indus*, the *Killin*, and the *Diplomat*. All these ships were on the direct track, took her for a British cruiser, and steamed innocently to meet her. After taking off their crews she sank them by gunfire.

Her next venture was less fortunate. She cut out an Italian steamer, the *Loredano*. Now Italy was one of the most important of the neutral Powers, and it was not advisable to give offence by tampering with her shipping. So von Müller merely stopped her and asked her captain to take over his prisoners; and when the captain refused he was told to continue his voyage. But, instead of doing so, he turned and made back to Hooghly. On the way he met the *City of Rangoon*, a big new ship with a rich cargo, and warned her of the danger ahead; whereupon she, being equipped with wireless, promptly gave the alarm.

The cat was now out of the bag. Every ship with a Marconi installation and within broad-casting distance picked up the message and scurried for port; and in every harbour of India and Ceylon the sailings were held up. The *Emden* was to make many more victims; but the hunt had begun. Directly the news reached Singapore, three cruisers, the *Hampshire*, the *Chikuma* and the *Yarmouth*, were hurried west to the coast of Ceylon.

Meanwhile the *Emden* had gone to False Bay to coal. On her way there she ran into the *Trabbock* and the *Clan Matheson*, which, having no wireless, had not been warned. They were promptly sunk. Two blank days followed, and the absence of ships in such frequented waters showed that the secret was out. Very soon, too, von Müller, listening in, began to pick up wireless messages which indicated that in the near future the neighbourhood was likely to become exceedingly unhealthy for a certain German cruiser.

The *Emden's* next move, therefore, was to shift her hunting ground and to cross the Bay of Bengal to the Gulf of Martaban, where she coaled under way, at a point not very far from Rangoon. Here she listened to further wireless conversations among her pursuers, from which it appeared that several British cruisers were working up from the south, and that she had only just missed one of them, the *Hampshire*, at the mouth of the Gulf. Von Müller now decided to double on his tracks, and by September 22nd he was back off the Malabar coast again. Here he carried out a spectacular *coup*. He bombarded Madras, the third city of India. The damage done was not great. Two tanks belonging to the Burmah Oil Company were destroyed, five people were killed, and a dozen or so wounded. But the moral effect of the achievement on a population largely composed of ignorant and credulous people was tremendous. Thousands of the inhabitants of Madras are said to have fled into the interior and for a season the wildest rumours startled the bazaars of India. Two months after the bombardment the present writer happened to be at Delhi, hundreds of miles from the coast. One day a strange and alarming story was being told and believed in the native city. It was said that the *Emden* (then lying a riddled wreck on the Cocos) was sailing up the river Jumna to the capture of Delhi Fort. The panic, however, was speedily averted. The next day the Indian Cavalry Regiment stationed in the city went a few miles out to train. That was the story, but the wiseacres of the bazaar knew better: it had gone out to deal with the *Emden*. And when in due course it returned, rumour had it that all was well and that the terrible German cruiser had been captured.

But, apart from the mischief which nonsense of this kind was liable to make among ignorant folk, the *Emden's* success in eluding capture and reappearing in a quarter supposed to be once more clear had very serious results. For a time all the sailings to and from India were thoroughly disorganized—a bad business when convoys of much-needed troops were waiting at the ports. And away down in Australia, where the first contingent was ready to sail, there was much heart-burning and some delay; so that, failing to appreciate the difficulty of rounding up one small and elusive cruiser in the mighty expanse of the Indian Ocean, public opinion was inclined to find fault with the British Navy.

At the same time it was hard not to feel a sneaking admiration for the bold outlaw, despite the trouble she was giving. Her daring, her cool disregard of the heavy odds against her, the certainty of her ultimate ruin, and especially the humanity with which, at great risk to herself, she had safeguarded the lives of the crews she captured, all commended themselves to a sea-faring people. Von Müller, we decided, was an unmitigated nuisance; but he was a bit of a sportsman.

After bombarding Madras, the *Emden* turned south towards Ceylon, again narrowly missing the *Hampshire*. She sank the *King Lud* and the *Tymeric*, and captured the *Gryfevale*, which she took on with her. She then steamed west to Minikoi, a small island to the south of the Laccadives; and between that spot and Cape Cormorin she made another haul. She captured the *Ribera*, the *Foyle* and—most fortunate for her—the *Buresk*. The first two, which were in ballast, she sank; but the *Buresk*, which she encountered at dead of night, steaming on the direct track with all lights burning, was a ship of 4,300 tons, bound for Hong Kong on Admiralty charter with a cargo of good Welsh coal. This was a wonderful piece of luck. Von Müller put all his prisoners in the *Gryfevale* and let her go; then he steamed south towards the Maldive Islands to cover his tracks and, if possible, to find a quiet spot where he might clean his ship and shift some of that excellent coal from the *Buresk's* bunkers to the *Emden's*.

His success was followed by another narrow escape. While he was coaling in the Maldives, the *Yarmouth* and the *Chikuma* were hunting round Minikoi; but when they reached the Maldives the *Emden* was off again. For a time they lost all trace of her, as well they might, for von Müller had gone far afield on another of his unexpected swoops. With superb impudence he was paying a visit to Diego Garcia, a tiny British island in the heart of the Indian Ocean. In this remote and lonely spot the inhabitants had not even heard of the war. In their innocence they gave the *Emden* (visitors being few and far between) a warm welcome, and supplied her with every facility for cleaning ship and coaling.

After this hospitable interlude she left for the north again, passing at a distance of three hundred miles one of her pursuers, coming down to Diego Garcia to look for her. Von Müller now returned to his old cruising-ground off Minikoi, where he picked up another Admiralty collier, the *Exford*, with 6,000 tons of Welsh coal aboard. This capture was the more welcome, since the British cruisers, while they had been baffled in their main quest, had been diligently rounding up the German colliers. Subsequently, between Minikoi and Ceylon, von Müller added five more ships—four of them big ones—to his bag. Shortly afterwards he had a lucky escape, the *Hampshire* and *Empress of Asia* crossing the *Emden's* course at a distance of only ten to twenty miles ahead of her; nothing but the fact that it was a showery morning, with bad visibility, saved her from capture.

Von Müller now decided to transfer his activities to the eastern waters of the Indian Ocean, where he hoped to keep a *rendezvous* with his surviving colliers. Also he had another object—nothing less than a raid on Penang, the British Malacca base. He crossed the ocean without being observed, and was off Penang on the early morning of October 28th.

In the harbour, which was guarded by a picket-boat, lay a Russian cruiser, the *Zhemchug*, and two French destroyers; while a third destroyer was out on patrol. Von Müller had painted his ship grey—the British colour—and rigged up a dummy funnel; and when the *Emden*, thus disguised, appeared at the entrance to the channel shortly after five o'clock in the morning, the picket boat took her in the uncertain light for a British ship, and let her pass. She ran in, hoisted German colours, and torpedoed the *Zhemchug*. Steaming on, she pounded the Russian at a range of three hundred yards, turned, gave her another torpedo, and went out again. The *Zhemchug* burst into flame and sank, and before the two French ships, taken completely by surprise, were able to fire a round, the *Emden* had vanished. The third French destroyer, however, the *Mousquet*, returning from patrol, came on her in the northern entrance, where she was actually engaged in stopping an incoming liner, the *Glenturret*. The *Mousquet*, hopelessly out-gunned, put up a stout fight, but in seven minutes the *Emden* sent her to the bottom.

This was perhaps von Müller's most audacious feat; and it was almost his last. He now made for the Cocos Islands, to the south-west of Sumatra, where he proposed to destroy the telegraph station and to meet his colliers. He reached the Cocos on the early morning of November 9th, but, though he again rigged his dummy funnel, the telegraph officials were not deceived, and while Lieutenant von Mücke, with a landing-party of fifty men, was on his way to the station, the S.O.S. went out. Before the wireless could be jammed, the *Minotaur* picked up the message; and then the energetic officials actually got a cable through to Admiral Jerram.

Now, unknown to the *Emden*, during the previous night the first Australian convoy had passed under escort forty miles east of the Cocos, and when, just before seven o'clock, the warning messages came through, it was only fifty-five miles to the north. Captain Silver, commanding the convoy, at once dispatched the Australian cruiser, the *Sydney*, under Captain Glossop, to deal with the *Emden*. So while von Mücke was blowing up the wireless mast and smashing the installation on Direction

Island, retribution was fast approaching. Shortly after nine o'clock smoke appeared on the horizon, and the *Emden* at once signalled the shore party to rejoin. The strange ship came up rapidly, however, and was soon identifiable as a British cruiser. In a few minutes von Müller decided that, if he was to get sufficiently clear of the island to have room for manœuvre, he would have to abandon von Mücke and his men. He had no intention of avoiding an action, and seems to have been under the impression that the stranger was merely a weak light cruiser from the East Indies squadron. It was therefore an unpleasant surprise to the Germans when they discovered, a little later, that their opponent was the *Sydney*, of 5,400 tons, with a speed of 25.7 knots and an armament of eight 6-inch guns. With such an adversary the *Emden* could hope neither to win in a fight nor to escape in a chase.

The action began at 9.40. It was a calm, clear morning, with every condition favourable for good shooting. The two ships raced in parallel lines between Direction Island and North Keeling, twisting, turning, and doubling on their tracks. But the *Emden* never had a chance. The *Sydney* could lengthen the range at will; she could pound her adversary from a distance, or close in and rake her with lyddite. After forty minutes of punishment the *Emden* had lost all her funnels, her foremast had been shot away, her steering gear was smashed, and her fire control positions were gone. She was badly holed, blazing fore and aft, and smothered in smoke; but, crippled and shattered though she was, she was game to the end. When von Müller found that his ship was sinking under him, he made a last desperate attempt to beach her on North Keeling. The *Sydney* dashed in to cut her off, but was just too late, and the *Emden*, her hull shattered and her decks a shambles, but her flag still flying, ran hard aground on a reef.

The *Sydney* then left her for awhile. When the fight began the *Buresk*, the captured collier which von Müller had brought with him across the Indian Ocean, had made off to the north. The *Sydney* now went after her, and soon overhauled her; but, though she surrendered at once, the Germans scuttled her before the prize crew could take possession. Captain Glossop then returned to deal with the stranded *Emden*. It was four o'clock in the afternoon before he got back to North Keeling Island, and the *Emden*, helpless wreck though she was, still flew German colours; and, since she made no answer to his repeated demands for her surrender, Captain Glossop was forced to open fire on her again. Von Müller has been criticized for allowing this further and unnecessary loss of life, but it is hard to find fault with such heroic obstinacy. After two salvos had rent the stricken ship she hoisted a white flag and hauled down her colours. The fight was over.

POLAND

THE LIGHTHOUSE KEEPER OF ASPINWALL[1]

Henryk Sienkiewicz

(1846–1916)

ON A time it happened that the lighthouse keeper in Aspinwall, not far from Panama, disappeared without a trace. Since he disappeared during a storm, it was supposed that the ill-fated man went to the very edge of the small, rocky island on which the lighthouse stood, and was swept out by a wave. This supposition seemed the more likely, as his boat was not found next day in its rocky niche. The place of lighthouse keeper had become vacant. It was necessary to fill this place at the earliest moment possible, since the lighthouse had no small significance for the local movement as well as for vessels going from New York to Panama. Mosquito Bay abounds in sandbars and banks. Among these, navigation, even in the daytime, is difficult; but at night, especially with the fogs which are so frequent on those waters warmed by the sun of the tropics, it is nearly impossible. The only guide at that time for the numerous vessels is the lighthouse.

The task of finding a new keeper fell to the United States consul living in Panama, and this task was no small one: first, because it was absolutely necessary to find a man within twelve hours; second, the man must be unusually conscientious—it was not possible, of course, to take the first comer at random; finally, there was an utter lack of candidates. Life on a tower is uncommonly difficult, and by no means enticing to people of the South, who love idleness and the freedom of vagrant life. That lighthouse keeper is almost a prisoner. He cannot leave his rocky island except on Sundays. A boat from Aspinwall brings him provisions and water once a day, and returns immediately; on the whole island, one acre in area, there is no inhabitant. The keeper lives in the lighthouse; he keeps it in order. During the day he gives signals by displaying flags of various colours to indicate changes of the barometer; in the evening he lights the lantern. This would be no great labour were it not that to reach the lantern at the summit of the tower he must pass over more than four hundred steep and very high steps; sometimes he must make this journey repeatedly during the day. In general, it is the life of a monk, and indeed more than that—the life of a hermit. It was not wonderful, therefore, that Mr Isaac Falconbridge was in no small anxiety as to where he

---

[1] From Jeremiah Curtin's translation of *Yanko the Musician*. Reprinted by permission of Little Brown & Co.

should find a permanent successor to the recent keeper; and it is easy to understand his joy when a successor announced himself most unexpectedly on that very day. He was a man already old, seventy years or more, but fresh, erect, with the movements and bearing of a soldier. His hair was perfectly white, his face as dark as that of a Creole; but, judging from his blue eyes, he did not belong to a people of the South. His face was somewhat downcast and sad, but honest. At the first glance he pleased Falconbridge. It remained only to examine him. Therefore the following conversation began:

"Where are you from?"

"I am a Pole."

"Where have you worked up to this time?"

"In one place and another."

"A lighthouse keeper should like to stay in one place."

"I need rest."

"Have you served? Have you testimonials of honourable government service?"

The old man drew from his bosom a piece of faded silk, resembling a strip of an old flag, unwound it, and said:

"Here are the testimonials. I received this cross in 1830. This second one is Spanish from the Carlist War; the third is the French legion; the fourth I received in Hungary. Afterward I fought in the States against the South; there they do not give crosses."

Falconbridge took the paper and began to read.

"H'm! Skavinski? Is that your name? H'm! Two flags captured in a bayonet attack. You were a gallant soldier."

"I am able to be a conscientious lighthouse keeper."

"It is necessary to ascend the tower a number of times daily. Have you sound legs?"

"I crossed the plains on foot." (The immense steppes between the East and California are called "the plains.")

"Do you know sea service?"

"I served three years on a whaler."

"You have tried various occupations."

"The only one I have not known is quiet."

"Why is that?"

The old man shrugged his shoulders. "Such is my fate."

"Still you seem to me too old for a lighthouse keeper."

"Sir," exclaimed the candidate suddenly in a voice of emotion, "I am greatly wearied, knocked about. I have passed through much, as you see. This place is one of those which I have wished for most ardently. I am old, I need rest. I need to say to myself, 'Here you will remain; this is your port.' Ah, sir, this depends now on you alone. Another time perhaps such a place will not offer itself. What luck that I was in Panama! I entreat you—as God is dear to me, I am like a ship which if it misses the harbour will be lost. If you wish to make an old man happy—I swear to you that I am honest, but—I have enough of wandering."

The blue eyes of the old man expressed such earnest entreaty that Falconbridge, who had a good, simple heart, was touched.

"Well," said he, "I take you. You are lighthouse keeper."

The old man's face gleamed with inexpressible joy.

"I thank you."

"Can you go to the tower to-day?"

"I can."

"Then good-bye. Another word—for any failure in service you will be dismissed."

"All right."

That same evening, when the sun had descended on the other side of the isthmus, and a day of sunshine was followed by a night without twilight, the new keeper was in his place evidently, for the lighthouse was casting its bright rays on the water as usual. The night was perfectly calm, silent, genuinely tropical, filled with a transparent haze, forming around the moon a great coloured rainbow with soft, unbroken edges; the sea was moving only because the tide raised it. Skavinski on the balcony seemed from below like a small black point. He tried to collect his thoughts and take in his new position; but his mind was too much under pressure to move with regularity. He felt somewhat as a hunted beast feels when at last it has found refuge from pursuit on some inaccessible rock or in a cave. There had come to him, finally, an hour of quiet; the feeling of safety filled his soul with a certain unspeakable bliss. Now on that rock he can simply laugh at his previous wanderings, his misfortunes and failures. He was in truth like a ship whose masts, ropes, and sails had been broken and rent by a tempest, and cast from the clouds to the bottom of the sea—a ship on which the tempest had hurled waves and spat foam, but which still found its way to the harbour. The pictures of that storm passed quickly through his mind as he compared it with the calm future now beginning. A part of his wonderful adventures he had related to Falconbridge; he had not mentioned, however, thousands of other incidents. It had been his misfortune that as often as he pitched his tent and fixed his fireplace to settle down permanently, some wind tore out the stakes of his tent, whirled away the fire, and bore him on toward destruction. Looking now from the balcony of the tower at the illuminated waves, he remembered everything through which he had passed. He had campaigned in the four parts of the world, and in wandering had tried almost every occupation. Labour-loving and honest, more than once he had earned money, and had always lost it in spite of every prevision and the utmost caution. He had been a gold-miner in Australia, a diamond-digger in Africa, a rifleman in public service in the East Indies. He established a ranch in California—the drought ruined him; he tried trading with wild tribes in the interior of Brazil—his raft was wrecked on the Amazon; he himself alone, weaponless and nearly naked, wandered in the forest for many weeks living on wild fruits, exposed every moment to death from the jaws of wild beasts. He established a forge in Helena, Arkansas, and that was burned in a great fire which consumed the whole town. Next he fell into the hands of Indians in the Rocky Mountains, and only through a miracle was he saved by Canadian trappers. Then he served as a sailor on a vessel running between Bahia and Bordeaux, and as harpooner on a whaling-ship; both vessels were wrecked. He had a cigar factory in Havana, and was robbed by his partner while he himself was lying sick with the vomito. At last he came to Aspinwall, and there was to be the end of his failures—for what could reach him on that rocky island? Neither water nor fire nor men. But from men Skavinski had not suffered much; he had met good men oftener than bad ones.

But it seemed to him that all the four elements were persecuting him. Those who knew him said that he had no luck, and with that they explained everything. He himself became somewhat of a monomaniac. He believed that some mighty and vengeful hand was pursuing him everywhere, on all lands and waters. He did not like, however, to speak of this; only, at times, when some one asked him whose hand that could be, he pointed mysteriously to the Polar Star, and said, "It comes from that place." In reality his failures were so continuous that they were wonderful, and might easily drive a nail into the head, especially of the man who had experienced them. But Skavinski had the patience of an Indian, and that great calm power of resistance which comes from truth of heart. In his time he had received in Hungary a number of bayonet-thrusts because he would not grasp at a stirrup which was shown as means of salvation to him, and cry for quarter. In like manner he did not bend to misfortune. He crept up against the mountain as industriously as an ant. Pushed down a hundred times, he began his journey calmly for the hundred and first time. He was in his way a most peculiar original. This old soldier, tempered, God knows, in how many fires, hardened in suffering, hammered and forged, had the heart of a child. In the time of the epidemic in Cuba, the vomito attacked him because he had given to the sick all his quinine, of which he had a considerable supply, and left not a grain to himself.

There had been in him also this wonderful quality—that after so many disappointments he was ever full of confidence, and did not lose hope that all would be well yet. In winter he grew lively, and predicted great events. He waited for these events with impatience, and lived with the thought of them whole summers. But the winters passed one after another, and Skavinski lived only to this—that they whitened his head. At last he grew old, began to lose energy; his endurance was becoming more and more like resignation, his former calmness was tending toward supersensitiveness, and that tempered soldier was degenerating into a man ready to shed tears for any cause. Besides this, from time to time he was weighed down by a terrible homesickness which was roused by any circumstance—the sight of swallows, grey birds like sparrows, snow on the mountains, or melancholy music like that heard on a time. Finally, there was one idea which mastered him—the idea of rest. It mastered the old man thoroughly, and swallowed all other desires and hopes. This ceaseless wanderer could not imagine anything more to be longed for, anything more precious, than a quiet corner in which to rest, and wait in silence for the end. Perhaps specially because some whim of fate had so hurried him over all seas and lands that he could hardly catch his breath, did he imagine that the highest human happiness was simply not to wander. It is true that such modest happiness was his due; but he was so accustomed to disappointments that he thought of rest as people in general think of something which is beyond reach. He did not dare to hope for it. Meanwhile, unexpectedly, in the course of twelve hours he had gained a position which was as if chosen for him out of all the world. We are not to wonder, then, that when he lighted his lantern in the evening he became as it were dazed—that he asked himself if that was reality, and he did not dare to answer that it was. But at the same time reality convinced him with incontrovertible proofs; hence hours one after another passed while he was on the balcony. He gazed, and convinced himself. It might seem that he was looking at the sea for the first time in his life. The lens of the lantern cast into the darkness an enormous triangle of light, beyond which the eye of the old man was lost in the black distance completely, in the distance mysterious and awful. But that distance seemed to run toward the light. The long waves following one another rolled out from the darkness, and went bellowing toward the base of the island; and then their foaming backs were visible, shining rose-coloured in the light of the lantern. The incoming tide swelled more and more, and covered the sandy bars. The mysterious speech of the ocean came with a fullness more powerful and louder, at one time like the thunder of cannon, at another like the roar of great forests, at another like the distant dull sound of the voices of people. At moments it was quiet; then to the ears of the old man came some great sigh, then a kind of sobbing, and again threatening outbursts. At last the wind bore away the haze, but brought black, broken clouds, which hid the moon. From the west it began to blow more and more; the waves sprang with rage against the rock of the lighthouse, licking with foam the foundation walls. In the distance a storm was beginning to bellow. On the dark, disturbed expanse certain green lanterns gleamed from the masts of ships. These green points rose high and then sank; now they swayed to the right, and now to the left. Skavinski descended to his room. The storm began to howl. Outside, people on those ships were struggling with night, with darkness, with waves; but inside the tower it was calm and still. Even the sounds of the storm hardly came through the thick walls,

and only the measured tick-tack of the clock lulled the wearied old man
to his slumber.

Hours, days, and weeks began to pass. Sailors assert that sometimes
when the sea is greatly roused, something from out the midst of night
and darkness calls them by name. If the infinity of the sea may call out
thus, perhaps when a man is growing old, calls come to him, too, from
another infinity still darker and more deeply mysterious; and the more
he is wearied by life the dearer are those calls to him. But to hear them
quiet is needed. Besides old age loves to put itself aside, as if with a foreboding of the grave. The lighthouse had become for Skavinski such a
half grave. Nothing is more monotonous than life on a beacon-tower. If
young people consent to take up this service they leave it after a time.
Lighthouse keepers are generally men not young, gloomy, and confined
to themselves. If by chance one of them leaves his lighthouse and goes
among men, he walks in the midst of them like a person roused from deep
slumber. On the tower there is a lack of minute impressions which in
ordinary life teach men to adapt themselves to everything. All that a
lighthouse keeper comes in contact with is gigantic and devoid of definitely outlined forms. The sky is one whole, the water another; and between those two infinities the soul of man is in loneliness. That is a life
in which thought is continual meditation, and out of that meditation
nothing rouses the keeper, not even his work. Day is like day as two beads
in a rosary, unless changes of weather form the only variety. But Skavinski felt more happiness than ever in life before. He rose with the dawn,
took his breakfast, polished the lens, and then sitting on the balcony
gazed into the distance of the water; and his eyes were never sated with
the pictures which he saw before him. On the enormous turquoise ground
of the ocean were to be seen generally flocks of swollen sails gleaming in
the rays of the sun so brightly that the eyes were blinking before the
excess of light. Sometimes the ships, favoured by the so-called trade
winds, went in an extended line one after another, like a chain of sea-
mews or albatrosses. The red casks indicating the channel swayed on the
light wave with gentle movement. Among the sails appeared every
afternoon gigantic greyish feather-like plumes of smoke. That was a
steamer from New York which brought passengers and goods to Aspinwall, drawing behind it a frothy path of foam. On the other side of the
balcony Skavinski saw, as if on his palm, Aspinwall and its busy harbour,
and in it a forest of masts, boats, and craft; a little farther, white houses
and the towers of the town. From the height of his tower the small houses
were like the nests of sea-mews, the boats were like beetles, and the
people moved around like small points on the white stone boulevard.
From early morning a light eastern breeze brought a confused hum of
human life, above which predominated the whistle of steamers. In the
afternoon six o'clock came; the movements in the harbour began to
cease; the mews hid themselves in the rents of the cliffs; the waves grew

feeble and became in some sort lazy; and then on the land, on the sea, and on the tower came a time of stillness unbroken by anything. The yellow sands from which the waves had fallen back glittered like golden stripes on the width of the waters; the body of the tower was outlined definitely in blue. Floods of sunbeams were poured from the sky on the water and the sands and the cliff. At that time a certain lassitude full of sweetness seized the old man. He felt that the rest which he was enjoying was excellent; and when he thought that it would be continuous nothing was lacking to him.

Skavinski was intoxicated with his own happiness; and since a man adapts himself easily to improved conditions, he gained faith and confidence by degrees; for he thought that if men built houses for invalids, why should not God gather up at last His own invalids? Time passed, and confirmed him in this conviction. The old man grew accustomed to his tower, to the lantern, to the rock, to the sand-bars, to solitude. He grew accustomed also to the sea-mews which hatched in the crevices of the rock, and in the evening held meetings on the roof of the lighthouse. Skavinski threw them generally the remnants of his food; and soon they grew tame, and afterward, when he fed them, a real storm of white wings encircled him, and the old man went among the birds like a shepherd among sheep. When the tide ebbed he went to the low sand-banks, on which he collected savoury periwinkles and beautiful pearl shells of the nautilus, which receding waves had left on the sand. In the night by the moonlight and the tower he went to catch fish, which frequented the windings of the cliff in myriads. At last he was in love with his rocks and his treeless little island, grown over only with small thick plants exuding sticky resin. The distant views repaid him for the poverty of the island, however. During afternoon hours, when the air became very clear he could see the whole isthmus covered with the richest vegetation. It seemed to Skavinski at such times that he saw one gigantic garden— bunches of cocoa, and enormous musa, combined as it were in luxurious tufted bouquets, right there behind the houses of Aspinwall. Farther on, between Aspinwall and Panama, was a great forest over which every morning and evening hung a reddish haze of exhalations—a real tropical forest with its feet in stagnant water, interlaced with lianas and filled with the sound of one sea of gigantic orchids, palms, milk-trees, iron-trees, gum-trees.

Through his field-glass the old man could see not only trees and the broad leaves of bananas, but even legions of monkeys and great marabous and flocks of parrots, rising at times like a rainbow cloud over the forest. Skavinski knew such forests well, for after being wrecked on the Amazon he had wandered whole weeks among similar arches and thickets. He had seen how many dangers and deaths lie concealed under those wonderful and smiling exteriors. During the nights which he had spent in them he heard close at hand the sepulchral voices of howling monkeys and the

roaring of the jaguars; he saw gigantic serpents coiled like lianas on trees;
he knew those slumbering forest lakes full of torpedo-fish and swarming
with crocodiles; he knew under what a yoke man lives in those unexplored wildernesses in which are single leaves that exceed a man's size
ten times—wildernesses swarming with blood-drinking mosquitoes, tree-
leeches, and gigantic poisonous spiders. He had experienced that forest
life himself, had witnessed it, had passed through it; therefore it gave
him the greater enjoyment to look from his height and gaze on those
matos, admire their beauty, and be guarded from their treacherousness.
His tower preserved him from every evil. He left it only for a few hours
on Sunday. He put on then his blue keeper's coat with silver buttons, and
hung his crosses on his breast. His milk-white head was raised with a certain pride when he heard at the door, while entering the church, the Cre-
oles say among themselves, "We have an honourable lighthouse keeper
and not a heretic, though he is a Yankee." But he returned straightway
after Mass to his island, and returned happy, for he had still no faith in
the mainland. On Sunday also he read the Spanish newspaper which he
bought in the town, or the *New York Herald*, which he borrowed from
Falconbridge; and he sought in it European news eagerly. The poor old
heart on that lighthouse tower, and in another hemisphere, was beating
yet for its birthplace. At times too, when the boat brought his daily
supplies and water to the island, he went down from the tower to talk
with Johnson, the guard. But after a while he seemed to grow shy. He
ceased to go to the town, to read the papers and to go down to talk poli-
tics with Johnson. Whole weeks passed in this way, so that no one saw
him and he saw no one. The only signs that the old man was living were
the disappearance of the provisions left on shore, and the light of the
lantern kindled every evening with the same regularity with which the
sun rose in the morning from the waters of those regions. Evidently, the
old man had become indifferent to the world. Homesickness was not the
cause, but just this—that even homesickness had passed into resignation.
The whole world began now and ended for Skavinski on his island. He
had grown accustomed to the thought that he would never leave the
tower till his death, and he simply forgot that there was anything else
besides it. Moreover, he had become a mystic; his mild blue eyes began
to stare like the eyes of a child, and were as if fixed on something at a
distance. In presence of a surrounding uncommonly simple and great,
the old man was losing the feeling of personality; he was ceasing to exist
as an individual, was becoming merged more and more in that which
inclosed him. He did not understand anything beyond his environment;
he felt only unconsciously. At last it seems to him that the heavens, the
water, his rock, the tower, the golden sand-banks, and the swollen sails,
the sea-mews, the ebb and flow of the tide—all form a mighty unity, one
enormous mysterious soul; that he is sinking in that mystery, and feels
that soul which lives and lulls itself. He sinks and is rocked, forgets him-

self; and in that narrowing of his own individual existence, in that half-waking, half-sleeping, he has discovered a rest so great that it nearly resembles half-death.

But the awakening came.

On a certain day, when the boat brought water and a supply of provisions, Skavinski came down an hour later from the tower, and saw that besides the usual cargo there was an additional package. On the outside of this package were postage stamps of the United States, and the address: "Skavinski, Esq.," written on coarse canvas.

The old man, with aroused curiosity, cut the canvas, and saw books; he took one in his hand, looked at it, and put it back; thereupon his hands began to tremble greatly. He covered his eyes as if he did not believe them; it seemed to him as if he were dreaming. The book was Polish—what did that mean? Who could have sent the book? Clearly, it did not occur to him at the first moment that in the beginning of his lighthouse career he had read in the *Herald*, borrowed from the consul, of the formation of a Polish society in New York, and had sent at once to that society half his month's salary, for which he had, moreover, no use on the tower. The society had sent him the books with thanks. The books came in the natural way; but at the first moment the old man could not seize those thoughts. Polish books in Aspinwall, on his tower, amid his solitude—that was for him something uncommon, a certain breath from past times, a kind of miracle. Now it seemed to him, as to those sailors in the night, that something was calling him by name with a voice greatly beloved and nearly forgotten. He sat for a while with closed eyes, and was almost certain that, when he opened them, the dream would be gone.

The package, cut open, lay before him, shone upon clearly by the afternoon sun, and on it was an open book. When the old man stretched his hand toward it again, he heard in the stillness the beating of his own heart. He looked; it was poetry. On the outside stood printed in great letters the title, underneath the name of the author. The name was not strange to Skavinski; he saw that it belonged to the great poet,[1] whose productions he had read in 1830 in Paris. Afterwards, when campaigning in Algiers and Spain, he had heard from his countrymen of the growing fame of the great seer; but he was so accustomed to the musket at that time that he took no book in hand. In 1849 he went to America, and in the adventurous life which he led he hardly ever met a Pole, and never a Polish book. With great eagerness, therefore, and with a livelier beating of the heart, did he turn to the title-page. It seemed to him then that on his lonely rock some solemnity is about to take place. Indeed it was a moment of great calm and silence. The clocks of Aspinwall were striking

---

[1] Mickiewicz (pronounced Mitskyevich), the greatest poet of Poland.

five in the afternoon. Not a cloud darkened the clear sky; only a few sea-mews were sailing through the air. The ocean was as if cradled to sleep. The waves on the shore stammered quietly, spreading softly on the sand. In the distance the white houses of Aspinwall, and the wonderful groups of palm, were smiling. In truth, there was something there solemn, calm, and full of dignity. Suddenly, in the midst of that calm of nature, was heard the trembling voice of the old man, who read aloud as if to understand himself better:

> "Thou art like health, O my birth-land Litva![1]
> How much we should prize thee he only can know who has lost thee.
> Thy beauty in perfect adornment this day
> I see and describe, because I am yearning for thee."

His voice failed Skavinski. The letters began to dance before his eyes; something broke in his breast, and went like a wave from his heart higher and higher, choking his voice and pressing his throat. A moment more he controlled himself, and read further:

> "O Holy Lady, who guardest bright Chenstohova,
> Who shinest in Ostrobrama and preservest
> The castle town Novgrodek with its trusty people,
> As Thou didst give me back to health in childhood,
> When by my weeping mother placed beneath Thy care
> I raised my lifeless eyelids upward,
> And straightway walked unto Thy holy threshold,
> To thank God for the life restored me,—
> So by a wonder now restore us to the bosom of our birthplace."

The swollen wave broke through the restraint of his will. The old man sobbed and threw himself on the ground; his milk-white hair was mingled with the sand of the sea. Forty years had passed since he had seen his country, and God knows how many since he heard his native speech; and now that speech had come to him itself—it had sailed to him over the ocean, and found him in solitude on another hemisphere—it so loved, so dear, so beautiful! In the sobbing which shook him there was no pain —only a suddenly aroused immense love, in the presence of which other things are as nothing. With that great weeping he had simply implored forgiveness of that beloved one, set aside because he had grown so old, had become so accustomed to his solitary rock, and had so forgotten it that in him even longing had begun to disappear. But now it returned as if by a miracle; therefore the heart leaped in him.

Moments vanished one after another; he lay there continually. The mews flew over the lighthouse, crying as if alarmed for their old friend. The hour in which he fed them with the remnants of his food had come;

---

[1]Lithuania.

therefore, some of them flew down from the lighthouse to him; then more and more came, and began to pick and shake their wings over his head. The sound of the wings roused him. He had wept his fill, and had now a certain calm and brightness; but his eyes were as if inspired. He gave unwittingly all his provisions to the birds, which rushed at him with an uproar, and he himself took the book again. The sun had gone already behind the gardens and the forest of Panama, and was going slowly beyond the isthmus to the other ocean; but the Atlantic was full of light yet; in the open air there was still perfect vision; therefore, he read further:

"Now bear my longing soul to those forest slopes, to those green meadows."

At last the dusk obliterates the letters on the white paper—the dusk short as a twinkle. The old man rested his head on the rock, and closed his eyes. Then "She who defends bright Chenstohova" took his soul and transported it to "those fields coloured by various grain." On the sky were burning yet those long stripes, red and golden, and on those brightnesses he was flying to beloved regions. The pine-woods were sounding in his ears; the streams of his native place were murmuring. He saw everything as it was; everything asked him, "Dost remember?" He remembers! he sees the broad fields; between the fields, woods and villages. It is night now. At this hour his lantern usually illuminates the darkness of the sea; but now he is in his native village. His old head has dropped on his breast, and he is dreaming. Pictures are passing before his eyes quickly, and a little disorderly. He does not see the house in which he was born, for war had destroyed it; he does not see his father and mother, for they died when he was a child; but still the village is as if he had left it yesterday—the line of cottages with lights in the windows, the mound, the mill, the two ponds opposite each other, and thundering all night with a chorus of frogs. Once he had been on guard in that village all night; now that past stood before him at once in a series of views. He is an Uhlan again, and he stands there on guard; at a distance is the public-house; he looks with swimming eyes. There is thundering and singing and shouting amid the silence of the night, with voices of fiddles and bass-viols "U-ha! U-ha!" Then the Uhlans knock out fire with their horse-shoes, and it is wearisome for him there on his horse. The hours drag on slowly; at last the lights are quenched; now as far as the eye reaches there is mist, and mist impenetrable; now the fog rises, evidently from the fields, and embraces the whole world with a whitish cloud. You would say, a complete ocean. But that is fields; soon the land-rail will be heard in the darkness, and the bitterns will call from the reeds. The night is calm and cool—in truth, a Polish night! In the distance the pine-wood is sounding without wind, like the roll of the sea. Soon dawn will whiten the east. In fact, the cocks are beginning to crow behind the hedges.

One answers to another from cottage to cottage; the storks are screaming somewhere on high. The Uhlan feels well and bright. Some one had spoken of a battle to-morrow. Hei! that will go on, like all the others, with shouting, with fluttering of flaglets. The young blood is playing like a trumpet, though the night cools it. But it is dawning. Already night is growing pale; out of the shadows come forests, the thicket, a row of cottages, the mill, the poplars. The well is squeaking like a metal banner on a tower. What a beloved land, beautiful in the rosy gleams of the morning! Oh, the one land, the one land!

Quiet! the watchful picket hears that some one is approaching. Of course, they are coming to relieve the guard.

Suddenly some voice is heard above Skavinski:

"Here, old man! Get up! What's the matter?"

The old man opens his eyes, and looks with wonder at the person standing before him. The remnants of the dream-visions struggle in his head with reality. At last the visions pale and vanish. Before him stands Johnson, the harbour guide.

"What's this?" asked Johnson; "are you sick?"

"No."

"You didn't light the lantern. You must leave your place. A vessel from St Geromo was wrecked on the bar. It is lucky that no one was drowned, or you would go to trial. Get into the boat with me; you'll hear the rest at the Consulate."

The old man grew pale; in fact he had not lighted the lantern that night.

A few days later, Skavinski was seen on the deck of a steamer, which was going from Aspinwall to New York. The poor man had lost his place. There opened before him new roads of wandering; the wind had torn that leaf away again to whirl it over lands and seas, to sport with it till satisfied. The old man had failed greatly during those few days, and was bent over; only his eyes were gleaming. On his new road of life he held at his breast his book, which from time to time he pressed with his hand as if in fear that that too might go from him.

FINLAND

HOW VÄINÄMÖINEN WAS BORN OF THE MOTHER OF THE SEA[1]

I HAVE heard it has been said; and I know it has been sung, how alone, one by one, the nights fell upon the earth; alone, one by one, the days grew light; alone Väinämöinen was born, alone the immortal bard was revealed. A woman bore him within her womb, the daughter of Ilma gave him birth.

She was a virgin, a virgin most beautiful, Luonnaaotar, the daughter of Ilma. Long time did she remain a virgin, alone amid the vast regions of the air, the immense ethereal spaces.

But the weariness of her days pressed upon her; she grew tired of her virginity, of her lone existence amid the air's vast spaces, its sad and desolate plains.

And she descended from her heights; she flung herself upon the sea, riding the white crests of the waves.

Then the wind arose; a storm wind blew from the east; the sea grew rough and the waves mounted high.

The tempest tossed her; from wave to wave she floated on the foam-crowned crests. And the breath of the wind caressed her bosom, and the sea woke life within her.

Seven centuries long, nine times the life of man, she bore her heavy burden. And he who should be born was not born, he whom none had engendered saw not as yet the day.

And the Virgin Mother of the Sea swam to the east and to the west; she swam to north-west and to south-west; she swam toward all the boundaries of the air. And within her body she suffered torment, and he who should be born was not born, he whom none had engendered saw not as yet the day.

And the virgin wept gently and said:

"Unhappy that I am! how sad are my days! Poor little one, how wandering is my life. Everywhere and always, beneath the great arch of heaven, driven onward by the wind, borne up by the waves upon the bosom of this vast ocean, upon its waves never-ending.

"Far better were it that I had remained the lonely daughter of Ilma than to float thus for ever as the Mother of the Sea. It is so cold! It is so cruel to be swept onward like an icicle in this watery waste!

"O Ukko, greatest of the Gods! thou who dost bear up the world, come

---

[1]Translated by Elizabeth D'Oyley from the French of L. Leouzon Le Duc's *Le Kalevala Epopée Nationale de la Finlande*, by permission of Ernest Flammarion, Editeur, 26 rue Racine, Paris, VI°.

to me, for much I need thy help. Haste thou, for I entreat thee. Deliver me from my anguish, free me from the burden within my womb. Come, O come quickly! The need of thy help groweth ever greater!"

A moment went by—one brief moment; and suddenly a broad-winged eagle took flight, cleaving the air with the loud beating of her wings as she sought a place for her nest, a place for her habitation.

East she flew; west she flew; she flew to the north-east and to the south, but she found no place wherein to make her nest or fix her dwelling.

Again she flew, and then she paused, and thus she pondered:

"Shall I build my nest in the kingdoms of the wind or in the midst of the sea? The wind will overturn my dwelling; the sea will overwhelm it in its waves."

Then the Mother of the Sea, the Virgin of the Air, raised her knee above the waves, offering to the eagle a place for her dwelling, for her well-loved nest.

The eagle, bird most beautiful, stayed her flight: she saw the knee of the daughter of Ilma above the blue waters; and to her it seemed a green hillock, a turf of fresh growth.

Slowly she hovered in the air. Then she dropped upon the upraised knee; and there she built her nest; and in the nest she laid six eggs, six eggs of gold and a seventh of iron.

And the eagle began to brood upon her eggs: one day she sat; a second day and a third. Then the Mother of the Sea, the daughter of Ilma, felt a burning warmth upon her flesh; it seemed to her that her knee was on fire and all her nerves were melting.

Swiftly she drew back her knee; she shook her limbs; and the eggs rolled down into the water, breaking in pieces amidst the waves.

Yet they were not lost in the mud, nor did they merge into the water. Their fragments changed into things of beauty.

From the lower fragments the earth was formed; mother of all beings; from the upper pieces came the heavens sublime; from the yellow came the glorious sun; from the white, the shimmering moon; the stars came from the mottled fragments, and the black parts made the clouds.

And time went by, and year followed year, for the sun and the moon had begun to shine.

But the Mother of the Sea, Ilma's daughter, wandered yet through the great waters, borne upon the mist-clad waves. Below her the watery waste; above her the clear sky.

And in the ninth year, and the tenth summer, she raised her head above the water and began to spread Creation about her.

Wheresoever she stretched out her hand, there she made cliffs arise; wheresoever her feet touched, she made caves for the fishes; wheresoever she dived, she made the ocean's depths yet deeper; When with her thighs she touched the land, she there spread out the shores; when with her feet she touched it, there she made the salmon pools; and wheresoever her head struck it, there were the gulfs pierced.

Then she sprang up, pressing onward to the open sea. There she made rocks, and brought forth reefs for the wrecking of ships and the losing of sailors' lives.

Already the islands had risen from the waves, the pillars of the air stood up, the earth, born at a word, spread its solid mass; veins of a million tints furrowed the stones and coloured the rocks. And Väinämöinen was still unborn, the immortal bard had not yet come forth.

Väinämöinen, the old, the steadfast, dwelt within his mother's womb for the space of thirty summers, thirty winters, for ever on the unfathomable deep, upon the foaming waves.

Deeply he pondered, wondering how he could exist, how he could pass his life within this dim retreat, this narrow dwelling-place where never the light of sun or moon could reach.

And he said:

"Break my bonds, O Moon! O Sun, deliver me! And thou, Great Bear, show me how to break through these unknown doors, these unknown ways, how to win forth from this gloomy dwelling-place, this stifling cage. Bring the voyager to land, the son of man beneath the open skies, that he may see the sun and the moon, and the splendour of the Great Bear, that he may rejoice in the glory of the stars!"

But the moon did not break his bonds, neither did the sun deliver him. Then Väinämöinen grew weary of his days, his life became irksome to him. Sharply, with the nameless finger, he struck upon the door of his prison; with his left toe he forced the barrier of bone; and with his nails dragged himself beyond the threshold, upon his knees across the gateway.

And now, plunged headlong in the deep, the puissant hero is thrall to the might of the waves.

For the space of five years, six years, seven years, and eight years, he tossed from wave to wave. At last, he came to rest upon an unknown headland, upon a land barren of trees.

There, using both elbow and knee, he stood to his full height, and looked upon the sun and the moon, admired the Great Bear's splendour, and rejoiced in the glory of the stars.

Thus Väinämöinen was born, thus was the illustrious bard revealed. A woman bore him in her womb, the daughter of Ilma gave him birth.

THE SMUGGLER[1]

Aino Kallas

PARBU–JAAN, the smuggler, sat on a bench in the cell for prisoners awaiting trial, expecting each moment to be called before the judge. His square-clipped sailor's beard rested every now and then on the thick shawl wrapped twice around his throat; at each slightest movement his stiff oilskin coat crackled. Weary with waiting, he let his eyes wander over the wall of the cell, but soon desisted, finding that he knew the room as well as his own fisherman's hut on the shore of Kilhelkonna; it was the third time that he sat within these walls. He glanced for a moment at his companions—two youths playing cards at the other end of the room. In reality they were pretending to be occupied by the game, the while they watched him with grinning faces, and open, boyish curiosity in their eyes. Parbu-Jaan weighed them up a moment with keen eyes, accustomed to look far over vast stretches of sea, and to which all objects seemed too close, a frown drawing his brows together as though he weighed the two lads and found them wanting in the balance.

Quickly, however, his face, expressive of cunning and determination, became wreathed in smiles and filled with good humour. He rose and paced across the room a couple of times, saying as he passed the youths:

"Stealing wood from the manor forest, hey?"

Tolerant forgiveness of the crime and contempt for its insignificance were mingled in his tone.

"Hit the nail right on the head," one of the youths said braggingly, and aping manliness.

Parbu-Jaan did not deign to look at them, but halted and stood tall beneath the barred window set high in the wall, his stalwart frame, over six feet, seeming to fill the room, and cast a giant shadow over all in it. His height enabled him to reach the window and to rest his chin on the ledge of stone, and for a moment he stood there motionless; then, with a gesture of disappointment, he turned towards the room. His gaze had fallen on a little, typical Kuresaare yard, one of the many which opened out between the stuccoed, steep-roofed houses skirting the ruined fort like the song birds, full of life and chirruping, cluster round the nest of the eagle-owl. He had looked down upon it all, vegetable patches, hens picking on a refuse-heap, a cock standing on one leg, a horse champing its bit. It had not escaped his notice that one hen mothered three duck-lings among her chickens; he had seen at a glance the black and yellow down on their bodies and their waddling walk. How they must long for water, he had thought, rising on his toes as if to get a glimpse of some-

---

[1]From *The White Ship*. Reprinted by permission of the author and of Jonathan Cape, Ltd.

thing on the distant horizon beyond the roofs, where the air quivered in the heat as behind a dim veil of glass. Athirst for what he could not see, yearning and disappointed, the pupils of his eyes expanded, his whole body called for salt after weeks of flavourless bread and water. The air was suffocating, and what little streamed through the crack in the window-frame seemed insipid, full of whirling atoms of dust. The sea remained invisible—far away behind the entrenchments and sand dunes.

He saw it in his mind—not a smooth sand for summer visitors at Kuresaare, but the wide lonely sea-flats of the Kilhelkonna shore. So clearly did it arise before him that he seemed to smell the rotting seaweed cast ashore by the sea, and to feel the crunching of little rosy sea-shells beneath his boots. He saw himself wading in the water which slowly deepened—in calm, translucent water, at the bottom of which he could see the seaweed covering the rocks wave slowly in the current, and a swarm of tiny fish darting away at his approach. The water rose slowly, penetrated the tops of his high boots, saturating his trousers, rising towards his waist . . . And then he was on board his boat anchored at the edge of the shallows. Did he not hear where he stood the restless creak of the rigging, the ceaseless beat of the waves driven against the stern by a favouring wind? But the boat lay immovable, the anchor clutched the white sand with its curved flukes, the sails drooped along the masts and the ship's sides were mirrored in the water. . . .

It must be gone—to-morrow—the day after—next week it must be in Memel. . . . His grim features become restless, his lips deep hidden in his beard no longer twitch with ready humour. His eyes glare like those of a beast of prey—behind his brow his wits are at work—he cudgels his brain striving to find a plan. . . . He must be set free this time. . . . That is the haven towards which he must fight his way. He must be as sure, as certain of himself, as when he steered his smuggler's craft past hidden rocks and watchful coastguards.

The blind alley in which he is vainly groping becomes unbearable, he turns again to the lads whom chance has given him for companions, and in their curious eyes he reads the thought that fills his own mind; they are wondering will he escape imprisonment this time or no?

"Brushwood thieves," he grinned contemptuously at them, drawing himself up sharply to his full height, so that his broad shoulders seemed to support his body like a spar on which all else was hung.

"Boys ahoy!—what would you say was my size?" he said.

One of the youths, the one who had spoken earlier, smiled slyly, winking at the speaker.

"Too big to be held by these walls, anyhow."

"Right," he thundered in pleasure.

"We were playing 'durak' for thy luck," the youth went on, growing bolder.

"I need no luck but my own," he answered, with head thrown back.

"They say the judge is a new one—come lately from the Mainland," the other lad put in hurriedly, anxious for a say in the matter.

Parbu-Jaan looked at the last speaker's long face, at his forehead hidden by the thick hair, at the bony contours of his nose and jaw.

"Whose boy art thou?" he asked with an attempt at good humour. "A new judge," he added thoughtfully, already forgetting the boy.

"Tare Tiiu's."

"Tiiu's . . . Tiiu's," repeated Parbu-Jaan mechanically.

He began to walk excitedly to and fro. A new judge! What if he should be able to repeat his old trick. . . . But it was too well known. . . . The walls of every tavern in Saaremaa had heard it, the very forests had echoed it. . . . He was surprised himself now at his own daring, admiration for himself grew within him as for a stranger. . . . Then also he had sat awaiting trial, his feet itching to be off, his vessel eager for departure. It was then that he shut his lips to a narrow line, took on an expression grave as of one in a church and asked to be allowed to speak to the judge: "Merciful Judge-Lord, the wife is welcoming a little stranger—ale ought to be brewed, and then the baptism—couldn't I go for a couple of weeks?" The judge hesitated—an old rascal, that Parbu-Jaan—but in the end consented.

"See that you are back here in two weeks' time." He had raced to the Kilhelkonna shore, hoisted sail, flown off to Memel for a load of rum and gunpowder. On the day agreed he had knocked at the prison door.

His thoughts returned to those old days, as if to gather strength from them. And in spite of his present plight laughter shook his frame, laughter that would free his spirit and restore his pride.

Memories tossed him up and down like a vessel tossed by the waves, tormenting and provoking him to laughter. This much he knew, that never would he be able to store too many such memories. He felt his craving for new adventures to string on to the old could never be slaked. He knew that never would he be himself again until he felt the deck planks sway again, beneath his feet with his hand upon the tiller.

An Autumn evening . . . the land showing as a dark streak, looming up strange and unfriendly even for him, as he steers towards it. The moon unnaturally large, a rift torn in the sky, gleaming dimly instead of casting light. He can hardly trust his eyes, the spray clouds his sight as with a curtain of mist; as a rope creaks or taps against the mast he starts. He feels that the darkness that cloaks the shore is hiding something hostile, a danger of which his senses do not grasp but only some occult instinct. Suddenly signal lights flare up on the shore . . . the coastguards! With his comrades he begins to throw barrels overboard, grimly watching them as they roll into the water and sink—everything overboard. Next his eyes take in the shore, marking trees, rocks and sandflats in the dim darkness, drawing the place, its distance from the shore more clearly in his memory than ever did surveyor on paper. The following day they lift the barrels from the bed of the sea with hooks.

Blood mingles in his memories, the sky glows an ominous red, he sees a hand clutch the gunwale of his boat, a large browned hand with knuckles and nails of iron—a hand whose owner is nothing to him—a hand rising from the depths to prevent his journey. His anger concentrates on the hand that dares to delay his boat, to him the hand is a living entity separated from all body. His hatchet swings through the air and the hand falls into the sea.

From this whirlpool his thoughts turn rapidly. Instead he sees a bright summer day, a smooth sea with flying gulls gleaming silver in the sunshine. He stands leaning against the mast of his boat, cunning, reserved, following with his eyes the Customs officials who search his vessel, running around like rats, nosing everywhere from hold to cabin, from cabin to deck. Without moving a finger he watches them, casting biting remarks at them between puffs at his pipe, advising them of secret hiding-places unknown to them. One after the other, they crawl on deck, discomfited as though suddenly drenched with water and he bids a polite good-bye to their chief, offering him a drink from his flask, bidding him welcome another time. But as the Customs boat grates on the sand, he seizes the coil of rope on which one of the searchers had sat, and between his hands rubs its end, which crumbles into brown leaves with a familiar smell—a twisted rope of tobacco.

Again he cast a yearning glance through the window. It is the middle of August, at night the sky gleams with stars, each one a compass. It is his pride to sail to Memel or the Swedish coast without a compass, trusting only to these tiny guides, which through the night vanish, light up, and shift as the yawl sails on.

"Was't thou who said there is a new judge?" he asked suddenly, turning to the boys.

"It was I," one of the boys replied, proud of his knowledge.

Parbu-Jaan smiled, his hand stroking meanwhile his beard. In his fancy he heard the sound of words and much talk, his own voice rising and gaining confidence, some one laughing outright . . . His hand clenched in a tight grip . . . Now he has gotten the idea . . . Just that . . . As yet he is not quite certain, the scheme is almost too dare-devil, but he must close his eyes to the danger. His state of mind is that of a diver in deep water; perhaps he may sink for ever, more likely he will rise again to the surface.

He looked at the boys and began already to play his new part—his keen, knowing eyes dilated and became vacant and stupid, his shoulders drooped, his hair fell over his forehead, hiding its strong, intelligent lines, the firm decision of his mouth is lost in loose, gaping lips.

"Well, whom do I look like now?" he asked, turning to the two youths and pushing his cap to the back of his head.

They stared at him startled, something of wild savagery had suddenly come over him, something terrifying and inexplicable; they looked questioningly at each other, perplexed and open-mouthed.

"Like Mad-Mats," whispered one into the other's ear.

"Right, boys. I am not quite right in my head, remember that. All night I have talked gibberish. I can no longer tell the moon from the sun . . . If anyone asks, say that."

The shifty eyes of the elder youth flashed and expanded, gleaming with understanding and admiration. The other stared, uncomprehending.

The elder youth bent suddenly towards Parbu-Jaan.

"What wilt thou give us?" he whispered.

Parbu-Jaan eyed him sternly, and broke into a laugh. He felt as proud of the boy as though he himself had trained him. The lad's early-developed business sense appealed to his own instincts.

"A gun and powder, of the best make." He threw the words hastily at him as the warder's steps sounded in the corridor.

The boy threw himself with his whole weight against the door, and beat on it with his fists.

The startled eyes of the warder appeared in the spy-hole, eyes used to darkness which appeared perpetually to dread any disturbance of the everyday round.

"What has happened here?" he said in a chiding tone.

Parbu-Jaan stood in a corner, muttering to himself. The youths had drawn as far as possible away from him.

"We want to be put in another cell," cried the elder youth. "We can't stand him—he isn't right here, all night we got no peace listening to him talk, talk, talk as fast as his tongue would let him."

The warder looked suspiciously at Parbu-Jaan.

"What has happened to him here?" he grumbled. For his own part, he would have been ready to let them all go, guilty and innocent alike, but being set to guard them, what could he do?

"What has addled his wits now?" he repeated to himself.

"Let us go to the judge," he said quietly and coaxingly as to a naughty child, laying his hand gently on Parbu-Jaan's shoulder and pushing him out of the room.

Parbu-Jaan obeyed without resisting, not for a moment forgetting his part, his lips moving all the while in babble of meaningless words.

In the court-room the judge, a bespectacled gentleman, waited with his clerk.

"This man has gone mad during the night," the warder humbly explained, as though the misfortune was partly his fault.

The judge cast a cold eye on Parbu-Jaan, and despite its coldness, Parbu-Jaan felt himself go hot.

"That remains to be seen," the judge said dryly.

He read the charge in a loud voice, Parbu-Jaan listening with his eyes wandering uneasily round the room.

"Two empty coffee sacks stamped with the Memel seal were found in the attic of Parbu's house," the judge finished his charge.

"Well, look now—don't lies get found out, gracious Judge-Lord," said Parbu-Jaan. "Sacks! As though coffee was ever carried in a sack—why, it would drip out."

"What nonsense art thou talking?" said the judge.

"No one carries coffee in a sack—coffee's a drink."

"Dost thou not know coffee, man?"

"How should I know gentle-folks' dainties?"

The judge looked at him for a while and then said:

"Come here—is not this thy compass?"

Parbu-Jaan reeled towards the table, purposely dragging his feet. With head on one side, he began to examine the compass.

"Well now, isn't that queer? It's moving—well, by . . . it's dancing like anything: what's the matter with it?"

"Man, remember with whom thou speakest. Who am I?"

"Thou art one of God's errand boys. When God draws up the laws on the tables of stone, thou bringest them down to us."

"Man, where wert thou last week?"

"I sat in the threshing-barn as God had created me, the wife washing my only shirt."

"Confessest thou or not?"

"Of course I confess whatever the Judge-Lord wishes. To everything I say only yea and amen."

"Thou wert then in Memel?"

"Certainly."

"When did that occur?"

"It is hardly twenty years ago."

"Have a care what you say, man."

"That is what I'm doing, and a care for my back too. I am not altogether mad, though not so clever as your Honour."

"Pah! I have no time for lunatics."

Parbu-Jaan's head drooped lower, and a smile vanished in his bushy beard. He dragged himself after the warder out of the court, the warder staring at him with respect mingled with fear. In the prison yard he paused—looked up at a window to where two youthful heads gazed curiously down at him, and waved his hand with a toss of his skipper's beard. His nostrils dilated as though the scent of the sea had struck them.

Six hours later he was bound for Memel, in the bright moonshine of an August night—with thousands of tiny, winking stars for a compass.

ICELAND

ONUND TREEFOOT[1]

T HERE was a man named Onund, who was the son of Ufeigh Club-
foot, the son of Ivar the Smiter; Onund was brother of Gudbiorg,
the mother of Gudbrand Ball, the father of Asta, the mother of King
Olaf the Saint. Onund was an Uplander by the kin of his mother; but the
kin of his father dwelt chiefly about Rogaland and Hordaland. He was
a great Viking, and went harrying west over the Sea. Balk of Sotanes,
the son of Blæng, was with him herein, and Orm the Wealthy withal, and
Hallvald was the name of the third of them. They had five ships, all well
manned, and therewith they harried in the South-isles; and when they
came to Barra, they found there a king, called Kiarval, and he, too, had
five ships. They gave him battle, and a hard fray there was. The men of
Onund were of the eagerest, and on either side many fell; but the end of
it was that the king fled with only one ship. So there the men of Onund
took both ships and much wealth, and abode there through the winter.
For three summers they harried throughout Ireland and Scotland, and
thereafter went to Norway.

In those days were there great troubles in Norway. Harold the Un-
shorn, son of Halfdan the Black, was pushing forth for the kingdom.
Before that he was King of the Uplands; then he went north through the
land, and had many battles there, and ever won the day. Thereafter he
harried south in the land, and wheresoever he came, laid all under him;
but when he came to Hordaland, swarms of folk came thronging against
him; and their captains were Kiotvi the Wealthy, and Thorir Longchin,
and those of South Rogaland, and King Sulki. Geirmund Helskin was
then in the West over the Sea; nor was he in that battle, though he had
a kingdom in Hordaland.

Now that autumn Onund and his fellows came from the west over the
Sea; and when Thorir Longchin and King Kiotvi heard thereof, they
sent men to meet them, and prayed them for help, and promised them
honours. Then they entered into fellowship with Thorir and his men;
for they were exceeding fain to try their strength, and said that there
would they be whereas the fight was hottest.

Now was the meeting with Harald the King in Rogaland, in that
firth which is called Hafrsfirth; and both sides had many men. This was
the greatest battle that has ever been fought in Norway, and hereof most
Sagas tell; for of those is ever most told, of whom the Sagas are made;

---

[1]From the translation of *The Saga of Grettir the Strong*, by Eirikr Magnússon and
William Morris.

and thereto came folk from all the land, and many from other lands, and swarms of Vikings.

Now Onund laid his ship alongside one board of the ship of Thorir Longchin, about the midst of the fleet, but King Harald laid his on the other board, because Thorir was the greatest bearserk, and the stoutest of men; so the fight was of the fiercest on either side. Then the king cried on his bearserks for an onslaught, and they were called the Wolf-coats, for on them would no steel bite, and when they set on naught might withstand them. Thorir defended him very stoutly, and fell in all hardihood on board his ship; then was it cleared from stem to stern, and cut from the grapplings, and let drift astern betwixt the other ships. Thereafter the king's men laid their ship alongside Onund's, and he was in the forepart thereof and fought manly; then the king's folk said,

"Lo, a forward man in the forecastle there, let him have somewhat to mind him how that he was in this battle."

Now Onund put one foot out over the bulwark and dealt a blow at a man, and even therewith a spear was aimed at him, and as he put the blow from him he bent backward withal, and one of the king's forecastle men smote at him, and the stroke took his leg below the knee and sheared it off, and forthwith made him unmeet for fight. Then fell the more part of the folk on board his ship; but Onund was brought to the ship of him who is called Thrand; he was the son of Biorn, and brother of Eyvind the Eastman; he was in the fight against King Harald and lay on the other board of Onund's ship.

But now, after these things, the more part of the fleet scattered in flight; Thrand and his men, with the other Vikings, got them away each as he might, and sailed west over the Sea; Onund went with him, and Balk and Hallvard Sweeping; Onund was healed, but went with a wooden leg all his life after; therefore as long as he lived was he called Onund Treefoot.

There were two Vikings called Vigbiod and Vestmar; they were South-islanders, and lay out both winter and summer; they had thirteen ships, and harried mostly in Ireland, and did many an ill deed there till Eyvind the Eastman took the land-wardship; thereafter they got them gone to the South-isles, and harried there and all about the firths of Scotland: against these went Thrand and Onund, and heard that they had sailed to that island, which is called Bute. Now Onund and his folk came there with five ships; and when the Vikings see their ships and know how many they are, they deem they have enough strength gathered there, and take their weapons and lay their ships in the midst betwixt two cliffs, where was a great and deep sound; only on one side could they be set on, and that with but five ships at once. Now Onund was the wisest of men, and bade lay five ships up into the sound, so that he and his might have back way when they would, for there was plenty of sea-room astern. On one board of them too was a certain island, and under the lee thereof he let one ship lie, and his men brought many great stones forth on to the sheer cliffs above, yet might not be seen withal from the ships.

Now the Vikings laid their ships boldly enough for the attack, and thought that the others quailed; and Vigbiod asked who they were that were in such jeopardy. Thrand said that he was the brother of Eyvind the Eastman, "and here beside me is Onund Treefoot my fellow."

Then laughed the Vikings, and shouted:

> "Treefoot, Treefoot, foot of tree,
> Trolls take thee and thy company.

"Yea, a sight it is seldom seen of us, that such men should go into battle as have no might over themselves."

Onund said that they could know nought thereof ere it were tried; and withal they laid their ships alongside one of the other, and there began a great fight, and either side did boldly. But when they came to handy blows, Onund gave back toward the cliff, and when the Vikings saw this, they deemed he was minded to flee, and made towards his ship, as came as nigh to the cliff as they might. But in that very point of time those came forth on to the edge of the cliff who were appointed so to do, and sent at the Vikings so great a flight of stones that they might not withstand it.

Then fell many of the Viking-folk, and others were hurt so that they might not bear weapon; and withal they were fain to draw back, and might not, because their ships were even then come into the narrowest of the sound, and they were huddled together both by the ships and the stream; but Onund and his men set on fiercely, whereas Vigbiod was, but Thrand set on Vestmar, and won little thereby; so, when the folk were thinned on Vigbiod's ship, Onund's men and Onund himself got ready to board her: that Vigbiod saw, and cheered on his men without stint: then he turned to meet Onund, and the more part fled before him; but Onund bade his men mark how it went between them; for he was of huge strength.

Now they set a log of wood under Onund's knee, so that he stood firmly enow; the Viking fought his way forward along the ship till he reached Onund, and he smote at him with his sword, and the stroke took the shield, and sheared off all it met; and then the sword drove into the log that Onund had under his knee, and stuck fast therein; and Vigbiod stooped in drawing it out, and even therewith Onund smote at his shoulder in such wise, that he cut the arm from off him, and then was the Viking unmeet for battle.

But when Vestmar knew that his fellow was fallen, he leaped into the furthermost ship and fled with all those who might reach her. Thereafter they ransacked the fallen men; and by then was Vigbiod nigh to his death: Onund went to up him, and sang:

> "Yea, seest thou thy wide wounds bleed?
> What of shrinking didst thou heed
> In the one-foot sling of gold?
> What scratch here dost thou behold?
> And in e'en such wise as this
> Many an axe-breaker there is
> Strong of tongue and weak of hand:
> Tried thou wert, and might'st not stand."

So there they took much spoil and sailed back to Barra in the autumn.

HOW *ELLIDI*, THE DRAGON–SHIP, AT THE COMMAND OF FRITHIOF THE BOLD, DROVE DOWN UPON THE WITCHES[1]

SO WHEN Frithiof and his men were come out of the Sognfirth there fell on them great wind and storm, and an exceeding heavy sea: but the ship drave on swiftly, for sharp built she was, and the best to breast the sea.

So now Frithiof sang:

> "Oft let I swim from Sogn
> My tarred ship sooty-sided,
> When maids sat o'er the mead-horn
> Amidst of Baldur's Meadows;
> Now while the storm is wailing,
> Farewell I bid you maidens,
> Still shall ye love us, sweet ones,
> Though *Ellidi* the sea fill."

Said Biorn: "Thou mightest well find other work to do than singing songs over the maids of Baldur's Meadows."

"Of such work shall I not speedily run dry, though," said Frithiof. Then they bore up north to the sounds nigh those isles that are called Solundir, and therewith was the gale at its hardest.

Then sang Frithiof:

> "Now is the sea a-swelling,
> And sweepeth the rack onward;
> Spells of old days cast o'er us
> Make ocean all unquiet;

---

[1]From *Three Northern Love Stories*. Reprinted by permission of the Trustees of William Morris.

> No more shall we be striving
> Mid storm with wash of billows,
> But Solundir shall shelter
> Our ship with ice-beat rock-walls."

So they lay to under the lee of the isles hight Solundir, and were minded to abide there; but straightway thereon the wind fell: then they turned away from under the lee of the islands, and now their voyage seemed hopeful to them, because the wind was fair awhile; but soon it began to freshen again.

Then sang Frithiof:

> "In days foredone
> From Foreness strand
> I rowed to meet
> Maid Ingibiorg;
> But now I sail
> Through chilly storm
> And wide away
> My long-worm driveth."

And now when they were come far out into the main, once more the sea waxed wondrous troubled, and a storm arose with so great drift of snow, that none might see the stem from the stern; and they shipped seas, so that they must be ever a-baling. So Frithiof sang:

> "The salt waves see we nought
> As seaward drive we ever
> Before the witch wrought weather,
> We well-famed kings' defenders:
> Here are we all a-standing,
> With all Solundir hull-down,
> Eighteen brave lads a-baling
> Black *Ellidi* to bring home."

Said Biorn: "Needs must he who fareth far fall in with diverse hap."
"Yea, certes, foster-brother," said Frithiof. And he sang withal:

> "Helgi it is that helpeth
> The white-head billows' waxing;
> Cold time unlike the kissing
> In the close of Baldur's Meadow!
> So is the hate of Helgi
> To that heart's love she giveth.
> O would that here I held her,
> Gift high above all giving!"

"Maybe," said Biorn, "she is looking higher than thou now art; what matter when all is said?"

"Well," says Frithiof, "Now is the time to show ourselves to be men of avail, though blither tide it was at Baldur's Meadows."

So they turned to in manly wise, for there were the bravest of men come together in the best ship of the Northlands. But Frithiof sang a stave:

> "So come in the West-sea,
> Nought see I the billows,
> The sea-water seemeth
> As sweeping of wild-fire.
> Topple the rollers,
> Toss the hills swan-white,
> *Ellidi* wallows
> O'er steep of the wave-hills."

Then they shipped a huge sea, so that all stood a-bailing. But Frithiof sang:

> "With love-moved mouth the maiden
> Me pledgeth though I founder.
> Ah! bright sheets lay a-bleaching,
> East there on brents the swan loves."

Biorn said: "Art thou of mind belike that the maids of Sogn will weep many tears over thee?"

Said Frithiof: "Surely that was in my mind."

Therewith so great a sea broke over the bows that the water came in like the in-falling of a river; but it availed them much that the ship was so good, and the crew aboard her so hardy.

Now sang Biorn:

> "No widow, methinks,
> To thee or me drinks:
> No ring-bearer fair
> Biddeth draw near;
> Salt are our eyne
> Soaked in the brine;
> Strong our arms are no more,
> And our eyelids smart sore."

Quoth Asmund: "Small harm though your arms be tried somewhat, for no pity we had from you when we rubbed our eyes whenas ye must needs rise early a-mornings to go to Baldur's Meadows."

"Well," said Frithiof, "why singest thou not, Asmund?"

"Not I," said Asmund: yet sang a ditty straightway:

> "Sharp work about the sail was
> When o'er the ship seas tumbled,
> And there was I a-working
> Within-board 'gainst eight balers;
> Better it was to bower,

> Bringing the women breakfast,
> Than here to be 'mid billows
> Black *Ellidi* a-baling."

"Thou accountest thy help of no less worth than it is?" said Frithiof, laughing therewith, "but sure it showeth the thrall's blood in thee that thou wouldst fain be awaiting at table."

Now it blew harder and harder yet, so that to those who were aboard liker to huge peaks and mountains than to waves seemed the sea-breakers that crashed on all sides against the ship.

Then Frithiof sang:

> "On bolster I sat
> In Baldur's Mead erst,
> And all songs that I could
> To the king's daughter sang;
> Now on Ran's bed belike
> Must I soon be a-lying,
> And another shall be
> By Ingibiorg's side."

Biorn said: "Great fear lieth ahead of us, foster-brother, and now dread hath crept into thy words, which is ill with such a good man as thou."

Says Frithiof: "Neither fear nor fainting is it, though I sing now of those our merry journeys; yet perchance more hath been said of them than need was: but most men would think death surer than life, if they were so bested as we be."

"Yet shall I answer thee somewhat," said Biorn, and sang:

> "Yet one gain have I gotten
> Thou gatst not 'mid thy fortune,
> For meet play did I make me
> With Ingibiorg's eight maidens;
> Red rings we laid together
> Aright in Baldur's Meadow,
> When far off was the warder
> Of the wide land of Halfdan."

"Well," said he, "we must be content with things as they are, foster-brother."

Therewith so great a sea smote them, that the bulwark was broken and both the sheets, and four men were washed overboard and all lost.

Then sang Frithiof:

> "Both sheets are bursten
> Amid the great billows,
> Four swains are sunk
> In the fathomless sea."

"Now, meseems," said Frithiof, "it may well be that some of us will go to the house of Ran, nor shall we deem us well sped if we come not thither in glorious array; wherefore it seems good to me that each man of us here should have somewhat of gold on him."

Then he smote asunder the ring, Ingibiorg's gift, and shared it between all his men, and sang a stave withal:

> "The red ring here I hew me
> Once owned of Halfdan's father,
> The wealthy lord of erewhile,
> Or the sea-waves undo us,
> So on the guests shall gold be,
> If we have need of guesting;
> Meet so for mighty men-folk
> Amid Ran's hall to hold them."

"Not all so sure is it that we come there," said Biorn; "and yet it may well be so."

Now Frithiof and his folk found that the ship had great way on her, and they knew not what lay ahead, for all was mirk on either board, so that none might see the stem or stern from amidships; and therewith was there great drift of spray amid the furious wind, and frost, and snow, and deadly cold.

Now Frithiof went up to the masthead, and when he came down he said to his fellows: "A sight exceeding wondrous have I seen, for a great whale went in a ring about the ship, and I misdoubt me that we come nigh to some land, and that he is keeping the shore against us; for certes King Helgi has dealt with us in no friendly wise, neither will this his messenger be friendly. Moreover I saw two women on the back of the whale, and they it is who will have brought this great storm on us with the worst of spells and witchcraft; but now we shall try which may prevail, my fortune or their devilry, so steer ye at your straightest, and I will smite these evil things with beams."

Therewith he sang a stave:

> "See I troll women
> Twain on the billows,
> E'en they whom Helgi
> Hither hath sent.
> *Ellidi* now
> Or ever her way stop
> Shall smite the backs
> Of these asunder."

So tells the tale that this wonder went with the good ship *Ellidi*, that she knew the speech of man.

But Biorn said: "Now may we see the treason of those brethren against us." Therewith he took the tiller, but Frithiof caught up a forked beam, and ran into the prow, and sang a stave:

> "*Ellidi*, hail!
>   Leap high o'er the billows!
>   Break of the troll wives
>   Brow or teeth now!
>   Break cheek or jaw
>   Of the cursed woman,
>   One foot or twain
>   Of the ogress filthy."

Therewith he drave his fork at one of the skin-changers and the beak of *Ellidi* smote the other on the back, and the backs of both were broken; but the whale took the deep and gat him gone, and they never saw him after.

Then the wind fell, but the ship lay waterlogged; so Frithiof called out to his men, and bade bale out the ship, but Biorn said:

"No need to work now, verily!"

"Be thou not afeard, foster brother," said Frithiof, "ever was it the wont of good men of old time to be helpful while they might, whatsoever should come after."

And therewith he sang a stave:

> "No need, fair fellows,
>   To fear the death-day;
>   Rather be glad,
>   Good men of mine,
>   For if dreams wot aught
>   All nights they say
>   I yet shall have
>   My Ingibiorg."

Then they baled out the ship; and they were now come nigh unto land; but there was yet a flaw of wind in their teeth. So then did Frithiof take the two bow oars again, and rowed full mightily. Therewith the weather brightened, and they saw that they were come out to Effia Sound, and so there they made land.

The crew were exceeding weary; but so stout a man was Frithiof that he bore eight men a-land over the foreshore, but Biorn bore two, and Asmund one. Then sang Frithiof:

> "Fast bare I up
>   To the fire-lit house
>   My men all dazed
>   With the drift of the storm:

And the sail moreover
To the sand I carried;
With the might of the sea
Is there no more to do."

HOW EARL ERIC HAKONSON CAPTURED THE *LONG SERPENT*[1]

Snorre Sturlason

(1178–1241)

THERE came first a flying report to Vendland that the Danish King,
Swend, had fitted out an army; and it was soon whispered that he
intended to attack King Olaf. But Earl Sigvald says to King Olaf:

"It never can be King Swend's intention to venture with the Danish
force alone to give battle to thee with such a powerful army; but if thou
hast any suspicion that evil is on foot, I will follow thee with my force
(at that time it was considered a great matter to have Jomsberg vikings
with an army), and I will give thee eleven manned ships."

The king accepted this offer; and as the light breeze of wind that came
was favourable, he ordered the ships to get under weigh, and the war-
horns to sound the departure. The sails were hoisted; and all the small
vessels, sailing fastest, got out to sea before the others. The earl, who
sailed nearest to the king's ship, called to those on board to tell the king
to sail in his keel-track:

"For I know where the water is deepest between the islands and in
the sounds, and these large ships require the deepest."

Then the earl sailed first with his eleven ships, and the king followed
with his large ships, also eleven in number; but the whole of the rest of
the fleet sailed out to sea. Now when Earl Sigvald came sailing close
under the island Svald, a skiff rowed out to inform the earl that the
Danish king's army was lying in the harbour before them. Then the earl
ordered the sails of his vessels to be struck, and they rowed in under the
island.

It is said that King Olaf and Earl Sigvald had seventy sail of vessels
and one more, when they sailed from the south.

The Danish king Swend, the Swedish king Olaf, and Earl Eric were
there with all their forces. The weather being fine and clear sunshine,
all these chiefs, with a great suite, went out on the isle to see the vessels
sailing out at sea, and many of them crowded together; and they saw
among them one large and glancing ship. The two kings said:

"That is a large and very beautiful vessel: that will be the *Long
Serpent*."

---

[1]Reprinted from Samuel Laing's translation of *The Heimskringla*.

Earl Eric replied, "That is not the *Long Serpent*." And he was right: for it was a ship belonging to Endric of Gimsar.

Soon after they saw another vessel coming sailing along much larger than the first; then says King Swend,

"Olaf Trygvesson must be afraid, for he does not venture to sail with the figure-head of the dragon upon his ship."

Says Earl Eric: "That is not the king's ship yet; for I know that ship by the coloured stripes of cloth in her sail. That is Erling Skialgsson. Let him sail; for it is the better for us that this ship is away from Olaf's fleet, so well equipt as she is."

Soon after they saw and knew Earl Sigvald's ships, which turned in and laid themselves under the island. Then they saw three ships coming along under sail, and one of them very large. King Swend ordered his men to go to their ships, "for there comes the *Long Serpent*."

Earl Eric says, "Many other great and stately vessels have they besides the *Long Serpent*. Let us wait a little."

Then said many, "Earl Eric will not fight and avenge his father; and it is a great shame that it should be told that we lay here with so great a force, and allowed King Olaf to sail out to sea before our eyes."

But when they had spoken thus for a short time, they saw four ships coming sailing along, of which one had a large dragon-head richly gilt. Then King Swend stood up, and said:

"That dragon shall carry me this evening high, for I shall steer it."

Then said many, "The *Serpent* is indeed a wonderfully large and beautiful vessel, and it shows a great mind to have built such a ship."

Earl Eric said so loud that several persons heard him, "If King Olaf had no other vessels but only that one, King Swend would never take it from him with the Danish force alone."

Thereafter all the people rushed on board their ships, took down the tents, and in all haste made ready for battle.

While the chiefs were speaking among themselves as above related, they saw three very large ships coming sailing along, and at last after them a fourth, and that was the *Long Serpent*. Of the large ships which had gone before, and which they had taken for the *Long Serpent*, the first was the *Crane*; the one after that was the *Short Serpent*; and when they really saw the *Long Serpent* all knew, and nobody had a word to say against it, that it must be Olaf Trygvasson who was sailing in such a vessel; and they went to their ships to arm for the fight.

An agreement had been concluded among the chiefs, King Swend, King Olaf the Swede, and Earl Eric, that they should divide Norway among them in three parts, in case they succeeded against Olaf Trygvesson; but that he of the chiefs who should first board the *Serpent* should have her, and all the booty found in her, and each should have the ships he cleared for himself. Earl Eric had a large ship of war which he used upon his viking expeditions; and there was an iron beard or comb above on both sides of the stem, and below it a thick iron plate as broad as the combs, which went down quite to the gunnel.

When Earl Sigvald with his vessels rowed in under the island, Thorkel Dyrdel of the *Crane*, and the other ship commanders who sailed with him, saw that he turned his ships towards the isle, and thereupon let fall the sails, and rowed after him, calling out and asking why he sailed that way. The Earl answered, that he was waiting for King Olaf as he feared there were enemies in the way. They lay upon their oars until Thorkel Nefia came up with the *Short Serpent* and the three ships which followed him. When they told them the same they too struck sail, and let the ships drive, waiting for King Olaf. But when the king sailed in towards the isle, the whole enemies' fleet came rowing within them out to the Sound. When they saw this they begged the king to hold on his way, and not risk battle with so great a force. The king replied, high on the quarterdeck where he stood,

"Strike the sails; never shall men of mine think of flight. I never fled from battle. Let God dispose of my life, but flight I shall never take."

It was done as the king commanded.

King Olaf ordered the war-horns to sound for all his ships to close up to each other. The king's ship lay in the middle of the line, and on one side lay the *Little Serpent*, and on the other the *Crane*; and as they made fast the stems together, the *Long Serpent's* stem and the *Short Serpent's* were made fast together; but when the king saw it he called out to his men and ordered them to lay the larger ship more in advance, so that its stern should not lie so far behind in the fleet.

Then says Ulf the Red, "If the *Long Serpent* is to lie as much more ahead of the other ships as she is longer than them, we shall have hard work of it here on the forecastle."

The King replies, "I did not think I had a forecastle man afraid as well as red."

Says Ulf, "Defend thou the quarterdeck as I shall the forecastle."

The king had a bow in his hands, and laid an arrow on the string, and aimed at Ulf.

Ulf said, "Shoot another way, king, where it is more needful: my work is thy gain."

King Olaf stood on the *Serpent's* quarterdeck, high over the others. He had a gilt shield, and a helmet inlaid with gold; over his armour he had a short red coat, and was easy to be distinguished from other men. When King Olaf saw that the scattered forces of the enemy gathered themselves together under the banners of their ships, he asked:

"Who is the chief of the force right opposite to us?"

He was answered, that it was King Swend with the Danish army.

The king replies, "We are not afraid of these soft Danes, for there is no bravery in them; but who are the troops on the right of the Danes?"

He was answered, that it was King Olaf with the Swedish forces.

"Better it were," says King Olaf, "for these Swedes to be sitting at home killing their sacrifices, than to be venturing under our weapons from the *Long Serpent*. But who owns the large ships on the larboard side of the Danes?"

"That is Earl Eric Hakonson," say they.

The king replies, "He, methinks, has good reason for meeting us; and we may expect the sharpest conflict with these men, for they are Norsemen like ourselves."

The Kings now laid out their oars and prepared to attack. King Swend laid his ship against the *Long Serpent*. Outside of him Olaf the Swede laid himself, and set his ship's stem against the outermost ship of King Olaf's line; and on the other side lay Earl Eric. Then a hard combat began. Earl Sigvald held back with the oars on his ships, and did not join the fray.

This battle was one of the severest told of, and many were the people slain. The forecastle men of the *Long Serpent*, the *Little Serpent*, and the *Crane* threw grapplings and stem chains into King Swend's ship, and used their weapons well against the people standing below them, for they cleared the decks of all the ships they could lay fast hold of; and King Swend, and all the men who escaped, fled to other vessels, and laid themselves out of bow-shot. It went with this force just as King Olaf Trygvesson had foreseen. Then King Olaf the Swede laid himself in their place; but when he came near the great ships it went with him as with them, for he lost many men and some ships, and was obliged to get away. But Earl Eric laid the *Iron Beard* side by side with the outermost of King Olaf's ships, thinned it of men, cut the cables, and let it drive. Then he laid alongside of the next, and fought until he had cleared it of men also. Now all the people who were in the smaller ships began to run into the larger, and the earl cut them loose as fast as he cleared them of men. The Danes and Swedes laid themselves now out of shooting distance all around Olaf's ship, but Earl Eric lay always close alongside of the ships, and used his swords and battle-axes, and as fast as people fell in his vessel others, Danes and Swedes, came in their place.

Then the fight became most severe, and many people fell. But at last it came to this, that all King Olaf Trygvesson's ships were cleared of men except the *Long Serpent*, on board of which all who could still carry their arms were gathered. Then *Iron Beard* lay side by side with the *Serpent*, and the fight went on with battle-axe and sword.

Earl Eric was in the forehold of his ship, where a cover of shields had been set up. In the fight, both hewing weapons, sword and axe, and the thrust of spears had been used; and all that could be used as weapon for casting was cast. Some used bows, some threw spears with the hand. So many weapons were cast into the *Serpent*, and so thick flew spears and arrows, that the shields could scarcely receive them; for on all sides the *Serpent* was surrounded by war ships. Then King Olaf's men became so mad with rage, that they ran on board of the enemies' ships, to get at the people with stroke of sword and kill them; but many did not lay themselves so near the *Serpent*, in order to escape the close encounter with battle-axe or sword; and thus the most of Olaf's men went overboard and sank under their weapons, thinking they were fighting on plain ground.

Einar Tambarskelver, one of the sharpest of bow-shooters, stood by the mast, and shot with his bow. Einar shot an arrow at Earl Eric, which hit the tiller-end just above the earl's head so hard that it entered the wood up to the arrow-shaft. The earl looked that way, and asked if they knew who had shot; and at the same moment another arrow flew between his hand and his side, and into the stuffing of the chief's stool, so that the barb stood far out on the other side. Then said the earl to a man called Fin,—but some say he was of Finn (Laplander) race, and was a superior archer:

"Shoot that tall man by the mast."

Fin shot; and the arrow hit the middle of Einar's bow just at the moment that Einar was drawing it, and the bow was split in two parts.

"What is that," cried King Olaf, "that broke with such a noise?"

"Norway, king, from thy hands," cried Einar.

"No! not quite so much as that," says the king; "take my bow, and shoot," flinging the bow to him.

Einar took the bow, and drew it over the head of the arrow. "Too weak, too weak," said he, "for the bow of a mighty king!" and, throwing the bow aside, he took sword and shield, and fought valiantly.

The king stood on the gangways of the *Long Serpent*, and shot the greater part of the day; sometimes with the bow, sometimes with the spear, and always throwing two spears at once. He looked down over the ship's side, and saw that his men struck briskly with their swords, and yet wounded but seldom. Then he called aloud,

"Why do ye strike so gently that ye seldom cut?"

One among the people answered, "The swords are blunt and full of notches."

Then the king went down into the forehold, opened the chest under the throne, and took out many sharp swords, which he handed to his men; but as he stretched down his right hand with them, some observed that blood was running down under his steel glove, but no one knew where he was wounded.

Desperate was the defence in the *Serpent*, and there was the heaviest destruction of men done by the forecastle crew, and those of the forehold, for in both places the men were chosen men, and the ship was highest; but in the middle of the ship the people were thinned. Now when Earl Eric saw there were but few people remaining beside the ship's mast, he determined to board; and he entered the *Serpent* with four others. Then came Hyrning, the king's brother-in-law, and some others against him,

and there was the most severe combat; and at last the earl was forced
to leap back on board the *Iron Beard* again, and some who had accom·
panied him were killed, and others wounded.

Now the fight became hot indeed, and many men fell on board the
Serpent; and the men on board of her began to be thinned off, and the
defence to be weaker. The earl resolved to board the *Serpent* again, and
again he met with a warm reception. When the forecastle men of the
Serpent saw what he was doing, they went aft and made a desperate
fight; but so many men of the *Serpent* had fallen, that the ship's sides
were in many places quite bare of defenders; and the earl's men poured
in all around into the vessel, and all the men who were still able to defend
the ship crowded aft to the king, and arrayed themselves for his defence.

Kolbiorn the marshal, who had on clothes and arms like the king's
and was a remarkably stout and handsome man, went up to the king
on the quarter-deck. The battle was still going on fiercely even in the
forehold. But as many of the earl's men had now got into the *Serpent*
as could find room, and his ships lay all round her, and few were the
people left in the *Serpent* for defence against so great a force; and in a
short time most of the *Serpent's* men fell, brave and stout though they
were. King Olaf and Kolbiorn the marshal both sprang overboard, each
on his own side of the ship; but the earl's men had laid out boats around
the *Serpent,* and killed those who leaped overboard. Now when the king
had sprung overboard, they tried to seize him with their hands, and
bring him to Earl Eric; but King Olaf threw his shield over his head, and
sank beneath the waters. Kolbiorn held his shield behind him to protect
himself from the spears cast at him from the ships which lay round the
Serpent, and he fell so upon his shield that it came under him, so that he
could not sink so quickly. He was thus taken and brought into a boat,
and they supposed he was the king. He was brought before the earl; and
when the earl saw it was Kolbiorn, and not the king, he gave him his life.
At the same moment all of King Olaf's men who were in life sprang overboard from the *Serpent;* and Thorkel Nefia, the king's brother, was the
last of all the men who sprang overboard.

Earl Sigvald, as before related, came from Vendland, in company
with King Olaf, with ten ships; but the eleventh ship was manned with
the men of Astrid, the king's daughter, the wife of Earl Sigvald. Now
when King Olaf sprang overboard, the whole army raised a shout of
victory; and then Earl Sigvald and his men put their oars in the water
and rowed towards the battle.

But the Vendland cutter, in which Astrid's men were, rowed back to
Vendland; and the report went immediately abroad, and was told by
many, that King Olaf had cast off his coat of mail under water, and
swam, driving under the long-ships, until he came to the Vendland
cutter, and that Astrid's men had conveyed him to Vendland; and many
tales have been made since about the adventures of Olaf the King.

But however this may have been, King Olaf Trygvesson never came back again to his kingdom of Norway.

By this victory Earl Eric Hakonson became owner of the *Long Serpent*, and made a great booty besides; and he steered the *Serpent* from the battle.

HOW THE NORSEMEN DISCOVERED AMERICA[1]

Snorre Sturlason

(1178–1241)

I

The Voyage of Biarne the Son of Heriulf

HERIULF dwelt first at Dropstock. His wife was called Thorgird, and their son was called Biarne. He was a promising young man. In his earliest youth he had a desire to go abroad, and he soon gathered property and reputation; and he was by turns a year abroad and a year with his father. Biarne was soon possessor of a merchant ship of his own. The last winter, while he was in Norway, Heriulf prepared to go to Greenland with Eric, and gave up his dwelling . . . Heriulf settled at Heriulfsness, and became a very distinguished man. . . .

Biarne came the same summer with his ship to the strand which his father had sailed abroad from in spring. He was much struck with the news, and would not unload his vessel. When his crew asked him what he intended to do, he replied, that he was resolved to follow his old custom of taking up his winter abode with his father.

"So I will steer for Greenland, if ye will go with me."

They one and all agreed to go with him. Biarne said:

"Our expedition will be thought foolish, as none of us have ever been on the Greenland sea before."

Nevertheless they set out to sea as soon as they were ready, and sailed for three days, until they lost sight of the land they had left. But when the wind failed, a north wind with fog set in, and they knew not where they were sailing to; and this lasted many days.

At last they saw the sun, and could distinguish the quarters of the sky; so they hoisted sail again, and sailed a whole day and night, when they made land. They spoke among themselves about what this land could be, and Biarne said that, in his opinion, it could not be Greenland. On the question, if he should sail nearer to it, he said:

"It is my advice that we sail close up to this land."

They did so; and they soon saw that the land was without mountains, was covered with wood, and that there were small hills inland. They left

[1]From Samuel Laing's translation of *The Heimskringla*.

the land on the larboard side, and had their sheet on the land side. Then they sailed two days and nights before they got sight of land again. They asked Biarne if he thought this would be Greenland; but he gave his opinion that this land was no more Greenland than the land they had seen before.

"For on Greenland, it is said, there are great snow-mountains."

They soon came near to this land, and saw it was flat and covered with trees. Now, as the wind fell, the ship's people talked of its being advisable to make for the land; but Biarne would not agree to it. They thought they would need wood and water; but Biarne said:

"Ye are not in want of either."

And the men blamed him for this. He ordered them to hoist the sail, which was done. They now turned the ship's bow from the land, and kept the sea for three days and nights with a fine breeze from south-west. Then they saw a third land, which was high and mountainous, and with snowy mountains. Then they asked Biarne if he would land here; but he refused altogether,

"For in my opinion this land is not what we want."

Now they let the sails stand, and kept along the land, and saw it was an island. Then they turned from the land and stood out to sea with the same breeze; but the gale increased, and Biarne ordered a reef to be taken in, and not to sail harder than the ship and her tackle could easily bear. After sailing three days and nights they made, the fourth time, land; and when they asked Biarne if he thought this was Greenland or not, Biarne replies:

"This is most like what has been told me of Greenland; and here we shall take to the land."

They did so, and came to the land in the evening under a ness, where they found a boat. On this ness dwelt Biarne's father Heriulf. . . .

II

And of Leif the Son of Eric the Red

It is next to be told that Biarne Heriulfsson came over from Greenland to Norway on a visit to Earl Eric, who received him well. Biarne tells of this expedition of his, on which he had discovered unknown lands; and people thought he had not been very curious to get knowledge, as he could not give any account of those countries, and he was somewhat blamed on this account. Biarne was made a court-man of the earl, and the summer after he went over to Greenland; and afterwards there was much talk about discovering unknown lands.

Leif, a son of Eric Red of Brattalid, went over to Biarne Heriulfsson and bought the ship from him, and manned the vessel, so that in all there were thirty-five men on board. Leif begged his father Eric to go as commander of the expedition, but he excused himself; saying he was getting old, and not so able as formerly to undergo the hardships of a sea voyage. Leif insisted that he among all their relations was the most likely to have good luck on such an expedition: and Eric consented, and rode from home with Leif when they had got all ready for sea; but when they were coming near to the ship the horse on which Eric was riding stumbled, and he fell from the horse, and hurt his foot.

"It is not destined," said Eric, "that I should discover more lands than this of Greenland, on which we dwell and live; and now we must not run hastily into this adventure."

Eric accordingly returned home to Brattalid; but Leif, with his comrades, in all thirty-five men, rigged out their vessel. There was a man from the South country called Tyrker with the expedition. They put the ship in order, and went to sea when they were ready. They first came to the land which Biarne had last discovered, sailed up to it, cast anchor, put out a boat, and went on shore; but there was no grass to be seen. There were huge snowy mountains up the country; but all the way from the sea up to these snowy ridges the land was one field of snow, and it appeared to them a country of no advantages. Leif said:

"It shall not be said of us, as it was of Biarne, that we did not come upon the land; for I will give the country a name, and call it Helloland."

Then they went on board again, put to sea, and found another land. They sailed in towards it, cast anchor, put out a boat, and landed. The country was flat and overgrown with wood; and the strand far around consisted of a white sand, and low towards the sea. Then Leif said,

"We shall give this land a name according to its kind, and call it Markland."

Then they hastened on board, and put to sea again with an on-shore wind from north-east, and were out for two days, and made land. They sailed towards it, and came to an island which lay on the north side of the land, where they landed to wait for good weather. There was dew upon the grass; and having accidentally got some of the dew upon their hands and put it to their mouths, they thought they had never tasted anything so sweet as it was. Then they went on board, and sailed into a sound that was between the island and a ness which went out northwards from the land, and sailed west past the ness. There was very shallow water in ebb-tide, so that their ship lay dry; and there was a long way between their ship and the water. They were so desirous to get to the land that they would not wait till their vessel floated, but ran to the land, to a place where a river comes out of a lake. As soon as their ship was afloat, they took the boats, rowed to the ship, towed her up the river, and from thence into the lake, where they cast anchor, carried their beds out of the ship, and set up their tents. They resolved to put things in order for wintering there, and they erected a large house. . . .

It happened one evening that a man of the party was missing; and it was the South-country man, Tyrker. Leif was very sorry for it; because Tyrker had been long in his father's house, and he loved Tyrker in his childhood. Leif blamed his comrades very much, and prepared to go with twelve men on an expedition to find him; but they had gone only a short way from the station before Tyrker came to meet them, and he was joyfully received. . . .

Leif said to him:

"Why art thou so late, my foster-father? and why didst thou leave thy comrades?"

He spoke at first long in Turkish, rolled his eyes, and knit his brows; but they could not make out what he was saying. After a while and some delay, he said in Norse:

"I did not go much farther than they; and yet I have something altogether new to relate, for I found vines and grapes."

"Is that true, my foster-father?" said Leif.

"Yes, true it is," answered he; "for I was born where there is no scarcity of vines and grapes."

Now they slept all night, and next morning Leif said to his men:

"Now we have two occupations to attend to, and day about; namely, to gather grapes or cut vines, and to fell wood in the forest to load our vessel."

And this advice was followed. It is related that their stern-boat was filled with grapes, and then a cargo of wood was hewn for the vessel. There was also self-sown wheat in the fields and a tree which is called Massur. Of all these they took samples; and some of the trees were so large that they were used in houses. Towards spring they made ready and sailed away; and Leif gave the country a name from its productions, and called it Vinland.

NORWAY

THE CORMORANTS OF ANDVÆR[1]

Jonas Lie

(1833–1908)

OUTSIDE Andvær lies an island, the haunt of wild birds, which no man can land upon, be the sea never so quiet; the sea-swell girds it round about with sucking whirlpools and dashing breakers.

On fine summer days something sparkles there through the sea-foam like a large gold ring; and, time out of mind, folks have fancied there was a treasure there left by some pirates of old.

At sunset, sometimes, there looms forth from thence a vessel with a castle astern, and a glimpse is caught now and then of an old-fashioned galley. There it lies as if in a tempest, and carves its way along through heavy white rollers.

Along the rocks sit the cormorants in a long black row, lying in wait for dog-fish.

But there was a time when one knew the exact number of these birds. There was never more nor less of them than twelve, while upon a stone, out in the sea-mist, sat the thirteenth, but it was only visible when it rose and flew right over the island.

The only persons who lived near the Vær at winter time, long after the fishing season was over, were a woman and a slip of a girl. Their business was to guard the scaffolding poles for drying fish against the birds of prey, who had such a villainous trick of hacking at the drying-ropes.

The young girl had thick coal-black hair, and a pair of eyes that peeped at folk so oddly. One might almost have said that she was like the cormorants outside there, and she had never seen much else all her life. Nobody knew who her father was.

Thus they lived till the girl had grown up.

It was found that, in the summer time, when the fishermen went out to the Vær to fetch away the dried fish, that the young fellows began underbidding each other, so as to be selected for that special errand.

Some gave up their share of profits, and others their wages; and there was a general complaint in all the villages round about that on such occasions no end of betrothals were broken off.

But the cause of it all was the girl out yonder with the odd eyes.

[1]From R. Nisbet Bain's translation in *Weird Tales from Northern Seas*. Reprinted by permission of Kegan Paul Trench, Trubner & Co., Ltd.

For all her rough and ready ways, she had something about her, said those she chatted with, that there was no resisting. She turned the heads of all the young fellows; it seemed as if they couldn't live without her.

The first winter a lad wooed her who had both house and warehouse of his own.

"If you come again in the summer time, and give me the right gold ring I will be wedded by, something may come of it," said she.

And, sure enough, in the summer time the lad was there again.

He had a lot of fish to fetch away, and she might have had a gold ring as heavy and as bonnie as heart could wish for.

"The ring I must have lies beneath the wreckage, in the iron chest, over at the island yonder," said she, "that is, if you love me enough to dare fetch it."

But then the lad grew pale.

He saw the sea-bore rise and fall out there like a white wall of foam on the bright warm summer day, and on the island sat the cormorants sleeping in the sunshine.

"Dearly do I love thee," said he, "but such a quest as that would mean my burial, not my bridal."

The same instant the thirteenth cormorant rose from his stone in the misty foam, and flew right over the island.

Next winter the steersman of a yacht came a wooing. For two years he had gone about and hugged his misery for her sake, and he got the same answer.

"If you come again in the summer time, and give me the right gold ring I will be wedded with, something may come of it."

Out to the Vær he came again on Midsummer Day.

But when he heard where the gold ring lay, he sat and wept the whole day till evening, when the sun began to dance north-westward into the sea.

Then the thirteenth cormorant arose, and flew right over the island.

There was nasty weather during the third winter.

There were manifold wrecks, and on the keel of a boat, which came driving ashore, hung an exhausted young lad by his knife-belt.

But they couldn't get the life back into him, roll and rub him about in the boat-house as they might.

Then the girl came in.

"'Tis my bridegroom!" said she.

And she laid him in her bosom, and sat with him the whole night through, and put warmth into his heart.

And when the morning came, his heart beat.

"Methought I lay betwixt the wings of a cormorant, and leaned my head against its downy breast," said he.

The lad was ruddy and handsome, with curly hair, and he couldn't take his eyes away from the girl.

He took work upon the Vær.

But off he must needs be gadding and chatting with her, be it never so early and never so late.

So it fared with him as it had fared with the others.

It seemed to him that he could not live without her, and on the day when he was bound to depart, he wooed her.

"*Thee* I will not fool," said she. "Thou hast lain on my breast, and I would give my life to save thee from sorrow. Thou shalt have me if thou wilt place the betrothal ring upon my finger; but longer than the day lasts thou canst not keep me. And now I will wait, and long after thee with a horrible longing, till the summer comes."

On Midsummer Day the youth came thither in his boat all alone.

Then she told him of the ring that he must fetch for her from among the skerries.

"If thou hast taken me off the keel of a boat, thou mayest cast me forth yonder again," said the lad. "Live without thee I cannot."

But as he laid hold of the oars in order to row out, she stepped into the boat with him and sat in the stern. Wondrous fair was she!

It was beautiful summer weather, and there was a swell upon the sea: wave followed upon wave in long bright rollers.

The lad sat there, lost in the sight of her, and he rowed and rowed till the insucking breakers roared and thundered among the skerries; the groundswell was strong, and the frothing foam spurted up as high as towers.

"If thy life is dear to thee, turn back now," said she.

"Thou art dearer to me than life itself," he made answer.

But just as it seemed to the lad as if the prow were going under, and the jaws of death were gaping wide before him, it grew all at once as still as a calm, and the boat could run ashore as if there was never a billow there.

On the island lay a rusty old ship's anchor half out of the sea.

"In the iron chest which lies beneath the anchor is my dowry," said she. "Carry it up into thy boat, and put the ring that thou seest on my finger. With this thou dost make me thy bride. So now I am thine till the sun dances north-westwards into the sea."

It was a gold ring with a red stone in it, and he put it on her finger and kissed her.

In a cleft on the skerry was a patch of green grass. There they sat them down, and they were ministered to in wondrous wise, how he knew not nor cared to know, so great was his joy.

"Midsummer Day is beauteous," said she, "and I am young and thou art my bridegroom. And now we'll to our bridal bed."

So bonnie was she that he could not contain himself for love.

But when night drew nigh, and the sun began to dance out into the sea, she kissed him and shed tears.

"Beauteous is the summer day," said she, "and still more beauteous is the summer evening; but now the dusk cometh."

And all at once it seemed to him as if she were becoming older and older and fading right away.

When the sun went below the sea-margin there lay before him on the skerry some mouldering linen rags and nought else.

Calm was the sea, and in the clear Midsummer night there flew *twelve* cormorants out over the sea.

JACK OF SJOHOLM AND THE GAN-FINN[1]

Jonas Lie

(1833–1908)

IN THE days of our forefathers, when there was nothing but wretched boats up in Nordland, and folks must needs buy fair winds by the sackful from the Gan-Finn, it was not safe to tack about in the open sea in wintry weather. In those days a fisherman never grew old. It was mostly women-folk and children, and the lame and halt, who were buried ashore.

Now there was once a boat's crew from Thjotto in Helgeland, which had put to sea, and worked its way right up to the East Lofotens.

But that winter the fish would not bite.

They lay to and waited week after week, till the month was out, and there was nothing for it but to turn home again with their fishing gear and empty boats.

But Jack of Sjoholm, who was with them, only laughed aloud, and said that if there were no fish there, fish would certainly be found higher northwards. Surely they hadn't rowed out all this distance only to eat up all their victuals, said he.

He was quite a young chap, who had never been out fishing before. But there was some sense in what he said for all that, thought the head-fisherman.

And so they set their sails northwards.

On the next fishing-ground they fared no better than before, but they toiled away so long as their food held out.

And now they all insisted on giving it up and turning back.

"If there's none here, there's sure to be some still higher up towards the north," opined Jack; "and if they had gone so far, they might surely go a little further still," quoth he.

So they tempted fortune from fishing-ground to fishing-ground, till they had ventured right up to Finmark. But there a storm met them, and

---

[1]From R. Nisbet Bain's translation in *Weird Tales from Northern Seas*. Reprinted by permission of Kegan Paul Trench, Trubner & Co., Ltd.

try as they might to find shelter under the headlands they were obliged at last to put out into the open sea again.

There they fared worse than ever. They had a hard time of it. Again and again the prow of the boat went under the heavy rollers, instead of over them, and later on in the day the boat foundered.

There they all sat helplessly on the keel in the midst of the raging sea, and they all complained bitterly against that fellow Jack, who had tempted them on, and led them into destruction. What would now become of their wives and children? They would starve now that they had none to care for them.

When it grew dark, their hands began to stiffen, and they were carried off by the sea one by one.

And Jack heard and saw everything, down to the last shriek and the last clutch; and to the very end they never ceased reproaching him for bringing them into such misery, and bewailing their sad lot.

"I must hold on tight now," said Jack to himself, for he was better even where he was than in the sea.

And so he tightened his knees on the keel, and held on fast till he had no feeling left in either hand or foot.

In the coal-black gusty night he fancied he heard yells from one or other of the remaining boats' crews.

"They, too, have wives and children," thought he. "I wonder whether they have also a Jack to lay the blame upon."

Now while he thus lay there and drifted and drifted, and it seemed to him to be drawing towards dawn, he suddenly felt that the boat was in the grip of a strong shoreward current; and, sure enough, Jack got at last ashore. But whichever way he looked, he saw nothing but black sea and white snow.

Now as he stood there, speering and spying about him, he saw, far away, the smoke of a Finn Gamme, which stood beneath a cliff, and he managed to scramble right up to it.

The Finn was so old that he could scarcely move. He was sitting in the midst of the warm ashes, and mumbling into a big sack, and neither spoke nor answered. Large yellow humble-bees were humming about all over the snow, as if it were Midsummer; and there was only a young lass there to keep the fire alight, and give the old man his food. His grandsons and grand-daughters were with the reindeer, far far away on the *Fjeld*.

Here Jack got his clothes well dried, and the rest he so much wanted. The Finn girl, Seimke, couldn't make too much of him; she fed him with reindeer milk and marrow-bones, and he lay down to sleep on silver fox-skins.

Cosy and comfortable it was in the smoke there. But as he thus lay there, 'twixt sleep and wake, it seemed to him as if many odd things were going on round about him.

There stood the Finn in the doorway talking to his reindeer, although they were far away in the mountains. He barred the wolf's way, and threatened the bear with spells; and then he opened his skin sack, so that the storm howled and piped, and there was a swirl of ashes into the hut. And when all grew quiet again, the air was thick with yellow humble-bees, which settled inside his furs, whilst he gabbled and mumbled and wagged his skull-like head.

But Jack had something else to think about besides marvelling at the old Finn. No sooner did the heaviness of slumber quit his eyes than he strolled down to his boat.

There it lay stuck fast on the beach and tilted right over like a trough, while the sea rubbed and rippled against its keel. He drew it far enough ashore to be beyond the reach of the sea-wash.

But the longer he walked around and examined it, the more it seemed to him as if folks built boats rather for the sake of letting the sea in than for the sake of keeping the sea out. The prow was little better than a hog's snout for burrowing under the water, and the planking by the keel-piece was as flat as the bottom of a chest. Everything, he thought, must be arranged very differently if boats were to be really seaworthy. The prow must be raised one or two planks higher at the very least, and made both sharp and supple, so as to bend before and cut through the waves at the same time, and then a fellow would have a chance of steering a boat smartly.

He thought of this day and night. The only relaxation he had was a chat with the Finn girl of an evening.

He couldn't help remarking that this Seimke had fallen in love with him. She strolled after him wherever he went, and her eyes always became so mournful when he went down towards the sea; she understood well enough that all his thoughts were bent upon going away.

And the Finn sat and mumbled among the ashes till his fur jacket regularly steamed and smoked.

But Seimke coaxed and wheedled Jack with her brown eyes, and gave him honeyed words as fast as her tongue could wag, till she drew him right into the smoke where the old Finn couldn't hear them.

The Gan-Finn turned his head right round.

"My eyes are stupid, and the smoke makes 'em run," said he; "what has Jack got hold of there?"

"Say it is the white ptarmigan you caught in the snare," whispered she.

And Jack felt that she was huddling up against him and trembling all over.

Then she told him so softly that he thought it was his own thoughts speaking to him, that the Finn was angry and muttering mischief, and *jojking* against the boat which Jack wanted to build. If Jack were to complete it, said she, the Gan-Finn would no longer have any sale for his fair-winds in all Nordland. And then she warned him to look to himself and never get between the Finn and the Gan-flies.

Then Jack felt that his boat might be the undoing of him. But the worse things looked, the more he tried to make the best of them.

In the grey dawn, before the Finn was up, he made his way towards the sea-shore.

But there was something very odd about the snow-hills. They were so many and so long that there was really no end to them, and he kept on tramping in deep and deeper snow and never got to the sea-shore at all. Never before had he seen the northern lights last so long into the day. They blazed and sparkled, and long tongues of fire licked and hissed after him. He was unable to find either the beach or the boat, nor had he the least idea in the world where he really was.

At last he discovered that he had gone quite astray inland instead of down to the sea. But now, when he turned round, the sea-fog came close up against him, so dense and grey that he could see neither hand nor foot before him.

By the evening he was well-nigh worn out with weariness, and was at his wits' end what to do.

Night fell, and the snowdrifts increased.

As now he sat him down on a stone and fell a-brooding and pondering how he should escape with his life, a pair of snow-shoes came gliding so smoothly towards him out of the sea-fog and stood still just in front of his feet.

"As you have found me, you may as well find the way back also," said he

So he put them on, and let the snow-shoes go their own way over hillside and steep cliff He let not his own eyes guide him or his own feet carry him, and the swifter he went the denser the snowflakes and the driving sea-spray came up against him, and the blast very nearly blew him off the snow-shoes.

Up hill and down dale he went over all the places where he had fared during the daytime, and it sometimes seemed as if he had nothing solid beneath him at all, but was flying in the air.

Suddenly the snow-shoes stood stock still, and he was standing just outside the entrance of the Gan-Finn's hut.

There stood Seimke. She was looking for him.

"I sent my snow-shoes after thee," said she, "for I marked that the Finn had bewitched the land so that thou should'st not find the boat. Thy *life* is safe, for he has given thee shelter in his house, but it were not well for thee to see him this evening."

Then she smuggled him in, so that the Finn did not perceive it in the thick smoke, and she gave him meat and a place to rest upon.

But when he awoke in the night, he heard an odd sound, and there was a buzzing and a singing far away in the air:

> "The Finn the boat can never bind,
> The Fly the boatman cannot find,
> But round in aimless whirls doth wind."

The Finn was sitting among the ashes and *jojking*, and muttering till the ground quite shook, while Seimke lay with her forehead to the floor and her hands clasped tightly round the back of her neck, praying against him to the Finn God. Then Jack understood that the Gan-Finn was still seeking after him amidst the snowflakes and the sea-fog, and that his life was in danger from magic spells.

So he dressed himself before it was light, went out, and came tramping in again all covered with snow, and said he had been after bears in their winter retreats. But never had he been in such a sea-fog before; he had groped about far and wide before he found his way back into the hut again, though he stood just outside.

The Finn sat there with his skin-wrappings as full of yellow flies as a beehive. He had sent them out searching in every direction, but back they had all come, and were humming and buzzing about him.

When he saw Jack in the doorway, and perceived that the flies had pointed truly, he grew somewhat milder, and laughed till he regularly shook within his skin-wrappings, and mumbled, "The bear we'll bind fast beneath the scullery-sink, and his eyes I've turned all awry, so that he can't see his boat, and I'll stick a sleeping-peg in front of him till spring-time."

But the same day the Finn stood in the doorway, and was busy making magic signs and strange strokes in the air.

Then he sent forth two hideous Gan-flies, which flitted off on their errands, and scorched black patches beneath them in the snow wherever they went. They were to bring pain and sickness to a cottage down in the swamps, and spread abroad the Finn disease, which was to strike down a young bride at Bodo with consumption.

But Jack thought of nothing else night and day but how he could get the better of the Gan-Finn.

The lass Seimke wheedled him and wept and begged him, as he valued his life, not to try to get down to his boat again. At last, however, she saw it was no use—he had made up his mind to be off.

Then she kissed his hands and wept bitterly. At least he must promise to wait till the Gan-Finn had gone right away to Jokmok in Sweden.

On the day of his departure, the Finn went all round his hut with a torch and took stock.

Far away as they were, there stood the mountain pastures, with the reindeer and the dogs, and the Finn's people all drew near. The Finn took the tale of the beasts, and bade his grandsons not let the reindeer stray too far while he was away, and could not guard them from wolves and bears. Then he took a sleeping potion and began to dance and turn round and round till his breath quite failed him, and he sank moaning to the ground. His furs were all that remained behind of him. His spirit had gone—gone all the way to Jokmok.

There the magicians were all sitting together in the dark sea-fog beneath the shelter of the high mountain, and whispering about all manner of secret and hidden things, and blowing spirits into the novices of the black art.

But the Gan-flies, humming and buzzing, went round and round the empty furs of the Gan-Finn like a yellow ring and kept watch.

In the night Jack was awakened by something pulling and tugging at him as if from far-away. There was as it were a current of air, and something threatened and called to him from the midst of the snowflakes outside—

> "Until thou canst swim like the duck or the drake,
> The egg thou'dst be hatching no progress shall make;
> The Finn shall ne'er let thee go southwards with sail,
> For he'll screw off the wind and imprison the gale."

At the end of it the Gan-Finn was standing there, and bending right over him. The skin of his face hung down long and loose, and full of wrinkles, like an old reindeer skin, and there was a dizzying smoke in his eyes. Then Jack began to shiver and stiffen in all his limbs, and he knew that the Finn was bent upon bewitching him.

Then he set his face rigidly against it, so that the magic spell should not get him; and thus they struggled with one another till the Gan-Finn grew green in the face, and was very near choking.

After that the sorcerers of Jokmok sent magic shots after Jack, and clouded his wits. He felt so odd; and whenever he was busy with his boat, and had put something to rights in it, something else would immediately go wrong, till at last he felt as if his head were full of pins and needles.

Then deep sorrow fell upon him. Try as he would, he couldn't put his boat together as he would have it; and it looked very much as if he would never be able to cross the sea again.

But in the summer time Jack and Seimke sat together on the headland in the warm evenings, and the gnats buzzed and the fishes spouted close ashore in the stillness, and the eider-duck swam about.

"If only some one would build me a boat as swift and nimble as a fish, and able to ride upon the billows like a sea-mew," sighed and lamented Jack, "then I could be off."

"Would you like me to guide you to Thjotto?" said a voice up from the sea-shore.

There stood a fellow in a flat turned-down skin cap, whose face they couldn't see.

And right outside the boulders there, just where they had seen the eider-duck, lay a long and narrow boat, with high prow and stern; and the tar-boards were mirrored plainly in the clear water below; there was not so much as a single knot in the wood.

"I would be thankful for any guidance," said Jack.

When Seimke heard this, she began to cry and take on terribly. She fell upon his neck, and wouldn't let go, and raved and shrieked. She promised him her snow-shoes, which would carry him through everything, and said she would steal for him the bone-stick from the Gan-Finn, so that he might find all the old lucky dollars that ever were buried, and would teach him how to make salmon-catching knots in the fishing lines, and how to entice the reindeer from afar. He should become as rich as the Gan-Finn, if only he wouldn't forsake her.

But Jack had only eyes for the boat down there. Then she sprang up, and tore down her black locks, and bound them round his feet, so that he had to wrench them off before he could get quit of her.

"If I stay here and play with you and the young reindeer, many a poor fellow will have to cling with broken nails to the keel of a boat," said he. "If you like to make it up, give me a kiss and a parting hug, or I shall go without them."

Then she threw herself into his arms like a young wild cat, and looked straight into his eyes through her tears, and shivered and laughed, and was quite beside herself.

But when she saw she could do nothing with him, she rushed away, and waved her hands above her head in the direction of the Gamme.

Then Jack understood that she was going to take counsel of the Gan-Finn, and that he had better take refuge in his boat before the way was closed to him. And, in fact, the boat had come so close up to the boulders that he had only to step down upon the thwarts. The rudder glided into his hand, and aslant behind the mast sat some one at the prow, and hoisted and stretched the sail; but his face Jack could not see.

Away they went.

And such a boat for running before the wind Jack had never seen before. The sea stood up round about them like a deep snow-drift, although it was almost calm. But they hadn't gone very far before a nasty pipin began in the air. The birds shrieked and made for land, and the sea rose like a black wall behind them.

It was the Gan-Finn who had opened his wind-sack, and sent a storm after them.

"One needs a full sail in the Finn-cauldron here," said something from behind the mast.

The fellow who had the boat in hand took such little heed of the weather that he did not so much as take in a single clew.

Then the Gan-Finn sent double knots after them.

They sped along in a wild dance right over the firth, and the sea whirled up in white columns of foam, reaching to the very clouds.

Unless the boat could fly as quick and quicker than a bird, it was lost.

Then a hideous laugh was heard to larboard—

> "Anfinn Ganfinn gives mouth,
> And blows us right south;
> There's a crack in the sack,
> With three clews we must tack."

And heeling right over, with three clews in the sail, and the heavy foremost fellow astride on the sheer-strake, with his huge sea-boots dangling in the sea-foam, away they scudded through the blinding spray right into the open sea, amidst the howling and roaring of the wind.

The billowy walls were so vast and heavy that Jack couldn't even see the light of day across the yards, nor could he exactly make out whether they were going under or over the sea-trough.

The boat shook the sea aside as lightly and easily as if its prow were the slippery fin of a fish, and its planking was as smooth and fine as the shell of a tern's egg; but, look as he would, Jack couldn't see where these planks ended; it was as if there was only half a boat and no more; and at last it seemed to him as if the whole of the front part came off in the sea-foam, and they were scudding along under sail in half a boat.

When night fell, they went through the sea-fire, which glowed like hot embers, and there was a prolonged and hideous howling up in the air to windward.

And cries of distress and howls of mortal agony answered the wind from all the upturned boat keels they sped by, and many hideously pale-looking folks clutched hold of their thwarts. The gleam of the sea-fire cast a blue glare on their faces, and they sat, and gaped, and glared, and yelled at the blast.

Suddenly he awoke, and something cried, "Now thou art at home at Thjotto, Jack."

And when he had come to himself a bit, he recognized where he was. He was lying over against the boulders near his boathouse at home. The tide had come so far inland that a border of foam gleamed right up in the potato-field, and he could scarcely keep his feet for the blast. He sat him down in the boathouse, and began scratching and marking out the shape of the Draugboat in the black darkness till sleep overtook him.

When it was light in the morning, his sister came down to him with a meat-basket. She didn't greet him as if he were a stranger, but behaved as if it were the usual thing for her to come thus every morning. But when he began telling her all about his voyage to Finmark, and the Gan-Finn, and the Draugboat he had come home in at night, he perceived that she only grinned and let him chatter. And all that day he talked about it to his sister and his brothers and his mother, until he arrived at the conclusion that they thought him a little out of his wits. When he mentioned the Draugboat they smiled among themselves, and evidently went out of their way to humour him. But they might believe what they liked, if only he could carry out what he wanted to do, and be left to himself in the out-of-the-way old boathouse.

"One should go with the stream," thought Jack; and if they thought him crazy and out of his wits, he ought to behave so that they might beware of interfering with him, and disturbing him in his work.

So he took a bed of skins with him down to the boathouse, and slept there at night; but in the day-time he perched himself on a pole on the roof, and bellowed out that now he was sailing. Sometimes he rode astraddle on the roof ridge, and dug his sheath-knife deep into the rafters, so that people might think he fancied himself at sea, holding fast on to the keel of a boat.

Whenever folks passed by, he stood in the doorway, and turned up the whites of his eyes so hideously, that every one who saw him was quite scared. As for the people at home, it was as much as they dared to stick his meat-basket into the boathouse for him. So they sent it to him by his youngest sister, merry little Malfri, who would sit and talk with him, and thought it such fun when he made toys and playthings for her, and talked about the boat which should go like a bird, and sail as no other boat had ever sailed.

If any one chanced to come upon him unexpectedly, and tried to peep and see what he was about in the boathouse there, he would creep up into the timber-loft and bang and pitch the boards and planks about, so that they didn't know exactly where to find him, and were glad enough to be off. But one and all made haste to climb over the hill again when they heard him fling himself down at full length and send peal after peal of laughter after them.

So that was how Jack got folks to leave him at peace.

He worked best at night when the storm tore and tugged at the stones and birchbark of the turf roof, and the sea-wrack came right up to the boathouse door.

When it piped and whined through the fissured walls, and the fine snowflakes flitted through the cracks, the model of the Draugboat stood plainest before him. The winter days were short, and the wick of the train-oil lamp, which hung over him as he worked, cast deep shadows, so that the darkness came soon and lasted a long way into the morning, when he sought sleep in his bed of skins with a heap of shavings for his pillow.

He spared no pains or trouble. If there was a board which would not run into the right groove with the others, though never so little, he would take out a whole row of them and plane them all round again and again.

Now, one night, just before Christmas, he had finished all but the uppermost planking and the gabs. He was working so hard to finish up that he took no count of time.

The plane was sending the shavings flying their briskest when he came to a dead stop at something black which was moving along the plank.

It was a large and hideous fly which was crawling about and feeling and poking all the planks in the boat. When it reached the lowest keel-board it whirred with its wings and buzzed. Then it rose and swept above it in the air till, all at once, it swerved away into the darkness.

Jack's heart sank within him. Such doubt and anguish came upon him. He knew well enough that no good errand had brought the Gan-fly buzzing over the boat like that.

So he took the train-oil lamp and a wooden club, and began to test the prow and light up the boarding, and thump it well, and go over the planks one by one. And in this way he went over every bit of the boat from stem to stern, both above and below. There was not a nail or a rivet that he really believed in now.

But now neither the shape nor the proportions of the boat pleased him any more. The prow was too big, and the whole cut of the boat all the way down the gunwale had something of a twist and a bend and a swerve about it, so that it looked like the halves of two different boats put to-gether, and the half in front didn't fit in with the half behind. As he was about to look into the matter still further (and he felt the cold sweat bursting out of the roots of his hair), the train-oil lamp went out and left him in blank darkness.

Then he could contain himself no longer. He lifted his club and burst open the boathouse door, and, snatching up a big cow-bell began to swing it about him and ring and ring with it through the black night.

"Art chiming for me, Jack?" something asked. There was a sound behind him like the surf sucking at the shore, and a cold blast blew into the boathouse.

There on the keel-stick sat some one in a sloppy grey sea-jacket, and with a print cap drawn down over its ears, so that its skull looked like a low tassel.

Jack gave a great start. This was the very being he had been thinking of in his wild rage. Then he took the large baling can and flung it at the Draug.

But right through the Draug it went, and rattled against the wall be-hind, and back again it came whizzing about Jack's ears, and if it had struck him he would never have got up again.

The old fellow, however, only blinked his eyes a little savagely.

"Fie," cried Jack, and spat at the uncanny thing—and back into his face again he got as good as he gave.

"There you have your wet clout back again," cried a laughing voice.

But the same instant Jack's eyes were opened and he saw a whole boat-building establishment on the sea-shore.

And, there, ready and rigged out on the bright water, lay an *Ottring*, so long and shapely and shining that his eyes could not feast on it enough.

The old 'un blinked with satisfaction. His eyes became more and more glowing.

"If I could guide you back to Helgeland," said he, "I could put you in the way of gaining your bread too. But you must pay me a little tax for it. In every seventh boat you build 'tis I who must put in the keel-board."

Jack felt as if he were choking. He felt that the boat was dragging him into the very jaws of an abomination.

"Or do you fancy you'll worm the trick out of me for nothing?" said the gaping grinning Draug.

Then there was a whirring sound, as if something heavy was hovering about the boathouse, and there was a laugh. "If you want the *seaman's* boat you must take the *dead man's* boat along with it. If you knock three times to-night on the keel-piece with the club, you shall have such help in building boats that the like of them will not be found in all Nordland."

Twice did Jack raise his club that night, and twice he laid it aside again.

But the *Ottring* lay and frisked and sported in the sea before his eyes, just as he had seen it, all bright and new with fresh tar, and with the ropes and fishing gear just put in. He kicked and shook the fine slim boat with his foot just to see how light and high she could rise on the waves above the water-line.

And once, twice, thrice, the club smote against the keel-piece.

So that was how the first boat was built at Sjoholm.

Thick as birds together stood a countless number of people on the headland in the autumn, watching Jack and his brothers putting out in the new *Ottring*.

It glided through the strong current so that the foam was like a foss all round it.

Now it was gone, and now it ducked up again like a sea-mew, and past skerries and capes it whizzed like a dart.

Out in the fishing grounds the folks rested upon their oars and gaped. Such a boat they had never seen before.

But if in the first year it was an *Ottring*, next year it was a broad heavy *Femboring* for winter fishing which made the folks open their eyes.

And every boat that Jack turned out was lighter to row and swifter to sail than the one before it.

But the largest and finest of all was the last that stood on the stocks on the shore.

This was the *seventh*.

Jack walked to and fro, and thought about it a good deal; but when he came down to see it in the morning, it seemed to him oddly enough, to have grown in the night and, what is more, was such a wondrous beauty that he was struck dumb with astonishment. There it lay ready at last, and folks were never tired of talking about it.

Now, the Bailiff who ruled over all Helgeland in those days was an unjust man who laid heavy taxes upon the people, taking double weight and tale both of fish and of eider-down, nor was he less grasping with the tithes and grain dues. Wherever his fellows came they fleeced and flayed. No sooner, then, did the rumour of the new boats reach him than he sent his people out to see what truth was in it, for he himself used to go fishing in the fishing grounds with large crews. When thus his fellows came back and told him what they had seen, the Bailiff was so taken with it that he drove straightway over to Sjoholm, and one fine day down he swooped on Jack like a hawk. "Neither tithe nor tax hast thou paid for thy livelihood, so now thou shalt be fined as many half-marks of silver as thou hast made boats," said he.

Ever louder and fiercer grew his rage. Jack should be put in chains and irons and be transported northwards to the fortress of Skraar, and be kept so close that he should never see sun or moon more.

But when the Bailiff had rowed round the *Femboring*, and feasted his eyes upon it, and seen how smart and shapely it was, he agreed at last to let Mercy go before Justice, and was content to take the *Femboring* in lieu of a fine.

Then Jack took off his cap and said if there was one man more-than another to whom he would like to give the boat, it was his honour the Bailiff.

So off the magistrate sailed with it.

Jack's mother and sister and brothers cried bitterly at the loss of the beautiful *Femboring;* but Jack stood on the roof of the boathouse and laughed fit to split.

And towards autumn the news spread that the Bailiff with his eight men had gone down with the *Femboring* in the West-fjord.

But in those days there was quite a changing about of boats all over Nordland, and Jack was unable to build a tenth part of the boats required of him. Folks from near and far hung about the door of his boat-house, and it was quite a favour on his part to take orders, and agree to carry them out. A whole score of boats soon stood beneath the pent-house on the strand.

He no longer troubled his head about every *seventh* boat, or cared to know which it was or what befell it. If a boat foundered now and then, so many the more got off and did well, so that, on the whole, he made a very good thing indeed out of it. Besides, surely folks could pick and choose their own boats, and take which they liked best.

But Jack got so great and mighty that it was not advisable for any one to thwart him, or interfere where he ruled and reigned.

Whole rows of silver dollars stood in the barrels in the loft, and his boat-building establishment stretched over all the islands of Sjoholm.

One Sunday his brothers and merry little Malfri had gone to church in the *Femboring*. When evening came, and they hadn't come home, the boatman came in and said that some one had better sail out and look after them, as a gale was blowing up.

Jack was sitting with a plumb-line in his hand, taking the measurements of a new boat, which was to be bigger and statelier than any of the others, so that it was not well to disturb him.

"Do you fancy they're gone out in a rotten old tub, then?" bellowed he. And the boatman was driven out as quickly as he had come in.

But at night Jack lay awake and listened. The wind whined outside and shook the walls, and there were cries from the sea far away. And just then there came a knocking at the door, and some one called him by name.

"Go back whence you came," cried he, and nestled more snugly in his bed.

Shortly afterwards there came the fumbling and the scratching of tiny fingers at the door.

"Can't you leave me at peace o' nights?" he bawled, "or must I build me another bedroom?"

But the knocking and the fumbling for the latch outside continued, and there was a sweeping sound at the door, as of some one who could not open it. And there was a stretching of hands toward the latch ever higher and higher.

But Jack only lay there and laughed. "The *Femborings* that are built at Sjoholm don't go down before the first blast that blows," mocked he.

Then the latch chopped and hopped till the door flew wide open and in the doorway stood pretty Malfri and her mother and brothers. The sea-fire shone about them, and they were dripping with water.

Their faces were pale and blue, and pinched about the corners of the mouth, as if they had just gone through their death agony. Malfri had one stiff arm round her mother's neck; it was all torn and bleeding, just as when she had gripped her for the last time. She railed and lamented, and begged back her young life from him.

So now he knew what had befallen them.

Out into the dark night and the darker weather he went straightway to search for them, with as many boats and folk as he could get together. They sailed and searched in every direction, and it was in vain.

But towards day the *Femboring* came drifting homewards bottom upwards, and with a large hole in the keel-board.

Then he knew who had done the deed.

But since the night when the whole of Jack's family went down, things were very different at Sjoholm.

In the daytime, so long as the hammering and the banging and the planing and the clinching rang about his ears, things went along swim-

mingly, and the frames of boat after boat rose thick as sea fowl on an
Æggevaer.

But no sooner was it quiet of an evening than he had company. His
mother bustled and banged about the house, and opened and shut
drawers and cupboards, and the stairs creaked with the heavy tread of
his brothers going up to their bedrooms.

At night no sleep visited his eyes, and sure enough pretty Malfri came
to his door and sighed and groaned.

Then he would lie awake there and think, and reckon up how many
boats with false keel-boards he might have sent to sea. And the longer
he reckoned the more draug-boats he made of it.

Then he would plump out of bed and creep through the dark night
down to the boathouse. There he held a light beneath the boats, and
banged and tested all the keel-boards with a club to see if he couldn't
hit upon the *seventh*. But he neither heard nor felt a single board give
way. One was just like another. They were all hard and supple, and the
wood, when he scraped off the tar, was white and fresh.

One night he was so tormented by an uneasiness about the new *Sek-
string* which lay down by the bridge ready to set off next morning, that
he had no peace till he went down and tested its keel-board with his
club.

But while he sat in the boat, and was bending over the thwart with a
light, there was a gulping sound out at sea, and then came such a vile
stench of rottenness. The same instant he heard a wading sound, as of
many people coming ashore, and then up over the headland he saw a
boat's crew coming along.

They were all crooked-looking creatures, and they all leaned right
forward and stretched out their arms before them. Whatever came in
their way, both stone and stour, they went right through it, and there
was neither sound nor shriek.

Behind them came another boat's crew, big and little, grown men and
little children, rattling and creaking.

And crew after crew came ashore and took the path leading to the
headland.

When the moon peeped forth Jack could see right into their skeletons.
Their faces flared, and their mouths gaped open with glistening teeth,
as if they had been swallowing water. They came in heaps and shoals,
one after the other: the place quite swarmed with them.

Then Jack perceived that here were all they whom he had tried to
count and reckon up as he lay in bed, and a fit of fury came upon him.

He rose in the boat and spanked his leather breeches behind and cried:
"You would have been even more than you are already if Jack hadn't
built his boats."

But now like an icy whizzing blast they all came down upon him, staring at him with their hollow eyes.

They gnashed their teeth, and each one of them sighed and groaned for his lost life.

Then Jack, in his horror, put out from Sjoholm.

But the sail slackened, and he glided into dead water. There, in the midst of the still water, was a floating mass of rotten swollen planks. All of them had once been shaped and fashioned together, but were now burst and sprung, and slime and green mould and nastiness hung about them.

Dead hands grabbed at the corners of them with their white knuckles and couldn't grip fast. They stretched themselves across the water and sank again.

Then Jack let out all his clews and sailed and sailed and tacked according as the wind blew.

He glared back at the rubbish behind him to see if those *things* were after him. Down in the sea all the dead hands were writhing and tried to strike him with gaffs astern.

Then there came a gust of wind whining and howling, and the boat drove along betwixt white seething rollers.

The weather darkened, thick snowflakes filled the air, and the rubbish around him grew greener.

In the daytime he took the cormorants far away in the grey mist for his landmarks, and at night they screeched about his ears.

And the birds flitted and flitted continually, but Jack sat still and looked out upon the hideous cormorants.

At last the sea-fog lifted a little, and the air began to be alive with bright, black, buzzing flies. The sun burned, and far away inland the snowy plains blazed in its light.

He recognized very well the headland and shore where he was now able to lay to. The smoke came from the Gamme up on the snow-hill there. In the doorway sat the Gan-Finn. He was lifting his pointed cap up and down, up and down, by means of a thread of sinew, which went right through him, so that his skin creaked.

And up there also sure enough was Seimke.

She looked old and angular as she bent over the reindeer-skin that she was spreading out in the sunny weather. But she peeped beneath her arm as quick and nimble as a cat with kittens, and the sun shone upon her, and lit up her face and pitch-black hair.

She leaped up so briskly, and shaded her eyes with her hand, and looked down at him. Her dog barked, but she quieted it so that the Gan-Finn should mark nothing.

Then a strange longing came over him, and he put ashore.

He stood beside her and she threw her arms over her head, and laughed and shook and nestled close up to him, and cried and pleaded, and didn't know what to do with herself, and ducked down upon his bosom, and threw herself on his neck, and kissed and fondled him, and wouldn't let him go.

But the Gan-Finn had noticed that there was something amiss, and sat all the time in his furs, and mumbled and muttered to the Gan-flies, so that Jack dare not get between him and the doorway.

The Finn was angry.

Since there had been such a changing about of boats over all Nordland, and there was no more sale for his fair winds, he was quite ruined, he complained. He was now so poor that he would very soon have to go about and beg his bread. And of all his reindeer he had only a single doe left, who went about there by the house.

Then Seimke crept behind Jack, and whispered to him to bid for this doe. Then she put the reindeer-skin around her, and stood inside the Gamme door in the smoke, so that the Gan-Finn only saw the grey skin, and fancied it was the reindeer they were bringing in.

Then Jack laid his hand upon Seimke's neck, and began to bid.

The pointed cap ducked and nodded, and the Finn spat in the warm air; but sell his reindeer he would not.

Jack raised his price.

But the Finn heaved up the ashes all about him, and threatened and shrieked. The flies came as thick as snow-flakes; the Finn's furry wrappings were alive with them.

Jack bid and bid till it reached a whole bushel load of silver, and the Finn was ready to jump out of his skins.

Then he stuck his head under his furs again, and mumbled and jojked till the amount rose to seven bushels of silver.

Then the Gan-Finn laughed till he nearly split. He thought the reindeer would cost the purchaser a pretty penny.

But Jack lifted Seimke up, and sprang down with her to his boat, and held the reindeer-skin behind him, against the Gan-Finn.

And they put off from land, and went to sea.

Seimke was so happy, and smote her hands together, and took her turn at the oars.

The northern light shot out like a comb, all green-red and fiery, and licked and played upon her face. She talked to it, and fought it with her hands, and her eyes sparkled. She used both tongue and mouth and rapid gestures as she exchanged words with it.

Then it grew dark, and she lay on his bosom, so that he could feel her warm breath. Her black hair lay right over him, and she was as soft and warm to the touch as a ptarmigan when it is frightened and its blood throbs.

Jack put the reindeer-skin over Seimke, and the boat rocked them to and fro on the heavy sea as if it were a cradle.

They sailed on and on till night-fall; they sailed on and on till they saw neither headland nor island nor sea-bird in the outer skerries more.

HOW DAMMITALL–WITH–THE–LIMP SAVED THE CREW OF THE *SEAL*[1]

Johan Bojer
(1872–)

THEN came the storm.

There was the usual swarm of boats lying over the banks, hauling in lines and nets. The air was raw and foggy, and there was a slight swell.

"There's good fishing to-day!" Peter Suzansa shouted across to the *Seal*, and Kristàver agreed with him. The nets were full of cod, and there would be thousands in the boat if they went on as they had begun.

"The air's awfully still!" cried a Nordlander, looking all round. There is a certain kind of stillness that makes the fishermen listen, and when one headman assumes a listening attitude, it is taken up in boat after boat, until all are trying, as it were, to find the scent. In fog every sound is suspicious, and now the cold sea-mist began to move and drift in a south-easterly direction, and that meant wind. Listen! Already there was a strange roar!

"We shall be having a visitor!" shouted a Nordland man, as he hauled and hauled at his nets to get them in in time. They must make for land at once.

"Hurry up, men!" shouted Peter Suzansa. In all the boats the men were working their hardest, hauling for their very lives; they knew this roar that was growing louder and louder, and their energy and their anxiety spread from boat to boat over miles and miles of sea. Make haste! A storm is coming!

This time it came so quickly that there was hardly time to do anything before the boats were in the midst of it, tossing up and down upon huge, foaming billows.

It was impossible to draw in the nets; the boats would only have been swamped. Knives were pulled from their sheaths and the nets cut off, the long chains of nets with all their burden of fish disappearing in the foaming water. The next moment a little sail was hoisted. Would it be possible to tack in towards land? The boat is driven along over waves like rolling mountains; the sail disappears into a deep valley and a new wave appears to be breaking over the very mast-top; but the next moment the little boat again mounts into view. The men on board are drenched to the skin and bale for their lives. They all know that in such a storm it is impossible to tack towards land; the only hope of safety is in sailing away, before wind and wave, at haphazard over the sea, as far as God wills.

[1]From Jessie Muir's translation of *The Last of the Vikings*. Reprinted by permission of the author and of Hodder & Stoughton, Ltd.

They ran before the wind; but the boats lay deep in the water with the weight of several hundred fish, so that the waves broke over the stern and made it useless to bale. The headman shouted an order that was repeated in shouts forward, and three men fell upon the fish and threw the precious cargo overboard into the foaming water, as if they were sacrificing to the sea to save their lives.

Even now, when every one had enough to do in looking after himself, comrade boats tried to keep in touch with one another. Peter Suzansa, on the *Sea Fire*, saw in front of him the *Seal's* brown sail, now high on the crest of a wave, then descending into a deep valley. Would it appear again? Yes! there it was!

It grew dark, and the sky was all black, scudding clouds. The wind whirled the spray into the air, where it tore about like wild, white wraiths; and the little sails were scattered and driven like storm-lashed birds in an ever wilder and wilder flight.

Where were they going? No one knew. When would they be able to turn? No one knew. Some time to-night, or some time to-morrow, they would perhaps be shattered upon a rocky cliff on the mainland; perhaps the wind would drive them seawards for days; perhaps in another moment their boat would capsize, and then—then there would be nothing more.

It was the first time Kristàver had sailed the *Seal* close-reefed. The sail was now as small as it could be, and did not reach half-way up the mast; and yet it was too large. It would be wrong to say that Kristàver was enjoying himself, but at last he was out with his boat in downright earnest, and how would it end? He had a huge pocket-book in his breast-pocket, and was responsible for four other lives on board. Incautious steering, the miscalculation of a wave, half a second in which his eyes were not everywhere, and the next moment they might be clinging to the keel of the capsized boat. It was not this, however, which occupied him most; it was the boat. She had capsized three winters in succession, but it was impossible to discover wherein the fault lay. There was some hidden cause which he would perhaps be able to extract from her now. As he stood in the drenching spray and the darkness, with his whole being intent upon the management of the boat, he felt that something was wanting in his mastery of her, and that at any moment she might play him a trick. The trough of that wave, for instance. If the stern were to be lifted so high that the rudder for one second hovered in the air, the boat would broach to, and then where would they be? Take care! Take care! There it was again—something wanting, insecurity in the rigging and boat. Confound it! He clenched his teeth: it was as though he and the boat were wrestling for the mastery.

Lars stood by the mast, minding the *priar*. This was important now that they were scudding before the gale. His sou'wester was pulled down over his ears and tied under his chin to prevent it flying away, and his eyes were fixed on his father. Every word that the headman shouted might mean life or death.

"Slack the *priar!*" his father shouted.

"Slack the *priar!*" all the men repeated.

And Lars hung on to the rope and carried out the order, and then once more fixed his eyes on his father, standing with the tiller in his hand, his face intent, his eyes everywhere. When a wave tossed the stern into the air, the headman seemed to be flying heavenwards; then they rode with the crest of the wave under the middle of the boat, and the water all round them was lashed into greenish white foam, making it seem quite light on board. Then the stern sank again, and his father with it into the depths, and Lars was on the point of shouting:

"Are you coming up again, father?"

But there he stood, just as calmly, at the tiller, ready to meet a new mountain of water; and now he rose again, and Lars felt as if he had got his father back once more. The boy began to repeat hymns, for all good spirits must help his father to-night; and if things went wrong, he was with his father at any rate, and if they ever got to land he would never leave him, never do anything to displease him.

They sailed on, they knew not whither. Whether it was to be right across the West Fjord, or out into the ocean, or straight upon a rock, God alone knew. Even if they had had a compass on board, it would have been impossible to see it, or to strike a match—in this weather. . . !

Now and then they heard cries that were not from birds but from human beings—human beings clinging to the keel of an upturned boat. It could not be helped; to-night every one had to do the best he could for himself, and those who still sailed knew that numbers of capsized boats were floating on the sea for miles round, and that those who clung to their keels must go on crying for help, for no one could heed them.

They sailed on and on. Darker it could not be, but it could get rougher. They could no longer distinguish between clouds and sea. The very heaven seemed to be falling upon them in white foam. No, it was a gigantic wave, and the wind broke the crest of it, and sent the spoon-drift flying about like white wraiths. Would the boat clear it? She did, but was almost swamped, and the men baled and baled—until the next wave came.

They sailed on, and it seemed to Lars that they were no longer on the sea, but flying through a weird, dark region, in which foaming billows pursued them like green and white hobgoblins that howled and tried to reach them, twisting and turning in a wild death-dance, flinging themselves upon the boat, from behind, from above, from the side, coming suddenly out of the depths to dance round her with foam-flecked faces, all round, everywhere. And his father stood on the thwart and was still keeping them off. How long would he be able to manage it? This was a long night.

The waves kept dashing over Kristàver, sometimes nearly knocking him down; but he nevertheless began to feel pleasure in his boat. She yielded so pliantly to the waves and cleared the most incredible billows, and every time he would have liked to pat her as one would a good horse, or cry:

"Well done, *Seal!*"

Was it possible for the wind to be worse? Great chasms seemed to be rent in the raging sky, and out of them darted fire, and the long, yellow stormy gleams threw weird reflections over the seething waters. When the boat rose on the crest of a billow and was borne along at its dizzy pace, it was almost as if she rose out of the water and flew through the air, as if even the keel lost touch with the water, with that on which the boat must keep a firm hold; and it was at such a moment the *Seal* first dived down into the trough of a wave, then broached to and capsized. The waves dashed over her, but now she was floating bottom upward.

There were cries from five men as she turned over; they were drowned in the roar of the wind and the waves, and that seemed to be the end.

But no! Two men were already hanging to the shrouds. The sea tossed the boat along, and two more who had been under her came up, and held on to the shroud on the other side. Where was the fifth?

Mechanically and half stunned the four men drag themselves up on to the boat, sitting astride over the keel to which they cling, so as not to be washed away. They have swallowed sea-water, and have been battered by the waves and the boat, and they have lost their gloves and sou'westers.

Kristàver had a feeling that Lars had come up, but he could not help crying out:

"Are you there, Lars?"

"Yes, father," came the answer.

"Hold tight!"

"Yes, father."

One man was missing, however, but Kristàver caught sight of a boot that was flung against the side of the boat, and managed to get hold of it, though he almost fell off into the water in doing so. It was Kaneles that he pulled up, and the man must have received a blow against the boat, for he was unconscious and made no attempt to hold on. No thought of letting go of him crossed Kristàver's mind; he would just have to cling with one hand to the keel, although it was as much as the others could do to hold on with both hands.

A capsized boat on the Lofoten Sea is such an ordinary thing, and they knew it. They were swept along, now high on the crest of a wave, now deep in the trough. It was such an ordinary thing to be drowned on a night such as this, and they knew it; but they nevertheless held on tight because every second was a second more to live, and they cried wild, agonizing cries for help, and the cry was the same from them all:

"Lord God! Help! Help!"

Every new wave that came foaming towards them was perhaps death itself, and involuntarily they crouched down before it to diminish the force of the blow. They cried again, though they knew there was no possibility of rescue; they cried in an agony of fear that stifled reason, they cried like animals that feel the piercing knife; their cries rose above the roaring of the wind, but no one answered.

The waves broke over them incessantly as they sat, flinging them hither and thither in the darkness. After a time Kristàver recollected that the boat would lie more quietly if he could cut the shrouds on one side so that the mast could float up.

"Lay hold there!" he shouted to Henry Rabben as he pushed Kaneles over to him. Henry gripped his unconscious comrade and held him fast. "Catch hold of my boot!" Kristàver shouted to Arnt Awsan, who instantly let go his hold of the keel with one hand and grasped the headman's foot. Kristàver then drew his knife from its sheath and let himself slip down over the side of the boat; and as a wave washed over his head he heard Lars cry:

"Oh, father! Take care!"

He soon came up again, however, with his knife between his teeth; the shrouds were severed, and in another moment the mast shot up from beneath the boat. But he had made a serious mistake. He had cut the shrouds on the lee side, and the mast came up on the weather side, and was immediately carried towards them on the top of a wave. If it hit any of them it would be certain death; it might sweep all five of them off at one stroke. No, it struck the boat with a resounding blow, and then retired to gather strength upon a new wave.

"Catch hold of my leg again!" cried Kristàver, and once more hung head downwards in the waves, and cut through the shrouds on the other side too.

The mast was now free. It was driven once more against the boat, but without hitting anyone, then retired again, carried away upon the waves with one end sticking up into the air, and finally disappeared from sight in the spray.

The boat tossed less now, and the four men sat holding the fifth between them. Until now they had not known that they were drenched to the skin, and so perished with cold that their teeth chattered; they had not felt that the flying spray so blinded them that they could hardly see one another.

How long they had been tossing about thus they did not know, when they thought they heard a shout in the darkness. They shouted back and shrieked for help; in the stormy yellow light that shone upon the foaming wave-crests they saw something—not a capsized boat, but a tiny sail, a boat coming towards them. They were saved! They cried again, like men begging for their lives. The stormy light shone more strongly upon them, and in its yellow glow the boat flew past. It was Peter Suzansa. He had meant to save them, and they could see him standing at the helm only a few yards off. He shouted, but in such a sea his boat would be dashed to pieces against theirs, and the old man knew it and could only leave them there and go on; but as he left his comrades to their fate he turned his head and looked at them, and a cry escaped from his lips, a cry that was taken up by all his men, as if they were begging for forgiveness because they could only save their own lives. Those on the upturned boat understood, and gave an answering cry of pain and anguish; and in another moment Peter Suzansa and his boat disappeared into the night.

Kristàver and his men still clung to their boat as if hope were not entirely gone. Kaneles was still unconscious, and Kristàver held him as before; but would he be able to do so much longer? The others had two hands to hold on with when the waves dashed over them, but Kristàver had only one, and Kaneles was heavy. Leave go of him? No! But what if he let himself be washed away?

"Kaneles!" he cried into the unconscious man's ear. "Try to wake up! Try to hold on! I can't keep up any longer!"

But Kaneles, who was such a strong lad and as elastic as an india-rubber ball, was now unconscious and unable to move a finger; and Kristàver felt that it would soon be all over with himself too. Here came a gigantic wave, and he would not be able to hold on himself and hold Kaneles up too. God forgive him if he had to leave go of the lad!

The wave dashed over them, and Kristàver bent before it; and when it had passed he still sat holding Kaneles.

He saw in fancy his father, the half-blind old man living in the little farm up on the mountain; and he still kept hold of the boy: they would have to be washed away together.

The water beat noisily under the boat, which lay high because it was full of air. Kristàver would have taken out his knife and bored a hole in it to let the air out, but he had no hand to spare and was not equal to anything more.

The same black masses of cloud were racing across the sky; the same gleams of stormy light broke from them over the sea, showing how high the spoondrift flew. But was that not another shout? Yes! There was a sail again. It was coming towards them, making straight for them. They shouted aloud, and in the yellow light they recognized the *Sea Flower*. She passed close by them. Jacob was at the helm, and he saw what Peter Suzansa had seen—that it was impossible to heave to and help them; and as he flew on he was followed by a cry, a despairing cry. Was he too going to leave them?

But that was not Jacob's thought. It would not be like Dammitall-with-the-limp to leave a comrade in the lurch. He and the *Sea Flower* had been out before on a winter's night, and they knew one another; they could venture what others would never dare to do. He roared an order that was repeated forward along the boat; they got the tack down, and she heeled over in the wind. The headman put her bow so as half to meet the waves, and started off as if about to tack. It was madness in such weather, but then it was Jacob who did it.

He was not quite sure what he really intended himself; he only meant to take a turn and keep on a level with the other boat, for he would not sail away from a comrade. The boat was filled by the waves breaking over the water-board, but the men kept on baling. Then they went about again, and Jacob knew that in the meantime the capsized boat must have drifted a good deal to leeward. He set his course at haphazard, and then, in the streak of yellow light, caught sight of a dark line upon the crest of a wave. There they were!

The *Sea Flower* bore down towards them, and Jacob could hear their cries. They must have seen him and taken heart again, and as he once more steered close by them, he shouted:

"Hold tight, boys, and wait a little!"

Such words of encouragement in the storm from one who was still sailing his own boat, made them feel half saved, and gave them strength to hold on. Jacob sailed away again into the blinding spray and darkness, but he had told them to wait and hold tight.

Once more the *Sea Flower* was forced up into the wind to gather impetus for a fresh effort to reach the other boat. She threatened to fill again and the men baled their hardest, and Jacob steered farther and farther to windward. No one but he would have done such a thing in a storm like this. And once more he went about and began to make straight for the capsized boat, which had again been driven farther to leeward.

"Keep a look-out for them!" he shouted, and the men along the boat repeated:

"Keep a look-out for them!"

The *Sea Flower* shipped more seas over her water-board, and her rigging and sail moaned under the pressure of the wind. But was not that the boat on the top of a wave down there? No, it was gone again!

A man standing by the tack shouted "There!" and pointed with his hand. "There!" shouted the others, pointing in the same direction.

Jacob stamped upon the thwart, and said: "Damn it all!" for he thought it was time to put an end to all this. He knew now what he meant to do, and he bore straight down upon the black line that stood out upon a wave far away to leeward.

"Two men on each side and haul them in!" he shouted.

"Two men on each side and haul them in!" the men repeated as they placed themselves in readiness.

It was a mad order, but at sea orders have to be obeyed. The fifth man remained by the tack to give the headman the direction.

At this moment Jacob had no thought for the risk he was taking. He knew perfectly well that there were ninety-nine chances out of a hundred that he would lose his steerage and then they would all be lost; but he had no time to consider this. The upturned boat rose into view again, and he was dashing down towards it on a gigantic billow.

"Stand by!" he shouted.

"Stand by!" the men repeated.

And the next moment the *Sea Flower* rode in the foam and the spray right over the keel of the *Seal*.

"Get hold of them!"

The *Sea Flower* trembled as she scraped over the keel of the other boat, but the men on both sides each hauled in his man. It was like getting big fish into the boat; it was done in half a second, and they were once more scudding through waves and blinding spray in the darkness.

The first thing Jacob was aware of was that his helm was *not* gone. The *Sea Flower* was as obedient as ever. The next thing he saw was that four men had been saved from the ship-wrecked boat; and he heard them cry: "O God! O God!" and then again, "O God!"

But this was not the time to go forward and pity them and say: "Poor fellows!" The steering, the wind, and the waves gave him enough to do. He only shouted to his men: "Are they all alive?" and as usual at sea, the men repeated the headman's words: "Are they all alive?"

"Yes!" said a voice from the middle of the boat.

"Yes!" they all repeated.

They ran before the wind again, flying on through the darkness, over mountains and into valleys, in a whirling tumult of white, shrieking spectres—sailing, sailing they knew not whither.

Toward morning they saw right before them a beacon-light. It was on the mainland, but how far north or how far south Jacob could not tell. They were flying in towards a rocky coast that they did not know. At any moment they might run upon a rock that stood up out of the water or lay hidden below the surface of the sea; but nevertheless they had to go on sailing.

The wind shifted round to the north, and they sailed down along the coast. They could hear the roar of breakers upon the shore side, and every now and then a gleam of stormy light showed them mountains covered with snow, and the white surf of waves breaking over rocks.

Now, however, the wind had so far fallen that Jacob took it into his head to sail in the direction he himself wished. He had no thought of making for land; the tack was put forward and he set out at haphazard through the darkness across the West Fjord again. This time it would be a long way to Lofoten.

Peter Suzansa that night had come safely in to Hammaröy, and it was with a heavy heart that he now sailed back across the West Fjord. He did not know how many men he knew might have been drowned, and he could not bear to think of Kristàver Myran and his men.

It was evening when he reached the station with its harbour lights, and he could see the hut, their Lofoten home, and thought how there would be plenty of room there now. As he tramped up the slippery wharf-steps, he saw people near but did not dare to ask any questions. The coming in of every boat that day was an event, and Peter, too, was soon surrounded by an inquisitive crowd; but he spoke to no one and went straight to the hut.

When he opened the door he paused. Was he dreaming? There were men lying asleep in the bunks!

He stared in astonishment, and then turned to the men following him. "Great God!" was all he said.

Dripping clothes were hanging round the stove, and sea-boots lay upon the floor in pools of water. The men came in and stood gazing at the sleepers. They had themselves been within an ace of going down, and they were drenched to the skin and thoroughly worn out; but all that was nothing compared with the fact that the crew of the *Seal* were lying in their bunks asleep.

While they were busy taking off their clothes and emptying the water out of their sea-boots on to the floor, Kristàver woke, and raising himself on his elbow, rubbed his eyes. Perhaps he was confused with some dream, but then he caught sight of Peter, who the night before had sailed past and left him clinging to his wrecked boat; and for a brief moment the two headmen looked at one another.

Then Kristàver yawned and passed his hand across his forehead.

"Have you got back?" he asked in a matter-of-fact tone of voice.

SWEDEN

THE OUTCAST[1]

Selma Lagerlöf

(1858–   )

(The following episodes are taken from Selma Lagerlöf's novel, *Bannlyst* which has been translated into English, under the title of *The Outcast* by W. Worster, M.A. and published by Messrs Gyldendal.

Sven Elversson and his comrades, starving in the Arctic, are said to have eaten a man. Sven, in reality, had had no part in the affair, though he had no memory of it. Returning home, he finds himself outcast from all.)

I

The "Naiad"

A FEW days after Christmas, Ung-Joel came back to Grimön, with a message from Olaus, to ask if Sven would take a share in the herring-fishery on board the motor-boat *Naiad*, belonging to his crew.

"He says it's hardly likely you could get taken on with any other crew," said Ung-Joel; "but seeing that you're my brother, I was to tell you. They'll not be the best of company, I doubt, that sail with Olaus."

Mor Elversson declared at once that it was out of the question; Sven should never have any dealings with any of them. But his father thought otherwise.

"It wouldn't be a bad thing, perhaps, if Sven tried to pick up the ways of the fishery on the coast here," he said. "And it's true enough he'd hardly get taken on with any other crew."

"Joel! How can you talk so?" cried his wife. "Who knows what they've been plotting and planning now, to send for him like that. Some new mischief, I'll be bound."

"Why, I only said 'twas a pity Sven shouldn't have a part in the fishery," said Joel mildly.

But Sven remembered his father's words on Christmas Eve, and it came into his mind now that perhaps it was his wish to get him away from home.

"You can tell Olaus I'll come," he said to his brother. "And thank him for offering. I'll go over to Fårön myself as soon as I can."

"Why not come back with me now?" said Ung-Joel. "Then you can get the things you want at our store. There was a telegram in this morn-

---

[1]Reprinted by permission of the author, from the translation by W. Worster.

ing that the herring are shoaling thick up at Smögen. By to-morrow they'll be getting away all about."

There was a hurry of preparation for a while, and then the two brothers set off, leaving Joel and Thala alone.

For a week or so they heard no news of Sven, then one Sunday Ung-Joel came out to visit them.

Mor Thala was eager to know how matters had gone with Sven and the crew—for all she knew, they might have killed him.

"I've heard nothing but what folk say," answered the boy. "And that's this. The crew of the *Naiad* before counted one man that had helped to kill a child, and one that had starved an old woman to death, one that had burnt down a place, and one that never sold but what he'd stolen, and two that were fast drinking themselves to death—and now they'd got another help, and that a man who'd eaten human flesh, so it would be hard to find a rougher crowd on one keel. I've heard nothing from Sven himself, but, from all accounts, he seems to be getting on all right with them."

"That's foolishness," said his mother. But for all her angry looks, she was glad to learn that no ill had come to Sven. "But don't forget as soon as you've word from Sven to come here and let us know. 'Tis the best you can do for your father and me."

A fortnight later, Ung-Joel came out to the island again.

"Here's what they're saying now," he began. "That the *Naiad* men won't be able to stand much more of Sven. They say here's the dirtiest, meanest, stinking little boat all along the coast getting gradually clean and workmanlike, the motor taken to working properly instead of going on strike when it's most needed, the rags of sails they used to help now and then been patched and put in order, the faded old flag done away with and a bright new one in its place, and the name painted clean on the stern with all the letters in gold; the food on board getting that decent you wouldn't know but what you were on shore, and clean pots and pans in the galley. And the way folk look at it is this: the *Naiad* men, they might at a pinch take any sort of scoundrel on board, but clean pots and pans and all the rest, it's more than they can put up with."

"Ah! you're making fun of me," said his mother. But it was plain to see that she was glad at heart. "And don't forget," she went on, "as soon as you've any word from Sven, come out and let us know. He's done no wrong, and we must know how it is with him, that he doesn't come to any harm."

But folk that live at Grimön have need of all their patience, waiting for news. All through another two weeks Mor Thala waited, before Ung-Joel came with news of his brother.

"I haven't seen him myself yet," he explained. "But I've heard what they say, that it can't be long now before there's an end of it with Sven Elversson and the *Naiad* crew. It seems that Olaus—he's the skipper—

has taken to seeing the men come on board to time, and more than once he's got his boat away with the rest of the fleet, instead of after, and got up in good time to the fishing-grounds and made a fair haul. And what with the nets being sound and whole, instead of torn in parts and rotten the rest; when they bring up full catches, and the man at the windlass isn't dead drunk and tips the whole lot into the water alongside; when they're beginning to earn good money on the *Naiad*, why, it's plain that Olaus from Fårön and Corfitzson from Fiskebäck and Bertil from Strömsundet and Torsson from Iggenäs and Rasmussen and Hjelmfeldt won't stay long on board. They might bear with a man that's eaten human flesh, but to sail on a well-found ship and make good hauls like all the other crews, and earn good money—it's more than any of them have ever done before."

Mor Thala scolded him roundly for a fool that could never so much as speak one serious word, but she was pleased enough at the news he brought.

"You wait and see, it'll all be well yet," she said. "Eh, Joel, Joel— I wasn't meaning you, lad, but your father. He's surely the wisest man in all Bohuslän. He knew what he was doing when he let Sven go and take a share in that boat, he did."

A week or so later, Ung-Joel came in with a new report.

"I've not seen Sven myself," he said, "for the herring are keeping away up to the north this year. But I've heard what folk say. That when Olaus from Fårön goes spending money he's earned on doing up his house on shore, and Corfitzson from Fiskebäck puts his in the bank, as soon as it's paid him, and Bertil gets his wife a new dress, and Torsson buys a new boat, and Rasmussen and Hjelmfeldt start bringing home food for their wives and little ones—why, there must be something wrong with the *Naiad* lot somewhere. They might take a man-eater with them on board and nothing surprising in that, but to see them now with a clean ship and decently at work and living almost like honest folk, it's more than any'd believe."

"I never heard your like for talking wicked nonsense," said Mor Thala, but she was happier than she cared to show. And she declared that all would go well with Sven in the end; folk would come to look at him differently before long.

"The trouble is," said Joel, "that folk have always looked on that one thing one way, and it's hard for any to see differently. And it won't be easy for him to win them. We must be thankful if we can but see that it's not too much for the lad himself."

A week or so later, the two brothers came sailing home to Grimön together. They looked ill at ease as they entered the house.

Neither mother nor father ventured to question Sven, but Mor Thala soon managed to get Ung-Joel by himself.

"Now what's happened?" she asked.

"Ay, what's happened," said Ung-Joel bitterly. "Little use that Olaus and Corfitzson and all the rest of them have turned better than they've ever been before, and can boast of a clean ship and a good season and a fine price for their fish, and the money well looked after, when they can't set foot in their own house but they're met by crying womenfolk. What's a man to do, when his own wife comes and begs and prays him and says better go on in the old way, bad as it was, than work and share with one that's done dreadful things like Sven. Says a man can't go near one that's done things like that without getting such himself that none can bear the sight of him after. Houses put to rights and boats and dresses and food and decency and comfort—they'd give it all and gladly, to be free of the one ugly thought. When things turn that way, what can a man do but go to Sven himself and beg of him to take his hand from off the ship and crew, and say he'd better go back to Grimön and stay there, where there's none that's likely to meet him and be the worse for it."

II

In the Nets

Some days later, Sven Elversson came down in the afternoon to Knape-fiord harbour, and found the *Naiad* lying in its usual place. Olaus from Färön and Corfitzson and the others whom he knew were on board, making ready, like the rest of the fishing fleet, to put to sea. They were going out with the drift nets, far into the Kattegat. And Sven Elversson felt a sudden desire to go with them, and spend a night at sea.

Olaus looked as if he were minded to refuse, but finding no good reason, he agreed. And as soon as a suit of oilskins had been found for Sven Elversson, they put off. The weather was better than they had had most of that summer, and they might hope to make a good haul. But Sven Elversson soon noticed that all on board were in ill-humour. They spoke unkindly to one another and to him. When he asked about the yield of the mackerel fishery early in the summer, they answered with oaths that a fisherman's life was the poorest that could be.

They reached the fishing grounds, and got the huge nets out, without a single pleasant word being spoken; the same gloom was noticeable later, when they had their meal. That night Sven Elversson sat up on deck; the watches relieved each other in turn, but none took the opportunity of having a chat with him. The men walked up and down silent, bitter and sullen all of them.

Sven Elversson felt depressed and unhappy over all this unfriendliness, but hoped the spirits of those on board would improve when the morning came, and it was time to haul in the catch. Something approaching cheerfulness was also apparent when the motor was started, and the two ends of the net were brought on board ready to haul.

Olaus and Corfitzson were hauling, the others stood ready to disengage the fish from the meshes as the net came in. And as the fish appeared, a full catch of splendid mackerel, glistening all colours of the rainbow, their faces brightened.

"You see, they won't have troubled us the night," said Corfitzson.

"Keep quiet, can't you!" snapped out Olaus, with an oath. "Want to tell them we're here? They'll find us soon enough without that. Feel here!"

He hoisted the net a little out of the water, and all saw, among the glittering fish, something big and dark. There was dead silence on board, and next moment the body of a man came on deck with the net.

One young fellow, who had taken Hjelmfeldt's place on board, tried to get the corpse free of the net, but the skipper's voice called to him sharply:

"Leave it alone. There's another of them here."

And a moment later a new command:

"Let them alone. There's more of them coming."

Just then Corfitzson and Olaus lifted on board a dreadful mass: two bodies twined together.

And when the last of the net was hauled in, there lay a huge mound of dead men, brown meshes, and fish in one confusion. The fish, still living, flapped and slithered about, making the whole horrible mass seem alive.

When the bodies were lifted on board, Sven Elversson was so affected that he wept. He wiped the tears away with the back of his hand, but could not stop them. He stamped his foot, but the tears still came. He was forced to leave his work at the net and walk away far astern.

There he stood until the net was in and the motor started for the homeward run. The silent crew, sullen, unwilling, and gloomy as before, had begun once more the work of clearing fish and mussels from the net, and getting loose the rest.

"All in the net to be thrown over," commanded Olaus.

When Sven Elversson heard the order, he went up to the rest. The tears still flowed from his eyes, but he did not heed them. He took his place with the crew, and set to work, helping with their dreadful task.

They came to one of the dead. Sven Elversson lifted him up, and loosened some of the meshes that had caught in the buttons of his uniform. It was an elderly man with a sailor's beard under his chin. Some one suggested that he was an Englishman. When he had got the body loose, Sven Elversson began hoisting it to the deck.

"All that's in the net to go overboard," said the skipper, bending down towards the corpse.

But Sven Elversson restrained him.

"Will you not let this be laid to rest in holy ground, Olaus?" he said.

Olaus did not answer directly.

"Best to get these horrors away from the ship," he said.

Sven Elversson clenched his teeth in the endeavour to keep back his tears, and said as firmly as he could:

"If you throw this overboard, you will have to throw me too."

He was astonished to hear himself speaking so, but he could not help it. He felt that he would stand by his word.

The others, too, saw that he meant what he said, and would never let the dead man go while he himself lived.

The skipper swore, and turned away, but made no direct refusal, and the others understood that he agreed.

Sven Elversson tried to lift the body, but it was too heavy for him. Then the young fellow newly joined came to his help, and together they laid the dead man by the bulwarks.

The next body was loosed from the net, and laid beside the first without question. Two men carried it up to where Sven Elversson stood. "This one's a German," they said.

To his surprise, Sven Elversson noted that the men on board had suddenly changed to a different expression, a different humour. They swore no longer, but spoke calmly and quietly. They no longer felt hatred towards these hosts of dead, that came and stole away their livelihood. They were accustomed to show respect and reverence to the dead, and something in their nature was more at ease to know that these drowned men of war were to be given decent burial.

Sven Elversson, too, felt strangely easier in mind. His soul felt more at rest now than ever since the first day of his misfortune.

He seemed to hear voices about him, thanking him for his charity to the bodies that once had been the dwellings of immortal souls.

"Now you are loosed from the burden that was laid upon you," said the voices. "Thus it was to come about. Your guilt is taken from you. You have risked your life to save the dead, and you have atoned for all."

His heart beat lightly and strongly, and he thought: "Let others condemn me now if they will, it will not matter, for in myself I know that I have fulfilled my penance and conquered."

THE SHIP[1]

Verner von Heidenstam

(1859–   )

LUCIDLY the summer night spread its shadow, but far out among the islands at Korsö gathered armed country-folk and islanders from Sandhamn and Harö.

A winter had snowed itself away since the Sunday when in Tistedal

---

[1]FromCharles Wharton Stork's translation, *The Charles Men*. Reprinted by permission of The American-Scandinavian Foundation, New York.

the muskets had been presented the last time before the king. Many of the oldest Charles men and those most broken with gout had already retired with their scanty pensions to their little farms, where they knotted their fish-nets by the window or looked over their old diaries. Serious, God-fearing, respected, they met at the church on Sundays; and generals and colonels, without regard to rank, embraced with moist eyes their brothers in arms of the long campaigns. The terms of peace had not yet been signed. When the cannon of the Russian fleet thundered once more among the islands, the veterans buttoned up their worn blue coats as tightly as before and unbuckled the broadsword from the bed-post. Then they each and all went out to defend hearth and home to the uttermost.

Captain Resslöf had appointed himself leader of the band that was assembled on Korsö. Already weary of his room, he stood among the people with a confident bearing. His razor and scissors had rested all winter in the drawer. His hair was so long, his beard was so white, and it was such a pleasure to look at him, that even the sullen and heavy islanders brightened whenever he turned toward them.

After the day's tempest, the surf was still rolling against the rocky seaward shore of the island, but in the hollow by the shining sound hardly a puff of air brushed over the pines under which the men, restless and expectant, counted the distant cannon-shots.

With shaking voice a pastor's son from Djurö stepped forward. He held his cap squeezed in his hand, and his pallor was greyer than ever in the nocturnal light:

"Captain, you have sent the sloops that brought us here to the inner islands to fetch more people. Two leaky rowboats are all we have to save ourselves in, if the enemy lands, but we are more than forty men. Conceal the truth no more! Our little band can no longer accomplish anything here. We have heard, of course, that Rika Fuchs with his Södermanlanders had already marched to Södra Stäk to beat the enemy or lose his life, and that Düker with his Dalecarlians and Westmanlanders is following soon after; but we know, too, that at Boo and along all the coast of Värmdon and Södertörn there will soon be nothing to look for on the cliffs but black ashes. Forgive my words, but we have all heard that Trosa is sacked, and that Nyköping is burning, so that the glare is visible away up toward Stockholm. In Norrköping Swedish peasants and soldiers plunder the wagons of the fugitives in the open street. At Vikboland the peasantry give signals to the Russian ships with sheets and bleached cloth to show that they surrender and swear loyalty to the Czar, and at Marstrand Tordenskjold has hoisted the Danish flag. Whichever way we look, the air is full of conflagration and smoke. It's all over with Sweden, our home, our home."

"I conceal nothing," answered Resslöf, "but rely upon it that the Swedes always get help at the eleventh hour. They seldom get it sooner."

The pastor's son smiled with a sneer, as he departed:

"It is night now, and the tenth hour has just gone by. Let us be hopeful!"

The men pressed close about Resslöf in great uneasiness. The cannon-shots were still thundering, but more faintly and farther out to sea.

Then the pale son of the pastor came once more across the rocks. He stumbled and slipped. He leaped. He pressed in among the crowd without letting himself be checked.

"Here's an uncanny thing, good people. Out at sea there a ship is coming with a lighted lantern in the bow, but with neither mast, nor sail, nor oars. And not a man can I make out on deck. Nobody is standing at the tiller. But the ship goes on just the same, though it moves slowly, slowly."

A murmur of superstitious fear ran through the peasants, but the taciturn islanders followed Resslöf to the topmost cliff by the inlet. They thought that the pastor's son had seen the ship in a vision, for they could not discover anything on the wide sea, around which glowed the nocturnal heavens.

Suddenly they all uttered a cry of astonishment, and the others, who followed them at a distance, began once more to murmur. From behind the rugged cape there drove forward heavily and slowly in the surf a brigantine, without sail and rigging, but with port-holes painted white, and at the stern under the lighted lantern stood a golden lion with paws raised as if to spring.

"That's a ghost ship," muttered the peasants.

Hesitatingly Resslöf ordered some of the bravest islanders to take their muskets and accompany him in one of the rowboats.

They neared the ship cautiously with noiseless strokes and raised muskets, but when they hailed, they received no answer. Some of the small panes in the after cabin gleamed, but that was the reflection of the night, and soon they all became equally dark. Only the bow light burned and flickered.

"God have mercy on us!" whispered Resslöf, pointing to the long strip of cloth which trailed in the water from the stern. "There are our colours. And now I can read the name. This is the brigantine *Swedish Lion!*"

"Yes, yes, it's the brigantine *Swedish Lion*," murmured the peasants on the island.

They shipped the oars. They lay to by the helm and climbed up on a rope of the fallen rigging, but when they entered the empty cabin through a broken window, they had to feel their way forward in the darkness with their hands.

"Isn't there a crew of a single man here?" inquired Resslöf, raising his voice.

No one answered, however, but all remained as quiet as before.

He then shoved up the hatch to the deck. Ship rats ran freely back and forth over the planks, but along the gunwales on both sides lay pale and motionless sailors, who had fallen at their post. He went from man to man, bending down to convince himself that they were all dead.

Thereupon he said to his followers:

"The eleventh hour is come. Bring the people on board now and make the two rowboats fast at the stern, before the surf and current drive the brigantine ashore. We can both bring ourselves safe to the inner islands and salvage a vessel of the Crown that has gone bravely through its fight."

The old man went off across the deck and sat down at the highest point of the stern, alone and apart from the others.

As soon as the people had been conveyed on board, they towed the brigantine in between the islands. Under the softly gliding prow the bays and sounds, illumined by the summer night, reflected the golden lion.

The reports of the cannon no longer rolled in from the sea. More slowly than a broken veteran proceeding to his cottage on a crutch the ship glided between the rocky islets. Women and children, who had hidden there under bushes and roots of trees, stepped out of their concealment. Joyful at hearing the words of their mother tongue from the deck, they flocked upon the beaches and piers with countless importunate questions.

"This is the *Swedish Lion* coming back from the fight," answered those on board.

With that the old Charles man by the flagstaff roused himself from his melancholy and stood up.

"It is more than that. Give me your hands!" he said to the younger men, drawing them close to him. "Hats off, good people, hats off! This devastated ship is like Sweden, who conceals herself behind her islands with her last troops and her dead. How the prisoners longed for her, those who have gone hundreds of miles away beside the rivers of Siberia! Lonely, in disguise, they stood on the deck of their whale-boat with the illimitable expanse of the Arctic Ocean before their sight, calling upon God every hour in their anguish that He should not quench the flame of their life till they were under the roof of their home. The roof of their home? It lies charred upon the ground. Beaten, beaten is our people, divided is our empire, and on our coasts the ruins are smoking. O inscrutable, eternal God, will the dawn never come? Be silent, be silent, good people: the dawn is coming. The captives in Siberian cities, as they sit dumbly at their handiwork, shall one morning leap up and see in the square a rider waving a white flag as a sign that peace has been declared. Thirsty mouths shall drink from Frederick's and Ulrica's gold-rimmed goblets, and the Christmas board shall again be spread by women who are not in mourning. Yet again the hay shall diffuse its fragrance in

Sweden. The church bells shall ring. For a whole year they shall ring every noontide for peace—and for the fallen. Where, indeed, are the old battalions with Grothusen's drum and the banners of Turkish silk? And he who held us together in the great strife and never would believe the sign that God had forsaken us, he in whose heroic nature all our yearning was concealed—where does he dwell? Ask the children that sing. Alas! they go hence one by one, the old brothers in arms. Wherever we fare through the country, walking or by post-chaise, we shall recognize in the mists of night the small white churches where eight or ten strong sons have laid the slabs above their graves. And where does there blossom in an alien land a field so remote that we may not sit down on the sward and whisper: 'Is this perchance the place where one of ours, one who fought and bled, is slumbering?' In their poor garments they loitered a short while before us by the bivouac fire, and then went away and fell. Such they were. So I recall them. So, too, they live in memory and say amid a grateful land: 'Beloved be the people that in the decline of their greatness made their poverty to be revered before the world!'"

AMONG THE SWEDISH SKERRIES[1]

Verner von Heidenstam

THE returning Swedish soldiers tramped from inn to inn with dusty clothing and worn-out shoes. On the cart in front of them jostled the Finnish women whom the king had ransomed from the Turks and married off among his soldiers, and beside them on the straw beneath the wagon-seat stood the cage of chameleons that Professor Eneman had fetched from Asia. The cart with the women was soon left behind, and the animals died, but between the sun-browned soldiers and grooms was still led Brandklipparen, though he was weary with years, stiff in gait, and no longer bore any conquering hero in the saddle.

A tall, thin man with restless eyes and knitted brows always walked a trifle in front of the others. His cheek was dusky as bark, but his teeth gleamed from the midst of the grizzled beard which he never took the time to cut off, since he had neither knife nor shears. The wretchedest vagabond would have scorned his bedraggled coat, but he carried with him all he owned—which was a sack and a cudgel. At the start of the journey, to be sure, he had been sent around to borrow money, but it had long since been strewn to the winds. So that strangers might not point their fingers at his poverty and his country, he called himself a plain private, but he was a royal guardsman, and was named Ehrens-

---

[1] Reprinted from Charles Wharton Stork's translation, *The Charles Men*, by permission of The American-Scandinavian Foundation, New York.

köld. In his youth he had, one October night, stabbed a certain Ensign Gyllenstjerne, and his wits still fluttered so uncertainly that, although he was the merriest with the ale-can, he lay awake at night with restless thoughts. Hardly did the dawn brighten, before he thumped on the floor of the hostelry with his wooden staff to waken his comrades.

At evening, when the exhausted band gathered round the table in the hall of the inn, he remained standing and cheerily raised the can toward all the inquisitive folk who climbed up outside the windows.

"Look, look!" whispered the beholders. "Every scar on that man's face and hands is a saga of some exploit. These are the heroes returning from Ilion!"

Later, when they saw Brandklipparen's rigid pace in the court-yard, they added: "And they have brought along the wooden horse."

But when Ehrensköld had told that it was Brandklipparen, while high-born countesses stepped out of the wagon with bread and sugar, so that they might be able to tell their descendants that Brandklipparen had once eaten out of their hand, he emptied his can to the dregs and beat on the table as a sign to his comrades that they should disperse.

"You don't let us either sit or sleep, with your homesickness," his comrades grumbled. "If a meal is laid out, you at once shout to us to get up and go on, even before the meat is carved."

Then he grew mistrustful and rancorous toward his former friends, and one morning he stole off ahead of the others.

He hardly needed to read the sign-posts or to ask his way. He knew that he went toward the north, that he always turned in on the most direct road. For year after year his homesickness had become more and more overpowering, and now that at last every step brought him nearer to the places of which he had never spoken, but on which he had always brooded, his longing only increased in strength. At times he would stand with hands crossed over his staff and stare at the road, but without himself being conscious of it, and he would then begin to walk on and on. If, on a rainy night, he happened to be turned with harsh words from a door where he had humbly called himself a poor Swedish baggage-driver who prayed to be given a piece of bread by the warm blaze, he forgot that he was no longer in military service. If, then, in the light of the embers, he saw through the window loaves of bread and a bowl of milk on the table, he bent the strips of lead, pulled out two or three small panes, and took for himself as much of the viands as he could reach. But as soon as he had appeased his thirst and stuffed his sack full of fragments of bread, he remembered that he was a good warrior, and before he departed he thrust in his stick, and brought it down on the table with such thundering violence that the bowls and loaves leaped. Then the people of the house, who ran in on all sides, understood that it was not a common thief.

He got to Stralsund before the others, but the city surrendered to the enemy, and their fleets barred the Baltic. After many adventures he at last found in Amsterdam a Dutch smack, which lay ready to sail for Bohus, and into which he was received on such terms that he had a bed on the straw in the cabin under the skipper's patchwork quilt.

But as soon as he heard the anchor-chain rattle, he struck his stick against the roof of the cabin and called to the skipper:

"Good father, when you get in sight of the Swedish skerries, you are to let me know, so that I can fix my beard and clothes, and go on deck."

The skipper promised to fulfil this request, but hardly did he get on deck before there was another knock on the cabin roof.

"Homeward, homeward bound," stammered Ehrensköld, taking the captain by the hand. "You have sailed the seas and experienced many things, father. Tell me, whence comes this delusion of the mind which determines that a man must know himself at home in order to be at peace with himself? Down there among the Turks, when poor Funck died of the fever, I had charge of the watch at the burial; but trust me, I could hardly hold my blade or remember the word of command. The stones lay so white—the cypresses stood so indifferent! If I myself had been laid in that place, I could not have slept in peace. I should have torn through the earth over my head and begged the Lord God for pity."

The skipper answered:

"Has not the same Father's hand formed every part of the earth and even the frail boards that now bear us in the storm? Turn over to the wall and take a good rest. You warriors of the land are bad sailors, and we're getting stiff weather."

The first thing next morning, when the captain was standing by the steersman, he heard fresh rapping on the cabin roof.

"I have a bullet here under my ribs, and I have never rightly understood whether it is that or homesickness which has so exhausted my strength that now I can't hold myself up straight without pain. Just this time of the morning, when it is half light, but the sun has not yet risen, is the hour of homesickness."

It was a restless passage, and the seas thundered. One night the captain came upon the cabin stairs with a horn lantern and threw the light on Ehrensköld. He sat awake on the straw with the staff beside him and the sack as a pillow, and his hair was now so long that it hung over his ears.

"My good sir," began the skipper, as he fastened the lantern to the hook in the roof, "we are now at the Swedish skerries outside Uddevall, but the storm holds heavy, and the night is misty and dark. We must turn and make to sea and wait for clearer weather."

"Yes, turn the smack, you there!" shouted Ehrensköld, so that the cabin rang. "I don't want to go home—what business have I at home, to be sure? In Kalmar church lies my father, and his scutcheon is on the wall. My brother is in captivity. My little sisters have become tall and married and old. They are no more the same. There are no little sisters any more. There is no home any more."

With such words he replied to the captain, but when the latter was about to go, he held him fast by the coat-sleeve.

"Don't listen to me!" he said. "Stick bravely to the same course as before! A good soldier mustn't come home like a coward after long and honest service with his king."

"But the smack, my good sir! It is my only property, and on it I command. I'm fairly sure I see the beacon-fire in the northwest, but the coast is dangerous here and full of pirates, who set out false lights."

Ehrensköld was no longer an enfeebled man. He sat straight up with one leg out of the bed and seized the captain in an iron grip.

"If you've any respect for an officer's will, then sail ahead. It's true I've nothing else to give you but the wretched rags that I shall still wear with honour when I go ashore; but by Kalmar Town I have a little estate, if it hasn't been taken from me. That you shall have in requital, if the sloop goes to wreck."

The skipper thought that homesickness had quenched his wits. He well knew that if the helm was not put down in time, they would be on the rocks. He wrestled to free himself. His coat-sleeve tore at the shoulder seam, and with naked arm he sprang to the ladder.

A blow shook the ship so violently that the candle in the lantern fell over and went out.

"Jesus! There, master, you have the Swedish skerries."

"Then may this moment be blessed! Not since I was a child have I sprung from bed in the morning with a lighter heart."

Ehrensköld heard shots and a struggle. He took the sack and stick and clambered up to the icy deck. The seas burst over him, but the dawn broke through the snowy mist, and he saw that the boat had stranded on a rocky isle and that a swarm of men were disarming the crew.

"Give us what you've got!" demanded a red-bearded man, raising his musket. "Stranded wreckage belongs to the folk on the shore."

Ehrensköld clenched his hand on the shaft of his stick and slung the beggar-sack in front of him.

"Take it! Take it! The peace of mind that I've just found, no bullets of yours can take from me; but if you hadn't a gun, a game of this sort should cost you dear. I am an officer of the Crown."

Cautiously Red-beard lowered his musket.

On the summit of the island glowed a false beacon that had burned down low, and behind the cliffs lay a galliot without a flag. Beside the extinguished stern-lantern sat a sickly, sallow young man wrapped in a splendid fox-skin pelisse and with two crutches on his knee.

"What's this, Norcross?" he cried, with a voice that was thin but shrilled piercingly like a whistle. "Hurry up there, hurry up there!"

Red-beard answered:

"The man here says that he's a Crown man, and in that case we might do better to give him a bullet than to let him slip ashore and carry the tale. Come, fellow, tell us who you are! I see your rags well enough, but no Crown uniform. Have you been away so long that you haven't heard tell of Lassë of the Highway? There he sits on the galliot. That's Commodore Gatenhjelm, look you!"

"My name," said Ehrensköld, "you may know if you first get me clothing according to my rank, but I care little for the harm you can do me, if only I may tread the soil of Sweden once more in this earthly life. I clearly see that ye are godless freebooters, and I recognize clearly another land than the bright and happy one I left—but in any case I am now home. I'm home! My life I can give up freely, but don't deny that I may first step down on the Swedish island!"

"That's reasonable," answered Gatenhjelm. "But hurry up there, hurry up!" He rapped still more impatiently on the railing with a crutch.

Ehrensköld threw his staff on the deck like a surrendered sword and stepped down on the island. He walked forward slowly several paces, as if the ground had taken fast hold of his feet. Then he knelt, stroked and caressed the cliff with his hands and bent down his cheek to it.

"Praise be to Thee, Heavenly Father," he whispered, "who hast led home Thy wandering son by such long and strange paths. Thine, Thine be the glory!"

With that Gatenhjelm gave a sign, and Norcross laid the musket to his eye and from the railing shot Ehrensköld through the head.

When the day arose, the pirates had already steered in with their prey to the coast of Bohus, but out on the island lay the dead warrior with his arms round the cliff.

HOW LEIF SON OF RODMAR FOUGHT THE SONS OF ATLE[1]

Gunnar Gunnarsson

ONE day in spring, when the wind blew freshly over the fjord, Leif sailed away with three ships. He stood on the poop and wondered that he had never thought before how hard it would be to part from Helga.

His old countryman clapped him on the shoulder and said:

"On a voyage it is best to keep the salt water outside the ship."

Leif smiled with a wry face. His heart had not yet been hardened.

Helga stood on the edge of the shore and saw the striped sails bellying in the breeze. The ships lay slanting on the water. They glided along as if in play, and became so quickly smaller.

---

[1]From *The Sworn Brothers* by permission of the author.

Helga stood alone on the shore. All the others who had been down to bid farewell to those departing had gone back again to the house. Helga stood there alone with the breeze. Everything was green and cheerful around her. Trees stood covered with new leaves, and flowers grew again from the ground. And there sailed Leif, taking the summer away with him. . . .

Leif had not sailed long before a great quiet came over him. Alone with the sea, and his own master! No one to obey! No one to consider! That was something to his taste, and under such circumstances there was no room in his heart for care and longing. Successive days awoke him, each with its own voice. Hungry in soul and body he crept each morning out of his sleeping-bag.

It suited his plans to sail to the British Isles; accordingly he was on his way thither. Otherwise he might have sailed to the land far toward the west which a beggar had once told him of. The only objection was that, according to the narrator, there were no people to trade with there and no one to pillage. He was out on a trading and Viking expedition. Besides, it was an absurd country, so entirely without inhabitants. If ever he had time and opportunity he might still wish to take a closer view of it. "Iceland," the beggar had called it, and had prophesied that he should some day see it. He wished to be certain about it, but it lay so far out of the way that he could not well include it in his voyage that summer.

If he did, he ran the risk of being obliged to spend the winter there. And he could not endure the idea of a whole winter without Helga. But he emphasized the fact to himself that if he now let Iceland alone, it was an act of his own free will.

The land out there in the west would not run away, so whether one went there a summer earlier or later was a point of minor importance. Leif, now voyaging alone, came to be quite intimate with the sea. He enjoyed standing at the helm and feeling the ship under his hand. He liked best sailing with all sails spread, and cutting his way through the water as it foamed. It was to him a great delight to sail in such a way that even old and experienced Vikings opened watchful eyes. He tortured his dragon-ship till it seemed to him the sea held its breath, ready to close its foaming jaws round its prey. When he thus kept his ship rocking right on the edge of destruction, clutching the quivering tiller fast in his thin hand, his heart felt light in his breast. He felt himself like a ruler over the sea.

The old Vikings watched Leif closely, and found that they had in him a guide after their own heart. They winked admiringly at each other when he sailed his maddest. His reckless courage filled them with expectation. They showed great willingness in obeying his wishes and orders. His young voice sounded sharply and pleasantly in their ears.

They took Leif's measure secretly and thoroughly approved of him. Though he was not so strong in body as warriors generally were, yet men with such restless eyes were rare. And the strength he had lay in hard lumps of muscle in the right places. When he greeted or thanked a man he clutched his hand as with an iron claw.

The Vikings found that they had reason to expect an eventful summer with much amusement and many dangers. They thought without regret that some of them might find their way to Odin before this Viking expedition was over. They had not much objection to sitting round the golden-bristled boar, though it should be this very winter.

Meanwhile, Leif had formed a fixed idea that he would show Ingolf that he could trade and get on in foreign lands on his own account. Accordingly, when he got there, he showed a caution which was not really according to his own mind, and which the Vikings had not expected. He traded with great foresight, bought chiefly corn and other necessary commodities, including wine and honey. He was also, in pursuance of his promise to Ingolf, cautious with regard to engaging in battle.

His men had expected great things in the direction of depredations on the coast, and were to a certain extent disappointed.

Leif had comparatively few men, and he did not engage in unequal warfare. In order, however, to get some booty, he practised unexpected attacks with quite a few picked men. With five or six followers he would row ashore in a boat in out-of-the-way spots. If they succeeded in getting on shore unobserved, they began to steal forward by remote paths and through deep and dark woods. These were occasions of incredible excitement and secret joy.

It was possible for days and nights to pass without their finding a place adapted for making an attack with so small a force. And when they had at last found a place, a considerable time might pass in watching for an opportunity. But when their well-prepared attack at length took place, it was overwhelming and irresistible. Even old and experienced Vikings had to acknowledge that they had never before taken part in such bold and exciting expeditions. And they loved Leif for the happiness he provided them in their old age. There was constant emulation among Leif's men to get leave to accompany him on these forays. But Leif showed an immovable firmness and foresight in choosing his companions. It was counted a great honour to be among those chosen.

The summer passed in sailing to and fro along the coasts of England and Ireland.

Leif diligently avoided collisions with other Vikings. There were, as a rule, many following him, and he never could be secure from an attack. It was therefore best to exhibit suitable caution. For the rest, he slept peacefully in his bearskin bag at night. Should it happen that he was involved in a fight without his own fault, he had nothing to do with that.

In many places where he came, he found that Haersten and Holmsten had been just before him with their six ships. Leif took no real trouble to overtake them. He remembered his promise to Ingolf, and had resolved to put his trust in chance. Chance had before shown him considerable kindness. But when, towards the close of summer, he directed his course homewards, chance had not yet come to his help. It was therefore with a certain disappointment in his mind that he turned homeward from his summer expedition. It was indeed no small disappointment to him that fate had not allowed him to meet Atle's sons.

Olmod the Old, who was voyaging with a fleet of five ships, made inquiries about his kinsman, Leif, wherever he went. In many places Leif had been just before him, but had sailed again no one knew whither.

Olmod the Old was continually on his scent, and sailed, so to speak, in his wake the whole summer, though without any success in overtaking him. He vowed offerings and gifts to Odin if he would help him to find his kinsman. But Odin seemed to have turned his eye from him.

Olmod kept himself likewise informed concerning the voyage of Atle's sons. From their movements he could not ascertain whether they intended evil against Leif or not. It did not really look as if they were following him. Perhaps they did not know what direction he was taking, but Olmod considered it best to be on the watch.

Late in the summer, Olmod lost every trace of Leif. But as a compensation he so nearly succeeded in overtaking Atle's sons that he at last caught a glimpse of their ships making out to sea on their way home. It seemed to Olmod that they were sailing rather early. Were they thinking of concealing themselves among the rocks and islands off the coast and giving Leif a warm reception when he turned home? Olmod the Old was from his own experience not unacquainted with stratagems. He kept a sharp eye on Atle's sons.

For some time he kept his ships hidden in a creek near the ordinary route in order to catch Leif, if possible. At last he could wait no longer. Leif, he thought, must have turned homeward by some other way, and as good sailing weather just then set in, he directed his course toward Norway. He had come to the conclusion that the safest thing was to try to find Atle's sons, or at any rate to get news of them. If he found that they had sailed the direct way home, there was scarcely anything to fear from them that autumn.

On a dark and stormy autumn day, with clouds driving across the sky and a tossing sea, Leif came sailing past Hisargavl. He was sailing along, thinking of his disappointment, when he suddenly found himself surrounded by ships bearing down upon him with their battle ensigns hoisted. For the sake of his promise, Leif counted the ships; they were six in number. He looked closer at them, and recognized them as those of Atle's sons. Then Leif felt a great contentment fill his mind. Here at last came his friends, the sons of Atle. And luckily all chance of flight was excluded. It would have been vexatious if he had had to break his word, but now it was all right. For Ingolf could not expect of him that he should surrender unconditionally in order to avoid battle with Atle's sons. He gathered his ships together and commanded them to lower sail; quickly he had boards for defence fixed on the quarter-deck, and cleared the ships for action. He went about and became gradually agitated with excitement and happy expectation. At last—at last the opportunity had come for seriously exchanging blows with Holmsten. One of them should in any case be a guest of Odin that evening. How he was to manage with his three ships against the six of Atle's sons did not worry Leif much.

While he issued his orders, he had only eyes for Holmsten's dragon-ship. There Holmsten came, also in a state of excitement. Now the long boat-hooks could reach the gunwale on Holmsten's ship. "Pull hard, men!" Leif had a great longing to salute Holmsten. The first spear whistled through the air. From both sides it was greeted with cheerful battlecries and gay laughter.

At length the two dragon-ships lay side by side, rocking violently upon the grey sea. Blows and shouts were exchanged above the high quarter-deck boards. Leif pushed his men roughly to one side. He had set eyes on Holmsten. A spear whistled past his ear, and he heard Holmsten laugh and shout:

"There is a spear in place of the one you sank here last autumn."

Leif twisted himself to one side, seized the spear, aimed at Holmsten, and sent it back.

"I have enough weapons, friend Holmsten! I will test the axe you once gave me on your skull."

Holmsten avoided the spear at the last moment by a leap to one side.

Now Leif was close to the gunwale. The fight went on energetically on both sides of him. The ships reeled violently and crashed noisily against each other. Salt spray concealed now and then the hot faces. Leif held his axe raised and shook it towards Holmsten.

"Now, when I cleave your head before long, it will not be through carelessness! Remember that, Holmsten."

Holmsten laughed derisively. He could not properly reach Leif because of his men.

"It will double my joy, friend Leif, to know you are lying cold at the bottom of the sea, by the side of your spear, while your friend Helga makes me comfortable."

Leif leaped up on the quarter-deck boards, swinging his axe high over his head, but was forced back. He tried again and again, but was met by a wall of weapons. One of Atle's sons' other ships hooked itself fast on to the other side of the dragon-ship. The battle raged furiously along both gunwales.

During an involuntary pause in the battle, Leif found time to look round him a little. One of his ships was already overpowered, and the other surrounded by three of the enemy's smaller ships; his own was so hard pressed that it was obviously only a question of how long he could hold out.

Leif saw clearly how untenable his position was. He did not envy Atle's sons their victory. He called those who had followed him on many bold expeditions to him, and said in a choked voice:

"If we are going to Valhalla, friends, let us take Holmsten with us, and as many of his men as we can!"

So he stormed the gunwale, followed by his best men, and succeeded in obtaining a foothold on Holmsten's dragon-ship. And now Leif was at his ease. Generously he dealt out blows and thrusts, and devoted himself energetically to the battle. He saw his men falling round him, and he himself had several wounds which he had not time to think about. He was not afraid of death, but meant to take Holmsten with him.

While Leif stood there, and dealt doughty blows around him in order to get at Holmsten, there came in sight a fleet of five ships by Hisargavl. The five ships were sailing swiftly, and the water foamed round their bows as they approached. At last Olmod the Old was about to overtake Leif. And he had bestirred himself, as it appeared. He gave himself no time to survey the situation, but drove his ships right in among the combatants. In his green cloak, with a golden helmet on his head, he stood in a dignified attitude by the mast and issued his orders.

"It looks as if you wanted a little help, Cousin Leif!" he shouted in the joy of battle. All other talking he left to his weapons.

Haersten saw quickly that his position was untenable, and gave orders for flight. But it was by no means so easy to get away in a moment. Holmsten's ship soon lay wedged in between those of Leif and Olmod the Old. Leif made use of the confusion which ensued among Holmsten's men at suddenly finding enemies on both sides, and made his way close up to Holmsten. When Holmsten saw him coming, he prepared to receive him in his cool and quiet way. But now Leif had become quite wild. When it seemed that he could not get forward quickly enough, he flung his axe at Holmsten's face. Holmsten dropped his weapons, threw up his arms, reeled, and fell.

Leif's joy at seeing Holmsten fall was so great that he forgot to be on his guard. One of his men pushed a shield in front of him just in time. The shield was cloven by the blow of an axe, intended for Leif. But Leif was not to die that day. Now he was himself again, picked up his axe, and continued the attack. After Holmsten's fall the opposition was soon broken.

A couple of Olmod's ships had recovered the ship Atle's sons had won from Leif. Olmod secured for himself Holmsten's ship as a reward for his trouble, and in order to be able to provide offerings and gifts to Odin. The remainder of Atle's sons' ships escaped in disorder.

Olmod came across Leif where he was sitting and binding up his wounds.

"You are bleeding much, cousin, and can be glad that you still have blood to bleed."

"That I owe to you, Cousin Olmod. What lucky wind was that which blew you here, just when you were most needed?"

"Ask, rather, what freak was it of Odin's that he did not let me overtake you before. I came to Dalsfjord the day after you sailed, and have pursued you in vain all the summer."

Leif looked up hastily. A sudden fear shot through him.

"What did you want me for?"

"That you have seen."

Leif was quiet again.

"Nothing more?" he asked.

"Don't you think I had cause enough? Did you expect me to follow your tedious tracks the whole summer, merely to bring you a greeting from Helga?"

DENMARK

THE LITTLE MERMAID[1]

Hans Christian Andersen

(1805–1875)

FAR out in the wide sea,—where the water is blue as the loveliest cornflower, and clear as the purest crystal, where it is so deep that very, very many church-towers must be heaped one upon another, in order to reach from the lowest depth to the surface above,—dwell the Mer-people.

Now you must not imagine that there is nothing but sand below the water: no, indeed, far from it! Trees and plants of wondrous beauty grow there, whose stems and leaves are so light, that they are waved to and fro by the slightest motion of the water, almost as if they were living beings. Fishes, great and small, glide in and out among the branches, just as birds fly about among our trees.

Where the water is deepest, stands the palace of the Mer-king. The walls of this palace are of coral, and the high, pointed windows are of amber; the roof, however, is composed of mussel-shells, which, as the billows pass over them, are continually opening and shutting. This looks exceedingly pretty, especially as each of these mussel-shells contains a number of bright, glittering pearls, one only of which would be the most costly ornament in the diadem of a king in the upper world.

The Mer-king who lived in this palace, had been for many years a widower; his old mother managed the household affairs for him. She was, on the whole, a sensible sort of a lady, although extremely proud of her high birth and station, on which account she wore twelve oysters on her tail, whilst the other inhabitants of the sea, even those of distinction, were allowed only six. In every other respect she merited unlimited praise, especially for the affection she showed to the six little princesses, her grand-daughters. These were all very beautiful children; the youngest was, however, the most lovely; her skin was as soft and delicate as a rose-leaf, her eyes were of as deep a blue as the sea, but like all other mermaids, she had no feet, her body ended in a tail like that of a fish.

The whole day long the children used to play in the spacious apartments of the palace, where beautiful flowers grew out of the walls on all sides around them. When the great amber windows were opened, fishes would swim into these apartments as swallows fly into our rooms; but the fishes were bolder than the swallows, they swam straight up to

---

[1]From *Fairy Tales*.

the little princesses, ate from their hands, and allowed themselves to be caressed.

In front of the palace there was a large garden, full of fiery red and dark blue trees, whose fruit glittered like gold, and whose flowers resembled a bright, burning sun. The sand that formed the soil of the garden was of a bright blue colour, something like flames of sulphur; and a strangely beautiful blue was spread over the whole, so that one might have fancied oneself raised very high in the air, with the sky at once above and below, certainly not at the bottom of the sea. When the waters were quite still, the sun might be seen looking like a purple flower, out of whose cup streamed forth the light of the world.

Each of the little princesses had her own plot in the garden, where she might plant and sow at her pleasure. One chose hers to be made in the shape of a whale, another preferred the figure of a mermaid, but the youngest had hers quite round like the sun, and planted in it only those flowers that were red, as the sun seemed to her. She was certainly a singular child, very quiet and thoughtful. Whilst her sisters were adorning themselves with all sorts of gay things that came out of a ship which had been wrecked, she asked for nothing but a beautiful white marble statue of a boy, which had been found in it. She put the statue in her garden, and planted a red weeping willow by its side. The tree grew up quickly, and let its long boughs fall upon the bright blue ground, where ever-moving shadows played in violet hues, as if boughs and root were embracing.

Nothing pleased the little princess more than to hear about the world of human beings living above the sea. She made her old grandmother tell her everything she knew about ships, towns, men, and land animals, and was particularly pleased when she heard that the flowers of the upper world had a pleasant fragrance (for the flowers of the sea are scentless), and that the woods were green, and the fishes fluttering among the branches of various gay colours, and that they could sing with a loud clear voice. The old lady meant birds, but she called them fishes, because her grandchildren, having never seen a bird, would not otherwise have understood her.

"When you have attained your fifteenth year," added she, "you will be permitted to rise to the surface of the sea; you will then sit by moonlight in the clefts of the rocks, see the ships sail by, and learn to distinguish towns and men."

The next year the eldest of the sisters reached this happy age, but the others—alas! the second sister was a year younger than the eldest, the third a year younger than the second, and so on; the youngest had still five whole years to wait till that joyful time should come when she also might rise to the surface of the water and see what was going on in the upper world; however, the eldest promised to tell the others of everything she might see, when the first day of her being of age arrived; for the grandmother gave them but little information, and there was so much that they wished to hear.

But none of all the sisters longed so ardently for the day when she should be released from childish restraint as the youngest, she who had longest to wait, and was so quiet and thoughtful. Many a night she stood by the open windows, looking up through the clear blue water, whilst the fishes were leaping and playing around her. She could see the sun and the moon; their light was pale, but they appeared larger than they do to those who live in the upper world. If a shadow passed over them, she knew it must be either a whale or a ship sailing by full of human beings, who indeed little thought that, far beneath them, a little mermaiden was passionately stretching forth her white hands towards their ship's keel.

The day had now arrived when the eldest princess had attained her fifteenth year, and was therefore allowed to rise up to the surface of the sea.

When she returned she had a thousand things to relate. Her chief pleasure had been to sit upon a sandbank in the moonlight, looking at the large town which lay on the coast, where lights were beaming like stars, and where music was playing; she had heard the distant noise of men and carriages, she had seen the high church-towers, had listened to the ringing of the bells; and just because she could not go there she longed the more after all these things.

How attentively did her youngest sister listen to her words! And when she next stood at night time, by her open window, gazing upward through the blue waters, she thought so intensely of the great noisy city that she fancied she could hear the church-bells ringing.

Next year the second sister received permission to swim wherever she pleased. She rose to the surface of the sea, just when the sun was setting; and this sight so delighted her, that she declared it to be more beautiful than anything else she had seen above the waters.

"The whole sky seemed tinged with gold," said she, "and it is impossible for me to describe to you the beauty of the clouds. Now red, now violet, they glided over me; but still more swiftly flew over the water a flock of white swans, just where the sun was descending; I looked after them, but the sun disappeared, and the bright rosy light on the surface of the sea and on the edges of the clouds was gradually extinguished."

It was now time for the third sister to visit the upper world. She was the boldest of the six, and ventured up a river. On its shores she saw green hills covered with woods and vineyards, from among which arose houses and·castles; she heard the birds singing, and the sun shone with so much power, that she was continually obliged to plunge below, in order to cool her burning face. In a little bay she met with a number of children, who were bathing and jumping about; she would have joined in their gambols, but the children fled back to land in great terror, and a little black animal barked at her in such a manner, that she herself was frightened at last, and swam back to the sea. She could not, however, forget the green woods, the verdant hills, and the pretty children, who, although they had no fins, were swimming about in the river so fearlessly.

The fourth sister was not so bold, she remained in the open sea, and said on her return home, she thought nothing could be more beautiful. She had seen ships sailing by, so far off that they looked like seagulls, she had watched the merry dolphins gamboling in the water, and the enormous whales, sending up into the air a thousand sparkling fountains.

The year after, the fifth sister attained her fifteenth year. Her birthday happened at a different season to that of her sisters; it was winter, the sea was of a green colour, and immense icebergs were floating on its surface. These, she said, looked like pearls; they were, however, much larger than the church-towers in the land of human beings. She sat down upon one of these pearls, and let the wind play with her long hair, but then all the ships hoisted their sails in terror, and escaped as quickly as possible. In the evening the sea was covered with sails; and whilst the great mountains of ice alternately sank and rose again, and beamed with a reddish glow, flashes of lightning burst forth from the clouds and the thunder rolled on, peal after peal. The sails of all the ships were instantly furled, and horror and affright reigned on board, but the princess sat still on the iceberg, looking unconcernedly at the blue zig-zag of the flashes.

The first time that either of these sisters rose out of the sea, she was quite enchanted at the sight of so many new and beautiful objects, but the novelty was soon over, and it was not long ere their own home appeared more attractive than the upper world, for there only did they find everything agreeable.

Many an evening would the five sisters rise hand in hand from the depths of the ocean. Their voices were far sweeter than any human voice, and when a storm was coming on, they would swim in front of the ships, and sing,—oh! how sweetly did they sing! describing the happiness of those who lived at the bottom of the sea, and entreating the sailors not to be afraid, but to come down to them.

The mariners, however, did not understand their words; they fancied the song was only the whistling of the wind, and thus they lost the hidden glories of the sea; for if their ships were wrecked, all on board were drowned, and none but dead men ever entered the Mer-king's palace.

Whilst the sisters were swimming at evening time, the youngest would remain motionless and alone, in her father's palace, looking up after them. She would have wept, but mermaids cannot weep, and therefore, when they are troubled, suffer infinitely more than human beings do.

"Oh! if I were but fifteen!" sighed she, "I know that I should love the upper world and its inhabitants so much."

At last the time she had so longed for arrived.

"Well, now it is your turn," said the grandmother, "come here that I may adorn you like your sisters." And she wound around her hair a wreath of white lilies, whose every petal was the half of a pearl, and then commanded eight large oysters to fasten themselves to the princess's tail, in token of her high rank.

"But that is so very uncomfortable!" said the little princess.

"One must not mind slight inconveniences when one wishes to look well," said the old lady.

How willingly would the princess have given up all this splendour, and exchanged her heavy crown for the red flowers of her garden, which were so much more becoming to her. But she dared not do so. "Farewell," said she; and she rose from the sea, light as a flake of foam.

When, for the first time in her life, she appeared on the surface of the water, the sun had just sunk below the horizon, the clouds were beaming with bright golden and rosy hues, the evening star was shining in the pale western sky, the air was mild and refreshing, and the sea as smooth as a looking-glass. A large ship with three masts lay on the still waters; one sail only was unfurled, but not a breath was stirring, and the sailors were quietly seated on the cordage and ladders of the vessel. Music and song resounded from the deck, and after it grew dark hundreds of lamps all on a sudden burst forth into light, whilst innumerable flags were fluttering overhead. The little mermaid swam close up to the captain's cabin, and every now and then when the ship was raised by the motion of the water, she could look through the clear window panes. She saw within, many richly dressed men; the handsomest among them was a young prince with large black eyes. He could not certainly be more than sixteen years old, and it was in honour of his birthday that a grand festival was being celebrated. The crew were dancing on the deck, and when the young prince appeared among them, a hundred rockets were sent up into the air, turning night into day, and so terrifying the little mermaid, that for some minutes she plunged beneath the water. However, she soon raised her little head again, and then it seemed as if all the stars were falling down upon her. Such a fiery shower she had never seen before, never had she heard that men possessed such wonderful powers. Large suns revolved around her, bright fishes swam in the air, and everything was reflected perfectly on the clear surface of the sea. It was so light in the ship, that everything could be seen distinctly. Oh! how happy the young prince was! he shook hands with the sailors, laughed and jested with them, whilst sweet notes of music mingled with the silence of night.

It was now late, but the little mermaid could not tear herself away from the ship and the handsome young prince. She remained looking through the cabin window, rocked to and fro by the waves. There was a foaming and fermentation in the depths beneath, and the ship began to move on faster, the sails were spread, the waves rose high, thick clouds gathered over the sky, and the noise of distant thunder was heard. The sailors perceived that a storm was coming on, so they again furled the sails. The great vessel was tossed about on the tempestuous ocean like a light boat, and the waves rose to an immense height, towering over the ship, which alternately sank beneath and rose above them. To the little mermaid this seemed most delightful, but the ship's crew thought very differently. The vessel cracked, the stout masts bent under the violence of the billows, the waters rushed in. For a minute the ship tottered to and fro, then the main-mast broke, as if it had been a reed; the ship turned over, and was filled with water. The little mermaid now perceived that the crew was in danger, for she herself was forced to beware of the beams and splinters torn from the vessel, and floating about on the waves. But at the same time it became pitch dark so that she could not distinguish anything; presently, however, a dreadful flash of lightning disclosed to her the whole of the wreck. Her eyes sought the young prince—the same instant the ship sank to the bottom. At first she was delighted, thinking that the prince must now come to her abode, but she soon remembered that man cannot live in water, and that therefore if the prince ever entered her palace, it would be as a corpse.

"Die! no, he must not die!" She swam through the fragments with which the water was strewn regardless of the danger she was incurring, and at last found the prince all but exhausted, and with great difficulty keeping his head above water. He had already closed his eyes, and must inevitably have been drowned, had not the little mermaid come to his rescue. She seized hold of him and kept him above water, suffering the current to bear them on together.

Towards morning the storm was hushed; no trace, however, remained of the ship. The sun rose like fire out of the sea; his beams seemed to restore colour to the prince's cheeks, but his eyes were still closed. The mermaid kissed his high forehead and stroked his wet hair away from his face. He looked like the marble statue in her garden; she kissed him again and wished most fervently that he might recover.

She now saw the dry land with its mountains glittering with snow. A green wood extended along the coast, and at the entrance of the wood stood a chapel or convent, she could not be sure which. Citron and lemon trees grew in the garden adjoining it, an avenue of tall palm trees led up to the door. The sea here formed a little bay, in which the water was quite smooth but very deep, and under the cliffs there were dry firm sands. Hither swam the little mermaid with the seemingly dead prince; she laid him upon the warm sand, and took care to place his head high, and to turn his face to the sun.

The bells began to ring in the large white building which stood before her, and a number of young girls came out to walk in the garden. The mermaid went away from the shore, hid herself behind some stones, covered her head with foam, so that her little face could not be seen, and watched the prince with unremitting attention.

It was not long before one of the young girls approached. She seemed quite frightened at finding the prince in this state, apparently dead; soon, however, she recovered herself, and ran back to call her sisters. The little mermaid saw that the prince revived, and that all around smiled kindly and joyfully upon him—for her, however, he looked not, he knew not that it was she who had saved him, and when the prince was taken into the house, she felt so sad, that she immediately plunged beneath the water, and returned to her father's palace.

If she had been before quiet and thoughtful, she now grew still more so. Her sisters asked her what she had seen in the upper world, but she made no answer.

Many an evening she rose to the place where she had left the prince. She saw the snow on the mountains melt, the fruits in the garden ripen and gathered, but the prince she never saw, so she always returned sorrowfully to her subterranean abode. Her only pleasure was to sit in her little garden gazing on the beautiful statue so like the prince. She cared no longer for her flowers; they grew up in wild luxuriance, covered the steps, and entwined their long stems and tendrils among the boughs of the trees, so that her whole garden became a bower.

At last, being unable to conceal her sorrow any longer, she revealed the secret to one of her sisters, who told it to the other princesses, and they to some of their friends. Among them was a young mermaid who recollected the prince, having been an eye-witness herself to the festivities in the ship; she knew also in what country the prince lived, and the name of its king.

"Come, little sister!" said the princesses, and embracing her they rose together arm in arm, out of the water, just in front of the prince's palace.

This palace was built of bright yellow stones, a flight of white marble steps led from it down to the sea. A gilded cupola crowned the building, and white marble figures, which might almost have been taken for real men and women, were placed among the pillars surrounding it. Through the clear glass of the high windows one might look into magnificent apartments hung with silken curtains, the walls adorned with magnificent paintings. It was a real treat to the little royal mermaids to behold so splendid an abode; they gazed through the windows of one of the largest rooms, and in the centre saw a fountain playing, whose waters sprang up so high as to reach the glittering cupola above, through which the sunbeams fell dancing on the water, and brightening the pretty plants which grew around it.

The little mermaid now knew where her beloved prince dwelt, and henceforth she went there almost every evening. She often approached nearer the land than her sisters had ventured, and even swam up the narrow channel that flowed under the marble balcony. Here on a bright moonlight night, she would watch the young prince who believed him-self alone.

Sometimes she saw him sailing on the water in a gaily-painted boat with many coloured flags waving above. She would then hide among the green reeds which grew on the banks, listening to his voice, and if any one in the boat noticed the rustling of her long silver veil, which was caught now and then by the light breeze, they only fancied it was a swan flapping his wings.

Many a night when the fishermen were casting their nets by the bea-con's light, she heard them talking of the prince, and relating the noble actions he had performed. She was then so happy, thinking how she had saved his life when struggling with the waves, and remembering how his head had rested on her bosom, and how she had kissed him when he knew nothing of it, and could never even dream of such a thing.

Human beings became more and more dear to her every day; she wished that she were one of them. Their world seemed to her much larger than that of the mer-people; they could fly over the ocean in their ships, as well as climb to the summits of those high mountains that rose above the clouds; and their wooded domains extended much farther than a mermaid's eye could penetrate.

There were many things that she wished to hear explained, but her sisters could not give her any satisfactory answer; she was again obliged to have recourse to the old queen-mother, who knew a great deal about the upper world, which she used to call "the country above the sea."

"Do men when they are not drowned live for ever?" she asked one day. "Do not they die as we do, who live at the bottom of the sea?"

"Yes," was the grandmother's reply, "they must die like us, and their life is much shorter than ours. We live to the age of three hundred years, but when we die, we become foam on the sea, and are not allowed even to share a grave among those that are dear to us. We have no im-mortal souls, we can never live again, and are like the grass which, when once cut down, is withered for ever. Human beings, on the contrary, have souls that continue to live, when their bodies become dust, and as we rise out of the water to admire the abode of man, they ascend to glorious unknown dwellings in the skies which we are not permitted to see."

"Why have not *we* immortal souls?" asked the little mermaid. "I would willingly give up my three hundred years to be a human being for only one day, thus to become entitled to that heavenly world above."

"You must not think of that," answered her grandmother, "it is much better as it is; we live longer and are far happier than human beings."

"So I must die, and be dashed like foam over the sea, never to rise again and hear the gentle murmur of the ocean, never again see the beautiful flowers and the bright sun! Tell me, dear grandmother, are there no means by which I may obtain an immortal soul?"

"No!" replied the old lady. "It is true that if thou couldst so win the affections of a human being as to become dearer to him than either father or mother; if he loved thee with all his heart, and promised whilst the priest joined his hands with thine to be always faithful to thee; then his soul would flow into thine, and thou wouldst then become partaker of human bliss. But that can never be! for what in our eyes is the most beautiful part of our body, the tail, the inhabitants of the earth think hideous, they cannot bear it. To appear handsome to them, the body must have two clumsy props which they call legs."

The little mermaid sighed and looked mournfully at the scaly part of her form, otherwise so fair and delicate.

"We are happy," added the old lady, "we shall jump and swim about merrily for three hundred years; that is a long time, and afterwards we shall repose peacefully in death. This evening we have a court ball."

The ball which the queen-mother spoke of was far more splendid than any that earth has ever seen. The walls of the saloon were of crystal, very thick, but yet very clear; hundreds of large mussel-shells were planted in rows along them; these shells were some of rose-colour, some green as grass, but all sending forth a bright light, which not only illuminated the whole apartment, but also shone through the glassy walls so as to light up the waters around for a great space, and making the scales of the numberless fishes, great and small, crimson and purple, silver and gold-coloured, appear more brilliant than ever.

Through the centre of the saloon flowed a bright, clear stream, on tne surface of which danced mermen and mermaids to the melody of their own sweet voices, voices far sweeter than those of the dwellers upon earth. The little princess sang more harmoniously than any other, and they clapped their hands and applauded her. She was pleased at this, for she knew well that there was neither on earth or in the sea a more beautiful voice than hers. But her thoughts soon returned to the world above her; she could not forget the handsome prince; she could not control her sorrow at not having an immortal soul. She stole away from her father's palace, and whilst all was joy within, she sat alone lost in thought in her little neglected garden. On a sudden she heard the tones of horns resounding over the water far away in the distance, and she said to herself, "Now he is going out to hunt, he whom I love more than my father and my mother, with whom my thoughts are constantly occupied, and to whom I would so willingly trust the happiness of my life! All! all, will I risk to win him—and an immortal soul! Whilst my sisters are still dancing in the palace, I will go to the enchantress whom I have hitherto feared so much, but who is, nevertheless, the only person who can advise and help me."

So the little mermaid left the garden, and went to the foaming whirlpool beyond which dwelt the enchantress. She had never been this way before—neither flowers nor sea-grass bloomed along her path; she had to traverse an extent of bare grey sand till she reached the whirlpool, whose waters were eddying and whizzing like mill-wheels, tearing everything they could seize along with them into the abyss below. She was obliged to make her way through this horrible place, in order to arrive at the territory of the enchantress. Then she had to pass through a boiling, slimy bog, which the enchantress called her turf-moor: her house stood in a wood beyond this, and a strange abode it was. All the trees and bushes around were polypi, looking like hundred-headed serpents shooting up out of the ground; their branches were long slimy arms with fingers of worms, every member, from the root to the uttermost tip, ceaselessly moving and extending on all sides. Whatever they seized they fastened upon so that it could not loosen itself from their grasp. The little mermaid stood still for a minute, looking at this horrible wood; her heart beat with fear, and she would certainly have returned without attaining her object, had she not remembered the prince—and immortality. The thought gave her new courage, she bound up her long waving hair, that the polypi might not catch hold of it, crossed her delicate arms over her bosom, and, swifter than a fish can glide through the water, she passed these unseemly trees, who stretched their eager arms after her in vain. She could not, however, help seeing that every polypus had something in his grasp, held as firmly by a thousand little arms as if enclosed by iron bands. The whitened skeletons of a number of human beings who had been drowned in the sea, and had sunk into the abyss, grinned horribly from the arms of these polypi; helms, chests, skeletons of land animals were also held in their embrace; among other things might be seen even a little mermaid whom they had seized and strangled! What a fearful sight for the unfortunate princess!

But she got safely through this wood of horrors, and then arrived at a slimy place, where immense fat snails were crawling about, and in the midst of this place stood a house built of the bones of unfortunate people who had been shipwrecked. Here sat the witch caressing a toad in the same manner as some persons would a pet bird. The ugly fat snails she called her chickens, and she permitted them to crawl about her.

"I know well what you would ask of me," said she to the little princess. "Your wish is foolish enough, yet it shall be fulfilled, though its accomplishment is sure to bring misfortune on you, my fairest princess. You wish to get rid of your tail, and to have instead two stilts like those of human beings, in order that a young prince may fall in love with you, and that you may obtain an immortal soul. Is it not so?" Whilst the witch spoke these words, she laughed so violently that her pet toad and snails fell from her lap. "You come just at the right time," continued she; "had you come after sunset, it would not have been in my power to have helped you before another year. I will prepare for you a drink with which you must swim to land, you must sit down upon the shore and swallow it, and then your tail will fall and shrink up to the things which men call legs. This transformation will, however, be very painful; you will feel as though a sharp knife passed through your body. All who look on you after you have been thus changed will say that you are the loveliest child of earth they have ever seen; you will retain your peculiar undulating movements, and no dancer will move so lightly, but every step you take will cause you pain all but unbearable; it will seem to you as though you were walking on the sharp edges of swords, and your blood will flow. Can you endure all this suffering? If so, I will grant your request."

"Yes, I will," answered the princess, with a faltering voice; for she remembered her dear prince, and the immortal soul which her suffering might win.

"Only consider," said the witch, "that you can never again become a mermaid, when once you have received a human form. You may never return to your sisters, and your father's palace; and unless you shall win the prince's love to such a degree, that he shall leave father and mother for you, that you shall be mixed up with all his thoughts and wishes, and unless the priest join your hands, so that you become man and wife, you will never obtain the immortality you seek. The morrow of the day on which he is united to another, will see your death; your heart will break with sorrow, and you will be changed to foam on the sea."

"Still I will venture!" said the little mermaid, pale and trembling as a dying person.

"Besides all this, I must be paid, and it is no slight thing that I require for my trouble. Thou hast the sweetest voice of all the dwellers in the sea, and thou thinkest by its means to charm the prince; this voice, however, I demand as my recompense. The best thing thou possessest I require in exchange for my magic drink; for I shall be obliged to sacrifice my own blood, in order to give it the sharpness of a two-edged sword."

"But if you take my voice from me," said the princess, "what have I left with which to charm the prince?"

"Thy graceful form," replied the witch, "thy modest gait, and speaking eyes. With such as these, it will be easy to infatuate a vain human heart. Well now! hast thou lost courage? Put out thy little tongue, that I may cut it off, and take it for myself, in return for my magic drink."

"Be it so!" said the princess, and the witch took up her cauldron, in order to mix her potion. "Cleanliness is a good thing," remarked she, as she began to rub the cauldron with a handful of toads and snails. She then scratched her bosom, and let the black blood trickle down into the cauldron, every moment throwing in new ingredients, the smoke from the mixture assuming such horrible forms as were enough to fill beholders with terror, and a moaning and groaning proceeding from it, which might be compared to the weeping of crocodiles. The magic drink at length became clear and transparent as pure water; it was ready.

"Here it is!" said the witch to the princess, cutting out her tongue at the same moment. The poor little mermaid was now dumb: she could neither sing nor speak.

"If the polypi should attempt to seize you, as you pass through my little grove," said the witch, "you have only to sprinkle some of this magic drink over them, and their arms will burst into a thousand pieces." But the princess had no need of this counsel, for the polypi drew hastily back, as soon as they perceived the bright phial, that glittered in her hand like a star; thus she passed safely through the formidable wood over the moor, and across the foaming mill-stream.

She now looked once again at her father's palace; the lamps in the saloon were extinguished, and all the family were asleep. She would not go in, for she could not speak if she did; she was about to leave her home for ever; her heart was ready to break with sorrow at the thought; she stole into the garden, plucked a flower from the bed of each of her sisters as a remembrance, kissed her hand again and again, and then rose through the dark blue waters to the world above.

The sun had not yet risen, when she arrived at the prince's dwelling, and ascended those well-known marble steps. The moon still shone in the sky when the little mermaid drank off the wonderful liquid contained in her phial,—she felt it run through her like a sharp knife, and she fell down in a swoon. When the sun rose, she awoke; and felt a burning pain in all her limbs, but—she saw standing close to her the object of her love, the handsome young prince, whose coal-black eyes were fixed inquiringly upon her. Full of shame she cast down her own, and perceived, instead of the long fish-tail she had hitherto borne, two slender legs; but she was quite naked, and tried in vain to cover herself with her long thick hair. The prince asked who she was, and how she had got there; and she, in reply, smiled and gazed upon him with her bright blue eyes, for alas! she could not speak. He then led her by the hand into the palace. She found that the witch had told her true; she felt as though she were walking on the edges of sharp swords, but she bore the pain willingly; on she passed, light as a zephyr, and all who saw her, wondered at her light undulating movements.

When she entered the palace, rich clothes of muslin and silk were brought to her; she was lovelier than all who dwelt there, but she could neither speak nor sing. Some female slaves, gaily dressed in silk and gold brocade, sung before the prince and his royal parents; and one of them distinguished herself by her clear sweet voice, which the prince applauded by clapping his hands. This made the little mermaid very sad, for she knew that she used to sing far better than the young slave.

"Alas!" thought she, "if he did but know that, for his sake, I have given away my voice for ever."

The slaves began to dance; our lovely little mermaiden then arose, stretched out her delicate white arms, and hovered gracefully about the room. Every motion displayed more and more the perfect symmetry and elegance of her figure; and the expression which beamed in her speaking eyes touched the hearts of the spectators far more than the song of the slaves.

All present were enchanted, but especially the young prince, who called her his dear little foundling. And she danced again and again, although every step cost her excessive pain. The prince then said she should always be with him; and accordingly a sleeping palace was prepared for her on velvet cushions in the anteroom of his own apartment.

The prince caused a suit of male apparel to be made for her, in order that she might accompany him in his rides; so together they traversed the fragrant woods, where green boughs brushed against their shoulders, and the birds sang merrily among the fresh leaves. With him she climbed up steep mountains, and although her tender feet bled, so as to be remarked by the attendants, she only smiled, and followed her dear prince to the heights, whence they could see the clouds chasing each other beneath them, like a flock of birds migrating to other countries.

During the night, she would, when all in the palace were at rest, walk down the marble steps, in order to cool her feet in the deep waters; she would then think of those beloved ones, who dwelt in the lower world.

One night, as she was thus bathing her feet, her sisters swam together to the spot, arm in arm and singing, but alas! so mournfully! She beckoned to them, and they immediately recognized her, and told her how great was the mourning in her father's house for her loss. From this time the sisters visited her every night; and once they brought with them the old grandmother, who had not seen the upper world for a great many years; they likewise brought their father, the Mer-king, with his crown on his head; but these two old people did not venture near enough to land to be able to speak to her.

The little mermaiden became dearer and dearer to the prince every day; but he only looked upon her as a sweet, gentle child; and the thought of making her his wife never entered his head. And yet his wife she must be, ere she could receive an immortal soul; his wife she must be, or she would change into foam, and be driven restlessly over the billows of the sea!

"Dost thou not love me above all others?" her eyes seemed to ask, as he pressed her fondly in his arms, and kissed her lovely brow.

"Yes," the prince would say, "thou art dearer to me than any other, for no one is as good as thou art! Thou lovest me so much; and thou art so like a young maiden, whom I have seen but once, and may never see again. I was on board a ship, which was wrecked by a sudden tempest;

the waves threw me on the shore, near a holy temple, where a number of young girls are occupied constantly with religious services. The youngest of them found me on the shore, and saved my life. I saw her only once, but her image is vividly impressed upon my memory, and her alone can I love. But she belongs to the holy temple; and thou who resemblest her so much hast been given to me for consolation; never will we be parted!"

"Alas! he does not know that it was I who saved his life," thought the little mermaiden, sighing deeply; "I bore him over the wild waves, into the wooded bay, where the holy temple stood; I sat behind the rocks, waiting till some one should come. I saw the pretty maiden approach, whom he loves more than me,"—and again she heaved a deep sigh, for she could not weep,—"he said that the young girl belongs to the holy temple; she never comes out into the world, so they cannot meet each other again,—and I am always with him, see him daily; I will love him, and devote my whole life to him."

"So the prince is going to be married to the beautiful daughter of the neighbouring king," said the courtiers, "that is why he is having that splendid ship fitted out. It is announced that he wishes to travel, but in reality he goes to see the princess; a numerous retinue will accompany him." The little mermaiden smiled at these and similar conjectures, for she knew the prince's intentions better than any one else.

"I must go," he said to her, "I must see the beautiful princess; my parents require me to do so; but they will not compel me to marry her, and bring her home as my bride. And it is quite impossible for me to love her, for she cannot be so like the beautiful girl in the temple as thou art; and if I were obliged to choose, I should prefer thee, my little silent foundling, with the speaking eyes." And he kissed her rosy lips, played with her locks, and folded her in his arms, whereupon arose in her heart a sweet vision of human happiness and immortal bliss.

"Thou art not afraid of the sea, art thou, my sweet silent child?" asked he tenderly as they stood together in the splendid ship, which was to take them to the country of the neighbouring king. And then he told her of the storms that sometimes agitate the waters; of the strange fishes that inhabit the deep, and of the wonderful things seen by divers. But she smiled at his words, for she knew better than any child of earth what went on in the depths of the ocean.

At night time, when the moon shone brightly, and when all on board were fast asleep, she sat in the ship's gallery, looking down into the sea. It seemed to her, as she gazed through the foamy track made by the ship's keel, that she saw her father's palace, and her grandmother's silver crown. She then saw her sisters rise out of the water, looking sorrowful and stretching out their hands towards her. She nodded to them, smiled, and would have explained that everything was going on quite according to her wishes; but just then the cabin boy approached, upon which the sisters plunged beneath the water so suddenly that the boy thought what he had seen on the waves was nothing but foam.

The next morning the ship entered the harbour of the king's splendid capital. Bells were rung, trumpets sounded, and soldiers marched in procession through the city, with waving banners, and glittering bayonets. Every day witnessed some new entertainments, balls and parties followed each other; the princess, however, was not yet in the town; she had been sent to a distant convent for education, and had there been taught the practice of all royal virtues. At last she arrived at the palace.

The little mermaid had been anxious to see this unparalleled princess; and she was now obliged to confess, that she had never before seen so beautiful a creature.

The skin of the princess was so white and delicate, that the veins might be seen through it, and her dark eyes sparkled beneath a pair of finely formed eye-brows.

"It is herself!" exclaimed the prince, when they met, "it is she who saved my life, when I lay like a corpse on the sea-shore!" and he pressed his blushing bride to his beating heart.

"Oh, I am all too happy!" said he to his dumb foundling. "What I never dared to hope for, has come to pass. Thou must rejoice in my happiness, for thou lovest me more than all others who surround me." —And the little mermaid kissed his hand in silent sorrow; it seemed to her as if her heart was breaking already, although the morrow of his marriage day, which must inevitably see her death, had not yet dawned.

Again rung the church-bells, whilst heralds rode through the streets of the capital, to announce the approaching bridal. Odorous flames burned in silver candlesticks on all the altars; the priests swung their golden censers; and bride and bridegroom joined hands, whilst the holy words that united them were spoken. The little mermaid, clad in silk and cloth of gold, stood behind the princess, and held the train of the bridal dress; but her ear heard nothing of the solemn music; her eye saw not the holy ceremony; she remembered her approaching end, she remembered that she had lost both this world and the next.

That very same evening, bride and bridegroom, went on board the ship; cannons were fired, flags waved with the breeze, and in the centre of the deck stood a magnificent pavilion of purple and cloth of gold, fitted up with the richest and softest couches. Here the princely pair were to spend the night. A favourable wind swelled the sails, and the ship glided lightly over the blue waters.

As soon as it was dark, coloured lamps were hung out and dancing began on the deck. The little mermaid was thus involuntarily reminded of what she had seen the first time she rose to the upper world. The spectacle that now presented itself was equally splendid—and she was obliged to join in the dance, hovering lightly as a bird over the ship boards. All applauded her, for never had she danced with more enchanting grace. Her little feet suffered extremely, but she no longer felt the pain; the anguish her heart suffered was much greater. It was the last evening she might see him, for whose sake she had forsaken her home and all her family, had given away her beautiful voice, and suffered daily the most violent pain—all without his having the least suspicion of it. It was the last evening that she might breathe the same atmosphere in which he, the beloved one, lived; the last evening when she might behold the deep blue sea, and the starry heavens—an eternal night, in which she might neither think nor dream, awaited her. And all was joy in the ship; and she, her heart filled with thoughts of death and annihilation, smiled and danced with the others, till past midnight. Then the prince kissed his lovely bride, and arm in arm they entered the magnificent tent, prepared for their repose.

All was now still; the steersman alone stood at the ship's helm. The little mermaid leaned her white arms on the gallery, and looked towards the east, watching for the dawn; she well knew that the first sunbeam would witness her dissolution. She saw her sisters rise out of the sea; deadly pale were their features; and their long hair no more fluttered over their shoulders, it had all been cut off.

"We have given it to the witch," said they, "to induce her to help thee, so that thou mayest not die. She has given to us a pen-knife: here it is! before the sun rises, thou must plunge it into the prince's heart; and when his warm blood trickles down upon thy feet they will again be changed to a fish-like tail; thou wilt once more become a mermaid, and wilt live thy full three hundred years, ere thou changest to foam on the sea. But hasten! either he or thou must die before sun-rise. Our aged mother mourns for thee so much, her grey hair has fallen off through sorrow, as ours fell before the scissors of the witch. Kill the prince, and come down to us! hasten! hasten! dost thou not see the red streaks on the eastern sky, announcing the near approach of the sun? A few minutes more and he rises, and then all will be over with thee." At these words they sighed deeply and vanished.

The little mermaid drew aside the purple curtains of the pavilion, where lay the bride and bridegroom; bending over them, she kissed the prince's forehead, and then glancing at the sky, she saw that the dawning light became every moment brighter. The prince's lips unconsciously murmured the name of his bride—he was dreaming of her, and her only, whilst the fatal penknife trembled in the hand of the unhappy mermaid. All at once, she threw far out into the sea that instrument of death; the waves rose like blazing flames around, and the water where it fell seemed tinged with blood. With eyes fast becoming dim and fixed, she looked once more at her beloved prince; then plunged from the ship into the sea, and felt her body slowly but surely dissolving into foam.

THE CRUISE OF THE *WILD DUCK*[1]

Holger Drachmann

(1846–1908)

I

"THE old man's dead," said Daniel Vibe, putting his head in at the window, where his friend, Klaus Tommerup, sat balancing himself on two legs of his chair with a tabby cat on his knee. Klaus interrupted his caresses, let the cat go, brushed the hairs off his arm, and asked—

"When?"

"At three o'clock this morning."

"Did he suffer much?"

"Not a great deal; I thought it would have been worse. The doctor came just at the end. He said it was a good thing."

"What?"

"The doctor said it was a good thing."

"I suppose it is," said Tommerup. "When a man has lived seventy-nine years and has spent fifty of them in grudging and grumbling, and quarrelling with his family, and dies decently at last, I suppose the doctor is right in saying it's a good thing."

Daniel Vibe did not answer. He pulled off his black gloves—he had already provided himself with gloves—and looked at his hands which were stained purple. It was warm standing there in the sun. Tommerup looked at his watch-chain, and then he asked his friend—

"I suppose you are going to buy the *Wild Duck* now, Daniel?"

"First, there's the funeral."

"But I want to know if you mean to buy the cutter."

"I'm thinking of it," said Vibe.

"Very good. Then we'll be off in a fortnight. It's wretched work going about like a chimney-sweep in a hole like this. I have done it myself, and I know."

He stretched out his hand through the window to his friend, who pressed it and walked away with drooping head, closely observed by a good many feminine spectators whose profiles were reflected in the little window mirrors all along the street.

Tommerup looked after him, and nodded approvingly.

"He does it well," he remarked, "very well."

Then he glanced in the opposite direction, down towards the little harbour, where two barges were loading bricks and a yacht was flying her flag half-mast high in honour of the only ship-owner and principal merchant of the town who had that morning exchanged time for eternity.

---

[1] From *The Cruise of the Wild Duck and Other Tales*, by permission of Ernest Benn, Ltd.

Neither the barges nor the yacht attracted Klaus Tommerup's attention. His glance passed over the half-rotten pier-head and fell upon a cutter-rigged boat; his dark eyes rested upon her with a sort of caress in them, and as he looked he sighed. Old Tommerup, his father, had departed this life the previous year, leaving his son a soap factory, heavily encumbered with mortgages, and sorely in want of capital; and the ledger which lay on the desk before him spoke of matters far enough removed from cutter-rigged boats and pleasure cruises. And at this moment the big tabby cat sprang on his master's back and drew his attention back to the book.

II

A fortnight had passed, but young Vibe did not consider it quite correct to leave home so soon after the event, "which had deeply affected one of the principal families of the town," as the local newspaper put it. He had cut his whiskers rather short—this was also a sacrifice to propriety—and his slender figure looked very well in his black clothes; but even the most elegantly garbed grief has its drawbacks. He was very much at a loss to know how to kill time without exposing himself to the disapproval of those ever-watchful critics who had only winked at certain of his youthful follies because he was the sole heir to old Vibe's corn and coal business. Now by his father's death he was promoted to a more serious position, and expected to behave seriously in consequence.

Daniel Vibe was a young man, but by no means an imprudent one. He went to the family physician and showed him a little red spot on his cheek. The doctor lifted his eye-brows, smiled, and said—

"I think perhaps you want a little change. You might be the better for a breath of sea air. Don't you think so? You would not object . . .?"

And on that Daniel Vibe bought the *Wild Duck*.

He got an old lawyer, the family factotum, who had assisted his father in a good many small matters that did not, strictly speaking, lie quite within his profession, to buy the boat for him privately. And the old *examinatus juris* was pleased to see young Vibe show so much business capacity. In the club they nodded approvingly when it came out at last that Vibe was the real purchaser; the doctor had let a word or two fall about young Vibe's health, and in that town nothing was unpardonable that was done with a good object. Klaus Tommerup went about whistling softly to himself; as his habit was when he had anything particular on his mind; and the next morning very early he was on board the boat doing sundry odds and ends of work about her. Later on in the day the owner himself arrived, wearing a short blue jacket, black trousers, a cap with a broad peak, and a bit of crape twisted round his anchor buttons. He looked on while the other worked, and so the morning passed.

III

"I suppose we ought to have a man on the boat?" asked Daniel Vibe the next day.

"It wouldn't be a bad plan to have some fellow to do the rough work," answered Tommerup, still busy on board, while his friend still stood on the pier-head and looked on.

"Who should we take, do you think?" asked the owner.

"I don't know—Hullo, what are all the people doing down there?"

Tommerup emerged from the cabin as he spoke, and a strong gust of wind blew his hair out on one side like a fan. There was really an unusual number of people—quite half a score in all—collected on the generally deserted pier. A stiff breeze sweeping down the fairway, whistled and howled in the cutter's rigging.

"What is it?" asked Vibe of a man near him, setting his legs wide apart in a jaunty, nautical way, rather as if he took the pier for the deck of a rolling ship. A tradesman of the town who was holding his tall hat on with both hands, explained that it was Prip's son who was believed to be capsizing out in the bay.

"What?" cried Tommerup, and sprang on to the jetty, "capsizing? But he has just made a new sail for the yawl, and he had plenty of ballast in her yesterday. I saw it myself."

"There is something wrong with him all the same," observed the tradesman, "and they have just sent to tell old Prip."

"I must have a nearer look at that," said Tommerup, incredulously; and he drew his friend with him to the other side of the pier under lee of the old goods-shed.

There before them lay the broad open bay, and the gusts of wind were sweeping over it, and the clouds of the clear, cool May morning were flying before the breeze above the heads of the "crowd" who held on their hats and exhausted themselves in conjectures as to the fate of the yawl. One believed that she had capsized already: another maintained that she was still up in the wind with flapping sail, and that she must drift out to sea unless, indeed, she were caught on the Quarantine Island, or left hanging on the reef of rocks out beyond the Northern Clapper.

The question was apparently open, and so was the bay; and the yawl at that distance looked so tiny that it was possible to entertain the most contrary surmises about her. All that was actually known was that old Prip's son, Sören, had gone out into the bay that morning to try the new smack sail which he had made himself. What had happened out there was not yet clear, but it was evident that something was wrong, and at this point in the debate Klaus Tommerup turned sharp round on his heel, and sprang back on board the *Wild Duck*, saying to his friend, "Come along."

"What do you mean?" asked Vibe, with a little hesitation.

"Cast off aft, and let us get away," answered Tommerup, shortly, as he set to work on the reef points of the mainsail.

"You go by yourself," said Vibe, adding more slowly, "I must be off on business."

Tommerup looked up and nodded at his friend with a little smile. And the next moment the *Wild Duck* glided out into the bay.

IV

Those who stood on the pier, among them young Vibe, who had found that his business was not so pressing after all, watched the cutter speed over the smooth water like a real wild duck, curtseying now and then as she met the swell, lying over first by fits and starts, and then more continuously, because it was really blowing pretty hard, and young Vibe congratulated himself with great emphasis on having given his comrade a hint to take in the two reefs in time.

"She behaves very well," declared the skipper of the yacht, with a side glance at the young man. "You should have gone with him yourself, Hr. Vibe; it's just the day for a big boat like that."

But Daniel Vibe only shrugged his shoulders, and then expressed himself to the ropemaker and the tanner and the watchmaker, in the most correct nautical terms, regarding the pretty behaviour of his vessel.

"Tommerup certainly sails her very well," he added, "but after all every one can't be a skipper by trade."

"Certainly not," answered the skipper of the yacht, rubbing his elbow.

And now as the *Wild Duck* grew gradually smaller and smaller, and the yawl was scarcely visible at all, the spectators disappeared gradually from the pier; and among the last who sauntered across the ill-paved landing-place was young Vibe.

"There's old Prip," said the tanner, pointing to a tall, thin figure leaning against a rusty anchor-stock, and holding his hand over his small grey eyes, to shade them from the sun, as he peered out across the bay.

"So it is," said Vibe; "let us hear what he has to say."

They directed their course straight towards him, but the old man did not seem to be in the least aware of their presence. It was not till Vibe's cap came directly across his line of vision that he let his hand fall, and twisted his forefinger round the bowl of the clay pipe which was jammed tight in a corner of his mouth.

"Good morning, Prip," said Vibe.

Prip grunted in reply.

"My boat has gone out to save the yawl, Prip," said Vibe, with some satisfaction.

There was no answer. The small, grey eyes blinked at the sun, and the forefinger went on pressing down the ashes in the bowl of the pipe.

"It's a lucky thing for your son," said the tanner.

The old man screwed up his eyes, opened them suddenly, and looked down on the stout little leather cleaner with an expression of amused indifference.

"I think Sören will be glad to see her, old man," said Vibe, with a touch of familiarity in his tone.

"I think," said the old man, taking the pipe out of his mouth for a moment, "that Sören will pitch into them well as soon as they get near enough to him."

With that the pipe resumed its usual place, and old Prip turned and strolled homewards to the old erection—something between a house and a shed—which lay on the far side of the harbour, where a tumble-down tar-kiln brought to mind the long since abandoned dockyard, which had once been the pride of the town.

V

It was blowing hard out over the bay, and the bay was not at any time to be trifled with. There was a narrow channel and a good deal of sand. It was something like two miles across to the high land on the opposite side. In the middle there was passage for big vessels, and generally there was a strong current. Out towards the sea the bay ran up into an inlet, where it was possible to put in quite snugly when it was blowing a gale outside. In this quarter lay several islets, among them the Quarantine Island; and there, too, was the long reef of rocks known as the Northern Clapper. There were not a few of these reefs or "clappers" round about. If you had a good boat which steered well, and if you knew the channel, there was very good sailing in the bay. The skipper of the yacht always said so, and Tommerup did not contradict him. But it is to be observed that these two gentlemen had so far done very little in their lives but sail in and out and round the bay.

Klaus Tommerup on board the cutter, lay up as far as he could, and so had the wind with him going free towards the high land on the opposite coast. He had lost sight of the yawl for an hour, and then perceived her behind one of the little islands. The smack sail was lowered, and the yawl lay in smooth water by a big rock; but Tommerup could see no one in her. He made straight for her, however, going as near as he dared venture into the shallow water. Then he backed his foresail and hailed her. A young man's head appeared above the gunwale of the boat and vanished again. Tommerup sounded the depth of the water, ventured a dozen fathoms nearer, and shouted once more. The head again appeared. It certainly belonged to Sören Prip.

"What's the matter?" inquired the man in the yawl.

"That's what I want to know," returned the man in the cutter.

"Go to the devil!" said the voice from the yawl.

Tommerup was slightly disconcerted. But not being of a hasty disposition, he shouted to the other again—

"Is there anything wrong? Can I do anything for you?"

"It's the step of the mast that's cracked. I can't hold her to the wind," Sören answered.

"Put the yawl off then, and I'll tow you," suggested Klaus.

"Put off yourself, and let me alone," the other retorted; and the head vanished once more.

Tommerup stayed where he was full five minutes longer, but the cutter had already twice touched the bottom; and he became impatient.

"Come out, man, I say," he shouted, "and let there be an end to this foolery! I can't lie here all day knocking my boat to pieces."

Sören Prip stood straight up. "I tell you," he said, "I sailed the yawl out, and I'm going to sail her home again, if I wait ever so long for the chance."

He held a bottle of beer to his mouth for a moment, and then laid the bottle and himself down again in the bottom of the boat.

Tommerup hauled in his foresail and stood off shore. Then, making a long tack, he bore down upon the Quarantine Island, as if he meant to land there; changing his mind, he sailed for a couple of hours up and down the channel, and as by that time it was late in the afternoon, and he began to feel hungry, he fancied the man in the yawl might be in the same case, and going down to leeward of the islet, he hailed him again.

There was no answer this time; no head appeared.

"That is certainly the man for us," thought Klaus Tommerup; and full of inward admiration for such steadfastness, he put the cutter about and sailed fast homewards.

VI

"You're quite right, that's the man for the *Wild Duck*," Daniel Vibe declared emphatically the next morning. The two friends sat in the cabin of the cutter which was again moored to the pier-head. A steady, pleasant breeze had been blowing for half an hour, following a stormy night and a wet daybreak. The breeze came from the other side of the bay, and, gliding into the harbour with the breeze, the top of a new smack sail presently became visible across the pier-head.

"Hullo!" cried Tommerup, "there he is!"

"Is that the man?" asked the owner of the cutter; and taking out the silver whistle with which he had provided himself as part of the necessary apparatus for a pleasure sail, he whistled quite in a man-of-war's fashion to the yawl.

Klaus looked at him, and then over at the yawl, as she came into the harbour. The little mast was still leaning backward with hardly any sail up, but the wind was with her, and she made way. Sören sat at the helm, and peered up at the deck of the cutter, as if the performance with the whistle, though it did not in any way concern him personally, afforded him a little amusement after the monotony of the previous day and night.

"Come alongside!" shouted Vibe.

The yawl glided quietly on its way.

"We want to speak to you!" shouted Tommerup.

"Oh, was that what you were whistling for?" asked Sören, and turned the tiller.

The yawl came alongside of the cutter; Sören sat still.

"Would you like to exchange vessels?" asked Vibe, pleasantly.

Sören measured the *Wild Duck* with his eye, and said—

"What shall I give in exchange for her?"

Tommerup laughed, and Vibe looked doubtful.

"Hr. Vibe is asking if you will engage with us?" said Tommerup.

Sören came a little nearer.

"Is your cargo coal?" he asked.

"What?" shouted Vibe.

"I mean, are we bound for England?"

"Are you mad?" exclaimed Vibe, looking quite startled.

Sören glanced from Vibe to Tommerup, and back again.

"Ah, well, after all," he continued, "that's dirty work, and it would be a sin to spoil the smart paint. So it's corn, then?"

"Can't you understand?" cried Daniel. "This is a pleasure boat."

"All right," said Sören, with perfect composure. "That saves the trouble of lading and unlading. It will be rather amusing to run over there just for the fun of it."

"But we are not going to England at all," Vibe announced firmly.

"Not?" said Sören, slowly, while he examined the roomy, well-fitted-out boat with critical eyes. "I thought that if Hr. Tommerup——"

"I am the owner of this vessel, not Tommerup," said Vibe, angrily. "And now let's have no more nonsense; will you come with us, or not?"

"Here I am," said Sören.

In the meantime Tommerup had taken out of his pocket, not a silver whistle, for which there wasn't after all any particular use, but his old tobacco pipe—a short cutty—which he filled, lighted, and began to smoke with philosophic calm. It is difficult to guess the thoughts of meditative people; but as Tommerup watched the breeze playing with the smoke, there is reason to think he was wishing that his soap factory was free and unencumbered, so that he might sell it and be his own master in a boat of his own.

VII

They sailed together, the three of them. When the weather was settled and the course fairly clear, Daniel Vibe took his place at the wheel, and Tommerup sat or lay by the stern railing. Sören's post was in the fore hatchway. If any change occurred, Tommerup's hand slipped inadvertently, as it were, on to the tiller, while Vibe's hand moved away as if unconsciously, and the owner contented himself for the moment with repeating in a loud voice the words of command softly suggested by his comrade. When the squall was over, or the shoal passed, the hands changed places again by the same tacit agreement. But if the course became more difficult, and the breeze dropped; or if the squall seemed likely to last long, Klaus Tommerup's body followed his hand to the tiller, while Daniel Vibe found a temporary refuge on the companion. Sören minded his own business, and paid no attention to anyone else. But when a reef or two had been taken in, and the owner happened, once in a way, to be still at the helm, Sören put the hard knuckle of his right forefinger between his teeth, and repeated half aloud to himself a favourite sentence, "We have a fine lot of stuff on board; real good stuff on board her."

So they sailed together, and each one naturally fell in time into the part which best suited him.

It was an August day—Daniel Vibe's twenty-ninth birthday. To receive the congratulations of his family, and to drink punch at the club in the evening, was not making enough of the day according to his ideas; and a real revel, with a big dinner, and so on, was not seemly, his relations thought, so soon after the great bereavement. He therefore provisioned the *Wild Duck* particularly well, and invited some of the best people of the town to come with him for a sail, which might perhaps last till the next day. Possibly this prospect deterred them; in any case the guests failed to put in an appearance. Daniel Vibe resolved to show that he could do without them; they set sail and glided out of the harbour. The weather was extremely promising, and the tanner and the chemist who had been invited at the last moment to fill the vacant places stood on the pier and repented in their hearts that they had made it a point of honour to decline.

Away they went. The captain was now in white trousers, light blue flannel shirt under his pea-jacket, and the peaked cap; and he still wore a bit of crape over his gilt buttons. His long fair whiskers made him look quite English, and he really was a very handsome birthday figure.

Of course he steered. The wind was fair and fresh. Tommerup thought the barometer showed a tendency to fall, but Daniel declared that he wouldn't ask advice from any weather-glass on his birthday. At breakfast he was evidently in the highest spirits. Sören sat forward and stared at the horizon, with his knuckle in his mouth, putting a word now and again into the conversation. As for Tommerup, he had brought a cushion up from the cabin and had made a comfortable place for himself in the stern. Beside him he placed a basket of provisions, to which he gave his undivided attention as soon as they were clear of the harbour swell. The soap factory had now come quite to a standstill, and the old woman—the solitary remnant of his father's household—who attended to his few wants, had announced that morning that her master did not give her an adequate sum for the weekly expenses, and that if it were not increased she must leave his service. Tommerup had managed to content her for the moment, but all the same, he had left his coffee and his bread and butter almost untouched, and there was a cloud on his broad, open brow as he walked down to the harbour with his cat under his arm. Klaus had not found it in his heart to leave the animal alone at home. The low, dreary old house had looked very melancholy indeed that morning in its owner's eyes, and he did not fancy it wore a much more cheerful aspect in the eyes of the cat. Tommerup's family had died out; he had no enemies in the town, and few friends; but he had his cat, and the cat's name was Jacob.

So he lay on the cushion which was stuffed with the best cork, and Jacob lay on his knee and blinked at the sun, and devoured the occasional mouthfuls of cold chicken which his master bestowed upon him.

VIII

Daniel Vibe was, as I have said, in excellent spirits. He meant that day to get right out to sea, he said, and they made straight for the other side of the bay.

Near the inlet they passed another little vessel belonging to the town, loaded with peat and potatoes—no unusual freight. The boat was heavily laden, the piles of peat were hanging over the sides; she beat up with difficulty against the tide.

Vibe scoffed at her master's seamanship.

"Faith," said he, "there's a fine trade!"

"The man gets a living for himself and his wife and child out of it, any way," remarked Sören, thoughtfully.

"What, has he got a family on board along with the peat?" laughed the captain.

"They don't live on peat," said Sören. "The man does a very good business, they say."

Tommerup said nothing, but nodded in a friendly way to the man, who responded by waving his cap.

"You ought to go in for something of that sort yourself, Tommerup," said Vibe. "Then you would have a chance of being your own master; while as it is——"

"As it is things are in a bad way," said Tommerup, stroking the cat's

back. "You mean that a peat barge that goes is better than a soap factory that stands still," he went on. "You are great at logic, Daniel.
Lend me your corkscrew."

"Yes, let's have a drink," said the captain.

They did have a drink. The first bottle of sherry was soon emptied,
and, in spite of Tommerup's objections, another was opened. Tommerup
refused to drink any more, but Vibe kept passing the bottle to Sören,
who did not refuse the captain's invitation. And he was not accustomed
to wine.

The Clapper was passed; the *Wild Duck* went curtseying out into the
open sea. The captain's pale face was a little flushed. His cap was on the
side of his head, and he looked rather rakish. Klaus sat and stroked his
cat, and looked up at the sky and across the cutter's sail.

"The wind is freshening," remarked Sören.

"So much the better," cried Vibe; but he added immediately, "Shall
we take in a reef?"

"It would be as well," said Tommerup. "Luff!"

They took in a reef, and in the afternoon, while the *Wild Duck* kept
out in the open, this is what happened.

Vibe sat at the helm, although the wind, as Sören had foretold, grew
fresher and fresher. The wine was doing its work; the captain was bolder
to-day. He meant to show them that he could sail his own ship. So he
stayed where he was, and a new bottle was opened, of which Sören had
a fair share.

Klaus Tommerup looked on for a little while and forbade the sailor
presently to drink any more.

"You let him alone!" cried Vibe. "I am the captain of this boat, and
it's my birthday."

Tommerup nodded. The vessel was labouring a good deal, and now
and then shipped a sea. So he put his cat inside the breast of his coat,
and buttoned him safely up, and then resumed his place on his cork
cushion, apparently indifferent, but really keeping a sharp look-out on
each of the helmsman's movements.

Sören drank, and was as happy as a child. He was wet through already, but the water did not seem to trouble him as much as it troubled
Jacob. The cat sat with his head out, but whenever a wave washed
over the boat he put it in and mewed.

"Hold her a little off, Daniel," said Tommerup.

Sören stood upright with his hands behind him, holding on to the topmost stay. At Tommerup's word he made a grimace, an action which,
strictly speaking, overstepped the limits of discipline.

"*We* are going to sail her to-day, aren't we, Sören?" cried the captain.

"So we are," laughed Sören; and again he accepted the bottle which
Tommerup himself had to pass to him.

The air became gradually more and more hazy. The sun shone red through the mist.

"I don't like the look of it," said Tommerup, glancing back at the shore, which was fading into the grey blue distance.

"Bosh!" said Vibe.

"We ought to turn back," answered his comrade. "It will be hard enough to beat up now and it will be fresher still before evening."

"Perhaps you're afraid?" cried the captain boldly.

At that moment Sören's feet slipped away from him, and he went flat down on his back on the wet deck.

Vibe grew pale. Sören was up again in a moment, but Tommerup looked severely at him, and Sören seemed a little ashamed. He had not appreciated the birthday sherry quite rightly. The drink had been stronger than the cutter's sailor.

And so came the first flash and the first peal of thunder. The sea turned purple and grey, and was specked inshore with innumerable white dots, and the wind whistled ominously. Tommerup rose to his knees, buttoned up his coat in spite of Jacob's evident objection, and put his hand on Vibe's shoulder.

"Get out of the way," he said. "We shall have the storm on us in a minute; it's no time for fooling."

But Vibe was obstinate.

"As you please," said Tommerup, and eased the mainsail. "Stand by the halyards, Sören; let go the peak halyard; let the throat halyard be!"

At this moment the cutter dipped her nose under an unusually high sea, which the helmsman had not parried. Sören clung to the hoop of the mast; the water rushed foaming aft, and filled the hole in which the helmsman stood.

Vibe let go the tiller and shot up out of the hole like a cork from a bottle. The boat careened right over, so that the mainsail dipped in the water. Vibe lost his balance, slid to leeward, and went overboard.

"Let go the foresail!" shouted Tommerup, and put the helm hard over with his foot. Then, turning quick as lightning, he snatched up the cork cushion, and threw it overboard, where Vibe's head appeared above the water.

The cutter shot up into the wind.

"Is there no rope?" shouted Tommerup. "Cut the jib halyard— cut it away with your knife, man! Now a turn of the rope round the oar and over with it. He is holding on to the cushion. That's right; pay out the rope. Now he's got it. All right, haul him in—here he is!"

And Klaus Tommerup bent over the railing, hauled in his comrade and pushed him into the cabin without ceremony. Jacob, who found himself also in an uncomfortable position, was mewing miserably, and he was sent into the cabin too.

"It's no good whining about it now," remarked his master.

Sören looked at him penitently.

"I deserve a thrashing, Hr. Tommerup," he said. "I did not think that the stuff was so strong."

"You must wait for your thrashing till we come ashore," answered the other. "It remains to be seen if we ever do. Down with the sail! Down with the throat halyard! Confound you, man, look alive! Here it comes." And while the *Wild Duck* was shrouded in the sheet of rain, and lay heeling over on her side with bare poles, he muttered to himself, "It's lucky for Daniel it didn't come sooner."

IX

Just in front of the inlet that ran out of the bay, on the island that had been long known as the Quarantine Island, there stood a yellow brick building with a high tiled roof, surrounded by ruined cottages and deserted gardens. The inside of the house corresponded to its exterior; half-ruined as it was, it still retained an air of dignity—a reminiscence of the days when epidemics were in fashion, and were treated with respectful consideration by the authorities. There are on our coast many such desolate outlying stations, mouldering fortresses, decayed depots. There is about them something of the sentiment that attaches to old castles and old soldiers.

The afternoon was passing into the evening, and there was more than a touch of autumn in the air. Right across the island, from the little harbour up to the highest rampart, there stretched a row of weather-beaten trees, with all their branches growing out on one side, not unlike a worn-out comb or toothbrush. The storm—for now it was really a storm—whistled wildly among these old veterans; there was not much else left for it to do. The coarse yellow grass outside the windows of the building waved to and fro, and the gusts of wind rattled against the convex panes.

In the large room, whose scanty furniture dated from the days of Napoleon—a silhouette of the Emperor on horseback still adorned the mirror—the inspector was sitting. What he was inspector of, no one quite knew. If he had inspected himself, as he sat in the deep armchair covered with flowery tapestry, he would have discovered himself to be a respectable old ruin, like the rest of the island. He had once been a strong, broad-shouldered man, but he was now bent with rheumatism, and there was in his eye a watery gleam that might perhaps be connected with the corner cupboard behind him, whose doors stood open, revealing two or three decanters. Before him on the little table stood a steaming mixture, which he now and then sipped with trembling hand.

Some distance from the armchair, by the gable window, sat a young girl with a book before her, that looked like a family volume of sermons She had been reading, but had paused to look attentively at the sea Then she went back to her reading, but evidently with an effort. It might be imagined that the book was a sort of necessity to which a girl might submit in a rather hopeless position, left to herself on a dreary island with a father like the one in the armchair, not knowing what to do with her youth and health, or how to find an outlet for her longings and her strength.

Now and then, as she glanced from the printed page to the armchair, there was visible in her eyes an expression of profound melancholy, out of keeping with her years, of weary resignation to an inevitable fate. But when she looked away from him with a little shudder, and glanced again through the casement at the world outside, her expression altered, revealing a gleam of resolution, the result possibly of continual intercourse with the sea.

Every ruin has some point round which the mouldering fragments may cling for a long time, and the sea has strength and freshness for every day. It is not to pass away till all things pass; and that hour is long in coming.

The girl's world lay there beyond those windows. It was little or great, according as you looked at it. At this moment it contained a single boat that with reefed mainsail and close-reefed foresail, in the red flush of the sunset, was beating up towards the inlet against wind and tide, and doing her utmost apparently to clear the rocky reef, the Northern Clapper, which lay to leeward of her.

The girl knew the pilot's boat, and the few other vessels along the coast. But she could not connect this one with any owner. She knew enough to be aware that the situation was very serious, and she watched still more intently, and presently uttered an exclamation of dismay.

"What's the matter?" asked the old man in the armchair.

She did not heed the question. Like a seabird with wounded wing, the boat drifted sideways, and the breakers on the reef were near—terribly near.

"Ah! . . . thank Heaven!" she cried.

"But what is it?" asked the voice from the armchair again.

"It's a boat which . . . It was making straight for . . . Now she has righted herself again. Look for yourself!"

"Not a trace of a boat," stammered the inspector, whose window looked to the west, while the gable looked to the east.

"They can't get up to the town, father; that is impossible. I think— yes, I really think," she repeated after a few moments' anxious scrutiny, "that they are coming over to us. Poor men! how wet they must be."

"Hot water," said the inspector, "that's what they'll want. Hot water and something in it!"

X

From the little harbour of the island three men walked up to the brick building. The one in the middle was supported by his stronger friends on either side.

They opened the outer door; there was a little sound of stamping and splashing in the brick-paved entry; then they knocked at the door, and finally entered the big room.

"Good evening. Excuse me," said Tommerup.

"By your leave," said Sören.

Daniel Vibe said nothing. They led him to the hard high-backed sofa, and he dropped on to it with a groan; it seemed to him that he was still sailing.

The young girl had been standing doubtfully in the middle of the room. Now she hastened to the door, and came back immediately with a clean towel and a glass of water.

"Your friend is ill. You have been in great danger?"

She addressed her remark to Tommerup, who, dripping wet as he was, nodded with some embarrassment, and struggled with the captain as with a child. Sören assisted him; and the floor round the three of them was like a little sea.

"We have a bed all ready," said the girl. "Would that not be the best thing?"

Vibe had recovered himself a little. He sat up and threw out his arms.

"Bed!" said he; "who talks of going to bed?"

He looked wildly round, and his glance fell on the little table beside the armchair. He staggered across the room, snatched up the glass and emptied it at a draught. The old man raised his large eyes approvingly, and spoke to his daughter in his harsh voice.

"I told you so," he said, jerking his elbow in the direction of the cupboard. "Hot water and the decanter."

The girl stood again as if uncertain what to do. She looked away from her father with a sigh, and seemed silently to ask Tommerup's advice.

"Yes, let us have something hot," he answered reassuringly, "and if you had any dry clothes?"

He pointed first at Vibe, then glanced at himself and Sören; and then he apologized for the condition of the floor.

The inspector's daughter blushed, though there was apparently no particular reason why she should blush because three strangers, dripping wet and much the worse for their trip, had visited the nearest island in stress of weather. She exchanged a few words with her father about the big wardrobe in the garret, and then disappeared.

There were now three men in the room, besides the ruin in the armchair. Vibe sat down again on the sofa. He was evidently much shaken, excited, nervous, and very pale; he was the living picture of a weak character, just escaped from a great danger, and still suffering from the effects of sea-sickness. He shook with cold in his wet clothes; the hot drink had done him a little good, but only a little, and he sat there shaking his head like an owl in a cage.

Tommerup surveyed the different objects in the room as well as the fading light permitted. The attention he paid to certain things seemed to indicate an old acquaintance with them. He tried to get up a conversation with the armchair but the attempt was sadly fruitless. The inspector only uttered a few unintelligible words and disjointed sentences, and ended with the assurance that they should soon have something hot.

"Ah yes," said Sören, who was amusing himself by letting his feet squelch in his shoes as he walked across the floor, "that isn't a bad idea —unless Hr. Tommerup has anything against it."

"I have nothing against it *now*," answered Klaus. "What do you say, Vibe? Come, pull yourself together a bit."

But that was more than the captain was capable of doing at present. He moved his head from side to side, and uttered a broken monologue, of which fragments such as "never sail again . . ." and "the confounded cutter . . ." were alone audible.

The door opened, and the daughter of the house came in with a light in her hand.

"The gentlemen can go in now and change their things," said she.

And so they did. The captain was helped in and out of his clothes like a child. To Tommerup's repeated suggestion that he should accept the bed that had been offered to him, he answered with a mixture of fretfulness and defiance—

"No, he was going to show them . . ."

In the meantime the table was laid for supper. A large jug was set steaming among the eggs and sausages and bread and butter, and what Vibe showed them was that he was thirsty rather than hungry. To the old man's evident satisfaction, he mixed himself first one glass and then another and then retreated to the sofa, and lay listening to the brief plain narrative of their expedition, which Tommerup gave on his comrade's behalf and his own.

But the simplicity with which the great events of the day were represented was not at all to Daniel Vibe's mind. Encouraged by the mixture, in the midst of concocting his third glass, he broke into Tommerup's story with such striking additions that his friend was silenced and Vibe continued alone.

They had really gone through unheard-of dangers. And if he himself had not had the confounded ill-luck to stumble and go overboard at the critical moment—an accident which however had given him a chance to display his dexterity in swimming—they would perhaps . . .

Sören could not contain himself. He began to laugh with half an egg and a slice of sausage in his mouth.

The captain grew angry.

"What are you grinning at, you idiot?" said he.

Klaus Tommerup interposed to keep the peace. The young girl who sat at some distance from the table watched him intently. From the armchair there came occasionally broken expressions of surprise and approval to which no one paid any attention at all.

Then the captain was seized with another attack of giddiness; his face turned yellow-white, and when he had disposed of another glass the tears streamed from his eyes, and he declared Klaus Tommerup to be his preserver and best friend. Sören nodded assent. Tommerup asked the girl to clear the table. The captain did not want to go to bed—not at all—he wanted to drink another glass to his friend and preserver, he wanted the armchair to pledge him—he wanted every one to be cheerful.

"All right," said Tommerup, laughing. "Let us be cheerful by all means," and he smiled reassuringly at the girl as if to say, "We must let him have plenty of rope."

"That's right," cried Vibe. "I am glad you are thawing at last."

Daniel Vibe, without exactly being a musician, was fond of singing. His taste lay rather in the music-hall direction. Rich young men in small towns—and in large ones, too—frequently have a turn for this kind of music. It requires no serious preliminary study, but chiefly a readiness to applaud noisily, and a purse opened freely to stimulate the singers who, like nightingales, trill their prettiest songs after sundown.

Daniel Vibe sang. Tommerup raised his eyebrows a little and glanced at the girl. She was listening with a faint smile to the funny falsetto voice. She could not hear the first words distinctly, but suddenly she set her lips together and moved her chair.

"That's enough of that," said Tommerup.

"What's wrong?" asked Vibe, and burst into careless laughter.

The wealthy young hero of the small seaport town was not endowed with a particularly refined nature and perhaps he did not know himself how coarse his song was. A glance from his friend now seemed to make him aware of the girl's presence for the first time.

"Oh, I see," he said, "the young lady. You needn't be afraid of me, Missy. You may trust me. . . ."

Here Tommerup spoke to him gravely.

"All right," Vibe went on, "just as you like. You're my preserver; . . . you're a regular brick, that's what you are. Come on, let's have a drink together, and the girl too. No one's going to hurt you, Missy; but you see, when a fellow's had such a close shave . . . and then to lie half drowned in the cabin . . . Tommerup, you're my friend, and if I'm not to sing, by Jove, you must."

Tommerup vainly endeavoured to soothe him. Nothing would do but a song. With his thoughtful air, and his good-humoured little smile, he at last agreed.

"All right," he said, "it's your birthday, and so you shall have your own way."

This is what he sang:

> "I am contented with my store;
>   Altho' I should not be the worse
> For just a very little more,
>   I covet not my neighbour's purse;—
>   For thine is thine,
>   And mine is mine,
>   Do what you will, mine it is still.
>
> "The sun that shines as bright for me
>   As for the richest man I meet;
>   The breeze that blows as fresh and free;
>   Good appetite and slumbers sweet;—
>   No money buys
>   What most I prize;
>   Bid what you will, mine it is still.
>
> "And while I'm roaming far away,
>   I'll hear perchance that one at home
> Looks out for me from day to day,
>   And wonders why I do not come;
>   Then hand in hand
>   We two shall stand;
>   The world may frown, she'll be my own."

After Vibe had relieved his mind by declaring the song too sentimental for grown-up men, Sören asked leave to say something, and proceeded to make a little speech in honour of Tommerup, ending by congratulating the captain on having had one man on board fit to look after himself and the boat and the others into the bargain.

Here Vibe again grew white; and when he had got the better of his reviving recollections of the terrors of the sea, he stared coldly at Sören, and rejoined that the whole thing was wholly and solely the fault of the *Wild Duck;* she was the wretchedest *Wild Duck*, the most miserable cutter he'd ever seen; and it was a shame that his old friend Tommerup had ever palmed her off on him.

Tommerup smiled, but Sören took the remark very seriously indeed.

"You can strike my name off the list of your crew, Hr. Vibe," said he; "and you can say I'm a common sailor, and that I loaf about at home doing nothing—you can say so and welcome. I can tell you there are worse ways of putting in the time than that. My father and my grandfather never did anything when they were my age but shoot, and sail, and fish, and all the same one of them's gone to his grave an honest man, and the other'll do the same; and so shall I, without cheating a soul out of a single farthing, and without letting every bad girl in the town make a fool of me. But when you begin grumbling at Hr. Tommerup, I tell you, you'd best go home and keep quiet, and it's a pity you didn't do it a good while ago."

"I say, Sören!" said Klaus.

"Oh, let him go on!" cried Vibe, flushing and turning pale, and then bursting into tears, as a weak man will at critical moments. He threw himself on the sofa, overcome with alcohol and emotion, and wept freely.

Sören looked perplexed, and Tommerup laid his hand consolingly on his friend's shoulder.

"I shall never set foot on the cutter again," he moaned, "never again."

"How are you going to get home, then?" muttered Sören.

"I'll knock a hole in her and sink her as soon as we get back," said Vibe.

"It would be better to sell her," responded the persistent Sören.

"Never!" was the answer.

"Well, then, you ought to give her to Hr. Tommerup," suggested Sören. "He has done enough to-day to earn her, and a good deal more."

Vibe did not answer at once; but presently he sat up, and extended his hand as he had seen travelling actors do and as he always did himself when he made a speech at the club.

"Tommerup, my friend, my preserver!" said he. "I owe you my life twice over to-day. First because you fished me out of the water, and then because you sailed us safely here. I give you the *Wild Duck*."

Tommerup was endeavouring to release himself from his friend's embrace.

"You'll have forgotten all about it to-morrow, Daniel," he answered, smiling.

"What!" said Vibe. "You think I'm drunk? Well, well . . . But I'll show you . . . Look here, my good girl, can you give me paper and pen and ink? I really mean it . . . and you'll be paid for it, too. . . . I'll give you a kiss afterwards. That's right . . . the old man over there shall be a witness. No, he's too far gone . . . Never mind, Sören and you shall be witnesses. There—it's a deed of gift *in optima forma*, as we lawyers say, and Tommerup can get it registered to-morrow at the office."

He succeeded in putting on the paper what follows:

Herewith, of my own free will, without any compulsion, I present the cutter *Wild Duck*, with all she contains, to my friend, Klaus Tommerup, as an acknowledgment of his having saved my life to-day.

Date   Signature.

XI

"That's done," said Klaus Tommerup an hour later, as he returned to the sitting-room from the apartment where he had put his magnanimous friend to bed, placing him for the time in Sören's charge.

It is sad to have to say that the former owner of the *Wild Duck* had gone to bed in a decidedly intoxicated condition. The kiss which he had tried to force on the young girl, shortly after the completion of his noble deed, had been rejected with disgust, and Tommerup, hitherto so patient, had interfered with a sharp rebuke. Vibe apologized and drank to their reconciliation, and by that time he was done for.

Tommerup stood again in the room. The inspector's daughter did not inquire after his friend's health. She was occupied—very sorrowfully occupied—with some one else.

Tommerup looked at the armchair. He could not conceal from himself that the inspector was done for also, and in a more wretched and helpless condition than his hare-brained friend.

They stood together before the armchair, and the old man stared up at them with fixed glassy eyes.

The young man touched the arm of the girl who stood with drooping head, and asked with profound reverence in his voice, "May I help you?"

She turned away from him to hide her shame—the shame that a father had brought upon his child. Tommerup lifted the old man out of his chair, and said to the girl:

"You might light me down the passage."

She took the light and went before him to her father's room, and there together, without exchanging a single unnecessary word, they put the inspector to bed.

Then they sat together in the sitting-room with the candle before them on the table. Tommerup poured out a large glass of cold water and swallowed it hastily.

"You must be very tired," said she. "Would you not rather——"

He took her hand and tried to bring back her old smile, and partly succeeded.

"I would rather talk to you," he replied.

She drew her hand gently away, laid it with the other in her lap, and waited. He hesitated, and she came to his aid.

"It is a long time since you have been to see us," she said. "Why has it been so long?"

Klaus Tommerup got up from his seat, moved a little away, and then came nearer.

"Won't you let me hold your hand?" he said. "It has been a very distracting day and . . . Forgive me . . . but you see, when I hold your hand I can explain things better to you. You don't know, of course, that everything has gone very badly with me since the last time that I was here, and I determined not to come back again until I could ask you to give me this hand that I am now holding . . . And it isn't my fault that I came to-day," he added, hastily.

She tried to draw her hand away, but what Klaus held, he generally held fast. She let it be, and looked at him gravely.

"Did you never think," she said, "that things might be going still worse here?"

He felt the reproach in her tone. In her sorrowful eyes he read an accusation of selfishness. At such a moment the best men are abashed, and have nothing to say for themselves, and so it was with Klaus. But presently he put his other hand over hers, and holding it between both his, he murmured—

"Poor girl! poor child! What an ass I am!"

She lowered her eyes, and he felt her hot tears falling on his hands. There she sat and there he stood, bending lower and lower over her.

The wind rattled the panes; the flame of the candle flickered. The storm was raging outside, and Tommerup felt that there was a storm also in the girl's heart. He was not much calmer himself.

What happened next? What always happens on such occasions? We know it all quite well and still we always like to hear it again. But at this moment they were interrupted by a doleful sound that came with the wind through the window.

Tommerup listened.

The same sound was heard again, only still more doleful.

Tommerup sprang up, a little to the girl's surprise, threw open the window, and called—

"Jacob!"

A cat sprang through the window on to the floor and thence to the sofa. Tommerup picked him up, laughing, and showed him to the girl. She had been a little disconcerted by this interruption, but now she was smiling too.

"It has really been a distracting day," said Klaus. "I left my best friend on board and forgot all about him. Heaven knows how he escaped drowning when the cabin filled."

He passed his hand caressingly down the cat's back, then he put him down and turned earnestly to the girl.

"I spoke just now," he said, "of my best friend. You can see by that what a fool I am, since I have made a close friend of that little creature. But Jacob did me a good turn just now. I was beginning to lose heart, and I should not do that. For however poor I am, there is some one here who is worse off still, and so. . . . Now give me both your hands, and promise me that you will stick to me through thick and thin. . . . Ah, don't cry—come here, come to me!"

He opened his arms, and the girl clung to him, and sobbed, with her arms round his neck—

"I will, I will. . . . Only trust me!"

It was rather late and the candle had burned very low, when Klaus Tommerup stepped into the room which had been allotted to the three companions. And he could not refrain from waking up Sören to tell him the news.

"Well, well," said Sören, and slapped his knee. "Then it's you, after all, who are keeping your birthday to-day! Anyhow, you have got a present."

"That I have," said Tommerup, with a beaming face.

Then he held up his candle-end and let the light fall on Daniel Vibe who was snoring loudly.

"He is sleeping it off," he observed. "A drunken man is an ugly sight to be sure. Just think, Sören, if that were your brother, or if either of us had a father like——"

"He is an ass," said Sören, rubbing his eyes, "but he has a good business at home yonder."

"So he has," said Tommerup; and he blew out the light.

XII

What remains to be told?

Nothing much, for everything went its natural way.

The second day from that evening Klaus went to see his friend who sat in the outer office, while the old lawyer, the pillar of the house, worked in the adjoining room.

There was a certain embarrassment in Daniel Vibe's greeting.

Tommerup took a half-sheet of paper out of his pocket-book and presented it to his friend.

Vibe coloured.

"I just wanted to give you back this paper," said Tommerup quietly. "I fancy you wrote it rather in a hurry."

"Not at all," said Vibe, glancing a little anxiously towards the adjoining room. "You have free leave to make use of it—that's to say, you may regard the cutter quite as your own."

Tommerup looked at him and he blushed a little more.

"You know very well, Daniel," said he, "that I should never press you to keep that promise, although I would sooner sail that boat than do anything else in the world—no, not exactly anything in the world, but sooner than most things. I only want to know how we stand; because yesterday after we landed you kept out of my way the whole afternoon. Either we can go on as we have done till now, and I have your leave to use the boat when I like, while you are still her owner and her captain; or else the *Wild Duck* is mine, honestly earned and honestly paid, and you have my leave to use her as much as you like, and to put on as much sail as you please."

"Heaven forbid!" exclaimed Vibe.

"Well then," said Tommerup, with his old smile, "the boat is really mine?"

"The boat is yours, confound her!" said Vibe.

"Thanks," said Tommerup; and he shook hands with his friend. "Don't be angry," he added, "if I ask you to exchange this bit of paper for a regular document, drawn up by the old fox in there. For this counts for nothing, as far as I can judge."

"Give me the paper," said Vibe. "I will give you a proper deed of gift this evening at the club."

They shook hands again—Tommerup, as he had always done, Vibe in a slightly altered way. But what could anyone guess from that?

The same evening Tommerup received his deed of gift. The new owner of the *Wild Duck* wished to give a punch supper, but the late owner excused himself on the ground of having a headache.

After that Tommerup often sailed with Sören across to the Quarantine Island and almost gave up going to the club. One pleasure has to make way for another. But one very wet autumn evening he came into the club again.

He did not notice anything unusual at first and was not at all aware that the other men there avoided him. But the apothecary who was every one's friend and every one's adviser, took him aside and explained with a good deal of circumlocution, that Daniel Vibe had several times told how Tommerup had taken him over to the Quarantine Island and made him drunk along with the "tipsy inspector and the little hussy his daughter," and so had tricked him out of the cutter.

Tommerup shook the rain from his coat-sleeves, looked up, asked the apothecary on his word of honour if what he said was true, and then went straight into the most select room of all, where Vibe sat among the other leading people of the place, playing high and drinking more rum-punch than was good for him.

Klaus was standing in front of Vibe before the latter had noticed his approach. Vibe grew rather pale.

"Look here, Daniel Vibe," said Tommerup, "I'm told you have played me a very dirty trick. As far as I could I have always been a true comrade to you. Will you say here before everyone that the apothecary lies when he says that you have said this and that about me in my absence?"

There was perfect silence in this very select room, and in those adjoining it. Vibe dropped his cards and stretched out a somewhat unsteady hand for his glass.

"Do you mean—do you mean to assault me?" he asked, looking round on his companions for assistance in case of need.

One of the other players who had been a friend of old Tommerup's, spoke up.

"Vibe has told us all," he said, "that that's how Tommerup managed it."

"Good," said Tommerup, and fastened a button of his coat. "Then I invite my former friend and comrade, Daniel Vibe, here on the spot to declare that he has slandered me falsely."

Vibe bent his head without answering.

"You see, gentlemen," continued Tommerup, with a very slight quiver in his voice, "that Hr. Vibe is in an awkward position. As far as I am concerned I have time to wait; I have always had time. But no one can wait indefinitely where his honour is in question. I expect at midday to-morrow a written apology from my former friend and I shall read it aloud here to-morrow evening. Should it not come, I shall declare Daniel Vibe to be a common slanderer, and I shall suggest that you should turn him out of your society, because he is not fit to be among decent people."

And so Tommerup went away.

The next morning Tommerup received his apology. It was couched in the briefest possible terms and hit the medium between excuse and denial so neatly that the recipient bit his lip and murmured, "The cunning old fox!"

None the less he went to the club and read the letter aloud—Vibe was absent—to the assembled members, and then he addressed the following little speech to them—

"This is not an excuse," said he, "such as I had a right to expect. But all the same I accept it, and I do not want to proceed any further in the matter. Hr. Vibe has a lot of people in his office, and he's a big man in this town and I am nothing. That's a fact I know I shall have to reckon with. But I part from you, gentlemen, persuaded that I have kept my good name untarnished and that is enough for me. If I stayed in the club I should necessarily be a cause of offence. My being here would always keep one man away, and you can spare me better than him. Thanks for the good times we have had here together, and farewell."

A month later the soap factory was sold, but Tommerup did not sell it himself. Some one else was kind enough to do it for him. All the outstanding claims had been collected by one person and that person proceeded to turn Klaus Tommerup into the street with nothing but a few absolutely necessary personal belongings, among them the cat Jacob.

Everything was sold—the whole property that for many generations had belonged to Tommerup's family; and so all claims were settled. Only the cutter, the *Wild Duck*, remained in his possession and in the meantime he lived on board her. The townspeople were discreet enough not to trouble him with visits.

The day after he had settled into his new quarters, old Prip, Sören's father, strolled down the pier. Tommerup put his head out of the companion. The old man stood still and took his pipe out of his mouth.

"Look here, Hr. Tommerup," said he, "Sören says there is room for you at home in the shed."

"I beg your pardon?"

"We have got two rooms ready for you; they are rather small, but they look west; you can see out across the bay. And we will share the kitchen; and so you can be married."

The old man replaced his pipe and walked away.

Tommerup gazed after him.

Shortly after, Sören made his appearance.

"Are you two mad?" shouted Tommerup to him.

"Not that I know of," said Sören. "You can't live with a wife on board the boat; anyhow not with children."

"Who told you I was thinking of getting married?" asked Tommerup, after a moment's despondent reflection.

Sören opened his eyes.

"Every one that has a sweetheart wants to get married. Why not let the parson arrange it? That's the easiest way."

Tommerup could not refrain from smiling.

"The question is, Sören, what shall we have to live on?"

"Peat and potatoes, of course. And you'll take me with you?"

Klaus Tommerup jumped up, sprang on the pier, and pressed Sören's hand.

"I had forgotten all about the peat," he cried.

"Yes, and the potatoes too," added the accurate Sören.

So the firm of Klaus Tommerup and Sören Prip really sailed with the above-mentioned freight, and it soon became evident that the *Wild Duck* with that freight could keep a man and his wife and child besides. The price of peat continued to rise, while the love at home did not go down. But whether Hr. Tommerup, after the shed was pulled down and a house put up in its place, and after the *Wild Duck* had a duckling in the shape of a smaller boat, and after both of these had been replaced by a big yacht—whether Tommerup then applied to the club for membership again, this story does not say.

JAPAN

HOW THE EMPRESS JINGO SAILED UNTO THE LAND CALLED CHOSEN[1]

THE Empress returned to the Bay of Kashihi, and loosing her hair, looked over the sea, saying:

"I, having received instructions of the Gods of Heaven and Earth, and trusting in the Spirits of the Imperial ancestors, floating across the deep blue sea, intend in person to chastise the West. Therefore do I now lave my head in the water of the sea. If I am to be successful, let my hair part spontaneously into two."

Accordingly she entered the sea and bathed, and her hair parted of its own accord. The Empress bound it up parted into bunches. Then she addressed her ministers, saying:

"To make war and move troops is a matter of the greatest concern to a country. Peace and danger, success and failure, must depend on it. If I now entrusted to you, my ministers, the duties of the expedition we are about to undertake, the blame, in case of ill-success, would rest with you. This would be very grievous to me. Therefore, although I am a woman, and a feeble woman too, I will for a while borrow the outward appearance of a man, and force myself to adopt manly counsels. Above, I shall receive support from the Spirits of the Gods of Heaven and Earth, while below I shall avail myself of the assistance of you, my ministers. Brandishing our weapons, we shall cross the towering billows; preparing an array of ships, we shall take possession of the Land of Treasure. If the enterprise succeeds, all of you, my ministers, will have the credit, while if it is unsuccessful, I alone shall be to blame. Such have been my intentions, do ye deliberate together regarding them."

The ministers all said:

"The object of the measure which the Empress has devised for the Empire is to tranquillize the ancestral shrines and the Gods of Earth and Grain, and also to protect her servants from blame. With heads bowed to the ground we receive thy commands."

The various provinces were ordered to collect ships and to practise the use of weapons. But an army could not be assembled. The Empress said:

"This is surely the will of a God."

So she erected the Shrine of Oho-miwa, and offered there a sword and a spear. Then the troops assembled freely. Hereupon a fisherman of

---

[1]From W. G. Aston's translation of *The Nihongi*. Reprinted by permission of Kegan Paul Trench, Trubner & Co., Ltd.

Ahe, by name Womaro, was sent out into the Western sea, to spy if there was any land there. He came back and said:

"There is no land to be seen."

Again a fisherman of Shika, named Nagusa, was sent to look. After several days he returned, and said:

"To the North-West there is a mountain girt with clouds and extending crosswise. This is perhaps a country."

Hereupon a lucky day was fixed upon by divination. There was yet an interval before they should set out. Then the Empress in person, grasping her battle-axe, commanded the three divisions of her army, saying:

"If the drums are beaten out of time, and the signal-flags are waved confusedly, order cannot be preserved among the troops. If greedy of wealth and eager for much, you cherish self and have regard for your own interests, you will surely be taken prisoners by the enemy. Despise not the enemy, though his numbers may be few; shrink not from him, though his numbers may be many. Spare not the violent, slay not the submissive. There will surely be rewards for those who ultimately conquer in battle, and of course punishments for those who turn their backs and flee."

After this a God gave instructions, saying:

"A gentle spirit will attach itself to the Empress's person, and keep watch over her life: a rough spirit will form the vanguard and be a guide to the squadron."

So when she had received the divine instructions she did worship, and for this purpose appointed Otarimi, Yosama no Ahiko to be the Director of the ceremonies in honour of the God.

Sail was set from the harbour of Wani. Then the Wind-God made a breeze to spring up, and the Sea-God uplifted the billows. The great fishes of the ocean, every one, came to the surface and encompassed the ships. Presently a great wind blew from a favourable quarter on the ships under sail, and following the waves, without the labour of the oar or helm, they arrived at Silla. The tide-waves following the ships, reached far up into the interior of the country. Hereupon the King of Silla feared and trembled, and knew not what to do, so he assembled all his people and said to them:

"Since the State of Silla was founded, it has never yet been heard that the water of the sea has encroached upon the land. Is it possible that the term of existence granted to it by Heaven has expired, and that our country is to become a part of the ocean?"

Scarce had he spoken when a warlike fleet overspread the sea. Their banners were resplendent in the sunlight. The drums and fifes raised up their voices, and the mountains and rivers all thrilled to the sound. The King of Silla beholding this from afar, felt that his country was about to be destroyed by this extraordinary force, and was terrified out of his senses. But presently, coming to himself, he said:

"I have heard that in the East there is a divine country named Nippon, and also that there is there a wise sovereign called the Tennō. This divine force must belong to that country. How can we resist them by force of arms?"

So he took a white flag, and of his own accord rendered submission, tying his hands behind his back with a white rope. He sealed up the maps and registers, and coming down before the Royal vessel, bowed his head to the ground, and said:

"Henceforward, as long as Heaven and Earth endure, we will obediently act as thy forage-providers, not allowing the helms of our ships to become dry, every spring and every autumn, we will send tribute of horse-combs and whips. And, without thinking the sea-distance a trouble, we will pay annual dues of male and female slaves." He confirmed this by repeated oaths, saying, "When the sun no longer rises in the East, but comes forth in the West; when the river Arinare turns its course backward, and when the river pebbles ascend and become stars—if before this we fail to pay homage every spring and every autumn, or neglect to send tribute of combs and whips, may the Gods of Heaven and Earth both together punish us."

HOW HIKO–HOHO–DEMI–NO MIKOTO MARRIED THE SEA–KING'S DAUGHTER[1]

THE elder brother, Ho-no-susori-no Mikoto, was endowed with a sea-gift, and was therefore called Umi no sachi-hiko:[2] the younger brother, Hiko-hoho-demi-no Mikoto, was endowed with a mountain-gift, and was therefore called Yama no sachi-hiko. Whenever the wind blew and the rain fell, the elder brother lost his gain, but in spite of wind and rain the younger brother's gain did not fail him. Now the elder brother spoke to the younger brother, saying:

"I wish to make trial of an exchange of gifts with thee."

The younger brother consented, and the exchange was accordingly made. Thereupon the elder brother took the younger brother's bow and arrows, and went a-hunting to the mountain; the younger brother took the elder brother's fish-hook, and went on the sea a-fishing. But neither of them got anything, and they came back empty-handed. The elder brother accordingly restored to the younger brother his bow and arrows, and demanded back his own fish-hook.

Now the younger brother had lost the fish-hook in the sea, and he knew not how to find it. Therefore he made other new fish-hooks, several

---

[1] From W. G. Aston's translation of *The Nihongi*. Reprinted by permission of Kegan Paul Trench, Trubner & Co., Ltd.

[2] Sea-gift-prince.

thousands in number, which he offered to his elder brother. The elder
brother was angry, and would not receive them, but demanded impor-
tunately the old fish-hook.

"These are not my old fish-hook: though they are many, I will not
take them."

And he continued repeatedly to demand it vehemently. Therefore
Hiko-hoho-demi-no Mikoto's grief was exceedingly profound, and he
went and made moan by the shore of the sea. Now there was an old man,
who suddenly came forward, and gave his name as Shiho-tsuchi no Oji.
He asked him, saying:

"Who art thou, my lord, and why dost thou grieve thee?"

Hiko-hoho-demi-no Mikoto answered and told him the matter from
first to last.

The old man said:

"Grieve no longer. I will devise a plan." So he unfolded his plan, saying: "The courser on which the Sea-God rides is a sea-monster eight
fathoms in length, who with fins erect stays in the small orange-tree
house. I will consult with him."

So he took Hiko-hoho-demi-no Mikoto with him, and went to see the
sea-monster.

The sea-monster then suggested a plan, saying:

"I could bring the Heavenly Grandchild to the Sea-palace after a
journey of eight days, but my King has a courser, a sea-monster of one
fathom, who will without doubt bring him thither in one day. I will
therefore return and make him come to thee. Thou shouldst mount him,
and enter the sea. When thou enterest the sea, thou wilt in due course
find there the Little Shore of Delight. Proceed along this shore and thou
wilt surely arrive at the palace of my King. Over the well at the palace
gate there is a multitudinous branching cassia tree. Do thou climb up
on to this tree and stay there."

Having so said, he entered into the sea, and departed.

Accordingly, the Heavenly Grandchild, in compliance with the sea-
monster's words, remained there, and waited for eight days, when there
did indeed appear to him a sea-monster of one fathom. He mounted on
it, and entered the sea, where he followed in every particular the former
sea-monster's advice.

At this time Toyo-tama-hime, the daughter of the God of the Sea,
came with a jewel-bowl in her hand and was about to draw water, when
she saw in the well the reflection of a man. She looked up and was startled,
so that she let fall the bowl, which was broken to pieces. But without
regard for it, she returned within and told her parents, saying:

"I have seen a man on the tree which is beside the well. His countenance is very beautiful, and his form comely. He is surely no ordinary
person."

When the God, her father, heard this, he wondered. Having prepared an eight-fold cushion, he went to meet him, and brought him in. When they were seated, he asked the reason of his coming, upon which he answered and told him all his case. Now the God of the Sea at once conceived pity for him, and summoning all the broad of fin and narrow of fin, made inquiry of them. They all said:

"We know not. Only the Red-woman has an ailment of the mouth and has not come."

So she was sent for in all haste, and on searching her mouth, the lost fish-hook was at once found. Upon this the God of the Sea chid her, saying:

"Thou Kuchime! Henceforward thou shalt not be able to swallow a bait, nor shalt thou be allowed to have a place at the table of the Heavenly Grandchild." This is the reason why the fish Kuchime is not among the articles of food set before the Emperor.

After this, Hiko-hoho-demi-no Mikoto took to wife the Sea God's daughter, Toyo-tama-hime, and dwelt in the sea palace. For three years he enjoyed peace and pleasure, but still had a longing for his own country, and therefore sighed deeply from time to time. Toyo-tama-hime heard this and told her father, saying:

"The Heavenly Grandchild often sighs as if in grief. It may be that it is the sorrow of longing for his country."

The God of the Sea thereupon drew to him Hiko-hoho-demi-no Mikoto, and addressing him in an easy, familiar way, said:

"If the Heavenly Grandchild desires to return to his country I will send him back."

So he gave him the fish-hook which he had found, and in doing so, instructed him, saying:

"When thou givest this to thy elder brother thou must recite the following: 'A big hook, and eager hook, a poor hook a silly hook.' After saying all this, fling it to him with a back-handed motion."

Then he summoned together the sea monsters, and inquired of them, saying:

"The Grandchild of the Heavenly Deity is now about to take his departure homewards. In how many days will you accomplish this service?"

Then all the sea-monsters fixed each a number of days according to his own length. Those of them which were one fathom long of their own accord said:

"In the space of one day we will accomplish it."

The one-fathom sea-monsters were accordingly sent with him as his escort. Then he gave him two precious objects, the tide-flowing jewel and the tide-ebbing jewel, and taught him how to use them. He further instructed him, saying:

"If thy elder brother should make high fields, do thou make puddle fields; if thy elder brother make puddle fields, do thou make high fields. Moreover, when thy elder brother goes to sea a-fishing, let the Heavenly

Grandchild stand on the sea-shore and do that which raises the wind. Now that which raises the wind is whistling. If thou doest so, I will forthwith stir up the wind of the offing and the wind of the shore, and will overwhelm and vex him with scurrying waves." And he taught him, saying: "If thy elder brother is angry and has a mind to do thee hurt, then produce the tide-flowing jewel and drown him therewith. As soon as he is in peril and appeals for mercy, bring forth the tide-ebbing jewel and therewith save him. If thou dost vex him in this way, he will of his own accord become thy submissive vassal."

When the Heavenly Grandchild was about to set out on his return journey, Toyo-tama-hime addressed him, saying:

"Thy handmaiden is already pregnant, and the time of her delivery is not far off. On a day when the winds and waves are raging, I will surely come forth to the sea-shore, and I pray thee that thou wilt make for me a parturition house, and await me there."

Thereupon the Sea-God placed Hiko-hoho-demi-no Mikoto on the back of a great sea-monster, and so sent him back to his own country.

Now Hiko-hoho-demi-no Mikoto followed implicitly the teaching of the Sea-God. First of all he offered his elder brother the fish-hook. His elder brother was angry and would not receive it. Accordingly the younger brother produced the tide-flowing jewel, upon which the tide rose with a mighty overflow, and the elder brother was drowning. Therefore he besought his younger brother, saying:

"I will serve thee as thy slave. I beseech thee, spare my life."

The younger brother then produced the tide-ebbing jewel, whereupon the tide ebbed of its own accord, and the elder brother was restored to tranquillity. After this the elder brother changed his former words, and said:

"I am thy elder brother. How can an elder brother serve a younger brother?"

Then the younger brother produced the tide-flowing jewel, which his elder brother seeing, fled up to a high mountain. Thereupon the tide also submerged the mountain. The elder brother climbed a lofty tree, and thereupon the tide also submerged the tree. The elder brother was now at an extremity and had nowhere to flee to. So he acknowledged his offence, saying:

"I have been in fault. In future my descendants for eighty generations shall serve thee as thy dog-men. I pray thee, have pity on me."

Then the younger brother produced the tide-ebbing jewel, whereupon the tide ceased of its own accord. Hereupon the elder brother saw that the younger brother was possessed of marvellous powers, and at length submitted to serve him.

After this Toyo-tama-hime fulfilled her promise, and bringing with her her younger sister, Tama-yori-hime, bravely confronted the winds and waves, and came to the sea-shore, riding on a great tortoise, and throwing a splendour over the sea. Now the months of her pregnancy were already fulfilled, and the time of her delivery was urgent. Then she spake quietly to the Heavenly Grandchild, saying:

"Thy handmaid is about to be delivered. I pray thee do not look on her."

The Heavenly Grandchild wondered at these words, and peeped in secretly, when behold, she had become changed into a great sea-monster of eight fathoms. Now she was aware that the Heavenly Grandchild had looked in upon her privacy, and was deeply ashamed and resentful. When the child was born the Heavenly Grandchild approached and made inquiry, saying: "By what name ought the child to be called?"

She answered and said:

"Let him be called Hiko-nagisa-take-u-gaya-fuki-ahezu no Mikoto. Hadst thou not disgraced me, I would have made the sea and land communicate with each other, and for ever prevented them from being sundered. But now that thou hast disgraced me, wherewithal shall friend-feelings be knit together?"

So she wrapped the infant in rushes, and abandoned it on the sea-shore. Then she barred the sea-path, and passed away.

Then Hiko-hoho-demi-no Mikoto made a song, saying:

> "Whatever befalls me,
> Ne'er shall I forget my love
> With whom I slept
> In the island of wild-ducks—
> The birds of the offing."

INDEX OF AUTHORS

INDEX OF AUTHORS